BK 631.4 U58S
SOIL
1957 .00 FV

⬧ W9-DJN-151

3000 157404 30017
St. Louis Community College

rganic matter

Crop residues
return

ro-organisms
pose
nic matter,
se minerals,
trogen

631.4 U58s
U.S.
SOIL 2.50

F.V.

WITHDRAWN

ontinues
from
rials beneath
athering,
lation,
aching

JUNIOR COLLEGE DISTRICT
of St. Louis-St. Louis County
LIBRARY
7508 Forsyth Blvd.
St. Louis, Missouri 63105

on what
a soil as
tained lo
the many
Successfu
fields acc
tions: W
the ideal?
into my farm budget? — CHARLES E. KELLOGG

THE

YEARBOOK OF

AGRICULTURE

1957

the yearbook
of agriculture
1957

THE UNITED STATES

DEPARTMENT OF

AGRICULTURE

WASHINGTON, D. C.

THE UNITED STATES GOVERNMENT PRINTING OFFICE

SOIL

FOR SALE BY THE SUPERINTENDENT OF DOCUMENTS, WASHINGTON 25, D. C., PRICE $2.25

Foreword

EZRA TAFT BENSON

Secretary of Agriculture

ALL MY LIFE I have had direct experience of the importance of soil. As a boy and young man I tilled it, worked with it, and got from it its bounty or, in bad years, wrested from it its reluctant yield. Then and later I learned to love it, respect it, and appreciate its values and limitations.

I LEARNED what every farmer knows—that each of the thousands of different kinds of soils requires its own care and skillful use, which also change from season to season as conditions of moisture, temperature, and crops change.

THESE TRUTHS, so simple to say here but so acutely complex when one's living depends on observing them, were brought home to me again, but more forcefully than ever, when I accompanied President Eisenhower early this year on a trip to survey the disastrous effects of drought in the Southwest, the Great Plains, and other sections. Farmers and ranchers in some of the States had suffered their sixth consecutive year of drought and needed help urgently.

THE PROBLEM demanded action of several kinds—emergency measures to provide for feed, refinancing of farm indebtedness, and urgent conservation needs; cooperation of State and Federal Governments, farmers and ranchers, and other citizens whose livelihood depends on agricultural well-being; and a long-range program looking to the best use of land and other natural resources.

MORE RESEARCH—continuing, thorough research—in the management of soil and water is a vital part of the long-range program. Not only must we learn more about the management of our soil and water; we must encourage the wider dissemination and application of the results of this research.

THAT IS WHY I am so keenly interested in this Yearbook of Agriculture and commend it to you and your neighbors. The facts in it are the product of years of patient, useful, practical research, and publishing it in this form is the best way I know of making it available to all Americans, wherever they live.

FOR TO ALL AMERICANS, wherever they live, soil is a basic treasure. Soils produce good yields and keep on doing so if they are well managed. The management of soil is among the oldest of the arts, but none is changing more rapidly than it. We know more about taking care of soil than our fathers and grandfathers did. There is much more that we should know.

Preface

ALFRED STEFFERUD

Editor

THIS BOOK IS, as a plant scientist might say, a new and adapted variety of *Soils and Men,* the 1938 Yearbook of Agriculture. The parent, a giant of 1,232 pages and 258,042 copies, is now out of print. That may be a manifest of its popularity and value. Surely it did help make Americans aware of the acute need to take care of their heritage. It warned: "The social lesson of soil waste is that no man has the right to destroy soil even if he does own it in fee simple. The soil requires a duty of man which we have been slow to recognize."

A PURPOSE of the present book is to indicate the extent to which that warning has been heeded—and at times to repeat it—and to describe the knowledge about soils that scientists and farmers have since gained.

THE 1938 YEARBOOK OF AGRICULTURE devoted considerable space to the classifications of soils, technical aspects of soil science, and the use of land (which we take to be different from the use of soil).

BECAUSE OUR KNOWLEDGE of soil has expanded greatly since 1938 and emphasis and needs have changed, this Yearbook of Agriculture is limited to the management of soil, itself a big and burgeoning subject. We plan to devote a subsequent Yearbook to the use and ownership of land. The material here about soil classification, the soils of the United States, and basic soil science is sufficient, we think, for the nontechnician to understand the principles of soil management that are set forth in this volume.

WE HAVE TRIED to help a farmer appraise his own requirements and help him decide which of the many available practices, machines, and materials are best for his situation. We have explained the continually increasing opportunities for more efficient soil management on a permanent basis—how the same soils can be farmed more efficiently than our fathers and grandfathers could farm them and how also more kinds of soil can be farmed efficiently.

vii

WE EMPHASIZE that for best results all parts of the soil-management system for a field must fit together—that systems of crop and timber management must be geared to the characteristics and requirements of both soil and plants.

A GLANCE at the table of contents will tell you more about the scope and organization: The place of soil management within the broad field of agriculture; how new scientific principles are developed; what we have learned about soils and the basic principles of their behavior; methods for achieving specific objectives, such as liming, cultivating, controlling moisture, increasing organic matter and storage of water, and preventing erosion; how systems of soil management support one another, and the requirements and methods of developing farm plans and systems of soil management for high production with conservation; soil-management systems for forest trees, gardens, and a few special crops that have requirements somewhat unlike those of the general run of field crops; and the opportunities for improved systems of soil management in the different regions of the United States.

THE MATERIAL AND SCOPE were planned by a Yearbook Committee, whose members are:

Charles E. Kellogg, Soil Conservation Service, Chairman
W. H. Allaway, Agricultural Research Service
Carleton P. Barnes, Agricultural Research Service
N. C. Brady, Cornell University
V. L. Harper, Forest Service
Carl P. Heisig, Agricultural Research Service
W. H. Pierre, Iowa State College
Harold E. Pinches, Agricultural Research Service
K. S. Quisenberry, Agricultural Research Service
F. G. Ritchie, Agricultural Conservation Program
Alfred Stefferud, Office of Information
Wynne Thorne, Utah State University
C. H. Wadleigh, Agricultural Research Service
Eric Winters, University of Tennessee

TWO OF THEM, Dr. Kellogg and Dr. Barnes, were members of the 1938 Yearbook Committee. Their devotion and wisdom in agricultural research and their distinguished work in the Department of Agriculture are reflected in their continuing concern that the results of the research and achievements of scientists be made public for the benefit of all.

Contents

ix

Practices

SOIL

We Seek;
We Learn

Charles E. Kellogg

Two hundred generations of men and women have given us what is in our minds about soils and soil fertility—the arts and skills and the organized body of knowledge that we now call science.

What is in our hearts they also have given us—the lore, traditions, and love for the land as the wellspring of our national life.

Men in ancient times used many practices that we use—manuring, liming, and crop rotations with legumes.

In the *Odyssey*, Homer told how Odysseus the far-wanderer was recognized at his homecoming first by his old dog "lying on a heap of dung with which the thralls were wont to manure the land."

The Romans had several good manuals for farmers, prepared by keen observers who sifted out the best from the experience they saw around them. Columella's *Husbandry*, written about A.D. 60, was a handbook for 15 generations. Some of his suggestions were good, even in the light of modern knowledge. He discussed amounts of material to be used, timing of operations, and application of combinations of practices to various kinds of soil.

Most of the actual knowledge farmers used during the long period from the fall of Rome to the French Revolution and for some time afterward was the home knowledge of farm people, passed on by father and mother to son and daughter. Their practices were highly traditional and slow to change. Yields of crops were low.

After Rome fell, the people of Europe were disorganized and lived in a dark age of disease, famine, and war for more than a thousand years.

But the Arabian culture flourished in the Near East, northern Africa, and southern Spain. Farming there was reasonably good, especially under irrigation. In the 12th century, for example, Ibn-al-Awan, a Moorish scholar, prepared an excellent handbook of agriculture. The experience he recorded and explained became significant to us much later through the Spanish influence brought into early settlements in the southwestern part of the United States.

Greater stability of governments came with the close of the Thirty Years War in 1648. Populations began to increase. Since yields remained low in much of western Europe, the growing populations began to press hard against the food supply. The new stability of governments stimulated intellectual activity, and out of it the first principles and skills of modern science were born. For the first time, economic problems were recognized and studied.

These new forces and ideas seemed to be unrelated for many years. In 1798 Thomas R. Malthus wrote his *Essay on Population*, in which he developed the idea that populations increase faster than the food supply and that it was probable that some people would die of starvation. He had no way of foreseeing the tremendous effects that technology would have on crop yields in Europe or on the development of vast new lands overseas.

Attempts were made to rationalize farming and to improve soil management. Near the beginning of the 18th century, Jethro Tull, an Englishman, invented the grain drill and the cultivator, which he called a "horse hoe." Weeds had choked grain fields; now crops could be sown in rows and cultivated.

Tull demonstrated that cultivation could be helpful, but he gave a wrong reason—that cultivation helped plants take in small particles of earth, especially clay. It is simply one example of how a practice, which is good on some kinds of soil, may be established through observation and advocated for all kinds of soil for the wrong reasons. The effect of Tull's insistence on much cultivation lasted a long time. Until recently farmers have overcultivated their soils beyond the need to incorporate organic matter and fertilizers, to make the soil receptive of rainwater, and to control weeds.

Jethro Tull's practices helped the further development of crop rotations to replace the earlier "two-field" system, in which a year of wheat alternated with a year of fallow.

The Norfolk "four-course" system, developed partly from experience in Holland, had such an advantage over wheat and fallow that it has persisted as a cornerstone of agriculture in the minds of many to this day.

In the original Norfolk system, turnips for cattle feed were grown as an intertilled crop, followed by wheat and 2 years of clover or clover mixed with grass. Sometimes the second year of grass was replaced by another year of wheat or other small grain. Soil fertility was maintained by the clover and manure. Weeds were controlled. The soil was kept in good physical condition by the roots of the meadow crop and by the organic matter returned in the manure. Yields of grain were doubled. Eliminating the fallow meant the soil could be used for crops and pasture all the time.

But here again, results that were so helpful to many of the soils of England were recommended too widely. Arthur Young, an English agriculturist, wrote in 1792 as follows:

"Hence then some courses [rotations] arrange themselves that are applicable, perhaps, to all the soils of the world.

"1, Roots, cabbage, or pulse.

"2, Corn [wheat].

"3, Grasses.

"4, Corn.

"and, 1, Roots [turnips], or cabbage.

"2, Corn.

"3, Grasses.

"4, Pulse, or maize, hemp, or flax.

"5, Corn.

"And in these the chief distinction, relative to soil, will be the number of years in which the grasses are left...."

It took a long time and much research to establish clearly that other systems are better for most kinds of soil that are unlike those of western Europe.

SCIENTISTS meanwhile were trying to find out what made plants grow. They assumed that one "principle" could be found. In the 16th century, Bernard Palissy, potter to French royalty and a man of great affairs who finally died in a dungeon of the Bastille, maintained that manures and plant residues returned to the soil the "salt" that plants removed. He regarded the ash left when plants burned as "a kind of salt" and the "principle" of plant growth. But experimental results were disappointing before chemistry had developed the skills necessary to distinguish among the many kinds of "salt."

Jan Baptista van Helmont, a Flemish chemist, thought he had proved water to be this "principle" in a famous experiment with a willow tree about 1635. He planted a small tree in 200 pounds of oven-dried soil. After growing 5 years, protected from dust and given only rainwater, the tree was removed. The soil was redried and weighed. Because the soil loss was only 2 ounces (which could be considered an experimental error) and the tree gained 165 pounds, he assumed that growth was due to the water alone. Now we know that the 2 ounces were critically important and that the bulk of the 165 pounds was carbon, oxygen, and hydrogen, mostly from the air. His results had wide acceptance, however.

John Woodward, of England, later reopened the question by growing plants in rainwater, river water, and muddy water from his garden. As growth was greatest from the muddy water, he concluded that earthy material must be the "principle."

Others found the answer in humus. They explained plant growth in terms of a passing of the "principle" from a dead plant or animal to the new plant. Some schools of "organic farming" hold to all or part of this idea today.

After the middle of the 17th century, most serious students of plant growth recognized that several items were necessary, although they could not be specific about them. More exact methods were necessary.

The French scientist, Antoine Lavoisier, who was led to the guillotine in 1794, greatly advanced scientific skills. Building on earlier work, as every scientist does, he perfected the quantitative balance, by which tiny amounts of substances can be weighed. He developed a table of chemical elements. It was incomplete, but it was a remarkable forward step. He showed that plants and animals used oxygen and survived by respiration—by the "burning" of organic food. He and others thus were able to account for a large part of the bulk of Van Helmont's willow tree.

EXPERIMENTATION in fields was begun in 1834 by the French agriculturist, J. B. Boussingault. Through measurement—weighing and chemical analyses—he made important attempts to account for the constituents of plants in relation to the soils in which they grew.

But the great change in agricultural theory came in 1840 when a German chemist, Justus von Liebig, published his findings. He made careful analyses of surface soils and plants and stated the balance sheet of plant nutrition: "The crops on a field diminish or increase in exact proportion to the diminution or increase of the mineral substances conveyed to it in manure."

The seemingly simple reasonableness of his views, his prestige as a scientist, and his skill in debate swept away all the alchemistic theories of plant growth.

Liebig's own theory, however, was

based on the assumption that soils were static, lifeless storage bins filled with pulverized rocks, which held the water and nutrients and which farmers stirred in tillage.

Neither Liebig nor his followers looked carefully at a real soil to see whether such an assumption was right. The researches that led to our appreciation of the dynamic processes going on in soils began much later.

The Rothamsted Experimental Station, long famous in agricultural history, was established near London in 1843. Painstaking experiments were begun, and systems of cropping have since been under continuous scientific study there. The chemistry of plant nutrition was further elaborated. Superphosphate was invented, and it and other fertilizers were tested. We owe a great deal to the researches in soil management conducted at Rothamsted as applied to much of western Europe and to like soils everywhere.

THE SOURCE OF NITROGEN in the soil was an early stumbling block to the balance-sheet theory of soil-plant relationships. People knew that wheat removed nitrogen, and good crops of wheat left an unmanured soil poorer in nitrogen. Yet, although clover removed nitrogen, the amount left in the soil was undiminished or increased.

The question was cleared up in the 1880's with the discovery that *Rhizobium* organisms grow in the nodules on the roots of leguminous plants and fix nitrogen from the air into forms that plants can use. The role of soil organisms in changing the nitrogen compounds in organic matter into forms available to plants had been explained a few years earlier.

The new soil science that was developing along the lines that Liebig laid down was a great advance. With the crop rotations begun in the Norfolk system, wider use of farm manures and chalk (as agricultural lime), and improved tillage, wheat yields had risen by 1850 to 16 bushels an acre in Germany, 14 in France, and 20 in Eng-

land. Then, with fertilizers and other improvements, by 1906 they had risen again to about 30 bushels in Germany and England and 20 in France. In 1950 they were more than 35 bushels in England.

Tillage methods and other soil-management practices also were improved through research. Grain production in western Europe went from about 590 million bushels to 1,260 million bushels between 1800 and 1900.

EARLY SOIL MANAGEMENT in the United States was largely copied from western Europe, except for that introduced into the Southwest by the Spaniards, who were familiar with the irrigation techniques the Moors perfected.

Practices of western Europe did not work well in the United States for several reasons. The soils of the Northeast are like the soils of western Europe, but those of the South and the West are quite different. The climate of western Europe is modified strongly by the sea, and most rains are gentle. The weather in nearly all of the United States has wider extremes than in western Europe, rains are more violent, and cultivated sloping soils are more subject to erosion. Land was abundant in America until the beginning of this century and relatively cheap in relation to labor costs.

Most farms in western Europe were small and intensively cultivated, but America was a big place with lots of room. Within a few years after clearing, the relatively acid and nutrient-poor soils along the Atlantic seaboard gave low yields. Many agriculturists emphasized the need for lime, fertilizers, and rotations with clover, but for more than 100 years after the American Revolution it was comparatively easy for young people to move West to soils that were richer to begin with.

Counties in New England that were 80 percent or more open cropland before the Civil War were 80 to 90 percent in forests by 1940. And the substitution of forest crops for field crops on many of the soils there still goes on.

Once the leached and acid soils of the forested uplands of the East had given up the nutrients stored in them by the trees and had begun to erode, the farmers on them were ready to move on. Farmers on the move in the United States during the 19th century wanted soils that were fertile and that would remain so.

Actually, only a few of our soils in the United States have within themselves the dynamic to remain productive. Those that do are mainly the alluvial soils along streams that receive frequent additions of nutrient-rich sediment from occasional overflow. Yet many of the dark-colored soils of the Middle West and Great Plains, developed under grass from nutrient-rich geologic materials in a drier climate, can return good yields of grain under cultivation without fertilizers for a long time. In the Great Plains, shallow soils with little room for water storage between infrequent rains and sandy soils easily moved by wind are even riskier than leached, erosive soils of the East.

SOME AMERICAN FARMERS, of course, did work out efficient, conserving systems, copied only in part from Europe. But until nearly the First World War, Americans looked to Europe for scientific leadership. It was the fashion for scientific scholars, including soil scientists, to go to Europe for advanced study. Most of them still looked to Europe when they came back. Few studied American soils and what American farmers were doing with them.

There were exceptions.

Edmund Ruffin, a Virginia farmer who fired the first shot at Fort Sumter and who killed himself when General Lee surrendered, was a great American agriculturist. His book, *An Essay on Calcareous Manures*, was reprinted five times by 1853. Liming was an old practice, but I believe Ruffin may have been the first farmer in the world to use lime specifically to correct a soil condition that he rightly judged to be acidity.

He reached this conclusion by study-ing Sir Humphry Davy's book, *Elements of Agricultural Chemistry*, and the soils on his own farm in Virginia. He experimented, explored for marl, studied, and wrote down his findings and theories. He explained the greater income to be had from good practices and scolded the many farmers who did not follow them or accept his advice. "Wornout" soils continued to be abandoned to broomsedge and Virginia pine, and slopes continued to erode.

Another great book appeared in 1860 and met a similar fate, *Report on the Geology and Agriculture of the State of Mississippi*, by E. W. Hilgard. It was the beginning of a new idea—the concept that different kinds of soil are products of climate and vegetation acting upon the rock materials produced by weathering.

Hilgard studied soils in many parts of the country before he became professor of agriculture in the University of California. His *Report on Cotton Production in the United States*, published as two huge volumes in the 1880 census, is a mine of information about the nature of soils and how they can and should be used.

Hilgard developed the idea of unique kinds of dynamic soils, each formed under unique combinations of climate and associations of native plants. To him these were the objects of soil study and the basis for recommendations to settlers.

He was ahead of his time. American farmers generally were not ready to rationalize their agriculture. Land was too abundant for people to see the need of conserving and building up the productivity of the soils on the farms they had cut out of the wilderness. Although widely available in colleges and libraries, Hilgard's great textbook, *Soils, Their Formation, Properties, Composition, and Relations to Climate and Plant Growth in the Humid and Arid Regions*, published in 1906, was read with understanding by relatively few. Much of what he had worked so hard to learn had to be rediscovered in later years.

Other scientists who studied soil erosion also were ignored. In his *Origin and Nature of Soils* (1891), the great American geologist N. S. Shaler drew attention to declining soil productivity. "Our successors," he wrote, "will look back upon our present administration of this great trust with amazement and disgust."

Farmers' Bulletin No. 20, *Washed Soils: How to Prevent Them,* published by the Department of Agriculture in 1894, gave a clear explanation of the problem. In the foreword, Assistant Secretary Charles W. Dabney declared, "Thousands of acres of land in this country are abandoned every year because the surface has been washed and gullied beyond the possibility of profitable cultivation."

FIELD EXPERIMENTS were begun during and after the Civil War, especially with the establishment of the land-grant colleges. Many experiments with lime, fertilizers, crop rotations, tillage, drainage, and irrigation were under way by 1890. They were mainly "testing" experiments, or trials. Not many were designed to study the soils themselves in order to determine the mechanisms of their behavior. Most of the experimenters took the soils for granted—as "storage bins" of fine rock material essentially as Liebig did a half-century earlier.

Chemistry was developing. It was applied to soils, crops, and animals. A workable concept about the soils themselves was lacking, but valuable information came from thousands of analyses and experiments. Men at nearly all State experiment stations were studying soil management by 1900, and a few fields and projects were laid out for the total analysis of crops and soils.

The researches of F. H. King at the University of Wisconsin and Cyril G. Hopkins at the University of Illinois were outstanding.

King studied the movement and storage of water in soils and the deep rooting of plants below the surface. He sought ideas from China, where peasants, poor and untrained in modern science and engineering, had been supplying food to a huge population for centuries. King's work greatly broadened the field of soil science in America; it was more than chemistry.

Hopkins' influence was great. He went about as far toward developing good soil-management systems for Illinois and for soils like those in Illinois as hard work with the simple tools of analytical chemistry and empirical field experiments made possible. Lime, finely ground, raw rock phosphate, and clover became his basic formula. His book, *Soil Fertility and Permanent Agriculture* (1910), reached many farmers and led to marked improvements in midwestern agriculture.

Still there was no theory or set of principles that could be used to bring into order the data coming from the experiment stations and the experiences of farmers—no way of applying the results of research and practical experience on millions of farm fields on more than 10 thousand kinds of soil. Not many people saw the need.

Milton Whitney, chief of the Bureau of Soils and the first leader of soil investigations in the Department of Agriculture, saw the need.

Dr. Whitney had imagination and the services of a growing staff of scientists. His own study of soils made him appreciate the importance of the differing characteristics of real soils outside the laboratory. He over-emphasized soil texture—the relative amounts of sand, silt, and clay—but his emphasis on the texture of the soil in the root zone was a forward step. Soil texture is a permanent characteristic of the soil itself that can be measured. He noted that the effects of climate on crop growth varied greatly with texture. He was impressed that characteristics of soils, their productivity, and the adaptability of crops to them varied from place to place.

He conceived an orderly field study, classification, and mapping of soils so that experimental studies in both fields and laboratories could be planned rationally and the results might be synthesized by kinds of soil and extended to farmers through the use of the maps. In that way, recommendations could be pinpointed to individual fields and farms, once the soils were identified.

Thus the Soil Survey was organized in 1899. The first results were disappointing, but gradually a corps of scientists were trained to study the real soils—all their characteristics to the depths that affect roots and water movement—in relation to the natural environment and to farm experience.

Dr. Whitney started other investigations. One was directed to find out the nature of clay too fine to be seen clearly with a microscope and yet the most active part of soils. Other research was aimed at the nature of the water in soils—the soil solution—from which it was supposed that plant roots took in their mineral nutrients. Research was begun to discover what toxic substances may inhibit plant growth.

Some of Whitney's views seemed almost wild at the time. His theory that all or most soils contained enough nutrients for crops and needed only water if they were used in a rotation and if a buildup of toxic compounds was avoided was proved false. So was Liebig's statement of the balance-sheet theory. Out of the clashes of opinion that followed, both theories were discarded in favor of a new theory that accounted for the evidence on which both were based.

CHEMISTRY meanwhile was advancing and was soon to make fertilizers better, cheaper, and more abundant. Sir William Crookes delivered a remarkable address in 1898 on the problem of wheat production for a growing population. Wheat yields were not keeping up with the need, and he foresaw an "impending catastrophe." He said the solution lay in the fixation of atmospheric nitrogen by chemical processes. That alone, he maintained, could save the countries whose people depend on wheat bread. It was an accurate forecast.

Technical processes for fixing the ni-trogen of the air into nitrogen compounds were just being developed.

During the next 12 years after Sir William spoke, methods were vastly improved. A chemical nitrogen industry developed enormously during the First World War, primarily for explosives. Nitrogen afterwards became available for use in fertilizers.

Soluble phosphatic fertilizers, discovered at Rothamsted in 1843, also were improved greatly during the first part of our century. The concentration of plant nutrients was increased. Methods were worked out for adding ammonia to superphosphate. Ways were developed for granulating the fertilizer.

Most supplies of potash fertilizer for American agriculture used to be imported from Europe. Shortages during the First World War stimulated exploration and development in the United States and elsewhere, and this primary fertilizer material also became more abundant.

The effect of fertilizers on improving the efficiency of crop production can scarcely be overemphasized. Although various natural products had been used for a long period, the general use of fertilizers in quantity depended on this development of an efficient chemical industry.

A BRILLIANT SCHOOL of soil scientists developed in Russia about 1870 under the leadership of V. V. Dokuchaev. These students noted that each kind of soil has a unique series of layers, or horizons, from the surface down to the geologic material at 3 to 5 feet, which have resulted from powerful soil-building forces acting on the geologic materials beneath.

Thus they established for the first time what Hilgard had hinted at—that soils are individual, natural bodies, each with its own morphology. This concept was as important to progress in soil science as the development of knowledge of anatomy was to medicine. One did not need to assume what a soil was. He could go directly to the soil itself and find its characteristics displayed in its own morphology as a summary of all its past environment.

Because of the language barrier, only hints of the far-reaching results of these ideas reached western Europe and America until 1914, when a textbook was published in German by K. D. Glinka. Hilgard in his earlier work and G. N. Coffey, in the Bureau of Soils, had conceived part of this new concept, but they had not reached it in a clearly integrated form.

The Soil Survey in the United States went on cooperatively between the Department of Agriculture and the State agricultural experiment stations, gathering data and learning about our soils. C. F. Marbut took charge of the Soil Survey under Whitney. He read and translated Glinka's book. He grasped the significance of the new concept at once. He personally studied the soils of the country and led young soil scientists everywhere along the new lines. It was not easy: Liebig's old balance-sheet theory of soils as storage bins was hard to dislodge, but Marbut was a great teacher.

With the new and broader theory, the data already accumulated in the experiment stations and from the Soil Survey took on new meaning. It became possible to develop a nationwide system of soil classification, which makes possible the orderly planning of soil research and the interpretation of the results to make them applicable to individual fields everywhere. Much of the work of mapping soils is still ahead of us, but a great deal has been done.

We know now that soils are dynamic and changing. Not only do soils support living plants and micro-organisms but these, in turn, have a lot to do with the formation and behavior of the soils. The system is not simply chemical and geological. It is also physical and biological.

As IN MANY OTHER FIELDS, Americans emphasize testing and the application of technology while depending on Europeans for the basic research in soil science. Even now, in the 1950's, the proportion of time and facilities for basic research on the behavior of soils and the nutrition of plants growing in soils is too low for the most economical benefits from the total effort in soil research. Practice can never get far ahead of basic principles, except accidentally.

Even so, the new ideas, developed partly within America and partly adapted from those of eastern Europe, had a stimulating effect. Emphasis on soil colloids (especially the fine clay) stimulated by Milton Whitney led to the discovery that clays are crystalline. Knowledge about the properties of these clay mineral systems has become a cornerstone of modern soil science.

Gradually total chemical analyses of samples of soil gave way partly to chemical examinations of the individual parts of the soil, of the soil solution, and of the exchanges between clay minerals and the solutions.

When we understand the processes going on in dynamic soils, we can change them by management to increase their productivity for plants.

Chemical treatments, liming, irrigation, tillage, drainage, and the growth of crops change the soils. Besides the characteristics of the original soils, the changes caused by cultural practices had to be understood, and the soil conditions had to be measured in the new situation. This called for chemical tests of nutrients and for other soil tests that could be widely applied.

For example, the soil scientist knew that untreated Norfolk fine sandy loam or Miami silt loam needed lime and fertilizers for good crop growth. He had to have methods that would give quantitative results, so that he could recommend specific amounts. Tests also were needed to assess the status of the soils after treatment in order to avoid deficiencies or the wasteful applications of material not needed.

Although homesteading ended about 1910, the public and many farmers and professional agriculturists generally did not see the serious problems of soil management that were coming.

These were problems of soil depletion through erosion and soil blowing, declining fertility, loss of soil structure, increased runoff, the flooding of small streams, and poorly adapted cropping systems for the local kind of soil. Farming during the early years of this century generally was exploitative, and most systems of soil management were planned on a short-run basis despite the warnings of Ruffin, Hilgard, Hopkins, King, and the others.

After the First World War, agriculture was depressed. It was hard to adjust total production downward from the great increases stimulated by the war. Farmers could scarcely make ends meet, and soil depletion increased.

The land-grant colleges were well established and were becoming better, but they had to cover all phases of agriculture in their teaching programs, and the attention to the different phases in research and off-campus education followed roughly the same proportion as in resident teaching. Thus the effort devoted to soil science was small in relation to the growing soil problems on farms.

H. H. Bennett, of the Department of Agriculture, started writing dramatically in the middle 1920's about the growing soil problem, which became worse when a general depression grew. He got attention where others had failed. He did much to awaken the country to the problem.

Bennett and his staff developed a grouping of the many kinds of soil under the "use-capability" concept. They placed major emphasis on relating the kinds of soil to their needs in simple terms. This emphasis started the conservation program on a sound basis. It brought out the major conditions each land user must deal with and furnished a guide to the combinations of practices required for sustained production.

More than 1.6 million farmers plan the use and management of their soil and water resources through about 2,700 soil conservation districts. Other thousands of farmers each year cooperate with their districts.

America's greatly expanded industry has given farmers new tools and chemicals. Research programs in the manufacturing technology of fertilizers and in their use also have expanded.

Instead of basing the use of fertilizers on the analyses of harvested crops, according to the balance-sheet theory of putting in what plants take out, the aim now is to supplement the soil in order to develop and to maintain a balanced supply of plant nutrients at economic levels.

This level of fertility for many kinds of soil is far higher than that of the natural soils. Certain nutrients must be added to the soils in amounts well above those removed annually by plants. Few arable soils require fertilizers containing all the plant nutrients. Some soils need several. Others require only one or two, even after long use. The amounts removed by plants and animals are important, but we have learned to take account of the amounts in the soil that are becoming available to plant roots and of processes going on in the soils that affect these supplies.

Conceivably we may be able some day to draw up a true balance sheet for a soil. To do so we shall need to understand better the mechanics of several processes and know how to measure them more precisely.

These include—besides analyses of plants, whole soils, and drainage waters—the amounts of nutrients in dusts that fall onto or are washed into the soil by rain, and those removed; the amounts removed by normal soil erosion and those added by the incorporation of new materials into the soil from the underlying rock material; the sources of nitrogen compounds in the soil; and the rate at which nutrients become available or unavailable to plants under different conditions.

These processes are influenced by drainage, irrigation, total amounts of nutrients and the balance between the nutrients and other substances, and different species of growing plants. All are modified by cultural practices.

The use of fertilizer and soil erosion are related. Erosion may change the chemical nature of soils, but the great damage is to soil structure. Commonly a mellow surface soil is removed, and a subsoil difficult to cultivate is uncovered.

The erosion of sloping soil is stimulated by tillage or weakened plant growth—by anything that exposes a bare soil to the direct action of wind and rain. On any highly erodible soil, even a highly fertile soil, exposure of the soil through cultivation results in erosion hazards. On many moderately erodible soils, however, the extent of erosion depends upon the vigor of the plant growth under good management practices, other than fertilization.

With low fertility and weak plants, erosion is serious; with high fertility and vigorous plant growth, it is not. Since the use of naturally infertile sloping soils, or of those that have been allowed to become infertile, means weak vegetation, erosion is increased. Thus the accelerated erosion of such infertile soils is more an effect of low fertility than it is a cause of the infertility.

A first step in the control of runoff and erosion on such soils, we have learned, is adequate fertilization. A fertile soil has a wider range of adapted crops, including grasses and legumes, than an infertile one. The problem may be solved with vigorously growing plants or with such plants and supplementary engineering works that would be ineffective by themselves or economically impractical at low levels of crop yields.

As a result of the developments in the use and supplies of fertilizers, a part of our emphasis in the study and teaching of soil management has been shifting from soil fertility to the physical properties of soils. In contrast to the early 1920's, few farm managers with adequate capital and skill need to allow soil fertility to be a limiting factor. We have methods of testing soils and recommendations for fertilizing for most kinds of soils. We have

reasonably good fertilizer materials at prices that generally have been going down.

In fact, the modern farmer is not primarily concerned with the productivity of his soil when it is first plowed. He is concerned with the responsiveness of the soil to management—the physical condition of the soil, the nature and stability of its structure, which controls its permeability by roots and water, and the maintenance of an adequate amount of available moisture.

Thus, from the lore, skills, and experience of many generations and the experiments, theories, and researches, we have learned a great deal about soils and how to use them.

We have learned that soils have depth and area. They can be defined, understood, classified, and mapped. Soil maps give us the means for firm connections between the experimental plots and the millions of fields. The capability of the soils for use can be predicted as a basis for farm decisions and the classification of land.

We have learned that any kind of soil is a complex combination of characteristics, no one of which has meaning by itself and apart from the others. A whole group of characteristics, each influencing the others, makes up the soil that will respond, for better or for worse, to the care we give it.

We have learned that the most efficient systems of soil management are combinations of practices, fitted to the unique kinds of soil in ways that realize the benefits of the many interactions among the separate processes and the several characteristics of the soil.

We have learned that soil-management practices can be adjusted with increasing accuracy to specific fields. Broadly defined combinations of treatments, or "shotgun" recommendations, can be replaced with specific ones that avoid the wasteful use of power, chemicals, and water.

We have learned that many of our so-called poor soils can be built up and maintained for efficient production and that there are few conflicts between those systems of management that give the greatest economic return and those that insure the continued improvement and conservation of the soils.

We have learned that many kinds of soil that gave low yields with the practices of only a generation ago can be used efficiently now. If those soils are protected under grass or trees, the United States can increase its acres of cropland very greatly if the need arises. Thus we have many choices in soil use and no real need to use unresponsive or high-risk soils for cultivated crops.

What we seek is not some kind of mythical natural balance between farmers and the soils they cultivate, but a cultural balance in which we use with understanding and precision all the tools of modern science, engineering, and economics.

The Basis of Fertility

Sterling B. Hendricks and Lyle T. Alexander

The old and new meet in soil management. From ancient days man has plowed, drained, terraced, and irrigated land. He has manured his crops and has used rotations, either blindly or by plan.

Early man was limited by not knowing how things happened. When a background of knowledge had developed to the point where the question of *how?* could be approached, further progress was possible. That progress was late, even in the period of recorded history—between 1800 and 1850.

Humphry Davy, an English chemist and a professor of the Royal Institution in London, made one of the first steps toward explaining the value of manure and ashes. He wrote in 1813: "If land be unproductive, and a system of ameliorating it is to be attempted, the sure method of obtaining the object is to determine the cause of its sterility, which must necessarily depend upon some defect in the constitution of the soil, which may be easily discovered by chemical analysis."

Twenty-seven years later, in 1840, Davy's ideas were still being debated and had not been put to wide use on farms. At that time the German, Justus von Liebig, the foremost organic chemist of his day, was turning his attention to the problems of soil fertility. In his book, *Organic Chemistry in its Applications to Agriculture and Physiology*, he pointed out that the chemical elements in plants must have come from the soil and air. If fertility is to be maintained, the loss from the soil must be replaced.

Even before Liebig had so emphatically pointed out the essential basis of fertility, others were conducting tests.

Prominent among them was John Bennet Lawes, who was devoting his estate at Rothamsted, north of London, to the purpose. In 1840 Lawes was trying out the effectiveness of crushed bones as a source of phosphate for plants. He found the bones to be quite ineffective, contrary to Liebig's teachings. Lawes reasoned that a more soluble type of phosphate compound was needed. To prepare such a material, he and his associate, J. H. Gilbert, in 1842 treated bones with sulfuric acid. The resulting fertilizer came to be known as superphosphate and is the basis of much of our present fertilizer industry.

The concern of Liebig, Lawes, Gilbert, and other agricultural chemists between 1840 and 1860 centered on the elements required in large amounts for plant growth. These include nitrogen, potassium, and calcium as well as phosphorus. The success of superphosphate (P) as a fertilizer quickly led to the wide use of soluble potassium (K) salts and compounds of nitrogen (N) in complete fertilizers. Thus, N–P–K as components of a complete fertilizer, or rather N–P_2O_5–K_2O, as we know them on our fertilizer tags, came into being.

The principles involved in nitrogen supply to plants and in the production of nitrogenous fertilizers have developed since 1850. Liebig thought that plants derived their nitrogen from ammonia in the air. The French agricultural chemist and farmer, J. B. Boussingault, however, in 1838 on his estate at Bechelbronn in Alsace showed that legumes can obtain nitrogen from the air only when the soil or medium in which they are growing has not been heated. Boussingault argued that the free nitrogen of the air is changed into compounds suitable for plant growth by something that is alive in the soil. Heat killed the living organisms. The time, 1838, however, was too long before the development of bacteriology as a science to allow the organisms to be found.

Fifty years after Boussingault's experiments, a Dutch scientist, M. W. Beijerinck, isolated bacteria from nodules on legume roots. He showed that the bacteria, which came to be known as *Rhizobia*, or root living, had to be present for nitrogen to be taken up by the legume. It was the rhizobia that were killed by Boussingault's heating of the soil. But the 50 years between Boussingault and Beijerinck had seen the development of bacteriology by the German physician, Robert Koch, and by one of the greatest benefactors of mankind, Louis Pasteur.

This was discovery. It served to explain the importance of legumes in land use, but it did not give the principles for changing the nitrogen of the air into soluble compounds.

The way in which nitrogen can be caused to react with other elements is basic to its fixation from the air. The principles of this fixation process are needed, both for an understanding of the part played by the legume bacteria as well as for the creation of a fertilizer industry. Both depend on catalysts, which are materials for speeding up reactions that otherwise are too slow to be effective.

Metallic iron is the most effective catalyst for promoting the combination of nitrogen and hydrogen to form ammonia, NH_3. This catalyst was developed by the German chemist, Fritz Haber, in the early years of the First World War.

Haber knew from the principles of chemistry that the catalyst could only increase the rate of combination of the nitrogen and hydrogen without changing the degree of their combination—that is, the equilibrium between nitrogen, hydrogen, and ammonia. To obtain the greatest degree of combination required pressures of many hundreds of atmospheres and temperatures of about 800° F. But even under those conditions, the combination did not take place unless the catalyst was present and iron was the best catalyst.

Haber's successful synthesis of ammonia answered the most serious problem of soil management and of world food production, a supply of nitrogenous fertilizers. More than 3 million tons of ammonia are now produced yearly in this way in the United States from the elemental nitrogen of the air and hydrogen, obtained chiefly from natural gas or petroleum refining.

The catalysts that promote nitrogen fixation by rhizobia growing on legume roots are still unknown. The German bacteriologist, H. Bortels, in 1930 showed, however, that free-living forms of nitrogen-fixing bacteria will grow in the absence of nitrogen compounds only if they have a supply of molybdenum. Bortels reasoned that some molybdenum compound must be the catalyst in bacteria for nitrogen fixation. On the basis of this idea, he showed in 1937 that nitrogen fixation by clover, beans, and peas was greatly enhanced by an adequate supply of molybdenum.

The practical application of Bortels'

findings first came in Australia, where large areas were known to be unsuited for pastures containing clover. The agronomist, A. J. Anderson, showed in 1942 that this condition could be corrected by use of a few pounds an acre of molybdenum compounds mixed with superphosphate, for the soils were deficient also in phosphate.

Another discovery about the association of nitrogen-fixing bacteria and legumes was made by a Japanese scientist, H. Kubo, in 1939. He learned that the nodules containing the bacteria are effective only when a red pigment is present. He demonstrated that this pigment is a hemoglobin much like that of blood, which has never been observed under other conditions in plants. Herein is a suggestion to explain the uniqueness of legumes among plants for nitrogen fixation, but much more must be found to explain the process.

The importance of a rather rare element such as molybdenum as essential for establishing legumes introduces the minor nutrient elements. A group of these elements, which are discussed in detail in the chapters that follow, are known to be essential for plant growth.

The first to be recognized was iron, the absence of which leads to a general yellowing, or chlorosis, of leaves. A French scientist, A. Gris, in 1844 described how chlorosis of some plants can be corrected by sprays of iron salts. Progress, however, was slow, and it was not until after 1900 that the importance of other minor-nutrient elements such as boron, copper, manganese, and zinc was appreciated.

The principle of essentiality of these elements has been stated by D. I. Arnon, of the University of California, in this form:

"An element is not considered essential unless a deficiency of it makes it impossible for the plant to complete . . . its life cycle; such deficiency is specific to the element in question and can be prevented or corrected only by supplying this element; and the element is directly involved in the nutrition of the plant quite apart from possible effects in correcting some unfavorable microbial or chemical condition of the soil or other culture medium."

Most minor—or "trace"—nutrients act as required parts of enzyme systems, the catalysts of living things, that speed up the reaction necessary for growth, although many of these enzymes are still to be discovered.

Thus molybdenum acts in nitrogen fixation as a part of some enzyme system; it also is required for the reduction of nitrates in plants, the enzyme required being nitrate reductase. The element is also required in animals for the oxidation of xanthine, a material similar to uric acid, which must be oxidized before it can be eliminated adequately.

A PRINCIPLE intimately involved in fertility, but with broader implications as well with regard to physical features of soils, is that of base or cation exchange. Today this is often a first factor to consider in management, as it involves liming of acid soils and amelioration of alkali soils.

The principle is that soils act to hold base elements such as calcium, sodium, potassium, and magnesium and the acid element hydrogen. Generally, one element can only be replaced by another. Thus, as calcium is removed from soil by plant growth, or by leaching with water, its place might be taken by hydrogen until the soil is too acidic for use. This is the tendency in most soils of the Eastern and Southern States.

The principle of base exchange was discovered just a little over a century ago by the Englishman, J. T. Way, an associate of Lawes at Rothamsted.

Way was concerned with the possible loss of water-soluble fertilizers from soil by leaching. He established instead that the soluble material was held and displaced an equal amount of material present in the soil. This was a fundamental principle. It foreshadowed by three decades the development of a part of modern chemistry, namely, the law of mass action, later (1867) stated by the Scandinavian scientists, C. M. Guldberg and Peter Waage.

The law of mass action formulated the idea that in a chemical reaction such as $A+B \leftrightarrows C+D$, in general, or $Na^+ + H$ soil$\rightleftarrows H^+ + Na$ soil, in particular, an equilibrium is attained. If, then, A is increased, the reaction will be driven toward the right; if D, toward the left. Thus, acid, H^+, increase displaces sodium, Na, so that it can be washed from soils. This is the basis for the use of sulfur as an acid-forming element in the recovery of alkali soils.

The principle of base exchange and that of mass action expressed in the reaction $Na^+ + H$ soil$\leftrightarrows H^+ + Na$ soil is in a very general form, in that inquiry is not made into the nature of H soil and Na soil.

This serves some of the requirements of management, but it does not explain, for instance, why Na soils often have very poor drainage and why one soil differs markedly from another when both have high sodium contents. The ends of management both for use of many soils under irrigation in the Western States or for recovery of land from the sea, as in the Netherlands, require a more detailed knowledge of Na soil.

Way, in the period near 1850, established that the base exchange was due chiefly to the very finely divided materials in the soil. Prominent among these materials were the clays, and Way made synthetic materials by precipitating aluminum and silicon compounds that somewhat resembled the clays and possessed base-exchange properties. But these synthetic materials, which have long been exceedingly important for softening water, differed markedly from clays in many of their properties, such as the capacity to remain suspended in water without change. An understanding of base exchange, then, became largely an effort to understand the nature of clays. This search was successful after 1925.

We can separate soils into fractions of various particle sizes by shaking them through sieves and by suspending them in water. The coarse fractions are sands. The intermediate ones down to the limits of microscopic magnification are silt. Those below these limits are the clays, which settle very slowly in water.

If a soil after separation into fractions is reconstituted with omission of the clay, its cohesive properties will be greatly diminished, particularly if the soil is a loam or heavier in clay content. The clay, then, apparently is the fraction involved not only in base exchange but also in interaction with water in soil. In management, as an example, the clay interaction with water is determinative for many properties, such as those underlying the tendency of soil to erode and its features of internal drainage.

The basic principles about clays are to be found on an atomic scale. You might think it strange that this is the case for such gross features of a field as its lime requirement, its tendency to erode, the draft requirement for plowing, or the required spacing of drains. These properties of the whole field, though, are only reflections of the most minute parts. While the four features are quite different in external appearance, they might depend on the same (or on only a few) minute features.

KNOWLEDGE ABOUT CLAYS on the atomic scale advanced only after a long period of development in the basic physics of atomic structure. In principle, to work with phenomena on a particular scale, the measuring instruments must have features on that scale. Thus, for measuring a mile to the nearest foot, a measuring tape need only be divided into feet, which would make it unsuited for measurement of thickness for a plastic film.

The desired basic information about clays was the arrangement of the atoms. The measuring method that proved useful in finding the arrangement was the diffraction of X-rays.

X-rays are like visible light in that they can be resolved into different wavelengths by diffraction and refraction. In visible white light, the resolution into the different component wavelengths or colors by refraction is shown in a rainbow. This resolution can also be done with an ordinary window screen and a light by diffraction, as can be seen by looking at a distant light through the screen. The degree to which the various colors are separated depends on the fineness of the screen—the smaller the separation of the wires, the greater is the color separation. The diffraction then can be used to measure the wire separation in the screen.

X-rays have wavelengths, equivalent to color in visible light, of about the same value as the separation of atoms in clays. The atoms in the clays, as in all crystals, irrespective of size, are arranged in an orderly and repeated manner much like the men in an army passing in review. This arrangement corresponds to the wires of the screen for visible light. Accordingly, the diffraction of the X-rays by the atomic arrangement in the clays can serve to measure the arrangement.

The kinds of atoms present in the clays are chiefly silicon, aluminum, and oxygen, with small amounts of the basic elements such as calcium, magnesium, sodium, and potassium, and the acid element hydrogen. They are the ones taking part in base exchange. This knowledge of composition came from the analysis by chemists of many pure clays collected from mineral deposits by geologists and mineralogists.

The diffraction of X-rays by a clay shows that the silicon atoms, which are relatively small, are each surrounded at the corners of a tetrahedron by larger oxygen atoms and that each oxygen atom is between two silicon atoms, which thus serve to link tetrahedrons together. The aluminum atoms, which are similar in size to silicon, are substituted, in part, in place of the silicon atoms. The tetrahedrons upon

linking are formed into sheets, and two of these atomic sheets are joined by aluminum atoms between them.

This arrangement of the atoms in the clays has three features, which are the basic ones underlying many properties of soils. These features are: The atoms are arranged in sheets; the surfaces of the sheets are largely the surfaces of oxygen atoms; and the attraction between atoms in the sheets depends on the relative number of oxygen, silicon, and aluminum atoms.

As a result of the atomic arrangement in sheets, the clays can be split between the sheets and thus reduced to particles that are exceedingly thin. The clays therefore are finely divided; that is one of the necessary features for formation of a mud.

OXYGEN ATOMS on the surface result in attraction of water molecule through binding with the hydrogen atoms of the water. In other words, the sheets have a high tendency to be wetted with water. In one type of clay, as a matter of fact, water molecules on the sheet surfaces separate the sheets and cause the clays to swell. It is for this reason that many of the alkali soils have such poor drainage. It is the basic reason for the cracking of many soils during prolonged droughts.

If the attraction of the atoms is not balanced on the scale of atomic dimensions, other atoms must be present for the balance. These atoms can only be present on the surfaces of the sheets. On the surfaces they can readily be separated in the water layers that are also there. Accordingly, they are the atoms that can be exchanged with others—the atoms of base exchange—the atoms involved in the acid reactions of soils and the liming requirements.

As knowledge of clays developed, it was found that there are several ways of making the atomic arrangements in sheets and that clays with different arrangements differ considerably in such properties as the amount of their base exchange and their tendencies to swell in water.

A first question about most soils is, "What is the clay type?"

This question is accompanied by, "What is the soil texture; how much clay is present?" Finally, "What is the base-exchange capacity?"

A guiding method for learning more about clays in soils was to work on pure clays and from their properties to assess their degree of contribution to the general properties of the soil. Other soil components also affect these properties, and the part played by organic matter or humus can be great. Can the principles basic to the action of organic matter also serve as a guide through some of the complexities of soil?

Until the time of Liebig, the idea was held that humus was directly used by plants and as such contributed to soil fertility. Liebig showed that plant growth instead depends upon inorganic compounds. Organic matter is useful for fertility only as it is broken down with release of the constituent nitrogen and phosphorus into inorganic forms. Even today, though, some nonagricultural persons maintain that humus has direct attributes in fertility.

With the advance near the end of the last century in knowledge of bacteriology and the requirements of micro-organisms for growth, it became evident that humus was, in part, a product of the action of micro-organisms and, in part, their sustaining food. The release of the nutrient elements required the destruction by micro-organisms of the organic matter from past crops or that of the native soil. From this point of view alone, the best practice would utilize the organic matter as rapidly as possible.

The organic matter has other properties. One is base exchange, or the capacity to hold nutrient elements, such as potassium, calcium, and magnesium, in saltlike combination much as do clays. Destruction of organic matter naturally reduces this exchange capacity of the soil.

The desirable effects of organic matter on the structure and, through these effects, on the physical properties of soil are of greatest importance. This is the discovery of no particular person but it is readily observed by all who are familiar with soils. It has to do with mellowness and friability, with the maintenance of a good tilth, and the preservation of a loose and uncompacted soil.

The question of principle would be to establish how organic matter contributes to desirable structure in soil.

The answer has not been found even by repeated inquiries into the nature of organic matter. Rather, it seems that something still is to be established about the interaction between organic matter and surfaces of clay minerals.

The most progress in this regard was the finding that some of the polymeric compounds related to the materials of plastics but containing more acid groups when added to clays or to soils have the desired action on structure. The principle, as vaguely formed, involves, in part, the presence of a number of acidic organic groups held together in one molecule that is resistant to attack by micro-organisms.

These acidic groups interact with the surfaces of the clay minerals. The natural materials possessing these properties, in part, are gums formed by bacteria. They are not very stable against further attack by bacteria, however, and have to be constantly renewed by supplying fresh organic matter for the bacteria to consume.

Fertility, the properties of clay, and the functioning of organic matter are examples of factors in soils for which basic principles have been sought.

Each principle is treated in chapters that follow. Other principles also are expressed, particularly with regard to the behavior of water in soils for which a basic understanding is well developed.

In the end, the search for principle is the only way by which we can gain information from one soil that is useful for farming another soil. Information about properties of the individual soils become an orderly and consistent part of knowledge about all soils.

What Soils Are

Roy W. Simonson

Soil is continuous over the land surface of the earth, except for the steep and rugged mountain peaks and the lands of perpetual ice and snow.

Soil is related to the earth much as the rind is related to an orange. But this rind of the earth is far less uniform than the rind of an orange. It is deep in some places and shallow in others. It may be red, as soils are in Hawaii, or it may be black, as they are in North Dakota. It may be sand, or it may be clay.

Be it deep or shallow, red or black, sand or clay, the soil is the link between the rock core of the earth and the living things on its surface. It is the foothold for the plants we grow. Therein lies the main reason for our interest in soil.

The soil mantle of the earth is far from uniform, but all soils have some things in common.

Every soil consists of mineral and organic matter, water, and air. The proportions vary, but the major components remain the same.

Every soil occupies space. As a small segment of the earth, it extends down into the planet as well as over its surface. It has length, breadth, and depth.

Every soil has a profile—a succession of layers in a vertical section down into loose weathered rock. The nature of the soil profile has a lot to do with the growth of roots, the storage of moisture, and the supplies of plant nutrients. The profile also is basic to scientific studies of soil. The profile carries within itself a record of its history for those who learn to read it.

A SOIL PROFILE consists of two or more layers lying one below the other and parallel to the land surface. The layers are known as horizons. The horizons differ in one or more properties such as color, texture, structure, consistence, porosity, and reaction.

Soil horizons may be thick or thin. Some are no more than a fraction of an inch. Others are several feet thick. Few horizons are at either extreme. Generally they merge with one another and lack sharp boundaries.

Horizons in a profile are like the parts of a layer cake without the clear bands of frosting between them.

Most soil profiles include three master horizons, identified by the letters A, B, and C. Some soils lack a B horizon and are said to have AC profiles. When a soil is used without proper care, the A horizon and even the B horizon may be eroded away.

The combined A and B horizons are called the solum, sometimes the "true soil." Together they form the major part of a profile. They are also direct results of the processes by which soils are formed.

All of the master horizons may be subdivided in the scientific study of soils. Such subdivisions are identified by the proper letter plus a subscript number, thus: A_1, A_2, A_3, B_1, B_2, B_3. The subdivisions of master horizons provide clues to the processes of soil formation and are important to the use and management of soils.

The A horizon, the uppermost layer in the soil profile, often is called the surface soil. It is the part of the soil in which life is most abundant in such forms as plant roots, bacteria, fungi, and small animals. It is therefore the part in which organic matter is most plentiful.

Because it lies at the surface, the A horizon is also the part of the soil that falling rain reaches first. Hence it normally is leached more than are the deeper horizons. Most A horizons have

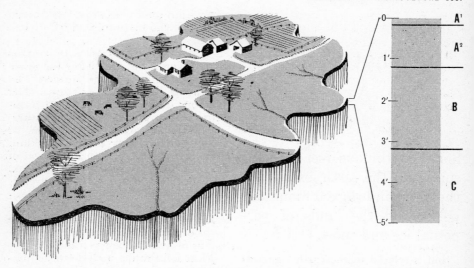

1. A single area of a soil type as it occurs in nature. At the right is an enlarged sketch of the profile with its major horizons.

lost soluble substances. Many have also lost some clay—mineral particles finer than a pinpoint. (About 10 thousand clay particles of average size laid end to end would equal 1 inch.) They may also have lost iron and aluminum oxides, which soil scientists generally call sesquioxides. Iron oxide is the familiar rust on an old piece of steel. Aluminum oxide is the dark tarnish on aluminum kettles.

Two subdivisions of the A horizon are common in soil profiles, although only one of the two may be present in a given profile. If a soil has been formed under prairie vegetation, as in the Corn Belt, it has a thick, dark A_1 and lacks an A_2 horizon. If the soil were formed under forest cover in the same region, the A horizon has two distinct subdivisions, a thin, dark surface layer (the A_1 horizon) and a much thicker, lighter colored layer beneath it (the A_2 horizon). The A_1 and A_2 horizons can be recognized in many uneroded soil profiles in humid regions, but both exist in few soil profiles of dry regions.

The B horizon lies immediately beneath the A horizon and often is called the subsoil. Lying between the A and C horizons, it partakes of the properties of both. Living organisms are fewer than in the A horizon but more abundant than in the C horizon. Color is often transitional between those of the A and C horizons. The B horizon generally is harder when dry (and stickier when wet) than its neighbors. It is frequently higher in clay than either of them. It may have a blocky or prismatic structure, usually combined with greater firmness. Concentrations of iron oxide or aluminum oxides or both, usually in combination with organic matter, mark B horizons of some soils.

THE C HORIZON is the deepest of the three major horizons. It consists of the upper part of the loose and partly decayed rock beneath the A and B horizons. The rock material in the C horizon is of the same kind as that which now forms the bulk of the soil above it. The C horizon therefore is said to be the parent material of soils. It may have accumulated in place by the breakdown of hard rock, or it may have been moved to where it now is by water, wind, or ice. The C horizon has less living matter than overlying ones and is therefore lower in organic matter. It is commonly lighter in color than the A and B horizons. The C horizon in most soils is more like the B than the A horizon. Some profiles, however, lack B horizons. Such profiles usually consist of faint or distinct A horizons grading downward into C horizons. The differences between the A and C horizons may then be small, especially if the A horizon is faint.

The master horizons and their subdivisions, recognized in scientific studies of soils, are shown in the second diagram. This hypothetical profile cannot be found in nature. All the horizons and subhorizons in it do not exist in any actual soil. Yet some of the horizons are part of every soil on earth. Moreover, the kinds and arrangement of horizons in a profile are a record of what has happened to that soil since it began to form. This history has meaning to the fertility, tilth, and productivity of soils for plants useful to mankind.

SOIL FORMATION proceeds in steps and stages, none of which is distinct. They are like the overlapping fibers in a piece of string—the eye can hardly tell where one fiber ends and another begins. Similarly, it is not possible to be sure where one step or stage in soil formation stops and another starts.

The two major steps in the formation of soils are accumulation of soil parent materials and differentiation of horizons in the profile. Each step can be thought of as consisting of several stages, which are hard to tell apart.

Some processes begin with the onset of rock weathering. Silicate clay minerals, for example, are formed and oxides are released from primary minerals, such as feldspars, before a rock disintegrates. Feldspars are minerals formed when molten lava crystallizes into hard rock, as happens deep in the earth. They consist of aluminum, silicon, and oxygen and one or more of calcium, potassium, and sodium. Silicate clay minerals are also mostly silicon, aluminum, oxygen, and hydrogen, but differ in atomic structure from feldspars.

Clay minerals may continue to be formed and oxides released within a soil as long as it exists. Minerals normally continue to decompose in a soil profile long after the distinct horizons form. Some processes in horizon differentiation, however, may begin only after there is a deep mantle of loose weathered rock. The two main steps in soil formation thus merge with one another.

STAGES in each of the major steps of soil formation, like the steps themselves, are far from being distinct.

The accumulation of soil parent materials follows from the weathering of rocks, which is slow, gradual, and continuous. It proceeds little by little from the time that the first changes take place in the solid rock mass. Many changes normally occur in a rock before it disintegrates. Decomposition of minerals usually proceeds long after a rock has disintegrated. Weathering continues without any sharp breaks. Thinking of it in stages is simply a way of looking at a continuous process one piece at a time.

Horizons in soil profiles may be considered faint, distinct, and prominent, although the stages in their differentiation are not clearly defined. Two or more faint horizons first appear when a soil profile begins to form. The earliest changes are small, and the horizons therefore are faint and hard to distinguish. If conditions are favorable, these horizons become distinct with the passing of time.

Additional horizons may also appear. Horizons change slowly and gradually as they become more and more distinct. These changes are like the steady upward movement of a barrel being rolled up an incline rather than like the jumps with which a boy goes upstairs.

Changes in color, structure, texture, consistence, porosity, and other properties occur in all horizons, but the

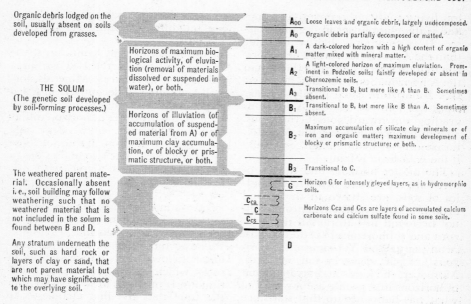

2. *A hypothetical soil profile that has all the principal horizons. Not all of these horizons are present in any profile, but every profile has some of them.*

same changes do not take place in every one. These various kinds of changes slowly differentiate horizons in a soil profile.

THE WEATHERING OF ROCKS provides soil parent materials.

Solid rocks disintegrate slowly under the influence of climate, which acts on them through sunshine, rain, frost, and wind. Heating and cooling, freezing and thawing, wetting and drying all tend to weaken the rock structure. The minerals in rocks react with water and air that enter through tiny cracks and crevices. Changes in the minerals then set up stresses and strains, which further weaken the rock structure.

The final effect of these forces is to break up a rock into small pieces, often into the constituent mineral grains. Gradually rocks thus disintegrate and decay. The loose and weathered rock materials may then become soil parent materials. As used here, parent rock means rock that is still solid and massive, whereas soil parent material is

the distintegrated rock at or near the present land surface.

Tremendous quantities of rocks have been weathered during the millions of years that have passed since the continents took form. A mantle of weathered rock, known as the regolith, now blankets the land surface generally. This regolith has been formed in some places by disintegration and decomposition of rocks on the spot. In many more places it has been moved about by water, wind, or ice.

The regolith may be slightly weathered and consist of fresh primary minerals, as it does in recent deposits left by glaciers in Alaska. It may be intensely weathered so that nothing but highly resistant minerals remain, as is true in parts of central Brazil. The wide range in degree of weathering is matched by similar ranges in composition of the regolith and in its thickness to hard rock. The composition and thicknesses are important to soil formation. The nature of the original rock and the stage of weathering of the regolith also affect the fertility and water relationships of soils.

PLANTS SOON GAIN A FOOTHOLD in the regolith. Sometimes they begin growing on rock before it has disintegrated. The pioneers are commonly simple forms, such as lichens. Micro-organisms, such as bacteria and fungi, also are early invaders. Larger and more complex plants soon follow. Small animals then join the biological community in the infant soil.

As these organisms grow and die, their bodies are left on and in the regolith. Parts of dead plants fall to the surface. Roots are left within the weathering rock mass. The addition and decay of organic matter gradually change the character and appearance of the surface layer of the regolith. It begins to differ from the deeper layers. It thus becomes a faint A horizon, marking the first stage in the differentiation of horizons.

Formation of an A horizon usually follows on the heels of weathering. By the time a regolith has been formed, horizon differentiation also will have started. Soil profiles with A and C horizons, both of which may be thin, therefore can be found in all but the very youngest regoliths. With the passing of time, a faint A horizon slowly becomes thicker and plainer, growing at the expense of the C horizon.

The B horizon makes its appearance after the A horizon has become distinct, as a rule, although A and B horizons may be formed together. Some soils have AC profiles for a long time before there is any indication of a B horizon.

Many soils in north central Iowa have thick, dark A_1 horizons with little evidence of any B horizons. These soils were formed from drift left by glaciers some 8,000 years ago. Eighty centuries have passed since horizon differentiation began, and an A_1 horizon probably has been obvious most of that time.

A_2 and B horizons have been formed in the former plowed layers of fields abandoned in eastern North Carolina a scant half century ago. These fields are now covered by pines about 45 years old. Under the trees, leaching has formed a thin A_2 horizon, and the accumulation of iron oxides and organic matter has formed a thin B horizon. The combined thickness of the two horizons is no more than 5 inches. Both of these new horizons lie within what was the A_2 horizon of a larger profile formed earlier. Changes reflected in the new profile are small, even though the horizons are distinct.

HORIZONS ARE FORMED in soil profiles because of gains, losses, and alterations.

The regolith, as a whole, gains some things and loses others. Changes in its composition go on all the time. The kinds and rates of changes are not the same throughout the regolith. Substances being gained or lost are not identical in the different parts of the vertical section.

Organic matter is usually added to the surface layer in greater quantities than to deeper ones. Clay and sesquioxides may be lost from the surface layer and accumulate in deeper ones. Minerals decompose slowly all the time, and organic matter decays rapidly. Minerals in the regolith react with air and water or with each other to form new compounds. The combined effects of these gains, losses, and alterations, going on slowly but constantly, differentiate horizons in soil profiles.

Gains in organic matter are an early step in the differentiation of horizons in most soils. They are important generally in differentiating A horizons. They are major processes in forming A_1 horizons, such as those in the soils once covered by prairie vegetation in the Midwest and the Great Plains.

Soils of the broad chernozemic belts of the world, shown in the map, have distinct A_1 horizons that owe their main features to gains in humus.

Humus seems to be a mixture of substances somewhat like wood in chemical composition and is formed by the decay of fresh plant or animal residues. During decay, the bulk of the organic matter is broken down to simple sub-

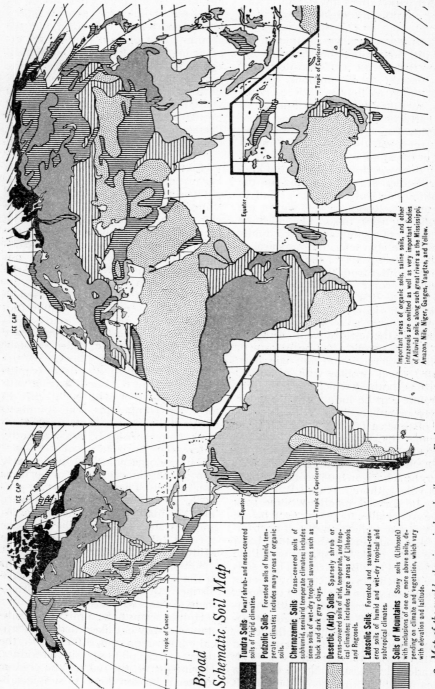

Broad
Schematic Soil Map

Tundra Soils Dwarf shrub- and moss-covered soils of frigid climates.

Podzolic Soils Forested soils of humid, temperate climates; includes many areas of organic soils.

Chernozemic Soils Grass-covered soils of subhumid, semiarid temperate climates; includes some soils of wet-dry tropical savannas such as black and dark gray clays.

Desertic (Arid) Soils Sparsely shrub or grass-covered soils of arid, temperate, and tropical climates; includes large areas of Lithosols and Regosols.

Latosolic Soils Forested and savanna-covered soils of humid and wet-dry tropical and subtropical climates.

Soils of Mountains Stony soils (Lithosols) with inclusions of one or more above soils, depending on climate and vegetation, which vary with elevation and latitude.

Important areas of organic soils, saline soils, and other intrazonals are omitted as well as very important bodies of Alluvial soils, along such great rivers as the Mississippi, Amazon, Nile, Niger, Ganges, Yangtze, and Yellow.

3. Map of the world, showing six broad soil zones. Each zone generally has similar processes of horizon differentiation prevailing over it. These are reflected in the character of the well-drained soils with undulating to rolling topography. Many kinds of soils are present in every zone.

stances, such as water and carbon dioxide. (Gas bubbles in soft drinks are carbon dioxide.) Black colors, as in chernozemic soils, do not always follow from additions of organic matter. Moderate amounts are added throughout the profile to many soils in the latosolic belts, mainly in the Tropics, but the dominant colors are still red and yellow.

Being the remains of living organisms, soil organic matter has nutrient elements in its structure and thus becomes a small storehouse for such elements. It also has direct effects on structure and tilth.

Gains in organic matter are not generally important in forming B horizons. Small amounts are transferred downward from A to B horizons in many soils. Usually the effects in horizon differentiation also are small. Large amounts of organic matter, as humus and more soluble forms, are moved down from the A horizon of some podzolic soils formed from sands. Thus much organic matter is being lost by the A and gained by the B horizon in such soils. The humus moves largely in suspension, tending to stop in the B horizon. More soluble organic matter moves in solution, and part of it may also stop in the B horizon.

Losses from the soil profile are due mainly to leaching or eluviation. Downward movement of substances in solution is known as leaching. The washing out of mineral and organic matter in suspension is called eluviation. The reverse of eluviation is illuviation, which means "washing in" rather than "washing out." The reverse of leaching is deposition. Losses may also be due to removals of nutrient elements by plants.

Water must move through a soil profile before leaching and eluviation can occur. The water comes from falling rain, which first enters the A horizon. In passing through the atmosphere, the water has absorbed a little carbon dioxide, which makes it slightly acid and helps it to dissolve minerals.

Once in the soil, the water dissolves minute quantities of mineral and organic matter, as sugar dissolves in coffee. The dissolved substances commonly move with the water as far as it goes. To this general rule, there are exceptions.

Material in solution may be carried deeper in the profile, below that into the regolith, or out into streams and eventually to the sea. If enough moves through the soil, water may also pick up clay, humus, or sesquioxides, as in muddy streams. Losses through leaching and eluviation and gains through illuviation are important to horizon differentiation in many soils.

Leaching and eluviation affect soils of humid regions more, on the whole, than they do those of dry regions. The rainfall is greater, so more water moves down and less moves upward through the profile. Examples of leached and eluviated A_2 horizons are common in soils formed under forest in the Eastern States and in the broad podzolic belts of the world.

Soluble salts (sodium chloride, or table salt, is an example), carbonates, and elements such as calcium, sodium, and potassium are slowly leached from the profiles of well-drained soils in humid regions. Leaching gradually removes the more soluble elements and also carries out some part of the less soluble ones, such as silicon, from most soils of the podzolic and latosolic belts. Slowly but surely, leaching depletes the plant nutrients in these soils. In extreme cases, among soils of the Tropics, the full supply of available nutrients is bound up in living and dead organic matter.

Leaching also plays a role in horizon differentiation in soils of dry regions. Soluble salts and carbonates in the well-drained soils are leached from the A horizon and also may be removed from the B horizon. Carbonates may be left in the lower B horizon but are left oftener in the C horizon.

Soluble salts, as a rule, are moved down and out of the profiles of well-drained soils. They have been leached to depths of 8 to 10 feet in the glacial till under many soils along the Canadian border in North Dakota. The A and B horizons of soil profiles in that region have combined thicknesses of 2.5 feet. In soils without free drainage, on the other hand, soluble salts and carbonates accumulate wherever the water table may stand in a profile, even at the surface itself. Generally speaking, leaching of A horizons is greater than that of B horizons in both arid and humid regions.

Eluviation operates mainly on A horizons. Clay, humus, and sesquioxides are lost from the A horizons of many soils. A part of these substances is carried out of the profile into the drainage waters. Mostly, however, the losses from the A horizon by eluviation are offset by gains in the B horizon. Many soils in humid regions show the effects of eluviation of substances from the A horizon accompanied by illuviation in the B horizon. Some soils in dry regions also bear the marks of eluviation and illuviation in their profiles.

Changes in the composition of mineral and organic matter are normal in soils the world over. Some of the changes proceed slowly. The decomposition of minerals is slow. The decay of organic matter is rapid. Whether fast or slow, alterations in composition continue throughout the regolith, including the soil profile. Changes that take place in a single week may be negligible, but Nature is patient and has plenty of time. The decomposition of minerals can become profound after many thousands of years.

Soil organic matter turns over rapidly. Most plant residues added to the A horizon by the growth of one season will decay before the next has come and gone. Because fresh supplies are added periodically, organic matter in the soil is in all stages of decay. A very small part of the total decomposes slowly enough to persist for several centuries. Some products of decay, such as humus, have direct effects on color, structure, and consistence of soil horizons. Others react with minerals to speed up their decomposition and

change. Some will dissolve sesquioxides, which can then move more rapidly. The decay of organic matter also releases nutrient elements that may later be used for plant growth.

Alterations of minerals and organic matter may make them more soluble or less soluble, or the solubility may be unchanged. Elements such as calcium, sodium, and potassium are shifted to more soluble forms when feldspars decompose. They then may be absorbed by roots or lost through leaching. Iron is released by decomposition of minerals much like (but not identical with) feldspars. It often combines with oxygen soon afterward to form oxides or rust, which is almost insoluble.

The breakdown of feldspars with formation of clay minerals has little effect on solubility. Both types of minerals are slightly soluble. The individual clay particles are smaller than feldspars, however, and move in the soil more readily.

Changes in the composition of minerals and organic matter may contribute directly or indirectly to horizon differentiation. When clay and sesquioxides are formed by decomposition of feldspars and other primary minerals, this in itself can make one horizon differ from another.

Differences in amounts of clay between A and B horizons in many soils reflect in part the differences in rates of formation of clay minerals in each of the two horizons. Changes in composition may also shift the solubilities of substances. This can then speed up or slow down leaching, eluviation, illuviation, and deposition.

Gains and losses from the regolith, especially from the soil profile, coupled with alterations in minerals and organic matter, determine the direction and rate of horizon differentiation.

They, in turn, depend on a host of simple processes, such as hydration, hydrolysis, solution, leaching, eluviation, and illuviation. These simple processes prevail in all soils. The balance is governed by such factors as climate, vegetation, and parent rock. The total combined effects of the simple processes fix the character of every soil, including its profile and its suitability for the growth of plants.

THE FIVE MAJOR FACTORS in soil formation are climate, living organisms, parent rocks, topography, and time. They control the weathering of rocks and the gains, losses, and alterations throughout the regolith, including the soil profile.

Temperature and rainfall govern rates of weathering of rocks and the decomposition of minerals. They also influence leaching, eluviation, and illuviation. Thus climate functions directly in the accumulation of soil parent materials and in differentiation of horizons. The indirect effects of climate are through its controls over the kinds of plants and animals that can thrive in a region. These living organisms, in turn, are of major importance in differentiating horizons in soils.

Because climate is so important to soil formation, the broad soil regions of the world tend to follow the distribution of climates. Soil and climatic regions are not identical, however, because five factors rather than one are important in soil formation.

Living organisms—plants, animals, insects, bacteria, fungi, and the like—are important chiefly to horizon differentiation and less so to the accumulation of soil parent materials. Gains in organic matter and nitrogen in the soil, gains or losses in plant nutrients, and changes in structure and porosity are among the shifts due to living organisms. Plants and animals may also mix horizons and thus retard their differentiation.

Plants largely determine the kinds and amounts of organic matter that go into a soil under natural conditions. They also govern the way in which it will be added, whether as leaves and twigs on the surface or as fibrous roots within the profile.

Some plants take their nitrogen from the air and add it to the soil as they die.

Deep-rooted plants reverse leaching processes in part. The roots may take up calcium, potassium, phosphorus, and other nutrient elements from the C horizon or even from the deeper regolith, only to leave some part of those nutrients in the solum when the plants die.

The effects of plants on the soil beneath them may be striking. Desert shrubs, such as shadscale, for example, concentrate sodium in the soil on which they grow. Enough sodium is taken up by the plant and added to the surface of the soil to make it far more alkaline than the soil between the bushes. Most effects are less dramatic than this, but all are important to horizon differentiation.

Horizons may be mixed by plants or animals. When trees tip over in a forest, the roots take up soil materials from several horizons. As the upturned roots decay, this soil material tumbles back down, mixing as it goes. Burrowing animals also mix horizons as they build their homes. Such mixing partly offsets horizon differentiation.

Bacteria and fungi live mainly on plant and animal residues. They break down complex compounds into simpler forms, as in the decay of organic matter. It has been suggested that the humus in soils is largely dead bodies of micro-organisms; much of it seems to have about the same composition, even though it exists under widely different types of vegetation. Some micro-organisms fix nitrogen from the atmosphere and thus add it to the regolith in their bodies when they die.

Parent rock is sometimes called a passive factor in soil formation. It must be weathered to form soil parent materials, which are further changed as horizons develop in a soil profile.

The character of the rock itself is a factor in the kinds of changes and how fast they go. Pure quartzite will disintegrate, for example, but little else can happen to it. Quartzite consists of quartz grains cemented together by silica. Quartz is also silica, a combination of silicon and oxygen. Highly resistant to weathering, quartz grains are well-nigh permanent. Small ones may dissolve very slowly, but no plant nutrients are released and no clay is formed as they do.

Most rocks are mixtures of many minerals, few of which are able to withstand weathering as well as quartz. The composition and structure of rocks strongly influence the rate of weathering and the products of that weathering. These in turn are both important to the kind of soil that may be formed.

Topography, or the lay of the land, affects runoff and drainage. Other things being equal, runoff is large on steep slopes and small on level ones. Drainage is rapid from mountainsides and slow from level plains. The amount of water that moves through the soil depends partly on topography. More water runs off and less enters the soil on steep slopes, as a rule, than it does on gentle slopes. The runoff also removes more of the weathered rock on steeper slopes, other things being the same.

Soil profiles on steep slopes generally have indistinct horizons and are shallower than those on gentle slopes. Low and flat topography often means that extra water is added to the soil. The extra water is reflected in gray or mottled colors or in higher amounts of organic matter in the A horizon. If water stands on the surface, peat deposits may be formed. Topography thus influences the moisture regime in soil and the erosion from its surface.

Time is required for soil formation— how much time depends on where the processes must start.

A tremendous interval is needed for development of soil from freshly exposed and fairly pure limestone. The limestone dissolves slowly while the rains come and go. As the mass of the limestone dissolves and is carried away, any impurities originally present are left to form a regolith. Millions of years may pass before parent materials have accumulated and horizons have been formed under such circumstances.

Much more time is needed, generally speaking, for the accumulation of soil parent materials than for the differentiation of horizons in the profile. This would be of the first importance if soil formation had to start from scratch. Because of weathering during past geologic time, however, a regolith now exists widely over the continents. In fact, soils have been formed on most land surfaces, perhaps many times, since molten lava first crystallized into rock about 2 billion years ago.

A soil profile may be formed in a fresh regolith within a few decades. R. L. Crocker and J. Major, soil scientists at the University of California, found the topmost 6-inch layer darker and higher in organic matter than the drift below within 30 years after it was left by a melting glacier in southeastern Alaska. Biological activity is low because of the cold climate, yet an A horizon was evident in 30 years. Where the drift has been exposed for 100 years, the A horizon contains as much organic matter as do many in soils of the eastern United States. The leaching of carbonates and increased acidity of the A horizon could also be measured by the end of the first century.

Differentiation of thin A_2 and B horizons within 50 years has also been observed in former plow layers in eastern North Carolina.

Soil profiles usually must be many centuries old before they have distinct B horizons.

Soils with B horizons high in humus have been formed in sands laid down on Roman ruins in parts of western Europe. The sands can be no more than 2,000 years old, but the profiles have prominent B horizons. Conditions for horizon differentiation in the sands were more favorable than they are generally. Furthermore, B horizons high in humus form more rapidly than do B horizons high in clay.

Soils formed from loess—windblown silty sediments—in eastern Iowa have distinct B horizons formed in about 20,000 years. Clay has accumulated in the B horizons of these soils, as have small amounts of sesquioxides.

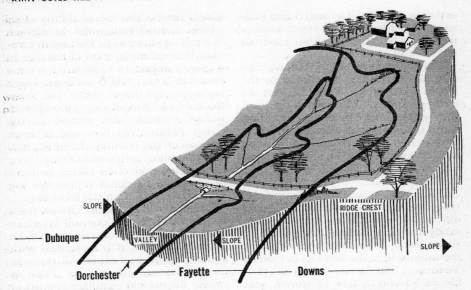

4. *A sketch showing how bodies of soil types fit together in a small landscape, much like the pieces in a jigsaw puzzle. Boundaries between adjacent bodies are gradations rather than sharp lines.*

Many soils with B horizons that are thick and either distinct or prominent must be much older than 200 centuries. Long intervals may therefore pass while horizons are being formed in soil profiles, even though parent materials are at hand for horizon differentiation.

None of the five factors of soil formation is uniform over the face of the earth. Variations in all of them are wide.

There are really many climates, many combinations of living organisms, many kinds of rocks, many topographies, and many different ages of land surfaces. As a result, there are hundreds of thousands of different local combinations of the factors of soil formation.

DIFFERENCES AMONG SOILS are local and regional.

Every farm consists of several local kinds of soils, known as soil types. A single farm usually has three to six types of soil within its boundaries. Soil types in the whole country number in the tens of thousands. Over the world,

they must number in the hundreds of thousands.

These thousands of soil types are not scattered about without rhyme or reason. Each one occurs in a definite geographic area and in certain patterns with others. Thus there are regional differences of importance.

Individual areas of soil types, commonly called phases, are three-dimensional bodies. They have length, breadth, and depth. A single body of a soil type is seldom large. Most are a few acres in size. Each soil type occurs on the earth as a number of separate bodies, which may be distributed over parts of several States or restricted to a small part of one. Each soil type can be defined by a description of the typical profile, the allowable deviations from that profile, and other features such as slope, stoniness, and physiographic position.

Every soil type has neighbors. It never occurs by itself. It tends to have the same neighbors wherever it may be found. A few other soil types usually are associated with it to form a char-

acteristic pattern. The individual bodies of neighboring soil types form a
mosaic, or patchwork, within a farm or
any area of like size.

The bodies fit together like the pieces
of a jigsaw puzzle, as shown in the
fourth illustration. They are not set
apart distinctly, as the sketch suggests;
they grade into one another without
sharp boundaries between them. Rarely does one find a sharp line between
associated soil types. That is one reason
why soil is a continuous mantle over
the land surface.

Differences among neighboring soil
types may be large or small. Marked
differences set apart Congaree fine
sandy loam in the small flood plain and
Ashe stony loam on the adjacent
mountainside in the Smokies of eastern
Tennessee. The former has an AC profile and is deep, free of stones, and
nearly level. It is fertile and has excellent moisture relationships. Ashe stony
loam has faint A, B, and C horizons
and is steep, stony, and of low fertility.
It has poor moisture relationships because so much of the profile is made
up of stones. Neighboring soil types
thus may differ greatly in features that
have an important bearing on use
and management.

Differences among soil types in the
same landscape may be small. Fayette
silt loam and Downs silt loam occur on
the same ridge in northeastern Iowa.

The pattern formed by Fayette,
Downs, and associated soils is shown in
the fourth drawing.

All soils shown in it might be found
on a single farm, but every farm does
not include all of them. Fayette silt
loam and Downs silt loam have the
same horizons in their profiles and
have been formed from the same loess.
Downs silt loam has thicker A_1, thinner
A_2, and slightly more friable B horizons than Fayette silt loam. Water relationships are about the same in the
two soils. Downs silt loam is higher
in organic matter and a trifle more
fertile.

Differences among associated soil
types generally are smaller than regional soil differences. Many soils
within a small geographic area, such
as a county, have some features in common. For example, most of the soils in
a county in eastern Colorado have the
same kinds of A and B horizons. These
horizons also have about the same
thicknesses. Similarities among soils
within a county are greater in the
Great Plains than they are in most
sections of the country. Even so, it is
true that many soils within a small area
have some, and often many, features
in common. Regional differences are
normally bigger than the local ones.

Regional soil differences follow from
two facts. First, any one soil type can
be found only in certain sections of the
country. Second, it is associated with
a small number of other soil types in
those sections. Fayette silt loam is
widely distributed in adjacent parts of
Illinois, Iowa, Minnesota, and Wisconsin. It is not to be found in other
States. Congaree fine sandy loam is
scattered through the Appalachians
and nearby Piedmont from Alabama
to Pennsylvania. The two soil types
never occur together, and each has its
own set of neighbors.

Regional soil differences can be related oftenest to the distribution of climate and living organisms. In places,
however, such differences reflect differences in topography, ages of land surfaces, or character of parent rocks.
The kinds of regional differences and
their size can best be illustrated by
comparisons of a few broad classes of
soils, each made up of several great
soil groups.

A GREAT SOIL GROUP consists of many
soil types whose profiles have major
features in common. Every soil type
in any of them has the same number
and kinds of definitive horizons, although they need not be expressed in
every profile to the same degree. The
Fayette, Dubuque, Downs, and Quan-
dahl soils, for example, are all members of a single great soil group.

The thousands of soil types in the
United States can be classified into

about 40 great soil groups. For the world as a whole, the number is perhaps half again as large. Collectively, the groups have wide ranges in their many characteristics, or properties.

They also have wide ranges in such qualities as fertility, tilth, ability to hold available moisture, and susceptibility to erosion.

Well-drained soil types with undulating to rolling topography tend to be similar over broad geographic belts. The similarities may extend across from one great soil group to another. Geographic belts marked by certain combinations of great soil groups can therefore be shown on maps of small scale.

Six broad belts are outlined on our schematic soil map of the world.

One consists of mountains and similar rough landscapes, in which many of the soils are stony, shallow, or both. The local patterns of great soil groups and soil types are especially complex in such areas.

The other five broad belts have simpler patterns, but each includes a number of great soil groups. For that matter, the soil types within a single farm commonly represent two or more great soil groups. The broad regions in the map therefore show major kinds of soils rather than complete patterns. Great soil groups other than the dominant ones exist in every belt. These are also important in many localities. The broad belts themselves have much meaning to farming and forestry.

The tundra region has a cold climate, which restricts biological activity and horizon differentiation. The soils are in cold storage for a large part of each year. The deep regolith is permanently frozen in some parts of the tundra. Well-drained soils of the tundra belt have profiles much like those of podzolic soils, although the horizons usually are thinner and less distinct.

PODZOLIC SOILS dominate a broad belt in the higher latitudes of the northern hemisphere and some smaller areas in the southern half of the world. They include the great soil groups known as Podzols (originally from Russian words meaning "ash beneath," referring to the A_2 horizon), Brown Podzolic soils, Gray-Brown Podzolic soils, and Gray Wooded soils. These groups were formed under forest vegetation in humid, temperate climates.

Podzolic soils commonly have distinct A_2 horizons. Some have B horizons that are accumulations of sesquioxides, humus, or both. Others have B horizons that are mainly accumulations of clay with minor amounts of sesquioxides and humus. Podzolic soils are more strongly weathered and leached than chernozemic or desertic soils but less so than latosolic soils. They are commonly acid, low in bases such as calcium, and low in organic matter. Levels of fertility therefore are moderate to low. Available moisture capacity is variable, depending on depth of soil and textures of horizons. As a group, however, the soils are responsive to scientific management.

LATOSOLIC SOILS dominate equatorial belts of Africa and South America. They are also dominant in southeastern parts of Asia and North America, as well as northeastern Australia and the larger islands of the western Pacific Ocean.

They include the great soil groups known as Laterites, Reddish-Brown Lateritic soils, Yellowish-Brown Lateritic soils, Red-Yellow Podzolic soils, and the several kinds of Latosols.

Red-Yellow Podzolic soils are so named because they have some features in common with each of the broad latosolic and podzolic groups, though they are more closely related to the former. Latosolic soils have been formed under forest and savanna vegetation in tropical and subtropical and humid to fairly dry climates. They do not extend into arid regions but may be found in alternately wet and dry zones where rainfall is low.

Latosolic soils are strongly weathered and leached, usually to great depths.

In fact, they are the most strongly weathered soils in the world. Despite the deep, strongly weathered regoliths, most of the soils lack distinct horizons, except for a darkened surface layer or A_1 horizon. Below this, the profile may remain unchanged for many feet. Red-Yellow Podzolic soils differ from others in having distinct A_2 horizons as well.

Red and yellow profile colors are common to latosolic soils because of the large amounts of iron oxides formed through intense weathering. Supplies of plant nutrients normally are low, but the capacity to fix phosphorus in unavailable forms is high. Most latosolic soils are easily penetrated by water and plant roots and are resistant to erosion. Red-Yellow Podzolic soils are more susceptible to erosion than others, being less permeable on the whole. Ease and depth of penetration by roots is illustrated by reports of tree roots extending down to 60 feet in the regoliths beneath latosolic soils in southeastern Brazil.

High porosities are also evident in the many fine tubular channels in such soils. Available moisture capacities are mostly moderate to high in latosolic soils, although they are low in some. Productivity is normally low when latosolic soils are used without benefit of modern science and industry.

CHERNOZEMIC SOILS have been formed under prairie or grass vegetation in humid to semiarid and temperate to tropical climates. These soils are most extensive in temperate zones, but some areas in the Tropics are also large. They include the great soil groups known as Chernozems, Brunizems or Prairie soils, Reddish Prairie soils, Chestnut soils, and Reddish Chestnut soils in temperate regions. In tropical and subtropical regions, the soils have been known as black cotton soils, Grumusols, regurs, and dark clays.

Chernozemic soils normally have dark A_1 horizons of great thickness, are fertile, and but slightly weathered. The A_1 horizons are among the most prominent found in soils, whereas the B horizons usually are much less distinct. The A_1 horizons of chernozemic soils are typically high in organic matter and nitrogen in temperate zones but not in tropical and subtropical zones. The profiles compare in depth to those of podzolic soils. They are not so deep as those of latosolic soils but are deeper than those of desertic soils. Chernozemic soils are less acid, higher in bases, and higher in plant nutrients generally than are podzolic or latosolic soils. They are much higher in organic matter and nitrogen, less alkaline, and lower in bases than desertic soils. Available moisture capacities of the soils are usually moderate to high.

Chernozemic soils of temperate zones are among the naturally most fertile soils in the world. They produce about 90 percent of the grain in commercial trade channels. Within the United States, they form the heart of the Corn Belt and wheat-producing regions. Production varies with seasonal weather, because the soils extend from the margins of humid into semiarid zones.

Chernozemic soils of tropical and subtropical zones commonly have unfavorable physical properties for tillage and plant growth. They are high in clay, plastic, and subject to great shrinking and swelling. Most of them are used for agriculture without benefit of modern technology, and their productivity under simple management is low. Problems in handling the soils are difficult.

DESERTIC SOILS have been formed under mixed shrub and grass vegetation or under shrubs in arid climates. The climates range from hot to cold. The soils are prominent in the great deserts of Africa, Asia, and Australia and in the smaller ones of North America and South America.

They include the great soil groups known as Desert soils, Red Desert soils, Sierozems, Brown soils, and Reddish-Brown soils.

Besides the desertic soils themselves, the deserts of the world include large proportions of sandy wastes, rocklands, and very shallow soils with the barest beginnings of horizons. Such lands lack agricultural possibilities.

Desertic soils have been very slightly weathered and leached. The shortage of moisture which restricts weathering and leaching also limits plant growth, leaving the soils low in organic matter and nitrogen. Limited rainfall is also reflected in the shallow profiles normal to the soils.

Their horizons are seldom prominent. Most of them are faint. The A horizon has commonly lost carbonates and perhaps some bases and clay and is lighter in color than the B horizon. The slightly darker B horizon has some accumulation of clay, but it is very low in organic matter. Levels of nutrient elements other than nitrogen are usually moderate to high in the soils. Available moisture capacities are variable, depending on thickness of profile and textures of horizons.

Marked contrast exists in the productivity of desertic soils used in a highly developed agriculture or under nomadic grazing—an example of the tremendous impact management may have on productivity.

Beyond the effects of management, however, each soil type or great soil group has an ill-defined range in use and management possibilities under a given agricultural technology. Each also differs in its response to changes in technology. The range in possibilities may be narrow, regardless of technology, as it is for steep slopes of Ashe stony loam in the Smokies. Soils of that kind will produce some forest but are not suitable for pasture or crops. On the other hand, Congaree fine sandy loam has a wide range in use and management possibilities. It is suitable for forest, pasture, and a variety of crops within the present agriculture. It would also be productive under a number of other levels of agricultural technology. Yields obtained from Congaree fine sandy loam in any agriculture depend greatly upon the level of management practiced.

Physical Properties

M. B. Russell

The physical properties of a soil largely determine the ways in which it can be used. On the size, shape, arrangement, and mineral composition of its particles and the volume and form of its pores depend other important physical properties.

The flow and storage of water, the movement of air, and the ability of the soil to supply nutrients to plants are examples of properties determined by the size and arrangement of the soil particles.

The proportions of the four major components of soils—inorganic particles, organic material, water, and air—vary greatly from place to place and with depth. The amount of water and air in a soil often fluctuates widely from season to season. The physical characteristics of the primary solid components of soil, however, are essentially unchanging.

Inorganic soil particles occupy about one-half of the total volume of most surface soils. Some of the particles can be seen very easily, but others can be examined only with an electron microscope. For many purposes it is convenient to divide the particles into size groups called separates.

Particles more than 2.0 millimeters in diameter are classed as gravel or stones and are not usually included in analyses of particle size. Particles under 2.0 mm. are divided into three major separates, each of which may be further subdivided.

Sand has particles between 0.05 and 2.0 mm. in diameter. The percentage of sand is determined by screening a thoroughly dispersed soil.

Silt has particles 0.002 to 0.05 mm. in size. Clay has particles less than 0.002 mm in diameter. The amount of silt and clay usually is determined indirectly from measurements of the speed of fall of the individual particles which have been well dispersed in water. The size of the individual particles is calculated from the settling speed.

THE PERCENTAGES of sand, silt, and clay determine the texture of the soil. The percentages in each of the several classes of texture are summarized in the illustration.

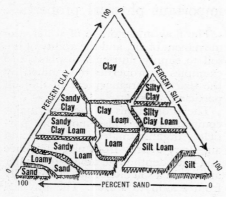

1. *The texture triangle shows the percentage of sand, silt, and clay in each of the textural classes.*

The physical properties and the chemical composition of the large and small particles differ greatly. The coarse separates—the stones, gravel, and sand—act as individual particles. They are composed mainly of rock fragments or such primary minerals as quartz.

Because of their size, these large particles have low specific surface (surface area per unit mass). Most of the important chemical and physical-chemical reactions in soils take place at the surface of the particles. The amount of such surface therefore strongly affects the ability of soils to react chemically.

The density of the larger soil particles usually is near 2.65 grams per cubic centimeter (gm./cc.). Soils containing large amounts of gravel or sand exhibit little or no plasticity and cannot retain large amounts of water or nutrients. They can easily transmit water and air, however, because large voids occur between their particles.

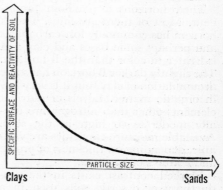

2. *Specific surface is important in determining the reactivity of soils. The amount of surface varies inversely with the size of the soil particles.*

The properties of silt particles are intermediate between those of sand and the clays, but mineralogically silts are more like sand because they are composed largely of primary minerals.

Silt particles have greater chemical activity because of their higher specific surface. Silts also exhibit more plasticity and cohesion than the coarser soil separates. The amount of chemical and physical-chemical activity in the silts, however, is not enough to give desirable physical behavior to soils that contain large amounts of such particles but little or no clay.

The clay fraction is the one that controls most of the important properties of a soil. In soils of the temperate regions, it is composed chiefly of secondary crystalline alumino-silicates, which are platy in form. Hydrated sesquioxides of iron and aluminum are the main components of the clay in the more completely weathered soils typical of many parts of the Tropics.

The clay minerals are secondary hydrated alumino-silicates, in which isomorphous substitutions may have occurred. These minerals are platelike in structure and show marked basal cleavage. Their crystalline structure is determined by the spatial arrangement of oxygen atoms, which by weight constitute roughly half of the mineral content, although on a volume basis the clays are roughly 90 percent oxygen.

The oxygen tetrahedron, which consists of four oxygen atoms in a close-packed arrangement around a silicon atom, is one of the basic structural units of the clay minerals. Such tetrahedra, by sharing oxygens, form sheets having the composition $(Si_2O_5)_n$.

Silica sheets are characteristic of the micas and the clay minerals. In these minerals the sheets are bonded through common oxygen atoms with sheets of aluminum or magnesium octahedra.

Kaolinite, a major clay mineral in many mature soils, especially in the Southeastern States, consists of silica and alumina sheets in a 1:1 ratio. Two other important types of clay minerals, montmorillonite and illite, are composed of silica and alumina sheets bonded together in a 2:1 ratio.

Ionic substitution of Al^{+++} for Si^{++++} and Mg^{++} or Fe^{++} for Al^{+++} are common in minerals of the 2:1 type. Such substitution destroys the balanced-charge condition of the idealized structure and gives the clay mineral crystal a negative charge. Some negative charge also comes from unsatisfied bonds at the edges of clay mineral crystals and from the dissociation of H^+ from the surface-exposed hydroxyl groups.

The negative charge of the clay minerals causes the clay particles to react with other charged particles, ions, and with dipolar molecules, such as water. The attraction between the negatively charged clay and such positive ions as H^+, Ca^{++}, Mg^{++}, and K^+ is one of the most important properties of a soil.

The attracted ions are held in a state of dynamic equilibrium with similar ions in the soil solution and can be replaced or "exchanged" from the soil particle in response to changes in concentration in the soil solution. This process of ionic exchange is a process of fundamental importance in soil management and plant nutrition.

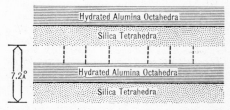

3. *Kaolinite crystals are composed of pairs of silica and alumina sheets held together by hydrogen bonds. The space between the crystal units is fixed and is largely inaccessible for surface reactions.*

The charged clay surfaces together with their associated exchangeable ions also react with water molecules, which become oriented when they are present in the strong electric field near the charged surfaces. The resulting layers of oriented water molecules give the characteristic properties of plasticity, cohesion, and shrinkage to clays and soils that contain large amounts of clay.

The individual particles occupy roughly one-half of the total volume in a soil. The remaining space, the voids between particles, is called the pore space. This is the volume occupied by water and the soil air. A measure of the total pore space is obtained by determining the bulk density, which is defined as the mass of a unit volume of dry soil. Values of bulk density range from less than 1.0 gm./cc. in well-aggregated soils high in organic matter to more than 2.0 gm./cc. for some highly consolidated soils.

Bulk density and other measures of the total porosity are useful in understanding certain types of soil behavior. They are of little value, however, in predicting performance if air or water transport is involved.

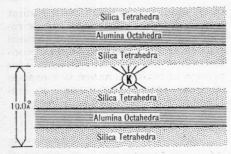

4. *The crystal unit of illite consists of a silica sheet on each side of an alumina sheet. Adjacent crystal units are held together by potassium bridges. The space between the units is partly accessible for surface reactions.*

5. *The crystal unit of clays of the montmorillonite consists of a silica sheet on each side of an alumina sheet. The interlattice spacing in the montmorillonite clays varies with the amount of water present. The entire surface of the crystal unit is accessible for surface reactions.*

It is necessary to consider the size distribution of the individual pores to understand the fluid transport phenomena that take place in soils. A geometric description of the size and shape of the voids in a system of regularly packed uniform spheres is difficult. In a soil composed of irregular particles of many sizes, such a description is impossible.

Soil pores can be classified in terms of their effective sizes by an analysis of the moisture desorption curve. This curve relates the moisture content of a soil to the pressure in the soil water. It also represents the moisture content observed at different heights in a vertical column of soil after excess water has drained from the lower end of the column.

The fraction of the total pore space that will be drained by successive reductions of pressure of the soil water can be readily determined from the desorption curve.

The pressure values can be translated into equivalent pore diameters through the use of the capillary rise equation. This equation relates the pressure, h, to the radius, r, of the soil pore. The density, d, and the surface tension, T, of water as well as g, the acceleration of gravity, also appear in the equation,

which is written as $h = \dfrac{2T}{rdg}$.

It is possible by repeated measurements of the volume drained at different pressures to determine the volume of pores having a given range of sizes. Such a size-distribution analysis is a more useful way of describing the soil voids than the single value obtained from measurements of bulk density.

Bulk density and porosity measurements reflect the arrangement or state of packing of the soil particles and are measures of the structure of the soil. Soils composed of coarse particles such as sands have single-grained structure; that is, each particle functions as an independent structural unit.

In soils that contain substantial amounts of silt and clay, many of the fine particles are grouped into secondary structural units, called aggregates.

The size, shape, and arrangement, particularly the amount of overlap, of the soil aggregates largely determine the porosity and pore size distribution of soils containing large amounts of silt and clay.

Soil aggregates are not permanent structural units, particularly in the surface of a cultivated soil. Consequently the degree of aggregation shows marked variations, depending on the texture and organic matter content of the soil and on climatic conditions and cultural practices.

Longevity of soil aggregates is re-

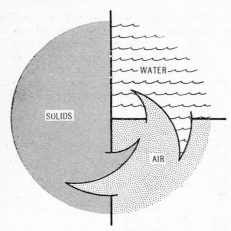

6. The volume fractions occupied by solids, water, and air are variable and affect soil behavior.

lated to the nature of the materials that hold the particles together. Organic colloids are the principal cementing agents for soil aggregates in the surface horizons of soils of temperate humid regions. Sesquioxides and silica act as important aggregating agents in some tropical and desert soils.

The organic colloids that are effective in giving stability to soil aggregates are intermediate products in the decomposition of plant residues. Such colloids are adsorbed on the surface of soil particles, probably through the mechanism of hydrogen bonding.

Added stability is imparted to the aggregate if the organic colloid undergoes an irreversible dehydration accompanied by shrinkage.

Under field conditions, the organic bonding compounds normally undergo further decomposition, which results in a loss of aggregate stability. A continuing supply of decomposing organic material therefore is of great importance in maintaining a high level of soil aggregation.

Soil aggregation greatly modifies the effects of texture as a factor affecting the important physical phenomena related to plant growth. That is particularly true for such transport processes as the movement of air and water and the flow of heat through the soil. Such properties as water retention, nutrient supplying power, and plasticity, however, are more closely related to soil texture, although structure may exert some modifying influence.

Water relations are among the most important physical phenomena that affect the use of soils for agricultural or engineering purposes. In particular, the flow of water in both saturated and unsaturated soils has a major effect on the field behavior of soils. Waterflow occurs through the soil pores. The resistance to waterflow is determined by the length and the cross-sectional area of the flow path.

The flow in saturated sands or gravels is rapid because such soils contain a high proportion of large pores. In partially saturated soils in which flow is limited to the water-filled pores, water transport is faster in fine-textured soils because they contain a larger effective transmitting cross section than do the coarse-textured soils in which the large pores are air filled.

Pore size distribution is strongly affected by aggregation as well as texture. Infiltration and movement of water through the soil therefore are greatly influenced by soil structure.

Water and air occupy the soil pores in reciprocally varying amounts. The amount and composition of the air in the soil have important direct and indirect effects on plant growth. Soil air differs from the atmosphere above the soil in that it usually contains 10 to 100 times as much carbon dioxide (CO_2) and slightly less oxygen and is saturated with water vapor. The roots of most plants and many of the soil micro-organisms require oxygen for their normal respiratory functions.

The composition of the soil air reflects a dynamic balance between two competing processes. The consumption of oxygen and the liberation of CO_2 by plant roots and soil organisms tend to increase the differences in composition between the soil air and the atmosphere above the soil surface.

Gaseous diffusion, however, tends to reduce the differences in composition.

The rate of diffusion of oxygen into and carbon dioxide out of the soil depends on the differences in concentration of each gas in the soil and the air and on the ability of the soil to transmit the gases.

Diffusion is proportional to the volume of air-filled pores and, for the pore sizes encountered in soils, seems to be largely independent of pore size.

Temperature and heating properties are important in determining the productivity and use of soils.

The temperature of field soils shows rather definite changes at different depths and at different seasons of the year. The changes are determined by the amount of the radiant energy that reaches the soil surface and by the thermal properties of the soil. The amount of radiant energy reaching the soil surface is determined by the angle at which the sunlight strikes the earth and by the nature of the atmosphere. Only the part of the energy that is absorbed causes changes in soil temperature.

Dark-colored soils having a low reflecting power capture a much higher proportion of radiant energy than do light-colored soils. Thus a fallow Brunizem absorbs nearly 80 percent of the radiation that reaches the soil surface. A grass-covered soil and quartz sand absorb, respectively, 65 percent and 30 percent.

The energy that has been adsorbed by the soil surface is disposed of in one or more of the following ways: By reradiation to atmosphere as longwave radiation, by heating of air above the soil by convection, by increasing the temperature of the surface soil, or by conduction to the deeper soil layers.

During daylight hours there is normally a net influx of heat to the soil surface. This situation is reversed during the night. Consequently the temperature of the exposed soil surface shows wider daily fluctuations than those of the air.

Soil temperatures vary in a charac-

teristic manner both on a daily and seasonal basis. The fluctuations in both instances are greatest at the surface and decrease in size at lower depths. A well-defined time lag, which increases with depth in the soil, also occurs in both the daily and seasonal variations.

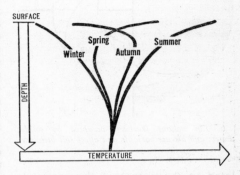

7. *Soil temperatures in temperate regions show characteristic seasonal variations, which decrease with depth.*

The observed fluctuations in soil temperature are related to the heat capacity and to the thermal conductivity of the soil. Both of these properties are strongly affected by the proportions of the total soil volume that are occupied by the solid, liquid, and gaseous soil constituents.

The thermal conductivity of water is greater than the corresponding value for the solid soil particles, which in turn is higher than that of air. Consequently the rate of heat flow in a soil is increased when the volume occupied by air is decreased. Such a reduction in the volume fraction of air can be obtained either by compacting the soil or increasing its moisture content. Modifications of this kind, however, cause a reduction in the temperature change that will result from the flow of a given amount of heat into or out of a unit volume of soil.

The foregoing relations are modified in frozen soils because the thermal conductivity of ice is nearly three times that of water, whereas its specific heat is only one-half that of water.

The reaction of soil to physical manipulation, such as is involved in tillage, is primarily an expression of the properties of cohesion, adhesion, and plasticity. These properties are largely determined by the size, shape, and arrangement of the soil particles and by the nature of the water films surrounding them.

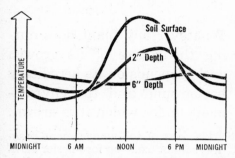

8. *Soil temperature fluctuates widely during a 24-hour period, but the variations become smaller below the soil surface.*

Water molecules, being highly dipolar, are strongly adsorbed and oriented on the negatively charged surfaces of soil particles. Also, water itself exhibits strong cohesion, as shown by its high surface tension. Therefore, as a result of drying, adjacent soil particles are drawn together with considerable force and the soil develops greater cohesion and mechanical strength.

Orientation of the particles into a tighter state of packing results in further shortening and strengthening of the water bonds between the particles. This results in shrinkage of the soil.

Soil loses its cohesion and becomes plastic in the presence of increasing amounts of water. This phenomenon is also associated with the water films and is most strongly shown by soils of high specific surface having platelike particles. Orientation of the soil particles parallel to the direction of the deforming force occurs. The soil then has little or no shearing strength and is readily deformed.

At a very high moisture content, soil loses its cohesive strength and its plastic properties and approaches a fluid in its mechanical properties. In this condition, the interparticle distances are so great that the effects of the oriented water molecules on the surfaces cannot influence the behavior of the particles.

The amount and kind of clay minerals, the nature of the exchangeable cations, and the content of organic matter are factors of major importance in all the foregoing rheologic reactions of soil. The phenomena of cohesion, plasticity, and shrinkage are the most strongly expressed in soils containing a large amount of clay of the montmorillonite type. Such properties are also enhanced by the presence of monovalent cations on the exchange complex.

Many important soil-management problems involving physical properties are associated with the kinds and the amounts of the clay and exchangeable bases in the soil. Increases in bulk density resulting from mechanical manipulation, such as occurs in tillage, are affected strongly by the amount of moisture in the soil. This relation is described by the compaction curve, which relates bulk density resulting from a given compactive effort to the moisture content.

Compaction curves of soils that vary in their content of clay, exchangeable cations, or organic matter content show marked differences in the critical moisture percentage and the maximum bulk density that are obtained.

Soils high in organic matter are less susceptible to compaction and exhibit less well-defined critical moisture percentages. Tillage on such soils therefore is less likely to result in excessive compaction even when performed over a wide range of moisture content.

Soil crusting is another form of consolidation important in soil management. Soil crusts are formed by the desiccation of a thin layer of dispersed surface soil. Such crusts, which vary in thickness from a few millimeters to several inches, frequently have considerable mechanical strength—they therefore may keep seedlings from emerging or cause injury to the stems of established plants.

Crust formation involves three processes—dispersion, segregation, and desiccation.

Dispersion accompanies the breakdown of the aggregates in the surface soil, which may result from excessive tillage or through the impact of raindrops. Because aggregate stability is low in the presence of excess water, raindrop impact is a major factor leading to the dispersion of unprotected surface soil.

Following the destruction of the aggregates, some segregation of particles of different sizes occurs in the dispersed surface soil. This segregation results in a closer packing of the soil particles and an increase in bulk density.

Mechanical strength of the dispersed soil is greatly increased by drying. Appreciable shrinkage accompanies the drying in soils high in clay or organic colloids. The cracking that results because of shrinkage reduces the mechanical impenetrability of the crust. Therefore the problem of crust formation on soils high in clay or organic matter is usually less acute than on silty soils.

All the physical properties discussed above affect plant growth through their relation in a qualitative sense to the root environment in the soil.

Of equal importance are the quantitative aspects of the soil as a habitat for plant roots. It is necessary that nutrients, air, and water are present in optimum concentrations for normal root development and plant growth. It is necessary also that enough of all of them be present throughout the growing season to meet plant needs.

It is important therefore to emphasize the depth of soil available for rooting as a major physical factor that influences soil management. Severe limitations are placed on the ways in which the soil can be used, in situations where the rooting volume is restricted by bedrock, cemented layers, a high water table, or other root barriers. Deep, permeable soils through which plant roots can develop extensively provide much wider possibilities for use in crop production.

Growth
of Plants

C. H. Wadleigh

Whatever any plant does during the course of its growth cycle depends on its hereditary background and the environment under which it is grown.

The best of soil-management practices cannot make up for inferior germ plasm—the substance by which hereditary characters are transmitted—in our crops. You have to grow the varieties with the most desirable capabilities for your climate and soil conditions. Soil management cannot make a silk purse out of a sow's ear.

Consider a few illustrations: Varieties of sugar beets that do not carry resistance to curly top disease are apt to be a total loss when they are grown in many of the Western States, regardless of cultural practices.

Even the best farmers in Minnesota cannot produce a profitable crop of wheat if they plant seed that does not carry resistance to a prevailing strain of stem rust.

California Common alfalfa grows luxuriantly in the Imperial Valley during the fall, but a northern variety like Ranger grown there at that time makes little growth because of its sensitivity to the length of day. The growth of Ranger practically stops in the fall with the onset of short days regardless of how favorable the weather and soil conditions may be.

Even though a plant has a good hereditary background for the most desired type of productivity, its potentialities cannot be reached fully in an adverse environment.

Cultural operations on the soil affect plant growth through their influence on the environment of an exceedingly important part of the plant—the roots. Even so, favorable conditions around the roots will be limited in their effects by the nature of aerial environment.

Why do plants grow?

By what processes and mechanisms do conditions about the tops and roots of plants influence growth?

Such questions cannot be answered fully. The secret of life is still a secret.

Yet progress in biological research constantly is increasing our understanding of why and how the wheels go 'round inside a living cell and why and how external conditions affect this "machinery."

GROWTH of an annual seed plant is in four stages: Seed germination, vegetative development, reproductive processes, and the maturing of the seed.

A mature seed contains a small, living, quiescent plant. This miniature plant is the embryo, or germ. When conditions of temperature, moisture, and oxygen are right, the embryo starts to grow. This process, including the bursting of the seedcoat, is germination. When the embryo plant has developed enough to lead an independent life without drawing on the nourishment stored in the seed, germination is complete.

Absorption of water is the first stage in germination. The rate at which seeds absorb water from the soil depends mainly on the moisture in the soil, the compactness of the soil around the seed, temperature, and the nature of the seedcoat. If the water content of the soil is down to the permanent wilting percentage, seeds cannot absorb enough water to germinate. Loose soil around the seed may prevent contact with a sufficient number of moisture-coated soil particles to transfer the amount of water needed for germination.

But excessive compaction of a moist soil may limit absorption of water by limiting the supply of highly essential oxygen. Thus the press wheel on seed planters should bring moist soil particles in close contact with the seed without too much compaction.

Seeds absorb water faster from a warm soil than from a cold one.

Some seeds have hard coats that water will not penetrate. They may need special treatment, such as scarifying (scratching the seedcoat) to make them more penetrable to water. Some seeds—like apple, rose, and iris—will not germinate even when the moisture supply is favorable unless they go through a series of changes known as afterripening—a process that usually involves exposure to low temperatures in a moist environment. Some seeds, like Grand Rapids lettuce, require exposure to light in the presence of moisture in order to germinate.

The second stage in germination is the digestion of stored nutrients and the transfer of these solubilized nutrients to the young plant or embryo. As water enters the seed, the seed coat is softened, facilitating the entry of oxygen and the release of carbon dioxide (CO_2), given off by respiration of the awakening seed.

With the absorption of water, the digestive compounds—enzymes—in the seed become active and digest or break down the complex stored foods, such as fats, starches, and proteins, into soluble forms. They are translocated to the embryo and are used in the formation and growth of the new cells that comprise the first shoot and root as they emerge from the seed.

These processes in the germinating seed are greatly affected by temperature. Some seeds will not germinate when the temperature of the soil is below 40° to 50° F. There is no specific optimum temperature for seed germination. The most suitable temperatures vary with the kind of plant; 65° to 80° are often favorable, depending on the kind of seed. Above 100°, germination is impeded. Therefore soil-management practices that aid in warming the soil in cool seasons may help seeds to germinate.

The digestion of stored foods in seeds and their reutilization in the growing embryo require relatively high levels of oxygen. Large amounts of CO_2 are given off. Facility for gaseous interchange around germinating seeds is highly important. That is why compacted soils or soggy, wet soils hinder or prevent germination.

As the young seedling pushes its way upward through the soil, mechanical work is done in thrusting soil particles aside and breaking any crust that may be present on the surface. When soils are seriously encrusted, more force may be required for a breakthrough than the little seedlings can muster, and they perish in the effort.

Cold, wet soils seem to foster the activities of the many kinds of disease organisms that are ready to attack weakened seedlings and thus cause serious agricultural loss.

Growers of cotton, sugar beets, soybeans, and other row crops know that one of their stiffest hurdles in producing a crop is getting a stand. In other words, attaining soil conditions that will provide optimum seed germination regardless of weather is important in getting high yields.

The little seedling, as it pops through the soil, starts on a new phase of development. It no longer depends on nutrient reserves in the seed. Its continued life and growth depend on its ability to make and use its own food supplies. The period of growth following seedling emergence and on to flowering is vegetative development.

Let us examine just what is meant by this word "growth" when applied to plants.

Growth consists of an irreversible increase in size. This usually (but not always) includes an increase in dry matter. Growth usually is accompanied by a change in form, shape, or state of complexity, which constitute the processes of development. Growth is measurable by a balance or a rule; development is characterized by descriptive adjectives.

How does growth take place?

Each crop plant is made up of billions of minute cubicles, the cells. A plant increases in size as the cells increase in number or size or both. If our cabbages stop growing, it means that the cells making up the leaves of the plants have stopped increasing in number and size.

The cells that provide the increases in number are only in certain parts of the plants—the meristems. They are the cambial layers (familiar as the "slipping" areas between the bark and wood of trees), the growing points of stem and root tips, and the blades of young leaves. Meristem cells can multiply by division. At a certain stage of their growth, the various contents of the cells are divided into two parts, and a new cell wall is laid down between the parts.

Some of the newly formed cells enlarge enormously with intake of water.

Other cells are destined to develop openings in consecutive ends to form the elaborate conductive system, or "plumbing," that is always present in the crop plants. Still others become strangely elongated and form thick walls, which are the fiber and wood cells that give rigidity to the framework of the plant.

Why do cells grow and thereby bring about the growth of our corn, cotton, or cabbage plants?

We do not know. We do know some of the essentials.

Every living cell contains a complex proteinlike substance, somewhat like egg white, called protoplasm. It is the physical basis of life.

Protoplasm contains fatty substances in addition to proteins. It is 80 to 85 percent water. It is distributed over the inner wall of the cell cubicle. Water fills the interior of a living cell, and this contains a host of substances, such as sugars, amino acids, hormones, organic acids, enzymes, minerals, and more complex materials that are essential for the life and function of the protoplasm.

An essential part of our discussion is how environment affects the components and thereby the life and growth of the cells that make up the growth of a plant.

Increase in size of a cell means that work was done and energy was utilized.

The energy comes from sunlight. Light energy from the sun is absorbed by chlorophyll—the green color in leaves—which in turn converts the CO_2 absorbed by the leaves and the water absorbed by the roots to simple sugars, a process called photosynthesis. The simple sugars are depositories of energy from the sun. They are the raw materials for the plant's diverse chemical syntheses and growth processes.

Thus light is essential for growth. A grower of greenhouse tomatoes in Cleveland knows that he can expect only half the production per plant from his fall crop as compared to his spring crop. The difference in production is merely a simple reflection of the difference in the light energy available to the tomato plants at the two seasons.

Carbon dioxide also is essential for growth. The atmosphere normally contains only 0.03 percent of CO_2. Under high light intensities during the summer, this low level of CO_2 in the air probably is the main limiting factor in the photosynthesis.

The production of an acre of a 100-bushel corn crop requires about 4 tons of CO_2. On a still summer day, the CO_2 level in the air of a cornfield drops very low. The corn under full sunlight could use 20 times the normal level of CO_2. We have evidence that the CO_2 produced by respiration of micro-organisms in the soil is an important factor in the supply of the gas to photosynthesizing plants: A well-fertilized soil rich in decomposing organic matter provides a much higher level of CO_2 in the air just above the soil than does a barren, infertile soil—proof that soil management can affect photosynthesis in the plant.

The greenness of leaves certainly affects the amount of light energy that will be absorbed and the sugars that will be synthesized. The loss of chlorophyll in leaves is called chlorosis—a malformation that may develop in relation to several kinds of disturbances in mineral nutrition of the plant or be induced by certain soil-management practices. I discuss this point in later paragraphs.

Air temperature affects growth in that the rates of chemical reactions increase with increase in temperature. Thus many of the biochemical processes in the living cell speed up with increasing temperature. This is particularly so with respiration, the process by which living tissues chemically combine oxygen and organic substances, such as sugars, with the resultant release of CO_2 and energy.

The rate of photosynthesis may also increase with increasing temperature, depending on the specific nature of the plant. The maximum rate for this process takes place at higher temperatures in tropical plants than in plants of temperate areas.

Respiration and photosynthesis tend to be counteractive in the usage and buildup of stored food (i. e., sugars) in the plant.

The temperatures at which these two seemingly counteracting processes permit maximum accumulation of food materials for growth vary with different kinds of plants. Little growth of sugarcane takes place at temperatures below 65° F., and maximum growth as well as accumulation of sugar occurs at 85° to 88°. On the other hand, Irish potatoes grow and yield the best at mean temperatures of around 60°. Aroostook County, in Maine, and Cuba are famous for the production of potatoes and sugarcane, respectively.

The distribution of prevailing temperatures is a key factor. Night temperatures are especially significant in the growth rate of plants. The Iowa farmer knows that his corn grows best on the nights that he swelters. Growth of most plants is superior under fluctuating night and day temperatures, when the night is appreciably cooler than the day.

Because freezing temperatures kill many kinds of plants, good management practices in orchards include provision for good air drainage down a slope to minimize frost damage at flowering time in the spring.

Light, temperature, and concentration of CO_2 in the air around a plant all have a direct effect upon the activity of the living cell in the growing plant. The effects are influenced by the behavior of the protoplasm—the stuff of life—in the cell. In essence, growth is largely dependent on the formation of new protoplasm. This proteinaceous substance is made up mainly of carbon, hydrogen, oxygen, nitrogen, and sulfur. It is dispersed in water. The first three elements come from the sugars made by photosynthesis. The sulfur and (in most cases) the nitrogen come from the soil.

The nitrogen in proteins is the key component. The nitrogen supply in the soil regulates the ability of the plant to make the proteins that are vital to the formation of new protoplasm. Inadequate supply of nitrogen in soils is one of the main limiting factors in agricultural production.

But we must not overlook the other essential mineral nutrients that plants obtain from the earth. Farmers of the United States spend more than a billion dollars a year to improve the fertility of their soils. Some of this fertilizer is used unwisely or ineffectively, but much higher levels of fertilization could be used profitably to improve plant growth when the soil is managed well.

Much of the annual fertilizer bill covers the purchase of phosphorus, which is vital to the processes in all living cells—plant or animal. Combined with certain organic substances, phosphorus provides the key mechanism by which biochemical energy is transferred from one step in a protoplasmic process to another. As the wiring in a house permits electrical energy to be transferred from one room to another, organic phosphorus compounds permit transfer of biochemical energy from one life process to another in the cell. When the cell manufactures sugar by photosynthesis, or releases energy through respiration, or synthesizes proteins for new protoplasm, organic phosphorus compounds control the biochemical steps in those processes and others.

The third major element supplied in the fertilizer bag is potassium. Potassium is essential for the growth of plants, and plants take tremendous amounts of it from the soil.

We do not know exactly what role potassium performs in the living processes of a plant cell. We have some evidence that potassium acts in enzymatic processes, especially those in transformations among different kinds of sugars.

Enzymes are proteinlike substances that catalyze (speed up) biochemical reactions. Many of them have a metallic element like iron or copper in their makeup, and these attached metals control the characteristic action of the enzyme.

A plant cell may contain hundreds of different enzymes that are active in different processes. Thus the concentration of a metal like potassium in the cell will regulate the activities of enzymes sensitive to it. Studies with bacteria show that potassium affects enzymes that control the use and transformation of sugars necessary in the life of the cell.

Tremendous amounts of calcium also are applied to our soils as superphosphate and as liming materials.

Lime does more than merely correct acidity of soil. The calcium in lime is a highly essential nutrient to plants. Calcium concentration in the cell affects the activities of certain enzymes, but it is especially important in combining with pectin to form calcium pectate—a sort of cementing material laid down between cells that aids in holding them together.

A deficiency of calcium first shows by death or distortion of the cells in the growing points of shoots and roots. In fact, the roots of most crop plants must have a supply of available calcium immediately at the growing root tips and cannot depend on calcium available in other parts of the root zone if the roots are to continue to grow.

The subsoil of very acid sandy soils in the Atlantic Coastal Plain often is devoid of roots, even though the soil is porous and water supply is adequate. Roots of crop plants cannot cope with the prevailing deficiency of calcium. Peanut pegs will not grow in a soil layer deficient in calcium even though calcium is supplied to the roots.

These observations indicate that growing plants do not have the ability to translocate calcium effectively from one part of a plant to another. Potassium moves from older leaves to the growing points under deficiency conditions, but calcium does not.

Magnesium is another metallic element that is used in plant growth in appreciable amounts. It is also active in enzyme systems, but it is especially significant in that an atom of magnesium is the central part of every chlorophyll molecule in cells of green leaves. Thus the magnesium taken up from the soil has a vital part in the photosynthetic process.

Sulfur is the sixth mineral element of major importance in the health and growth of plants. Sulfur is a component of important amino acids—organic acids containing nitrogen groups— present in plant cells. Amino acids are the building blocks of proteins. Certain amino acids that also contain sulfur are essential in the makeup of the various proteinaceous constituents of protoplasm.

Sulfur is just as essential as nitrogen in making new protoplasm for plant cells, but its deficiency in the soil is not so prevalent.

Around industrial areas where sulfur dioxide is going into the atmosphere from furnace stacks, plants may absorb a major part of their sulfur from the air through the leaves. Sulfur dioxide in the air at concentrations of 1 part per million can kill the cells in leaves.

Besides the six so-called major mineral nutrients, seven others are some-times designated as the trace elements. They are iron, manganese, zinc, copper, boron, molybdenum, and chlorine. These seven are not less essential than the six major mineral nutrients, but they are required at much lower levels. They are considered in detail in later chapters, but we discuss them here primarily as they influence the growth of plants.

A deficiency of iron in plants is reflected in yellowness of leaves. Iron is not a part of the chlorophyll molecule, but it is essential for the formation of chlorophyll. Iron is the central atom of heme—a complex atom similar to chlorophyll that comprises the red pigment of blood hemoglobin. These iron-containing compounds regulate respiration in plant cells through their association with enzymes. Some soils are on the borderline in providing adequate iron to plants, and management practices may have an effect. Thus soils in the peach orchards around Grand Junction, Colo., may readily bring about severe iron-deficiency chlorosis in the trees. The tendency is augmented by overirrigation, plowing under cover crops, or excessive phosphate fertilization.

Manganese is essential in certain enzyme systems of the plant cell. Too little manganese is reflected in a type of chlorosis of the leaves. An interrelationship may exist between iron and manganese in the effects on growth processes—that is, a high level of manganese may intensify iron-deficiency chlorosis.

Zinc also is an essential part of certain enzyme systems. Plants that do not get enough of it have small, thickened leaves on shortened internodes of the stem. Chlorotic areas develop between veins of leaves. Corn, tung trees, and citrus are especially sensitive to a deficiency of zinc.

Copper is present in the active part of such enzymes as polyphenoloxidase, an enzyme that is important in the respiratory processes of many plants.

Boron is somewhat like calcium in that it is essential in continuous supply to the main growing points of plants. Otherwise the tips of growing roots and shoots die. Storage tissues become corky. Sugars and starches tend to accumulate, instead of being transferred from cell to cell and from tissue to tissue. Plants are sensitive to an excess of boron in the soil; in fact, levels exceeding only 1 part per million in the soil solution are toxic to sensitive plants, such as beans and lemon trees.

Molybdenum needs to be present in only minute amounts. It is essential in the enzymatic processes, which convert nitrate nitrogen taken up from the soil to organic nitrogen forms, which are used in synthesizing amino acids and proteins.

Chlorine needs to be present in the form of the chloride ion in minute amounts. Its role in plant metabolism has not been established.

All these mineral nutrients that are essential for the growth and function of plants are taken up from the soil by the roots. Before we explore how and why these elements enter the roots, it is important that we consider at least one more important component of the living cell—water.

WATER is the medium that disperses the protoplasm in the cell. It is a medium by which physical force is effected on the cell wall to bring about expansion and growth.

Only a small part of the water taken up by the roots from the soil is retained in the cells of the plants. Most of the water that is absorbed is conducted to the leaves, where it is lost by evaporation or transpiration. Since the evaporation of 1 gram of water requires 539 calories, the high rate of water loss that takes place from leaves on hot summer days acts as an evaporative cooler. One mature tomato plant in a warm, arid climate will transpire a gallon of water in a day. As much as 700 tons of water may be needed to produce 1 ton of alfalfa hay. The water that is transpired by a cornfield in Iowa in a growing season is enough to cover the field to a depth of 13 to 15 inches.

The loss of water from plants is controlled by incident light energy, relative humidity, temperature, wind, opening of pores (called stomata) in leaves, and supply of water in soil.

Incident light energy is the most important factor because the evaporation of water requires a source of energy. Relative humidity is also important because evaporation takes place much more rapidly in a dry atmosphere than in a humid one. The other factors I mentioned are of a relatively minor consequence.

If water loss by transpiration exceeds water intake by the roots, a water deficit develops in the plant, expansion of growing cells ceases, and the plant stops growing. If the water deficit continues, the plant wilts. If it becomes too severe, the plant tissues wither and die.

By what means can plant cells absorb and retain water when the atmosphere is evaporating it from the leaves and the soil is impeding its entry into the roots? An illustration:

When salt is applied to shredded cabbage, the tissue fluids diffuse out of the leaf slices and dissolve the salt, making a brine. The cabbage shreads become limp, or flaccid. If the limp shreads are washed free of brine and placed in pure water, they again become stiff or turgid. This exemplifies one of the most fundamental characteristics of the water relationships of plants. It is the diffusion of water through a semipermeable membrane—more commonly called osmosis. When two solutions differing in concentration are separated by a membrane impermeable to the dissolved substance, water moves from the solution of lower concentration to the one of higher concentration. (Water in the shredded cabbage diffuses out to the more concentrated brine surrounding the shreds.)

The force with which water moves across such a membrane is called osmotic pressure, which is measured in atmospheres (1 atmosphere equals 14.6 pounds to the square inch). A 4-percent sugar solution has an osmotic pressure of about 3 atmospheres. Thus, if this 4-percent sugar solution were separated from pure water by a semipermeable membrane, the driving force causing the water molecules to cross the membrane and enter the sugar solution is 3 atmospheres, or 44 pounds to the square inch. If this 4-percent sugar solution were contained in a nonexpandable cell having a limited capacity for water, the hydraulic pressure on the walls of the cell would equal the osmotic pressure of the solution. This hydraulic pressure on the walls is the turgor pressure of plant growth. It is the force that causes cells to expand and plants to grow.

Now if the cell containing the 4-percent sugar solution were surrounded by a 2-percent sugar solution having an osmotic pressure of 1.5 atmospheres, the net driving force across the cell wall causing water to enter would be only 1.5 atmospheres, calculated thus: Inside pressure of 3.0 atmospheres minus outside pressure of 1.5 atmospheres equals a driving force of 1.5 atmospheres. Hence the hydraulic, or turgor, pressure of the cell solution pushing outward on the cell wall would also be only 1.5 atmospheres.

If the osmotic pressure of the bathing solution equalled that of the cell solution, then turgor pressure, the force effecting cell expansion, would be zero. Hydraulic forces other than osmotic pressure are involved in the suction of water into cells and the creation of the wall pressure effective in the turgor and growth of cells.

Evaporation of water from leaf cells around the terminals of the conductive tubes induces a water deficit in these cells that is transferred down through the conductive tubes to all parts of the plants, including the roots.

We do not ordinarily think of water as having the tensile properties of a rope, yet if we look at a drop of water on a piece of wax paper, we see that the water coheres into a spherical droplet having a minimum of surface exposed. This tendency of water to form into discrete drops illustrates the high surface tension of water—the high affinity of one water molecule for another.

This cohesion between water molecules is so great that in very fine tubes water can actually be pulled up to great heights. This is the mechanism by which water is brought to the tops of tall trees 200 feet or more in height; the actuating force for the movement of water up the very fine tubes in the stem is the transpirational pull developed by evaporation of water from the leaves.

The force of the transpirational pull up the stem can greatly exceed the osmotic pull by cells for water. If that happens, the cells lose water and turgidity, and the plant wilts. This emphasizes the key importance of water supply from soil to the roots in meeting the water needs while maintaining turgidity of cells so essential for growth.

We come now to the vital contributions of roots in the growth of our crop plants. Not only do they absorb water that is so essential in rather tremendous amounts, but they also take in the many mineral elements necessary for the life of plant protoplasm.

Roots also take up some elements (silicon, sodium, strontium, selenium, arsenic, cobalt, iodine) that are not essential to the plant. Excessive accumulation of these and of the essential elements can be toxic to the plant.

The way by which soil management affects plant growth is mostly through influences on the environment of the roots. It follows therefore that in some degree we should fit tillage practices to the peculiarities of the roots of the crop we are growing.

Different crops vary greatly in the nature and extent of their root systems. The roots of spinach and celery are confined mostly to the surface foot of soil. Most of the roots of potatoes are within the surface 2 feet. Corn, cotton, and tomatoes permeate an open soil to a depth of 4 feet or more. Alfalfa and asparagus roots readily penetrate good soil to a depth of 8 to 10 feet or more. Cucumber roots extend laterally 5 or 6 feet in the plowed layer. Asparagus roots make little lateral spread in comparison with their depth.

The concentration of roots of many plants in the plowed layer has an important bearing on tillage practices. Deep cultivation may effect severe root pruning and damage the plant. Roots of some crops proliferate much more than others. Potatoes and celery are known to have roots that do a poor job of permeating the soil, but the grasses have roots usually characterized by a high degree of proliferation.

A study at the University of Iowa of the roots of a single winter rye plant illustrates how extensive the root system of a grass plant may be. The plant was grown for 4 months in 1 cubic foot of loam soil. Then the roots were carefully liberated by spraying with water for several hours. It was determined that this one plant had approximately 13,800,000 roots, with a length of more than 385 miles and a surface area of about 2,550 square feet. The root hairs of this plant numbered approximately 14 billion, with a total length of more than 6,600 miles and a surface area of about 4,320 square feet. These calculated figures illustrate the high proportion of the linear growth of a plant that takes place beneath the ground surface.

Each species of plant has certain inherent characteristics of its root system, such as length and depth of penetration and degree of proliferation, but soil conditions may modify the characteristics.

Root penetration is seriously inhibited by the presence of compacted layers in soils. The prevalence of compacted layers at the plowsole effectively confines roots of crops in many of our cultivated soils in the surface 6 to 8 inches. The adverse effect on roots of soil compaction resulting from tillage and harvesting machinery has become a serious agricultural problem.

Roots cannot penetrate ledges or hard layers except through cracks. Thus on shallow soils the roots may be confined to a thin layer. Studies carried out during the Second World War by the Department of Agriculture on guayule, a shrub that produces rubber latex, illustrate the point. Two-year-old plants on a Lewisville silty clay in San Antonio, Tex., sent their roots down 16 feet, but 30-year-old guayule plants on an Ector stony loam in Brewster County, Tex., had their roots confined to the surface 2 feet by the prevalence of limestone flagstones alternating with dry shale.

When roots penetrate soils made up of interspersed layers of sandy material and clay loam, proliferation usually is much greater in the layers of clay loam than in those made up of sandy soil.

Roots make practically no growth into soil depleted in moisture down to and below the permanent wilting percentage. Roots are hydrotropic—they will grow in a direction toward increasing available moisture if they are not impeded by a very dry layer.

Roots may grow upward to a moist layer maintained at the soil surface. Frequent light sprinklings of water on lawns tend to keep the roots of grass near the surface of the soil and thereby impair the ability of the grass to withstand drought and to absorb nutrients present in the soil below the surface a few inches.

Roots of most plants will not enter wet, saturated soils.

High water tables limit root penetration and may even kill roots that had previously penetrated below the water table. High water table conditions that restrict roots to a shallow surface layer during the spring impair the capacity of the plant to stand a drought during the summer.

Wet soils impair root activity to the extent that they restrict aeration—exposure to air. Soil pores filled with water leave no room for air. Roots are actively alive and need a continuous supply of oxygen to remain healthy.

There is also a need for dissipation of the carbon dioxide given off by root respiration. An accumulation of carbon dioxide at the root surface can be toxic. Facility for gaseous transfer in a soil is a good measure of its suitability as a physical medium for root growth.

Plants killed by flooding of soils usually die from physiological drought. Flooding keeps air from the roots. Unaerated roots of most plants cannot absorb water.

THE TEMPERATURE of the soil also affects the development of roots, but it does so through its influence on cell activity, particularly respiration. It is pertinent therefore to consider in more detail how the cells in the surfaces of roots absorb water and nutrients.

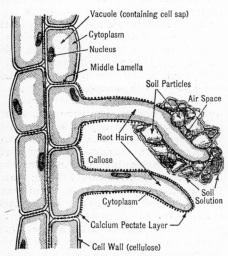

1. Surface cells of a root. The development of root hairs and their penetration among soil particles are shown. (From Experiment Station, Hawaiian Sugar Planters' Association)

The drawing illustrates a small section of the absorbing surface of a root. Note that root hairs are tubular extensions from the wall of the surface cell located one-fourth inch to 1 inch back from the growing point of the root. Note also that the root hairs make close contact with soil particles as the hairs protrude in an irregular course through interstices among the particles. Furthermore, the film of water that surrounds each soil particle touches the surface of the root hair. There is also illustrated the vital air pore spaces that must maintain oxygen supply to the root cells and transport carbon dioxide away from the roots. Parts of the root not covered by root hairs also maintain intimate contact with the soil particles and their surrounding moisture films.

We have noted that a single plant may have an astronomical number of root hairs, which provide a seemingly enormous surface for contact with soil particles. The roots of a winter rye plant were found to have a total surface of 6,870 square feet. The plant was grown in a cubic foot of loam soil. Such a soil will have a specific surface of about 20 square feet to a cubic centimeter. The surface on all the millions of particles contained in a cubic centimeter of loam will add up to about 20 square feet. Calculations show that the particles in a cubic foot of such a soil will have a total surface of about 560,000 square feet. That is, what we regarded as an enormous root surface was really only a little over 1 percent of the soil surface available for contact. In other words, even this highly proliferous root system did not come in contact with 98 percent of the soil particle surface.

Water enters the roots from the soil particle films as a result of osmotic forces in cells or through the pull of transpiration transferred from the leaves. Cells must be alive and active to absorb water. If the oxygen supply is deficient, the root-absorbing cells may become asphyxiated and stop absorbing water, and the plant wilts.

Unduly low temperatures may also impede water absorption by root cells. Sudden hot spells in spring when the soil is still comparatively cool cause cotton plants to wilt, even though soil moisture is adequately available. Too low a temperature around the roots limits absorption of water. Toxic substances that impair the health of root cells also impede the absorption of water.

As the roots absorb water from the films surrounding the soil particles, the films become thinner, and the remaining moisture is held by the soil particle with greater tenacity.

At the moisture content of field capacity—the soil moisture content a few days following a heavy rain when free internal drainage has stopped—the soil particles hold the moisture with a force equivalent to 0.01 atmosphere.

When the plant has removed the soil moisture down to the permanent wilting percentage, the soil particles hold the moisture with a force equivalent to about 15 atmospheres.

The movement of moisture along the surfaces of particles towards the root surface is slower as the moisture films become thinner. Thus both energy of retention and movement may contribute to impeding water entry into roots at low levels of soil moisture.

The moisture held by the soil between field capacity and the permanent wilting percentage is termed the available soil moisture.

Sandy loams hold about 1 inch of available water per foot of depth. Clay loams hold about 2 inches of available water per foot of depth. The soil moisture reservoir available to a plant is equal to the depth of the active root zone of the plant times the amount of available water per foot of soil. Thus spinach growing in a sandy loam will have a soil-moisture reservoir equivalent to a 1-inch layer of water, but a deep-rooted alfalfa field in a clay loam will have a moisture reservoir of 12 inches. Obviously the status of the soil-moisture reservoir is of key importance in enabling growth of plants during extended periods of drought.

The mineral nutrients absorbed by the roots are adsorbed on the surfaces of the soil particles or dissolved in the moisture films surrounding the particles. Maybe you assume that the minerals move into the absorbing cells of roots along with the entry of water. That is not necessarily so. Although minerals move in along with water pulled by transpiration, they also will move in even if transpiration is nil.

The accumulation of mineral ions by root cells is an active life process effected by energy released by respiration of the cell. Any condition in the root environment such as low temperature, lack of aeration, and the presence of toxins that impair respiration will likewise adversely affect absorption of mineral ions.

As is evident in the drawing, in order for minerals to reach the vacuoles of a cell, they must move through the cytoplasm around its inner wall.

The cytoplasm—cytoplasm plus nucleus equals protoplasm—has remarkable powers of accumulating and retaining certain minerals. For example, a root cell may accumulate potassium in its vacuoles to 20 to 30 times its concentration in the soil solution. The cells retain the accumulated potassium against the high tendency for outward diffusion as long as it is actively alive. If the cell is full, the potassium will immediately diffuse out.

Although potassium and sodium are quite alike chemically, the cytoplasm in the roots of many plants differentiates them—accumulating potassium while excluding sodium. Since nutrient absorption depends on energy released from respiration, it also follows that the supply of respiratory substrate (sugars) in the root cells regulates mineral intake. The sugars providing this energy are transported down from the leaves. In this manner, conditions of the aerial environment affecting photosynthesis and sugar accumulation may have a direct bearing on absorption of mineral nutrients by the roots.

The mineral reservoir available to the plant is conditional, as is the soil moisture reservoir, upon the extent and proliferation of the root system. Since the plowed layer is the main source of minerals in most soils, it is obviously important that the roots develop maximum permeation of this layer.

Thus we see that the vegetative growth of a plant is the resultant of a complex interrelationship of a large number of environmental factors upon the constituent cells in the plant. In a number of crops, the grower has no economic interest beyond the phase of growth termed vegetative development,

Potatoes, sugarcane, sugar beets, hay crops, and the leafy vegetables are examples, but the farmer growing cotton, soybeans, fruits, grains, and seeds must produce something besides stems and leaves.

Why does a plant go into the flowering stage? We do not know exactly. When a plant has reached a certain age and the proper environmental conditions prevail, certain cells in the growing points initiate the development of tissues that become flower parts.

Investigations by Department of Agriculture scientists some 20 years ago showed that the flowering of many plants is controlled by length of day. Some flower during the long days (short nights) of early summer and others flower during the shorter days (longer nights) of late summer and early fall. Other species of plants are induced into flowering by exposure to low temperature. For example, sugar beets, cabbage, and cauliflower must go through a cold period before they will flower.

Soil-management practices may affect flowering through their influences on vegetative vigor. Vigorous plants are usually delayed in flowering but this may be compensated for by increased intensity of flowering.

The maturation of seed is largely influenced by the previous vegetative status of the plant, weather conditions, and soil moisture. The problem of soft corn is a good illustration of the economic importance of the right growing conditions and good weather and seed maturation.

The production of our crop plants is determined by their inherent capabilities to grow within the limitations imposed by environmental conditions. The farmer can do relatively little to improve the weather conditions prevailing on his fields, but he can have a major influence through soil management upon the environment of the roots of his crops: A plant is a living entity derived from soil, sunshine, air. The soil is not the least of these three.

Soil Moisture

L. A. Richards and S. J. Richards

The efficient use of the available supply of soil moisture is usually a major aspect of soil management. It may dominate crop selection, time and rate of planting, tillage operations, weed control measures, and programs of fertilization.

Soil moisture is seldom ideal for best crop yields. Some soils are too wet, even for a part of the year, and artificial drainage may be profitable. In some places a lack of soil moisture limits crop yields, and irrigation or moisture-conserving practices are used.

Statistical studies for semiarid and subhumid climates usually show a significant correlation between effective precipitation and crop yields. Irrigation often is feasible, even when the investment is considerable. Without irrigation in semiarid and subhumid regions, soil-management practices strongly emphasize the efficiency of use of the available moisture supply.

In humid climates, if other factors are favorable, deficiency of soil moisture may limit crop growth oftener than is generally realized. The possibility of a significant deficiency depends on the crop and the soil as well as the climate. Studies of evapotranspiration in relation to climate indicate that yield-depressing droughts occur with almost statistical regularity in many climates, even though the average precipitation during the cropping season may exceed the total amount needed by the crop.

Supplemental irrigation in humid climates is often feasible because of proximity to a water source and is becoming more widely practiced.

Technicians have gained much information on the effect of soil-management practices in determining the amount of water that enters the soil and the amount that runs off and is lost by surface drainage. Terracing, contour furrows, contour cultivation, and basin listing are used for reducing runoff. Crop residues are left to protect the soil surface from puddling and evaporation. All cultural practices affecting soil structure, at the surface and below, are involved. These and other subjects related to infiltration, erosion, and evaporation have a direct and controlling effect on soil moisture, and are treated in later chapters. Chapters are devoted also to irrigation and drainage. This discussion deals with the general principles relating to the retention and conduction of water by soil—principles that apply to soil management under a variety of conditions of climates, crops, and soils.

THE RETENTION of water by soil is related to the size and arrangement of the soil pores: In the soil pore system water moves and is retained for plant use. The ratio of the volume that is not occupied by soil particles to the bulk volume of the soil is called the porosity.

Fine-textured soils tend to have higher porosity than coarse soils—when all of the pores are filled with water, a fine soil usually contains more water than a coarse soil. Sandy soils tend to have a preponderance of large pores. Clay soils, which contain many fine particles, tend mainly to have small pores. During and following the entry of rain and irrigation water, sandy soils with their large pores usually conduct water more rapidly than fine-textured soils. For that reason and because they contain less water to begin with, sandy soils retain less water for plant use.

If a bucket of soil is connected to a water reservoir as at A, the soil will

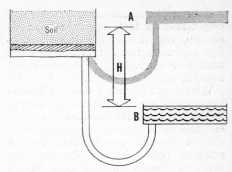

1. A system for measuring the water content of soil in relation to the suction supplied by a hanging column of water.

approach saturation. When the reservoir is lowered to B, some (but not all) of the water drains back into the reservoir. The soil retains a certain amount, depending on interconnection and size distribution of pores in the soil. With such an arrangement, each lowering of the reservoir will produce an additional outflow of water from the soil. A layer of permeable material with fine pores, such as a porous ceramic plate, can be placed in the bottom of the bucket to keep air from getting into the suction line. The suction of the vertical column of water extending down to the free water surface in the reservoir is counterbalanced after each outflow increment by an increased suction developed in the water films remaining in the soil. This suction depends on force action at the soil and water surfaces.

The suction required to empty a soil pore depends on its size. The volume of water retained in a soil at a given suction is therefore related to the volume of pore space smaller than a given size. The water content of a soil at a specified suction and structure is called retentivity. The water retention curve is based on a number of retentivity values. Such curves provide a picture of pore size distribution.

The terms "soil suction" and "soil moisture tension" have identical meaning and may be used interchangeably. In this example, the suction is controlled, and the soil moisture makes a corresponding adjustment. Under field conditions, the soil moisture content changes and the suction changes accordingly. Suction is reduced when water is added to the soil by rainfall or irrigation and, conversely, suction is increased when soil moisture is depleted by drainage, root absorption, or evaporation.

Suction is related to the relative wetness of soil and, over a restricted range, can be measured with a tensiometer. This is a standard soil moisture instrument consisting of a porous cup, which is connected to a vacuum gage and filled with water. Commercial instruments usually employ a Bourdon gage, as shown at the left in the illustration.

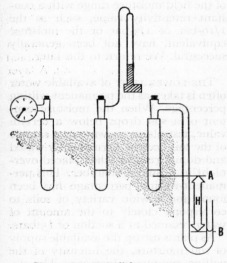

2. Tensiometers use dial gages, mercury manometers, or water columns for measuring soil suction. The length H on the water manometer represents suction head in the soil adjacent to the cup.

A mercury manometer, mounted above the ground on the tensiometer tube, often is employed for suction readings in experimental work. The tensiometer unit on the right in the drawing is shown with a water manometer attached. Suction is read directly from the gage or scale in pressure units and sometimes is called soil

moisture tension. Pressure in the manometer at A is the same as in the porous cup at the same level, so the suction in the cup, and in the soil adjacent to it, is equal to that produced by the vertical length of water column from A to B. This equivalent length of water column H is called suction head and is a convenient measurement for relating suction differences to the water-moving force in soil. If the porous cup of a tensiometer were installed in the soil bucket of the preceding figure, the instrument would give a reading corresponding to the height H.

Suction values are often expressed in terms of cm. (centimeter) of water column. A larger unit is sometimes more convenient. The barometer is used for measuring atmospheric pressure and the bar is a metric unit of pressure, which is approximately equal to the pressure of the atmosphere at sea level. One bar corresponds to 1,021 cm. of water column at 20° C. One millibar therefore corresponds closely to 1 cm. of suction head.

MOISTURE RETENTION CURVES show the relationship between soil moisture and suction.

Moisture content may be expressed in various units. Moisture percentage on a dry basis is commonly used and is the weight of water per 100 units of weight of dry soil. For field applications, expressing soil moisture content as the water ratio is convenient. This is the volume of water per unit bulk volume of soil and is numerically the same as the surface depth of water per unit depth of soil. (The water ratio is determined by drying a known bulk volume of soil or by multiplying the moisture percentage, dry weight basis, by 1 percent of the bulk density of the soil when the latter is expressed in grams per cubic cm.) The equivalent surface depth of water in a soil depth interval is found by multiplying the soil depth by the average value of the water ratio in the interval. This is convenient because rainfall and irrigation water are also expressed in terms of the equivalent surface depth of water.

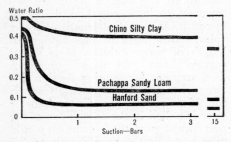

3. Water retention curves for three soils. Water content is expressed in terms of the water ratio which is the volume of water per unit bulk volume of soil.

The accompanying curves show the moisture retention properties of a fine-, a medium-, and a coarse-textured soil. Core samples having field structure were initially saturated, and successive water contents were determined by weighing after equilibrium was established at successively increasing suction values. Suction control apparatus like that illustrated above could be used for such measurements. With the soil supported on a layer of material with fine pores, it is more convenient to obtain the pressure difference across the supporting layer by increasing the air pressure inside the soil chamber. With this arrangement, the outflow of water from the soil takes place at atmospheric pressure and is easy to measure. Cessation of outflow indicates that hydraulic equilibrium is attained between the soil and the suction control surface. The suction value in the soil is then equal to the excess air pressure in the chamber.

Over the suction range from zero to 150 bars, soil moisture retention is represented by a smooth, continuous curve. There is no water content or suction value in this range at which the water appears to undergo a marked change in properties or state. Older terms used for classifying soil water, such as gravitational, capillary, and hygroscopic water, are hard to identify with physical properties of the system.

Pore size distribution determines the shape of a retention curve at the low suction end. At the saturation point— that is, zero suction, when all the pores become filled—the volume of water per unit bulk volume of soil equals the porosity. For the sandy soil in the figure, small increases in suction at the wet end of the curve caused a large decrease in water content, thus indicating the presence of pores having large size. For the clay soil, on the other hand, no water outflow occurred below a suction of 100 millibars. This means that starting with saturation under field conditions, downward drainage to a water table at a depth of 1 meter would still leave this soil saturated clear to the surface.

Attempts to identify the upper limit of the field moisture range with a constant retentivity value, such as the 1/10-bar or 1/3-bar or the moisture equivalent, have not been generally successful. We return to this later.

THE LOWER LIMIT of available water often is taken as the permanent-wilting percentage. When the moisture content of a soil drops below a certain value, test plants growing in a sample of the soil become permanently wilted and do not recover when placed overnight in a humid chamber. This permanent-wilting percentage has been found for a wide variety of soils to correspond closely to the amount of water retained at a suction of 15 bars.

As plants use up the available supply of soil moisture, the intensity of the wilting symptoms increases. The degree of wilting of leaves depends on the balance between water uptake by the roots and evaporation from the leaves, so that weather and the characteristics of the crop also are involved.

Corresponding to the range of wilting symptoms is a wilting range of soil moisture. The so-called permanent-wilting percentage corresponds to a selected degree of wilting and represents a somewhat arbitrary point in the wilting range. The usefulness and significance of the 15-bar percentage depends directly on the fact that it corresponds closely to the permanent-wilting percentage. Under certain cropping conditions, soil moisture in the field is depleted below the 15-bar percentage. The minimum moisture for wheat grown in the Great Plains is well below the 26-bar percentage in the 60- to 120-cm. depth interval.

The suction range corresponding to the wilting range can be obtained by locating the measured moisture content values on the retention curve and reading the corresponding suction values. This is not a very reliable procedure because of the large rate of change of suction with respect to moisture content. By this method, however, it is estimated that for various plants and soils wilting takes place in the suction range from 10 to 60 bars.

Curves relating soil moisture to suction for a given soil sample are not single valued. The water uptake curve lies beneath or below the water release curve, and the time required for soil to reach hydraulic equilibrium is much longer. Moisture release curves are believed to be more generally representative of field conditions and therefore are much more commonly dealt with. The hysteresis effect, however, must not be ignored or forgotten.

The water retained by a given soil at high suctions is associated with the surface area of the soil particles. The surface area per unit mass of soil is called the specific surface. Specific surface values are surprisingly high. A clay, for example, may have as much as 25 acres of surface area for 1 pound of soil. A sandy soil will have much less—from 3 to 5 acres of surface area a pound. At suctions of the order of 10 bars and above, the retention curve is nearly flat. A small change in soil-water content (that is, a small change in film thickness) produces a large change in suction. Suction is a convenient measure of the physical condition of water in soil and the tenacity with which water is held by soil.

Vapor transfer of water through soil occurs by molecular diffusion through the connected gas-filled pore space. This mechanism is relatively more important in dry soils because more pore space is available for transmitting the vapor and also because the vapor pressure difference, which is the direct cause of vapor diffusion, is likely to be higher.

At constant temperature, the aqueous vapor pressure in soil pores changes only slightly with the water content of the soil in the plant growth moisture range. The vapor pressure of soil at the wilting point is below the vapor pressure of the same soil at saturation by less than 2 percent. In other words, the air contained in soil that is dry enough to cause crop plants to wilt is still more than 98 percent saturated, and the vapor pressure difference that is due to differences in water content alone will be small in the root zone for agricultural crops.

Temperature, however, has a strong effect on the vapor pressure of soil water, and temperature gradients produce marked vapor pressure gradients in the soil air system. Steep temperature gradients are most likely to occur near the soil surface or where there is a freezing zone in the profile. There is evidence that, except very near the soil surface and then mainly for longtime effects involving weeks or months, vapor transfer of water in soil in the root zone of growing crops is not very significant agriculturally.

LIQUID AND FILM FLOW are the main mechanisms responsible for water transfer in soil. Marked progress is being made in applying hydraulics to the processes involved. It is useful to have general principles that apply to and describe water movement in all soils.

A prime element in this theory is the law that flow is proportional to the driving force. This is a basic relation that holds for heat and electricity and for a long time has been known to apply to soil moisture. Only recently, however, have methods for measuring the driving force and the proportionality factor been developed to such a stage that they can be applied to soils under field conditions. The effect of temperature on liquid and film flow of water in soil can be taken into account, but in many instances temperature effects do not appear to be very significant.

The flow law may be expressed by the equation $v = ki$, in which v is the volume of water crossing unit area perpendicular to the flow in unit time. The proportionality factor k is called the hydraulic conductivity, and i is the water-moving force. At each point in the soil, the effective velocity v is equal to the product of the conductivity and the driving force. The latter may be conveniently expressed relative to gravity and has two components. These are the gravity force and a pressure-gradient force. The gravity force per unit amount of soil water is of constant magnitude and always acts in the downward direction with an intensity we refer to as 1 g. The pressure-gradient force, on the other hand, may vary both in direction and magnitude. For flow of water in unsaturated soil, the pressure force, expressed in g units, is equal to the gradient of the suction head. This is the change in suction head per unit distance through the soil in the direction of the greatest rate of increase in suction.

Examples will illustrate the value of instrument readings and a flow theory. Consider cores of the sand, loam, and clay for which the water retention curves were given earlier. For arbitrarily selected values of the water ratio R equal to 0.10, 0.20, and 0.43, the suction values S would be 250, 500, and 750 millibars, respectively. If these soil cores, while resting on a table as shown in the illustration, are pressed into contact, water will move from the sand to the loam and both will lose water to the clay even though the latter has a much higher moisture content. It is possible to specify these flow directions because in the horizontal direction there is no component of the gravity force, and flow takes place in the direction of the increase in

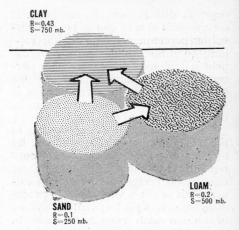

CLAY
R=0.43
S=750 mb.

LOAM
R=0.2
S=500 mb.

SAND
R=0.1
S=250 mb.

4. *The relationship of suction to the movement of water is illustrated by the soil cores on a table. The water ratio R and suction S are indicated for each soil. Lateral water flow, which is indicated by the arrows, is controlled by suction difference rather than moisture content difference.*

suction. The suction values indicated were taken from the retention curves but could have been measured with tensiometers.

As another example, consider a wick rolled up from a piece of cheesecloth that is immersed in water, pressed out lightly, and supported from above by the fingers. With just a slight water deficit, no dripping occurs when the roll is horizontal; if either end is lowered, however, dripping occurs immediately from the low end. The flow equation, which holds for water in any porous medium, states that flow stops only when the suction-gradient force is upward and equal in magnitude to the downward gravity force. This condition of zero water-moving force is always met when water is at static equilibrium under gravity. Suction and the suction gradient in the cheesecloth roll, as in the case also for soil, are determined by water content and the water content gradient in the roll.

In the horizontal position, the suction difference required to counterbalance gravity is small because the vertical distance is small. With the roll in the vertical position, the vertical distance

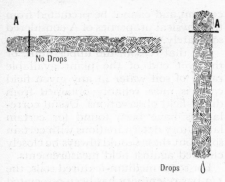

5. *A device for illustrating hydraulic effects from underlying soil layers. The cheesecloth roll retains water in the horizontal position. When rotated to the vertical, however, outflow commences immediately because of the suction difference produced by the longer vertical column.*

in the roll is greater and the suction difference necessary to counterbalance gravity will be greater. For static equilibrium, there must be one unit of increase in suction head for each unit of increase of elevation. In order to meet or establish this condition, water is moved downward by the gravity force. This causes the lower part of the wick to become saturated, the suction is reduced to zero, and water drips from the lowest point.

This illustrates a second law of soil moisture which is of the nature of a boundary condition; namely, that free outflow will occur from soil or other porous medium only if the suction reduces to zero.

The outflow process maintains the suction at the bottom of the wick at the zero value until the suction head at the top of the wick is equal to the elevation of the top above the drip point. This makes the upward suction gradient equal to one unit of suction head per unit of vertical distance and corresponds to an upward suction force of 1 g. This cancels gravity and brings the water-moving force in the roll to zero; the flow stops. The amount of water the end of the roll that is marked "A" will hold depends on the underlying hydraulic system that controls the water-moving force and the suction

head at A. This example has application to field soil and will be referred to again.

The rate at which water drains from the root zone following an application of water is of importance to farmers. This rate depends directly on the suction gradient. If the profile is dry and wetting is shallow, drainage will be speeded up by a downward suction gradient. If the same soil is deeply wetted, the downward suction gradient will be smaller and surface soil will remain wetter for a longer time. The downward suction force is decreased by the presence of a shallow water table because, by definition, the suction is zero at the water table. The water table is the locus of points in the soil-water system where the suction is zero.

A soil layer in which the hydraulic conductivity is low slows the drainage of overlying soil. It is recalled that the flow velocity is equal to the product of the conductivity and the water-moving force. Velocity is low in the restricting layer because the conductivity is low. Velocity is low above the restricting layer because the water-moving force is low. A temporary water table forms or tends to form just above the restricting layer. This lowers the suction gradient, lowers the downward water-moving force, and consequently lowers the drainage rate in overlying soil. Thus the water-moving force acting to remove water from surface soil depends importantly on hydraulic conditions, including water distribution, in the underlying soil. This was illustrated by the example of the cheesecloth roll. In the horizontal position, the water-moving force in the end marked A quickly dropped to zero and drainage ceased. In the vertical position, however, the water-moving force at A was controlled by hydraulic conditions at a lower depth, and water loss from A by downward drainage took place rapidly and occurred over a longer time and to a greater degree.

The condition for static equilibrium of water in a field profile is seldom attained. It might occasionally be approached under conditions of a high steady water table and with negligible evaporation at the soil surface. Usually, however, the water-moving force is not zero. The moisture content of field soil changes with time, whether or not plant roots are present. The velocity of water movement in surface soil decreases with time following wetting, but it is not easy to specify the time after which the movement rate becomes negligible for agricultural purposes.

THE WATER RETAINED in soil for crop use is important to farmers and is frequently measured and studied. The upper limit of the plant-available range is often referred to as the field capacity and is determined by oven-drying samples of soil that are taken from the profile at some time following a rain or an irrigation. Values obtained for a given soil depend on the sampling time and moisture distribution in the profile.

Attempts have been made to estimate field capacity from laboratory measurements on soil samples. The water retained in an air-dried and screened sample of soil that is saturated and brought to equilibrium on a porous plate at a suction of 1/10 bar has been found to correlate reliably with water contents observed in the field following the irrigation of sandy soils in certain localities. Similarly, the moisture equivalent, which corresponds closely to the 1/3-bar retentivity, has been related to field capacity for some medium-textured soils.

The futility of looking for a laboratory determination that can be generally used for indicating the field capacity of all soils may be indicated by reference again to the example of the roll of cheesecloth. Numerous laboratory measurements could be made of the intrinsic moisture properties of a sample clipped from the wick, such as the end A, but the water-moving force that caused drainage from A in the vertical position was determined by hydraulic conditions elsewhere in the

column and cannot be predicted from the physical properties of A considered separately.

For that reason, the upper limit, or the wet end of the plant available range of soil water in any given field case, is most reliably obtained from direct field observations. Useful correlations have been found for certain laboratory determinations with certain soils, but these should always be closely checked against field measurements.

For some medium-textured soils, the 1/3-bar retentivity has been associated with field capacity. As a result, it is sometimes concluded incorrectly that suction at field capacity is near the 1/3-bar value. A day or two following deep wetting by rain or irrigation, tensiometers usually indicate soil suction in the range from 20 to 100 millibars.

The lower limit of available water is a much more definite figure. Because of the low value of the capillary conductivity in the wilting range, it can be reliably related to intrinsic physical properties of a sample of soil. The wilting percentage is normally taken as the lower limit of available water, and for most practical purposes it is indistinguishable from the 15-bar percentage.

It has been customary to refer to all of the water retained in a soil between the field capacity and the wilting percentage as available water. Because of the interaction of variables related to crop and soil and their effect on depth of root zone, and also because of the uncertainties of climatic factors, the recommended time for irrigation may vary from 50 to 85 percent depletion of the available water.

THE WATER-CONTENT CHANGE due to downward drainage of water from a field soil is illustrated by the parallel straight lines in the accompanying figure, where the data on soil moisture content are plotted against time, using logarithmic scales.

The Pachappa sandy loam was the same as that represented by the middle retention curve in the earlier drawing.

This is a deep, uniform soil with unrestricted drainage and no water table. After a deep wetting of the profile, the soil surface was covered with plastic sheeting to prevent evaporation, and moisture samples were taken on the days following irrigation indicated in the figure. The volume of water per unit volume of soil was calculated for each soil sample, and the equivalent depth of water W_D in each of the several surface layers of depth D is plotted in the figure as a function of time T. For this profile it was found that the ratio W_D/D was substantially independent of depth so that all of the data can be represented by the single equation $W_D/D = aT^{-b}$, where a and b are constants. W_D/D is the average water ratio in the layer of surface soil of depth D. Because the soil surface was sealed, the rate of change of the depth of water in each surface layer of soil is equal to the downward drainage velocity, v_D, at the depth D of the lower boundary of the layer. The equation for v_D follows directly from the foregoing equation and may be written in the form

$$v_D/D = -abT^{-b-1}.$$

These equations are shown plotted to linear scales and give a complete picture of the moisture content and the flow velocity as functions of both depth and time for this profile.

CHANGE in water content due to the combined action of drainage and evaporation was also measured and is shown in the set of straight lines in the additional figure, again using logarithmic scales. It is apparent that with surface evaporation the straight lines representing moisture change with time are no longer parallel. The nearer the surface, the more rapidly the water content of the soil changes with time. The straight-line relation with log scales indicates that the rate of water loss from surface layers of this soil, with or without evaporation, is proportional to the water content and is inversely proportional to the time following irrigation.

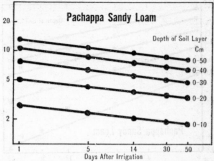

6. *Water content changes produced by drainage in a fallow soil that is protected from evaporation. The data points, which are plotted on logarithmic scales, indicate the equivalent surface depths of water contained in the various soil layers.*

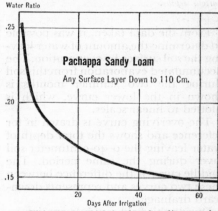

7. *This curve, which is plotted to linear scales, summarizes the data from the preceding figure. The volume of water per unit bulk volume of soil was found to be independent of depth for this particular field test.*

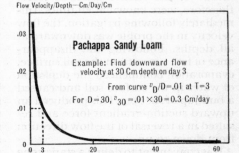

8. *The downward flow velocity as a function of time and depth. This curve is derived from the curve in the preceding figure.*

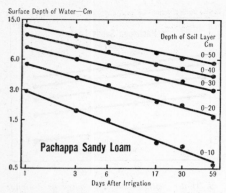

9. *Water-content changes in fallow soil as produced by drainage and evaporation. The data points, which are plotted on logarithmic scales, indicate the surface depth of water contained in soil layers of various depths.*

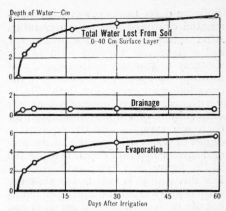

10. *The accumulated loss of water from a layer of fallow soil. These curves are plotted to linear scales and are based on the straight line for the 40-cm. layer in figure 9.*

From the data taken, it was possible to determine the amount of water leaving the soil surface by evaporation. The accumulated evaporation from this soil during the two summer months is shown in the lower curve, which is plotted to linear scales.

The overlying curve is drawn in for reference and shows the total depth of water leaving the 0–40-centimeter soil layer during the same period. The middle curve is the difference between these two curves and represents downward drainage.

During this field test, information on the suction and the suction gradient in the profile was obtained with tensiometers. Both the direction and the magnitude of the suction-gradient force, therefore, were known at all times. Immediately following irrigation, the flow velocity in the profile was downward at all depths. Following the disappearance of free water from the soil surface, evaporation commenced the depletion of water in the surface soil and caused a buildup of suction. This produced an upward suction-gradient force and resulted in a reversal of the flow direction from down to up.

It is convenient to define a static zone as that layer in the soil below which flow is downward and above which flow is upward. In the static zone, the

suction-gradient force is equal and opposite to gravity and the net water-moving force is zero. The position of the static zone in the profile was known from the tensiometer readings.

In this soil, the static zone moves downward through the profile at a fairly rapid rate. By the 14th day following irrigation, the static zone had passed below the 50-centimeter depth. It is clear that, in the soil layer above the static zone, water loss no longer occurs by drainage but moves upward in response to surface evaporation. Except in a very shallow surface layer, it was determined that this upward flow was film flow because soil salts moved with the water. Water movement in the vapor phase does not transport salt, and vapor transfer was found to be of significant magnitude only in the surface 10 or 15 cm. of soil.

In considering this example of water flow in a field profile, one should keep in mind that the foregoing data represent a deep uniform soil without restricting layers or a water table. Other soils, having different textural layers, a flow barrier, or a water table, will represent different hydraulic conditions, but the flow law that states that the flow velocity is equal to the product of the conductivity and the water-moving force holds for all cases and provides a background of theory for understanding and predicting field-flow problems, especially since the capillary conductivity and the water-moving force can be measured under field conditions.

The capillary conductivity function, like water retentivity, is an intrinsic physical property of the soil. It can now be evaluated over the whole soil-moisture range that will permit the growth of plants. The capillary conductivity of Pachappa soil is shown on log-log scales in the accompanying figure. It is apparent that the capillary conductivity falls off very rapidly as the suction increases. The capillary conductivity at a suction of 0.2 bar is 10,000 times the value at 10 bars. Nevertheless, it is believed that film flow in the wilting range is far from negligible because it is primarily this slow movement of water in the film phase that supplies water to the root system and makes it possible for certain species to survive long periods of drought.

The capillary conductivity function should play an increasingly useful role in understanding and applying available information to the moisture problems that enter into soil management. Clay soils, for example, have low conductivity at low suctions compared with sandy soils, but at high suction values the fine-textured soils have much higher capillary conductivity than the coarse-textured soils.

Consider the problem of the salinization of surface soil from a shallow ground water table. The movement of water from a water table at a depth of 1 meter in a sandy soil in response to surface evaporation may be completely negligible, whereas, in a soil like the Pachappa, the capillary conduction of water to the soil surface from a 1-meter water table is more than adequate to maintain an evaporation rate that is limited only by the external evaporative conditions. That is, the evaporation of water from the soil surface would be at the same rate as from a free water surface. The movement of

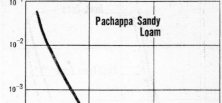

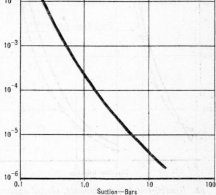

11. Capillary conductivity, which is the effective flow velocity when the water-moving force is one g, changes rapidly with suction. This physical property makes possible a quantitative treatment of soil moisture phenomena as observed in the field.

water to the soil surface from a shallow water table can now be predicted from theory, and the theoretical approach will play an increasingly useful role in field operations relating salinity, leaching, and drainage.

SOIL WATER MEASUREMENTS, for management purposes, involve two aspects.

One is the volume or quantity of water present in the soil that can be used by crops. This information has been obtained in the past by oven-drying soil samples to determine the quantity of water present. Information on the wilting point or the minimum to which the soil moisture is reduced by the crop is necessary for each individual sample in order to determine the available water. Field samplings of soil-moisture content are still widely made and are quite useful for guiding management practices, particularly in dry-farm areas. Newer methods involving neutron scattering are now being used in experimental work and may prove to be feasible in practical agricultural operations.

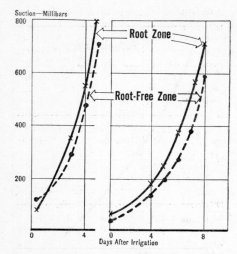

12. *Readings of two instruments, plotted against time, indicate film flow in the tensiometer suction range. One tensiometer cup (solid line) was in soil permeated by roots. In adjacent soil, another tensiometer was enclosed in a guard such that no roots came closer than 2½ cm. to the tensiometer cup (dashed line).*

The other aspect of measuring soil moisture relates to the physical status of the water in soil. In saline soils, this must involve the concentration of the soil solution as expressed in terms of osmotic pressure, but in nonsaline soils, a measurement of soil suction gives an indication of the tenacity with which the water is held and an indication of the availability of the water to plants. Because it gives a direct measure of soil suction, and also because of the very large significance of suction readings to the hydraulics of soil water, the tensiometer will always be a standard soil-moisture instrument.

Tensiometers are commonly used in irrigation agriculture as an aid in irrigation control. The question sometimes is raised as to the representativeness of a tensiometer reading and the extent to which the reading is disturbed by plant roots at the surface of the cup.

Some information on this point is given by the curves in the accompanying figure that show the reading of a tensiometer in soil directly in contact with roots and the reading of a tensi-

ometer in the same root zone where the tensiometer was enclosed within a larger porous cup so that no plant roots came within 2.5 cm. of the tensiometer cup.

The curves indicate that for this sandy loam the reading of the tensiometer that was protected from direct root action increased almost as rapidly as the nearby tensiometer, which was subjected to direct root action. The capillary conductivity for this soil in the tensiometer range of suction apparently was adequate to move water for some distance during the interval between irrigations.

In sandy soils having low contents of silt and clay, the capillary conductivity decreases rapidly as the suction increases. The suction developed in such soils at the plant roots where the moisture is absorbed is not transmitted rapidly to the cup, and wilting symptoms may develop before the tensiometer attains its maximum reading. Tensiometers will work reliably only up to suctions of about 850 millibars. This limitation must always be kept in mind, but apparently there is still a wide range of usefulness for these instruments in research on the control and measurement of moisture.

Several types of electrical resistance blocks give readings that in general respond to the soil water suction. In other words, in nonsaline soils, an electrical resistance unit comes to about the same reading, independent of the kind of soil, when a certain value of the suction is attained. There is still considerable room for improvement in instruments to measure moisture.

The subject of soil moisture is growing and developing. The flow and distribution of water in soils can be described in terms of hydraulic laws and intrinsic soil properties. Better instruments for measuring soil moisture condition and soil properties are still needed, but progress toward more efficient utilization of water in agriculture will be accelerated as the basic laws and principles relating to soil moisture become more widely used.

Use of Moisture by Plants

Sterling A. Taylor

The growth of plants reflects the rate at which energy is used to remove water from the soil to supply their needs.

Most of the water that plants take up from the soil passes out into the atmosphere as transpired water. Consequently the rate of transpiration determines more than anything else how fast water must be taken up.

Plants wilt whenever the rate of transpiration exceeds the rate at which water enters their roots. A wilted plant does not grow. If something happens to reduce the rate of transpiration— such as an increase in the relative humidity of the air or a drop in leaf temperature—the rate of uptake might exceed the rate of transpiration (or depletion), and the plant will regain turgidity—fully distended tissues—and grow again.

Weather conditions govern almost entirely the transpiration rates for turgid plants, which need more water on hot, dry, windy days than on humid, cool, or calm days. Likewise plants have greater need for water in hot, dry climates than in cool or humid climates. The needs also are greater in regions where solar radiation is high than in places where much of the sun's energy is intercepted and absorbed in the atmosphere.

The transpirational needs of crop plants are small on cool, cloudy, calm days, when the atmosphere is nearly saturated, but they might need more than one-half inch of water a day on hot, windy days when relative humidity is low.

The total water requirement for the crops is the sum of the daily requirements for every day of the season. It drops as low as 6 to 8 inches for short-season crops in humid climates. It may be 30 to 40 inches for long-season crops in arid climates.

Solar radiation strongly influences the amount of evaporation and transpiration that takes place. It is therefore a good indication of the rate at which plants require water.

The amount of solar energy arriving at the earth's surface averaged 542 calories a square centimeter a day at Albuquerque, N. Mex., in 1954; it was 288 at Astoria, Oreg. The maximum at Astoria was 585 calories a day in May; at Albuquerque it was 777 a day in June. The minimum at Albuquerque was 295 calories per square centimeter a day in December. At Astoria the minimum was 79.

Solar radiation is high throughout the dry regions of Washington, Oregon, Idaho, Utah, Nevada, California, Arizona, New Mexico, Texas, Oklahoma, Wyoming, and Kansas, where it reaches average values above 700 calories a square centimeter a day for one or more months in the year. The rate of water use is highest there.

In the humid localities of New York, Maine, Minnesota, Pennsylvania, Maryland, Rhode Island, and Massachusetts, the mean monthly solar radiations did not exceed 600 calories a square centimeter a day in 1954. The rate of water use by plants was lowest in those States.

The amount of solar radiation and rate of water use by plants were intermediate at places where measurements were made in Florida, North Carolina, Georgia, Indiana, Arkansas, Louisiana, North Dakota, and Nebraska.

The areas of high solar radiation usually have higher temperatures and lower average relative humidities. Much more soil water therefore is required for a given plant there than in areas of lower solar radiation. Local winds and other conditions can modify these generalizations.

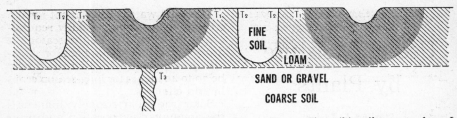

1. *Water penetrates a dry soil uniformly in all directions, as shown at T_1, until it strikes a coarse layer. It will not enter this coarse layer readily but moves laterally in the fine soil, as shown at T_2. Finally, when the soil is wet enough, it will enter the coarse soil at a few points and be channeled away as in a drain (T_3). Water continues to drain for several days after source is removed. Field capacity is the amount of water remaining after 24–48 hours of free drainage.*

WATER CAN BE STORED in the soil in limited amounts. The soil itself limits the amount that can be stored for future plant use. Some farmers supply large excesses of water to the soil during irrigation in the false belief that all the water that enters the soil will be held there until it is evaporated or used by the plant.

Excess water actually may do serious damage when it carries nutrients below the root zone or raises the water table in low-lying areas to a point where drainage may become necessary to keep the land productive. The term "field capacity" is used sometimes to express the amount of water that remains in the soil moisture reservoir after the applied surplus has leaked away.

Part of the excess water drains out rather fast in soils that have good internal drainage. It enters the water table if one exists, or it might enter dry soil and eventually create a new water table.

The movement of water into dry soil from irrigation or rain continues uniformly in all directions until it strikes a wormhole, root channel, or a change in texture or structure. Then its movement is retarded.

Soils of coarse texture or structure that are overlain by finer soil will retard the movement of water and tend to increase the amount of water retained in the finer overlying soil.

An underlying layer of fine soil may have the same effect if the water transmission rate is appreciably less in the fine material. The movement of moisture in soil does not stop when one stops applying water to the surface. Rather, the movement continues for hours or days.

Plants cannot remove all the water retained in the soil.

Lyman J. Briggs and H. L. Shantz, of the Department of Agriculture, found that about the same amount of water remained in a given soil at the end of a long, dry summer in the desert regions of Utah, regardless of the species and the size of the many kinds of plants that grew there. Different soils, however, contained different amounts of water at the end of the summer and also when plants growing in them wilted permanently.

In speaking of the availability of water to plants, they said that the permanent wilting of plants represented a point—the permanent wilting point—on a curve that relates time and the amount of water left in the soil. This point is reached when the forces opposing the further removal of soil moisture exceeds the forces exerted by the plant.

FORCES OF MOISTURE retention in soil increase as the soil dries out—the energy that must be expended to remove each additional increment of water from the soil increases; the moisture stress increases as the soil dries out.

When the soil is near field capacity, the forces that retain water in the soil increase only a little with each increment of water removed. The forces of retention increase progressively more

FINER SOIL

2. *Water penetrates dry soil uniformly in all directions* (T_1) *until it strikes an impermeable clay layer. Water enters this clay layer slowly so it moves laterally in the loam* (T_2). *As soil becomes wetter, it penetrates slowly into the clay* (T_3), *but most of the water remains in the soil, creates an excess of water, and results in poor drainage and reduced yield of crops. Water continues to drain slowly for many days. Field capacity does not exist in this soil.*

rapidly as water is removed. By the time the soil moisture has been reduced to the wilting point, the forces of retention are increasing very rapidly as moisture is removed. This fact led F. J. Viehmeyer and A. H. Hendrickson, of California, to suggest that water could be used with equal facility by plants in the moisture range from field capacity to permanent wilting point.

The concept that water is retained by forces in the soil and withdrawn when plants exert greater force was expressed by Willard Gardner, of Utah.

He showed that such terms as "field capacity" (amount of water in the soil when free drainage becomes negligible) and "permanent wilting point" or "wilting coefficient" (the amount of water in the soil when plants wilt and fail to recover unless water is added) are points on a continuous curve that relates soil moisture content to the energy required to remove water from the soil.

Therefore the facility with which plants can get water must increase as the energy required to remove water increases. Evidence to support this idea has accumulated until there is little doubt that the energy of retention affects the ease with which plants can take up water.

Plants frequently can get water fast enough to supply all their needs even though the energy required to remove the water might increase. When that is the case, plant growth may not be retarded or diminished by the lower availability of water. For some deep-rooted crops, such as alfalfa, or orchards, the surface soil might be reduced to a moisture content near the wilting point before the plant is unable to get water fast enough from greater depths to supply its needs.

Retardation in growth often occurs in dry regions where water is needed by plants at a faster rate, even though the moisture content of the surface soil is much higher than permanent wilting. Growth in the dry regions of Utah is progressively retarded as the average force of moisture retention in the soil comprising the root zone increases beyond 1 atmosphere. Field capacity corresponds to about one-third atmosphere and the wilting point to about 12 atmospheres in the same region.

M. E. Bloodworth, in experiments in Texas, learned that the rate at which water moves upward in the stem of the cotton plant decreases as the average moisture tension increases. When the soil was quite moist, the upward movement was rapid but was followed by a rapid drop in the rate of upward movement in the stem as the tension increased. When the soil became moderately dry, with tensions near 1 atmosphere, the rate of upward movement declined to about 50 percent of that when the tension was near field capacity. The further decrease in rate of moisture movement in the stems of plants was only 12 percent as the soil dried to the range of wilting, near 15 atmospheres of tension. The stresses developed within the plants must have been considerably greater when they

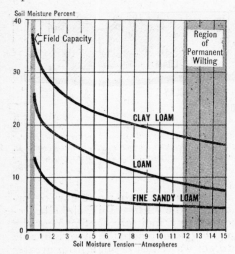

Soil Moisture Percent

3. The forces that retain water in the soil increase progressively faster as the soil dries. By the time the moisture has been reduced to the permanent wilting region, the tension increases very rapidly. The amount of water retained in this clay loam at the wilting point is more than the fine sandy loam contains at field capacity. The amount of extractable water is about 18 percent in clay loam and only 8 percent in fine sandy loam. Very little water is removed from fine sandy loam above 4 atmospheres tension, but in clay loam appreciable water is removed up to about 10 or 12 atmospheres tension.

grew in the dry soil in order for water to move through them almost as fast as it did through plants grown in moister soil.

Research in California demonstrated that for plants grown under controlled conditions the net water removed in a day was about the same when soils were nearly dry as when they were moderately moist.

Observations in Utah confirmed that the total water removed in a week from the entire root zone of alfalfa and sugar beets was almost as great when the average tension in the root zone approached 8 atmospheres as when it was near 1. If the plant wilted, however, the removal was retarded greatly.

When the tension approached 8 atmospheres before irrigation was applied, yields of alfalfa hay and sugar beet roots were reduced—the plant must have been under stresses that retarded growth more than they retarded moisture uptake and movement through the plant. Since the rate of flow of water in the plant dropped as tension in the soil moisture increased, the plant must have been under great stress and water must have moved for an increasing proportion of time in order for the total amount of water removed in one day to be nearly constant.

MOISTURE REMOVAL from the soil is determined by the active absorbing area of roots, the average velocity that water moves from the soil to the roots, and the rate of increase of active root area. The growth of roots into moist soil and the movement of water from moist soil to the absorbing root therefore influence the amount of water that can be removed by a plant in any given time. If water moved to the active root surface at the same rate, then the uptake from any portion of soil in the root zone would be proportional to the root activity. As soil dries out, however, water moves progressively more slowly.

Because more roots normally are in the surface soils, most of the water plants use is taken up from the surface soil immediately after a good irrigation or rain. The surface soil therefore dries out faster than the soil at lower depths. And, because water moves more slowly in dry soil, the plant then takes up a larger proportion of the water it uses from deeper soil, where the root activity is less.

Moisture removal patterns from soil in which crops are growing, as well as from laboratory models, have shown this to be true. The rate of soil moisture removal is proportional to root distribution when the water is retained throughout the root zone at uniform tension. As soon as nonuniformity occurs in the form of tension gradients in the soil, the removal rate from any unit of soil depends more upon how fast the water moves to the roots (and how fast roots move to water) than upon how many roots there are in the soil being considered.

A greater force per unit area must be exerted at the surface of a plant root in a dry soil than in a moist one if water is to move to the plant at any needed rate.

For example, assume that two identical fields of Millville loam are side by side except that one is moist with average tensions about 0.5 atmosphere, the other has tensions near 2 atmospheres. If the weather is such that water is needed at the rate of 0.015 inch an hour and a force of 0.75 atmosphere at the root surface will supply it in the first soil (moist), a force gradient 30 times as large would be required to supply the water at the needed rate in the dry soil. To get this gradient, the force would need to be 9.5 atmospheres at the root surface in the drier soil. In the dry field, the physiological condition of stress in the plant tissue caused by high suction force needed at the root surface would probably be enough to cause retardation of growth. The amount of water utilized by the plant would be about the same in both instances, but growth would be more in the moist soil.

The term "moisture stress" is used to indicate that an undesirable physiological condition might be created in the plant tissue because of the large forces that must be exerted to get water from soil as a result of either high tension or salt in the soil water or the slow rate with which water moves to the plant to be taken up.

DIFFERENT SPECIES OF PLANTS reach their peak requirements for water at different parts of the season. The peak rate of use and the total seasonal requirement vary with the kind of crop as well as the climate.

Annual crops have a small water requirement while they are still young and small. At the same time, however, the roots are limited to a small volume of soil so that the soil might need frequent but light irrigations. The plants are especially sensitive to shortage of

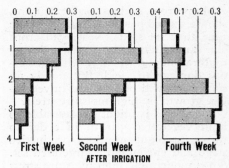

First Week   Second Week   Fourth Week
AFTER IRRIGATION

4. *The rate of soil moisture removal under sugar beets grown on Millville loam is almost proportional to the root distribution for a short time after a good irrigation or soaking rain. As the surface soil dries out, less water is removed from it and more water is removed from deeper depths, where root concentrations are less. As the surface soil approaches the permanent wilting point, only a small amount of water is removed in the surface soil, but large amounts are removed from the 3- to 4-foot depths, where the water is at lower tensions. Growth is retarded by the fourth week, even though almost as much water was removed from the soil as was removed during the earlier weeks.*

water at this stage of growth, and even short periods of drought might retard growth so seriously that the plant can never catch up to those that did not suffer.

When the plants are larger and have a more extensive root system, their water requirement is higher, but the roots can reach a larger reservoir of moisture and the plant is less sensitive, so that it can withstand short periods of wilting during the heat of the day without damage.

Sensitivity to moisture stress corresponds to the period of most rapid growth. Seeds might germinate rather slowly if the moisture tension is high, but they will still live until the moisture conditions are right. The plant grows most rapidly during the seedling stage and it is most sensitive then to high moisture stress. If not enough moisture is available, the seedling will die or it may be permanently retarded in growth. As the plant gets older and larger, its relative growth rate and its sensitivity to high moisture stress diminish gradually.

Many crops, such as corn and grains, show a second peak of sensitivity at the time they set seeds. Nearly all crops can stand high moisture stress during maturation and ripening without serious damage to yield. But nearly all such crops will be retarded in vegetative growth by high moisture stress.

Sometimes it might be desirable to limit vegetative growth in order to throw the plant into the reproductive stage and encourage a large seed set. Since moderately high moisture stress limits vegetative growth but has little effect on seed production and maturation, an excellent way exists to encourage seeding. It is to withhold water until the soil moisture tension in the root zone approaches the wilting point.

This technique might be quite useful in seed production of alfalfa, clover, and birdsfoot trefoil where there is a tendency for plants getting normal moisture supply to continue to set small amounts of seed over a long period, and at no time is there a large amount of seed to harvest. By withholding water and obtaining moderately high stress, larger amounts of seed are set. Then, if water continues to be withheld, there will be little additional vegetative growth and little additional seed set, thus allowing considerable amounts to be harvested at one time.

Perennial crops require water earlier in the growing season than do the annual crops. The root systems of most perennials are already well established in the spring, so that as soon as conditions are right for growth there will be a relatively high demand for water. The requirement will be somewhat less if the leafy portion does not cover the ground completely, because less transpiring surface is exposed to the sun's radiation. Since the roots are already well established, the plants do not show the same sensitivity to moisture deficiency as do annual crops in the seedling stage. Their well-developed roots enable them to endure lower soil moisture.

The period of maximum use of water generally corresponds to the period of fastest vegetative growth. In the case of fruits and fruit trees, water should be available at low tension during the period of rapid expansion of fruit size. If the fruits are enlarging more or less uniformly through the season, an increase in moisture stress at any time will cause a retardation in growth and result in smaller fruits at harvest. Fruits that remain small during the summer and enlarge in the fall are affected only slightly by moderate stress during the summer but require abundant moisture during enlargement.

Excess water lowers the growth and use of water by most agricultural crops except rice. Plant roots need to be aerated so that the waste carbon dioxide produced by the roots can be dispelled and be replaced by oxygen. Whenever waterlogging or compaction stops this process, the rate of moisture uptake is retarded, and the plants might wilt. Plant growth will cease, and the plants will die if the condition continues long enough.

POINTS TO REMEMBER about the use of moisture by plants:

Proper balance of moisture in the root zone of growing plants is necessary for healthy, vigorous growth.

Aeration will limit growth and the uptake of water if soil is too wet.

As soil dries out, the plant is placed under increasing stress until the rate that water can move to the plant root and be absorbed is no longer fast enough to prevent retarded growth and decreased vegetative yields.

During dry, hot weather, the limiting stress in plants might occur at relatively low soil moisture tensions of 1 atmosphere or less.

During cool, humid weather, tensions might become 4 atmospheres or higher before plant growth is retarded.

Limiting plant stress is reached at lower soil moisture tensions in soil containing few roots than in soil with large numbers of roots.

pH, Soil Acidity, and Plant Growth

W. H. Allaway

When crop plants do not grow well, one of the first questions the soil scientist usually asks is, "What is the pH of the soil?" or, "Is the soil acid, neutral, or alkaline?"

The reason for these questions lies in the fact that the pH, or degree of acidity of the soil, often is a symptom of some disorder in the chemical condition of the soil as it relates to plant nutrition.

A measurement of soil acidity or alkalinity is like a doctor's measurement of a patient's temperature. It reveals that something may be wrong but it does not tell the exact nature of the trouble.

The acidity or alkalinity of every water solution or mixture of soil and water is determined by its content of hydrogen ions and hydroxyl ions. Water molecules break up, or in chemical language, ionize, into two parts—hydrogen ions and hydroxyl ions. When there are more hydrogen ions than hydroxyl ions, the solution is said to be acid. If there are more hydroxyl ions than hydrogen ions, the solution is alkaline (or basic). Solutions with equal numbers of hydrogen and hydroxyl ions are called neutral.

Only a very small percentage of the water molecules present are broken up into hydrogen and hydroxyl ions at any one time. If one attempts to express the concentration of these ions in conventional chemical ways, some cumbersome decimal fractions result. In order to avoid these cumbersome numbers, the Danish biochemist S. P. L. Sorenson devised a system called pH for expressing the acidity or alkalinity of solutions.

The pH scale goes from 0 to 14. At pH 7, the midpoint of the scale, there are equal numbers of hydrogen and hydroxyl ions, and the solution is neutral.

pH values below 7 indicate an acid solution, where there are more hydrogen ions than hydroxyl ions, with the acidity (or hydrogen ion concentration) increasing as the pH values get smaller.

pH values above 7 denote alkaline solutions, with the concentration of hydroxyl ions increasing as the pH values get larger.

The pH scale is based on logarithms of the concentration of the hydrogen and hydroxyl ions. This means that a solution of pH 5 has 10 times the hydrogen ion concentration of a solution of pH 6. A solution of pH 4 has 10 times more hydrogen ions than one of pH 5 and 10 times 10, or 100 times, the hydrogen ion concentration of a solution of pH 6.

A measurement of the pH of a solution of a strong, or highly ionized, acid measures essentially the total strength of the acid. But a pH determination of a solution of weak, or slightly ionized, acid measures only a part of the total strength of the acid, because pH is a measure of hydrogen ions only and does not measure all the acid molecules that can potentially ionize to form hydrogen ions.

In a soil, hydrogen ions exist in a number of different chemical combinations and states of adsorption on the surfaces of solid particles. The number of hydrogen ions in the soil solution at any one time is small in relation to the number held in a less active form in various nonionized molecules and on the surfaces of the solid particles.

When the soil is limed in order to bring it to neutrality, enough lime must be added to react not only with the so-called free hydrogen ions of the soil solution but also with those held in the less active forms. This is so because as the neutralization of the soil progresses, ionization of the less active forms of hydrogen likewise progresses and new free hydrogen ions are formed as long as the supply of less active forms holds out.

Thus it is possible to think of the total acidity of a soil as being composed of two parts.

One part, often called the active acidity, is made up of the hydrogen ions in the soil solution. These are the hydrogen ions measured when the pH of the soil is determined.

The second, and much larger, part of the total soil acidity is often called potential acidity. The potential acidity is due to hydrogen ions held in various chemical combinations and adsorbed on the surfaces of solid particles. These hydrogen ions are in chemical equilibrium with the free hydrogen ions of the active part of the soil acidity, and as the free hydrogen ions of the soil solution are neutralized or removed from the soil solution in other ways, hydrogen ions from the less active (or potential acidity) source enter the solution.

Most of the hydrogen ions in the potential acidity forms are held on surfaces of solid particles of clay or soil organic matter. These clay and organic particles are very small, and consequently have a large surface area per unit weight. They make up what is called the colloidal fraction of the soil. Since most of the potential acidity of soils is due to hydrogen ions held on the clay and organic particles, it follows that fine-textured soils, which are high in clay and organic matter, can have a higher total acidity than sandy soils of low clay and organic content.

There are different kinds of clay in different soils, and these different kinds of clay can hold different amounts of hydrogen ions in the potential acidity form. Generally speaking, the clay found in soils of cool-temperate and

Approximate Amounts of Finely Ground Limestone Needed to Raise the pH of a 7-inch Layer of Soil as Indicated [1] [5]

Soil regions and textural classes	Limestone requirements		
	From pH 3.5 to pH 4.5 Tons per acre	From pH 4.5 to pH 5.5 Tons per acre	From pH 5.5 to pH 6.5 Tons per acre
Soils of warm-temperate and tropical regions: [2]			
Sand and loamy sand..............	0.3	0.3	0.4
Sandy loam.....................	....	.5	.7
Loam..........................	....	.8	1.0
Silt loam......................	....	1.2	1.4
Clay loam.....................	....	1.5	2.0
Muck..........................	[3] 2.5	3.3	3.8
Soils of cool-temperate and temperate regions: [4]			
Sand and loamy sand..............	.4	.5	.6
Sandy loam.....................	....	.8	1.3
Loam..........................	....	1.2	1.7
Silt loam......................	....	1.5	2.0
Clay loam.....................	....	1.9	2.3
Muck..........................	[3] 2.9	3.8	4.3

[1] All limestone goes through a 2-mm. mesh screen and at least ½ through a 0.15-mm. mesh screen. With coarser materials, applications need to be greater. For burned lime about ½ the amounts given are used; for hydrated lime about ¾.

[2] Red-Yellow Podzol, Red Latosol, etc.

[3] The suggestions for muck soils are for those essentially free of sand and clay. For those containing much sand or clay the amounts should be reduced to values midway between those given for muck and the corresponding class of mineral soil. If the mineral soils are unusually low in organic matter, the recommendations should be reduced about 25 percent; if unusually high, increased by about 25 percent, or even more.

[4] Podzol, Gray-Brown Podzol, Brown Forest, Brown Podzol, etc.

[5] From USDA Handbook No. 18, p. 237.

Cation Exchange Reactions When an Acid Soil Is Limed

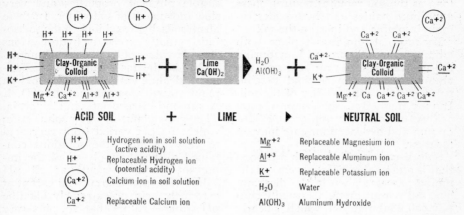

H+	Hydrogen ion in soil solution (active acidity)	
H+	Replaceable Hydrogen ion (potential acidity)	
Ca+2	Calcium ion in soil solution	
Ca+2	Replaceable Calcium ion	

Mg+2	Replaceable Magnesium ion
Al+3	Replaceable Aluminum ion
K+	Replaceable Potassium ion
H2O	Water
Al(OH)3	Aluminum Hydroxide

arid regions can hold a greater quantity of potential-acidity hydrogen ions than can the kind of clay found in soils of warm-temperate and tropical regions. General relationships between kind of soil, pH, and the amounts of lime required are shown in the table.

The hydrogen ions of the potential acidity form are held to the colloidal material because of their electrical charges. The colloidal material is predominantly negatively charged. The hydrogen ions are positively charged, and the attraction between the unlike charges accounts for most of the binding of hydrogen ions to the colloidal surfaces. When hydrogen ions change from the potential to the active acidity forms, their places on the clay-organic colloidal material are taken by other ions carrying positive charges. Ions of calcium, magnesium, potassium, and sodium are positively charged and may take the place of hydrogen on the colloidal complex.

Ions with positive charges are called cations. The process whereby positively charged ions of one kind are replaced on the surfaces of the clay-organic colloidal material is called cation exchange. The total amount of all kinds of cations held by the clay-organic complex at any one time is called the cation-exchange capacity. The ions held to the clay-organic surfaces are called

exchangeable or replaceable cations.

The basic process involved when lime is added to an acid soil is the replacement of hydrogen ions held by the clay-organic colloidal material with calcium ions from the lime.

The diagram shows this process. The small numbers by the symbols for the different cations indicate the number of positive charges carried by that cation. Where no number appears, one positive charge is present. The numbers of different kinds of ions involved in an exchange reaction depend on the number of charges carried by each ion. Thus one calcium ion with its two positive charges will replace two singly charged hydrogen ions. Three doubly charged calcium ions are required to replace two triple charged (or, in chemical terms, trivalent) aluminum ions.

Aluminum ions have a unique role in soil acidity. In the diagram it can be seen that the replaceable aluminum ions of the acid soil have been replaced by calcium in the neutral soil. The aluminum ions thus replaced react with the soil water to form insoluble hydroxides and oxides.

Aluminum is one of the ions of positive charge that react with basic solution to form insoluble oxides and hydroxides. Aluminum occurs as a replaceable cation in acid soils in far greater quantity than any of the other cations that show this property. So long as the soil remains neutral, these aluminum oxides and hydroxides remain insoluble and inert in the soil.

Because calcium ions replace both aluminum and hydrogen ions during the neutralization of an acid soil, the aluminum ions can be said to contribute to the total acidity of the soil. In most methods for determining total acidity of soils, the replaceable aluminum and hydrogen ions are lumped together.

Soils become acid through a process that is almost the direct reverse of the liming process shown in the diagram. The soil parent materials usually contain colloidal material, which is nearly saturated with basic cations like calcium and magnesium. But through the centuries during which soil development takes place, hydrogen ions carried by downward percolating waters gradually replace these calcium and magnesium ions. The calcium and the magnesium are carried away by the drainage waters.

The replacement of bases by hydrogen ions from the water moving through the soil profile is a slow process, but soil formation usually takes place over many centuries. The more water moving down through the soil, the faster the process. Therefore the soils of humid regions are generally more acid than the soils of subhumid regions, and acid soils are rarely found in arid regions. Also, since sandy soils can hold lesser amounts of replaceable bases, these sandy soils usually become acid more rapidly than do fine-textured soils.

Many important chemical properties of the soil are dependent on the kind of replaceable cations held by the clay-organic colloidal fraction of the soil. Calcium, potassium, and magnesium held as replaceable ions constitute the major source of these important plant nutrients in most soils.

The physical properties of the soil are often affected also by the replaceable cations. In some of the alkali soils of the West, excesses of replaceable

sodium ions bring about very undesirable physical properties and very slow movement of soil water. In these alkali soils, hydroxyl ions in the soil solution greatly exceed the hydrogen ions and pH values of 8 to 10 are common.

One of the most important experiments dealing with the effect of pH on plant growth was conducted by D. I. Arnon and his associates in California. They grew plants in water solutions in which the pH varied from very acid to very alkaline; the solutions contained a liberal supply of all the important plant nutrients at all pH values. The plants grew well except at extremely acid or extremely alkaline pH values—values that are only very rarely encountered in field soils. Throughout the range of pH values common in soils—that is, from about 4 to 9—plant growth was not greatly affected by the pH of the solution.

This experiment of Dr. Arnon and his associates might well cause one to question why soil scientists so frequently measure the pH of the soil in order to diagnose troubles in crop production. One might also question the value of tables of the pH values at which various plants grow best.

The answer to these questions lies in the fact that the effects of pH on plants growing in soil are indirect, while Dr. Arnon's solution culture experiments were designed to measure the direct effects of pH. The solution cultures used contained neither deficits nor excesses of the essential plant nutrients.

In soil, however, the solubility and availability to plants of many important nutrients is closely related to the pH of the soil. It is this indirect effect of pH on the availability of plant nutrients that justifies the frequent use of pH measurements for diagnosis of soil problems, and makes tables of so-called pH preferences of plants useful under many conditions.

Changes in the acidity of soils may change the availability to plants of different nutrients in different ways. As the pH of an acid soil is increased by the addition of lime, ions such as aluminum, iron, manganese, copper, and zinc become less soluble. In acid soils these ions may be found in dissolved form in quantities sufficient to become toxic to plants. As the soil is neutralized, these ions form inert oxides and hydroxides, and the toxicity is corrected. As the pH of the soil is increased still further, the solubility of these ions becomes so low that deficiencies of those (iron, copper, manganese, zinc) needed by plants may occur.

Bacteria and other micro-organisms living in the soil convert nitrogen, sulfur, and phosphorus from organic compounds, in which these nutrients are unavailable to plants, to simpler inorganic forms that plants can take up. Neutralizing an acid soil usually makes the soil condition more favorable to the growth of bacteria and may thus indirectly speed up processes by which important nutrients become available to plants.

The bacteria that live in association with the roots of legumes are less effective in their important role in nitrogen fixation in acid soils than in neutral or alkaline soils.

In farm practice, compounds of calcium and magnesium are the basic materials used to treat acid soils.

Along with the decrease in acidity, the addition of these materials increases the supply of calcium and magnesium for use by plants growing on the soil. In some cases, a lack of available calcium or magnesium may be the most important defect of an acid soil.

The availability to plants of the phosphorus in soils is changed in a rather complex manner when the acidity of the soil changes. Phosphate availability in many soils is highest when the soil is neutral or slightly acid, and it declines as the soil becomes either strongly acid or alkaline.

Boron and molybdenum are other plant nutrients that show changes in availability with changes in the pH of the soil. Boron deficiencies frequently occur when too much lime is added to an acid soil. On the other hand, molybdenum is most often deficient in acid soils, and becomes more available as the soil is limed.

In any discussion of the relationships between pH and nutrient availability in soils it should be emphasized that these relationships differ in different soils. In organic soils (peats and mucks), the relationships between pH and nutrient availability are not the same as for mineral soils. Copper, for example, may be deficient in acid organic soils but is rarely so in acid mineral soils.

Many soils are naturally alkaline and contain an excess of lime. The availability of plant nutrients in these naturally alkaline soils quite often differs from the availability of nutrients that results when a naturally acid soil is treated with an excess of lime. For example, many naturally alkaline soils have an adequate supply of available boron, whereas overliming of a naturally acid soil usually brings about boron deficiency.

Since the relationships between pH and the availability of plant nutrients are complex, pH measurements of soils are not easy to interpret in the solution of problems of soil fertility.

While the measurement of pH may give some valuable clues concerning the reasons for poor plant growth, it is generally necessary to follow up these clues with additional tests before an accurate diagnosis of the trouble can be made.

Among the many recent publications about chemical reactions in soils the following may be cited: *Chemistry of the Soil*, by F. E. Bear (Reinhold Publishing Corp., New York, 1955); *Clay Mineralogy*, by R. E. Grim (McGraw-Hill Book Co., Inc., New York, 1953); *Cation Exchange in Soils*, by W. P. Kelley (Reinhold Publishing Corp., New York, 1948); *Soil Conditions and Plant Growth*, by E. J. Russell and E. W. Russell (Longmans, Green and Company, New York, 1950); "Formation Constants for CU (II)—Peat Complexes," by N. T. Coleman, A. C. McClung, and D. P. Moore (Science, February 24, 1956).

The Chemistry of Soil pH

N. T. Coleman and A. Mehlich

Every substance dissolved in water or mixed with water is acid, neutral, or alkaline. Vinegar, containing acetic acid, is a substance that is acid. Water itself is neutral, as are solutions of salt and other such compounds. Lime, baking soda, and lye give alkaline solutions.

The reactions of these and all other substances are typical of the substances themselves and of the ways in which they react with water.

Water itself is composed of one atom of oxygen and two atoms of hydrogen. Its chemical formula is H_2O. Liquid water, however, is really a mixture of H_2O, H^+, and OH^-. H^+, called the hydrogen ion, is a positively charged hydrogen atom, and OH^-, the hydroxyl ion, is a negatively charged unit consisting of one hydrogen and one oxygen atom.

The hydrogen ion and hydroxyl ions come from the breakdown, or ionization, of the water molecule according to the scheme:

$$H_2O \rightleftarrows H^+ + OH^-.$$

This reaction does not produce very many H^+ or OH^- ions because the water molecule is very stable. In fact, only about one molecule in 10 million is ionized at any one time.

The extent to which water ionizes can be expressed more exactly in terms of an ionization constant, Kw. This is defined as:

$$Kw = [H^+][OH^-]. \quad (1)$$

$[H^+]$ and $[OH^-]$ are the concentrations of hydrogen ions and hydroxyl ions, expressed as equivalents per liter. One equivalent of a singly charged ionic species is the weight in grams of that species, which contains 6.023 x 10^{23} particles.

The value of Kw is 10^{-14} at 22° C., and in any aqueous system at this temperature the product of the concentrations of hydrogen and hydroxyl ions is 10^{-14}.

Equation 1 can be written in a more useful form by dividing both sides into 1 and taking logarithms. That is:

$$\log \frac{1}{Kw} = \log \frac{1}{[H^+]} + \log \frac{1}{[OH^-]} = 14. (2)$$

The values of $\log 1/[H^+]$ and $\log 1/[OH^-]$ generally are referred to as pH and pOH, respectively. These values are indices of the acidity or alkalinity of a system.

Any system in which pH and pOH are equal is neutral. At 22° C., when $Kw = 10^{-14}$, neutrality corresponds to pH = pOH = 7. When pH is less than 7, the system is acid. When pH is above 7, it is alkaline.

Soils vary in pH from about 4, for strongly acid soils, to about 10, for alkaline soils that contain free sodium carbonate.

The pH range for most agricultural soils is 5 to 8.5.

IN SOLUTIONS, pH is related to hydrogen-ion concentration in a straightforward manner. That is not the case for soils, which consist of a solution phase, the soil water, and a solid phase, the mineral and organic particles of the soil. The pH of a soil-water system is an approximate reflection of the hydrogen-ion concentration of the soil solution, but it does not reflect the total acidity of the system. This is because of the cation-exchange properties of soils.

The tiny mineral and organic particles of soils have cation-exchange capacities—the particle surfaces are negatively charged, and the positively charged ions, or cations, sit on or near the particle surfaces. These positive ions are called exchangeable cations.

The cation-exchange capacity of a soil is the quantity of positive ions necessary to neutralize the negative charge of a unit quantity of soil, under a given set of conditions. Cation-exchange capacity usually is expressed as milliequivalents (6.023 x 10^{20} particles) of cations required to neutralize the negative charge of 100 grams of soil at pH 7.

The cation-exchange capacity of a soil depends on the amounts and kinds of finely divided mineral and organic particles present. Sandy soils generally have low cation-exchange capacities because of their small proportions of negatively charged material. Soils high in organic matter have substantial cation-exchange capacities because of the large negative charge developed by humus. As far as clays are concerned the cation-exchange capacities of the montmorillonoid and vermiculite-like minerals, found in Midwestern soils and soils of the dry areas, are large. Those of kaolin minerals, which predominate in Southeastern soils, are small. The finely divided micas are intermediate.

The fine-grained mineral and organic particles of soil differ as to the source and characteristics of their negative charge as well as to its magnitude. There are two general sources of cation-exchange capacity, a permanent charge and a pH-dependent charge.

All clay minerals appear to possess permanent charges resulting from their crystal structures. As the name implies, the permanent charge of soil minerals persists under all conditions. The montmorillonoid minerals, which occur in many soils of the Midwest, have permanent charges of 80 to 120 milliequivalents per 100 grams. The kaolin minerals, which are predominant in soils of the Southeastern States, have much smaller permanent charges, varying from 1 to about 8 milliequivalents per 100 grams.

Clay minerals also have pH-dependent charges, which result from the ionization of hydrogen ions from SiOH groups around the edges of the crystals and perhaps for other reasons. Such charges do not develop below a pH of about 6, and do not contribute to the effective cation-exchange capacity of acid soils. As pH is increased above 6, the pH-dependent charge increases progressively, reaching a maximum at a pH of around 10.

The pH-dependent charge which can be developed by clays depends on the exposed edge area of the crystals and on the nature of the clay. It probably is around 20 milliequivalents per 100 grams for montmorillonoid clays, and is much smaller for micas and kaolins. Cation-exchange capacity at pH 7 includes all of the permanent charge and a part of the pH-dependent charge.

Because of the chemical nature of soil organic matter, it probably has only pH-dependent charge, resulting from the ionization of hydrogen from carboxyl and phenol groups attached to organic matter particles. Of these two kinds of groups, the carboxyls ionize largely between pH 4 and pH 7, while the phenol groups ionize only at alkaline reactions. The cation-exchange capacity of soil organic matter, measured at pH 7, averages near 200 milliequivalents per 100 grams. Thus 1 percent of organic matter contributes about 2 milliequivalents per 100 grams toward the cation-exchange capacity of a soil.

The relationships between cation-exchange capacity and pH for clay minerals and organic matter can be illustrated schematically, as in figure 1.

For the mineralogical clay specimens the effective cation-exchange capacity does not vary with pH below about 5. This may not be the case with soil clays. The effective cation-exchange capacity of organic matter is near zero at a pH below about 4, and increases continuously as the pH is raised.

Though clay minerals and soil organic matter generally are considered

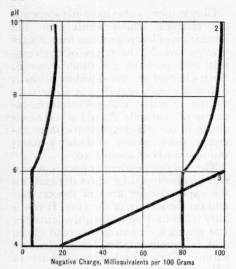

1. The negative charge, or effective cation-exchange capacity, of clays and organic matter varies with pH. Those of kaolinite (curve 1) and montmorillonite (curve 2) are constant below pH 6 but increase at more alkaline reactions. The negative charge of humus (curve 3) increases linearly with pH.

to be responsible for the cation-exchange capacity of soils, other substances may contribute as well. Iron, aluminum, and titanium oxides, as well as noncrystalline iron and aluminum silicates and phosphates, may add greatly to the cation-exchange capacities of some soils.

Under any given set of soil conditions, the permanent charge and that part of the pH-dependent charge that is ionized are balanced by the presence of cations in the vicinity of the particle surfaces. The kinds of balancing ions, or exchangeable cations, depend on the previous history of the soil.

Hydrogen, aluminum, calcium, magnesium, potassium, and sodium are the most abundant exchangeable cations. Their proportions vary from soil to soil, depending on inherited characteristics and past management practices. Hydrogen and aluminum are the predominant exchangeable cations in most acid soils. Calcium and magnesium balance the negative charge in nearly neutral soils, while strongly al-

kaline soils contain large proportions of exchangeable sodium. The strength with which ions are bound to soil particles depends on the nature of the ions and of the particle charges. Hydrogen is bound very strongly to pH-dependent charges but weakly by permanent charge.

IN MOST SOILS the amounts of exchangeable cations are much larger than the amounts of cations in the soil water. With acid soils it is convenient to speak of "active acidity" and "total acidity." Active acidity is measured as the pH of a soil-water mixture. The total acidity of a soil is equivalent to the amount of a base (such as calcium hydroxide) necessary to neutralize it.

Total acidity always is greater than active acidity. It would take only about 3 pounds of ground limestone to neutralize the active acidity of the top 6 inches of an acre of a soil with a pH of 4. Many times that amount of lime would be needed to neutralize the total acidity.

It is possible to have acid soils of identical pH but with very different total acidities. Many of the sandy soils of the Atlantic Coastal Plain have a pH of about 5. Often 1 thousand to 2 thousand pounds of calcium carbonate per acre is required to neutralize soil acidity. Other Coastal Plain soils, high in organic matter, also have a pH near 5. As much as 40 thousand pounds of calcium carbonate is required to neutralize the acidity of the plow layer of many such soils.

NEUTRALIZATION CURVES OR BUFFER curves are useful for studying and illustrating the acid characteristics of soils. They are prepared by adding to a soil sample small increments of an alkaline substance, such as sodium or calcium hydroxide, and measuring the pH after each addition. Curves relating soil pH to percentage base saturation are obtained in that way. The percentage base saturation is the proportion of the cation-exchange capacity that is balanced by basic metal cations such as

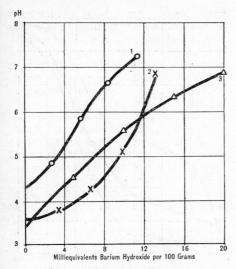

pH

Milliequivalents Barium Hydroxide per 100 Grams

2. *Neutralization curves of acid soils. Curve 1, kaolin clay; curve 2, montmorillonoid clay; curve 3, organic soil.*

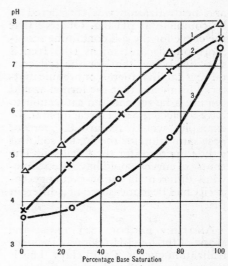

pH

Percentage Base Saturation

3. *The pH-percentage base saturation relationships for soils having different sources of cation-exchange capacity. Curve 1, kaolin clay; curve 2, organic matter; curve 3, montmorillonoid clay.*

calcium, magnesium, sodium, and potassium. Neutral soils are base saturated; acid soils, containing exchangeable hydrogen and aluminum, are base unsaturated.

If a partially base-saturated soil is progressively neutralized in this way, the quantity of base necessary to reach pH 7 is a measure of the total acidity of the sample. When an acid-washed or otherwise base-depleted soil is treated in the same way, cation-exchange capacity is measured.

The second diagram illustrates the kind of neutralization curves obtained with several soils. The curves can be divided into three general areas. For each soil there is a region of buffering, or resistance to change in reaction with addition of base, in the low pH range. This reflects the neutralization of acidity associated with the permanent charge of the clay or the carboxyl-group charge of soil organic matter. This portion of the buffer curve is followed by an inflection, or endpoint, evidenced by an upswing in the curve between pH 6 and 8. The midpoint of this upswing, which commonly occurs around pH 7–8, often is taken to reflect the cation-exchange capacity. It comes at different additions of base for different soils. The third region is a zone of buffering at pH above about 8. This is due in part to the neutralization of weakly acidic groups and in part to the decomposition of minerals which occurs at strongly alkaline reactions.

The shape of the low-pH end (region 1) of the neutralization curve depends on the base used in the titration and on the nature of the soil. Generally, buffer curves obtained with sodium hydroxide lie above those obtained with calcium hydroxide. That is, more calcium than sodium hydroxide is required to raise the pH of an acid soil to a predetermined point.

Differences due to the nature of the cation-exchange material in the soil can best be brought out by examining curves in which pH is plotted against percentage base saturation. This is illustrated by the third figure, which shows such graphs for soils containing different kinds of clay and different amounts of organic matter.

Calcium hydroxide was the base used,

and neutralization was considered to be complete at pH 8.2. Observe that the curve for the soil containing montmorillonoids and micas (the Iredell soil) lies below that for the soil containing kaolin minerals or organic matter. This means that the former would require a larger calcium saturation to have a selected pH. To reach pH 6, for example, would require 80 percent base saturation for the Iredell soil, but only 40 percent for the Cecil soil. The course of curves would have been somewhat different if cation-exchange capacity had been measured at a different pH.

ANOTHER FACTOR INFLUENCES the shape of the low pH region of the neutralization curves of acid clays. This is the mechanism involved in the neutralization reaction. Acid clays contain both hydrogen ions and aluminum ions as exchangeable cations. The proportions of the two vary with the characteristics of the clay and the previous history of the sample. Generally, the permanent charge on clays is countered by metal cations such as calcium, magnesium, and aluminum. Appreciable quantities of hydrogen ions do not neutralize permanent charge because hydrogen-clays are unstable and spontaneously decompose to yield aluminum ions (also magnesium, iron, and others) and silicic acid. The former migrate to exchange spots, and the clay becomes aluminum saturated.

Apparently exchangeable calcium, magnesium, and sodium largely neutralize the portion of the pH-dependent charge of clays that exists in a particular situation. Hydrogen counters the part that is not ionized.

When hydrogen-saturated soil is neutralized with calcium hydroxide, the reaction is:

$$\text{Soil}\Big\langle{}^{\text{H}}_{\text{H}} + \text{Ca(OH)}_2 \rightarrow \text{Soil} - \text{Ca} + 2\text{H}_2\text{O}.$$

When aluminum-saturated soil is neutralized:

$$\text{Soil}{-}{}^{\text{Al}}_{\text{Al}} + 3\,\text{Ca(OH)}_2 \rightarrow \text{Soil}{-}{}^{\text{Ca}}_{\text{Ca}} + 2\text{Al(OH)}_3.$$

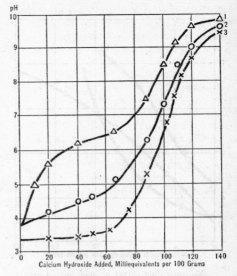

4. *The neutralization of acid montmorillonite as related to the kind of neutralizing base and the nature of the acid clay. Curve 1, aluminum-saturated clay plus sodium hydroxide; curve 2, aluminum-saturated clay plus calcium hydroxide; curve 3, hydrogen-saturated clay plus calcium hydroxide.*

Aluminum ions in water solution hydrolyze, or react with water, to give hydrogen ions and aluminum hydroxide. For this reason, aluminum salt solutions are acid. The hydrolysis reaction occurs between pH 4 and 5. In the neutralization of aluminum-saturated soils, however, the combination of ion exchange and hydrolysis reactions is not complete until a higher pH is reached.

The fourth graph shows the shape and position of neutralization curves obtained with samples of the same clay (montmorillonite) saturated initially with either hydrogen or aluminum ions. The curve for the hydrogen clay lies far below that for the aluminum clay.

Aluminum saturation of the part of the permanent charge not neutralized by calcium, magnesium, and other basic metal cations is the rule in acid soils. About the only exchangeable hydrogen in most mineral soils is due to the portion of the pH-dependent charge that is neutralized between pH 6 and the pH chosen to make an "exchangeable hydrogen" determination. Because of this, it is more appropriate to use the term "exchange acidity" rather than "exchangeable hydrogen."

REGION 3, THE high pH portion of the neutralization curve, is observed when the base used is sodium hydroxide or when calcium hydroxide is used and the soil system is protected from the carbon dioxide of the air. When an acid soil is titrated with calcium hydroxide, equilibrium being continuously established with air containing a given amount of carbon dioxide, a curve similar to that in the fifth graph results.

Under those conditions, region 3 has turned into a straight line parallel to the calcium hydroxide axis. In this case, with the carbon dioxide content of the air being 0.03 percent, the pH stays constant at pH 8.3. The straight line expresses equilibrium between exchangeable calcium, excess calcium carbonate, water, and carbon dioxide. The equilibrium pH, as well as the calcium and bicarbonate concentrations of the soil water, depends on the carbon dioxide level. The quantity of excess calcium carbonate present is immaterial as far as reaction is concerned.

The pH of strongly alkaline soils is high because of the hydrolysis of exchangeable sodium, with the formation of sodium carbonate. Free calcium and magnesium carbonates may be present, but the calcium carbonate-carbon dioxide equilibrium does not control soil reaction.

Just as pH is not an index to total soil acidity, neither is it a guide to total alkalinity, or the amount of acid required to bring the soil to neutrality. In alkaline soils the soluble and insoluble metal carbonates are largely responsible for total alkalinity. The hydrolysis of exchangeable cations can account for high pH's but not for large total alkalinities.

THE MEASUREMENT of soil pH often is regarded as a simple and straight-

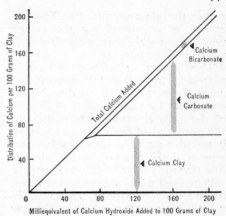

5. *The distribution of calcium in clay-water-carbon dioxide systems. The slanting line with a slope of 45° shows the total amount of calcium added to a clay-water system in equilibrium with the carbon dioxide of the air For calcium hydroxide additions of less than 50 milliequivalents per 100 grams, all of the calcium is bound to the clay. For larger additions of calcium hydroxide, constant amounts of calcium bicarbonate and calcium clay are in equilibrium with excess calcium carbonate.*

forward determination. That is not the case. In fact, pH, particularly in soil systems, is a most uncertain quantity both with regard to measurement and to interpretation.

We originally defined pH as —log hydrogen-ion concentration, but have seen that this is not the case in soil systems. In soil-water systems that are not too concentrated, pH approximates the hydrogen-ion concentration of the soil solution. This, in turn, depends on the cation-exchange capacity of the soil and percentage base saturation, soil-water ratio, and electrolyte content.

The device commonly used for measuring soil pH is a pH meter equipped with two electrodes, which are inserted into a soil-water mixture. One of these, the glass electrode, reflects the concentration of hydrogen ions. The essential part of this consists of a thin bulb of glass, which separates the soil suspension or paste from an acid solution of known concentration. An electrical potential, proportional to the hydrogen-ion concentration of the solution into which the electrode dips, develops across the glass membrane. This potential is registered by the meter, which has a scale that reads directly in pH units from 0 to 14.

The second electrode, which is placed in the soil-water mixture, is a calomel electrode. It is used as a reference point for measuring the potential of the glass electrode. Unfortunately, the potential of the calomel electrode is not the same in all soil-water systems, and pH measurements made with this assembly are difficult to interpret.

When soil pH is measured with glass and calomel electrodes, the value obtained depends on whether the salt bridge that connects the calomel electrode to the soil-water system is in contact with soil particles or with soil solution. With acid soils, lower pH's are obtained when the salt bridge contacts soil particles. This is called the suspension effect. The factors responsible for the suspension effect are not completely understood, but its existence makes the interpretation of soil pH uncertain.

There are a number of organic compounds called indicators, which change color depending on the pH of their surroundings. One such substance is phenolphthalein, which is colorless below pH 8.3 and is red above this pH. The indicators are widely used for measuring the pH of solutions. They are little used for estimating soil pH because of numerous practical difficulties. Foremost among these is the difficulty of seeing indicator color changes in the presence of soils. Indicators have the more fundamental disadvantage that they are either positively or negatively adsorbed by soil particles, and that they may change color at different pH's in contact with soil than in true solution.

THE GENERAL pH-BASE saturation relationships for different kinds of soils already have been indicated. In addition, there are a number of factors that can be varied. They have large effects on measured soil pH. These include the soil-water ratio, the electrolyte content, and the carbon dioxide level.

The pH of a soil varies considerably with its water content. For acid and neutral soils, pH generally is lower for large soil-water ratios than for small. A 1:1 soil-water paste may have a pH one unit or more lower (a tenfold difference in "active acidity") than a 1:5 suspension. This is another manifestation of the suspension effect, and generally has been attributed to differences in hydrogen ion concentration in contact with the glass electrode. The correct explanation appears to be much more complicated and must await further work.

With soils that have a high pH and contain free sodium carbonate and other soluble salts, pH also increases with the water-soil ratio. That is because dilution increases the hydrolysis of sodium-clay, leading to a larger hydroxyl ion concentration in the soil solution. Hydrolysis of exchangeable sodium occurs very readily because hydrogen ions from water have a strong affinity for weakly acidic groups on clay and organic matter.

Because of the effects of soil-water ratio on measured values of soil pH, it is advisable to standardize this. A ratio of one part of soil to one part of water often is used. In studying the salted soils of dry regions, the pH of a soil saturated with water often is measured.

Some research workers have suggested measuring the pH of soil samples at field moisture contents. That is not desirable, since the high external resistance that is encountered under these conditions leads to errors.

The concentration and kind of soluble salts in the water phase profoundly affect soil pH. With acid soils this is largely an ion exchange phenomenon, with cations of the salt replacing exchangeable hydrogen and aluminum ions from the soil particles. The acidity of the solution increases because of increased hydrogen ion concentration or the partial hydrolysis of aluminum ions. As salt concentration is increased, soil pH falls rapidly at first and then becomes insensitive to further changes. Seasonal fluctuations

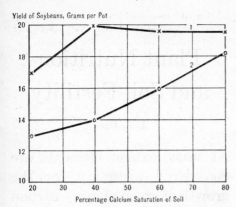

6. *The yield of soybeans as related to the percentage of calcium saturation of two North Carolina soils. Curve 1, organic soil; curve 2, White Store soil containing montmorillonoid clay.*

in salt content, due to fertilization or the mineralization of organic matter, can change soil pH by 0.5 unit.

Since soil reaction varies with salt content, pH often is measured in salt solutions of definite concentration. One normal potassium chloride and 0.01 molar calcium chloride have been used. Such procedures iron out experimental fluctuations to some extent, and for that reason may be desirable.

Measurement of soil pH in dilute calcium chloride solutions appears to offer several advantages. Calcium is the most abundant basic metal cation in most soils, and addition of calcium chloride solutions does not usually change the proportions of the exchangeable cations very much.

Furthermore, there is a general relationship between the concentrations of any two ions in the water phase of a soil-water mixture which permits a description of soil reaction in a way that is independent of the soil-water ratio and of salt content. This relation, which has been called the "ratio law," is that the concentration of hydrogen ions in a soil solution divided by the square root of the concentration of calcium ions is a constant that is characteristic of the soil. The ratio law may be written as: $[H^+]\sqrt{[Ca^{++}]} =$ constant, or as $pH - \frac{1}{2} pCa =$ constant.

Since the value of $pH - \frac{1}{2} pCa$ does not depend at all on the soil-water ratio or the salt content, it is a more definite index to soil reaction than is pH.

Another advantage is that both pH and pCa are determined on a clear soil solution, and difficulties due to the suspension effect are avoided.

Considerable attention should be paid to the effect of the addition of soluble calcium salts to acid soils. When gypsum, or calcium sulfate, is added to acid soils, soil pH falls and the aluminum and manganese concentration of the soil solution increase, sometimes to levels toxic to plants.

The effect of salt concentration on the pH of neutral soils is due largely to increases in the apparent strength of acidic groups. With alkaline soils, increasing salt concentration lowers pH by reducing the hydrolysis of the exchangeable cations, largely sodium.

The pH of soils containing free carbonates of calcium and magnesium is greatly influenced by the bicarbonate concentration in the soil solution. The bicarbonate concentration is proportional to the carbon dioxide content of the air in contact with the soil. The carbon dioxide content of the atmosphere is about 0.03 percent. A soil containing free calcium carbonate has a pH of 8.3 when in equilibrium with this concentration of carbon dioxide. The carbon dioxide content of the soil air may be much larger than that of the atmosphere. Plant roots and microorganisms usually liberate carbon dioxide faster than it can escape from the soil to the atmosphere. Soil air may contain as much as 10 percent carbon dioxide, although contents of about 2 percent are more common. This carbon dioxide content would result in a pH of about 7.1.

When soil samples are taken from the field and prepared for pH measurement, they usually are allowed to equilibrate with the atmosphere. Because of the dependence of pH on carbon dioxide level, the pH measured in the laboratory may be different from that in the field.

Fertility

Plant Nutrition and Soil Fertility

L. A. Dean

At least sixteen elements are considered necessary for the growth of green plants—carbon (C), hydrogen (H), oxygen (O), nitrogen (N), phosphorus (P), sulfur (S), potassium (K), calcium (Ca), magnesium (Mg), iron (Fe), manganese (Mn), zinc (Zn), copper (Cu), molybdenum (Mo), boron (B), and chlorine (Cl).

We commonly refer to these elements as the plant nutrients and as essential elements. An element is said to be essential if the plant cannot complete its life cycle without it and if the malady that develops in its absence is curable only by that element.

Plants obtain carbon, hydrogen, and oxygen from water and carbon dioxide, and the other nutrients from the soil.

We classify plant nutrients as the macronutrients and micronutrients (or—to use an older term—minor elements). This classification is based on the relative amounts that are found normally in plants and does not imply relative importance.

The micronutrients are iron, manganese, zinc, copper, molybdenum, boron, and chlorine.

Green plants contain sodium, iodine, and cobalt, which are essential to animals but have not been proved to be essential to green plants. Although sodium is not considered as an indispensable element, it does enhance the growth of some plant species. Silicon and aluminum occur almost universally in plants, but they perform no recognized function.

The essential elements originate and are distributed within the soil in several ways. A study of these matters gives an insight into the nutrient-supplying power and reserves of soils.

Overall chemical analyses indicate that the total supply of nutrients in soils is usually high in comparison with the requirements of crop plants. Much of this potential nutrient supply, however, is tightly bound in forms that are not released to crops fast enough to produce satisfactory growth. Thus interest has developed in measuring the available nutrient supply as contrasted to the total quantities involved.

Soils are composed of three physically separable phases: Solid, liquid, and gaseous. The nutrient supply originates with the solid phase. The usual path to the plant is from the solid particles to the surrounding liquid and thence into the plant root.

The actual transfer involves the movement of ions. The positively charged ions, called cations, include K^+, Mg^{++}, Ca^{++}, Fe^{+++}, Mn^{++}, Zn^{++}, and Cu^{++}. The anions, those of negative charge, include NO_3^-, $H_2PO_4^-$, SO_4^{--}, Cl^-, $HB_4O_7^-$, and $HMoO_4^-$. The liquid phase, which contains these ions, frequently is referred to as the soil solution. Chemical and biological processes occurring in the soil solution and at the interfaces with solid soil particles create the ions necessary for plant nutrition.

Materials of organic origin—one of the two broad classes of materials that constitute the solid phase of soils—consist of a large series of products ranging from fresh plant and animal tissue to the more or less stable black or brown degradation product, which is humus, formed by biological decay.

The organic matter of soils is a potential source of nitrogen, phosphorus, and sulfur. It contains more than 95 percent of the total nitrogen, 5 to 60 percent of the total phosphorus, and 10 to 80 percent of the total sulfur.

Biological processes are required to convert these organic sources to an ionic state that is available to plants.

Within the biosphere a continuous turnover of these elements takes place among soils, plants, animals, and sometimes atmosphere. Thus there is a nitrogen cycle, a phosphorus cycle, and a sulfur cycle.

We can consider soil organic matter to be one of the storage points in these cycles. Energy must be expended before the elements again reenter the cycle. For the growth of nonlegumes in the absence of fertilizer or manures, the soil organic matter is the origin of the nitrogen supply of crops. But only a part of the phosphorus and sulfur supplied to crops is derived from this organic matter.

The inorganic or mineral fraction—the other broad solid phase of soils—comprises the bulk of most soils. It derives from rocks and their degradation products. The composition, mineralogy, and nutrient-supplying power of the larger particles—that is, the sand and silt—are quite different from those of the fine particles or clay fraction. The minerals that comprise the sand and silt fractions contain most of the elements essential for plant growth as a part of their structure.

Mineral decomposition is necessary before the nutrients in this form are available to plants. These minerals decompose very slowly in the soil. For example, experiments have been conducted with finely ground feldspar and apatite, common primary minerals of soils bearing potassium and phosphorus, respectively. When they were applied in quantities comparable with which they usually are found in soils, the rates of supply of the nutrients were insufficient for the good growth of plants.

The clay fraction of soils is composed of secondary minerals and amorphous materials that differ typically from the components of the sand and silt. The clays are products of weathering and are not found in unaltered rocks. They also are somewhat more stable toward decomposition by weathering processes. The soil clay is composed mostly of two groups of substances—the clay minerals and the hydrous oxides.

The clay minerals are composed mainly of three mineralogical types— kaolinite, montmorillonite, and illite, which are important to soil chemistry and the mineral nutrition of plants because of the cation-exchange properties they exhibit.

The hydrous oxides are predominantly compounds of iron and aluminum. They have a part in the fixation of phosphates and so influence the availability of phosphorus in soils.

THE CATION-EXCHANGE properties of soils arise in the clay mineral fraction and the organic matter fraction. This exchange is the reversible process by which cations are exchanged between the solid and liquid phases.

The exchangeable cations are held at the surface of the solid phase because of the negative charges of unbalanced forces. When these particles are bathed in water, some of the cations enter the water until a steady state between the numbers of cations associated with each phase is set up. Conversely, if a soluble salt (potassium chloride, for example) is introduced into the liquid phase, cations of potassium are formed as the salt dissolves and the steady state is disrupted. In this instance, potassium ions will exchange for other ion species held as exchange cations, and a new equilibrium is established. The net result is that a part of the soluble potassium is converted to an exchangeable cation status and as such is a part of the solid phase of the soil. The amounts held are low in sandy soils and large in clay and organic soils.

This capacity of soil to hold exchangeable cations is termed the cation-exchange capacity and usually ranges between 2 and 50 milliequivalents per 100 grams of soil. One milliequivalent of calcium per 100 grams of soil is equal to 400 pounds per acre of calcium—the amount of calcium in 1,000 pounds of pure limestone.

The important exchangeable cations are hydrogen, calcium, magnesium, potassium, and sodium. Other cations that may appear, but in smaller amounts, are ammonium, manganese, zinc, copper, and aluminum. These different ion species are held to the solid phase with different binding energies. Calcium is the nutrient most tightly held, and potassium the least. The ease with which ions are exchanged one for another is related to the binding energies.

The base-exchange properties of soils influence plant nutrition and the desirability of the soil as a growth medium in a number of ways. Nutrient cations held as exchangeable bases are in a readily available state, but are not readily leached from soils. In fact, other things being equal, leaching losses decline with an increase in the cation-exchange capacity. Cation exchange acts as a buffer, which hinders rapid changes in nutrient level or cation balance.

The balance between amounts of exchangeable hydrogen and exchangeable bases governs the acidity of soils. In an acid soil, a large number of the exchange sites are occupied by hydrogen. Soil acidity is usually corrected by replacing these hydrogen ions with calcium ions—by liming the soil.

Some nutrient elements form anions and enter into the reactions involving soil and plants in that form. The most prevalent nutrient anions in soils are NO_3^-, Cl^-, SO_4^{--} and $H_2PO_4^-$.

When the soils are bathed in solutions containing NO_3^- and Cl^- ions, there are no chemical reactions of importance involving these ions and the solid soil phase. Nearly always is that also true of the SO_4^{--} ions.

The phosphate fixation properties of soil are responsible for the normally low concentration of phosphate ions in the soil solution and for the restricted movement of phosphate in soils. In comparison with the exchange cations, the binding energies holding the fixed phosphate ions are high. These fixed phosphate ions, however, do contribute to the reservoir that supplies phosphorus to plants.

BECAUSE THE LIQUID PHASE (or water) in soils contains dissolved soluble salts, it is referred to often as the soil solution. The assumption is that nutrient ions present in the soil solution are immediately available for plant nutrition.

Studies of the soil solution and the water-soluble materials of soils date back to the early attempts to relate soil composition to nutrient uptake:

The soluble materials in soils range from tiny amounts in some acid soils of the humid regions to the saline conditions sometimes encountered in the soils of the arid regions.

Crops usually require greater amounts of nutrients than the soil solution contains at any given time.

The soil solution is highly dynamic. Ions are continuously being removed by plant roots.

Simultaneously other ions are renewing this solution through cation exchange and the slow breakdown of soil minerals.

Other ions, notably the nitrate ion, are entering the soil solution by way of biological activity.

We may conclude from the foregoing that plant roots draw their nutrients from several sources—the soil solution, an assortment of minerals and inorganic compounds, the exchange cations, and the soil organic matter. It is indeed difficult to distinguish the contribution of a given fraction. Further, reactions and exchanges between fractions are continually taking place. All this stresses the fact that the available nutrient supply is not readily defined.

Two questions now arise: How do plants feed? What is the feeding power of plants?

THE PROCESSES by which the mineral nutrients are absorbed and accumulated by plants is the plant phase of the soil-plant interrelationships.

No mechanism or series of mechanisms that explains the processes has received complete acceptance. Perhaps these phenomena are best understood if the uncontested observations concerning them are considered:

The process embraces the transfer of the nutrient ions across the interfaces of soil and root into the cellular structure of the plant.

An expenditure of energy by the plant is required.

No absorption takes place in the absence of metabolic activity by a plant. When this activity of a plant is inhibited by lack of oxygen or low temperatures, nutrient accumulation drops.

Nutrient absorption involves ion exchange. Cations may be absorbed in exchange for H^+ ions of the plant which are released to the soil. Anions may be absorbed in exchange for OH^- and HCO_3^- ions. A degree of selectivity is exhibited in nutrient absorption. Cations and anions enter the plant independently. The cations K^+ and NH_4^+ are rapidly taken up, while Ca^{++} and Mg^{++} are absorbed at a much slower rate. The anions NO_3^- and Cl^- are absorbed faster than SO_4^{--} and $H_2PO_4^-$.

The rate of nutrient accumulation is not independent of the concentration in the soil solution, and (except for instances of high concentrations) this rate of absorption is proportional to the concentration of a specific ion species. Ion accumulation or absorption thus is regulated by both external and internal factors.

A number of root factors are involved in the overall accumulation of plant nutrients. The surfaces of roots, like those of the soil, carry a negative charge. They also exhibit cation-exchange properties like those of soil.

The most active ion absorption is associated with younger tissues—those capable of growth and elongation. Roots are known to vary in their capacity to absorb nutrients. This is their feeding power. The extensiveness of the root systems, and thus the volume of soil they tap, is involved.

Other effects are involved, however. An example is the differential feeding power for phosphate rock. Species such as buckwheat and certain legumes (as compared with the grasses) show a preferential ability to utilize this material as a source of phosphorus. This ability is not related to the extensiveness of their root systems.

A number of theories have been advanced to explain such observations.

One is that roots excrete materials, such as organic acids or carbon dioxide, which in turn exert a dissolving action on soil or fertilizer particles. Other theories involve a variation in the base-exchange capacity of the root system.

Our present knowledge emphasizes an active rather than a passive role for roots in nutrient accumulation.

NUTRIENT UPTAKE from soil by plants accounts for about 10 percent of the total dry weight of crops. The actual amounts are highly variable. Among the many factors involved are the size of the crop, its age and species, and the properties of the soil.

Chemists have sampled crops at various stages of growth and have analyzed them for their nutrient content. Such information gives an insight to the overall requirements.

Arthur Hawkins, in experiments conducted at the Maine Agricultural Experiment Station, found the highest content of nutrients in potato plants, including tubers, to be about 143 pounds of nitrogen, 26 pounds of phosphoric acid, 232 pounds of potash, 56 pounds of calcium oxide, 30 pounds of magnesium oxide, and 11 pounds of sulfur per acre.

Of those amounts, 8 percent of the total was absorbed during the first 50 days after planting. During the succeeding 30 days, 70 percent of the total nutrient absorption for the season was accomplished. Thus, during the early stages of growth, the rate of nutrient absorption is slow, but as the season progresses the rate increases sharply. The peak rate of absorption was for potash—about 6 pounds an acre a day.

The amounts given for the potato crop are considerably higher than for the usual field crops. A corn crop of 50 bushels an acre, for example, contains about half these amounts.

This pattern of nutrient absorption is not unlike that for overall plant growth as measured by increase in dry weight. The main difference is that the period of peak nutrient absorption precedes that for peak growth by a week or more.

Besides the variations in the total amounts of nutrients absorbed, differences also exist in the amounts relative to each other. Our potato crop absorbed more potassium than any other nutrient. Nitrogen was second. The amount of calcium was relatively small. This particular relationship is not common to all crop species or all soil-management practices. The total and relative amounts of nitrogen or potassium that are absorbed vary with the soil fertility and the fertilizer practices.

Ammonium, potassium, and nitrate ions are loosely held by the soil, and plants readily absorb them. If the elements are plentiful, plants will accumulate them in excess of those amounts required for normal growth and function. This phenomenon is commonly called luxury consumption.

The normal physiological function of plants may be upset by accumulations of some nutrients. Excessive nitrogen, for example, may prolong the vegetative cycle or even prevent flowering.

By comparison, the phosphorus content of plants is surprisingly constant. Phosphate ions are tightly held by soils and are accumulated by plants at a relatively slow rate.

Some species—including many of the legumes—have a relatively high calcium content. Our 7-ton potato crop contained 56 pounds of CaO, and the ratio of K_2O to CaO was 4.15. We would expect a 3-ton crop of alfalfa hay to contain about 80 pounds of CaO and to have a K_2O to CaO ratio of 1.5.

SIMILAR RELATIONSHIPS exist for the trace—or micro—nutrients, but the amounts involved are much smaller. The amount of boron in the 7-ton potato crop (if determined) would have been about 0.2 pound.

In the case of boron (and to a lesser degree the other micronutrients) if the soil contains excessive amounts, toxic quantities are absorbed by plants and growth is restricted. The need for a reasonable balance in amounts of available nutrients in the soil has been postulated.

When the available supply of a given nutrient becomes depleted, this supply is a limiting factor in plant growth. Then the addition of increments of this nutrient to the soil as a fertilizer will result in increased yields of dry matter.

EXCESSIVE INCREMENTS of some nutrients may cause decreases in yields.

Eilhardt Mitscherlich, a German agricultural scientist, was the first to suggest an equation to relate nutrient supply and growth. This equation, although it has many recognized limitations, has been widely used in the solution of practical problems of crop production. It has been the basis used by economists in predicting fertilizer needs and economic usage. If more than a single nutrient, two for instance, are in limiting supply, the addition of either alone may produce but small increases in growth as compared with a combination of both. This effect is termed a nutrient interaction.

A field experiment with oats conducted at the Iowa Agricultural Experiment Station illustrates such a nutrient interaction. The results from the treatments, expressed as bushels per acre, are listed thus: No fertilizer, 15; nitrogen only, 20; phosphorus only, 28; nitrogen and phosphorus combined, 54.

The application of nitrogen and phosphorus singly resulted in net increases of 5 and 13 bushels of oats, respectively. On the other hand, a combination of the same quantities of nitrogen and phosphorus produced an increase of 39 bushels. This example illustrates the importance of maintaining a reasonable balance of nutrients.

Nitrogen and Soil Fertility

Franklin E. Allison

Crop yields in regions where rainfall is adequate are determined more by soil nitrogen than by any other mineral element supplied by the soil.

Improved agricultural methods and better crop varieties are demanding more and more of this element. Soils alone seldom can meet the increased demand because they were never well supplied with nitrogen or because they have lost much of their original supply during 50 to 100 years of cultivation.

Nitrogen is of special importance because plants need it in rather large amounts, it is fairly expensive to supply, and it is easily lost from the soil. A major factor in successful farming is the farmer's ability to manage nitrogen efficiently.

The functions of nitrogen in plant and animal life are many. Essentially all life processes depend directly on it. Nitrogen occurs chiefly as protein and nucleoproteins with smaller and widely varying amounts of amines, amino acids, amino sugars, polypeptides, and many miscellaneous compounds.

The more active nitrogenous compounds occur largely in the protoplasm and nuclei of the cells of plants and animals. Among them are the enzymes that speed up biological processes; they are proteins.

An abundant supply of the essential nitrogen compounds is required in each plant cell for a good rate of reproduction, growth, and respiration. Even the green leaf pigment chlorophyll, which enables plants to use the energy of sunlight to form sugars, starches, and fats from carbon dioxide and water, is a nitrogenous compound.

Closely associated with the nitrogenous constituents are the many non-nitrogenous substances, which serve chiefly as sources of energy for the various cell activities.

Some nonprotein nitrogen compounds do not appear to be especially active biologically but probably serve chiefly as a part of the structure of the organism, just as cellulose and lignin do. One of them is chitin, a complex organic substance related to the carbohydrates. It occurs in bacteria, fungi, lichens, and worms and in the shells of lobsters, crabs, shrimp, and insects.

Nitrogen occurs chiefly in the young, tender parts of plant tissues, such as tips of shoots, buds, and the opening leaves. This nitrogen, present chiefly as protein, is constantly moving and undergoing chemical changes. As new cells form, much of the protein may move from the older cells to the newer ones, especially when the total nitrogen supply of the plant is too low. Then the plant makes the maximum use of a minimum supply.

The transfer of nitrogen from cell to cell may proceed to such an extent that only the growing tips still are functioning properly. The older cells may turn yellow, and many of them, even whole leaves, die and drop off. This yellowing and dropping of the leaves farthest from the growing shoots is the main symptom of nitrogen deficiency. Growth then is of a non-succulent, high-carbohydrate, dwarfed type.

The proper functioning of nitrogen in plant nutrition requires that the other essential elements, particularly phosphorus, potassium, calcium, and magnesium, be present in adequate supply. If the supply of one or more of them is inadequate, the addition of much nitrogen to most common crops may produce limited growth, and this may be very abnormal. Such plants often are unusually susceptible to diseases, and they mature late. But if the nutrient balance and total supply have been adequate from the seedling stage, plants throughout show the stocky growth and dark-green foliage that is a mark of health and vigor.

Plants tend to take up most of the available supply of nitrogen during the early stages of growth. The young plants gorge on nitrogen and hold it for later use. This excess of nitrogen may meet the needs of the plant for several days, but it is not adequate indefinitely for a rapidly growing crop: There has to be a continuous formation and release of available nitrogen from soil organic matter or it must be supplied from outside sources to insure a steady rate of growth and an adequate supply later for the synthesis of storage protein for producing seed.

For a crop like grass that is grown for pasturage, it is even more important that adequate nitrogen be available throughout the growing season. Because pasture plants are not allowed to reach maturity, the need for nitrogen does not diminish as the season advances.

As maturity approaches in a grain crop, most of the protein moves from the vegetative parts of the plants into the seeds. A 30-bushel wheat crop, for example, commonly contains about 50 pounds of nitrogen in the grain and less than 20 pounds in the rest of the plant. This storage protein remains inactive as long as the seed is inactive but changes rapidly when germination begins.

THE PRIMARY SOURCE of soil nitrogen is the air.

Harry A. Curtis, of the Tennessee Valley Authority, calculated that there are about 34,500 tons of nitrogen over every acre of the land area. That is about four-fifths of the atmosphere. This inexhaustible supply remains constant, because nitrogen is being returned to the atmosphere at about the same rate as it is being removed.

Higher green plants cannot utilize gaseous nitrogen directly. It must first be combined with other elements. The process of producing such combinations is called nitrogen fixation. Nitrogen is an inert element and resists combining with other elements. Such combinations are brought about in several ways, chiefly by electrical discharges in the atmosphere, by various chemical reactions in industrial processes, and by several species of micro-organisms living in or on the soil, in plant tissues, and in fresh and salt waters.

Nitrogen fixed by lightning combines with the oxygen of the air to form oxides of nitrogen. These oxides are washed out of the air by rain or snow and reach the soil in the forms of nitrous and nitric acids. The amount of nitrogen that enters the soil in these forms is usually not more than 2 pounds an acre a year.

Rains commonly wash about 2 to 6 pounds of ammonia and organic nitrogen from the air. The total amount of nitrogen brought down by rains annually varies with the rainfall, frequency of electrical storms, and nearness to industrial areas where ammonia is being released. An average figure for cropped areas in the humid-temperate region is usually considered to be about 5 pounds of combined nitrogen an acre a year. As I stated, two-thirds or more of this is not newly fixed nitrogen but is combined nitrogen, chiefly ammonia that escaped from the soil or was released as a result of the burning of coal and other materials. A small percentage consists of micro-organisms and other forms of organic matter carried into the air by the wind.

Large amounts of nitrogen are fixed in industrial nitrogen-fixing plants as ammonia and calcium cyanamide.

The synthetic ammonia process is the more economical. In this process, nitrogen and hydrogen gases are made to combine under pressure in the presence of a catalyst. Such fixed ammonia now constitutes the main commercial source of nitrogen used in agriculture. It is commonly applied in the form of ammonia and ammonium salts, and as urea and nitrates produced from ammonia. As a result of the rapid expansion of the industry, chemical nitrogen was available in 1956 in adequate amounts and at prices somewhat below those a few years earlier. The capacity of 50-odd anhydrous ammonia factories in the United States in 1956 was about 4.1 million tons of ammonia, compared to 1.8 million tons in 1951.

Nature's method of fixing nitrogen still constitutes the chief source of nitrogen for farm crops. This nitrogen is fixed by microscopic plants that exist wherever plant life can exist. Some of them live in nodules on the roots of plants, chiefly legumes. Others lead an independent existence. These microscopic forms fix atmospheric nitrogen at ordinary temperatures and pressures.

Legumes may fix 200 pounds or more of nitrogen an acre each year if effective strains of the proper root nodule bacteria are present in the soil or are added to the seed as commercial inoculants. These bacteria penetrate the root hairs, live in the root nodules formed, and in cooperation with the higher plant take nitrogen from the air for the use of both the bacteria and the crop. An average fixation value is usually 50 to 100 pounds, depending on the kind of legume. When available soil nitrogen is abundant, legumes are likely to use it in preference to atmospheric nitrogen. The amount of nitrogen fixed in nitrogen-deficient soils parallels closely the amount of carbohydrate photosynthesized by the plant and its dry weight.

Farmers in the past depended largely on legumes as a source of nitrogen to supplement animal manures and soil nitrogen. They have turned more and more in later years to synthetic ammonia to meet crop needs. It is largely a matter of economics, which is in turn influenced by the type of farming and the use to be made of the legume. For example, in livestock farming legumes are especially valuable as feed and as suppliers of nitrogen. But in grain farming, where their feed value is not realized, they may be a more expensive source of nitrogen than commercial fertilizer nitrogen.

Several nonleguminous plants have root nodules that are produced by bacteria or fungi and can use atmospheric nitrogen. Most of these plants, such as the alder and various species of *Casuarina, Elaeagnus*, and *Cycas*, are trees or shrubs and of little value in agriculture. Nitrogen-fixing trees, both leguminous (black locust, *Acacia*, and *Mimosa*) and nonleguminous, are of considerable importance in the growth of some forests.

Bacteria are the chief free-living micro-organisms that fix nitrogen. A few fungi and yeasts also can do so. A few genera of blue-green algae, often observed as a green scum on ponds, also can use atmospheric nitrogen and are of economic importance where paddy rice is grown.

We do not know exactly how much nitrogen is fixed by nonsymbiotic (free-living) soil organisms, such as azotobacter and clostridia. J. G. Lipman and A. B. Conybeare, of the New Jersey Agricultural Experiment Station, estimated it to be an average of 6 pounds a cultivated acre a year in the United States. Others have given higher values. An accurate value for such fixation cannot be given because the errors involved in sampling and analyzing soils are larger than the values to be measured. This nonsymbiotic fixation of nitrogen is important, but this source of nitrogen does not meet the needs of large crops.

There has been much interest in recent years, especially in the Soviet Union and Germany, in the possibility that nitrogen-fixing bacteria may live on the outside of plant roots and supply the crop with nitrogen. It is reported that as early as 1942 the Soviet Union inoculated 5 million acres of crops with a commercial preparation of azotobacter. Such preparations have been valueless in most countries.

MISCELLANEOUS SOURCES of nitrogen not obtained directly from the air, including a few manufactured products and various byproducts and wastes, are a large part of the supply of nitrogen for crops on many farms. This nitrogen originally came from the air, but after fixation it has taken on various forms.

Nitrate of soda from Chile, which used to be the world's leading source of fertilizer nitrogen, has been pushed into the background by the abundant supplies of domestic synthetic ammonia. Chilean nitrate remains an important fertilizer material, and costs largely determine whether it or synthetic nitrogen is used.

Ammonium sulfate, a byproduct of the coke industry, is also one of the important sources of fertilizer nitrogen. Coal thus is a secondary source of nitrogen. All ammonium sulfate sold in 1957, however, was not produced from coal. Some of it (and also some sodium nitrate) was produced in nitrogen-fixation plants from synthetic ammonia.

Animal manures are one of the chief and best sources of nitrogen for crops. Slaughterhouse byproducts and press cake, such as cottonseed meal, are also excellent sources but have practically disappeared from fertilizers. They are of more value when used as feeds.

Miscellaneous industrial and canning wastes find their way by various routes to the farm. The amount of nitrogen they supply is not large, and its availability to crops varies widely. Low availability may be due to the inert nature of the product itself or the high proportion of carbohydrate to nitrogen in the added material. Leather scraps and some urea-resin compounds are examples of inert materials. Canning wastes are typical of those that commonly contain such a high proportion of carbon to nitrogen that on decomposition little nitrogen is released to the growing crop.

Sewage sludge and garbage wastes are becoming more important as sources of crop nitrogen, yet only small percentages of these city wastes reach the farms. In the raw state they are decidedly objectionable for health and sanitary reasons, high in moisture, and unsuitable for general crop use.

Sewage sludges that are activated

and dried commonly contain 5 to 6 percent nitrogen and are satisfactory sources of nitrogen. The digested product usually contains less than half as much nitrogen, and its availability is considerably lower.

Myron S. Anderson, in Department of Agriculture Circular 972, discusses the various types of sludges and presents data on the availability of the nitrogen. He states that heat-treated sludges are usually safe for use from a sanitary standpoint, but unheated digested sludges should be used with caution if vegetable crops are to be grown.

The cost of converting raw sewage and garbage into forms suitable for use as fertilizers and their comparatively low content of nitrogen make them uneconomical to produce if the sole aim is to produce fertilizer. Nevertheless they will undoubtedly be produced to a greater extent in the future because cities must dispose of their wastes regardless of costs.

Other sources of nitrogen are the various crop residues. Green manures are essentially in the same status, although if they are legumes most of the nitrogen is obtained by them directly from the air.

THE CHEMICAL NATURE of soil nitrogen is not well understood.

All but a small part is present in organic forms. Our knowledge of the organic part is inexact because widely varying types of nitrogenous compounds gain entrance to the soil and soon start to decompose. The destructive processes are affected by almost every factor that affects life itself. Furthermore, accompanying the biological degradation process are numerous synthetic processes. The micro-organisms that decompose the various compounds use a portion of the nitrogen to form new cells, which in turn die and become a new source of soil organic matter. The cycle never ends.

Protein is believed to be the chief form of nitrogen in soils although direct quantitative determination has not been made. Indirect procedures, involving treatment with acids, followed by identification of the breakdown products, chiefly amino acids, have usually been used in such studies.

J. M. Bremner, of the Rothamsted Experimental Station in England, concluded that up to 50 percent of the nitrogen in some soils is present as protein. Because micro-organisms decompose protein readily, it is not present as free protein but is probably in the form of ligno-protein and clay-protein complexes. In fact, there is some evidence that the amino acids present after chemical treatment of soils may have been there before such treatment as amino acids combined with (and protected by) clays, rather than as constituents of proteins.

Chitin, already mentioned as a constituent of plants and animals, is also a common soil constituent. It is somewhat resistant to biological attack, but some micro-organisms decompose it.

Heterocyclic nitrogen compounds, such as purines and pyrimidines, occur in soils to some extent, but the amount is believed to be small.

Lignin and several other organic materials combine with ammonia to form compounds that are resistant even to treatment with acids and alkalies. Considerable nitrogen may be present in such forms, but we have no proof of that.

Organic-inorganic complexes are important parts of soils. Laboratory studies have shown, for example, that protein to the extent of 8 percent of the weight of some clays can combine with them. Any protein held in such a complex is attacked much more slowly by micro-organisms than if no clay is present. Several other compounds, including humic acids and amino acids, are so held.

Some nucleic acids, found in the nuclei of bacteria and in the cells of higher plants, are present in soils. The amount of soil nitrogen present in that form may be less than 10 percent.

Crop residues, also present in varying stages of decomposition, contain chiefly protein and its degradation products. During decomposition, such compounds as histidine, arginine, creatinine, choline, cyanuric acid, and lysine are formed. The amounts of each present at any one time are small and are likely to be transitory. Some of them have been thought to have effects on plant growth far greater than might be expected from the concentrations present, but seldom have such effects been demonstrated.

Inorganic forms of nitrogen, chiefly ammonia and nitrates, are always present in soils in quantities varying from traces to perhaps 5 percent of the total. The amount present in cropped soils is small.

Many soils can hold ammonia nitrogen so tenaciously that it is released only slowly to micro-organisms and to higher plants. The minerals in soils that are responsible for this fixation and holding of ammonium ions are vermiculite, montmorillonite, biotite, and weathered illite, which usually contains the other three minerals.

The quantities of such fixed ammonium normally present in cultivated surface soils is believed to be small. The ammonium-fixing power of subsoils is usually higher than that of surface soils and is increased by drying and heating. Low recoveries of nitrogen in the crop, following additions of ammonia to subsoils, might be expected on the basis of laboratory studies on soils high in the minerals I mentioned, but we have no field data to prove or disprove this.

THE NITROGEN CONTENT of virgin soils in various parts of the United States, according to Oswald Schreiner and B. E. Brown, of the Department of Agriculture, varied from 0.01 to 1 percent or higher in the surface layer when first put under cultivation. The nitrogen level tended to vary with the climate and native vegetation, which are so important in soil formation. They put the approximate nitrogen content of the surface 6 inches of virgin soils in the various regions as follows: Brown Forest soils of the

Northeastern States and Red and Yellow soils of the Southeast, 0.05 to 0.20 percent; Prairie soils of the Central States, 0.10 to 0.25 percent; Chernozem soils of the eastern Dakotas, Nebraska, and Kansas and farther south, 0.15 to 0.30 percent; Chestnut soils in the western parts of those States, 0.10 to 0.20 percent; Brown soils still farther west, 0.10 to 0.15 percent. The western desert soils are very low in nitrogen.

The variation in nitrogen content with depth is pronounced in the soils of the different regions. Soils in the East generally are shallow. Soils in the Central States are deeper. Under virgin conditions, there was an average of about 4 thousand pounds of nitrogen an acre in the upper 40-inch layer in the Red and Yellow soils of the Southeast and 16 thousand pounds in the Chernozem soils of the Central States. The figures emphasize that many of our soils were not high in nitrogen when first brought under cultivation, but most of them contained more nitrogen then than they do now.

The statement that virgin soils are not necessarily fertile soils may seem strange to some readers, but that is true of many of our soils. The main factors that determine content of soil nitrogen, aside from the effect of farming operations, are temperature, rainfall, soil texture, the type of minerals present, and vegetation. Temperature and rainfall largely determine the plant cover under virgin conditions.

The nitrogen content of soils in the United States usually tends to increase from south to north.

Hans Jenny, at the Missouri Agricultural Experiment Station, found that the average content of nitrogen and organic matter in the soils of the central part of the country increases two to three times for each fall of 18° F. in annual temperature. This temperature effect corresponds closely to the known effect of temperature on the rate of both chemical and microbiological activities as observed in the laboratory.

This effect of temperature does not always hold for tropical soils, some of which are as high in nitrogen as are soils of the Temperate Zone. In tropical soils, other factors may mask the effect of temperature—poor aeration in regions of high rainfall; absence of wetting and drying, with the accompanying increased oxidation; and absence of killing frosts.

Dr. Jenny also observed that in the grassland soils of the Central States the nitrogen content increased with rainfall. This finding would probably not hold for many other regions, especially where the rainfall is very high. Generalizations about the effect of climatic factors on soil nitrogen obviously need to be limited to definite regions.

The type of vegetative cover on a soil affects the nature of the soil that forms and its nitrogen content. In the humid places where forests predominate, the Podzol soil that forms is a shallow soil, and most of the organic matter and nitrogen is concentrated in the upper foot or less. The higher rainfall causes much leaching and the removal of most of the bases originally present. In contrast, Chernozem soils, formed under conditions of somewhat limited rainfall, retain their bases and are deep soils, largely because of the depth of penetration of the grass roots.

Soil texture influences the amount of nitrogen that accumulates in soil. A clay or clay loam commonly contains two or three times as much nitrogen as a very sandy soil in the same type of climate. A part of the difference is due to the combining of organic nitrogen constituents with some of the clay minerals. Poorer aeration and less leaching also favor the retention of nitrogen in soils of finer textures.

THE NITROGEN CONTENT of cultivated soils after 50 years or more of cropping is usually much lower than when first plowed, unless the soil initially had little nitrogen. The nitrogen content in virgin soils, kept under constant conditions for centuries, is stabilized.

Cultivation introduces a new set of factors, and soil nitrogen immediately starts to respond to the new conditions and seeks a new level at which income and outgo of nitrogen are in balance.

Cultivation accelerates microbiological activities and the rate of release of ammonia from soil organic matter. A considerable part of this nitrogen may be lost through leaching and erosion while the soils are without adequate vegetative cover, but a larger proportion is removed in the crop. Besides, less vegetative material usually is returned to the soil than under virgin conditions.

Unless adequate nitrogen and the other essential elements are added as animal manures, legumes, or as commercial fertilizers, the productivity of the soil gradually declines. Even if they are added and crop production is maintained, the nitrogen level seldom stays at the virgin level. The higher the soil was originally in nitrogen, and the warmer the climate, the greater the decline in soil nitrogen is apt to be.

Studies of the decrease in soil nitrogen when soils are first put under cultivation show that the rate of decline is usually high the first few years and becomes less in later years. Reductions of 25 to 50 percent of the original nitrogen in the Central States have commonly occurred during the 75 or more years of cultivation. Usually about half of the loss occurred in the first 20 years and one-fourth in the next 20 years.

It seems that the nitrogen content now has about reached stability in many localities, at least where farm-management practices are good. In dry-farming regions, where wheat is the main crop, the surface soils commonly have lost about a third of their nitrogen since 1900. At the southern end of the Wheat Belt and below it, the losses have usually been near one-half. Losses from eastern and southeastern soils probably have been about the same magnitude in terms of percentage of the original content.

In all sections of the United States

are soils that have not shown nearly as marked losses in nitrogen as the figures would indicate. Examples are the soils that have been in sod or trees for much of the time and have not been stirred very often. The examples emphasize that farming practices determine the extent and rate of change in soil nitrogen. In fact, the trend toward lower soil nitrogen levels often can be reversed slowly.

THE RELEASE of soil nitrogen to crops occurs as a result of the activities of many kinds of micro-organisms. Two broad groups are primarily responsible for making it available to higher plants—the ammonifiers (ammonia-producers) and the nitrifiers (nitrite- and nitrate-producers). The ammonifiers comprise most of the bacteria and fungi that live in soil. They decompose soil organic matter primarily in order to obtain a supply of energy for growth. In the process they liberate ammonia, some of which they use themselves. The rest is set free as a byproduct. The nitrifiers then oxidize the ammonia to nitrites and then to nitrates. Some chemical oxidation of nitrites to nitrates may occur also in acid soils. Ammonia and nitrates are the main sources of nitrogen for plants and hence do not accumulate in the presence of an actively growing crop.

Little ammonification and nitrification take place in the Temperate Zone during the winter. The rate of activity of micro-organisms above 45° F. increases twofold or threefold for each rise of 18° if moisture is adequate and the soil is not highly acid. Nitrate formation reaches a maximum in the late summer and decreases in early fall. The total amount of nitrates in the soil may be highest in late summer because of the high temperature and also because of less leaching and the slowing down of crop demands as maturity approaches.

Any nitrate that accumulates in late summer is largely leached out during the winter and early spring in the humid region unless a cover crop is grown. This yearly soil nitrate pattern under cultivated crops does not hold under sod crops; rarely is there more than a trace of available nitrogen in such soils at any time. There is less decomposition of soil organic matter under a sod, and any released nitrogen is quickly assimilated by the crop. The mass of undecomposed carbonaceous roots present also serves to keep nitrates low. Grasses can use much more nitrogen than they usually get.

Good soil aeration also favors the release of nitrogen from soil organic matter. The degree of aeration is determined largely by soil texture, drainage, and cultivation. Aeration in cultivated soils is usually adequate for a satisfactory rate of formation of ammonia if it is adequate for healthy plant growth.

An increase in the rate of oxidation of native organic matter, as evidenced by increased production of carbon dioxide, is sometimes observed after green manures and other fresh plant materials are added. Presumably nitrogen is also released, but it may be assimilated soon by the microflora.

This increased destruction of native organic matter, which has been demonstrated by tracer techniques, is due to the increase in microbial growth with the accompanying increase in the production of cell enzymes. They attack the added plant material and native organic matter simultaneously. The magnitude of the effect on the latter usually varies from a negligible increase to a 100-percent or 200-percent increase in carbon release from soils during the first week. A rapid decrease in the rate of release follows. Within a few days, a negative effect may be observed. This phenomenon is of more scientific than practical interest; the overall effect during a growing season is small. Any such effect is much more than compensated for by the new soil organic matter formed from the added plant materials.

The net amount of nitrogen released from an organic material depends on the nitrogen content of the material, the completeness with which it is destroyed, and the amount of nitrogen used by the decay organisms. If the material is high in available energy and contains less than 1.5 percent of nitrogen, most of the nitrogen will be used by the micro-organisms. If the nitrogen content is above 1.5 percent, most of the extra nitrogen will be released for plant use.

The percentage of soil nitrogen released annually to a cultivated crop varies widely and is affected by many factors. G. E. Smith, of the Missouri Agricultural Experiment Station, estimated the percentages released yearly to corn in that State to be 1.25 to 2.5 percent of the total from a clay or clay loam, 1.5 to 3 percent from a silt loam, and 4 to 6 percent from a sand or sandy loam. It is fortunate that humus is rather resistant to biological attack because it is usually more valuable for maintaining soil tilth and permeability to air and water than it is as a source of nitrogen.

Great interest has been shown in rapid methods for estimating the amount of nitrogen that a soil can furnish a crop. No method has been proposed that is entirely satisfactory. The most used method, and probably the best, is to determine nitrate formation in a few grams of soil kept in the laboratory at constant temperature for about 2 weeks. The amount of nitrate formed is then compared with that formed in similar soils where crop yields have been determined.

LOSSES OF NITROGEN from soils may occur through crop removal, erosion, and leaching, and as gases. The comparative importance of the four channels varies with the soil, crop, and soil-management practices.

Losses through crop removal are proportional to the size of the crop. Such losses can be lowered only by changing the farming system. Grain and hay crops, for example, may be fed to animals on the farm rather than be sold.

Erosion control is especially impor-
tant because erosion tends to loosen and float away much organic matter. The nitrogen in such eroded material may be several times higher than in the soil left behind.

Leaching removes large amounts of nitrates from soils but no more than traces of other forms of nitrogen. The losses occur most readily from the more sandy cultivated soils, especially in warmer climates and in places where the rainfall is enough for the surface water to penetrate to the ground water several times a year.

Losses of gaseous nitrogen from soils occur chiefly as ammonia, free nitrogen gas, and nitrous oxide. Traces of certain substances, such as amines, hydrocyanic acid, and nicotine, may also escape from growing plants.

Ammonia, applied as a fertilizer, often is rapidly lost from soils to the extent of 25 percent or more. Such volatilization is largely limited to alkaline soils, although they need not be much above pH 7. It is accelerated by drying, especially if the temperature is high and the ammonia is near the surface. It occurs most readily from sandy soils and also from decaying masses of nitrogenous organic materials at or near the soil surface even if the soil is slightly acid, since the ammonia formed may raise the pH locally. Failure to incorporate manure with soil may help explain the low recovery of its nitrogen in the crop.

Losses of nitrogen from soils in the form of free nitrogen gas and oxides of nitrogen are chiefly the result of bacterial action. Such losses are of considerable economic importance. Denitrifying bacteria that produce these gases are widely distributed. Ordinarily they use atmospheric oxygen for growth, but if the supply is deficient they can obtain oxygen from nitrates. In doing so they release gaseous nitrogen. The losses are greatest if soil aeration is poor and if nitrate fertilizers are applied in the presence of masses of plant materials that are undergoing decomposition.

The efficient use of the nitrogen

sources available to the farmer involves the prevention of unnecessary losses, the return of manures and crop residues, use of Nature's methods of fixation, and the addition of commercial sources of nitrogen to bring the yield up to a satisfactory level.

Attention should be given more to the use of good farm-management practices than to just the maintenance or building up of soil nitrogen.

The level at which soil nitrogen can be held varies for each soil and for each climatic zone and is affected by the cropping system. With good farm management, including adequate use of fertilizers, good crops can be produced on soils of any nitrogen level if the environment can be made suitable for the crop. This does not imply, though, that abundant soil nitrogen is not highly desirable and favorable to larger and more profitable crops.

In the control of soil erosion and leaching, a greater use of sod crops, catch crops, and cover crops, especially on rolling or hilly land, is needed. Application of soluble forms of nitrogen as short a time as possible before needed by cultivated crops will greatly increase the proportion that is utilized. This statement applies chiefly to the more sandy soils in regions where much leaching occurs just before and during the growing season.

All crop residues should be returned to the soil unless insect infestation, diseases, or the crop to be grown make this impractical. The residues supply some nitrogen, help to hold soluble soil nitrogen, and replenish the supply of active organic matter. Special attention needs to be given to the preservation and use of animal manures.

Gaseous losses of ammonia can be minimized by not applying anhydrous ammonia or ammonium salts to alkaline soils; if they are used, one has to make certain that they are well mixed with the soil. Highly nitrogenous organic matter added to all soils should be handled in the same way.

Losses of nitrogen gas and oxides of nitrogen can be reduced by avoiding the application of nitrates to soils that are poorly aerated and drained. Large applications of undecomposed plant materials also may favor such losses by reducing the oxygen in the soil.

More legumes should be grown in many areas, especially where moisture is not limiting and there are enough livestock to utilize them. The deep-rooted perennial or biennial ones that fix the most nitrogen and require the least cultivation are most beneficial to the soil. Because the amount of nitrogen fixed on nitrogen-deficient soils is likely to parallel closely the total dry weight of the legume, it is important that growth conditions, apart from nitrogen, be made satisfactory.

Nitrogen fixation by free-living soil micro-organisms can probably be increased by the addition of crop residues, such as cornstalks and straw, that are low in nitrogen.

Commercial nitrogen should be used as a supplement to the other forms of nitrogen to the extent needed. Other elements should be supplied in such quantities as to keep the proper nutrient balance.

Soil Phosphorus and Fertility

Sterling R. Olsen and Maurice Fried

Phosphorus is present in all living tissue. It is particularly concentrated in the younger parts of the plant and in the flowers and the seed.

It is necessary for such life processes as photosynthesis, the synthesis and breakdown of carbohydrates, and the transfer of energy within the plant. It is a major part of the nucleus of the cell and is present in the cytoplasm, where it is involved in the organization of cells and the transfer of hereditary characteristics.

Growth is arrested when the supply of phosphorus in the soil is too low, and phosphorus from the older tissues moves to the younger tissues. Usually, therefore, signs of too little phosphorus appear first in the lower leaves, which are the older ones. The symptoms may be a lack of chlorophyll, a deepening of the green color, or a red color in the leaves. Usually also the roots are stunted and poorly branched. A deficiency of phosphorus may delay maturity of the plant.

Different species of plants and different parts of a plant vary in their content and requirement of phosphorus. The cobs in a 75-bushel corn crop contain about 0.1 pound of phosphorus, but the stover may contain 5 pounds and the grain about 12 pounds. The roots of the corn plant contain less phosphorus than the tops. The plants that produce the 75 bushels may take up 20 pounds of phosphorus. Although 35 bushels of wheat may contain only half as much phosphorus as the 75-bushel corn crop, the required level of readily available phosphorus in the soil is probably greater for wheat than for corn.

The amount of phosphorus removed by a harvested crop depends on its total yield, its phosphorus content, and on how much of the plant is actually removed. If only the grain is removed, as in sweet corn, the soil loses less phosphorus than when the whole corn plant—silage corn, as an example—is harvested. Grass harvested for seed may remove less phosphorus than grass harvested as hay.

The phosphorus content of a particular species tends to be low when the available supply is low, but the amount in a plant may be increased by using phosphate fertilizer. The increase usually is small, but if it is needed it can improve the plant and its nutritive value.

Since phosphorus is an essential nutrient of plants, the total amount of phosphorus in cultivated and virgin soils is one of our important natural resources. It ranges from less than 100 to 4,000 pounds an acre and averages about 1,000 pounds.

The coastal areas in the South Atlantic States and Gulf States are lowest in total phosphorus. High concentrations occur in Tennessee, Kentucky, and the Pacific Northwest.

Virgin surface soils and their subsoils contain similar concentrations of total phosphorus, but many tilled soils do not. The liberal use of phosphate fertilizers has resulted in accumulations of phosphorus in the surface soil in some areas—notably in potato-growing areas and places close to phosphate deposits. Some soils in potato areas have received as much as 100 pounds of phosphorus an acre for each potato crop. Since less than one-fourth of that amount may be removed by the crop, accumulations have resulted.

As phosphorus does not move appreciably in the soil, the accumulations are primarily in the first foot of soil.

On the other hand, some soils have been in agricultural production long enough to deplete the total phosphorus supply, and unless fertilizer phosphorus is added equivalent to the amount removed by crops, the phosphorus in the surface layer will decrease further.

Most of the total phosphorus supply is tied up chemically in a form that is not usable by the crop in a single growing season—it is not available to the growing plant. The available soil phosphorus originates from the breakdown of soil minerals, from soil organic matter, or from the previous addition of phosphate fertilizer. The available soil phosphorus usually is only about 1 percent of the total soil phosphorus.

The available soil phosphorus is not necessarily related closely to the total soil phosphorus, partly because the chemical nature of the phosphate minerals and organic compounds is not the same in all soils. The differences in agricultural soils are due primarily to management practices, which affect the available phosphorus much more than they affect the total phosphorus. While high fertilization increases available soil phosphorus more than total soil phosphorus, crop removal without fertilization rapidly lowers the available phosphorus without changing very much the total content.

Phosphorus occurs naturally in soils in the form of the calcium phosphates, hydroxyapatite and fluorapatite; iron phosphate and aluminum phosphate; various primary and secondary minerals, in which a phosphate group substitutes for a silicate group in a crystal lattice; and as organic phosphorus, which may constitute as much as 75 percent or as little as 3 percent of the total soil phosphorus.

As the soil matures by weathering processes and plant growth, these natural forms of phosphorus change into other forms, which accumulate in the surface layers and the clay fraction of the soil.

The original source of most of the inorganic phosphorus is the apatite group of minerals. These forms tend to disappear as weathering proceeds and the soil becomes more acid. The content of iron phosphate and aluminum phosphate increases because they are more stable under acid conditions. The clay minerals and hydrous oxides of iron and aluminum, which result from weathering, can adsorb phosphorus on their surfaces. Thus the phosphorus content of the clay fraction increases with weathering unless clay is lost by erosion. The exact nature of the phosphorus associated with the clay fraction is unidentified, but it is probably in iron, calcium, and aluminum phosphates that are present as tiny particles.

The amount of organic phosphorus increases as the organic nitrogen increases. Soil micro-organisms change the organic phosphorus to inorganic phosphorus at a faster rate as the soil pH increases. Therefore the amount of organic phosphorus tends to be larger in acid soils than in alkaline soils. Organic phosphorus occurs in soils as inositol hexaphosphate, other inositol phosphates, phospholipids, and unidentified compounds.

Phosphorus applied to soil as fertilizer is changed into forms similar in some respects to the native forms already present. A characteristic feature of soil phosphorus is its low solubility in water or the soil solution.

Acid soils contain a large excess of iron and aluminum. Alkaline and calcareous soils contain calcium. All three readily combine with water-soluble phosphates (such as superphosphate) and convert them into sparingly soluble forms.

The process of changing soluble phosphates into less soluble phosphates in soils is called fixation, or reversion. The nature of fixation may affect the efficiency of the phosphorus fertilizers differently on different types of soil.

Hydrated iron and aluminum oxides in acid soils are known to adsorb soluble phosphorus from fertilizers to form iron and aluminum phosphates. The amounts of hydrated aluminum and iron oxides in soils increase in general as the weathering processes continue. It is highest in regions of high temperature and rainfall (where kaolinite is the dominant clay mineral) and lowest in regions of low rainfall.

Acid soils with their higher content of hydrous oxides will fix phosphate to a greater extent than alkaline soils of similar texture. Within a group of acid or alkaline soils, the fixed phosphorus is less available on clay loams than on sandy loams, because of their higher clay mineral content. The amount of phosphorus adsorbed by a given soil series of varying textures is related closely to the surface area of the soil particles.

DIFFERENCES in the solubility of fixed forms of phosphorus result from differences in the pH of the soil at the time the fertilizer is applied.

Iron and aluminum phosphates are least soluble at pH 4. Their solubility increases as the pH increases from 4 to 8.5. J. F. Fudge, at the Alabama Agricultural Experiment Station, found that liming an acid soil to pH 6.3 increased tenfold the phosphorus concentration of the displaced soil solution. The calcium phosphates begin to form around pH 6. Their solubility decreases as the pH increases to about 7.5. In the presence of excess calcium carbonate, the solubility of the calcium phosphates increases between pH 7.5 and 9. This effect of pH holds true for the native and fixed forms of phosphorus. The availability is at a maximum in the pH range 6.5 to 7. As the pH increases from 7 to 8.5 in alkaline soils, the availability of phosphorus again drops. This may be due to a change in the rate or capacity of the roots to adsorb phosphorus or to a decrease in the concentration of the H_2PO_4 ion.

In neutral, alkaline, and calcareous soils, soluble phosphorus from fertilizers reacts with exchangeable calcium ions, soluble calcium salts, and calcium carbonate to form slightly soluble calcium phosphates. The form of calcium phosphate that appears first may be dicalcium phosphate, but this form is unstable in the presence of excess calcium ions and changes into hydroxyapatite or similar calcium phosphates. A calcium fluorphosphate has been found on the surface of large limestone particles in a soil that had been limed and then treated with superphosphate for many years.

A MAJOR PROBLEM of concern to the farmer involves the availability of the native and fixed forms of phosphorus to plants and the soil-management practices that can be followed to get the maximum benefit from fertilizer.

The availability of the soil phosphorus depends primarily on its degree of water solubility, since the plant obtains its phosphorus from the soil solution. Repeated restoration of the water-soluble phosphorus is necessary to meet the phosphorus requirements of the plant.

One has a clearer idea of the relation of forms of soil phosphorus to their availability if he knows how the plant gets its phosphorus from the soil.

The immediate source is the phosphorus dissolved in the soil water or solution. At least three events occur as the plant grows and absorbs phosphorus from this soil solution.

First, the amount or concentration of phosphorus in the soil solution immediately around the root drops. The amount of phosphorus in the soil solution is insufficient to meet the needs of the plant.

Second, the solid-phase phosphorus in contact with the soil solution enters the soil solution to replace the phosphorus absorbed by the root.

Third, the root grows into fresh areas of soil solution, repeating processes one and two.

Organic phosphorus, converted to inorganic form by microbial action, also acts as a source of supply to renew the soil solution phosphorus. If the concentration of phosphorus in the soil solution is too low or the rate of renewal from the solid-phase phosphorus is too slow, plant growth is retarded. Under these circumstances, a farmer could expect an increase in yield and quality of his crop from the application of phosphate fertilizer.

During periods of rapid growth, the phosphorus in the soil solution may be renewed from the solid phase 10 times or more a day in fertile soils. If the level of restoration is too low to maintain the phosphorus concentration needed for optimum growth, yields will be lower.

Plant growth usually brings about a reduced concentration of phosphorus in the soil solution. Very fertile soils heavily fertilized for many years may not show a perceptible change in solution phosphorus concentration from the growth of one or two crops, but they will follow the same pattern subsequently.

The addition of a water-soluble phosphate fertilizer or manure usually increases the concentration of the soil solution phosphorus. Recommendations for phosphate fertilization and soil-management practices that affect the phosphorus fertility levels of soils are designed to attain the optimum concentration of soil solution phosphorus, but this level is not known for all soils and crops.

The solubility of fixed forms of phosphorus increases after a water-soluble phosphate fertilizer is added and drops as a result of crop removal, aging, and weathering processes. The changes in solubility of fixed forms because of aging and weathering are ascribed to drying and crystal growth.

Dehydration—loss of water—causes a decline in the solubility of the fixed forms. Small crystals are less stable than large crystals; by growing, the crystals become less soluble.

Also, as mixing occurs upon cultivation and plowing, the fixed forms are exposed to fresh soil surfaces that have lower amounts of fixed forms per unit volume of soil. These fresh surfaces contain the metal ions, which react with soluble phosphorus and thereby further lower the solubility of the fixed forms. The decreases cause a gradual decline in the availability of phosphorus. This decline in availability generally is most rapid on soils in which the fixed phosphorus is in the least soluble forms.

An important difference between the native and the fixed forms of phosphorus in soils is the relative size of the particles. Native forms occur mainly as larger particles than the fixed forms. A greater percentage of the total phosphorus in fixed forms is in contact with the soil solution where it can replace the phosphorus removed by plants. An example: Some old rotation plots on calcareous soils had received superphosphate or manure for 39 years. About 30 percent of the residual or fixed forms but only 2 percent of the native forms were available to plants.

The smaller particle size or larger surface area of the fixed forms of phosphorus is to be expected, since the hydrated oxides and clay minerals that react with the phosphate fertilizer are also present as fine particles of colloidal size. The adsorbed phosphorus appears to remain on the surface of the individual soil particles and therefore continues in a fine state of subdivision.

Some organic substances modify the adsorption of phosphorus by soils. The decomposition of crop residues and soil organic matter releases various organic acids, such as isocitric acid and tartaric acid, which react with iron and aluminum to form soluble, complex, metal-organic ions. These complex ions have but slight tendency to combine with phosphorus.

Other decomposition products, not well defined, may be adsorbed on the same sites that could hold the phosphorus and thereby prevent phosphorus from being adsorbed. These effects of organic matter modify the reaction of fertilizer phosphorus with the soil.

Organic matter from manure and crop residues increases the availability of both native and fixed phosphorus. But there are temporary periods when phosphorus availability may drop during stages of rapid microbial growth. The phosphorus becomes bound in various organic compounds within the bodies of the micro-organisms, but most of this phosphorus is released in time as inorganic phosphorus, which is available for plant growth. The crop residues low in phosphorus and high in carbon, such as straw, are most likely to decompose and immobilize some phosphorus for a time.

The rate of mineralization of organic phosphorus increases as liming raises the pH. This effect probably is associated with several factors—the activity of the micro-organisms increases, the iron and aluminum oxides become less active in adsorbing organic phosphorus, and the greater amount of roots and crop residues supplies more energy material for the organisms.

Conserving organic matter and adding fresh crop residues affect phosphate availability. Organic matter increases the availability of phosphorus of both fixed and native forms. Mixing superphosphate with manure before it is put on the soil makes the superphosphate more efficient.

The total available supply of phosphorus depends on the plants and the chemistry of soil phosphorus. Maximum benefits from maintaining a high phosphate fertility level are not realized unless other nutrients are supplied at proper levels.

Many experiments show that only with adequate levels of nitrogen and potassium will the plant utilize high levels of available phosphorus.

L. C. Dumenil and J. Hanway, at the Iowa Agricultural Experiment Station, found no effect of phosphorus alone on corn yields, but phosphorus increased the yield 10.2 bushels when nitrogen was added. Phosphorus increased the yield 23 bushels when both nitrogen and potassium were applied.

THE pH OF THE SOIL affects the root system and its capacity to absorb other nutrients.

If the pH of the soil is more than 8, the plant may be unable to absorb enough iron, zinc, and manganese, even though the availability of phosphorus is high.

When the pH is below 5, the concentrations of manganese and aluminum may be large enough to be toxic to the plant, and molybdenum becomes deficient in some soils. Liming these soils may lower the toxicity of aluminum and manganese and increase the availability of molybdenum and phosphorus. In such cases, the beneficial effect of liming cannot be attributed only to an increase in the availability of phosphorus.

A significant factor of plant behavior with respect to the availability of fixed phosphorus is the relatively high need for phosphorus in the early stages of growth. Curves of growth and total phosphorus uptake usually show that 50 percent of the total plant phosphorus is absorbed when only 20 percent of the total growth has occurred. The smaller root system during the period of early growth and competition for available phosphorus by microorganisms explain the need for large supplies of available phosphorus in the

early stages of growth. These factors favor annual applications of soluble phosphorus fertilizers at planting time for annual crops.

SPECIES OF PLANTS differ markedly in their capacity to absorb soil and fertilizer phosphorus. At Beltsville, Md., phosphorus from phosphate rock was found to be most available to buckwheat. Legumes (alfalfa, crotalaria, and Ladino clover) extracted more phosphorus from phosphate rock than grasses (orchardgrass, bromegrass, perennial ryegrass, millet, and oats).

One explanation for these differences in uptake is that plants vary in their capacity to absorb cations, such as calcium, from the soil solution. A lowering of the calcium content of the soil solution increases the solubility of phosphorus. A plant with a high capacity to adsorb calcium on its root surfaces, such as buckwheat and the legumes, reduces the calcium concentration in the soil solution more than does a plant with a low capacity, such as oats. Therefore the buckwheat absorbs more phosphorus than oats because of the higher solubility of the phosphorus in the soil solution.

Another explanation is that plant roots release carbon dioxide to the soil solution. Carbon dioxide lowers the pH and increases the solubility of calcium phosphate. More carbon dioxide is given off by roots of a high exchange capacity than by roots with a low exchange capacity. This mechanism could also explain the relative differences between buckwheat and oats. It would be least effective on iron phosphate and aluminum phosphate or acid soils generally and most effective on calcium phosphates.

Crops with a low capacity to absorb the relatively insoluble calcium phosphates should benefit if they follow a crop with a high capacity. Planting pasture mixtures that combine these two types of crops may make it possible for the species with a low capacity to absorb these phosphates.

M. Drake and J. E. Steckel, of the

Massachusetts Agricultural Experiment Station, reported that oats grown in association with red clover gained 32 percent in yield and 62 percent in total phosphorus uptake compared to oats alone.

PLACING THE FERTILIZER in bands reduces soil contact and increases the phosphorus concentration in a small area. The proportion of the added phosphorus fixed in the more unavailable forms is greater when the fertilizer is broadcast and mixed with the whole mass of acid soils.

Band placement of phosphorus fertilizer greatly increases the availability of the phosphorus in acid soils. In alkaline or calcareous soils, placement and thorough mixing with the soil lead to about the same results, except possibly with potatoes.

The time phosphate fertilizer is applied is more important on acid soils than on calcareous soils. The major change in solubility of concentrated superphosphate occurs within 2 or 3 days after mixing.

Water-soluble phosphorus diffuses away from a fertilizer particle through the soil a distance of about 1 inch; then its movement becomes very slow. Within this small zone around the fertilizer particle, water-soluble phosphorus in the soil increases. Any mixing from cultivation or plowing, however, will expose the phosphate-rich soil around the fertilizer particle to soil capable of adsorbing more phosphorus, with the result that the phosphorus will transfer to other soil surfaces. The greater the adsorption capacity for phosphorus, the more significant the reduction in solubility will be.

Farmers with acid soils usually get best results by applying phosphorus at planting time, but farmers with alkaline or calcareous soils may satisfactorily apply the phosphorus several months before planting.

The availability of soil phosphorus is also affected by the available moisture supply. J. L. Haddock observed at the Utah Agricultural Experiment Station that conditions of soil moisture were as important in making phosphorus available to sugar beets as either phosphorus applications or placement.

Drying tends to make phosphorus less available. That may be due to a drop in amount of phosphorus in solution or to other factors associated with root activity and the production of carbon dioxide. The effects of soil moisture on phosphorus availability emphasize the importance of maintaining high rates of water infiltration and of reducing evaporation losses on non-irrigated soils subject to drought.

Less than 20 percent of the applied phosphorus is utilized by the crop the year of application. When a farmer follows a practice of applying phosphate as inorganic fertilizer or manures to his soil each year, or even every 2 or 3 years, the amount of phosphorus the crop removes is usually less than the amount of phosphorus added.

Residual phosphate accumulates in the soil, with the result that the plant-available phosphorus level increases.

In several areas intensively farmed or devoted to large cash crops, phosphate fertilization has been so high that the soils no longer respond very much to applications of phosphate. This phosphate fertilizer probably could be utilized more efficiently on soils on which chemical tests show low values for extractable phosphorus.

If the level of available phosphorus is low, as indicated by a soil test for extractable phosphorus or by plant response to applied phosphorus, a large application is needed to bring the available phosphorus level within a suitable range.

In high-fixing acid soils, the residual or carryover effects of phosphorus for a second crop usually are small, unless the soil has been fertilized for many years. At the start of a phosphate fertilization program, therefore, the rate may have to be high, and annual applications may be necessary. As the residual phosphorus gradually accumulates in the soil, the rate and frequency of application may be reduced.

Soil Potassium and Fertility

R. F. Reitemeier

Plants need large amounts of potassium, one of the three major fertilizer elements. It is supplied to roots by natural sources in the soil and by fertilizers, manures, and mulches.

Our soils, except acid sandy soils and organic soils, such as peat and muck, usually have high contents of potassium—often 2 to 3 percent in the surface foot. The total potassium content of our soils generally increases from east to west; that is, in the direction of less severe soil weathering. The content tends to increase from south to north in the eastern half of the country.

Potassium (K) is a silvery-white, soft, highly reactive metal, much like sodium. In nature it does not occur in a free metallic state but is combined in many compounds and minerals. It is found in all living matter, and its salts are used as fertilizers. The term "potash" originally was used for K_2CO_3 (potassium carbonate), produced in the burning of plants, but commonly is applied also to KOH (caustic potash) and to potassium salts such as KCl (muriate of potash) and K_2SO_4 (sulfate of potash). In fertilizer and soil analyses, however, potash signifies the hypothetical potassium oxide, K_2O.

Soil potassium exists in a number of forms. One form is soluble in water. Some forms are insoluble even in strong acids. Others are of intermediate solubility. Most soil potassium is not available to plants even after years of cropping.

A large proportion of it is in primary high-potassium minerals in the silt and sand fractions. These minerals include two micas (muscovite and biotite) and two feldspars (orthoclase and microcline). The minerals in soils of arid regions are relatively unweathered and therefore are effective suppliers of potassium to plants. Biotite seems to decompose most readily. It can be an important source of potassium for crops in tropical soils when temperature and moisture are high.

Many soils also contain potassium-bearing, clay-size minerals, the hydrous micas or illites, which have less potassium and more water than the primary micas. Because of their smaller size, which gives them a greater exposed surface area, some forms of illite effectively supply potassium. The high potassium-supplying power of some soils in the Corn Belt is attributed to this source.

Such clay minerals as illite, montmorillonite, vermiculite, and kaolinite, and soil organic matter have cation-exchange capacity—that is, the ability to retain on their surfaces cations that can be replaced rapidly by other cations. Potassium ions often constitute from 1 to 3 percent of the exchangeable cations in the soil.

Exchangeable potassium is the important reservoir of readily available potassium. It may be derived from potassium-bearing minerals or from fertilizers, other soil additives, or crop residues. It generally represents only a small part of the total potassium. For example, in a soil containing 40 thousand pounds of potassium (to convert to potash, K_2O, multiply by 1.2) an acre at plow depth, the exchangeable potassium might be 400 pounds; that is, 1 percent of the total.

In turn, the soluble potassium that is free to move with the soil water amounts to a small fraction of the exchangeable quantity, about 1 to 5 percent. The soluble and exchangeable forms are in equilibrium with each other. A reduction of the soluble form by crop removal or leaching is followed instantly by a transfer from the exchangeable form so as to maintain the equilibrium relationship.

When a soluble potassium salt is added to the soil, a transfer occurs in the opposite direction, from solution to exchange surfaces, and the equilibrium is reestablished rapidly at a higher available potassium level. Because of this relationship, no distinction is made between soluble and exchangeable forms in the usual determination of exchangeable potassium by salt or acid extractions or other methods.

When a soluble potassium fertilizer, such as muriate of potash, is applied to some soils that contain expandable lattice clay minerals (like montmorillonite and vermiculite and some forms of illite) a substantial part of it may be converted into a form which is not readily available. Drying appears necessary for this fixation by montmorillonite, but not by illite. G. Brown, of the Rothamsted Experimental Station, in England, has named a potassium-fixing form of illite in Irish soils "degrading illite."

Fixation and release in these minerals are viewed as the comparatively slow entry and exit of potassium ions within the layers of cations located between silica layers of the lattice. When a large fraction of these cation sites is occupied by potassium ions, the lattice is contracted. The degree of subsequent availability of the fixed potassium depends on such factors as the kind of crop, type of mineral, moisture content, and the levels of exchangeable potassium, calcium, and hydrogen.

The illite of some river sediment soils in the Netherlands, named "ammersooite" by J. Temme and H. W. van der Marel, fixes fertilizer potassium so firmly that potatoes and clover cannot be grown successfully without extremely high potash applications, although sugar beets, oats, barley, and wheat yield satisfactorily.

Fixed potassium should not be considered as a total loss but as an addition to the reserve supply forms, which helps to reduce leaching and luxury consumption of soluble and exchange-

able forms. Its availability generally is intermediate between that of exchangeable and natural nonexchangeable forms. In the case of illites, fixation may be regarded as the restoration of potassium previously lost from the crystal lattice by weathering, leaching, and cropping.

Another equilibrium exists between exchangeable and clay lattice forms, but this equilibrium is more sluggish than that between soluble and exchangeable forms. The overall equilibrium may be represented as follows: Soluble $\rightleftharpoons$ Exchangeable $\rightleftharpoons$ Lattice (fixed; illitic).

The time required for equilibrium to be established between each pair of forms increases from left to right. An increase of soluble potassium, as from a fertilizer application, results in a movement of some potassium to the right, and a decrease, as from cropping, in a movement to the left.

The release of the nonexchangeable forms to the more readily available exchangeable and soluble forms has been increased by cropping, freezing and thawing, liming, and drying. Drying fixes potassium in some soils if the readily available level is high but releases it if the level is low.

The exchangeable form is never depleted completely by cropping but it often reaches a minimum level characteristic of the soil and the cropping situation. In soils containing all the various forms, the exchangeable potassium value is usually lowest at harvest time and highest in the spring before planting.

Other cations can affect some of the forms of potassium.

When water is added to a soil, a small fraction of the exchangeable potassium changes to the soluble form because of replacement by calcium and magnesium ions originally in solution. During a drying period, some soluble potassium replaces an equivalent amount of calcium and magnesium in the exchangeable forms.

Both the fixation and the release of potassium in illite are favored by an increase in the exchangeable calcium relative to exchangeable hydrogen, which is the basic process in liming. The increased calcium ions evidently expand some of the clay mineral lattice interlayers sufficiently to facilitate the entry or exit of potassium ions.

Ammonium ions and hydrogen ions (actually hydronium ions, H_3O^+) are of about the same size as potassium ions and therefore interfere and compete with potassium in fixation and release reactions involving the interlayers of expandable lattice minerals. Ammonium added to a soil containing vermiculite, montmorillonite, or degrading illite thus may become fixed and thereby decrease the fixation of subsequently added potassium. The converse would occur where the potassium was applied first.

LOSSES OF SOIL POTASSIUM occur in cropping, leaching, and erosion.

Soils that cannot supply significant amounts of natural and fixed nonexchangeable potassium (such as organic soils; acid, coarse-textured soils; and acid soils that do not contain illites) have no reservoir of reserve potassium to maintain the exchangeable form at a moderate or high level. Potassium removed from such soils by cropping must be replaced frequently by potassium in fertilizers.

Exchangeable potassium is subject to leaching with water by exchange with hydrogen and other cations, and leaching losses in permeable soils in humid regions must be replaced. If clay is abundant in the subsoil, potassium leached from the surface soil may become concentrated there in exchangeable and fixed forms. Erosion of surface soil in extreme cases may cause an appreciable loss of available potassium by the removal of fertilizer particles and of soil particles and organic matter that have high exchangeable potassium content. Because the total content of potassium usually does not vary abruptly with depth, erosion does not alter appreciably the total potassium of the surface soil.

Crops remove large amounts of potassium from soil, as compared with other nutrients except nitrogen and calcium. The actual amounts are affected by the species, variety, and size of plant and by such factors as level of available potassium, supplies of other elements, soil moisture, soil aeration, and temperature. The potassium contents needed for average to good acre yields therefore should be regarded only as approximate needs.

The grain portion of barley, oats, and wheat crops contains about 10 pounds. The straw contains about 30 pounds. Corn grain contains 15 pounds and the stover about 50 pounds. The aboveground part of a cotton crop may have a content of 40 pounds, of which about one-third is in the lint and seed. Various grasses contain 25 to 50 pounds. Alfalfa and sweetclover contain 100 to 150 pounds, and other legumes 50 to 75 pounds. Potatoes contain 150 pounds, 100 pounds in the tubers and 50 pounds in the vines. A 15-ton crop of celery may contain 200 pounds of potassium.

When a high supply of readily available potassium is present and other growth conditions are favorable, the uptake by crops may far exceed average requirements. That may result from an increase in the size of the plants and from the luxury consumption of potassium.

Annual crops do not take up potassium at a constant rate but approximately according to the size of the plant at each stage.

In experiments with potatoes at the Virginia Truck Experiment Station, R. L. Carolus learned that during the 8th week of growth the crop absorbed about 1 pound of potassium an acre a day but absorbed 4 pounds a day between the 10th and 12th weeks. The potassium supply during the period of greatest growth should be enough to meet a high rate of demand.

Plant roots readily absorb soluble and exchangeable potassium, as must be obvious from the high potassium requirements of some annual crops.

Potassium apparently enters the root cells in combination with the organic compounds produced in metabolic processes within the plant. Once inside the roots, the potassium evidently reverts to an ionic form and can move rapidly through the plant. Although it is retained moderately tightly by living cells, it does not become permanently combined in organic molecules or structural components and is easily removed at the death of the cell.

During the time that seeds, fruits, and nuts develop, potassium moves to them from the leaves. Cereal plants normally appear even to lose a portion of their potassium to the soil as they approach maturity. Appreciable fractions of the potassium content of plants are lost sometimes by the leaching of potassium from the leaves by rain. This high mobility has hindered the determination of the essential functions of potassium in the growth of plants.

POTASSIUM IS NECESSARY for several basic physiological functions—the formation of sugars and starch and their movement between different parts of the plant, the synthesis of proteins, normal cell division and growth, and the neutralization of organic acids.

Potassium also assists different plants in a number of more specialized ways. It enhances the size, flavor, and color of some fruits and vegetables. It increases the resistance of some plants to particular diseases. Potassium improves the rigidity of straw and stalks, so there is less lodging. It increases the oil content of oil-bearing seeds. It helps overcome influences of adverse weather, such as low soil moisture and low temperature, and of poor physical soil conditions, such as compaction and inadequate aeration.

You may not be able to notice any deficiency effects in plants that have moderately inadequate levels of potassium because the usual symptom of this degree of deficiency is a general reduction in growth. That is not easy to detect unless you compare the size of the plants with that of others that are growing in a similar place and are getting enough potassium. Furthermore, this is a general deficiency symptom for many nutrients. Analyses and tests of the soil and plant may reveal a potassium deficiency.

The onset of characteristic visual symptoms, which signifies a more severe deficiency, means that production has already been seriously impaired. The application then of fertilizer potassium cannot overcome the damage already incurred, especially in annual quick-growing crops.

If legumes, such as clovers and alfalfa, and grasses are growing together, a shortage of potassium may lead to the reduction or disappearance of the legume without the occurrence of any severe deficiency symptoms. Grasses and weeds can thrive at levels of available soil potassium that are inadequate for forage legumes.

The general leaf pattern when potassium is low begins with a yellowing of the tips and edges. The yellow area then gets broader. The tissues at the edges and later the entire leaf die as the deficiency becomes more severe. These symptoms appear first in the older leaves and later in the younger leaves, because in line with the general tendency of potassium to concentrate in the rapidly growing tissues it moves from the older leaves (at their expense) to the younger leaves.

At first, in clover and alfalfa you usually see small, white spots around the edges of the leaf. As the deficiency worsens, the spots become more numerous, the edges and entire leaf turn yellow, the edges are scorched, and the older leaves drop.

In corn, the tips of the older leaves first become yellow. Streaks of yellow run lengthwise through the leaves. The edges become scorched. The stalks are weak and short. The ears are small, poorly filled, and chaffy at the tip.

A deficiency symptom in cotton, known as cotton rust, first appears as yellowish, mottled margins of the leaf and yellow spots between the veins. They finally merge to make a dry, curled, reddish-brown leaf, which drops prematurely. Unopened and partly opened bolls containing cotton of poor quality result from this extreme deficiency of potassium.

THE SUPPLY of potassium to plants often affects and is affected by the level of other nutrients.

In soils containing expandable lattice clay minerals, an increase in exchangeable calcium sometimes causes the fixation or release of nonexchangeable potassium, depending on whether the exchangeable potassium level is relatively high or low. Under the condition of very high soluble or exchangeable calcium and very low exchangeable potassium, the calcium may depress the immediate supply of potassium to plants. That appears typical also of some calcareous soils.

But normally within a wide range of saturation of the cation-exchange capacity with calcium, the calcium has only a minor effect on the uptake of exchangeable potassium. Actually an increase in the exchangeable potassium level may reduce the uptake of calcium or magnesium and cause the luxury consumption of potassium, even though the absolute potassium level is very low relative to the level of the other two cations, as is customary. Such an effect has been observed in alfalfa, clover, tomatoes, apples, and prunes.

The usual effects of nitrogen and phosphorus, the other two major fertilizer nutrients, are associated with nutrient balance in the plant. If the supply of nitrogen and phosphorus is high relative to that of potassium, growth may be rapid at first, but the potassium concentration in the plant may become reduced to a deficiency level. Thus, even though the total potassium uptake by the plant may be increased by the high nitrogen and phosphorus levels, additions of potassium to the soil would be necessary to maintain the nutrient balance required for rapid, continued growth. In situations of high available potas-

sium level and low nitrogen or phosphorus supply, luxury consumption of potassium is to be expected.

SODIUM IS NOT CONSIDERED to be an essential plant nutrient, but some plants (for example, beets, celery, turnips, and cabbage) require it for maximum production even in the presence of ample potassium.

Another group of plants, including barley, oats, wheat, cotton, tomatoes, asparagus, and alfalfa, respond to sodium when the potassium supply is inadequate.

A third large group of crops respond to sodium slightly or not at all at any potassium level. Among them are corn, rye, potatoes, lettuce, and soybeans. Sodium or potassium generally will depress the uptake of the other cation, but the results of this mutual relationship in any particular situation will depend on the levels of available sodium and potassium and the relative ease of absorption of the two cations by the plant.

THE EFFICIENT MANAGEMENT of soil with respect to potassium must be based on a number of soil-management factors: The kind of crop, the rotation system, the livestock-management system, the nature of the soil, the liming and fertilizer practices, and the weather.

Satisfying the potassium requirements of a cropping system should be based first on the natural potassium-supplying ability of the soil. In this regard soils range from organic and acid sandy soils (which cannot be depended on for any natural reserve supply) to clay soils that contain large amounts of relatively unweathered potassium minerals, which do not have to be supplemented by potash fertilizer.

Soils having little or no reserve potassium supply and low cation-exchange capacities require the frequent additions of small or moderate amounts of potassium. Large single applications to such soils may result in higher losses through leaching and unbalanced nutrient relations in the crop through luxury consumption. Leaching losses from rain can be serious in winter-fallowed soil of regions in which winters are warm. A winter cover crop reduces this loss. The continued removal of hay crops, however, severely depletes the soil potassium, and it must be increased by adding potash.

When rotations include row crops that respond markedly to potash (for example, cotton, tobacco, and potatoes), a potash application should be made to these crops at planting time. Excessive rains after planting may make additional applications necessary to replace leaching losses.

Legume crops that are removed from the land severely lower the available potassium level of soils. Liming of acid soils improves various growth conditions and thereby increases potassium requirements of legumes, but it also reduces the leaching of potassium. In a study at the North Carolina Agricultural Experiment Station, Adolph Mehlich found that even clay subsoils would not retain potassium effectively until they were limed.

If sodium is applied to the soil, either as sodium nitrate or as a treatment for a sodium-responsive crop, the extent of the substitution of this cation for potassium should be considered in estimating potash applications.

Loams and clays containing an abundance of illitic clay minerals or unweathered primary potassium minerals can be expected to supply from a moderate fraction to all of the potassium required for a cropping system. Younger soils in this group can be cropped for many years before fertilizer potash has to be included in the soil-management program. The exact length of time, of course, depends on the amount of potassium in crops removed from the land and on other losses from the soil.

IN A SOIL-PASTURE-LIVESTOCK management system on such soils, the potassium cycle would be as follows: Mineral, to exchangeable, to soluble, to plant, to animal, to manure, to soluble, to exchangeable, to mineral (fixed). After the forage plants have absorbed soluble soil potassium which has been replaced from the exchangeable form and released earlier from mineral lattice forms, the pastured animals consume it during their feeding. A large fraction of it is returned to the soil in the animal manure, some of which becomes, in turn, soluble, exchangeable, and finally fixed in mineral lattices. The main loss of potassium in this cycle arises from the removal of the animals and animal products from the land.

Byron T. Shaw, of the Department of Agriculture, has estimated that in such a system, 75 to 90 percent of the potassium removed from the soil would be returned to it. Other cropping and livestock systems will conserve a smaller fraction. If sheltered animals are fed hay from the same farm, losses of potassium may occur if the manure is improperly conserved before it is applied to the soil.

If the straw of small grain and corn crops is not removed from the land, only about one-fourth of the potassium in the crop is permanently lost from the soil. The harvested portions of potatoes, celery, other vegetable crops, and tobacco contain much higher fractions of the total crop potassium. Much of the potassium in leaves of deciduous fruit and nut trees that drop on the ground eventually will return to available soil forms. In places where the native potassium supply is inadequate to replace losses, fertilizer potash must be applied. In many soils, a fraction of it will be fixed, and the availability of the application to the current crop will be lowered accordingly. This fixed potassium will be slowly available in the future, however, and so improve the ability of the soil to supply potassium.

The determination of currently available potassium is made by a soil test or by a plant tissue test. Information about the reserve supply is obtained from other laboratory measurements and from the history and general knowledge of the particular soil.

Sulfur and Soil Fertility

Howard V. Jordan and H. M. Reisenauer

Plants get sulfur from the soil, rain and irrigation water, fertilizers, insecticides, fungicides, and the atmosphere.

Sulfur is essential to life. Many plants use about as much sulfur as they do phosphorus.

Sulfur (S) is a nonmetallic element that occurs in several forms. The stable form under ordinary conditions is a pale-yellow, brittle, crystalline solid, which burns with a blue flame to give sulfur dioxide and combines with many metals to form sulfides. Large amounts are extracted in Texas and Louisiana.

Soil supplies of sulfur are so meager in some places that deficiencies exist; in other places supplies are very low.

Considerable sulfur—upwards of 40 pounds an acre, which is enough for crops—is released in industrial areas in the smoke of burning coal and carried to the soil in rainwater.

Atmospheric sulfur, which is utilized by plants, also is present in large amounts in industrial areas.

Sulfur accretion from rainwater in nonindustrial localities may be only about 4 pounds an acre a year, and atmospheric sulfur is of little importance there.

All water used for irrigation in the Western States contains dissolved sulfur in a form usable by plants, but the amount depends on how much water is applied and its sulfur content.

Crop production has been maintained in some areas of potential sulfur deficiency by the application of fertilizers, in which sulfur may be only an incidental component. The trend in the preparation of commercial fertilizers is toward higher concentrations of the major nutrients, and some or all of the sulfur is being eliminated—a development that may intensify the problem of supplying sulfur.

Some plants of the crucifer, or mustard, family (cabbage, cauliflower, kale, turnip, radish) and the lily family (onions, asparagus, and many flowering plants) have particularly high requirements of sulfur. A 15-ton crop of cabbage and a 20-ton crop of turnips absorb on the order of 40 pounds of sulfur an acre. A 15-ton crop of onions takes up about 19 pounds.

Legumes, cotton, and tobacco utilize relatively large amounts, ranging from 20 pounds an acre for 4 tons of alfalfa to about 15 pounds an acre for good yields of the other crops.

Small grains, grasses, and corn are less sensitive to sulfur. They require 10 pounds an acre or less.

The sulfur generally is well distributed through the plant.

It usually is absorbed from the soil as the sulfate ion, in which form it is readily mobile within the plant. The sulfate form is converted in plant metabolism to a reduced form, mainly the sulfhydryl group.

Sulfur in plant compounds may be reconverted to the sulfate form and reutilized in the formation of other sulfur-containing compounds in a different part of the plant. Relatively large amounts may be moved in this way—from older tissues to newer tissues in sulfur-deficient plants and into the seed and fruit of maturing plants.

Sulfur may also enter the leaves as sulfur dioxide from the atmosphere.

Sulfur is a constituent of all plant proteins, some plant hormones, the mustard-oil glycosides, and glutathione. The sulfur content of plant proteins (in which sulfur occurs as the amino acids, cystine and methionine) never exceeds 2 percent. The amino acids are important in animal nutrition and may improve the quality of protein in flour for bread making.

The plant hormones that contain

sulfur—thiamin and biotin—act as
plant growth regulators and also are
important in animal nutrition.

The mustard-oil glycosides impart
flavor to plants. Glutathione sup-
posedly is involved in plant respiration.

Sulfur appears to influence several
plant processes. Protein synthesis is
retarded in the sulfur-deficient plants,
and as a result amino acids and other
nitrogen-containing compounds may
accumulate in the tissues. Sulfur may
favor the development of nodules and
the subsequent nitrogen fixation by
legumes. Sulfur seems to be associated
with the formation of chlorophyll, as
shown by the yellow color of sulfur-
deficient plants. Anthocyanin pigments develop in some plants that lack
sulfur, an indication that sulfur affects
carbohydrate metabolism.

SYMPTOMS OF SULFUR DEFICIENCY in
plants generally are like those of nitrogen deficiency. The plants are stunted
and are pale green to yellow in color.
Such chlorosis often is severe on the
older leaves, but on some plants,
notably citrus, tobacco, and cotton,
it is worst on new growth. In contrast
to the pattern for nitrogen deficiency,
the severely chlorotic leaves of sulfur-
deficient plants do not die back in
early stages of the deficiency and do
not show a characteristic pattern.

On some plants, like turnips, a
marked redness develops in the lower
leaves. It starts in the leaf veins and
gradually spreads to the interveinal
tissue as the deficiency gets worse.

Sulfur deficiencies in nonlegume
crops occur most commonly at high
levels of nitrogen fertilization. As the
organic matter of the surface soil declines with continued cultivation, nitrogen deficiencies may develop in
crops; the responses to nitrogen fertilization are readily demonstrated.

Because the soil organic matter is
the main store of both sulfur and nitrogen, however, sulfur released by the
decomposition of organic matter declines in proportion to the decrease in
release of nitrogen. When all of the

*1. Places where responses of crops to applied sul-
fur have been demonstrated by field experiments.*

nitrogen available for use by a nonlegume crop is supplied from decomposition of the soil organic matter, the
sulfur released at the same time is adequate for crop needs. But if the supply
of soil nitrogen is supplemented with
heavy applications of sulfur-free nitrogenous fertilizer, the amount of
nitrogen available for crop use may be
excessive in relation to the sulfur.

Under such high-nitrogen and low-
sulfur conditions, plant-growth processes are disrupted, and plants develop
symptoms of sulfur deficiency. Sometimes total growth has been reduced
by fertilization with nitrogen alone,
whereas combined applications of nitrogen and sulfur have given the normal yield increases expected from the
nitrogen application.

Deficiencies of sulfur may result from
combined additions of nitrogen fertilizers and high-energy, low-sulfur organic materials. Then the available
sulfur is tied up by the resulting large
increase in the microbes in the soil.
This effect has been noted more commonly in greenhouses than in experiments in the field.

SULFUR may be toxic to plants.

Sulfur dioxide in the atmosphere in
any sizable concentration kills plants.
The countryside near smelters sometimes is nearly denuded of vegetation.
Most species are injured by exposure
for only an hour to air containing one
part in a million of sulfur dioxide. This
sort of atmospheric contamination has
been controlled somewhat in modern

installations that discharge the gases from high stacks or recover the sulfur at the point of discharge.

Plants also may suffer from high concentrations of soluble sulfates in the soil profile. Such conditions normally develop only in arid or semiarid regions and in poorly drained soils. Very likely this sensitivity comes about because high concentrations of sulfate tend to limit the uptake of calcium.

MOST OF THE SULFUR in soils of humid regions is in the organic fraction and is high in the soils that accumulate organic matter.

The supply is much less plentiful in weathered soils. Thirteen Chernozems described in the *Atlas of American Agriculture, Part III* contain a mean of 1,080 pounds of sulfur an acre in their A horizon. Twelve Prairie (Brunizem) soils contain a mean of 792 pounds, and 43 Red-Yellow Podzolic soils contain a mean of 420 pounds.

Total sulfur is more abundant in the surface than in lower soil horizons. In a number of soils in Ohio, the depths at 0–6 inches, 6–12 inches, 12–18 inches, and 18–24 inches contained 1,056, 830, 686, and 528 pounds of total sulfur an acre, respectively.

The transformation of sulfur in the soil organic matter into forms available for plant use is largely a microbial process. If the soil is well aerated, the organic sulfur is oxidized to sulfates, which plants can use directly.

An interesting application is the use of a commercial product that is fortified with an efficient sulfur-oxidizing microflora and sold as inoculated sulfur. Inoculation hastens the oxidation process. Inoculated sulfur sometimes is more effective than the elemental sulfur.

If the soil is waterlogged or if for other reasons anaerobic conditions prevail, the oxidation is retarded, and even added sulfates may be reduced to elemental sulfur, hydrogen sulfide, or related products.

Sulfates are usable by plants and are mobile within the soil profile.

A study of sulfur supplies and requirements for crops in the Southeastern States was begun in 1953 by the Department of Agriculture in cooperation with 12 experiment stations in the South and the Tennessee Valley Authority. Sulfur extracted from soils with sodium acetate-acetic acid solution is taken as a measure of available sulfur. In the Southeast, particularly in the light-textured soils of the Coastal Plain, the distribution of this extractable sulfur is almost the reverse of that of total sulfur.

These Southeastern soils have a unique pattern in distribution of extractable sulfur. Surface horizons typically contain 3 parts per million (6 pounds an acre) or less. A definite accumulation occurs in some lower horizons. This zone of accumulation may occur at a depth of 6 inches or it may be as much as 30 inches beneath the surface. Concentrations as great as 280 parts per million (560 pounds an acre) have been found in the zones. The contrast with the distribution of total sulfur is evident. The accumulation zones are correlated with horizons having an increase in clay content, a reduction of pH, or both.

Extractable sulfur, accumulated in the lower horizons, may be unavailable to shallow-rooted crops but may be available to deep-rooted plants, except in early stages of growth. Thus cotton responded to sulfur in certain soils in Alabama, but alfalfa and sericea lespedeza did not. Seedling plants often are deficient in sulfur throughout the Southeast; as their roots extend into deeper horizons, however, the deficiencies may disappear and yields may be normal or nearly normal.

Deficiencies of sulfur may persist throughout the growing season in the Northwest—an indication that subsoil accumulations of extractable sulfur do not occur there. Sufficient research has not been completed to determine how widely the pattern extends beyond the Red-Yellow Podzolic group, however.

Additions of sulfur in rainwater may be adequate for crop production in

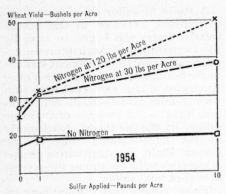

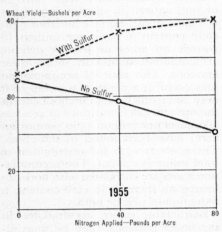

2. These charts show how increased applications of nitrogen fertilizer to wheat in Washington increased the requirement of the crop for sulfur. On this Palouse silt loam, which is low in sulfur, application of 1 pound of sulfur per acre increased wheat yields up to 7 bushels per acre in 1954. The crop yield was reduced in 1955 when nitrogen was applied alone, but it increased 11 bushels per acre with both nitrogen and sulfur.

industrial areas, but they only supplement the supplies in areas of potential deficiency of sulfur.

Rainwater is said to add about 209 pounds of sulfur an acre annually near Chicago, 127 pounds near Gary, Ind., and 40 to 60 pounds near smaller industrial centers. Even the smaller additions are enough for normal crop production.

In the Southeast, in the area south of the Virginia-Kentucky border and in areas away from industry, rainwater has added only 5.4 pounds of sulfur an acre a year. In six rural areas in Nebraska, a 2-year study gave a corresponding value of 6.2 pounds an acre a year. An estimated 6 pounds of sulfur an acre a year are added in precipitation in Washington. Sulfur accretions of this amount alleviate, but do not end, deficiencies of sulfur if other supplies are inadequate.

Additions of sulfur in the irrigation water may be enough to supply the total crop requirements. Western river waters contain 6 pounds to 2 thousand pounds of sulfur an acre-foot of water. The average is 50 pounds. The sulfur content of most rivers is lowest near their source and increases as the flow is supplemented with drainage water from irrigation projects. In only a very few areas in the West is sulfur fertilization of irrigated crops required for the maximum yields.

The sulfur content of well waters, though highly variable, generally is lower than that of river waters.

As to fertilizers, normal superphosphate contains about 11 percent of sulfur in the form of gypsum. Ammonium sulfate contains about 24 percent, and potassium sulfate about 16.5 percent. The average mixed fertilizer sold in the United States has about 7.5 percent.

In the Northwest, increases in yields of alfalfa from applications of superphosphate and potassium sulfate, formerly attributed to the primary constituents of those fertilizers, were found later to be largely responses to sulfur.

The equivalent of about 1.4 million tons of sulfur was applied in primary fertilizers in the United States in 1955. Additions in secondary nutrient fertilizers, liming materials, manures, and miscellaneous items (including insecticides and fungicides) brought the total close to 2 million tons that year.

That total is large, but the additions of sulfur from those sources were not uniformly distributed and perhaps were inadequate in some areas where soils were deficient and rainfall and irrigation water added little sulfur.

Fertilizers that are essentially sulfur-free have been used increasingly. Ammonium nitrate, anhydrous ammonia, urea, and ammonia solutions are examples among the nitrogen carriers. The use of concentrated superphosphate and other phosphorus carriers with little sulfur has been expanding.

We recommend that farmers in areas of potential deficiency should have a planned program of adding sulfur instead of depending on incidental applications in ordinary fertilizer materials.

Losses of sulfur from soils are due mainly to leaching, erosion, and removal by crops.

Some sulfur is lost from soils of humid regions in drainage water. Measured losses from eight soil types in Illinois maintained in fallow ranged from 1.5 to 57 pounds of sulfur an acre a year; the average was 30 pounds. The larger losses occurred from the more permeable and more fertile soils. Annual losses from a Fayette silt loam with 10 percent slope in Wisconsin were approximately 1 pound an acre when crops were grown and 3 pounds an acre from uncropped soil.

The measurements in both States were made in lysimeters that permitted runoff and probably are fairly applicable to sloping upland soils. Earlier measurements, made in lysimeters that did not permit runoff, were considerably higher.

Sulfur losses from erosion have been estimated to average about 6 pounds an acre.

The losses may deplete soil supplies of sulfur, except perhaps in industrial and irrigated areas where accretions may exceed losses.

A balance sheet of the sulfur economy of soils and crops in the United States would appraise these additions and losses. It would be expected that soils well supplied with organic matter and occurring near industrial areas would not at present need sulfur fertilization. Requirements in such areas may change, particularly if sulfur-free fertilizers come into wide use or coal is replaced as fuel.

Iron and Soil Fertility

R. S. Holmes and J. C. Brown

Most soils contain an abundance of total iron, which all plants need, but many interacting factors affect and limit the iron that plants can use.

An accumulation of the heavy metals—copper, manganese, zinc, and nickel—in relation to available iron may induce iron deficiency in plants in acid soils.

Lime-containing soils, however, are most apt to contain too little iron; plants on such calcareous soils may have an abnormal growth, which is called lime-induced chlorosis. Its symptoms are yellow foliage, lack of vigor, and unproductiveness. It is common in the arid Intermountain and Southwestern States.

A deficiency of iron exists in almost every major fruit-growing area.

It is difficult to supply iron in a form available to plants. Such soil amendments as ammonium sulfate have been used to furnish plant nutrients and at the same time increase the soil acidity, which affects iron solubility. Some new compounds, called iron chelates, have been found to correct many deficiencies of iron.

One of the functions of iron is to be a catalyst in the production of chlorophyll, the green pigment in plants.

You can recognize iron deficiency by looking at the new, growing leaves. The tissue between the veins becomes lighter in color than the veins. The areas between the veins become yellow as the deficiency advances. Only a branch of a tree may be affected, or perhaps only a few trees in an orchard are chlorotic. The entire tree in severe cases is affected, plants lose part of their leaves, and dieback results. If the condition is not corrected, the plant becomes unproductive and dies. Young peach trees in some places cannot be kept alive longer than 2 years because of iron chlorosis.

The iron that is proportional to chlorophyll in the plant is called active iron. Enough active iron for normal chlorophyll development can be present only after a certain minimal amount of residual iron is in the leaf. Active iron affects the iron-porphyrin protein complex, which acts as an oxygen carrier, transporter of electrons, activator of oxygen, and decomposer of hydrogen peroxide (H_2O_2). Iron becomes active biologically only when it becomes a part of these complex organic compounds. Factors that limit the supply of iron to a plant limit the life of the plant.

THE IRON IN SOILS of humid sections comes from the weathering of many iron-containing minerals of the parent material of the soil.

Among the more common iron-bearing primary minerals are hornblende, biotite, and chlorite. The iron in those minerals is largely in the ferrous state (that is, a combining value of 2, such as $Fe^{++} O^{--}$). When they and other minerals are weathered during soil formation, most of the iron is changed to the ferric state (that is, the combining value has been increased to 3— e. g., Fe_2O_3) and forms different iron compounds. The kind of parent material and the conditions under which it is weathered influence the distribution and kinds of iron compounds formed in the soil.

We have two groups of conditions under which the iron of the parent material is most altered in the process of soil formation.

One is when rainfall is high, temperature is low, and an organic cover has accumulated. In such conditions, which prevail in much of the North-

eastern States, a large part of the sodium, potassium, calcium, and magnesium of the parent material is dissolved and leached away and a more acid residue is left in the top horizons of the newly formed soil. A great deal of the iron, in turn, becomes reduced and dissolved and is transported to the lower, less acid horizon, where it is precipitated and forms new iron compounds, such as iron hydrates, oxides, and some organic iron complexes. Those compounds vary in color and ease of solubility. The more hydrated iron compounds are the most easily dissolved and reduced (that is, oxygen is removed) of all the inorganic iron minerals. The organic iron in acid soils is somewhat soluble in water, and the iron in this form tends to be protected from oxidation-precipitation.

The other set of conditions occurs when little organic cover has accumulated, but rain is abundant and temperatures are high. Such conditions prevail in many tropical areas. Here the more active base elements are also removed, as in the first set of conditions, and an acid material is formed, accompanied by oxidation. The iron is converted largely to hydrated oxides, which are retained in place. Some of the hydrated iron subsequently becomes dehydrated to Fe_2O_3.

Sizable amounts of the iron compounds form coatings on clay, silt, and sand particles in many soils. The coating may give them their color. The colors of other soils are due to the presence of the iron compounds as such. For example, some soils have various shades of red and reddish brown or yellow and yellowish brown because of the presence of hydrated iron oxides.

Thus all manner of modifications affect soil-forming processes. It is true, however, that in almost all soils that have developed enough to have clay and nonclay components, the clay fraction is several times higher in iron than the nonclay part.

We can get a general idea of the total iron content of many soils from an analysis of the soils and colloidal material of 30 alluvial soil profiles in the Mississippi River lowlands and 15 of its major tributaries.

The percentages of Fe_2O_3 in the whole soil of the A horizons of these profiles ranged from 1.8 to 6.5, with an average of 3.9 percent. The percentages of Fe_2O_3 in the colloidal or clay material of the same soils ranged from 7.7 to 12.6, with an average of 9.9 percent. The estimated iron content in the nonclay part of the soils was 0.7 to 2 percent. These soils may be considered as composite samples of the various soil areas drained by the Mississippi River. Their iron content was influenced by a yearly rainfall of 30 to 60 inches.

Iron deficiency also occurs in acid soils. Oftener than we think, iron may be a limiting factor in the growing of plants that prefer an acid soil—blueberry, cranberry, rhododendron, azalea, and many others. Many of the deficiencies can be corrected by increasing the acidity in the soil by using soil amendments, such as sulfur or ammonium sulfate, or by supplying a soluble iron chelate.

Iron chelates (which we define later) have been used successfully in the culture of blueberry, azalea, and some other acid-preferring plants on soils not acid enough to grow them well.

But asparagus, spinach, cucumbers, squash, and many other plants do not grow well on acid soils. We do not know definitely whether such plants require a particular soil reaction or other soil conditions that are affected by the reaction. Until more is known about this important question, the selection of plants adapted to the soil or the use of soil amendments to control the soil reaction is recommended.

Because the soils of the arid and semiarid regions are less weathered and leached than those formed under heavier rainfall, many of them are calcareous and alkaline in reaction. The iron is less altered and is more uniformly distributed in the soil profile. Rainwater in many places had little

to do in soil development or formation of profiles, except that it leached the soluble salts from the surface soil.

Extensive areas of the arable soils of the intermountain districts of the United States, however, are alluvial fans, lake terraces, stream terraces, and bottom lands. Many of them show some weathering in place and profile development, but much of this material, before its deposition, already had been partially disintegrated by frost, wind, and water erosion. The soils contain variable (but usually small) amounts of organic matter. Most of them are well supplied with the inorganic elements, but because of their alkaline nature the soluble iron is low. Iron chlorosis often occurs in some plant species. It is most serious in the culture of fruits and ornamentals. It is less prevalent in certain field crops. In fact, almost all the soils west of 100° longitude are arid and have problems of iron chlorosis when some plants are grown.

THE SOIL IRON available to plants is altered markedly by its environment. The organic matter in an acid soil normally increases the content of soluble iron, but apparently in an alkaline soil it does not. The carbonates and bicarbonates formed from decomposing organic material in an acid soil aid the reduction and solubility of iron. The reverse is true in a calcareous or alkaline soil.

Decomposing organic matter in alkaline soils often intensifies the chlorosis in fruit trees. Peach trees irrigated with water containing 267 parts per million (p.p.m.) of bicarbonate became stunted and chlorotic. When water from another source containing 76 p.p.m. of bicarbonate was used, the trees began to grow, and the new growth was green. Apparently there is no satisfactory general explanation for the relationship of bicarbonates to iron chlorosis.

The relative amounts and ratios of calcium, potassium, phosphorus, and nitrogen in plants are altered with the development of iron chlorosis. Chlorotic leaves have a higher ratio of potassium to calcium and phosphorus to iron and contain more nitrogen than green leaves. These conditions may be a result of chlorosis rather than a cause.

The concentration of certain heavy metals—copper, zinc, cobalt, manganese—have a direct bearing on iron chlorosis. No general statement can be made about the harmful concentration of any one of them. One plant species may tolerate more of a certain minor element than another. Sorghum and wheat, for example, made good growth at a copper concentration that caused chlorosis in a variety of soybean.

Iron chlorosis in acid, sandy soils in Florida is thought to be caused by an accumulation of copper applied to the soil and plants as fertilizer and sprays. These soils now contain about 700 pounds of copper and manganese an acre. Similar virgin soils contain 5 to 10 pounds of copper and 30 to 40 pounds of manganese an acre. Many orange groves have become unthrifty and chlorotic in recent years.

SEVERAL METHODS have been devised to overcome a lack of iron: Controlling the soil moisture by irrigation, ample drainage, some cover crops, and shallow cultivation; grafting and budding susceptible varieties on chlorosis-resistant rootstocks; adding soil amendments that contain soluble iron; adding amendments that make the soil iron more available; spraying the plants with solutions of iron salts; and injecting iron salts into the trunks and limbs of trees.

The treatment of soils with acidifying materials, such as sulfur or ammonium sulfate, to make iron more available, has been more successful on acid soils than on calcareous soils.

Soluble inorganic iron salts applied to alkaline, calcareous soils are absorbed by some plants but not by others. Because iron is not readily translocated in many plants, spraying with soluble iron salts is not always successful.

Satisfactory results can be obtained by injecting iron into trees, but growers have not liked the method because the individual treatments take so much time. Holes are drilled in the base of the tree a few inches apart and gelatin capsules filled with iron salt (ferrous citrate, ferric citrate, or ferric phosphate) are placed in the holes. The holes are then sealed with grafting wax or emulsified asphalt.

The selection of plants that are not susceptible to iron chlorosis and the use of iron chelates have been two of the most promising ways of dealing with chlorosis.

Where the proper and unsusceptible plant material has been used in fruit culture, the results have been good. For example, Concord and many other American grapes (*Vitis labrusca*) are susceptible to chlorosis, but many European varieties (*V. vinifera*) have a high degree of resistance to chlorosis. These resistant varieties have been used as rootstocks for Concord grapes grown on alkaline, calcareous soils.

For 5 years the Concord graft on Malaga, Muscat, Rose of Peru, and Tokay rootstocks were vigorous, productive, and practically free from chlorosis. On the other hand, the self-rooted Concord plants were chlorotic from the beginning, and 98 percent of them were dead at the end of 5 years. Grafting *V. labrusca* varieties on resistant *V. vinifera* rootstocks thus appears to offer a method of controlling chlorosis in grapes.

We know of no satisfactory rootstock for the peach.

IRON CHELATES are reagents, such as citric acid, which bind the iron ion through two or more positions within their structures. The iron ion is held in such a way that it cannot free itself to form another compound when treated with such common precipitating agents as phosphate or hydroxide. Some of the synthesized chelates that combine with iron are very soluble, yet the iron is retained in a soluble complex form available to plants as a nutrient. Very likely many organic compounds formed from soil organic matter chelate, or complex, metal ions, such as Fe, Cu, and Mn. Many of these organic compounds may be readily destroyed by micro-organisms.

The characteristics of a satisfactory chelating agent for soil applications are: The chelated metal ion is not easily replaced by other metals; the metal-ion complex is stable against hydrolysis in all kinds of soil; the chelating agent is not decomposed by soil micro-organisms; the chelate is water soluble and not easily fixed in the soil colloidal fraction; the metal ion is available to the plant at the root surface and after it enters the plant; the chelating agent is not toxic to plants; and the chelating agent is available to the grower.

Ivan Stewart and C. D. Leonard, of the Florida Citrus Experiment Station at Lake Alfred, corrected iron chlorosis in citrus trees by adding iron chelate, Fe-EDTA (iron-ethylenediamine tetraacetic acid) to an acid, sandy soil. Their investigations have stimulated research on the practical importance of metal chelates for the correction of iron deficiency in many countries.

The chelating agents that have been used in soils to test their effectiveness in correcting iron chlorosis are ethylenediamine tetraacetic acid (EDTA), hydroxethyl ethylenediamine-tricetic acid (HEEDTA), diethylenetriamine pentaacetic acid (DTPA), cyclohexane trans 1,2-diaminotetraacetic acid (CDTA), and an aromatic aminopolycarboxylic acid (APCA). The relative effectiveness of these chelates in making iron available at pH 7, in decreasing order, is: CDTA, APCA, DTPA, HEEDTA, EDTA.

Fe-APCA has been the most satisfactory chelate used thus far on alkaline calcareous soils. Ten pounds to the acre corrected chlorosis in greenhouse studies with soybeans. As much as 1,000 pounds an acre was not toxic. Fe-DTPA has been the next most satisfactory chelate. Fe-HEEDTA and Fe-EDTA have been good sources of iron on acid soils, but were ineffective on alkaline calcareous soils. The higher cost of producing Fe-APCA limited its practical use in 1957.

Less expensive chelates having some of the characteristics of APCA were being produced and tested in the field. APCA was the least toxic of the chelates tested. Several companies produce Fe-DTPA and Fe-EDTA.

It is important to understand the metabolic fate of chelates in plants, since the compounds, if they persist in plant fluids, may affect the mineral metabolism of the plant and other growth processes. The effect of very small applications of APCA on the mineral metabolism of soybeans suggests that this compound may have a favorable physiological effect besides its capacity to chelate iron in the soil.

Zinc and Soil Fertility

Lloyd F. Seatz and J. J. Jurinak

Zinc is essential for plants and animals. Many of our major farm regions contain areas that do not have adequate quantities of available zinc to support normal plant growth.

Zinc deficiencies in the field were first observed in Florida in 1927 on crops growing in peat soils. Zinc was used in the 1930's to cure nutritional difficulties in citrus in Florida and California. Deficiencies on other tree crops, such as pecans and tung, were encountered later in Florida and along the gulf coast. Corn and other crops on the Coastal Plain of the Eastern States have since been found to suffer from too little zinc.

Deficiencies also are common on

calcareous (limestone) and noncalcareous soils throughout the West, particularly for cherries, apples, peaches, pears, apricots, citrus, and walnuts. Zinc deficiency in field crops in the West has increased since 1950. Regions affected include the Columbia Basin in Washington and the Sacramento Valley in California. The highly phosphatic soils of central Tennessee and Kentucky when heavily limed have also produced zinc-deficient crops, particularly corn and Sudangrass.

Several reasons can be offered.

Increased fertilization has produced larger yields, which have tended to remove larger amounts of available zinc from the soil than formerly. Other soils, naturally low in zinc, may develop zinc deficiencies when they are brought under cultivation. The Columbia Basin in Washington is an example of this type of area.

TWO FACTORS GOVERN the ability of a soil to provide enough to a growing plant—the total supply of zinc in the soil and its availability to the plant. Zinc-deficiency disease therefore may be caused by a naturally low zinc fertility level or by fixation processes, which retain, or fix, zinc in a form that the plant cannot utilize.

Most soils in the United States usually have more than enough zinc for the requirements of normal plant growth, but crops may have zinc-deficiency disease. Thus the major problem is one of availability.

Occasionally the total supply of zinc in the soil—as in regions that support an intensive cropping program and that have strongly weathered and coarse-textured soils of low inherent fertility—may be the limiting factor.

Chemical tests are used to determine the ability of the soil to supply zinc to plants. Zinc is extracted from the soil with reagents and the results are compared with crop response or deficiency. Acidified potassium chloride solution, 0.1 normal hydrochloric acid, 0.04 normal acetic acid, and acidified ammonium acetate have been used as the extracting agents, but the most promising for both acid and calcareous soils is dithizone.

This method was introduced in 1951 by Ellsworth Shaw and L. A. Dean, of the Department of Agriculture. When dithizone-extractable zinc from a soil sample is less than 0.4 to 0.5 parts per million, symptoms of zinc deficiency can be expected from crops growing in that soil.

Biological methods based on the sensitivity of the fungus *Aspergillus niger* to zinc have been used with some success. The bioassay technique of determining the ability of soil to supply zinc takes about 8 days for incubation and analysis. The actual working time to analyze one sample is less than with chemical methods.

The concentration of zinc is highest in the surface soil and declines with depth. The reason lies in the uptake of zinc from the subsoil by plants and its translocation to the leaves. When the leaves fall and decay, zinc is released from the plant tissues and is fixed in the surface soil. The continuation of this fixation process near the surface depletes the subsoil of zinc and increases the possibility of deficiency to deep-rooted perennials, as fruit trees.

MANY SOIL FACTORS are associated with the deficiency of zinc in plants. One of the first factors to be correlated with deficiency was soil reaction, or soil pH. It was observed that less zinc was taken up after lime was put on an acid soil. The reduced availability of zinc, as the pH of the soil is increased, is generally attributed to the formation of insoluble zinc hydroxide, although undoubtedly other factors related to the adsorptive and exchange properties of the soil exert some influence on zinc availability as the pH of the system is altered by liming.

It is commonly thought that zinc availability is at a minimum in the soil pH range of about 5.5 to 7.0. Zinc is readily available at lower pH values. As the reaction rises above pH 7, the situation becomes more complex.

Evidence from experiments suggests that the positively charged zinc ion may be converted to a negatively charged zincate complex. The conversion would tend to reduce further the solubility of zinc in alkaline soils, where the predominance of calcium ion would favor the formation of very insoluble calcium zincate. The effect of possible zincate formation on zinc availability has not been established. The data, however, indicate that care must be exercised when attempting to define the chemical nature of the zinc ion in alkaline soils.

Adsorption studies in comparatively simple systems indicate that the clay fraction of the soil exerts a strong attractive force for zinc ions. A part of the attraction is related to the similarity in size and charge between magnesium and zinc ions. The similarity allows zinc ion to react with the clay mineral lattice, where it may substitute or possibly exchange for magnesium in the clay mineral, thus making it relatively unavailable. Inferences based on the knowledge of the electronic structure, small size, and charge of zinc ion allows one to predict that zinc will be tenaciously adsorbed by clay and other soil minerals. And indeed, at low concentrations, the zinc ion manifests itself in such a fashion.

The influence of excess soil phosphate on the availability of zinc has not been clearly defined. Excess phosphate has been associated with low availability of zinc in the major fruit regions of the West. The indiscriminate use of phosphate fertilizers in orchard management is not recommended there. Many soils of Kentucky and Tennessee that support crops suffering from zinc deficiency have a high content of native phosphate. These examples support the contention that zinc interacts with the phosphate radical to form an insoluble zinc phosphate complex, and so lowers its availability. Soils of the citrus regions of Florida, however, have not shown an increase in soil fixation of zinc within the limits of ordinary phosphate applications.

Attempts were made at Washington State Agricultural Experiment Station in 1953–1954 to induce zinc deficiency in field corn and beans by a heavy application of phosphate fertilizer. The phosphate treatments did not alter their uptake of zinc.

The detrimental effects of phosphate fertilization on zinc uptake may be due to the depressing action of the calcium ion in superphosphate. No conclusive evidence has shown this to be the case, but the apparent contradiction of various workers as to the effect of phosphate on zinc nutrition supports the view that the interaction is not a simple zinc-phosphate relation but that other factors must exert an influence.

Zinc ion has also been shown to be strongly adsorbed on commonly occurring lime minerals. The minerals are calcite (calcium carbonate), dolomite (calcium-magnesium carbonate), and calcian-magnesite (magnesium carbonate with calcium impurity).

The lime minerals containing magnesium carbonate exhibited a greater adsorptive capacity for zinc ion because of the compatability of zinc ion with the magnesium carbonate crystal lattice. Thus, if the available zinc present in the soil is near the critical level, the presence of appreciable amounts of lime minerals may present an additional hazard to proper zinc nutrition of plants. Zinc deficiency could well be worsened in soils of semiarid and arid regions where these minerals are widely distributed, and zones of lime accumulation can be found frequently within the root zone of crops. The practice of land leveling for irrigation may increase the importance of zinc adsorption on lime minerals by bringing the zone of lime accumulation nearer the surface.

The effect of liming with calcitic and dolomitic limestone on acid soils thus lowers zinc availability by increasing soil pH; it may also increase temporarily the adsorptive capacity of the soil for zinc. The ability of the lime minerals to increase the adsorptive capacity of any given soil, whether acid or alkaline, for zinc ions would probably be important only in soils of coarse texture where clay is not the dominating fraction of the soil.

Deficiency of zinc in California has been associated with soils of a high content of organic matter. Symptoms have been observed in spots that formerly were corrals or barnyards. In soils of average organic matter content, however, the destruction of the organic fraction has little influence on the amount of zinc extracted from the soil—an indication that the organic fraction in most soils does not affect greatly the availability of zinc. In organic soils, or soils where an appreciable portion of the adsorptive capacity derives from the organic complex, however, the organic fraction would have a more vital part in making zinc available.

ZINC DEFICIENCY in plants causes several abnormalities in structure.

The palisade cells of leaves from most affected plants are larger and are transversely divided, rather than columnar, as in normal leaves. Zinc deficiency therefore may lead to cell enlargement rather than to cell differentiation. Other abnormalities may be a reduction in the number of chloroplasts, the absence of starch grains, the presence of oil droplets in the chloroplasts, the presence of calcium oxalate crystals, and the accumulation of phenolic materials in the leaves. These changes in chemical composition indicate that zinc is related to normal metabolism of carbon within plants.

The roots of zinc-deficient plants are also abnormal. Tomato roots may have a series of swellings with whorls of root hairs near the root tip. Secondary roots may develop later in them. Cell structure is also deranged; cells even in the meristematic, or actively growing, region may be enlarged, and an irregular arrangement with many air spaces may occur among the cells. Older tissue becomes necrotic and has flaky masses of exfoliated cells. The metabolic prod-

ucts of the root cells also are abnormal. Tannin, fats, and calcium oxalate crystals are present in abnormally large amounts. Starch is absent.

Zinc is also related to seed production in several plants. A threshold value of zinc has been established for peas and beans below which the plants produce only small, seedless pods. When plants are supplied zinc in concentrations above this value, the pods are larger and contain seeds.

Zinc may be translocated from other parts of the plant to the seeds at maturity, because the viability of the seeds is not affected by the concentration of zinc supplied the plants.

Zinc seems to be distributed fairly well within the plant. The concentration varies with the amount of available zinc in the soil, the kind of plant, the part of the plant sampled, and the stage of growth. Differences in varieties and in environmental factors probably affect the zinc content. Generally the zinc content of normal plants is higher than that of zinc-deficient plants grown in a similar environment, although a considerable overlap seems to exist.

E. Archibald and F. B. Wann, of Utah State University, have discovered that the limiting value for the zinc content of the leaves of several fruit trees (below which the development of zinc deficiency may be expected) is 0.0123 percent. Normal leaves contained between 0.0123 and 0.0345 percent of zinc. A critical value for tung is reported to be 0.0010 percent of zinc. Other research workers have reported that the percentage composition of zinc in the leaves of normal plants is considerably lower than the above values—as low as 0.0004 percent of zinc in normal leaves of some plants.

Frank Viets and his coworkers in Washington reported values ranging from 10.5 to 32.7 p.p.m. of zinc, with an average of 16.86 for selected parts of several crops that were growing on a normal area without zinc deficiency. In an area where crops showed a zinc deficiency, the values varied from 9.3 to 22.5 p.p.m., with an average of 15.44

p.p.m. When the crops were fertilized with zinc, the average content of the crops became 22.58 and 18.34 p.p.m.

Both the tops and roots of corn at several sampling dates did not show great or consistent differences in zinc concentration between normal and zinc-deficient plants. The total zinc uptake, however, was much greater for normal plants than for zinc-deficient plants, indicating greater growth for the normal plants.

P. R. Stout and G. Pearson, of California, discovered that plants very low in zinc have a higher concentration of zinc than larger plants that also are deficient in zinc. When zinc was added to the culture solution, the amount of internodal to nodal and embryonic tissue increased, and the zinc concentration of the entire plant dropped. The concentration in the plant again increased when more zinc was added.

The zinc concentration in actively growing parts of plants is higher than in older tissue. Zinc tends to accumulate in and around the primary veins of the leaf blade in actively growing corn leaves. The highest zinc concentration in cornstalks is at the node; concentration falls off quite rapidly both above and below the node. In oats, 20 to 30 percent of the zinc in the plant is in the leaves, mainly in the chloroplasts. Zinc is bound to the protein material in the chloroplasts along with their colored pigments.

A deficiency of zinc in a plant may affect its content of other elements. Leaves of corn plants that show zinc deficiency have more potassium and phosphorus than leaves of normal plants.

ZINC IS a necessary component of several enzyme systems, which regulate various metabolic activities within plants. It is a part of the enzyme carbonic anhydrase, which regulates the equilibrium between carbon dioxide, water, and carbonic acid. It also functions as a part of two enzymes, dehydropeptidase and glycylglycine dipeptidase, which have a part in specific aspects of protein metabolism.

Zinc also is needed for the formation of auxins, which are growth-promoting substances in plants. Because one of the symptoms of zinc deficiency is a failure of the stem tissue between the nodes to elongate, resulting in rosetting, it was thought that zinc deficiency might be related to a low content of auxin. This phase of the function of zinc in plants has been studied by F. Skoog and his associates at the University of Wisconsin. They learned that plants deficient in zinc were low in auxin. The auxin content of the plants increased when zinc was applied. Further investigation showed that zinc seems to limit the production of one of the compounds that serves as a building block in the formation of the complex auxin compound.

Zinc is associated with water relations in plants. High osmotic pressures resulting from zinc deficiency are due to reduced water uptake, which was restricted by the failure of cell walls to grow because of lack of auxin.

The observation that zinc deficiency does not develop so readily in mild sunlight as it does in bright sunlight may be associated with auxin activity. Plants grown under blue light exhibit zinc deficiency symptoms more readily than those grown under red light. Light of high intensity and of short wavelengths inactivates auxin.

Plants differ in their ability to extract zinc from the native soil supply. Crops that followed crotalaria as a cover crop in Florida exhibited zinc deficiency, but crops that followed a cover crop of native weeds did not. Analysis of the plants showed that the weeds accumulated much more zinc from the limited soil supply than the crotalaria did.

Dr. Viets and his coworkers studied the relative ability of 26 different crops to utilize native soil zinc. They classified the plants in three groups.

In the very sensitive group (plants that cannot get enough zinc from the soil) are beans, soybeans, corn, hops, grapes, lima beans, flax, and castor beans.

The mildly sensitive group includes

potatoes, tomatoes, onions, alfalfa, sorghum, Sudangrass, sugar beets, and red clover.

Insensitive plants are peppermint, the cereals, peas, asparagus, mustard, carrots, safflower, and grasses.

ZINC DEFICIENCY of trees is known as rosette, mottle leaf, littleleaf, and yellows. The terms tend to describe the usual symptoms of zinc deficiency although such symptoms are not always brought about by too little zinc.

The deficiency in citrus is usually known as mottle leaf. Affected leaves have irregular chlorotic areas between the leaf veins. The leaves may be normal in size in the early stages of the disease, but new leaves as they develop become progressively smaller. Rosetting does not usually occur in citrus.

Pecans that get too little zinc have a bronzing of the leaves and rosettes of small leaves on shortened branches. Yellowish mottled areas appear on young leaves. They turn reddish brown on older leaves and may die and cause many small holes in the leaf.

The disease is called little leaf or rosette in deciduous fruit trees, such as apple, cherry, peach, apricot, and plum. Rosetting occurs, and dense clusters of small, yellowish leaves grow at the end of twigs that are bare of normal lateral leaves. The internodes are shortened. Little leaf produces small, chlorotic, narrow leaves. Chlorotic mottling progresses inward from the margin in the interveinal tissue. Considerable dieback of the branches occurs in severe stages of little leaf. The number of blossoms and fruits set usually is greatly reduced, and fruits that are produced are of poor quality.

A typical symptom of lack of zinc in most field crops is chlorosis of the interveinal tissue, particularly of the lower leaves. The younger leaves in severe cases may also be chlorotic. The lower leaves may turn brown to purple and die. The internodes may become short, and the plants are stunted. In severely affected corn the bud may become almost white.

Zinc deficiency disease usually can be cured by applying zinc to the plants in an available form.

Application of zinc-containing materials to the soil either as a soluble salt or in a chelated form is a common way. The effectiveness of soil applications is determined by how strongly the soil fixes the applied zinc. For that reason the application of soluble zinc salts may not be effective on soils with a high zinc-fixing capacity. Sometimes band placement of the zinc-containing fertilizer has increased its effectiveness.

The use of zinc chelates is an effective way of providing zinc to plants under high soil-fixing conditions. The chelating agent is made up of complex molecules capable of reacting with the zinc and combining it into the complex molecular structure. The zinc therefore is not fixed by the soil and remains in a soluble and available form to the plants. Often applications of chelated zinc have corrected deficiencies where applications of soluble salts, such as zinc sulfate, have not been effective.

Foliar sprays have been effective in correcting zinc deficiency, particularly on tree crops. For citrus a single spray of a solution containing about 5 pounds of zinc sulfate per 100 gallons of water corrected zinc deficiency for 1 to 3 years. Foliage injury is reduced by adding 2 to 3 pounds of hydrated lime, soda lime, or lime sulfur to the spray. Wetting and adhesive agents sometimes have given a beneficial effect at low concentrations. Sprays applied just before flush growth give a longer effect than those applied before dormancy.

Concentrated sprays of 25 pounds of zinc sulfate to 100 gallons of water are effective on apples and pears when applied as a dormant spray just before the buds open. Zinc dusts have been less effective than sprays.

Grapes are usually treated by daubing the freshly cut pruning wound with a solution containing 2 pounds of zinc sulfate to a gallon of solution.

Sometimes, especially on sweet cherries and walnuts, when sprays are not effective, injections of zinc-containing materials are helpful. Zinc-coated nails and pieces of galvanized iron may be driven into the trunk and the main branches. Another means of injecting zinc into the tree has been to bore several holes into the trunk about 3 inches apart and to pack 2 to 3 grams of zinc sulfate into each hole. The holes are then filled with wax.

Field crops usually are fertilized with zinc fertilizers in the row or in bands slightly below and to the side of the seed at the time of planting. Top-dressing and sidedressing with zinc salts after the crop is growing have not been satisfactory. Fertilizer manufacturers in some areas add zinc sulfate to the mixed fertilizer so that farmers can apply the necessary fertilizer elements in one operation without having to mix zinc sulfate with the fertilizer.

Zinc sulfate sprays have also been satisfactory on field crops when the spraying is done early in the season before serious deficiencies arise.

Boron and Soil Fertility

Darrell A. Russel

The modern American kitchen contains enough boron to produce 16 tons of alfalfa hay. This boron is in the enamel in freezers, stoves, refrigerators, sinks, dishes, and glassware.

But many thousands of acres of agricultural soils in the United States contain only enough available boron to produce a ton or two of alfalfa hay. That amount is the equivalent of the boron in an iron cookstove, an icebox, and a good set of china dishes.

Many crops are affected by a deficiency of boron in the soil. Sugar beets, alfalfa, and clovers are the most commonly affected of the agronomic crops. Celery, beets, cauliflower, apples, grapes, pears, walnuts, sunflowers, and asters are a few of the many vegetable, fruit, nut, and ornamental crops that may suffer from too little.

BORON WAS FIRST USED as a fertilizer about 400 years ago when borax (then called Tincal or Tincar) was shipped from central Asia to Europe. Not until 1915, however, was boron suggested as an essential element for plant growth, when P. Mazé of France made this suggestion as a result of his work with corn grown in nutrient solutions. Katherine Warington, at the Rothamsted Experimental Station in England, provided the first proof in 1923 that boron was an essential element.

An inadequate supply of boron in the soil was shown to be the cause of heart rot and dry rot of sugar beets and mangolds in Germany by E. Brandenburg in 1931.

L. G. Willis and J. R. Piland, of the North Carolina Agricultural Experiment Station, were among the first in the United States to show that legumes, especially alfalfa, responded to borax fertilizer. The two agronomists published the results of their research in 1938. Boron deficiencies have been reported since then in 41 States and for 90 or more crops.

Most of the boron in soils is in the form of the highly insoluble mineral tourmaline. The total boron content of the soil varies between 20 and 200 pounds in the plow depth of an acre.

The total boron content of the soil is not a reliable guide to the adequacy of boron for crop growth, because less than 5 percent of the total may be available for the use of plants. The determination and measurement of the available forms of boron have been of concern since 1931.

AVAILABLE BORON occurs in two broad forms, inorganic and organic.

The inorganic forms (chiefly calcium, magnesium, and sodium borates) resulted originally from the slow dissolution of minerals containing boron. Soil micro-organisms and plants utilized this boron in their growth, transforming the boron to organic forms. Upon the death of the micro-organisms and plants, the organic boron was oxidized to inorganic boron.

The amount of boron available for reuse, plus that made available through the continued weathering of unavailable forms, is adequate for crop growth in some soils. The loss of available boron through crop removal, leaching, and reversion to unavailable forms, coupled with higher requirements for boron through better crop varieties and improved cultural practices, has resulted in an inadequate supply of boron available for crop growth on many agricultural soils.

Loss of boron through crop removal is unavoidable. Nevertheless such losses must be recognized, and the nutrients that are removed (boron, as well as the other essential elements) must be replenished eventually by the application of fertilizer.

Each ton of alfalfa hay contains 1 ounce of boron. A ton of sugar beets contains 2.5 ounces of boron. One hundred bushels of peaches contains 4 ounces of boron, while 100 bushels of corn contains only 0.4 ounce of boron.

The seriousness of boron losses by crop removal depends, then, on the kind of crop and on whether the crop is utilized on the farm and returned to the soil as manure.

Leaching losses are considerable, particularly in the acid soils of humid regions. Joe Kubota, K. C. Berger, and Emil Truog, working with soils in Wisconsin, found that the rate of boron movement in the soil was related primarily to soil texture. Boron fertilizers applied to soils that were uniformly light-textured throughout the profile moved to a depth of 24 inches, or deeper, in 6 months. Little of the boron moved below the 12-inch layer in the heavier soils.

Many other factors influence the availability of soil boron. One of the most important is the pH of the soil.

James A. Naftel, working in Alabama in 1937, discovered that small additions of boron to the soil counteracted the harmful effects of overliming and that the application of lime to the soil often results in a lower availability of soil boron.

R. V. Olson and K. C. Berger, in research in Wisconsin in 1946, investigated the effect of soil reaction on boron fixation. They found that fixation was closely related to the clay content and to the soil pH as changed by the addition of sodium hydroxide, calcium hydroxide, and hydrochloric acid. They demonstrated that clays fixed the most boron, silts fixed an intermediate amount, and sands fixed very little. The cations used had little influence on the boron fixation, but the alkalinity they produced resulted in fixation.

The fact that the boron that is fixed because of a rise in pH can be made available again by lowering the pH to its original value indicates that a reversible chemical reaction is involved. This reaction is quite rapid.

The evidence suggests further that most of the boron is fixed by a soil mineral or group of minerals, the activity of which predominates in the clay fraction of soils but is also present in the silt fraction. The pH of the soil has a great effect, direct or indirect, on the ease with which this fixation occurs.

The organic matter also influences the fixation of boron. A. Maquori, G. Stradaioli, and E. Perici in Italy learned that organic boron is the most soluble boron in soils. The Wisconsin scientists, Dr. Olson and Dr. Berger, found that oxidation of the organic matter in soils caused significant increases in the amount of boron released to the available form as well as decreases in the amount of boron that could be fixed by the soil.

Dry weather accelerates the appearance of symptoms of boron deficiency in crops in soils low in available boron. L. P. Latimer, of the New Hampshire Agricultural Experiment Station, found that drought in June and July was the chief predisposing factor causing boron deficiency in apples. The actual role of dry weather in causing boron to become unavailable has not been ascertained.

R. Q. Parks, at the Ohio Agricultural Experiment Station, found that drying of the soil in the laboratory increased the fixation of boron. Boron deficiencies have been observed to be more severe in places in the field where the soil had dried out excessively in dry years, according to J. C. Walker and his associates at the Wisconsin Agricultural Experiment Station.

Dr. Berger has stated that it is doubtful whether the plow layer of a field will dry out enough in most years to cause appreciable fixation of boron. If boron were fixed to any extent, most soils would be deficient in boron; soils in arid regions would be particularly deficient. That obviously is not so.

Dr. Berger suggested that the reason for the appearance of boron deficiency symptoms in dry years, as contrasted to wet years, is that most of the available boron is in the surface, or organic, layer of the soil. When this layer becomes dry, plants feed in the layer to a limited extent because of the lack of water. Instead, plants feed from the lower soil horizons, which are usually low in organic matter and low in available boron.

Boron deficiency in dry years therefore occurs because the supply of available boron has been reduced—not by fixation but by the inability of plant roots to feed in the surface horizon. Some boron fixation may be caused by the drying of surface soils in extremely hot and dry weather, but it is doubtful if much boron is fixed below 2 inches.

THE GEOGRAPHIC EXTENT of boron deficiencies in the United States is difficult to describe. The greatest areas of deficiency are in the humid regions where soils are generally acid.

When Kenneth C. Beeson, of the United States Plant, Soil, and Nutri-tion Laboratory, mapped the boron deficient areas in the United States in 1945, the presence of boron deficiencies had been reported in only 31 States. A current map of the boron-deficient areas shows that boron deficiencies have been found in every State east of the Mississippi River and generally in the first two rows of States west of the Mississippi, as well as the Pacific States. Only seven States reported all their soils to be supplied adequately with available boron.

Dairy farms in particular are among the first farms to show deficiencies of boron in most areas. Alfalfa is grown extensively on many of them, and alfalfa has a high boron requirement. Unless the dairyman conscientiously returns manure to his fields, the loss of boron through crop removal may soon deplete the available boron.

The supply of available boron is exhausted rather quickly in places where vegetable crops are grown commercially. Yields of vegetable crops usually are high because of the large amounts of fertilizer used. Since several crops may be harvested from a field each year, the loss of boron by crop removal may soon mean deficiencies.

Orchards are established preferably on deep, well-drained, well-aerated soils. These conditions favor the loss of boron by leaching. Applications of nitrogen fertilizer, by increasing the tree growth, increase the boron requirement and thereby augment the deficiency.

SYMPTOMS of boron deficiency vary with the type and age of the plant, the conditions under which it grows, and the severity of the deficiency.

The first visual symptom generally is the death of the terminal growing point of the main stem. The lateral buds then produce side shoots, but the terminal buds on the shoots die also. Further rebranching may occur. This multibranched plant is often described as having a rosette appearance.

Further symptoms are a slight thickening of the leaves, a tendency for the leaves to curl, and sometimes chlorosis.

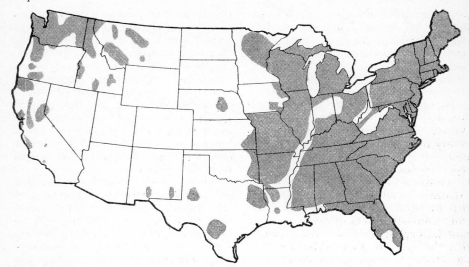

The shaded areas indicate parts of the United States where deficiencies of boron may exist. Farmers in those regions should watch for symptoms of boron deficiency in crops, especially those with a high boron requirement.

The petioles and even the leaves become brittle. Flowers may not form; if they do, fruit may not set. The roots generally are stunted.

Each crop has more or less characteristic growth abnormalities associated with a deficiency of boron, but these symptoms are manifestations of the general boron-deficiency symptoms found in all crops. Rosetting in alfalfa, snakehead in walnuts, and dieback in apples are all caused by the death of the terminal growing points.

Dr. Walker, of the Wisconsin Agricultural Experiment Station, reviewed the histological effects of boron deficiency in a symposium published in Soil Science in 1944. One of the first effects of boron starvation is increased cell division in the cambium, accompanied by less cell differentiation. The cell walls remain thin, and parenchyma tissue increases at the expense of conductive tissue.

The reduction in normal development of conductive tissue leads indirectly to many of the characteristic external symptoms, such as leaf distortion, stunted growth, and increased

anthocyanin in the leaves. Internal discoloration appears first in a relatively few cells, but necrosis gradually extends until large areas of dead or dying cells result. The byproducts of the dead cells also may become factors that influence the growth of the surrounding cells.

Thus a series of symptoms of boron deficiency occurs. The mildest are manifested only by reduced growth and certain chemical changes. The second stage of symptoms is characterized by cellular changes. Finally, macroscopic changes occur that lead to the premature death of the plant.

The symptoms yield many clues as to the function of boron in plants.

Fifteen functions have been ascribed to boron. Boron has an effect on flowering and fruiting processes, pollen germination, cell division, nitrogen metabolism, carbohydrate metabolism, active salt absorption, hormone movement and action, the metabolism of pectic substances, water metabolism, and the water relations in plants.

Further, boron is said to be a constituent of membranes, to serve in precipitating excess cations, to act as a buffer, to be necessary in the maintenance of conducting tissues, and to exert a regulatory effect on other elements.

Hugh C. Gauch and W. M. Dugger, Jr., of the Maryland Agricultural Experiment Station, have proposed a 16th function of boron in plants that embodies many of those suggested previously by other scientists. They have presented evidence supporting the hypothesis that boron is necessary for the translocation of sugar in plants.

In order for highly polar compounds, such as sugar, to move through cell walls and other membranes, energy must be expended. Boron may lower the polarity of the sugar—thus reducing the energy required for translocation—by either or both of two modes of action. The boron may combine directly with the sugar and thus move with it. It is more likely, however, that boron is a constituent of the membranes and that sugar may then form a temporary union with the boron until it (the sugar) has passed through the membrane.

The observations of many workers lend credence to the theory. E. S. Johnston and W. A. Dore in 1928 found that the leaves of boron-deficient plants have comparatively high concentrations of sugars and starch. At Cornell University, Dr. R. H. White-Stevens found that carbohydrates were deficient in the meristems and roots of boron-deficient plants, even though the leaves contained an excess of carbohydrates in all forms. Certain parts of the plant appear to die, then, because of a lack of sugar when adequate boron is not present. Boron-deficiency symptoms may therefore be an expression of sugar deficiency.

The amount of boron required by the plant at any one time is very small. But plants must continue to absorb boron throughout their life cycle—an indication that more boron is required as new cell membranes are formed. Most of our evidence shows that boron is relatively immobile in the plant—

additional evidence that boron is associated with cell membranes.

THE RELATIONSHIP of boron to other plant nutrients has been the subject of much study. The tendency of plants to maintain a constant amount of total cations, on a chemically equivalent basis, however, leads to some rather complex relationships. Thus, if the potassium content of a plant is increased, the concentration of calcium or other cations probably will be decreased. To ascribe the effect of boron on cation concentration as either a direct or an indirect effect then becomes difficult.

Because the symptoms of boron deficiency and calcium deficiency in the growing point of a plant are similar, the two elements seem to be related in plant growth. Harold Jones and George Scarseth, in greenhouse experiments on limed and unlimed soils in Indiana, discovered that plants would take up various amounts of calcium and boron, depending on the availability of the two elements in the soil. Plant analyses showed that normal growth occurred only when a certain balance in the intake of calcium and boron existed.

These two agronomists found a low boron requirement for plants when there was a low calcium uptake and a high boron requirement when there was a high calcium uptake. Their work with alfalfa showed that a calcium-boron ratio in the plant of 80:1 to 600:1 resulted in normal plant growth.

When I was engaged in work with alfalfa in Illinois, I learned that alfalfa plants exhibited boron-deficiency symptoms only when the calcium-boron ratio was approximately 800:1 or higher.

I also obtained evidence that optimum ranges of ratios for magnesium-boron, copper-boron, and nitrogen-boron existed for alfalfa.

The relationship of potassium to boron in the plant is far less important than that of calcium to boron.

The main work on potassium-boron ratios has been done by Eldrow Reeve and John W. Shive at the New Jersey Agricultural Experiment Station. They discovered that the concentration of potassium in the external substrate was more important in plant growth than the internal potassium-boron ratio.

CROPS MAY BE CLASSIFIED as to their boron requirement in various ways.

One system is based on the boron content of the plant when it begins to show deficiency symptoms. Thus the critical level of boron for alfalfa is 20 parts per million (p.p.m.). For apple leaves and sugar beets, the critical level is 14 p.p.m. Tobacco has a critical level of 10 p.p.m. Lettuce shows deficiency symptoms when the boron content drops to 30 p.p.m. or lower.

A second classification system is based on the boron content of crops grown normally in a soil adequately supplied with available boron. Crops with a low content of boron generally have a low requirement of boron, and crops with a high content of boron have a high requirement of boron.

Gabriel Bertrand and his associates in France did extensive research to determine the boron content of plants grown in a normal soil. They ascertained the boron content of 30 species of plants grown in the same soil. The strikingly unequal ability of the different species to take up boron ranged from 2.3 p.p.m. for barley and not more than 5 p.p.m. for corn, wheat, and rye, to as high as 94.7 p.p.m. for the poppy. Beets contained 75 p.p.m., turnips 49 p.p.m., and tobacco only 25 p.p.m. of boron when grown in the same soil as the poppy and the barley.

A third classification was used by Dr. Berger in his review, "Boron in Soils and Crops," published in 1949 in Advances in Agronomy. His system is based on the amount of available boron in the soil and the production of normal crops not deficient in boron. Among the crops that grow normally in a soil containing less than 0.1 p.p.m. of available boron are barley, corn, wheat, oats, soybeans, green beans, strawberries, white potatoes,

flax, brome, and most grasses. Crops that grow normally in a soil containing 0.1 to 0.5 p.p.m. of boron include cotton, tobacco, lettuce, tomatoes, sweetpotatoes, cherries, and peaches. Crops requiring a high content of available soil boron (0.5 p.p.m. or more) for normal growth are alfalfa, sweetclover, red clover, sugar beets, red beets, turnips, cabbages, radishes, celery, and apples.

Because deficiencies of boron can be corrected with boron fertilizers, the progressive farmer watches his crops and soils for evidences of deficiency. Deficiency symptoms in a crop are a fair warning to the farmer that he has already delayed too long in using boron fertilizers. Crop yields start to decline before deficiency symptoms become apparent.

CHEMICAL ANALYSES of the crop or the soil are excellent diagnostic aids in predicting the level of available boron in the soil, but many soil-testing laboratories were not equipped in 1957 to make the analysis for boron either in the soil or in the plant.

Special equipment is required for the analysis. The usual chemical glassware is made of borosilicate and leads to contamination when a hot solution or a concentrated acid is used. The very small amount of boron extracted from a boron-deficient soil often may be less than the boron dissolved from the walls of a flask unless boron-free glassware is used.

The determination of a fraction of a part per million of boron in such a complex mixture of mineral and organic matter as the soil is no easy task. The procedures required for the determination of boron in the soil are therefore not so short and simple as for the determination of phosphorus and potassium.

Generally boron is extracted from the soil with boiling water, but care must be exercised during the extraction so that the boron is not volatilized into the atmosphere. The extract containing the boron must then be concentrated. The actual analytical procedures in use today usually require that a very strong, concentrated sulfuric acid solution be used in measuring the boron. Such solutions are unpleasant and dangerous to use.

The chemical analysis of plant tissue, as a routine procedure for the evaluation of soil fertility, has not achieved as common acceptance as the chemical analysis of the soil. Nevertheless, many investigators have shown that deficiency symptoms for the various plant nutrients appear when the nutrient in question drops to certain concentration levels within the plant. The complex relationships among the various nutrients required by plants make the interpretation of plant analyses fully as difficult as the interpretation of the soil analyses.

Further complicating factors in plant analyses are the stage of growth of the plant when it was sampled and the part of the plant (stems, leaves, whole plant, roots) used in the analyses. These factors are subject to wide variations. Probably the best method of evaluating the fertility status of a soil is one that is based on a combination of soil and plant analyses. Whenever such an approach develops on a more widespread basis, the use of the spectrograph would be feasible. Nearly all elements important in plant growth, except nitrogen, can be analyzed concurrently with the spectrograph, and only one sample need be used.

BORON FOR FERTILIZERS comes from mineral deposits in Death Valley and the Mojave Desert and from the brine of Searles Lake, all in California.

Borax (sodium tetraborate) and other sodium borates have been the most commonly used materials for agriculture. These materials contain 10.5 to 13.6 percent of boron, depending on whether or not it is a regular or high-grade fertilizer borate.

New boron minerals for fertilizers have been introduced. Colemanite, a calcium borate, is less soluble than sodium borate. It is recommended for use on sandy soils in areas of high rainfall because it leaches out of the soil less rapidly than borax. It contains 10.1 percent of boron.

Some sodium borates have been developed especially for use as sprays or dusts. Such materials are highly soluble and are highly concentrated in boron. They are applied directly to the foliage of fruit trees, vegetables, and other crops in areas of high soil alkalinity.

All boron materials may be mixed with regular fertilizers, which are then known as borated fertilizers, before being applied to the soil. In several States it is recommended that all fertilizers for legumes contain a certain amount of boron.

Boron often is applied to the soil as a contaminant in other soil amendments or soil fertilizers. Barnyard manure may contain approximately 20 p.p.m. of boron. Superphosphate contains 5 to 20 p.p.m. of boron. Even lime contains boron, 1 ton containing the equivalent of 1 ounce of borax.

Since the boron content of the usual fertilizer materials is low and the rate of application of these materials is also low, these secondary sources of boron cannot be expected to provide an adequate amount of boron for crops.

The amount of boron that should be applied to a soil deficient in available boron depends on a number of factors—the crop, the soil, the season, the method of application, and the source of boron. For a given crop, boron fertilizer can be applied in larger amounts to soils that have a high organic-matter content, a high exchange capacity, or a high pH, than could be applied to light, acid soils of low organic-matter content. The rate of application of borax fertilizer for alfalfa varies from 15 to 60 pounds an acre. The lower rates of application are generally used on the light, acid soils of the Coastal Plains. The heavier rates are recommended in the Midwest and the West.

A few words of caution are necessary. Borax is one of the oldest weedkillers known. The active ingredient is boron. In regions of low rainfall, the boron content of the soil is high. In these regions, the boron content of water used for irrigation is sometimes great enough to cause injury to crops.

Carl S. Scofield and L. V. Wilcox, of the Department of Agriculture, found that 0.5 p.p.m. of boron in irrigation water injured some crops. A boron content of 1.0 p.p.m. caused injury to most crops, even those with high boron requirements.

The boron that occurs in injurious concentrations in irrigation water may be derived from the solution of exposed outcrops of soluble boron minerals, from underground waters, or directly from volcanic gases dissolved in percolating waters. The areas in which boron toxicity may occur are not large; nevertheless, the injury to crops in some of these areas is serious. These areas are located primarily in southern California, western Nevada, and parts of Arizona.

Certain control measures are available for eliminating or preventing the accumulation of toxic concentrations of boron in soils. Thorough leaching of contaminated soils is usually recommended when possible. Mixing irrigation water high in boron content with water low in boron content is recommended as a method of utilizing all the water available for irrigation without building up toxic concentrations.

Borax, or other boron fertilizers, therefore must not be used indiscriminately. The effect may be disastrous. Fortunately, the effect in humid regions is temporary; the boron soon leaches from the soil. In the absence of official recommendations, farmers should use borax at the rate of only a few pounds to the acre and only on small areas until experience shows the need for boron and the proper amount to use.

Boron fertilization is becoming a necessary and accepted practice in many areas of the United States, just as plastic is becoming more widely used in the kitchen. But just as the housewife knows that plastic has its limitations, the farmer knows that the use of boron has its limitations.

Copper and Soil Fertility

Walter Reuther

Soils high in organic matter and weathered, sandy soils are likely to be deficient in copper. A great deficiency may cause serious stunting of growth and visible symptoms of disease in plants, but moderate deficiency may merely reduce yields.

Copper once was regarded as a plant poison, as indeed it may be when too much of it is used on soil. As a matter of fact, a 5-percent solution of copper sulfate was one of the first spray formulations used for the chemical control of weeds. Concentrations of 0.1 percent to 0.2 percent of copper in the form of water suspensions of insoluble hydroxides, carbonates, or oxides are an effective fungicide. Research workers noted long ago that solutions containing as little as 1 part per million of soluble copper killed algae and fungus spores.

Bordeaux mixture, the first widely used fungicide applied to foliage by spraying, is prepared by dissolving 5 to 10 pounds of copper sulfate in 100 gallons of water and adding approximately an equal weight of lime (calcium hydroxide) or soda ash (sodium carbonate).

Many researchers before 1927 observed that Bordeaux sprays sometimes had stimulating effects on vigor and yield that were not associated with the control of fungus diseases. Other research workers noted that minute amounts of copper were distributed through all plant tissues. Some thought that the stimulating effects of small amounts of copper on plants and fungi were due to some indirect action of copper or to "an irritation response." Others thought that copper might be an essential element in the metabolism of plants and animals.

The first credible evidence that copper was an essential element in the nutrition of lower plants was provided by H. Bortels, a German scientist, in 1927. He showed that a deficiency of copper in the culture medium of the common bread mold, *Aspergillus niger*, reduced growth by 50 percent and changed the color of the spores from black to brown. The addition of minute amounts of copper to the cultures produced normal growth and black spores.

Confirmation of his results was soon provided by other scientists, who discovered that copper is essential for the normal growth of a wide variety of fungi and yeasts and also of green plants and animals. R. V. Allison and his associates in 1927 showed that the almost complete failure of many crops to grow on the peat soils of the Florida Everglades could be cured by fertilization with copper. They postulated that the disorder was due to a lack of sufficient copper for normal plant growth.

THE SYMPTOMS of copper deficiency in green plants vary considerably with species and perhaps other complicating factors. No general description of visual copper deficiency symptoms can therefore be made.

Crops showing a moderate response in vigor and yield to applications of copper to soil may not exhibit striking symptoms of disease other than lack of normal vigor. Usually some parts of fields or orchards in which moderate responses to copper are obtained have a few plants that show acute pathological symptoms of copper deficiency.

Symptoms of copper deficiency of citrus were among the first to be recognized as such in the field and are fairly typical of symptoms on other tree crops. Primary symptoms of the disease are gum pockets under the bark, stained spots on the bark of terminal twigs and defoliation on them, the formation of multiple buds in the leaf axils and shortening of internodes, a dying back of the twigs, and a characteristic staining of the fruit because of the formation of gum-soaked areas in the rind. Affected fruits frequently split open and drop before they attain full size. In Florida, where it was first noted and described, the disease was known as exanthema, dieback, or ammoniation. The last term indicates that growers recognized that it was associated with heavy applications of "ammonia" (nitrogen) fertilizers.

Copper deficiencies of other tree crops have been reported in other sections of the United States and the world. Usually shoots die back and the foliage may show marginal or spotted necrosis and chlorosis. Multiple bud formation, rosetting (shortening of shoot internodes), malformation of leaves, and an excessive gumming also may occur.

A disease of grains called white tip, yellow tip, or reclamation disease has been reported in various parts of the world. It responds to copper fertilization. It is characterized by a necrosis of the tips of older leaves and a marginal chlorosis of the tips of younger leaves, which may remain unrolled and tend to wilt readily. The heads may be dwarfed and distorted. Grain production may be reduced more than the vegetative growth.

Symptoms of copper deficiency have been described for sugarcane, a number of vegetable crops, peanuts, and other plants.

THE FUNCTIONS OF COPPER in the mineral nutrition of plants appear to be numerous, varied, and complex. In fact, none of the essential nutrient elements has a single, simple job in the economy of plant growth and development. Copper is no exception, although evidence concerning many of its functions is quite meager.

Copper seems to be concentrated more in the rootlets of plants than in leaves or other tissues—it may therefore have an important function in root metabolism.

Analyses of the tissues in a copper-deficient plant indicate it to be abnormally high in proteins and amino acids, although similar effects have been noted with several other deficiencies of essential plant nutrients.

Heavy fertilization with nitrogen tends to increase the severity of pathological symptoms of copper deficiency. Plants supplied with ammonium nitrogen in culture solutions respond favorably to higher levels of copper than do plants supplied only with nitrate nitrogen, an indication that copper is related somehow to utilization of ammonium nitrogen by plants. All the evidence suggests that copper is important in the utilization of proteins in the growth processes of plants.

The rate of photosynthesis of leaves on copper-deficient plants is abnormally low. The concentration of copper in chloroplasts (minute corpuscle-like bodies in plant cells in which the green pigment chlorophyll is concentrated) is larger than in the leaf as a whole. We have evidence that copper is involved in oxidation-reduction reactions in plants.

Copper probably functions as an enzyme activator or as an integral part of enzyme molecules involved in certain reactions. For example, potatoes grown in the Netherlands on soil that is low in available potassium but has adequate copper tend to blacken in storage because of the oxidation of tyrosine (and related phenolic compounds) by the enzyme tyrosinase to the black pigment, melanin.

On the other hand, potatoes grown on soil low in potash and low in copper have a high content of tyrosine (as do potatoes grown in low-potash and high-copper soil) but have much less tendency to produce blackening of cut surfaces. Potatoes grown on low-copper soil exhibit less than one-tenth of the tyrosinase activity of potatoes grown on normal copper soil. The black pigment, melanin, is probably like that produced in the spores of

Aspergillus niger and inhibited in production in spores of that organism when grown when copper is deficient.

Plants suffering from copper deficiency are low in ascorbic acid oxidase activity. Other enzymes that appear to involve copper are cytochrome C and laccase.

Because of its inherent physical and chemical properties, copper forms a vast array of compounds with proteins, amino acids, and other organic compounds that commonly occur in the juices of plants and animals.

Two groups of such copper compounds, known as complexes and chelates, are probably of particular significance in the special functions that copper performs in the life processes of plants and animals. In complexes, because of its special properties, copper is held securely by a number of single chemical bonds to other atoms in molecules of proteins, amino acids, and related species of compounds. Chelates are similar to complexes, except that copper is held with tremendous security by extremely strong multiple chemical bonds.

THE COPPER CONTENT of tissues of plants suffering from copper deficiency is abnormally low.

Among the tree crops, copper concentration in tissues of citrus has perhaps been the most extensively studied in various parts of the world. If copper in citrus leaves falls below about 4 p.p.m. (parts per million) in dry matter, severe copper deficiency symptoms are almost certain to be observed. In the range of about 4 to 5 p.p.m., mild to moderate deficiency symptoms may occur. Copper deficiency rarely occurs when the copper concentration in leaves is 6 p.p.m. or more. A copper concentration above 16 p.p.m. in normal citrus foliage is uncommon, unless contamination from foliage sprays is responsible.

About the same relationship between copper concentration in leaves and incidence of deficiency symptoms has been noted in a large number of other tree crops and many vegetable and agronomic crops.

Analyses of fibrous roots of citrus indicate that copper concentration in them may be about 5 to 10 times the concentration found in the leaves of the same trees, but we are not sure how the concentration of copper in roots of plants is related to copper deficiency.

Small grains that suffer severe copper deficiency (severe stunting, necrosis of foliage, distorted heads) may contain a normal concentration of copper in the aboveground tissues.

F. Steenbjerg found that in Denmark fertilization of such plants with a small amount of copper sulfate actually reduced copper concentration in tissues while at the same time it increased growth and yield considerably. Heavy fertilization with copper restored normal yield and growth and increased copper concentration in the tissues. This type of irregular relationship of concentration in tissues, incidence of deficiency symptoms, and response to copper fertilization, however, is the exception rather than the rule.

THE COPPER CONTENT of soils, according to limited analyses, varies quite widely.

Most mineral soils that have a texture between loam and clay have a total content of native copper of 10 to 200 p.p.m.—usually 25 to 60 p.p.m.

Very sandy soils, such as are common in the Atlantic Coastal Plains, contain 1 to 30 p.p.m. of native total copper, with most between 3 and 15 p.p.m.

Organic soils contain about the same range of native total copper as mineral soils. As a rule, the subsoil (B horizon) may contain somewhat less copper than the topsoil (A horizon). In some soils, the total copper does not vary significantly with depth. In others, the subsoil may contain significantly more copper than the topsoil.

No good chemical method has been developed for assaying the amount of copper in soil available to plants. Rough correlations have been found between the copper removed by several soil extractants (acid or salt solutions) and the copper content of plants growing thereon or to response to copper fertilization. Such relationships are rule of thumb, and their use to determine needs often is limited to a small range of soil types and plant species.

Probably the most reliable—but not infallible—index of the copper status of soil with respect to a particular crop is the copper content of the foliage of the crop growing on it.

IN FLORIDA, I and my coworkers found that copper extractable by strong acid digestion of soil correlated reasonably well with the copper content of the tissues of plants grown on it. No doubt "wet ashing" soil with strong oxidizing chemicals liberates all the copper associated with the organic matter fraction of the soil, and subsequent extraction with more dilute acid displaces that held by exchange or other reactions on the surface of the clay, but leaves intact most of the copper within the crystal lattice of clay particles. Oxidation of Florida soils (containing 95 to 98 percent of sand) with concentrated nitric and sulfuric acids and digestion of the residue with dilute sulfuric acid brought more than 90 percent of the total copper content of the soil into solution.

A biological method of estimating availability of copper in soils has been widely used and appears to be fairly reliable. A specially prepared copper-free nutrient solution is inoculated with spores of the common bread mold, *Aspergillus niger*, a small amount of the soil to be assayed is added, and the culture is incubated for several days. The spore color developed is compared with a series of standards to estimate micrograms of available copper. Black spores indicate adequate available copper, and progressive shades of lighter color indicate increasing degrees of copper deficiency.

THE REACTIONS of copper with soil are not so clearly understood as are those of other essential elements.

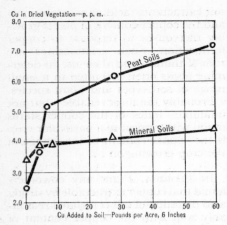

1. *The relationship of copper content of pastures and forage crops to the application of copper sulfate to soils in Sweden.*

Some copper may be held by the colloidal fraction of the soil in much the same way as base elements, such as calcium or magnesium. A major part of copper, however, evidently is fixed with a degree of security such that it cannot be displaced readily by other common soil cations (such as calcium, magnesium, or potassium) in the ordinary range of soil acidity.

FOR EXAMPLE, scientists in Florida found that a normal NaCl (common table salt) solution at pH 6.0 would displace less than 5 percent of copper added to sandy soil at the rate of 100 pounds of copper to the acre and that most such soils could fix about three times as much added copper as ammonia ion. A high proportion of copper added to hydrogen or calcium-saturated clay was held in nonexchangeable form; that is, it could not be "exchanged" or displaced and leached out readily by solutions of other cations commonly found in soils and fertilizers.

Soil holds copper most securely in the range from pH 7 to 8, appreciably less securely at pH 6, and progressively less securely as the soil becomes more acid. In addition, the kind of minerals present in the clay fraction may influence the reaction of copper with soils.

Because of these reactions of copper with soil, a high proportion of copper added to soil as a fertilizer or fungicide residue is fixed rather permanently in the top few inches of the soil, unless the soil is very acid or cultivated deeply. This tight fixation may be due to the formation of complexes and chelates of copper with ligno-proteins and other humate compounds in soil organic matter and to a lesser extent to some analogous complexes with clay.

Thus organic matter, the kind and amount of clay minerals, and acidity are all major factors affecting the availability of copper in soils.

COPPER FERTILIZATION of most soils deficient in copper usually produces a satisfactory crop response.

On mineral soils, a single application of 5 to 25 pounds of copper sulfate (bluestone) an acre usually is enough to correct the deficiency with pasture and field crops.

For organic soils, 50 to 200 pounds of copper sulfate an acre may be required for normal yields of vegetable and field crops. Other soluble salts, such as copper chloride or nitrate, have been used with results equal to copper sulfate. Insoluble oxides of copper and various copper ores also have been used. They may be quite effective if the rates are adjusted for copper content and the materials are finely divided.

In the sandy soils used for citrus orchards in Florida, annual applications of 15 to 50 pounds of copper sulfate an acre formerly were recommended for the control of ammoniation (copper deficiency) of citrus. In time, however, this practice led to toxic accumulations.

It is now recommended that a total of 50 to 100 pounds an acre of copper sulfate be added over a period of years to newly planted citrus orchards on virgin soil prone to be copper deficient. It is applied as an ingredient of mixed fertilizer (usually about 30 pounds of copper sulfate or the equivalent per ton) in several applications a year for 5 to 6 years before the trees begin heavy bearing. No further copper is recom-

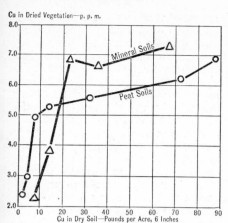

Cu in Dried Vegetation—p. p. m.

Mineral Soils

Peat Soils

Cu in Dry Soil—Pounds per Acre, 6 Inches

2. The relationship of copper content of pastures and forage crops to the copper content (perchloric acid extractable) of soils in Sweden.

mended until indications of deficiency are again apparent.

On the muck soils of Michigan, farmers are advised to apply to responsive crops initial applications of 100 pounds an acre of copper sulfate and continue smaller annual applications until a total of about 250 pounds an acre has been applied. This provides enough residual available copper for many years.

Copper-deficient plants usually respond quickly and satisfactorily to foliage sprays of such copper compounds as Bordeaux mixture. Foliage sprays are often valuable emergency treatments when symptoms of copper deficiency are first observed. Soil applications usually are the most practical way of supplying the copper requirements of plants unless copper sprays are required routinely for the control of disease.

It was found in nearly all instances studied that single applications of copper to the soil produce strong residual effects, which may persist for many years. This is because copper is held tightly by the soil, it is not subject to leaching out of the main root zone, and the amount removed when a crop is harvested is small compared to the amounts usually applied. For example, about 30 years of heavy cropping are

required to remove 1 pound of copper from an acre of citrus in the fruit.

AS TO ANIMALS, it is generally recognized that the blood of those that suffer from copper deficiency is low in hemoglobin—that is, they have a type of anemia. Copper is not a part of the hemoglobin molecule, but it seems to be essential for the formation of hemoglobin. Other symptoms of copper deficiency in animals are retardation of growth, failure to fatten, coarsening and depigmentation of hair, poor reproduction, diarrhea, abnormalities of bone formation, nervous disorders, and general weakness. Incipient copper deficiency may first show up as a reduction in reproductive efficiency.

THAT TOXIC LEVELS of copper in the soil or nutrient solution can cause reduced growth, chlorosis of the foliage, and abnormal, stunted root development of such plants as corn, beans, and squash was demonstrated in 1917 by Dr. R. H. Forbes, of the University of California.

His analyses indicated that copper-stunted plants contained somewhat more copper in the foliage and much more copper in the roots than healthy plants. He concluded that the abnormally high concentration of copper in injured roots was combined largely with proteins and localized mainly inside the root in the promeristem and central stele and not in the outer epidermal or cortical tissues.

Later studies have disclosed that toxic amounts of copper in the soil or nutrient medium may reduce growth, depress the iron concentration in leaves, and cause symptoms of iron chlorosis. Copper toxicity also may interfere with the uptake of certain other heavy metals and phosphorus and otherwise derange the normal process of nutrient accumulation by roots. This is associated with stunting, reduced branching, and thickening and abnormal dark coloration of rootlets.

Somewhat similar toxic effects can be produced by other heavy metals, such as nickel, cobalt, zinc, and manganese. Nickel is appreciably more toxic than copper. Cobalt is slightly less toxic. Zinc and manganese are about one-tenth and one-thirtieth as toxic, respectively.

Instances of toxic concentration of copper developing in agricultural soils as a result of accumulation in many years of residual copper from the Bordeaux fungicides or from copper sulfate fertilization have been reported in Florida and France.

Toxic effects of high copper in citrus orchard soils in Florida are manifested in severe cases by a marked reduction in tree vigor and yield, severe chlorosis of foliage, and dieback of the twigs. Similarly, copper toxicity symptoms of several crops have been reported in some old vegetable fields having a large amount (more than 400 p.p.m.) of copper in the topsoil, the result of many years of frequent spraying of celery with Bordeaux mixture to control fungus diseases.

The chlorotic foliage of affected citrus trees in Florida has an abnormally low iron content, and the sparse, dark, stubby fibrous roots in the topsoil have an exceedingly high copper content. Such copper toxicity symptoms of citrus in most instances are associated with an acid soil condition (pH 4.0 to 5.5) produced by application of acid-forming fertilizers and large residues of sulfur used to control pests.

If the copper level in the soil is not too high, normal vigor of affected trees can be restored by applying one-fourth to one-half pound of chelated iron (iron ethylenediamine tetraacetate, or Fe-EDTA) per tree and sufficient lime or soda ash to raise the pH of the topsoil to about pH 7. The iron chelate quickly corrects the chlorosis by supplying iron to the top—presumably mainly through the healthy roots in the subsoil, which are not affected by copper toxicity. The heavy liming usually reduces the availability of copper enough to permit the gradual restoration of normal rooting in the topsoil.

Studies with pots of virgin Florida

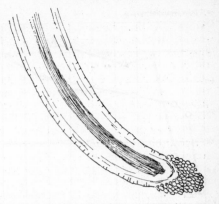

3. The tip of a corn root that is exposed to a toxic concentration of copper. The dark part indicates that copper is localized in the inner promeristem and central stele portion of the root.

orchard topsoils containing about 5 p.p.m. or less of total copper indicate that the addition of 10 to 25 p.p.m. of copper may benefit citrus seedlings, and additions of 50 to 200 p.p.m. may reduce growth and cause chlorosis. The degree of toxicity obtained is controlled largely by the exchange capacity (related primarily to the organic matter content) and degree of acidity of these very sandy soils.

We have evidence also that a high phosphate content of soils reduces copper toxicity, as judged by total growth of seedlings in pots. Paradoxically, high phosphorus may increase the incidence of chlorosis symptoms on such soils.

Field studies of acid, sandy soils in citrus orchards in Florida indicate that slight toxic effects in the trees may occur when the copper level in the soil reaches about 1.6 milliequivalents of copper per milliequivalent of exchange capacity in 100 grams of dry soil. At twice this concentration, mild to severe toxic effects are likely to be observed. In other words, the lower the clay and organic matter content of a soil, the lower is the amount of added copper required to produce toxicity.

Scientists in France found that copper accumulated over many years in acid soils from residues of Bordeaux sprays in vineyards may be toxic to a variety of crops. Pot tests indicated that addition of about 200 p.p.m. of copper from copper sulfate produced a toxic reaction in soils low in copper, but otherwise comparable to Alsatian vineyard soils, which were found to contain as much as 400 p.p.m. of copper. Among the crops tested, vines were most resistant to copper toxicity; clover and alfalfa were most sensitive.

Symptoms of copper poisoning were found in southern France in spinach and gladiolus grown in a field once occupied by a peach orchard that had been sprayed heavily for many years with Bordeaux mixture. Only the parts of the field having quite acid soil (pH 4.5 to 4.7) were affected; the copper content of that soil was 98 to 130 p.p.m.

Future research in disease control and soil fertility with copper-containing compounds should evaluate the residual effects, because nearly all the copper applied to crops will normally be fixed in the few inches near the surface of the soil.

Manganese and Soil Fertility

G. Donald Sherman

Plants require tiny amounts of manganese to grow and mature properly. Otherwise they fail as completely as if they lacked the major elements.

Paul M. Harmer, in research work at Michigan Agricultural Experiment Station, reported a 100-bushel increase an acre in yields of potatoes after the manganese-deficient soil in which they were growing received a liberal application of manganese sulfate. He obtained an increase of 561 bushels of potatoes an acre after he had applied

a small amount of manganese sulfate in Bordeaux sprays.

Cereal crops grown on manganese-deficient soils often fail to yield enough to replant the field. The cereals need less manganese than alfalfa does. Peppermint, spearmint, and rhubarb grow normally on a soil in Michigan that had too little manganese for onions, potatoes, alfalfa, oats, and beans.

Manganese-deficient soils have been found in many parts of America.

Chemical analyses have disclosed that the manganese content of plants of the same crop vary greatly.

Manganese with the aid of iron assists in the synthesis of chlorophyll, since all chlorophyll tissues have the highest concentrations of manganese.

In research with field peas in Michigan, I found that manganese controls the state of oxidation of several oxidation-reduction systems in the plant. Conditions existed in manganese-deficient plants that favored the oxidation of iron, ascorbic acid, and glutathione to their respective oxidized forms. In a normal plant these constituents occur in their reduced form.

The staining of iron in plant tissue showed the deposition of ferric iron, an insoluble form of iron, in the veins of pea leaves of a manganese-deficient plant, whereas the normal plant gave no test for ferric iron in the veins of the leaves. The normal leaf had an even distribution of ferrous iron, an available and active form of iron, throughout the leaf tissue; the manganese-deficient leaf showed only small amounts of ferrous iron in tissue near the veins. Recalling the pattern of the chlorosis (yellowing) developed on pea leaves, the results showed an almost complete absence of iron in the chlorotic, yellow parts of the leaf. The manganese-deficient leaves contained more iron, which supports the function of manganese in the movement of iron in plants.

SYMPTOMS of a deficiency of manganese have been established for most of the agronomic and horticultural crops by growing the plants in purified cultures devoid of manganese and in soils known to be deficient in manganese.

Plants that have net-veined leaves generally develop a deficiency symptom of a definite and similar pattern. Manganese deficiency leads to a chlorosis in the interveinal tissue of their leaves. The veins remain dark green; the color persists even when the chlorotic parts die. Some plants of this group develop symptoms similar to deficiency symptoms of iron and zinc and to the toxicity symptom produced by too much boron.

Plants with leaves that have parallel veins developed a general chlorotic condition and secondary symptoms— such as a gray speck of cereals and Pahala blight of sugarcane.

Symptoms of manganese deficiency commonly are known by descriptive popular names—in cereals, gray speck, white streak, dry spot, and leaf spot; in field peas, marsh spot; in sugarcane, streak disease and Pahala blight; and in spinach and beans, yellow disease.

Gray speck in oats is typical of the symptoms in other cereals and grasses. The manganese-deficient plants develop a grayish lesion on the base of the leaf. The lesion increases in size and becomes bright yellow or orange at the edge of the leaf—the halo stage. Tissue within the lesion dies and is known as dry speck or dry spot condition. The leaf tip is green. The basal part is dead. Chlorosis of all the green tissue follows rapidly.

Investigations in Michigan by Dr. Harmer and me showed that different types of manganese-deficiency symptoms develop in different varieties of oats. We grew four varieties of oats— Gopher, Wolverine, Iogold, and Huron—on the same manganese-deficient soil under identical conditions. Huron was the least susceptible to the manganese deficiency. Gray speck on it was confined to small, oval, grayish spots on the leaves. Long, grayish lesions, which changed to the halo appearance, and necrosis of the leaf developed in Wolverine, a very susceptible type.

Too much available manganese in the soil also harms plant growth. Excessive amounts exist in some soils of Kentucky and Connecticut. Tobacco and other crops grown on them develop a severe chlorosis. Pineapples on some soils in Hawaii become chlorotic because of too much manganese. One can detect a spotted condition (caused in the early stages by the uneven distribution of chlorophyll) by holding the leaf toward the sun.

AMONG THE FACTORS that influence the availability of manganese in the soil is the basic chemistry of manganese in the soil. Seldom is a soil depleted of its manganese by leaching to the point that it cannot adequately supply the plant with available manganese. The factors that contribute to the development of a manganese-deficient condition are of two general groups: Deficiencies produced by the chemical conditions in the soil and those produced by biological factors.

Soils with a reaction above pH 6.0 favor the oxidation of manganous manganese, a divalent form of manganese. The oxidation-reduction conditions in strongly acid soils favor the reduction of manganic manganese (the insoluble, high-valence form) to the manganous manganese, an available form.

The manganese can be leached from a strongly acid soil, but leachates from an alkaline soil show only traces of manganese. The manganese content of strongly acid soils subject to much leaching is low, especially if the leaching occurs during cool weather. An example is the soils along the Atlantic coast in the Southeastern States. Despite their low content of manganese, these soils in their native condition did not produce manganese-deficient conditions in respect to plant growth. A soil capable of reducing manganic manganese can maintain a low but adequate supply of manganous manganese, which is easily replaceable, since the equilibrium favors the available manganous manganese.

The liming of strongly acid soils to an alkaline reaction has been the commonest cause of manganese deficiency. An acid soil with a low content of active manganese should receive only enough lime to change the reaction to pH 5.7 to 6.0. The application of lime to a slightly acid organic soil that does not need lime will depress the growth of some crops, among them onions, potatoes, beets, cereal crops, legumes, and tree crops.

The continuous application of lime to soils having a high content of easily reducible manganic oxide may produce a manganese-deficient condition. The reapplication of lime will cause a steady depletion of the easily reducible manganic oxide as a result of its conversion to inert manganic oxides.

Acid organic soils can be made alkaline by methods other than the direct application of lime.

The burning of organic soils, especially those well supplied with lime, produces an alkaline condition. The reaction of organic soils after burning often ranges from pH 6.8 to 8.2. Before burning they were able to supply the plant with enough available manganese for normal growth. After burning, they have a high capacity for the oxidation of manganese and its subsequent fixation as inert oxides. Thus a manganese-deficient condition is brought about. Organic soils that have been deeply burned require heavy applications of manganese fertilizers.

The alkalinity of some organic soils in Michigan has been caused by alkaline water from springs. An alkalinity so produced causes a soil to become manganese-deficient by the reversion of its oxidation system in respect to manganese.

Imperfectly drained mineral soil of a high organic content may naturally overlime itself in some places. A manganese deficiency is produced in the spots that fluctuate between well-drained and waterlogged conditions between seasons. The soil has a high amount of calcium and magnesium. The waterlogged condition during a part of the year and the subsequent withdrawal of the water remove the manganous manganese. After the withdrawal of the excess water, conditions for rapid oxidation of manganese rapidly set in and cause a deficiency.

The leaching of strongly acid soils removes the manganous manganese from the soil because the conditions in them favor the reduction of the manganic manganese. Perhaps they lose so much manganese from overleaching that too little manganese is left to support normal plant growth.

Regardless of how small the active manganese content of strongly acid soils may be, this manganese exists under conditions favorable to its maximum availability. It is doubtful if many cases of manganese deficiency are due directly to this cause, but it is the indirect factor that sets the stage for many of the manganese deficiencies in soils. It is often the agent that reduces the copious supply in the parent material from which the soils were formed.

Several investigators have proved that bacteria are responsible for the inability of plants to obtain available manganese from the soil.

F. C. Gerretsen, of the Netherlands, reported that a gray speck disease would not develop on a manganese-deficient soil when formalin was added to the soil. He concluded that gray speck was caused by certain bacteria in the soil. G. W. Leeper and R. J. Swaby, Australian soil scientists, have shown that bacteria can oxidize manganous manganese to manganese dioxide.

MANGANESE EXISTS in the soils in several forms, which determine its availability to plants.

The exchangeable and water-soluble manganese (which is the divalent manganous ion) is the only form available to the plant. The manganous-manganic equilibrium and the capacity of the soil to oxidize manganese control the level of available manganese. When a manganous salt is added to an alkaline media, a white precipitate is formed; it soon turns brown and settles out rapidly. It has been identified as manganous hydroxide, which undergoes partial oxidation to the hydrated manganic oxide, an insoluble form of manganese. The addition of a reducing agent will reverse this reaction to the hydroxide form, the white precipitate.

Substantial evidence supports the existence of this system in the soil: First, because the rate of fixation is related to the concentration of hydroxyl ion rather than bacterial activities and, secondly, the existence of the hydrated oxide can be established by its properties. The addition of reducing agents will cause the increase in concentration of manganous ions. The dehydration of the hydrated oxide will cause a splitting of manganous oxide and manganese dioxide.

A manganese cycle in soils has been developed and its basic principles are: Manganous manganese > colloidal hydrated $MnO.MnO_2$ > inert MnO_2.

The reaction can be reversed by the addition of a reducing agent. Dehydration will cause the following split of the dehydrated oxide:

$$(MnO)x(MnO_2)y.(H_2O)_z > xMnO + y MnO_2 + _zH_2O.$$

The reaction is considered to be reversible. Thus the treatment of manganese deficiency can be approached by using these fundamental reactions.

First, the deficient condition can be corrected by direct applications of manganous salts. If the soil has a high capacity for the fixation of manganese, their efficiency will be low.

Secondly, the fixation capacity of the soil can be reduced by applying acid-forming material, which reduces the hydroxyl concentration. The formation of the hydroxide is the first step in the fixation, and subsequent oxidation of the manganese to the hardly soluble hydrated oxide can be reduced by decreasing the hydroxyl concentration of the soil through its acidification.

Lastly, manganese deficiency can be corrected by the application of reducing agents. The application of hydroquinone, stannous chloride, hydrazine sulfate, and sodium azide have corrected manganese-deficient soil by increasing the available manganese.

Likewise the correction of manganese toxicity can be accomplished by taking advantage of the manganese cycle in soils. The soluble and available manganese can be reduced by increasing the hydroxyl concentration in soil by the application of lime and by using mulches to prevent dehydration through exposure to wind and sun.

SEVERAL METHODS for the correction of manganese-deficient soils have been discovered and are recommended for use by farmers, gardeners, and greenhouse operators. The methods recommended include the direct application of manganese and indirect methods, which are based on the reversion of the manganous-manganic equilibrium.

The common method of correcting manganese deficiency is to apply manganese salts to the soil. The rate of application is determined by the type of soil and by its fixation capacity.

Applying 50 to 100 pounds per acre of manganese sulfate to mineral soils, in which the manganese deficiency has been caused by overliming, generally will give adequate results. On soils having a slightly acid to neutral reaction, 50 to 100 pounds of manganese sulfate may be applied; 100 to 200 pounds may be put on those having a neutral to slightly alkaline reaction, and 200 to 400 pounds on soils having a strongly alkaline reaction.

At 1957 prices, manganese sulfate was the most economical means of applying soluble manganese. The use of insoluble manganese compounds, such as pyrolusite, was not considered economical because heavy applications of those compounds, finely ground, are needed to produce the same effect as smaller amounts of manganese sulfate.

An early method of correcting unproductive manganese-deficient soil was to change its reaction with the application of sulfur and other acid-forming materials. The method was economical and gave good results on organic soils. Sulfur should be used only on soils where it will bring about a relatively permanent change in reaction. Some organic and sandy soils can be economically treated in this way; among them are peat soils; soils in Michigan, Indiana, and New York; and the soils of the Coastal Plains.

To apply manganese directly to a soil with a high-fixation capacity is an inefficient way to correct a manganese-deficient condition. Two other methods are more efficient and economical. The first is to apply manganese sulfate and sulfur together. The sulfur increases the availability of the manganese by retarding its oxidation through the reduction of the hydroxyl ion concentration. Plants growing on a manganese-deficient soil that got 400 pounds of manganese sulfate and 500 pounds of sulfur had 2.5 times more manganese in their tissues than plants growing in similar soil that got 400 pounds of manganese sulfate alone.

The other method is to apply manganese sulfate as a spray to the foliage. This method was used at the Rhode Island Agricultural Experiment Station in 1925. Many citrus growers have used it. It is economical wherever it is possible to spray the plant. The sprays have been successful on general crops, such as potatoes and cereal crops.

Manganese deficiency in a soil may be corrected temporarily by steam or sterilization by dry heat. This treatment causes a great increase in soluble manganese in the soil. The explanation for this phenomenon lies in the dehydration of the hydrated oxides, especially $MnO.MnO_2$. The aftereffects of steam sterilization can be explained by its effect on the solubility of manganese. When a soil containing large amounts of oxides of manganese is sterilized by this means, a manganese toxicity condition is produced in respect to plant growth. This effect will disappear eventually.

The improvement of soils that have a content of soluble manganese toxic to plant growth requires a treatment that will cause the oxidation of the soluble manganese. This is done by using lime and mulch to protect hydrated oxides from dehydration.

Trace Elements

P. R. Stout and C. M. Johnson

We hear a lot these days about trace elements. Advertisements imply they are a magic guarantee of success for any gardener and farmer. What are they?

Originally the term "trace elements" came from a custom of the analytical chemist to report the presence of elements that he could detect but were present in such small amounts as to be insignificant. Preparation of an ultimately pure chemical has never been attained because—if for no other reason—it must always come in contact with apparatus used in processing it.

The more refined grades, such as Chemically Pure, are analyzed, and the percentage of the principal chemical and the amounts of "impurities" associated with it usually are reported on the label. Elements that cannot be estimated accurately but can be detected qualitatively are simply reported as being present in trace amounts—hence the term "trace elements."

The plant physiologists ordinarily use salts available on the market to prepare the culture solutions for growing plants. In that way they determine the kind and amount of chemical elements the plants need. (A salt is a chemical compound formed when the hydrogen of an acid has been replaced by a metal. Salts are named according to the acid and the metal from which the salt is derived. Copper sulfate, for example, is a salt derived from copper and sulfuric acid.)

It often happened in earlier experiments that plants would grow adequately in solutions of a few salts. All of the six then unknown minor elements could have been supplied from contaminants in three salts—calcium nitrate, magnesium sulfate, and potassium phosphate—from which plants get calcium, magnesium, sulfur, nitrogen, potassium, and phosphorus.

The early research men discovered also that an additional salt containing iron was necessary, for without iron—or with even a tiny amount—young plants would soon become chlorotic, or yellow, and would cease to grow.

The scientists consequently presumed that plants could synthesize all of the complex chemical compounds needed in their life processes from 10 chemical elements, of which 7 came from the salts added to the culture solutions. The other 3 elements—carbon, hydrogen, and oxygen—were provided by the atmosphere and water; all of the hydrogen would come from water.

Today we recognize 16 elements as essential for the growth of the higher plants. To the original 10 elements have been added manganese, boron, zinc, copper, molybdenum, and chlorine. These six are the plant nutrients that would have been grouped within the category of "trace elements" if detected in the usual analytical control of Chemically Pure grade of salts.

The term "micronutrient" has been coming into use to signify plant nutrients that are essential to plants but are needed only in very small amounts. (The term "macronutrient"—macro meaning "large"—refers to elements needed in larger amounts.)

The term is preferred to "minor elements" or "trace elements" because the amount of micronutrients must also be considered in specific terms, just as one must do for nitrogen, potassium, or phosphorus. For example, we speak of the fertilization of a clover field at the rate of 200 pounds of superphosphate to the acre and 1 ounce of molybdenum to the acre, rather than 200 pounds of the one and a trace of the other.

In keeping with the idea that a micronutrient is a chemical element needed in small amount, iron is also a micronutrient. The 10 essential elements thus included 9 macronutrients, with iron as a micronutrient.

Animals normally get the micronutrients they need from plants.

When we add the nutritional requirements of animals and some species of micro-organisms (that is, fungi, algae, and such "lower" plants) to those of higher plants, we have to include 5 more micronutrients—cobalt, iodine, vanadium, fluorine, and sodium.

Therefore, in the general biochemistry of living organisms, present-day knowledge must consider the roles of 12 micronutrient elements.

Iron, zinc, boron, copper, and manganese have become of such widespread importance in connection with soil fertility that a chapter is devoted to each of them in this volume. The micronutrients that we discuss here are molybdenum, chlorine, vanadium, cobalt, iodine, fluorine, and sodium.

The term "trace elements" in biology should be reserved for chemical elements that have not been demonstrated to be required nutrients. In the future, if a trace element is to be transferred to the status of a nutrient element, adequate experiments must be conducted under rigidly controlled conditions to prove a living organism needs it and to determine how much of it is needed.

Thus any one of the chemical elements in nature can be regarded as potential candidates for recognition as a micronutrient. But before a trace element can gain such recognition, its need must be proved. We can prove that an element is essential for a living organism by trying to grow the organism, whether plant or animal, in a medium that is sufficiently free from the element to demonstrate that the organism cannot grow without it. We cannot prove the nonessentiality of a chemical element, however, for the simple reason that the complete absence of a chemical element from a growth medium can never be guaranteed—impurities will get into it.

If any single cubic foot of soil were

subjected to critical chemical analysis, the chances are good that any one of the chemical elements in nature could be found in it. The same is true of plants grown in that soil. Every inorganic chemical compound of which soils are composed is soluble to some degree, and plants will absorb some fraction of any simple compound found in solution. For example, many analyses of plants have shown the presence of silver and gold. Those elements exist in soils, and plants absorb them—but their presence in trace amounts is not evidence that plants need them.

With the coming of nuclear reactions of modern physics, many new radioactive isotopes (radioactive atoms having the same chemical properties as ordinary elements) have been prepared that formerly did not exist in nature. Plants have the ability to absorb them as well as newly synthesized elements—for example, technetium (atomic number 43) and plutonium (atomic number 94).

The unraveling of the relationships of micronutrient elements in plant and animal nutrition has been one of the great contributions of modern science toward an understanding of the nature of the world in which we live. Much remains to be done, but the successes achieved to date point to an expanding interest in research into micronutrient elements and their use in farming.

MOLYBDENUM as a plant nutrient is the latest to have attained significance in soil management. Its use as a fertilizer has been increasing so rapidly that it seems destined for recognition as a major micronutrient.

An amazing feature of molybdenum as a nutrient element is the small amount required: We speak of fractions of ounces rather than pounds. For many soils that have too little molybdenum, fertilization with an ounce of molybdenum to the acre is liberal, and there is no need to repeat the application perhaps for several years.

Usually a soluble molybdenum compound, such as sodium molybdate or molybdic acid, is mixed with superphosphate fertilizer. When the phosphate is spread upon the field, molybdenum is distributed with it. In practice, soils low in molybdenum have always been low in phosphate, so that the problem of distributing small amounts of molybdenum has been solved most readily through the use of molybdenized phosphatic fertilizers.

The varied avenues of research that have led to our understanding of molybdenum in the nutrition of plants and animals make an interesting chapter in the history of science.

A connection between molybdenum and biological systems was not suspected before 1930, when the first clue was given by H. Bortels of Germany. He was studying the growth of microbial cultures of *Azotobacter croococcum*. Bortels considered molybdenum as a catalyst that aided the conversion of gaseous nitrogen to usable forms by these nitrogen-fixing micro-organisms.

Several other discoveries between 1930 and 1942 made scientists realize that molybdenum is vital in life processes of micro-organisms, higher plants, and animals. Research with molybdenum in biological systems has accelerated rapidly since then. Between 1930 and 1942, following Bortels' experiments, there occurred five different types of experiments, each of which broadened our knowledge.

C. B. van Niel noted in 1935 that a sandy, calcareous soil near the Hopkins Marine Station of Stanford University in California could not support nitrogen-fixing *Azotobacter*. Additions of molybdenum in the amount of 0.5 part per million (p.p.m.) to culture solutions resulted in growth of *Azotobacter* because molybdenum restored the ability of the micro-organism to fix gaseous nitrogen. This experiment demonstrated that some natural soils of low fertility might be improved by supplying molybdenum to its free-living, nitrogen-fixing micro-organisms.

R. A. Steinberg, of the Department of Agriculture, working with culture solutions of high chemical purity, in

1936 showed that *Aspergillus niger*, a common mold, could not grow without molybdenum in its culture medium. Dr. Steinberg's experiments extended considerably the place of molybdenum in biology, since *Aspergillus niger* does not fix nitrogen. Other physiological roles for molybdenum therefore were brought into our thinking.

W. S. Ferguson and his associates, studying a local disease of dairy cattle in Somerset, England, in 1938 discovered that molybdenum in excessive amounts was the injurious factor. They later demonstrated that some pastures consistently grew fodder having a high enough content of molybdenum to result in the teart disease. Thus the concentrations of molybdenum in different soils was recognized as ranging from too little to nurture *Azotobacter* to amounts high enough to be toxic to farm animals.

The basis of the broad, general role of molybdenum in biology was fairly well completed in 1939 and 1940 by the demonstrations that molybdenum was essential for the growth and development of higher plants.

At the University of California, as a result of a program to produce high degrees of purity in chemicals used to grow plants, D. I. Arnon and P. R. Stout showed in 1939 that tomato plants could not complete their life cycle when growing on their highly purified water cultures unless supplemented with molybdenum. Molybdenum additions of 0.01 p.p.m. of the culture solution permitted normal growth, however.

Also at California in 1940, D. R. Hoagland, with the same sources of salts and culture solutions, extended these experiments to demonstrate a molybdenum requirement for plum tree seedlings. C. S. Piper, of the Waite Institute in Australia, made similar demonstrations with oats in the same year. It thus appeared that molybdenum was required for the growth and development of higher plants in general—a fact that has held true in all later experiments with many species.

Because of the very small amounts of molybdenum required in plant nutrition and its inevitable inclusion as a contaminant or impurity in waters, salts, containers, and almost anything used for experiments in plant nutrition, some investigators could not conceive of a natural soil so free of molybdenum as to show a deficiency for plants. Consequently, it was thought that molybdenum deficiencies might remain a matter demonstrable only under closely controlled conditions of the experimental laboratory.

Any such ideas were dispelled by A. J. Anderson, of the Commonwealth Scientific and Industrial Research Organization in Australia.

He laid out an elaborate series of field experiments on hilly pastures near Adelaide in 1942 in an area where very low productivity had baffled investigators for years. It was known that ash from burned eucalyptus contained a material that could restore fertility for a short time. From Anderson's ingeniously arranged series of field trials, which included molybdenum as a possible fertilizing element, he was able to prove that the reason for the declining yields in the pastures was due to the low molybdenum status of the soil; that the deficiency could be overcome in proportion to molybdenum applications up to one-sixteenth ounce to the acre; that the main effect of molybdenum came from supplying the nitrogen-fixing organisms associated symbiotically with clover plants; and that the additions of large amounts of lime could release enough soil-absorbed molybdenum to give the same results as applying molybdenum at the rate of one-sixteenth ounce an acre.

Dr. Anderson's notable contributions led to further experiments and field demonstrations of the practical value of using molybdenum on other molybdenum-deficient soils. Yields were multiplied fourfold to tenfold at a cost of 25 cents an acre.

The influence of molybdenum was disclosed in other field demonstrations as a primary need of the plant rather than a secondary one of symbiotic nitrogen-fixing micro-organisms.

The whiptail disease of cauliflower and broccoli in New Zealand was found in 1945 to be an out-and-out molybdenum deficiency that could be cured by spraying foliage with solutions of molybdenum salts or by adding molybdenum to the soils.

Brassica crops—cabbage, kale, cauliflower—are uncommonly sensitive to the molybdenum status of soils. The whiptail disease in acute forms produces plants in which the leaf tissue, except small areas close to the midrib, dies. The leaves continue to elongate, however, and are often twisted. Heads of cauliflowers do not fill, even though the deficiency is not enough to produce whiptail in the leaves. Control measures for whiptail vary, but the disease can always be corrected by applications of molybdenum. Some vegetable growers apply a pound or more an acre of soluble molybdenum salt.

Molybdenum treatments of horticultural and field crops must take into account relations of molybdenosis (teart disease) in crop production and livestock problems. Molybdenosis results from ingestion of excessive amounts of molybdenum by ruminants. Technicians in New South Wales recommended the control of whiptail in cauliflowers by watering the plants with a solution of 1 ounce of ammonium molybdate in 10 gallons of water per 10 square yards of seedbed 1 or 2 weeks before transplanting.

In Florida, the recommendations are to use varieties of cauliflowers less susceptible to molybdenum deficiency; to lime the soil to as high pH as compatible with other crops (for example, potatoes) grown in the rotation; and to use fertilizers that do not give rise to physiological soil acidity. These practices lessen the risk of building up molybdenum concentrations in foliage, which might serve as feed for ruminants. The scientists in New Zealand cautioned against the use of excessive amounts of molybdenum on peats and copper-deficient fields.

Molybdenum deficiencies in the field may come about in two ways.

The weathering of soil results in removing molybdenum to very low total amounts, as has been reported on a molybdenum-deficient serpentine soil in California. This soil, derived from magnesium silicate parent material, remains nearly neutral even under intensive weathering. In those circumstances, molybdenum released during weathering is not absorbed by soil clays and is carried away in drainage waters.

An opposite kind of molybdenum-deficient soil often is acid and is well supplied with total molybdenum, but the molybdenum is fixed in forms unavailable to plants or soil micro-organisms. Liming them frequently releases adequate molybdenum to crops.

The most acutely molybdenum-deficient soil that we know of is Cressy shaley clay loam of Tasmania. E. F. Fricke, of the Tasmanian Department of Agriculture, showed that failure of oats because of blue chaff disease was due to too little molybdenum. Heavy liming or adding an ounce of molybdenum to the acre corrected the disease. The main value of liming was to release molybdenum fixed by the acid soil in an unavailable form.

More than 20 crops have been helped by fertilization with molybdenum. Among them are alfalfa, sweetclover, peas, citrus, cauliflower, cantaloup, and lettuce.

Soils in need of molybdenum are quite limited in the United States. They exist on the Atlantic coast, the eastern part of Washington, and Hawaii. Elsewhere, particularly in Australia and New Zealand, molybdenum has assumed a much greater agricultural importance.

Because of the vital role of molybdenum in nitrogen fixation by micro-organisms and of nitrogen transformation processes in plants, we can be certain that molybdenum will receive an increasing amount of attention.

In animal nutrition, molybdenum receives emphasis almost entirely in connection with teart disease.

Green fodder containing 20 p.p.m. (on a dry-weight basis) is regarded as a borderline concentration, above which the frequency of molybdenosis is increased. Some investigators feel that subclinical manifestations of molybdenosis are not recognized generally, so that susceptibility of some ruminants, such as dairy cattle, may begin at concentrations as low as 5 p.p.m.

Plants may accumulate 100 p.p.m. or more of molybdenum without obvious signs of toxicity to the plant itself. At these higher levels, acute molybdenosis results in severe diarrhea and debilitation of the animal. Chronic molybdenosis causes fading of hair color; the entire syndrome almost parallels that of copper deficiency. Indeed, where cattle are pastured on high-molybdenum fields, molybdenosis may be prevented or corrected by administration of copper salts directly to the animal, as, for example, in drinking water. As much as 1 gram of copper a day for a full-grown beef animal may be needed. Much smaller quantities of copper suffice if injected directly into the blood stream. Although molybdenosis can be controlled by administration of copper, the methods used to provide copper effectively pose serious management problems, particularly with range animals.

These interrelations between molybdenum and copper in animal nutrition are the prime reason for recommendations that molybdenum deficiency in plants should be corrected with minimal amounts of molybdenum applied to soils. It often happens that soils low in molybdenum are also low in copper. Consequently the amount of molybdenum in fodder tolerated by ruminants is lowered proportionately.

Molybdenum interrelations with copper have been expressed in an opposite way by A. T. Dick and L. D. Bull, of the Commonwealth Scientific and Industrial Research Organization. They observed a rapid accumulation of copper in the livers of sheep grazing on pastures containing less than 0.1 p.p.m. of molybdenum in dry plant material.

The rate of copper accumulation was judged sufficient to produce chronic copper toxicity and eventual death of the animals.

In places where pastures are developed through use of molybdenum and copper, it is clear that the welfare of grazing ruminants calls for careful management in applying the two elements as fertilizers.

Sulfate levels of soils introduce a third component into the complex interplay of molybdenum and copper in the nutrition of plants and animals. Both sulfate and molybdate ions are of the same size and charge and compete with each other for adsorption sites on plant roots. If the soil sulfate levels are increased, therefore, less molybdate can be absorbed by plants. Sulfate also enters into the molybdenum-copper status of animals.

Dr. Dick and Dr. Bull observed that molybdenum, in presence of high sulfate in the diet, mobilizes copper from the livers of sheep. H. R. Marston, also of the Commonwealth Scientific and Industrial Research Organization, showed that molybdenum toxicity in rats on low-copper diets was increased if sulfate intake was raised.

To detect influences of copper, molybdenum, and sulfur in diets, black sheep are convenient. If a normally black sheep is given a raised level of molybdenum, the newly emerging wool is light gray—almost white. If a copper supplement is given at the same molybdenum level, the next growth of wool is black. Increasing sulfate in the diet at the same level of molybdenum and copper brings forth gray. Responses are rapid, so that the color of the new wool may be changed in a day or so. When wool is clipped from such experimental animals, the record of dietary levels is seen clearly in the color changes corresponding with the diet.

The accompanying illustration shows one of the patterns established in the wool of a black sheep that was periodically given extra molybdenum in its diet. Once wool is formed, the color does not change.

Banding of black sheep's wool due to changes of molybdenum-copper ratios in diet. A. Normal black, crinkly fleece—diet contains 1 p.p.m. of Mo and 15 p.p.m. of Cu. B. Molybdenum in diet increased to 100 p.p.m. C. Three-day fasting with corresponding band of normal, black wool. D. Resumed diet with 100 p.p.m. of molybdenum. E. High molybdenum diet with copper raised to 50 p.p.m. F. Fleece shorn.

Influences of mineral components in the dietary balance of ruminants are beginning to come to light, but complete understanding is far away.

Recent findings from dietary studies with rats and sheep have implicated both manganese and the protein level in diets as modifying factors in the copper-molybdenum-sulfur complex. Recognition of molybdenum as a plant micronutrient has accelerated agricultural research along lines that in themselves may prove to be worth as much as the economic advantages so far derived from molybdenum fertilizations.

COBALT is accumulated from soils by plants, which in turn become the primary source of cobalt for animals.

Plant physiologists have been unable to demonstrate a cobalt requirement for higher plants. Nevertheless fertilization of pastures with cobalt salts is practiced commonly on cobalt-deficient lands. The reason is that unless forage on deficient land is supplemented with cobalt, farm animals that graze adequate-looking pastures waste away and eventually die as a result.

The malady now known to be cobalt deficiency, or more specifically a vitamin B_{12} deficiency, has a long history, as attested by the many names for the same disease. In the British Isles, the

disease was called pining, dasing, vinkish, and pine of the Cheviots. In the United States it was the salt sickness of Florida; in East Africa, the nakuruitis of Kenya; the enzootic marasmus in western Australia; bush sickness in New Zealand; and coast disease of southern Australia.

The barrier to progress in combating these diseases was broken in 1935 by H. R. Marston and his coworkers in Australia. They turned their attention toward understanding the causes of the coast disease, which was associated with some Australian coastal pastures, where originally healthy ruminant animals would lose weight, become anemic, and die if put upon the "coasty" pastures and allowed to remain there. In the same year, E. J. Underwood in western Australia showed that low cobalt in ruminant feeds caused enzootic marasmus.

A reasonably satisfactory control of bush sickness has resulted in New Zealand from feeding limonite (hydrous iron oxide) to cattle. Thereupon the Australian scientists improved the health of afflicted animals with drenchings of iron salts. They examined closely the iron salts for possible contaminants that might be the real principle required for ruminant metabolism. They discovered very small amounts of cobalt in the iron salts, and subsequently showed that coast disease was the result of acute deficiencies of both cobalt and copper. Treatment of afflicted animals with cobalt or copper singly revealed the separate natures of the two deficiencies. In the country where the disease occurred, applications of cobalt salts to pastures protected grazing animals but did nothing to increase the yields of plants. Copper applied to the same fields did increase plant yields and provided the copper requirements of sheep and cattle as well.

Ruminants have a higher requirement of cobalt than other herbivores. Horses and rabbits do well on pastures where fodder is acutely deficient for cattle or sheep.

Ingestion of 0.1 mg. of cobalt a day is quite enough to meet the cobalt requirements of a sheep. If one assumes a heavy carrying capacity of 7 sheep to the acre, soils must supply 0.01 of an ounce an acre each year. Cobalt is the mighty pygmy of micronutrients. The second step forward in the understanding of cobalt nutrition came in 1948 with the discovery by E. Lester-Smith in England and E. L. Ricks and his associates in the United States that the antipernicious anemia factor of liver extracts was a deep-red organic compound containing cobalt. It was named vitamin B_{12}.

A third step came from many clues in the feeding of poultry and pigs that protein of vegetable origin was inferior to animal protein. Hens confined to diets entirely of vegetable origin produced eggs of poor hatching quality and chicks of substandard ability to survive. The unknown food accessory became known as APF, or the animal protein factor. Cow dung was known to be a rich source of APF, as were tankage, yeast, and protein-free liver extracts. Shortly after vitamin B_{12} became available, it was shown that this vitamin was a main part of APF.

Vitamin B_{12} is produced only by micro-organisms. All animals seem to require this cobalt-containing vitamin. Considerable amounts of B_{12} are synthesized in the lower alimentary canal and thus appear in feces. B_{12} is not absorbed in the lower intestine in quantities sufficient to be useful to most animals, however, although it may be possible for some herbivora to secure B_{12} in that way. Ruminants are aided by micro-organisms in the paunch, which, with cobalt, synthesize B_{12} before it passes into the true stomach and thus to the upper intestine, where B_{12} can be absorbed.

The animal world thus depends on plants to synthesize its food and micro-organisms to synthesize small quantities of vitamin B_{12}, an indispensable food factor.

A problem that remains to be solved is whether cobalt is required for the growth of higher plants. All attempts so far have failed to produce satisfactory evidence of such need.

Four species of blue-green algae were studied for mineral nutrient requirements in 1954 by O. Holme-Hansen, G. Gerloff, and F. Skoog at the University of Wisconsin. Two species were nitrogen fixers. Two were not. Each species demonstrated a requirement for cobalt. Within the range of growth where yield was limiting for one of the species (*Nostoc muscorum*), the addition of one billionth gram of cobalt resulted in a yield increase of 19 milligrams dry weight. In other words, the lowest cobalt requirement of *Nostoc muscorum* was 0.05 p.p.m.—a figure that compares interestingly with analyses of fodder giving rise to cobalt deficiency in sheep. It is considered that fodder containing 0.08 to 0.10 p.p.m. of cobalt will meet the animal's dietary requirement. Pasturage containing 0.02 to 0.03 p.p.m. will not suffice.

The cobalt status of soils in relation to the plants grown on them and the animals that eat the plants raises questions of the meaning of soil fertility, as we think of it. If the end product of a farm is beef, mutton, or wool, a cobalt-deficient soil, though covered with a good stand of plants, would be no better than a soil completely incapable of supporting crops of any sort. If the end product were to be horses, the deficiency in the fodder might remain unnoticed. We ascribe fertility of soils only to their ability to support plant life. Awareness of the value of these recently discovered micronutrients has presented some new ways of improving many problem soils. They are showing complicated interrelations that require new investigations.

CHLORINE was proved to be a plant nutrient in 1954 by T. C. Broyer and his associates at the University of California during experiments to investigate cobalt as a possible plant nutrient. They spent a lot of effort in trying to make chemically pure culture solutions which would supply only the nutrient elements then known to be required for plant growth. They found finally that nothing but severely diseased plants could be grown on them. Chlorine turned out to be the element that had to be added before plants would grow in the solutions.

They kept sufficient chemical control of the solutions to produce the disease in severe forms. Leaves displayed symptoms of wilt, chlorosis, necrosis, and (on tomatoes) an unusual bronze discoloration. The symptoms were characteristic of no other known nutritional or pathological disease. Sugar beets, carrots, cabbage, lettuce, barley, wheat, cotton, and subterranean clover were among the other species that were severely restricted in growth without supplementary chlorine.

Chlorine is perhaps the most surprising trace element to transfer to the status of a micronutrient element, because plants need more of it than any of the other micronutrient elements, except possibly iron.

In the leaves of tomato plants suffering from an acute deficiency of chlorine, chlorine is present in the order of 7 micromoles (250 p.p.m.) per gram (dry weight) of leaf tissue. Molybdenum-deficient plants with equal visual stress contain 0.001 of a micromole per gram (0.1 p.p.m.). Thus, on a weight basis, the amount of chlorine required is several thousand times greater than the amount of molybdenum. On an atom-for-atom basis—because 3 chlorine atoms weigh about the same as one molybdenum atom—the chlorine requirement is in the neighborhood of 8,000 times greater than the molybdenum requirement.

The reason why chlorine escaped notice so long is its wide distribution in nature. As one of the principal components of sea water, chlorine is picked up by winds from sea spray so that tiny bits of sea salt are carried everywhere. Consequently it is an ever-present source of contamination in the atmosphere and in chemicals needed for the compounding of culture solutions.

The needs of higher plants for chlorine in relation to fluorine, iodine, and bromine were studied by C. M. Johnson and associates at the University of California in 1955. Neither fluorine nor iodine can serve the functions of chlorine, though bromine can assist materially. Bromine substituting for chlorine in plant nutrition is reminiscent of the sparing effect of sodium for potassium. Low-chlorine plants cannot be brought to equivalent yields of plants adequately supplied with chlorine, however large the amount of bromine supplement. The amount of bromine in nature is so much less than that of chlorine that it is doubtful whether bromine is at all significant in plant nutrition.

From the point of view of soil fertility, plants require 1 pound of chlorine for each 4 thousand pounds of dry matter they produce. Large crops therefore would need 5 pounds or more of chlorine to the acre.

Chlorine, unlike other nutrient elements contained in native rocks, is not fixed by colloids of soil materials. In fact, it exhibits the phenomenon of negative absorption—meaning that chlorine atoms are actually repelled from negatively charged clay surfaces. Unlike all the other micronutrient elements, all chlorine compounds that are formed in soils are highly soluble.

RAINWATER is a continuing source of supply of chlorine. Analyses of annual chlorine acquisitions from the atmosphere have been made in many parts of the world. Lower recorded values are in the order of 10 pounds of chlorine an acre a year; many coastal stations report the deposition of hundreds of pounds of chlorine an acre.

Plantlife, particularly in the humid land masses of the earth, depends on rain to bring supplies of chlorine from the sea. Assuming a low average chlorine deposition of 10 pounds an acre a year, the total amount would exceed 5 million tons for the continental United States each year.

As long ago as 1891, A. Muntz, a pioneer geochemist who studied the contributions of airborne cyclic salt in geological distributions of chlorine, pointed out that without this source of salt, the land soon would be drained of its chlorides, and living beings would suffer. We now can give further meaning to cyclic salt and in greater detail than Muntz could have had in mind. He might have arrived at his statement from the knowledge that chlorine is required for animal life. Since we now are aware that plants must have chlorine in order to grow, it is easy to understand why herbivores can remain supplied with chlorine wherever there is enough plantlife to draw upon for their other food needs.

Whether chlorine will ever be found to be limiting to plant growth under field conditions remains an open question. In places where chlorine is recognized as a problem, it is because of the excessive amounts accumulated with other salts in saline soils or irrigation waters from saline lakes, streams, or wells. The amount of chlorine brought far inland may be so low, however, as to become borderline for crop production, especially if a high proportion of the rain is from clouds originating from transpiration or evaporation water from inland places rather than from the sea. Rainstorms vary greatly in the salt content of their water. A succession of rains of a low content of chlorine conceivably could reduce some soils to low enough chlorine values to limit plant growth.

VANADIUM was shown to be an element of biological significance by H. Bortels in 1930. Molybdenum or vanadium was used by the free-living soil micro-organism *Azotobacter croococcum* as a "catalyst" in fixing nitrogen. Interest in molybdenum and its applications to agriculture since has expanded enormously, but the relationships of vanadium to biology have remained largely a matter of academic interest. Vanadium has been included in many field trials, particularly on soils of low molybdenum status. The field tests mostly have been without effect,

but in some there have been suggestions of responses to vanadium.

Because of the early demonstrations of Dr. Bortels and others that vanadium substitutes for molybdenum in nitrogen fixation by *Azotobacter*, one might expect field trials in low-molybdenum areas to show responses to vanadium as well as to molybdenum. Field responses to vanadium, however, have been too indefinite to be of help in establishing a measurable role for the element in agriculture.

These observations strongly suggest that the number of species of nitrogen-fixing micro-organisms capable of using either molybdenum or vanadium is limited. It also means that the important symbiotic nitrogen-fixing rhizobial micro-organisms are not included among those where effective substitution of vanadium for molybdenum can take place.

D. I. Arnon and Gunilla Wessel, at the University of California, demonstrated in 1953 that vanadium is essential for the growth of *Scenedesmus*, a green alga. Strangely, the requirement of *Scenedesmus* for vanadium is high, and the same cultural techniques have failed to give responses with other algae that have been tested. We have been unable to demonstrate a vanadium requirement for higher plants, and we know of no successful attempts to do so in other laboratories. The failure may be due to inadequate skill in controlling chemical environments with respect to vanadium.

O. Warburg, of Germany, suggested in 1955 that additions of vanadium to suspensions of *Chlorella*—a single-celled green alga—allow this plant to photosynthesize more efficiently with green light of low intensity, but no vanadium effect was observed with white light at higher intensity.

The incompleteness of our knowledge of the place of vanadium in plant nutrition is not due to lack of effort but rather to a lack of positive observations. Further progress in the research rests on more refined chemical controls of cultural media and environment or on the discovery of other species which, like *Scenedesmus*, need much vanadium.

SODIUM is found in all plant materials in amounts large enough to be analyzed.

None of the hundreds of published references to sodium offers evidence that it is necessary for the growth and development of the higher plants, but there is agreement that plants do use sodium advantageously, particularly in places where low supplies of potassium would otherwise limit growth.

Our present understanding of sodium in plant nutrition as it might influence soil fertility is that sodium can partly substitute for plant needs otherwise satisfied by potassium. The phenomenon is known as the sparing effect of sodium for potassium. In experiments designed to exclude sodium from water cultures, however, higher plants can develop and grow if adequate potassium is provided. Many observations suggest that some higher plants, such as the sugar beet, may grow a little better if sodium is included in the culture medium.

Sodium is indispensable for animals. Dr. Arnon and M. B. Allen in 1955 proved that sodium is an essential micronutrient element for growth of *Anabaena cylindrica*, a nitrogen-fixing blue-green alga.

Sodium is widespread in nature. It is an important component of feldspar minerals in rocks. It and chlorine are the dominant chemical elements in sea water. Thus cyclic salt from the seas returns sodium to the land, as with chlorine. Large sodium reserves occur in the native rocks, which through weathering contribute much more sodium to the seas than is returned via the atmosphere in rains.

The removal of excess sodium in soils is a major problem in the reclamation of saline and alkali lands. Sodium toxicities to crops are often observed, and unfavorable soil structures occurring from high sodium contents of soils are matters of primary concern in many semiarid places.

Low sodium in soils may never be recognized as limiting soil fertility because so much of it exists in native rocks and in rainwater. Animals satisfy their desire for common salt from salt blocks in the field.

IODINE AND FLUORINE are needed by animals, but as far as we know they are not needed for the growth and development of any form of plantlife.

Deficiencies of iodine in people and livestock have been serious in the past, but goiter, which is associated with iodine deficiency, is easily recognized and easily treated with iodized salt. It is doubtful whether any good purpose would be served in trying to introduce iodine into foodstuffs through soil fertilization procedures. It would be expensive and perhaps less effective than the prophylactic measures now in use.

IODINE is known to almost everyone as a blackish-gray, volatile, solid dissolved in alcohol (tincture of iodine). It always occurs in plant materials, but sometimes may be too low to meet animal requirements for the iodine needed to maintain activity of the thyroid gland. Foods containing less than 0.01 p.p.m. can give rise to goiter in livestock. The general syndrome of goiter is complicated by other substances, besides iodine, that can be absorbed by the thyroid tissues in competition with iodine. Greater amounts of iodine consequently may be required in diets that contain such substances.

Suggestions that iodine is a plant nutrient have never been confirmed. Iodine is toxic to plants in concentrations of 0.1 p.p.m. in culture solutions. For soil applications, as little as 3 pounds of iodine to the acre have been toxic to plants. We know of no authenticated instances that fertilization with iodine has increased plant yields. The fact that plant toxicity is produced from such low amounts suggests high reactivity of iodine in some plant biochemical systems. Iodine therefore remains an element of active interest for investigation by plant physiologists.

FLUORINE, like iodine, is always contained in soil-grown plants. Both are indispensable in animal nutrition, but neither has been shown to be required by plants.

Fluorine also is a common component of rock phosphates. Some deposits having several parts per hundred of fluorine are roasted at high temperatures to remove fluorine before they are marketed as phosphatic fertilizer.

But fluorine, however, is required for animal life—at least by animals that have bone skeletons. It is an important constituent of apatite, the calcium phosphate mineral of which bones and teeth are composed.

Skeletons cannot form in the normal way without small amounts of fluorine. Bones of rats fed low-fluorine diets do not form properly; the lower jawbone is particularly deformed. The fluoride ion is slightly smaller than the hydroxyl (OH) ions found in the crystal structure of apatite and therefore readily exchanges for hydroxyl ion if present in small amounts.

Administered orally, the fluorine from fluoride salts is absorbed by bones and teeth. A small amount of fluoride substituted in the apatite structure hardens the mineral—an advantage, especially for teeth. The crystal structure is warped and weakened without some fluorine. There is a critical point, however, above which the structure is again weakened by having too many fluorine atoms for the most compact crystalline structure.

Fluorine concentrations above 2 p.p.m. in drinking waters are considered excessive and can be removed by passing the water through filters made of ground bone. Difficulties have been reported with livestock that drink water containing 10 to 20 p.p.m. of fluorine; their tooth enamel was so soft that rapid erosion resulted and made it difficult or impossible for the animals to chew.

SILICON AND ALUMINUM we mention just for the sake of completeness. They dominate the soil mass and are present in large quantities. They are always found in plant materials, sometimes in high concentrations. An example is silica in cereal straw.

The two elements provide an example of the general proposition that plants adsorb materials from soils whether they are needed in their physiological processes or not. We know that silicon is necessary for normal development of diatoms—small one-celled organisms whose siliceous skeletons have given rise to huge deposits of "diatomaceous earth."

Studies with culture solutions, especially directed toward discovering whether silicon and aluminum are of use to plants, generally have resulted in indefinite or negative conclusions: It is quite possible to grow plants in solutions as nearly free from these chemical elements as has been possible to attain by refined purification procedures without interfering seriously with plant growth.

In researches with culture solutions, particularly when cereals or beets are grown, the addition of silica to the solutions seems to give rise to sturdier plants. Whether silica is necessary for their growth and continuation of life cycles is not known. There have been many reports of beneficial results from the application of sodium silicate to field crops, but the reasons for the response are obscure. The assumption usually has been that the additions of silicon have resulted in a better phosphate status of the plants fertilized with silicon because soil-adsorbed phosphates were released by alkaline silicate salts.

Whatever the place of silicon and aluminum in the nutrition of plants and animals, we can rest assured that if they are needed by plants their requirements are in micro amounts. It seems quite unlikely, moreover, that the two elements will ever become of importance from the point of view of soil fertility for the reason that they constitute the dominant portion of the soil mass and always appear in soil solutions and plants.

Organic
Matter

F. E. Broadbent

Soil organic matter is a substance and a process. It is a mixture of materials—plant and animal remains and products of decay processes that have been going on months or years.

Organic matter is produced in living organisms and is composed of a great many compounds of carbon. In soils it occurs in intimate admixture with inorganic soil constituents, which are derived from rocks and minerals.

Most of the benefits conferred on soils by organic matter are due to the never-ending decomposition of plant and animal residues, which are ultimately converted into simple inorganic compounds, such as carbon dioxide, water, and nitrate.

It is not very helpful to try to distinguish between relatively undecomposed residues on the one hand and material in a more advanced state of decay on the other, although the term "humus" often is applied to the latter.

Wherever plants grow, their roots, leaves, stems, and twigs are the raw material for the organic-matter process, and all the intermediate substances between them and the simple end products make up the organic fraction of soils. A small part of it is living—the cells of such micro-organisms as bacteria, molds, and actinomycetes.

The changes the chemical activities of these living cells bring about are far more important than their proportion by weight might lead us to believe.

Their most important basic function is to destroy complex organic materials: If organic matter were an end product rather than an intermediate product in the biochemical factory of the soil, all the carbon dioxide in the atmosphere would be tied up sooner or later in the organic matter in the soil.

The organic fraction is not a mixture of inert substances accumulating by reason of their immunity to microbial attack. Whenever fresh residues are applied, the decomposition of "humified" materials already present is speeded up, so that complete turnover of the organic matter eventually occurs.

THE CHEMICAL COMPOSITION of plant residues that provide the starting material of most soil organic matter is fairly well understood. Their major constituents are in three groups.

The polysaccharides are a large class of natural carbohydrates, whose molecules are derived from the condensation of several or many molecules of simple sugars (monosaccharides). The polysaccharides include cellulose, the so-called hemicelluloses, starch, and pectic substances.

Lignins are complex materials that occur in the woody tissues of plants. Lignins possess a high degree of resistance to attack by most chemicals and micro-organisms. When lignin molecules are broken into tiny fragments by drastic chemical procedures, characteristic compounds having in common the benzene ring with a three-carbon side chain can be identified. Lignin is probably formed from condensation of many aromatic nuclei to form a large complex molecule with certain side groups attached.

Proteins, the principal nitrogen-containing constituents, are formed by linkage of many simpler units called amino acids. Proteins have high molecular weights (up to 10 million) and compose much of all living matter.

Besides these three groups, a variety of other, less important, substances occurs in plant residues.

We get some general ideas about the

chemistry of soil organic matter when we consider the changes that micro-organisms in the soil cause in the principal plant constituents.

The polysaccharides, which make up the bulk of mature plant tissues, are easily decomposed by many species of soil microbes. They are converted chiefly to carbon dioxide and water. New cells of molds, actinomycetes, and bacteria also are formed. They contain polysaccharides, which differ somewhat from those found in higher plants. The result is that soil organic matter contains very little polysaccharide of plant origin, but it does contain some polysaccharide of microbial origin.

Lignins, being less susceptible to microbial attack than polysaccharides, tend to accumulate as the decomposition process goes on, but they do not remain unaltered. Some of the side chains are split off, and methoxyl groups are cleaved. Phenolic hydroxyls are left in their place, and the number of acidic groupings, such as carboxyl, is increased. Perhaps internal condensation of the molecule also occurs as some of the linkages holding the aromatic rings together are broken.

These changes modify the properties of lignin. They make it more reactive in some ways (such as in retention of nutrient elements) but less susceptible to biochemical oxidation. Thus, although soil organic matter contains a substantial fraction of lignin-derived material, its chemical properties differ a good deal from unchanged plant lignin. Some soil molds contain a substance that resembles lignin in several respects; it also may accumulate.

Plant proteins are excellent food for soil micro-organisms. They contain the nitrogen essential for building microbial cells. Micro-organisms generally contain a higher percentage of nitrogen than do higher plants. Some bacteria contain as much as 90 percent of protein. Nitrogen therefore accumulates in soil organic matter, not because plant protein is resistant to microbial attack but because nitrogen is an important constituent of microbial cells

and is used over and over again as old cells die and new ones are formed.

The proteins in soil organic matter do not behave the same as plant proteins or microbial proteins out of the soil.

Soil scientists have wondered why organic nitrogen in soils is converted so slowly to soluble inorganic forms that can be used by plants. Because much of this nitrogen is present as proteins, which normally are readily broken down by micro-organisms, we have several theories to explain why rapid decomposition of protein does not seem to occur in soils.

Part of the explanation is that clay minerals exert a protective action on protein molecules, trapping them within the lattice of the clay crystal in a space too small for bacteria to enter. But many micro-organisms can produce extracellular enzymes, substances much smaller than the bacterial cells, which can function some distance away from the organisms that produced them. But enzymes are proteins, too, and they can also be absorbed by clays, so that their activities are diminished in a soil environment.

Other theories are based upon the formation of organic complexes resulting from reactions between proteins and other constituents of soil organic matter, such as lignin. Such complexes are assumed to be quite resistant to microbial attack, exerting a protective action on proteins by reason of chemical composition.

Not all the organic nitrogen in the soil is present as protein. Some occurs in the form of chitin, a polymer of amino-sugar units. Chitin is a constituent of many soil fungi, but perhaps most of it comes from the remains of insects. Still another form of soil nitrogen may be one that, unlike protein, resists microbial attack and is probably the result of interaction between ammonium ion and lignin derivatives, by means of which the nitrogen atom is placed in an aromatic ring. When more is known about the nitrogen bound in this manner, we may be able to explain some of the puzzling things about nitrogen availability in soils.

Organic matter is not the same in all soils.

The type of vegetation, the nature of the soil population, drainage, rainfall, temperature, and management affect the kind and amount of the organic matter: Soil organic matter is a product of its environment.

A soil developed under deciduous forest in a cool, humid climate obtains most of its organic matter from leaf fall on the surface, and the material is concentrated in the upper few inches of the soil. A grass-prairie soil receives residues from a large mass of fibrous roots and has a fairly uniform distribution of organic matter through a considerable depth. Little organic matter is found in arid soils where vegetation is sparse, because the raw materials are lacking, but when they are brought into agricultural production through irrigation the organic matter level often increases.

Hans Jenny, at the Missouri Agricultural Experiment Station, showed that there is an inverse relationship between mean annual temperature and the level of organic matter in regions of comparable rainfall. Higher temperatures seem to stimulate microbial decomposition more than they stimulate the production of plant tissue.

This relationship has great practical importance as a guide in establishing feasible limits at which levels of organic matter can be maintained. For example, a farmer in Louisiana could not economically maintain the organic matter in his soil at the same level as does the farmer in Minnesota. The decay processes that break down organic matter are more rapid in the warmer climate and go on for a longer period during the year.

MATURE PLANT RESIDUES that provide the raw material for the soil organic matter process usually are about 50 percent carbon and less than 1 percent nitrogen.

Carbon in the residues is converted to carbon dioxide by enzymatic processes. Some of the energy released is used in the cellular processes of soil microbes. Some of the carbon and nitrogen from the residues is built into the cell constituents of the micro-organisms.

All the nitrogen in the plant protein ordinarily is needed for building microbial protein, but only a small part of the plant carbon is needed for synthesis of new cells. In other words, mature plant residues constitute an unbalanced ration for the soil population of micro-organisms, with carbon in excess—a way of saying that the carbon-nitrogen ratio is wide.

As decomposition proceeds, much carbon is lost as carbon dioxide and very little is used for building microbial cells, whereas essentially all the nitrogen available is conserved by incorporation into new protein molecules. The result is a narrowing of the carbon-nitrogen ratio. If additional nitrogen is supplied when the carbon-nitrogen ratio is wide, it also will be assimilated by the soil population up to a point where the population is as large as the food supply permits it to be.

Because decomposition is accompanied by narrowing of the carbon-nitrogen ratio, it does not follow that artificially lowering the ratio by addition of fertilizer nitrogen will stop or greatly lower the amount of carbon lost.

There are two reasons: Most of the energy needed to keep the soil population functioning and to drive the myriad soil processes comes from the conversion of organic carbon to carbon dioxide. Soil micro-organisms are inefficient in their ability to use the energy so released to build new cells.

To produce a pound of organic matter from plant residue carbon and fertilizer nitrogen would require the destruction of perhaps 10 to 20 pounds of the plant residue to provide the energy for the process. In the overall carbon cycle in nature, most of the production of organic materials is due to the activities of higher plants, which obtain the necessary energy for their chemical factories from sunlight. A small amount

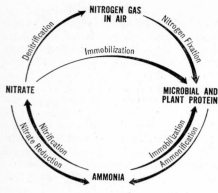

1. The soil nitrogen cycle.

of synthetic activity is due to the soil micro-organisms, but most of them do not make a net contribution to the supply of combined carbon in soil at all, because they must obtain their energy from destruction of carbon compounds.

Because of its importance in the nutrition of plants and as an element essential to all forms of life, nitrogen and the changes it undergoes are often discussed as a separate cycle. It is impossible to separate the so-called carbon and nitrogen cycles in nature because one cannot go on without the other. The nitrogen transformations that occur depend mostly on energy derived from the carbon cycle.

The atmosphere is a vast reservoir from which nitrogen can be withdrawn and started in the soil cycle by nitrogen-fixing bacteria and algae.

The best known nitrogen fixers are the rhizobia—bacteria that can penetrate inside the roots of legume plants and form nodules. In these nodules they live in a symbiotic relationship that enables them to get their carbohydrate from the plant. They in turn provide the plant with a usable form of combined nitrogen for they bring nitrogen gas from the atmosphere into chemical combination.

The rhizobia probably furnish the major part of the nitrogen that goes into the soil cycle, but they cannot fix nitrogen unless they are living in the legume nodule.

Many other species of bacteria, free living in soil, can also fix nitrogen without the aid of a host plant, but apparently they contribute less than the rhizobia.

Fixed nitrogen in inorganic fertilizers has become more and more important in the nitrogen cycle wherever cultivation is intensive.

The first step in the nitrogen cycle is the conversion of nitrogen gas to protein. Nitrogen in protein is essentially immobilized and does not proceed further through the cycle until protein is decomposed and ammonia is released. That process is called ammonification or mineralization. If the carbon-nitrogen ratio is greater than about 30:1, any ammonia that is produced will be reassimilated as rapidly as it is formed and be converted into microbial protein. This assimilation process is called immobilization.

Don Kirkham and W. V. Bartholomew, at the Iowa Agricultural Experiment Station, developed mathematical equations to calculate the rates of mineralization and immobilization of nitrogen from experimental data. Their research showed that both processes go on at the same time. If immobilization is faster than mineralization, no available nitrogen is present in a soil. If the reverse is true, available nitrogen will increase.

When the C–N ratio of protein-containing organic residues becomes narrower than about 15:1 (so that considerable nitrogen in excess of microbial needs is present), the ammonia resulting from protein breakdown enters another phase, nitrification.

Through activities of a specialized group of bacteria, ammonia is oxidized to nitrate, a form that may be assimilated readily by plants and thus reconverted to protein. Nitrate may also be reduced to nitrogen gas or nitrous oxide in the process of denitrification, thereby returning nitrogen to the atmospheric reservoir from which it came and completing the cycle.

Leaching also may take nitrate out of the soil cycle.

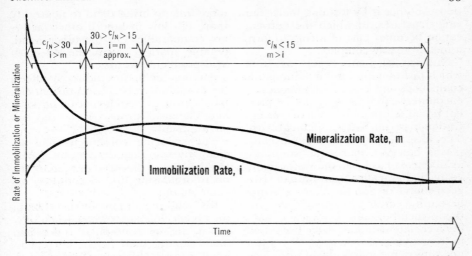

2. *The relationship between carbon: nitrogen ratios and nitrogen availability during decomposition of plant residues.*

ORGANIC MATTER is a source of plant nutrients, particularly nitrogen, phosphorus, and sulfur.

Soil organic matter usually contains 5 or 6 percent of nitrogen, nearly all of which is unavailable to crop plants. The significance of the processes that convert the large organic reserves to usable forms can be seen easily, and the importance of continual turnover of organic matter as a factor in soil fertility also becomes apparent.

Soil organic matter contains much less phosphorus than nitrogen, but it is enough in many soils to account for more than half of all the phosphorus present. Among the phosphorus compounds in soil organic matter are the inositol phosphates, which form stable, insoluble salts with iron and aluminum and are themselves quite resistant to biochemical attack; nucleic acids and their derivatives; and phospholipids.

The phosphorus cycle is similar in some respects to the nitrogen cycle. For example, when carbon-phosphorus ratios are large, immobilization of available phosphorus will occur. When the ratio is small, however, net increases in inorganic phosphate are produced.

Sulfur is a constituent of proteins. It occurs in organic combination in the amino acids cysteine and methionine, for example. It is present in plant and animal residues and in soil microbes. Like nitrogen and phosphorus, it must be converted to a soluble inorganic form before it can be assimilated by growing crops. The conversion of organic sulfur compounds to sulfate is therefore an important part of the organic matter process. Because protein breakdown is involved, this phase of the sulfur cycle is linked to the carbon cycle.

ANOTHER WAY organic matter functions as a source of plant nutrients is through release of adsorbed cations—calcium, magnesium, and potassium.

Like soil clays, colloidal particles of the organic fraction are negatively charged and attract positively charged ions to their surface. On a basis of unit weight, the retentive capacity of organic matter is greater than that of the most reactive clays, so the importance of this material in plant nutrition is far beyond its weight percentage.

Cation retention occurs in at least two ways. One is by the formation of salts of the carboxylic acids, which constitute a part of the organic fraction. Another is by forming molecular ring structures, in which the nutrient cation becomes part of a ring to form a metal-organic complex.

Nutrient elements, such as iron, which form highly insoluble inorganic compounds under conditions frequently encountered in soils, may not be present in soil solution in sufficient concentration to permit the best plant growth. The formation of iron-organic complexes, however, makes the iron more available. It has been known for many years that so-called iron-humate is a good source of iron for plants growing in solution culture. More recently, synthetic metal-organic complexes, having a chelate structure, have been used in remedying deficiencies of certain micronutrients, particularly iron. The greater solubility of these synthetic compounds accounts in part for their greater effectiveness as suppliers of certain elements.

THE FORMATION of metal-organic complexes sometimes stabilizes a soil nutrient that otherwise might not be retained in sufficient quantities for good plant growth. Adequate amounts of available boron usually exist in soils with high organic matter content—an indication that organic matter can protect the boron against leaching without making it unavailable.

A characteristic result of microbial attack on plant residues is the formation of acidic groupings, usually carboxyl groups. These carboxylic acids ionize and influence the hydrogen-ion concentration, or degree of acidity of the soil solution. They can also form salts and complexes and so affect the equilibrium of bases in soil solution.

The principal effect of organic matter on soil reaction, or pH, is not in making a soil acid (although many organic soils are highly acid), but in increasing the buffer capacity of the soil. Stated another way: The presence of organic matter tends to lower the tendency of the soil pH to change when acid or alkaline materials are added. Soils high in organic matter require more lime to bring them to neutrality than soils low in lime if other factors are comparable. On the other hand, organic matter lessens the effect of acid-producing fertilizers.

Soil organic matter indirectly affects the availability of certain nutrient elements through its influence on physical and chemical properties of the soil environment.

The reducing conditions that accompany waterlogging are due partly to depletion of dissolved oxygen by the micro-organisms that decompose organic matter.

Reducing conditions often occur in the absence of excess water when oxygen in the soil atmosphere is depleted more rapidly than it can be replenished through diffusion of air through the soil pores. This rate of oxygen depletion depends on the level of microbial activity, which, in turn, is governed by the kind and amount of organic matter used for food by the soil population.

Vigorous microbial activity may therefore result in an increase of substances in the reduced state. For example, some of the iron in the soil will be reduced to the ferrous, or divalent, state, which has a much higher solubility than the trivalent, or ferric, form in which most of this element normally occurs in well-aerated soils. Availability of iron therefore is increased by vigorous microbial activity accompanying the breakdown of the organic matter.

A similar situation exists with regard to manganese, which can be reduced from tetravalent manganese found in soils as manganese dioxide to the more available divalent form through microbial activity.

THE BEST KNOWN functions of organic matter are those relating to physical properties.

An adequate level of organic matter improves soils that are too heavy and those that are too light. A heavy clay soil may be hard to work and slow to absorb water and have a tendency to puddle, so that rainfall or irrigation water has a tendency to run off rather than soak in. Such a soil is also likely to be poorly aerated.

Organic matter makes heavy soils more friable—easier to work—and promotes a crumbly structure. It stabilizes the soil crumbs so that they are held together under the slaking action of water. As a result, the soil absorbs water more rapidly. Runoff and erosion decline. A more porous structure permits better aeration in the root zone. Less crusting permits better emergence of seedlings.

On the other hand, the faults of light, sandy soils are that they will not hold much water—penetration is too rapid. Aeration is good, but there is likely to be a deficiency of nutrient elements. Organic matter improves the water-holding ability of such soils and enhances the supply of nutrient elements. These elements are less susceptible to leaching when organic matter is present, because of its ability to adsorb them. Other nutrients are slowly made available as needed during decomposition of organic matter.

These desirable physical properties are not entirely dependent on a high organic matter level. As we have seen, soil organic matter is in equilibrium with its environment.

The level that can be maintained economically in a soil depends on its texture, the way it is managed, and climate.

LONG BEFORE the modern soil scientist appeared on the scene, farmers were well aware of the importance of soil organic matter. Perhaps they also realized that the manure they turned under did not last very long in the soil. For although it is true that there are few soil properties that are not affected directly or indirectly by organic matter, it is also true that much of its value results from its breakdown. The key to management of this valuable soil constituent is in control of the organic matter process so that the desired byproducts are obtained.

Living Organisms in the Soil

Francis E. Clark

A teaspoonful of soil may contain billions of living organisms. On them crop growth, soil fertility, and even soil development depend in many ways.

Among the soil's inhabitants are specialists that rot organic matter, transform nitrogen, build soil tilth, produce antibiotics, and otherwise affect plant welfare.

Bacteria are the smallest and the most numerous of the free-living organisms in the soil. About 25 thousand of them measure an inch. Despite their minute size, their total weight in the top foot of an acre of fertile soil may be as much as a thousand pounds, or 0.03 percent of the weight of the soil. Poor soils and some sandy soils may harbor few bacteria.

The bacteria are little more than tiny blobs of jellylike protoplasm enclosed in a cell membrane. Most of them subsist on waste organic materials.

Those that derive both their cell carbon and their energy from organic substances are called heterotrophic bacteria. They use energy previously stored by other microbes or by higher plants. Their metabolism—or ability to carry on such life processes as oxidizing sugar to carbon dioxide and water—is like that of the higher animals, all of which depend on the energy stored in carbohydrates, fats, and proteins.

A few bacteria possess pigments that enable them to trap the energy in light. They obtain their cell carbon directly from the carbon dioxide of the atmosphere. Green plants similarly possess this photosynthetic ability.

Still other bacteria, called autotrophic or chemosynthetic, draw upon the atmosphere for their carbon supply and obtain their energy by oxidizing relatively simple chemical materials. In this group are bacteria that oxidize carbon monoxide to carbon dioxide, sulfur to sulfates, hydrogen to water, ammonia to nitrous acid, and nitrous acid to nitric acid.

Most soil bacteria require nitrogen that previously has been combined either into mineral forms (such as ammonium and nitrate) or into organic nitrogen compounds (such as plant proteins and animal proteins).

Only a limited number of micro-organisms are able to make use of nitrogen gas as it commonly occurs in the air. Among the soil bacteria that can do so are the legume-nodule bacteria, or rhizobia, which use nitrogen from the air in partnership with leguminous host plants. The nitrogen taken from the atmosphere is available to both partners. Consequently legumes can be grown on soil that is poor in nitrogen but otherwise is favorable.

The amount of nitrogen fixed by nodulated legumes varies greatly, but the average is estimated to be 50 to 150 pounds of nitrogen an acre each year.

The right kind of legume bacteria must be present for each legume plant. If the legume is native to an area or has been grown for several years on the soil, the correct bacteria usually have become established. But for newly introduced legumes, for soils in which the correct rhizobia do not survive during the intervals between crops, and for soils in which there are only weak or parasitic strains of nodule bacteria, inoculation of the legume seed at planting time with nitrogen-fixing bacteria is desirable or necessary.

Packaged inoculants containing nitrogen-fixing bacteria are available at many seed stores. Because the inoculants are prepared for specific legumes or groups of legumes, the names of which are printed on the package, the purchaser needs only to specify to the dealer the legume seed he wishes to treat. Inoculant labeled as effective on one legume, such as soybeans, is not at all suitable for other legumes, such as clovers or garden peas.

Legume inoculant sufficient to treat a bushel of seed costs 15 to 55 cents, depending on the type of seed and the amount of inoculant purchased.

Directions on the package should be followed as closely as possible. The user should plant the inoculated seed within a very few hours after he treats them. Meanwhile the seeds should not be exposed to heat, drying, or sunlight. He should not purchase or use inoculant that is older than the expiration date stamped on the label.

Gardeners or farmers who have highly fertile soils or who apply liberal quantities of nitrogenous fertilizer can expect little or no additional benefit from legume inoculants. Commercial operators or farmers who grow large acreages of legumes commonly consider seed inoculation to be a desirable procedure and one that entails little extra cost.

The use of inoculant insures that the legume seedlings will be exposed to the right kind of nitrogen-fixing bacteria early in the growing season.

There also exist in the soil free-living, or nonsymbiotic, forms of bacteria, such as *Azotobacter*, that can use atmospheric nitrogen. These types occur in relatively small numbers. Their effect on fertility has been questioned. Increases of 50 pounds of nitrogen an acre a year have been attributed to *Azotobacter*. Some persons say nonleguminous crops and even compost piles should be inoculated with these bacteria, but we have little evidence that such inoculation is economically sound.

Some of the pigmented bacteria that are capable of photosynthesis also can use atmospheric nitrogen. They exist mostly in stagnant water and mud. They are believed to be of little importance in the nitrogen fertility of ordinary field soil.

Soil bacteria are not distributed uniformly through the soil. They commonly occur in clumps or colonies of few to thousands of individual cells.

Because bacteria depend largely on organic matter for their food, they occur most abundantly near organic residues. The upper layers of the soil profile are enriched almost continuously by plant wastes, and they contain many more bacteria than the deeper layers do. Even within the plow layer, islands of activity can be expected wherever food material exists.

One site of intensive microbial colonization is at the surface of plant roots. We usually think that plant roots are in contact with the soil solution or soil particles, but actually the roots and root hairs are almost fully coated by a film of micro-organisms—as we can see through a microscope. The microbiological environment in the immediate vicinity of plant roots is known as the rhizosphere. Microbes are usually 10 to 50 times more numerous there than in soil away from the roots.

ACTINOMYCETES are microscopic organisms that in many respects resemble the bacteria. Their individual cells are of about the same size in cross-section, but (unlike the bacteria) the actinomycetes form long, threadlike, branched filaments. Therefore they sometimes are called the ray fungi. The actinomycetes in most soils are only about one-tenth to one-fifth as numerous as the bacteria.

Because their cells are much bigger, the total weight of actinomycetes in an acre-foot of soil roughly equals the weight of the bacteria. The actinomycetes usually constitute a greater fraction of the total microbial population in soils of low moisture content and in organic material that is in the later stages of rotting than they do in wet soils or in rapidly rotting residues.

Most actinomycetes live at the expense of organic residues on or in the soil. The slightly musty odor of newly plowed grass sods or of old grain and straw is due mainly to actinomycetes.

The actinomycetes as a group are important in the decomposition and the humification of organic residues. One species causes potato scab. Other species produce antibiotic substances, which have great value as medicines to mankind.

FUNGI that grow above the ground often can be seen. Their cottony, colorless, or variously colored growths on bread, jellies, shoes, and clothing are commonly spoken of as mold.

Their presence is less apparent in the soil. Many of the filamentous fungi living in the soil can be seen only with a hand lens or a microscope.

Numerically, the fungi are fewer in soil than the bacteria or the actinomycetes. They account for perhaps no more than 1 percent of the total census of the three groups, as determined by laboratory methods. In actual amount of cell substance, their total acre-weight roughly equals the combined acre-weight of the bacteria and the actinomycetes.

Many different fungi exist in soil. Some are microscopic yeasts and simple molds. Some are big and complex forms, like mushrooms and bracket fungi, whose sporulating bodies at the surface may be several inches wide.

Fungi have no green pigment—chlorophyll—and therefore must feed on organic materials. Many species are parasitic on plants and animals. Nonparasitic species attack a variety of substances in the soil, including such complex plant materials as cellulose and lignin.

Fungi are important in decay because they can initiate decomposition and because they grow vigorously once they have gained a foothold. They can attack organic residues on the surface of the ground, as well as stored agricultural products and household items, whose moisture contents are too low to permit bacterial invasion. When air circulation is good, fungi rapidly convert organic wastes into cell substance and to carbon dioxide and water.

The absence of oxygen sharply limits the growth of nearly all fungi. Fungi are inactive in waterlogged soil. They are present in acid soils and even contribute to their development.

Under many coniferous and some mixed hardwood-coniferous stands of trees, the profuse penetration of fresh forest litter by fungi and the formation of a strongly acid surface organic layer, called mor, influence the development of podzolized soils.

Conversely, the formation of peaty organic soils is due partly to the inability of fungi to grow in waterlogged conditions. Many plant constituents, such as cellulose and lignin, therefore escape decomposition, and the accumulation of organic matter sharply exceeds decomposition. The two processes again come into balance when the water table recedes or the accumulated organic matter is built up to the surface of the water.

Some fungi can colonize the surfaces of plant roots and also can penetrate them and form fungus-root associations, known as mycorhizae. Such associations occur most conspicuously in the forest. They seem to benefit the higher plant. The fungal association causes the development of many short roots in pines and some other trees. Part of the superior feeding ability of the fungus-bearing roots is believed due to their much greater absorptive area. Mycorhizal roots often present several hundred times more absorbing surface than nonmycorhizal roots.

Algae are the simplest of the forms of plant life that commonly bear photosynthetic pigments. Their differences in pigmentation divide them into various subgroups, such as the blue greens, the greens, the reds, and the browns.

The algae range from the unicellular and microscopic types to the easily visible fleshy and filamentous types.

They occur in greatest abundance as seaweed and as pond scums. They form only a minor fraction of the total microflora in most soils. In watersoaked soil, shallow ponds, and rice paddies, dense surface growths of algae commonly occur.

Sometimes a sudden, profuse development of red algae on a light-colored soil after a heavy rain is interpreted as signs of witchcraft or "bleeding" soil.

Most of the soil species live on moist surfaces, but some forms live deeper in the soil. Any algae growing below the surface of the soil must do so by using plant residues or soil organic matter as their food supply. Only in the presence of light can algae manufacture their own carbohydrates by using light energy to combine carbon dioxide and water.

Some algae can fix atmospheric nitrogen. They usually are given credit for the long-continued nitrogen fertility (albeit of a low level) in the rice paddies in the Orient.

Algae at times are important in soil formation and in the initial colonization of some soil surfaces. Accumulated algal remains are the dominant constituent of some aquatic peats.

Apart from their nitrogen fixation and their contribution to formation of organic soil, the role of algae in the soil appears insignificant. Algal growth in reservoirs where water is being held for drinking purposes is objectionable to the extent that it imparts undesirable odors and flavors to the water.

Because they can use light energy for rapid development when they are grown in tank or vat culture, the algae are of further interest as a possible source of food for man and animals.

The algae complete their individual life cycles within the span of a few days or even hours. Algal growth can be harvested continuously from tanks containing soluble fertilizer salts and with the solutions properly kept in balance and exposed to light. Yields, calculated on an acre basis per year, appear to be as high as 40 tons of dry matter. Even more important than this tremendous total yield is the fact that the algal dry matter has a protein content of more than 50 percent—much higher than that of any other harvested plants.

All the engineering problems of mass culture have not been solved, but the best current estimates on costs of production are in the range of 10 to 30 cents per pound of dry matter produced. Even though there appears no immediate likelihood that innumerable short-term algal harvests will compete with annually harvested crops, such as wheat, the possibility of culturing algae as a food supply is worthy of mention.

THE SOIL MICROFLORA influences the soil as a medium for plant growth.

The bacteria, actinomycetes, and fungi are agents of decay. Collectively they are indispensable in the mineralization of plant and animal residues. They continually recycle important chemical elements, sometimes on a grand scale. In the atmosphere above the surface of an acre, there is approximately 20 tons of carbon dioxide. The living organisms in an acre of fertile soil return that much carbon dioxide to the atmosphere in a year. Microbes thus have an essential part in the carbon cycle in nature, in which carbon that has been combined photosynthetically by plants is again set free as carbon dioxide by respiration and decay.

Micro-organisms participate in many different ways in the nitrogen cycle in nature. The ability of the rhizobia and some free-living forms to fix atmospheric nitrogen is well known. Nitrogen stored in the soil is almost entirely organic nitrogen. The activity of the soil microflora in the release or mineralization of such nitrogen is a link in making it available to plants.

Many different species participate in the release of ammonia from organic nitrogen. Ammonification occurs under both aerobic and anaerobic conditions—with and without air.

The ammonia released may be used again by other organisms (including higher plants). It seldom is washed from the soil by water. Ammonia escapes to the atmosphere under some conditions. If it remains free in the soil, it is transformed by nitrification.

Nitrification consists of two steps. First, the ammonia is oxidized to nitrite by a specialized group of bacteria represented mainly by the genus *Nitro-*

somonas. The nitrite is further oxidized to nitrate by other specialists, such as *Nitrobacter.* Some commonly occurring heterotrophic bacteria and fungi can oxidize ammonia to nitrites and nitrates to a limited extent.

Microbial decomposition of organic matter releases not only its carbon and nitrogen, but the many other contained minerals as well. The mineralization of organic phosphorus in some Prairie soils during the growing season supplies much of the phosphorus taken up by the crop.

Microbes also affect the availability of various minerals in their inorganic combinations. Iron, manganese, and sulfur are transformed from unavailable to available forms by microbial oxidations and reductions.

Products of microbial oxidation exert solution effects upon soil parent material and on insoluble forms of fertilizer. When rock phosphate is composted with sulfur and manure, the sulfuric acid formed by biological oxidation makes the insoluble phosphate available. Plants may get more phosphate from poorly soluble phosphate materials when they are grown in the presence of microbes than when they are grown under sterile conditions. Sulfur applied to soils as a corrective for excessive sodium salinity is ineffective until it has been oxidized to sulfate by the soil flora.

The soil microflora provides nutrients in available forms and also conserves those present from fixation or flocculation in unavailable forms. In the case of phosphorus, biological interference with mineral fixation is accomplished in part by the elaboration of organic acids. The acids combine with iron and aluminum and thus keep them from forming insoluble iron phosphate and aluminum phosphate. In soils that have little available iron, the tendency of microbially produced organic acids to combine with iron and to hold it in solution benefits plants.

But not all activities of the soil microflora are beneficial to the growth of crops. The mineral nutrients the microbes need for growth and activity are the same as those required by the higher plants. If a mineral is scarce and the supply of available energy material is abundant, the soil organisms are extremely able competitors for the scarce nutrients.

Competition for nitrogen commonly occurs after a large amount of straw is put on the soil. The available soil nitrogen becomes tied up in microbial tissue to such an extent that plant growth suffers. With time, the available energy material, as represented by the straw, becomes depleted; consequently fewer micro-organisms are able to live. As some of them die and the remaining ones attack substances richer in nitrogen than the initially applied straw, nitrogen again becomes available in amounts satisfactory for crop growth. For the period immediately following application of straw, sufficient nitrogen can be assured by application of fertilizer nitrogen. The supply is thus made adequate both for the crop and for the microflora.

Microbes also effect transformations that make nutrients unavailable to higher plants. Thus manganous and ferrous compounds become largely insoluble when they are oxidized to manganic and ferric compounds. Nitrate nitrogen may be reduced to gaseous nitrogen under anaerobic conditions in order that bacteria may satisfy their oxygen demand. The loss of combined nitrogen in such an instance is entirely apart from any demand for nitrogen for bacterial growth. The nitrate is torn down simply for the oxygen in it.

Micro-organisms indirectly affect plant growth through their influences on the composition of the soil air; on the moisture-holding ability of the soil and the rate of water movement in soil; and on the soil temperature.

Microbes take part in forming water-stable crumbs—that is, small soil aggregates that are composed of many individual soil particles held together as a unit and not slaking down in water and are essential in many soils for good tilth. Microbial crumb formation is closely linked to the decomposition of organic wastes.

Different species of microbes and different types of organic residues vary in their ability to induce the formation of stable aggregates. The action of a given species and a particular residue in turn varies in different soils.

During periods of intense microbial activity, the cells and filaments of the organisms, gums produced by them, and the miscellaneous intermediate products of decay all serve to bind soil particles together. All these binding materials are in turn subject to decomposition. Repeated additions of organic matter therefore are required for continued effective participation of the microflora in the formation of crumbs.

Excellent soil structure commonly occurs in grassland. The extensive microflora associated with the plant roots, together with the binding action of roots and root hairs, provide greater opportunity for crumb formation than do intermittent applications of manures.

Microbial effects on the physical conditions of soils are not always beneficial. The growth of organisms in a fine-textured soil interferes with the downward movement of water whenever the soil pores become clogged with microbial bodies. In the use of water-ponding for recharging an underground water supply, or of flooding to leach excess salinity from the soil, microbes are undesirable to the extent that they interfere with the movement of water.

Even the ability of microbes to induce crumb formation is not always desirable. Some surface mulches during decomposition induce the formation of a layer of small surface crumbs that are more subject to wind movement than are the fine soil grains initially present. In such cases crumb formation intensifies the hazard of severe wind erosion.

PROTOZOA are single-celled, microscopic forms of life. They belong to the animal kingdom. They are slightly larger than bacteria—some can be seen with the naked eye. They are mor-

omplex structurally than the bacteria
ut are less numerous in the soil. Even
o, a teaspoonful of soil may contain
everal millions of protozoa. Fertile
oils contain approximately 200 pounds
f protozoa per acre-foot of soil.

As the soil protozoa feed largely on
acteria, soil conditions that favor the
rowth of bacteria also favor the
rowth of protozoa.

Apart from their predatory action on
acteria, the role of protozoa in the
oil is little understood. At one time the
rotozoa were believed harmful to soil
rtility to the extent that they de-
oured beneficial soil bacteria. Such a
ondemnation no longer appears justi-
ed. Microbial processes, such as decay
nd nitrogen fixation, proceed as fast
or even faster) when protozoa are
resent as when they are absent.

Closely related to the protozoa are
e slime molds. Sometimes they are
onsidered to be animals because dur-
g their feeding stage they so closely
esemble the amoeboid protozoa. They
ourish in damp earth and on decay-
g organic matter. They feed largely
n bacteria. After their feeding stage,
e individual cells flow together and
rm large jellylike masses, which be-
ome immobile and produce spores.
he slime molds during their fruiting
ate more closely resemble sporulating
ungi than protozoa.

NEMATODES are nonsegmented worms.
Most of them are microscopic or nearly
o in size. A few forms do attain lengths
f several inches or several feet. The
est known types agriculturally are
ose that parasitize plant roots.

A far more numerous group both in
umbers and species are those that
ed on the soil microflora and on
rotozoa and other very small animals.
uch types may number several mil-
ons in a cubic foot of soil. The total
eight of all the nematodes in an acre-
oot of fertile soil may be 50 pounds.

The direct participation of the non-
arasitic nematodes in the processes of
ecay is negligible. Nor does either
roup have any important role in soil

mixing. Both groups move mostly
through the existing soil spaces without
increasing pore size or making tunnels.

MITES AND INSECTS are present in
field and forest soils. The mites and
small, wingless insects, such as the
springtails, are the most numerous, but
the larval, grub, and adult stages of the
higher insects most frequently present
serious agricultural problems.

The insects of direct agronomic importance are the subject of a later
chapter. It suffices here simply to point
out the abundance of mites and insects
in the soil and to mention their relationships to organic decomposition
and the physical condition of soil.

Mites range from microscopic to
barely visible in size. They occasionally reach populations of several billions
to the acre. The group includes types
that feed on other small animals, but
the species that feed on plant wastes
and on fungi are the most numerous.
They and the springtails are the smallest animals that participate significantly in the breakdown of plant residues.

Insect life in the soil is represented
by many thousands of species that are
diverse in appearance, life cycles, and
feeding habits. Various insects attack
living plants above the ground. Others
continue the maceration and digestion
of plant litter at the soil surface. If leaf
fall is heavy, as in a forest, insects work
over the organic material so thoroughly that they are responsible for much
of its decomposition and for mixing
the rest with the surface soil.

Their activity leads to the development of a characteristic mineral-or-
ganic layer, which is designated as
insect or arthropod mull. Insects also
affect the porosity of the soil and its
water intake rate by their numerous
burrows and galleries. As many as 84
emergence holes of cicadas have been
counted in a square foot of soil surface.

Insects also carry on extensive soil
transport. An outstanding example is
the old termite mounds in the Tropics,
which are 6 to 10 feet in average height
and up to 50 feet in diameter. As many

as 30 mounds may occur in an acre. Their construction involved the transport of something like 10 million pounds of soil in an acre.

EARTHWORMS are perhaps the one group of soil organisms most familiar to the public. Farmers, fishermen, bird watchers, gardeners, and organic gardening enthusiasts know them well.

When conditions are favorable, earthworms become the dominant animal life in the soil. At such times their weight equals or exceeds that of all the other soil-dwelling animals combined.

Earthworms flourish best in well-drained soils that contain abundant organic matter and a continuous supply of available calcium. They are susceptible to drought, cold, waterlogging, and extremes of acidity or alkalinity. Earthworms number several million to an acre in favorable soils. Their total weight in an acre of fertile soil may be one-half ton.

Earthworms are important agents in mixing surface organic residues with the underlying soil. The earthworms in an acre can bring to the surface 20 tons of soil a year. Their burrowing activity is most intense in the surface 6 inches, although some tunnels extend to depths of 6 feet. Earthworm channeling improves soil aeration and increases movement of water into and through soils.

Earthworms contribute to the formation of soil structure by their cast-forming activities. The earthworm in feeding ingests soil along with organic wastes. The organic material is humified in the gut. The residue, together with calcium carbonate and mucus secreted from the gut wall, is ejected as a granular cast. Some species eject their casts in the soil. Others drop them only on the soil surface.

If the surface organic residues are heavy, the soil reaction is favorable, and the types of earthworms that form surface casts are dominant, there accumulates a characteristic granular soil known as mull or earthworm mull. Such a mull is found on many forest soils that have a deciduous cover, bu it is usually absent in coniferous stands Pine needles rich in resin are unaccept able to earthworms as food material.

Most species of earthworms feed o fresh plant residues or on fresh anima dung, but a few species feed only o humic substances in the soil or on th fungal mycelia.

Sharp differences of opinion exis concerning the relationship of earth worms to soil fertility. Some person insist that earthworms almost single handedly are responsible for good fer tility. Such a viewpoint has little bas in fact. The organic residues ejecte by earthworms are poorer in nutrien than the original residues ingested.

We have no good evidence that pas sage of soil particles through a worm gut increases the availability of th nutrients they contain.

The beneficial effects of earthworm on plant growth are largely those assc ciated with improved aeration and im proved tilth.

Earthworms are to be considered a indication of a good soil fertility rathe than its cause.

DO CHEMICAL FERTILIZERS, even whe they are applied at customary rate damage the nutritive value of crops? Are they detrimental to the earth worms and to the soil microflora? The answer in both cases is no.

The nutrients released to plants b decaying organic matter cannot b told from the nutrients applied in fe tilizer materials. Ammonia nitroge released during the decay of plant pr teins or animal proteins is indistir guishable from that washed from th atmosphere during thundershowe and carried down in rainwater an also from that in any one of sever ammonia-bearing fertilizers.

For soils with favorable calciun moisture, and aeration regimes, fe tilizer applications are beneficial earthworms to the extent that they ir crease plant growth and the amount residues for return to the soil.

The snails and slugs deserve bri

mention. Although the gardener is usually aware of only those that feed on living plants, most snails and slugs feed on dead and dying vegetation. They are typically scavengers and, like the earthworms, are important in the decomposition of organic matter.

MAMMALS and birds sometimes seek shelter or nesting sites in the ground. Many of them scarcely affect the soil as a medium for plant growth.

A notable exception is the soil-dwelling rodents. Although their acreweight is usually only about a few pounds even in the uncultivated land, their soil transporting activities sometimes are considerable. In building their tunnels and nests, they transport large quantities of subsoil to the surface. The open burrows in turn catch dry or waterborne surface debris and humus-rich surface soil. Water movement into the subsoil may be facilitated by the presence of rodent burrows. In some circumstances this is desirable; in others it is not. The farmer applying irrigation water does not always express himself in temperate language when he finds gopher holes.

Toxic Elements in Soils

Firman E. Bear

We got the word "toxin" from the Greek word for huntsman's bow. "Toxic" came to refer to the effects of the poisons that man applied to the tips of arrows he used for hunting.

A toxic element is one that brings injury and sometimes death to the living organism that absorbs it.

Plants may suffer injury and die from high concentrations of salts, even salts that carry essential elements. Water of a high content of salt may be toxic to animals. Plants may be harmed by relatively small amounts of a particular element in the soil; animals may be injured by eating the plants in which that element has accumulated.

SELENIUM probably is the most troublesome. It is a serious hazard to livestock and probably to people in a wide semiarid belt that extends from inside Canada southward across the United States into Mexico.

Selenium (Se), a nonmetal, resembles sulfur in its chemical properties. The so-called metallic selenium is a silvery-gray, crystalline solid. Selenium tends to be present in largest amounts in areas where the soils have been derived from Cretaceous rocks. Such soils average about 5 parts per million of total selenium, but some contain as much as 80 p.p.m. Lack of rainfall has prevented the solution of the selenium minerals and the removal of their salts in drainage waters.

Cultivated crops and native grasses seldom contain enough selenium to be dangerous to animal life. The selenium content of wheat from such areas is usually only a few parts per million. When such wheat is mixed with wheat from other regions and with other foods, no trouble is likely, at least among people outside these areas.

The primary problem is selenium-accumulating forage plants, in which the concentration of selenium may reach 15,000 p.p.m. Even at much smaller concentrations, selenium may harm animals that eat considerable amounts of the forage.

The major selenium-accumulating forage plants are certain species of *Astragalus* (vetch), *Xylorrhiza* (woody aster), *Oonopsis* (related to goldenrod), and *Stanleya* (of the mustard family).

Astragalus is the most widely distributed. About 24 of its more than 200 species are selenium accumulators.

The accumulator plants seem to need selenium to grow well. The element tends to be toxic to nonaccumulating plants. It apparently replaces sulfur in the sulfur-containing amino acids.

Accumulator plants not only are troublesome in themselves as forage for livestock—they increase the concentration of selenium in the soil in which they grow. They leave the accumulated selenium behind in soluble form in their dead tissues for more ready absorption by the next accumulator.

Two types of livestock injury are recognized. Alkali disease causes malformation and sloughing off of hoofs. Blind staggers, a more advanced form, leads to death within a short time. Eggs of hens fed seleniferous grain have low hatchability. Concentrations of 5 p.p.m. of selenium in food or 0.5 p.p.m. in milk or water are considered dangerous for people.

The degree of injury to livestock is related to the condition of the range, notably in very dry years. Selenium-accumulating plants tend to be deeper rooted than the grasses. They survive more severe aridity. They may remain as the principal forage for grazing in time of drought.

Selenium toxicity to livestock can be overcome partly by feeding linseed oil meal as a supplement. Sodium arsenite has been found useful as a remedy, but it is too poisonous to have around the ranch. Considerable experimental work has been done with the less toxic arsanilic acid and related compounds, but they are less effective than the arsenite. Sulfates are a partial antidote for selenate toxicity but they are not effective in overcoming the toxicity of selenites or of the organic compounds of selenium.

To solve the selenium problem, a multiple approach has been suggested—a careful survey and mapping of the soil of the seleniferous areas, development of a more complete list of accumulator plants, and more exact descriptions of the symptoms of injury to livestock that have eaten selenium-containing forage and grains. The worst areas should be fenced off and posted with warnings to stockmen. Everyone should be aware of using selenium-containing water.

ARSENICAL SPRAYS, when used repeatedly, have brought about accumulations of arsenic to the point of toxicity in orchard soils, notably in Washington. Many orchards have had 15 lead-arsenate cover sprays of 100 gallons a tree yearly for a long time.

Arsenic (As) is a gray, brittle, crystalline substance. It occurs combined with sulfur, oxygen, and other elements, and as the element. The arsenates are fixed by soils in a relatively insoluble state and are not lost by leaching. They tend therefore to accumulate. Nevertheless, as much as 12 p.p.m. of water-soluble arsenic has been found in the top 6 inches of soil in orchards.

Barley and alfalfa seedlings are injured at concentrations of 2 p.p.m. of water-soluble arsenic. The tips of their leaves turn yellow a few days after they emerge.

Arsenic toxicity is particularly troublesome where old orchards have been removed and attempts are being made to replace them or to grow grass, grain, or vegetables on the sites.

Plants vary in their tolerance for arsenic. Apples, pears, grapes, and raspberries are among the most tolerant fruits. Rye, asparagus, cabbage, potatoes, and tomatoes are among the most tolerant field crops. Bluegrass, orchardgrass, and ryegrass are among the most tolerant forage plants.

Least tolerant plants include peaches and apricots among the fruits; barley, wheat, peas, and beans among the field crops; and alfalfa, clovers, vetch, and Sudangrass among the forages.

Other fruit, field, and forage crops are intermediate in tolerance.

Most plants, wherever grown, contain traces (normally less than 0.1 p.p.m. dry weight) of arsenic. Plant growing on soils in which arsenate have accumulated have been found to contain as much as 14 p.p.m.

Arsenic toxicity is evidenced by slow stunted growth and late maturity of lants. Shot-hole and marginal scorch ccur on the leaves of the more sensitive ruits, notably peach and apricot and ometimes cherries. The leaves drop rematurely. Legumes tend to die in he seedling stage, following the appearance of small spots of dead tissue cattered over the leaves. Grain crops urn yellow and die back from the tips f the leaves. Arsenic-poisoned corn eems to suffer from too little moisture. njury is most pronounced during warm, dry months.

Treatment for arsenic toxicity consts in the use of 1 to 2 tons of iron sulate to the acre, or triple-superphoshate at about the same rate, or, for each trees, zinc sulfate at the rate of to 10 pounds a tree. At pH values bove 6, a chelated form of zinc, about pound to a tree, is preferred.

Other methods of dealing with this roblem include growing only the most lerant types of trees and crop plants nd deep plowing to bury the surface il to a depth of 1 to 2 feet. The plowg does not suffice for peaches. The ost important period is when the ees or crops are being established. he best method in replanting ornards is to set the young trees in 2 to cubic feet of uncontaminated soil.

Arsenites seem to be more troubleme than arsenates.

The ferric forms (or oxidized comounds) of iron therefore are more usel than the ferrous forms (or reduced mpounds) as correctives.

Plants on soils treated with ferric mpounds contain much less soluble senic than those growing on soils not treated. Aluminum sulfate is not a tisfactory substitute for the corresonding iron salt.

MOLYBDENUM serves in plants as a talyst in enzyme systems that funcn in reducing nitrate to ammonium preparation for the synthesis of nino acids and proteins. It has a simr part in nitrogen fixation by the dule bacteria of legumes and by the nsymbiotic bacteria. As far as is now known, toxicity of

molybdenum enters the agricultural picture only in relation to livestock production. The element appears to be essential as a respiratory catalyst, but trouble is experienced at concentrations above 10 p.p.m., dry weight, in green forage.

Areas of serious molybdenum toxicity to livestock have been found in California and Florida. The indications are that the element may also be present in toxic amounts in the forage of widely scattered places in the semi-arid regions of the West.

The total molybdenum content of soils usually is about 1 to 3 p.p.m. Soils containing 75 p.p.m. of molybdenum have been found in Hawaii. The molybdenum content of soils in the localities of California where cattle are injuriously affected usually do not exceed 10 p.p.m. Molybdenum differs from most of the essential trace elements in that its availability is highest at soil pH values that approach neutrality. Most of the other trace elements are most available in acid soils.

One remedy for molybdenum deficiency for plants growing on acid soils is to lime the land liberally. Applications of superphosphate tend to have similar but less pronounced effects. Conversely, the available molybdenum in the soil can be reduced by acidulation with sulfuric acid, partly because the pH value of the soil is lowered and partly because it provides a competitive ion for absorption by the plant.

One of the best methods of overcoming molybdenum toxicity is to grow forage crops on the land for harvesting as hay until the more readily available supplies of molybdenum have been removed from the soil and hauled away with the hay.

FLUORINE usually is present in plants within a range of 2 to 20 p.p.m. dry weight. We have no evidence that it is useful as a plant nutrient. Tea is the best known accumulator of fluorine; its dried leaves may contain as much as 400 p.p.m.

In acid soil and following applications of soluble fluorides, the fluorine content of some plants can be raised to levels of 500 p.p.m. or higher. Injury usually results before the fluorine content has been raised to 50 p.p.m. At higher levels the plants may die.

Soils normally contain 100 to 300 p.p.m. of total fluorine, with increasing concentrations in the subsoil. Soils derived from rocks high in phosphate may contain as much as 8,000 p.p.m.

Fluorine is often added to soils in fertilizers and insecticides. It is brought down in the rain, notably in areas around factories where fluorine-containing ores are processed. Yet, as far as we know, fluorine toxicity to plants seldom or never occurs in open fields away from such factories.

A possibility exists that plants on strongly acid soils are poisoned by fluorine accumulations from applications of fluorine-containing insecticides. Any such toxicity can be overcome by liming materials and soluble phosphates, which immobilize the soluble fluorides and tend to produce the highly insoluble, fluorine-containing mineral apatite.

Most of the toxicity of fluorine to plants has been by way of the atmosphere, particularly near factories that process phosphate and aluminum. Atmospheric fluorine may also cause trouble in cities where large amounts of soft coal are burned and around ore refineries. Active volcanoes discharge large amounts of fluorine, which have caused serious injury to livestock grazing nearby.

Instances of injury from volatilized fluorine have occurred in Tennessee. In Maury County the fluorine was emitted in the thermal processing of phosphate rock, which normally contains about 4 percent of fluorine. During the high-temperature operations, as much as 90 percent of the fluorine is given off as silicofluoride. On coming in contact with moist air, silicofluoride yields hydrofluoric acid, a gas that is highly toxic to the leaves of plants. Only about one-third as much fluorine is liberated in the sulfuric acid

method as in the thermal process of manufacturing available phosphates.

In Blount County, Tenn., the source of the fluorine was the cryolite that was being used in the production of aluminum. About 7 pounds of fluorine per acre were being brought down annually in that area. Somewhat large amounts were found in the rain around the phosphate rock-processing factories in Maury County. Still larger amount fell on the city of Knoxville. Less that a pound of fluorine falls on an acre i rain in nonindustrial areas.

Animals are subject to injury from high fluorine intake by way of feed and water. Serious injury to livestock oc curred in the places mentioned.

We have limited evidence as to the need of animals for fluorine. But fluorine seems to be useful because it is a constituent of teeth and bones. It helps reduce the tendency to tooth decay if taken i proper amounts. Excess amounts lea to disintegration of the teeth and bone Such troubles are experienced in area near deposits of phosphate rock when the water tends to contain more tha normal amounts of fluorine.

Equally serious problems arise whe pulverized phosphate rock is fed livestock as a substitute for bonemeal but that danger can be avoided b roasting the rock at high temperature to drive off the fluorine.

A person takes in about 0.5 to 1 milligrams of fluorine daily. If larg amounts are consumed, the excess excreted in the urine. The only know injury from moderate excess is to th teeth and bones. Evidence of deficien cy, indicated by excessive tooth deca appears to be much greater than th of toxicity from too high consumptio

In some cities enough fluoride added to the drinking water to rai its fluorine level to 1 p.p.m. We hav indications that the incidence of cari is reduced when that is done.

BORON TOXICITY came into prom nence during the First World Wa when the United States was forced develop its own supplies of potash sa ɔ replace those formerly purchased ʾom German producers. The most asily developed source was that at earles Lake in California. When ʒixed fertilizers containing potash ʾom that source were first used for ʾops, widespread damage resulted, ɔotably to potatoes and vegetables. Investigations disclosed that boron ʾas present in these fertilizers in toxic ɔncentrations. Some shipments of ɛarles Lake potash salts contained as ʒuch as 20 percent of borax, of which ʒore than 11 percent is boron. Steps ʾere taken immediately to refine the ɪlts, and the problem was solved.

Plants need boron, but the amount ʾquired is about 25 to 75 p.p.m. Many ɪants absorb much larger amounts if ʒe boron is available, often to the ɔint of readily apparent injury. Some ɪants will accumulate up to 200 p.p.m. ɔybeans, sweetpotatoes, and sunflow-ʾs are among these accumulator plants. Boron differs from the other essential ace elements in that the tolerance of ʒe plant for more than the amount ʾquired is limited. Any excess results ʒ the development of yellowish-brown ɔots around the edges of the leaves, ɪrticularly the oldest ones. The brown ɔots may be distributed over the en-ʾe leaf in severe cases.

The boron problem is not confined ɪ the manufacture and use of fertiliz-ʾs. It enters also in the development ɪd use of irrigation waters in arid gions. Boron often is present in arid ɪils and in the irrigation water used ɪ them as water-soluble sodium bo-ʟte. Some water carries so much that ɪ cannot be used for irrigation.

In rating irrigation waters for crop ʾoduction, the boron limit for sensi-ʋe crops is usually set at about 0.66 p.m. For semitolerant crops, the limit ɪ set at about 1.33 p.p.m., and for tol-ɑnt crops at 2 p.p.m.

Most of the beans and all of the nut ɪd fruit trees are classed with the sen-ɪive crops. Alfalfa, sugar beets, on-ɪns, carrots, and cabbages are among ɛ most tolerant crops. The remaining ɔps are mostly semitolerant.

The water-soluble forms of boron in humid regions have long since been carried off in drainage waters. The boron that remains is in the form of highly insoluble minerals, notably tourmaline. The total boron in the soils of humid areas normally is 25 to 100 p.p.m., of which about 1 percent is soluble in hot water.

About 0.35 p.p.m. of hot-water-soluble boron in soil is adequate for most crops, although some require considerably higher soluble-boron levels. The difficulty lies in knowing the point at which toxicity may develop for a particular crop.

It has become standard practice in the more intensively farmed parts of the humid regions to add 5 pounds of borax to each ton of mixed fertilizer. For topdressing established alfalfa, as much as 100 pounds of borax may be added to each ton of fertilizer.

A broadcast application of 10 pounds of borax to the acre can be made in most cases without hurting the crop. If that amount is placed only along the row, however, plants may be injured. Applications of 50 to 100 pounds of borax to the acre have been broadcast successfully for cauliflower and beets in deficient heavy soils. Great care is needed in using borax for crops on very sandy soils; on them the less soluble mineral colemanite is preferred.

MANGANESE AND IRON are a pair of trace elements that may interfere with each other as catalysts in enzyme systems that perform necessary functions in living organisms. One that is present in excess may substitute for the other to the extent that plants are injured.

Studies with culture solutions have shown that a deficiency of iron—evidenced by a characteristic yellowing of the leaves—can be induced by limiting the supply of iron available to the plant and by raising the supply of manganese to abnormally high levels in relation to those of iron. Catalase, peroxidase, and cytochrome oxidase activities are depressed then.

That is proof that a balance is involved. The problem is to determine for each plant—in its environment—what constitutes the best ratio of available iron to manganese in the nutrient solution or soil. That may apply to the many other pairs of essential and nonessential trace elements and to the secondary and major elements.

The important point is that a deficiency of one element and an excess of another may produce virtually identical effects on a plant: The element in excess has a toxic effect on the plant.

Often or always we can define toxicity, in relation to mineral nutrition of plants and animals, in terms of balance. On that basis, any element may be toxic in excess, and deficiency and toxicity are opposites.

Most soils in humid regions are naturally acid or may become acid soon after they are put to agricultural use. The reaction of such soils tends to fall to about pH 5 unless lime is applied to them. The pH values may fall to 4 or lower in some places, or they may remain well above 5—depending on the nature of the rock material from which the soil was formed and the nature of any rock material that lies immediately beneath the soil.

The purpose of liming soil is to raise its pH value usually to around 6, such a value having been found to be favorable for best growth of most crops, notably the legumes. One of the reasons is that availability of manganese in acid soils is often so high as to result in toxicity. Liming the soil causes a lowering in the solubility of manganese and presumably brings the iron and manganese into better balance in relation to plant needs.

THE SOLUBILITY OF ALUMINUM, a toxic element in acid soils, is also greatly reduced by liming acid soils.

An explanation is suggested by the discovery that soluble aluminum greatly reduces the degree of activation of isocitric dehydrogenase and malic enzyme by manganese. This cannot be overcome by supplying excessive amounts of manganese.

We have evidence that traces of aluminum may be essential to some plants But there is little likelihood of any deficiency, for most soils contain relatively large amounts of total aluminum. The range in humid temperate climates is 1 to 8 percent. Tropical soils may contain somewhat higher percentages, along with much higher percentages of iron. The combined amounts of these two elements, calculated as the oxides, may total as much as 80 percent in a Latosol.

To be troublesome to crop plants aluminum must be present in soluble form in concentrations of 10 to 2 p.p.m. or more. Such concentration are not likely to occur even in acid soils unless use is made of some highly soluble, acidifying fertilizer salt, such as ammonium sulfate. The sulfuric acid resulting from oxidation of sulfides in some swampy locations may have a similar effect. In either instance unless lime is applied, the concentration of soluble aluminum tends to increase beyond the tolerance of many crop plants.

Yet some plants grow well on acid soils, indicating a high degree of tolerance for soluble aluminum or for another element of similar character that may be present in excess under such conditions. Thus blueberries, cranberries, oats, peanuts, potatoes, rye redtop, watermelon, rhododendron and azalea are plants that tolerate acid soil. Corn, cotton, strawberry tomato, timothy, and vetch are fairly tolerant.

The greatest difficulty is experienced with alfalfa, asparagus, beets, and celery. Lettuce, onions, and spinach are especially sensitive to soluble aluminum.

Some plants are noted for their capacity to accumulate aluminum. A Australian oak was found to contain jellylike deposit of aluminum succinate. The ash of a part of the trunk of that tree was nearly 50 percent aluminum. Analyses of leaves of *Symploc tinctoria* (sweetleaf) showed aluminum concentrations of 3 to 4.5 percent.

OTHER TOXIC ELEMENTS exist in soils om place to place, usually near ore ?posits and around ore refineries and places where they have been applied constituents of fungicides or insecti-des. Among them are barium, nickel, ›pper, zinc, and lead.

Barium is toxic to plants only in ex-eme conditions, such as those around ırite mines, where soil concentrations high as 33,500 p.p.m. of total barium ıve been reported. Brazil nuts are ›ted for their high content of bar-m—up to 4,000 p.p.m. Barium car-›nate has been used as a rat poison ıd is toxic to plants.

Nickel is toxic to plants at relatively w concentrations. Soils derived from ırpentine rocks are notably high in ckel—a fact that may explain the ck of productiveness of such soils, al-ıough there is evidence that excess anganese and a deficiency of molyb-›num also may be involved.

Total nickel in soils ranges usually ›tween 10 and 40 p.p.m., but values high as 140 p.p.m. have been re-›rted. The nickel content of plants is ually between 0.5 and 2 p.p.m. Tox-.ty in tomatoes developed at 40 p.m. of nickel in the plants. Growth ›pped at 150 p.p.m.

Copper is more likely to be deficient an excessive in soils, both in relation the needs of plants and of the ani-als that consume them. Nevertheless, pper is under suspicion as a toxic ?ment after continued use of copper lfate as a fertilizer and as a fungicide, rticularly for plants growing on ındy soils. Notable cases of bad effects ›m copper have been reported in rus groves in Florida.

The copper content of soils usually nges between 10 and 40 p.p.m. and at of plants between 2 and 20 p.p.m. uch higher values are known for cer-ın soils, and more than 500 p.p.m. of pper have been found in celery. Ap-.cations of as little as 10 pounds of pper sulfate an acre has retarded ınt growth on sandy soils. Yet as ıch as 10,000 pounds of copper sul-.e per acre has been applied to cop-per-deficient peats without crop dam-age. Copper sulfate is an antidote for molybdenum toxicity.

Excessive concentrations of zinc exist in some acid soils as a result of the presence of nearby deposits of zinc ores. The zinc content of soils usually is 20 to 200 p.p.m. and that of plants be-tween 30 and 50 p.p.m. Ragweed (*Am-brosia*) is noted as a zinc accumulator, nearly 4,000 p.p.m. of zinc having been found in one specimen growing near a zinc-mineral outcrop. Zinc toxicity has been troublesome around zinc smelters. The toxicity to plants is readily over-come by liming the soil.

Lead poisoning of livestock has been experienced from time to time around lead mines, where concentrations as high as 45,000 p.p.m. of total lead have been reported in soils, and in places where animals have had access to lead-containing paints.

Considerable controversy has been aroused on the subject of residues of lead arsenate sprays on fruits. There is little evidence of injury to plants from lead poisoning except where lead ar-senite has been used as a spray. Lead arsenate is usually preferred for spray-ing because it is less soluble and more stable than the arsenite.

ALMOST ANY SOIL ELEMENT is toxic to plants when it is present in abnormally high concentrations. Such abnormali-ties may be natural to the soil, or they may be the result of applications of salts of the several elements in fertiliz-ers, insecticides, or fungicides. Sewage sludges often have abnormally high amounts of some of the trace elements. Often one or more species of plants thrive under such conditions and may serve as indicator plants. Often they accumulate the elements to relatively high concentrations. Livestock grazing on them may be poisoned.

But the question still remains as to whether such toxicity is a direct result of the presence of the element in excess or an indirect result of its replacement of some similar element that is essential to the living organism.

How To Determine Nutrient Needs

Frank G. Viets, Jr., and John J. Hanway

You can tell whether soil need fertilizers by the health an productiveness of the plant that grow on it.

Plants in poor health may be stunt or—when nutrients are critically low—show signs of sickness on leaves, stem or fruits. In some plants, however, t need for more or different nutrients less easily seen. Often they may not a pear stunted or show deficiency sym toms, but they will respond to the add tion of nutrients to the soil. This hidd hunger will become more common farmers increase their yields.

Three steps are necessary to dete mine the nutrient needs of soil:

The problem must be diagnosed.

The degree of deficiency must determined.

The amount of fertilizer needed f the desired yield must be found.

PLANTS AND SOIL conditions must examined in detail in the field. The is no way of getting around that. T diagnosis can then be checked by si ple fertilizer tests in the field or gree house, by quick tests of plant tissu and by analysis of soils and plants.

Often you can easily see that a cr is not making proper growth. Som times plants exhibit general or speci symptoms of poor nutrition. Too lit sulfur and nitrogen, for example, p duce a general chlorosis—a yellow pale-green color over the entire pla Some deficiencies, like that of ir show up mostly in the younger tissu the young leaf blades are white or p yellow but the veins may be normal

Although symptoms are a useful guide o the need for nutrients, one has to be areful in interpreting them, particularly when two or more deficiencies xist at the same time. Climate also nay affect the expression of symptoms. Therefore the diagnosis should be confirmed by chemical tests of the plant issues or by applying the nutrient to he soil or the foliage and seeing how he plant responds.

Of particular importance in diagnos is the influence of the soil profile. 'oor drainage may induce symptoms f deficiency. An example is so-called me-induced chlorosis, or iron deficiency, which is common on susceptible rops or poorly drained sites in the Vest. Plants in fields where surface soil as been removed by erosion or in reparation for irrigation often are decient in nitrogen, phosphorus, iron, otassium, or zinc, especially if the subil contains lime. Overliming can induce some deficiencies on acid soils. Deficiencies of one or more elements ·equently occur where sand or gravel nderlies shallow soil.

It is important but not always easy) exclude other possible causes of oor growth or symptoms that look ke mineral deficiencies. Some insects uck juices from plants and so reduce rowth. The toxins of some insects derm plants and produce symptoms ke those of mineral deficiency. Nemaodes may retard development of roots. Some plant diseases, particularly the irus diseases, produce leaf patterns nat can be confused with symptoms f mineral deficiency. So do various rganisms that produce dead areas a leaves. Root rot can reduce the bility of a plant to forage for nutrients. Excess salts in the soil reduce the eny of water into plants and restrict neir growth without producing specfic symptoms of deficiency. This probm is common in western irrigated eas and may become so in the Eastn States. Accumulation of sodium on e clay of soils leads to an alkali contion that often is linked with poor owth or no growth of crops and the

presence of deficiency symptoms of iron and sometimes zinc.

The damage done by drought may be mistaken for nitrogen deficiency in grains, corn, sorghum, and grasses.

Frost damage may also produce symptoms that may appear to be deficiencies of nutrients.

Applying fertilizers too close to the seed at planting or sidedressing fertilizers at too high rates or too close to the plants may produce injuries that reduce growth or kill plant tissues.

Improper cultivation may result in deficiency symptoms. Lightning may sear small areas in a field.

After you have made a field diagnosis, you can confirm it by pot experiments in a greenhouse or strip tests in the field. These tests are made by adding (singly or in various combinations) the fertilizer elements suspected of being deficient and observing the plant growth that results.

THE NEXT STEP is to determine the extent of the deficiency.

One way to do that is to make an experiment in the field itself. The deficiency is estimated by adding nutrients and determining what effect the additions have on the plants. The fertilizer containing the nutrient is added to the soil or sprayed on the plants at various rates of application—more than one nutrient may be deficient, and several rates of each nutrient may be added in combination with different rates of the others.

Several kinds of information may be had from these experiments. The simplest is the response curve of yield in relation to the amount of nutrient supplied. It gives information about the supplying power of the unfertilized soil in terms of bushels or tons of produce. If the increase in yield is great, the experiment shows that the soil has too little of the nutrient in question. The shape of the response curve also shows how much nutrient is needed to produce the desired yield level under the existing set of conditions.

Other methods of evaluation of the

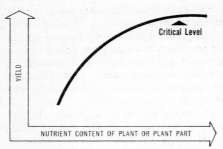

1. A theoretical curve of yield in relation to plant composition, where only one nutrient limits growth. As the nutrient content increases above the critical level, yield does not increase.

available nutrients involve chemical analyses of unfertilized plants. Such estimates usually are based on only the tops of plants, because it is hard to test the roots. The chemical analysis and the yield of the plant tops allow one to calculate the amount of a nutrient element removed from the soil by the plants. The amount removed by the unfertilized plants can be used as an estimate of the power of a soil to supply nutrients.

The method has limitations, however, because factors other than the availability of the nutrient may restrict plant growth and thereby reduce the amount of the nutrient removed.

L. A. Dean, of the Department of Agriculture, in 1954 proposed a method of plotting the phosphorus uptake by plants grown with a series of applied rates of phosphate. The method gives an estimate of the available phosphate in the soil in terms of the phosphate that is applied. The nutrient uptake must be proportionate to the nutrient applied if this method is to be used conveniently.

R. D. Munson and George Stanford, of the Iowa Agricultural Experiment Station, later applied this method to nitrogen studies with German millet grown in pots.

Field studies on the applicability of this method of estimating nutrient availability have been started at several experiment stations.

Another way to estimate the nutrient availability can be used in a field or greenhouse. It makes use of an isotope of the nutrient element. An isotope used for tagging—identifying—a fertilizer differs from the normal or common form of the element either in it weight or its ability to emit radiation that can be detected. These isotope are useful in research studies because they can be detected readily, but they enter in the same kinds of chemical reactions in the soil and are absorbed by plant roots just like normal isotopes.

The tagging isotope is incorporated into fertilizer. Then the amount of nutrient taken up from the fertilizer can be determined accurately by calculating the proportion of normal isotope to "tagged" isotope in the plant grown on the soil.

F. E. Koehler and his associates a the Nebraska Agricultural Experiment Station used radioactive phosphorus in concentrated superphosphate to determine how much phosphate in alfalfa came from the fertilizer and how much from the soil. The phosphate was drilled about 2 inches deep in the alfalfa sod. Alfalfa in a 6-year, non manured rotation was compared with alfalfa in the same rotation, in which 12 tons of manure an acre was added each time sugar beets were grown. In the nonmanured rotation, 39 percent of the phosphorus in the plant came from the fertilizer. In the rotation in which the available phosphorus had been built up by manure, only 29 per cent came from the fertilizer. The soil could supply more.

Maurice Fried and Dr. Dean, of the Department of Agriculture, proposed a new method of calculating availability of nutrients in the soil by the use of radioisotopes. They use the amount of nutrient applied and the amount of nutrient in the plant obtained from the fertilizer in the calculations. The result is the "A" value—or amount of available nutrient expressed in terms of that applied. A soil high in available nutrient will give a high "A" value, because not much nutrient is taken up from the fertilizer. A soil low in available nu

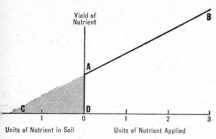

2. *Theoretical yield of nutrient line* AB, *obtained om fertilizer application. Line* AD *is direct meas-·e of nutrient available from unfertilized soil. Line :D is an estimate of nutrient in soil in terms of that bplied obtained by extending line* AB *to* C.

·ients will give a low "A" value, be-·ause the crop takes much of its nutri-·nt from the fertilizer.

The method is of limited usefulness ·1 comparing different soils because ·ιe "tagged" fertilizer or standard re-·cts differently with the soils. To com-·are several methods of soil manage-·ιent on the same soil, however, the ·A" value procedure is good. To illus-·ate its usefulness, data obtained by ·. L. Hausenbuiller, of the Washing-·ιn Agricultural Experiment Station, ·ιay be cited. Sagemoor fine sandy ·am cropped with row crops for 20 ·ιars had an "A" value of 22 pounds ·: phosphorus an acre, whereas the ·ιme soil that got 77 pounds of phos-·horus an acre annually and grew the ·ιme crops had an "A" value of 157.

THE SITE for a field experiment ·ιould be chosen carefully. It must be ·pical of the soil conditions to be ·sted. Because the effect of the added ·ιtrients is indicated by the difference ·:tween plants on treated and un-·eated plots, the experimental area ·ιould be as uniform as possible. Only ·en can you be sure that the differ-·ιce between plots is due primarily to ·e treatments that are applied and not due to variations in the soil. Because it is impossible to find areas · soil that are absolutely uniform, we ·ιploy replication and randomization · reduce and estimate the error in ·easuring the effect of the treatments.

Replication means that each treat-ment is repeated one or more times in the experiment. Usually the site is di-vided into blocks of plots. Each treat-ment is applied to one plot in each of the blocks. The average of all plots treated alike is considered the best value to use in estimating the effect of that treatment.

Randomization means that within each block the treatments are assigned to individual plots in a random man-ner. This insures that each treatment has an equal chance of being assigned to any given plot. Thus, if the soil on one plot is better than the soil on another, each treatment has an equal chance of being assigned to the better plot.

The results of a field experiment can be applied specifically only to the site tested and the year the experiment was conducted. Similar experiments must be conducted on similar soils in differ-ent years to determine whether the re-sults are applicable to other fields and other years.

Such experiments in the field take much time, effort, and money. It is not possible to conduct adequate field ex-periments on all fields and the different crops, soil types, and management con-ditions. Cheaper and quicker tests therefore have been developed to ex-tend the results obtained from field experiments, which serve as a source of soil and plant samples to be used in standardizing the other tests.

Tests in the laboratory and green-house under conditions different from those in the field can provide only rela-tive estimates of nutrient availability in the field, but such tests, when properly standardized, provide reliable infor-mation much faster and cheaper than is possible in field experiments.

Laboratory and greenhouse tests in-clude tests of soil samples and tests of plant tissues.

Because the soil sample must be typical of the soils in the area to be tested, several subsamples are taken at various scattered points within the area. A sample should always repre-sent only one soil condition. If two or more types are in the sampling area, each should be sampled separately.

Usually each composite sample is mixed thoroughly and air-dried soon after it is collected. For certain tests, especially for potassium, there have been indications that samples of some soils should be tested in the moist condition, as taken from the field. Only samples from the surface soil usually are collected and tested, but often the results of tests of subsoil samples may be just as important as the tests of surface soil.

The soil tests may involve the growing of plants or micro-organisms on the soil sample or they may include chemical analyses of the soil sample. Each kind of test is useful, and each has its limitations. The test used in any particular case will depend on the information desired.

The tests in which plants are grown include pot tests and Neubauer tests. The same kinds of plants are grown as in a field, but the estimates of availability of nutrients they provide are only relative values. The limited amount of soil that is used is uniformly mixed and does not represent the actual soil profile, which has varying physical properties and chemical characteristics at different depths. The tests do not measure the influence of management practices, climatic factors, and the varying moisture conditions that exist in the field. Therefore these tests also must be standardized against field experiments.

In pot tests, plants grow in pots or cans in the greenhouse. Usually 1 to 10 pounds of the bulk soil sample is weighed into individual pots. Clean, white sand or washed gravel may be mixed with the soil to improve its physical condition. Nutrient solutions or fertilizers are added at different rates to the soil in some of the pots. As in field experiments, it is desirable to replicate each treatment.

Pot tests have been conducted with most field and vegetable crops, such as oats, millet, alfalfa, clovers, corn, wheat, and tobacco. Romaine lettuce and sunflowers are often used and

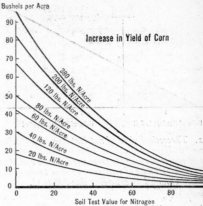

Bushels per Acre

Increase in Yield of Corn

280 lbs. N/Acre
200 lbs. N/Acre
120 lbs. N/Acre
80 lbs. N/Acre
60 lbs. N/Acre
40 lbs. N/Acre
20 lbs. N/Acre

Soil Test Value for Nitrogen

3. Yield increases of corn to be expected from application of different rates of nitrogen fertilizer relation to soil test values for nitrogen availabili Where relationships such as this have been develop the soil test value can be used to predict yield creases to be expected from fertilizer application (Data of Hanway and Dumenil—Soil Science ciety of America Proceedings 19: 77–80.)

have special value in studies of min elements in soils because of their sens tivity to deficiencies.

The plants are seeded or transplant into the pots and allowed to grow f 3 to 6 weeks. Water is added to ke the soil moist. The plants are harveste dried, and weighed. Chemical analys may be made to determine the amou of each nutrient element taken up.

Pot tests have the advantage that t plants are grown under uniform co ditions. The tests may be conducted field experiments are: Each pot is li a plot in a field experiment, and sir lar kinds of data are obtained.

Pot tests may be used also to co pare plant response on different so under uniform conditions. They oft furnish the best estimates of nutrie availability to use for comparing t reliability of different chemical tes

In Neubauer tests, many seedli plants are grown in a small amount soil, so that there is an intensive upta of available nutrients in a short tim A chemical analysis determines t amount of nutrients absorbed by t plants.

One hundred carefully selected see

of rye, wheat, or barley are weighed and planted in 100 grams of soil diluted with quartz sand. Similarly 100 seeds are planted in quartz sand alone. After 14 to 18 days of growth, the roots and tops of the seedlings are harvested and analyzed.

The difference in the amount of nutrients in the seedlings grown in the soil and those grown in the sand indicates the amount of nutrients the seedlings obtained from the soil. This amount expressed as milligrams per 100 grams of soil is referred to as the Neubauer number. These numbers may be interpreted in relation to certain limit values, which are assumed to be the minimum values for satisfactory yields of crops. For example, 6 milligrams of P_2O_5 (phosphoric oxide) is the limit value of phosphorus for wheat. If the value obtained for a soil sample is less than 6, it indicates that the soil will not supply enough phosphorus for a satisfactory yield of wheat. The technique is useful for both major and trace elements.

Micro-organisms can be used in testing soils and can be grown in a laboratory more easily than the higher plants.

Two basic procedures are used. In plaque tests, the growth of the micro-organisms is measured. In incubation tests, the chemical compounds produced by micro-organisms (such as the nitrate nitrogen resulting from the decomposition of soil organic matter) are determined by chemical analysis of the soil after incubation with the micro-organisms.

Plaque tests are made by growing bacteria (*Azotobacter*) or fungi (*Aspergillus* and *Cunninghamella*) on samples of moist soil. Different nutrient solutions, each containing all but one of the essential nutrients, are added to different portions. The samples are then inoculated with the bacterium or fungus. The micro-organisms grow on the moist soil 4 to 6 days in an incubator. The amount of growth is measured by the diameter of the colony of micro-organisms, or the pad of growth is removed, dried, and weighed. The differ-

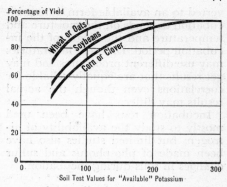

4. *The relationship between percentage of yields without added potassium for different crops and soil test values for available potassium (where yield with adequate added potassium is 100 percent). Since different crops have different nutrient requirements, the interpretation of the soil test result must depend on the crop to be grown.*

ence in the growth produced on the soil alone and on the soil plus added nutrient indicates the availability of a nutrient in the soil. Sometimes the nutrient content of the growth also is determined. The production of spores of the fungi is also noted. The plaque method has been used mostly in studies of phosphorus and potassium. It is used also to determine amounts of nitrogen, magnesium, copper, zinc, and molybdenum.

Incubation tests are based on the fact that micro-organisms in soils convert many compounds to available forms.

An example is the decomposition of organic matter whereby nitrogen, phosphorus, and other nutrient elements are changed from organic forms that cannot be absorbed by plants to mineral forms that plants can use. This process occurs in soils in the field. The incubation tests in the laboratory merely measure the amounts mineralized when moisture and temperature are controlled. A small sample of soil is incubated for a time. The amount of the nutrient element converted to an available form during the incubation period is extracted from the soil and measured by chemical analysis.

The amount of the nutrient converted to an available form during incubation depends on the moisture and temperature and the length of the incubation period. Different laboratories may use different procedures and may get results that are equally reliable for correlations even though the actual results may differ.

Incubation tests have been used mostly to study the availability of nitrogen, but limited studies also have been made of phosphorus and sulfur changes in soils during incubation.

CHEMICAL TESTS of soil samples may be made to determine the total amount of an element in the soil, or to show the amount of an element that is soluble in some reagent, like a weak acid or salt solution. Knowing the total amount of an element present in the soil generally does not help much in estimating its availability to plants.

In the most widely used soil tests, a reagent is used to extract a small, more readily soluble portion of the total amount of the nutrient in the soil. To extract phosphorus, for example, one may use dilute sulfuric or hydrochloric acid, dilute hydrochloric acid with ammonium fluoride, sodium acetate, sodium bicarbonate, or water saturated with carbon dioxide.

If suitable reagents are used, a good correlation can be obtained between the amount extracted and the availability of the nutrient. Because each nutrient has its own properties, different reagents usually are needed for extraction of the different nutrients. Furthermore, because the chemical characteristics of soils vary extremely, a reagent that is suitable for extracting a nutrient from one group of soils may be of no value in estimating the availability of that nutrient in another group of soils. Therefore the reagents must be adapted to the element and to the soils to be tested.

Sometimes the same reagent may be used on different soils, but the interpretation of the test results must be changed for variations in soils, crop, and climate. Examples: Potassium is usually extracted with a salt solution, but phosphorus is usually extracted with a dilute acid or alkaline solution.

Dilute sulfuric acid as an extractant for phosphorus may give satisfactory results on acid soils but is not reliable on neutral or alkaline soils. A solution of sodium bicarbonate or a very dilute solution of hydrochloric acid with ammonium fluoride can be used to test for phosphorus in either acid or alkaline soils, but a given test value must be read differently for different soils.

Tests results must be reproducible—that is, if a soil sample is tested time and again, the same result should always be obtained. The laboratory techniques often are as important as the reagents used. The proportion of reagent to soil, the manner and time of agitation or contact with the soil, and often the temperature must be the same each time the procedure is repeated. Speed and cheapness are desirable in such tests, but not at the expense of accuracy.

Chemical tests are used widely to estimate needs for lime and the major fertilizer elements, nitrogen, phosphorus, and potassium.

THE NEED FOR LIME usually is estimated from the pH or reaction of the soil sample. The reaction may be determined with a pH meter or a colorimetric indicator.

A pH meter measures the electrical potential between two special electrodes. The magnitude of this potential is related to the pH. When the electrodes are placed in a soil-water suspension, the pH meter indicates the pH of the system.

Colorimetric indicators are compounds that have different colors at different pH's. For example, bromcresol green is yellow at pH 3.8 and blue at pH 5.4 and gradually changes from yellow to blue as the pH changes from 3.8 to 5.4. Other indicators change color over other pH intervals. By mixing suitable indicators with soil, the soil pH can be determined by the color that results.

The actual amount of acid present in a soil with a given pH depends upon its texture, the kind of clay in it, and its content of organic matter. These properties must be considered in addition to pH in estimating the need for lime.

The actual amount of acid in a sample of soil can be measured by titrating—measuring the amount of a standard base required to neutralize the acid in the soil.

Titrations are rather tedious and are seldom used in testing samples from farm fields. C. M. Woodruff, of the Missouri Agricultural Experiment Station, has developed a procedure to estimate the amount of acid by measuring the change in pH of a buffered solution—one that resists changes in pH—when the solution is mixed with the soil sample. This method is used in many soil-testing laboratories.

Some indirect methods of testing for the need for lime have been used in the past but are being discarded. One is the thiocyanate test. Soluble ferric iron in the soil reacts with thiocyanate to produce a red color. The intensity of the red color is a measure of the amount of soluble iron. The amount of ferric iron present depends somewhat on the degree of acidity of the soil.

In areas where soils have a low cation-exchange capacity, tests for exchangeable calcium and magnesium often are made to determine whether lime should be added to supply these nutrients.

Essentially all of the nitrogen in soils is present in the organic matter and must be changed to mineral form before plants can use it. Chemical tests to determine the ability of soils to supply nitrogen have been difficult to develop and standardize. Tests for the amount of nitrogen present in available forms at any one time usually are of little value in predicting nitrogen needs of a crop. Tests for the total amount of organic matter in certain soils have been used with some success. Scientists at the Iowa Agricultural

Experiment Station developed an incubation test to estimate the rate at which soil micro-organisms convert organic nitrogen to the nitrate—mineral—form. A moist sample of soil is incubated at 35° C. for 2 weeks. Then the nitrates produced during this period are washed out of the soil with water, and the amount is determined chemically. Correlations show a good relationship between the test results and crop response to nitrogen fertilizers on soils in Iowa.

An alkaline permanganate distillation procedure was developed by Emil Truog and others at the Wisconsin Agricultural Experiment Station. In this test, the amount of ammonia released from the soil during the distillation period is measured. The ammonia is assumed to be an estimate of the amount of nitrogen that will be converted most readily to available forms.

The forms of phosphorus present and their availability vary in different soils. Many reagents—water, carbon dioxide in water, different kinds and concentrations of acids, alkaline solutions, salts, and mixtures of these reagents—are used to extract phosphorus.

The phosphorus soluble in the reagent is extracted by adding the soil sample to the chemical solution, shaking it for a short time, and filtering. The amount of phosphorus extracted by the solution is determined by suitable chemical procedures. These procedures usually involve adding reagents that react with phosphorus to produce a characteristic color. The amount of color produced is determined by use of a photometer or by visual comparison with standard colors or solutions.

The amounts of potassium that can be replaced readily by another cation such as ammonium, sodium, or hydrogen, generally are considered to be a good estimate of potassium availability in soils. The amount of potassium replaced by another cation in many soils depends on the moisture content of the soil sample. Proper conditioning before testing is essential for a reliable test with such soils. Extracting the potassium from the soil is accomplished by mixing or leaching the soil sample with an acid or salt solution and determining the amount of potassium in the solution. The potassium in the solution may be determined with a flame photometer or it may be precipitated and the amount of precipitate determined. The precipitation procedure requires careful techniques. The temperature must be kept constant at some predetermined value.

Many laboratories make tests for soluble salts, calcium, magnesium, boron, and other elements.

Tests for soluble salts usually measure the electrical conductance of a soil-water suspension or a water extract of the soil. Soluble salts in water increase the electrical conductance.

Tests for calcium and magnesium usually measure the amount of them that is replaced by an exchange reaction with an acid or salt solution similar to potassium tests.

Boron tests involve extracting soils with hot water and measuring the water-soluble boron. Special boron-free glassware is required.

The reliability of any of these chemical tests depends on the data that have been obtained showing the relationship between the test results and results of experiments in the field.

We emphasize that all soil tests give relative values for nutrient availability and do not measure the pounds per acre of a nutrient that is available for crop use. Actually, the amount of a nutrient that is available to plants from any soil will vary from year to year. Moisture and temperature influence nutrient availability to plants, and with nutrients, such as phosphorus and potassium, a chemical equilibrium exists between the available and unavailable forms in the soil. As plants use the available form, more becomes available to them. Therefore the actual amount available depends on how effectively the plants absorb nutrients from the soil and how long the plants grow and take up nutrients.

Furthermore, only the surface soil commonly is tested—but crops get nutrients from as deep as their roots extend into the soil. Nutrient availability in the subsoil often is far different from that in the surface soil.

Thus a soil test value for phosphorus that shows 30 pounds of "available" phosphorus an acre in the surface soil does not mean that a crop can obtain 30 pounds of phosphorus from that soil. It is absurd, therefore, to make calculations of the type that indicate a given yield of a crop will require 50 pounds of phosphorus and that—because the soil test value is 30 pounds an acre—another 20 pounds of phosphorus should be added.

The soil test value is useful only as it is related to nutrient availability as measured by crop response to added nutrients.

Soil-testing laboratories in most States use chemical soil tests to estimate nutrient availability in farmers' fields.

Soil-testing kits are commercially available for testing soil samples. Individuals should be warned that the results obtained with these kits often are inaccurate. The reagents used in the kits may not give reliable results for the soils being tested. The interpretation of the test result may not apply to the soils being tested. Slight changes in the techniques followed in making the tests may result in serious errors in the results obtained.

PLANT TISSUE TESTS are valuable in evaluating the nutrient status of plants.

The chemical composition of plants varies according to the supply of nutrients available for their growth. The percentage of any nutrient in the plant follows a response curve as nutrient availability is increased. Because plants growing in the field reflect the effect of all factors that have influenced nutrient availability to the plant (including soil, climate, management, and characteristics of the plant itself), an analysis of the plant may provide information not obtained by analysis of soil samples. Tissue testing, as it is called,

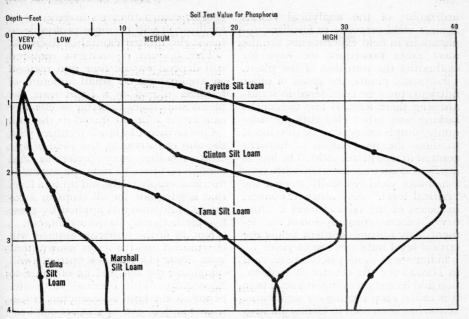

5. *The distribution of "available" phosphorus in the profiles of different soil types in Iowa. Because tests of surface soil samples do not reflect these differences between soil types, individual relationships must be developed between the soil test values and the crop response to added fertilizer for each soil type.*

is particularly useful in detecting mild deficiencies before they become acute and deficiency symptoms appear.

Tissue testing includes quick tests and accurate laboratory analyses.

Quick tests usually are made directly in the field and involve simple chemical tests that produce a color that is proportionate to the amount of certain soluble forms of the nutrient present. For example, one powder used to test for nitrogen changes from white to red in the presence of nitrate nitrogen. A pink color indicates a medium amount of nitrate in the plant. Such tests are usually made on the midribs or stalks of plants like corn and on the petioles or leaves of crops like potatoes or sugar beets. The test simply measures the amount of certain forms of the nutrient flowing in the "blood stream" of the plant. Nitrate nitrogen, phosphorus, and potassium lend themselves best to this technique.

The chemical determinations in the quick tests provide only semiquantita-

tive estimates of the amounts of a nutrient present in a particular form. The results for some nutrients, like nitrogen, are influenced by such factors as the time of day the tests are made. A person who knows how to use and interpret the tests can get much help from them in the diagnosis of nutrient deficiencies.

ACCURATE LABORATORY ANALYSES are used to determine quantitatively the nutrient content of some part of the plant—like the petioles or young leaves. These parts indicate most accurately the nutrient condition of the plant. Since nutrient contents of such plant parts generally change as the petioles or leaves age, the parts selected are usually chosen so they will be of the same age. Thus, for sugar beets, petioles of the most recently matured leaf are used. For fruit trees, young, but fully developed leaves of the current season's terminal growth are chosen.

Such analyses, coupled with standardization of the analytical results against yield response to fertilizer applications in field experiments, are the most exact procedure we have for evaluating the nutrition of the plant.

For some plants, the levels of other nutrients must be considered in standardizing these tests. If one element is lacking and other elements are adequate, simple curves can be developed to show the relationship of nutrient content to maximum yield. The lowest nutrient content associated with near maximum yield is usually termed the "critical level." Any nutrient content in excess of the critical level is "luxury"—excess—consumption of the element. Any nutrient content below the critical level indicates loss of yield.

Foliar—leaf—analysis has been used in Hawaii for the control of fertilization and irrigation of sugarcane. There it is called crop logging on sugarcane. It also has been used in California with sugar beets and citrus and deciduous fruits. Commercial laboratories collect the samples, make the analysis, and interpret the results. Foliar analysis shows considerable promise for other crops as research develops adequate methods and interpretations.

DETERMINING HOW MUCH nutrient materials to add is the practical goal in testing for nutrient availability.

A farmer wants to know what profit he can expect if he buys extra fertilizers. The tests therefore must be interpreted to estimate the increase in crop production that will result from additions of nutrients.

The amount of nutrients the farmer applies will be influenced by the amount of yield increase to be expected from applications of different amounts of the nutrient, the cost of the nutrient application, and the value of the crop produced.

When the farmer's capital is limited, the amount applied also depends on the returns to be expected from other enterprises on the farm. If, for example, the same amount of money invested in livestock will produce a greater return than an investment in fertilizer, it will be more profitable to invest the limited capital in livestock.

The amount of nutrient required will depend on the time and method of application. A small amount of fertilizer placed in a band near the plants sometimes may be as effective as a larger amount mixed in the soil.

One farmer may apply fertilizer with the aim of increasing the yield of one crop. Another may prefer to add enough fertilizer to raise the available nutrient supply in the soil up to a level that is adequate for all crops in a rotation. The amounts applied by these two methods may be quite different.

Not all of the nutrients applied will be utilized by the crop grown that year. Some of the added nutrients will remain in the soil and be of value to later crops. This residual value depends on the kind and amount of nutrients added, the method of application, characteristics of the soil, the cropping system, and climate. The residual value should be considered when deciding on the amount of nutrients to apply.

For some nutrients, particularly the trace elements, how much to add may not be important because the amount needed may cost little—but excessive amounts may be toxic to plants.

ONE MUST KNOW, then, not only how available the soil nutrients are but also how effective the added nutrients will be. Added nutrients do not have the same availability in all soils. Depending on the chemical properties of the soil, more or less of the added nutrient may react with the soil and be fixed in unavailable or less available forms. For any given type of soil, the effectiveness of added nutrients in increasing crop production can best be determined by field experiments in which different amounts of them are added.

Experiments that provide the needed information should include a wide range of amounts of nutrient applied from zero to amounts adequate to produce the maximum yield possible.

The experiments should also be designed to measure the residual value of the nutrient applications in succeeding years. Such experiments should be conducted on soils with different levels of nutrient availability for each different soil type, crop, and climatic condition.

Because such complete information seldom is available, the available data must be interpreted for the different conditions. Obviously this interpretation should be made by a person with knowledge of the effects of the various factors if the interpretation is to be reliable.

Different methods may be used in developing a relationship between the results of laboratory and greenhouse tests and the results obtained from field experiments. The objective of any of these methods is to develop a satisfactory relationship that can then be used to predict from test results what increase in crop production can be expected from added nutrients.

One method is based on the idea that a given level of nutrient availability in the soil will result in a relatively constant percentage of the yield that would have been obtained had the nutrient been present in adequate amounts. An example: The level of phosphorus availability in a soil may be such that it will result in only 60 percent of the yield possible had adequate phosphorus been applied. This may be 30 bushels on a soil that will produce 50 bushels an acre with adequate phosphorus or it may be 60 bushels an acre on a soil that will produce 100 bushels when enough phosphorus is applied.

Where this idea applies, percentage yields are essentially a method of expressing the yield data obtained in field experiments in terms of nutrient availability. This concept can be applied better to phosphorus and potassium in soils than to nitrogen.

Expressing the yields obtained in field experiments as percentage yields permits one to group the field experimental results from soils with different yield potentials into one correlation. Not all soils should be grouped together in one correlation, even if the percentage yields are used. Various factors influence nutrient availability in different types of soils, and the differences between soils may not be reflected in the laboratory or greenhouse test results. For example, if samples of only the surface soil are tested, differences in nutrient availability in the subsoils may be great but will not be reflected in the test results. Separate relationships should be developed for the different soil types. Furthermore, different correlations must be developed for different crops since the percentage yield at a given level of available nutrients varies for different crops.

Percentage yields do not indicate the actual increase in yield that can be obtained by adding nutrients. The use of percentage yields involves a step that need not be taken even though the correlations with test results are often better using percentage yields than actual yield increases.

A direct method that involves actual yield increases obtained in field experiments can be used (and should be used) for each group of similar soils even if relationships with percentage yields have been developed initially. Data must be available from a number of field experiments on a group of similar soil types that differ in nutrient availability.

A curve can be fitted to the data showing the relationship between the test results and the yield increases obtained for each rate of nutrient application. A graph can then be plotted of several such curves. The curves will indicate the yield increases to be expected at any test level from different rates of nutrient application.

This method has the advantage that the yield increase to be expected from different rates of application are estimated directly. It can be used for any nutrient as long as individual relationships are developed for different groups of soils of like yield potentials.

In view of the wide variety of soils, climatic conditions, crops grown, and methods of applying nutrients that influence test correlations and amounts of nutrients required, it is not surprising that adequate field experimental information is seldom available. Until such data are available, the interpretation of test results and the recommendations of how much nutrient to add should be made by someone with a good knowledge of soils and soil fertility.

Knowledge of the soils being tested, the nutrient requirements of the crops grown, and the effect of various factors on nutrient availability under different conditions permits extension of the available information to various situations for which adequate data are not available. Lack of such knowledge may lead to errors in recommendations.

When properly interpreted, tests of nutrient availability in soils can be used to predict yield increases to be expected from nutrient applications. This is basic information the farmer needs, but he must also consider other factors before he can reach a logical decision as to how much of the nutrients to apply.

Several books about the deficiencies of various elements may give further help. Among them are *Hunger Signs in Crops—A Symposium*, published by the American Society of Agronomy and the National Fertilizer Association, Washington, D. C., and edited by Gove Hambidge; *Visual Symptoms of Malnutrition in Plants*, written by J. E. McMurtrey, Jr., and published as chapter 8 in *Diagnostic Techniques for Soils and Crops* by the American Potash Institute, Washington, D. C., in 1948; and *Diagnosis of Mineral Deficiencies in Plants by Visual Symptoms*, written by T. Wallace and published by The Chemical Publishing Co., New York, in 1953.

Further information on the use of quick tissue tests is given in *Plant Tissue Tests as a Tool for Agronomic Research*, by B. A. Krantz, W. L. Nelson, and L. F. Burkhart, 1948, in the book, *Diagnostic Techniques for Soils and Crops*, and *The Purdue Soil and Plant Tissue Tests*, by A. J. Ohlrogge, Purdue University Agricultural Experiment Station Bulletin 584, published in 1952.

Soil Reaction and Liming

K. Lawton and L. T. Kurtz

A farmer in the Midwest who plans to grow alfalfa probably will have his soil tested because he knows that alfalfa grows poorly or not at all in strongly acid soils.

But when he selects ornamentals to landscape his home he might find the soil not acid enough to grow acid-loving plants like azaleas.

He knows generally that most of the common field crops grow well in slightly acid soils: When he limes to grow alfalfa he will have favorable soil reaction for corn and soybeans.

But many soils of humid areas naturally are too acid for the maximum production of many field crops. Many crops and plants grow best only if the soil reaction is suitable. Adjustment of soil acidity to the proper level often is important in good management.

Liming to reduce soil acidity is an extensive and routine practice in most of the eastern half of the United States. Soil acidity develops gradually in humid regions as the calcium and magnesium are slowly lost from the soil by leaching and is speeded by crop removals and by use of the soil.

Soils in the western Great Plains and in dry regions usually are neutral or slightly alkaline, rather than acid. Liming there is seldom necessary and often is harmful. The natural high-lime condition in some places contributes to nutritional disorder and poor production of some crops. Lime-induced chlorosis of fruit trees is an example.

Location is not a sure indication that

a soil needs lime. Although soils of the Eastern States generally need liming, the degree of acidity varies, and scattered areas of naturally calcareous soils—neutral to moderately alkaline—occur from Florida to Iowa. They may be a result of calcareous soil material or perhaps are shelly-spots associated with ancient lakes or marshes.

Many soils naturally are extremely acid, and only poor yields of field crops can be obtained on them even if fertility is adequate. They need moderate liming to correct soil acidity for maximum yields of corn and small grains.

Additional liming to a slightly acid or neutral range is necessary for maximum yields of other crops, particularly alfalfa and some other legumes.

Besides their value as crops, legumes are associated with nodule bacteria (rhizobia) and so can supply much of the nitrogen needed by following crops. Liming then influences the legume crops and also nitrogen fertility.

Before nitrogen fertilizers were readily available on the market, legumes were necessary in almost all systems of farming. Fixation through legumes was the one way to add nitrogen to the soil. Liming to encourage good growth of legumes used to receive more attention than now.

Availability of nitrogen from sources other than legumes should not detract very much from emphasis on the need for lime. Liming has been recommended for some sections on a fairly scientific basis for 50 years, but half of the acreage in these areas would still benefit from liming.

BENEFITS FROM LIMING result from more than mere reduction of soil acidity. Two major plant nutrients, calcium and magnesium, are supplied by liming materials. Soils that have too little calcium and magnesium for best plant growth often are highly acid. Liming may supply calcium and magnesium and correct the soil acidity at the same time.

Calcium and magnesium are removed in crops in large amounts, and those removals, along with leaching, contribute to the gradual development of acidity, a normal soil process in humid areas.

Finely ground limestone is the liming material used in many sections. Calcium carbonate is the active agent in limestone for reducing soil acidity. The calcium carbonate reacts with and neutralizes the soil acidity. The calcium then becomes part of the soil supply that can be utilized by plants.

Dolomitic limestone contains magnesium carbonate and calcium carbonate and therefore supplies magnesium, another nutrient. Even some of the high-calcium limestones contain significant percentages of magnesium.

Basic slag, a byproduct of the steel industry, is an important liming material in some regions, particularly in the Southeast. Calcium silicate is the active ingredient in the neutralization.

Marl and chalk are soft, impure forms of limestone and are sometimes liming materials.

Oyster shells, in which the neutralizing agent is calcium carbonate, also are used.

Hydrated lime and burned lime, which contain calcium hydroxide and calcium oxide, are effective but usually are more expensive and are not applied very extensively. They supply little magnesium.

OTHER BENEFITS, besides neutralizing soil acidity and supplying nutrients, may result from liming.

Regulation of soil acidity is a means of controlling some crop diseases. An example is potato scab, which is less severe in acid soils.

Liming influences the solubility of many compounds in the soil. Large amounts of iron, aluminum, and manganese may come into solution in a strongly acid soil and may be adsorbed on the surface of the soil particle in a form that plants can easily take up. Sometimes high levels of easily soluble manganese and aluminum are believed to be toxic to crops—a condition that liming can correct.

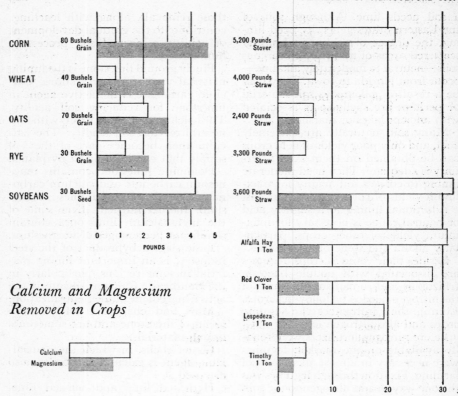

Calcium and Magnesium Removed in Crops

1. Losses of calcium and magnesium vary with climate, soil permeability, soil acidity, fertility, and cropping practices. The figures here were obtained by R. S. Stauffer, of the University of Illinois, from uncropped lysimeters containing undisturbed soil profiles.

Liming influences the form of phosphorus in the soil. Phosphates are believed to react in highly acid soils with the active iron and aluminum to form complex substances. Calcium is the dominant ion on the surface of the soil particle in properly limed soils, and the phosphates apparently can be utilized more readily. In alkaline soils, phosphates react with the surface of calcium carbonate particles and crops utilize them less readily.

Myriad bacteria, fungi, and other kinds of micro-organisms abound in fertile soils. Some of the organisms are active in the decay of crop residues and manures in the soil. Decay processes release some of the nitrogen, phosphorus, and other mineral nutrients from these residues for subsequent crops. The activity of the micro-organisms and consequently the phosphorus and nitrogen fertility generally increase when an acid soil is limed.

The solubilities of iron, manganese, phosphorus, copper, zinc, and boron generally are less in alkaline soils than in slightly acid soils. But molybdenum is more soluble in alkaline soils than in acid soils, and liming may result in increased uptake of this micronutrient by crops. Some concern that liming may cause a deficiency of some nutrients or a toxic excess of molybdenum is probably warranted for a few soils.

Liming to adjust the soil to a slightly acid or near-neutral reaction will not induce deficiencies of phosphorus or the micronutrients in most soils and cropping situations. Underliming is far more common than overliming. If a deficiency of boron or phosphorus is induced by recommended applications of lime materials, the soils probably were already near the borderline and would soon have needed phosphate or borax fertilizers anyway.

Excessive liming should be avoided, of course. Overliming is less likely on silt or clay soils than on sandy soils. Medium-textured and heavy-textured soils of the middle States have a high capacity for lime. Sandy soils and highly weathered soils have low capacities and are more easily overlimed. Soil organic matter also has a high capacity for lime.

Frequency of liming varies with climate, soil, and cropping practices. Soils of heavy texture may require reliming only once in 10 years. Applications on other soils should be made oftener. The need for reliming—like the need for initial liming—can best be determined by testing the soil.

THE ACIDITY in most soils is on the surface of the soil particles. An acid soil should not be thought of as a mixture of inert soil particles in a solution of dilute acid. The acid ions stick almost completely to the surface of the soil particles.

This ability to hold cations on the particle surfaces resides chiefly in the clay, fine silt, and organic matter. Coarser particles have little ability to hold cations in this exchangeable form.

The exchange capacity of a soil under natural conditions is occupied with ions of hydrogen (acid), calcium, magnesium, potassium, and sometimes sodium. If a large proportion of the exchange capacity is occupied by hydrogen, the soil is acid and liming is needed. Liming will be unnecessary if a high proportion of the exchange capacity is occupied by calcium and magnesium.

This exchange capacity of many soils in nature is more than half-filled with acid ions. Such soils are extremely acid. Liming materials furnish calcium

2. *A line dividing the humid from the subhumid sections indicates where soil processes tend to develop acid soils.*

and magnesium to replace and neutralize the acidity.

A liming material must neutralize the hydrogen and furnish calcium and magnesium. Calcium sulfate (gypsum) supplies calcium but is not effective as a liming material. The carbonates or silicates of calcium and magnesium are effective because the activity of the acid is essentially eliminated in the reaction between the liming materials and the soil acidity.

In a well-limed agricultural soil, about 80 to 90 percent of the exchange capacity is ordinarily occupied with calcium plus magnesium; there are about 5 to 10 times as many calcium ions as magnesium ions. Potassium may be expected to occupy 2 to 5 percent of the capacity, and hydrogen (acid) the rest. Critical values for the balance among these ions have not been set, although normal ranges are well established.

To ASSIST in determining needs for lime and fertilizers, soil-testing laboratories are operated in every State through the agricultural experiment stations and extension service. Soil-testing services also are available from many private companies and consulting services. Tests to indicate the lime needs of farm soils and recommendations for method and time of application are made.

Methods of sampling, costs of testing, and operations vary in different States, but the county agent or local extension representative has information for ob-

Annual Losses of Calcium and Magnesium
From Soil by Leaching

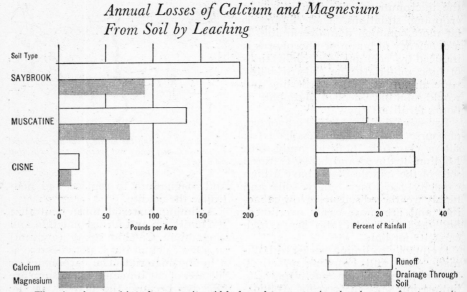

3. *The mineral composition of crops varies widely from the amounts given here because of crop maturity of the crop and differences in soils, varieties, climate, and seasons. Ratios between the grain and nongrain portions of the crop also vary.*

taining tests and making recommendations about liming.

Two general methods, with many modifications, are used in most States to determine the need for lime. A widely used method is based on the determination of the pH of a soil-water mixture. The other general method is to measure the amount of acidity exchanged from the soil sample when it reacts with a standard buffer solution.

The pH of the soil-water mixture usually is determined electrometrically with a glass electrode manufactured to be sensitive to only hydrogen ions. The procedure is standardized at a narrow (1:1, 1:2, or sometimes 1:5) soil-solution ratio.

Color indicators are also used satisfactorily for determining pH in many soil-testing laboratories. These indicators are dyes that change color according to the acidity present so that the color indicates the "free" acidity or pH of the soil. The litmus test, one of the early tests for soil acidity, was based on this principle.

Indicators now in use have wide changes in color. The color may be yellow in acid soils, green in neutral soils, or blue in slightly alkaline soils. Mixtures of dyes are prepared to give enough color change so that several steps of acidity can be read. Indicators have been formulated in liquid or powder or impregnated in paper strips.

The determination of the pH does not give a direct measure of the amount of exchangeable acidity but only the "free" or ionized acidity. Therefore pH must be interpreted by the soil technician to make a recommendation of an amount of lime. Soils containing considerable clay and organic matter need more lime than do sandy or highly weathered soils of the same pH level. Texture and organic matter content consequently are often taken into account when making recommendations for lime. Sometimes the type of clay also is considered.

Methods have been designed to measure all of the exchangeable acidity. The soil sample is allowed to react with a solution that is especially formulated to react with the soil acidity. The amount of acid released from the soil to this buffer solution can be measured and expressed as the amount of limestone needed.

A method of this type was developed by C. M. Woodruff, of the University of Missouri, and is used in many soil-testing laboratories in this country. The buffer solution, when mixed with the soil, lowers in pH by one-tenth of a unit for each half ton of lime required by the soil. In the laboratory, the soil sample is mixed with the solution and allowed to stand while the reaction takes place. The electrodes of the Missouri Limemeter are then placed in the mixture of the soil and buffer and the amount of limestone needed per acre is read from that instrument. The Missouri Limemeter is a special type of pH meter for use with this procedure.

In Arizona, Colorado, Idaho, New Mexico, North Dakota, South Dakota, Utah, and Wyoming, the lime requirement is not determined routinely on soil samples because only rare soils are sufficiently acid to need liming.

FARMERS AND GROWERS in most sections usually can buy a number of forms of lime. Each material neutralizes soil acidity, supplies calcium, and leaves no harmful residue in the soil. In this sense, calcium sulfate (gypsum) and calcium chloride do not qualify as liming materials even though they are more soluble forms of calcium than those considered as lime.

The selection of a liming material generally is based on its availability, the price per unit of calcium and magnesium, convenience in handling, and (in special cases) its rate of reaction with soil or its magnesium content.

The capacity of a liming material to neutralize soil acidity is expressed as its neutralizing value (N.V.), usually in terms of calcium carbonate as 100.

Because of the existence of forms of lime other than carbonates and the presence of impurities, the neutralizing value of commercial liming materials may run below 50 percent and as high as 200 percent.

Most high-calcium limestones and other natural forms of lime have neutralizing values between 75 and 95 percent. When appreciable amounts of magnesium carbonate (N.V. 119 percent), calcium hydroxide (N.V. 135 percent), calcium oxide (N.V. 178 percent), or magnesium oxide (N.V. 250 percent) are present, the neutralizing value of the lime source will be greater than 100 percent.

All liming materials can be classified in four forms, including carbonate, oxide, hydrate, and silicate compounds of calcium and magnesium. Ground limestone makes up more than 95 percent of all lime used in the United States, but a number of other liming materials are quite satisfactory.

This group of materials includes slag, marl, chalk, shells, and certain refuse and byproduct limes. Many of them occur naturally and are relatively inexpensive near their source.

Limestone is a sedimentary deposit. In rock form it consists of calcium and magnesium carbonates. It is widely distributed over the United States, and surface formations can be quarried and crushed rather easily. Limestone therefore is by far the commonest and one of the cheapest sources of lime. Deposits that consist almost entirely of calcium carbonate are called calcitic limestone. Those that contain magnesium carbonate up to almost 50 percent are referred to as dolomitic or high-magnesium limestone. As a rule, the dolomitic material has a higher neutralizing value, is a harder stone, and does not decompose so rapidly in acid soils as calcitic limestone. If these materials contain less than 80 percent by weight of calcium carbonate equivalent, they are considered low grade.

Marl is calcium carbonate that was deposited through chemical precipitation of calcium or by the biological action of certain aquatic plants and shell-forming animals in shallow lakes and swamps. It generally occurs as a soft, earthy, or mushlike material in layers or beds a few inches to many feet thick and overlying sand, clay, or areas of peat or muck. Small amounts of magnesium carbonate and quantities of clay, sand, and organic matter may be present in marl. The neutralizing value of a good marl is considered to be 90 to 95 percent on a dry basis. As a rule of thumb, 2 cubic yards of marl is equivalent in neutralizing soil acidity to a ton of ground limestone. Deposits in Michigan, Wisconsin, Minnesota, Ohio, Washington, and other States generally contain considerable moisture and must be excavated with power shovels, draglines, and scoops.

Shells constitute a small (but sometimes important) local source of calcium carbonate. Ground or burned oyster shells are used extensively as a liming material in parts of Delaware, Maryland, and New Jersey. Neutralizing values as high as 95 percent have been reported for some shell piles. Dust from the manufacture of buttons also has been used in a few places.

Refuse-lime includes a number of byproducts of the chemical industry, purification sludges from agricultural processing plants, and lime used in water-softening processes. Some of them contain both calcium carbonate and hydroxide. Others are referred to as precipitated or finely divided calcium carbonate. Most of these sources of discard lime, including those of sugar beet and water-softening plants, paper mills, and other industries generally have such a high content of water that they are hard to handle and spread.

Piles of refuse-lime from gasworks and acetylene plants may contain sulfur impurities and traces of gas, which may injure seeds. On exposure to air, however, the sulfides are oxidized quickly to sulfates, and the gases escape in a short time.

Refuse-lime, which has a high neutralizing value, often can be obtained at little or no cost. Labor and transportation costs and the size of the pile may determine the extent of their use in a locality.

The oxide form of lime is sold under such names as burned lime, quicklime, caustic lime, lump lime, and unslaked lime. It is produced commercially by heating any form of calcium or magnesium carbonate, driving off the carbon dioxide, and leaving oxides of calcium and magnesium. This material is caustic and disagreeable to handle. Its neutralizing value is 150 to 185, according to the impurities in it, its percentage of magnesium, and the completeness of burning.

Burned lime that comes in contact with moisture becomes slaked. In this process, the oxides of calcium and magnesium take on water and become hydroxides. Other commercial names for it are hydrated lime, slaked lime, caustic lime, and agricultural hydrate. Like the oxide, it is usually marketed in bags as a fine powder. Hydrated lime has the objectionable characteristics of burned lime, but it reacts quickly with acid soils.

Calcium hydroxide has a theoretical neutralizing value of 135, but that of the commercial product usually is 125 to 145, because it contains some carbonates and possibly oxides, depending on the degree of slaking.

Only a small amount of oxide and hydrate is used for liming purposes, but their advantage over ground limestone is the rapid rate of reaction with soil. The National Lime Association estimated in 1948 that about 1.2 percent of the total tonnage of all lime used came from this source.

Wood ashes have some use as a liming material, although they are relatively scarce. Their rather low neutralizing value ranges from 30 to 70 percent, expressed as calcium carbonate. The ash of hardwoods, such as maple, elm, oak, and beech, contains about one-third more calcium than the ash of softwoods. Freshly burned wood ashes contain calcium mainly as the oxide, but, on exposure to moisture, they are largely in the carbonate form by the time they are applied to soil.

Coal ash has little or no liming value and benefits ascribed to it are probably a result of improvement in the physical condition of soil.

Blast furnace and basic slags (byproducts in the smelting of iron ore) and calcium silicate slag (from rock phosphate reduction furnaces) are satisfactory liming materials. At furnace heats, silica in iron ore and rock phosphate combines with calcium of the limestone or phosphate rock to form calcium silicate. This compound breaks down in acid soils to liberate calcium and metasilicic acid. Slag must be finely ground if it is to be effective. A typical basic slag contains 6 to 10 percent of calcium silicate, 40 to 50 percent of calcium oxide, 4 to 5 percent of magnesium oxide, and 5 to 20 percent of phosphoric oxide.

Experiments comparing slag and limestone in several Southeastern States indicate that slag contains enough boron to raise yields of several legumes more than limestone does.

THE QUALITY of a liming material is determined by purity and fineness.

The rate of reaction with soil is essentially a function of the size of the lime particle and (to a lesser extent) the type of liming material and the degree of mixing with the soil. The finer the lime, the greater is its specific surface, and consequently the more rapid are the changes brought about by liming.

Burned lime, agricultural hydrate, and refuse-lime normally have a very fine texture and require no grinding. Particles of limestone and basic slag larger than those passing an 8-mesh sieve, however, dissolve very slowly even in strongly acid soils. Almost all States require that at least 80 percent or more of the material pass through a sieve that has 8 to 10 meshes to the square inch.

When limestone rock is crushed, ground, and coarse-screened, a material ranging from coarse particles to dust is produced. The relative proportion of coarse, medium, and fine particles determines its reactivity. Because the cost of grinding increases as fineness increases, however, it is not practical to grind all limestone to pass, say, a 50- or 60-mesh sieve—a fineness that would make almost all of it available within 3 years.

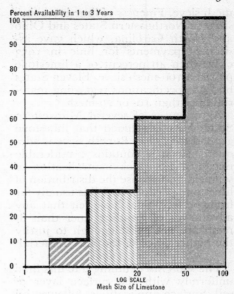

4. *The relative availability of ground limestone, as influenced by its particle or mesh size.*

Many farmers have used agricultural meal, a common grade of limestone of medium fineness, of which 95 percent or more will pass an 8-mesh sieve and 25 percent or more will pass a 100-mesh sieve. In some types of farming, such as truck gardening, a fine lime is desired, especially for rapid reaction. Pulverized limestone, 65 percent or more of which passes a 100-mesh sieve, or hydrated lime may then be used.

Dolomitic limestone, which is less soluble than calcitic stone, commonly is ground fine for agricultural use.

Some agronomists believe that much of the agricultural limestone has been too coarse to produce the desired effects of liming, and that finer grinding is practical, because grinding is only a small part of the total cost of limestone delivered and spread.

In the Agricultural Conservation Program, the specifications of 16 States for standard ground limestone require that 25 percent or more of the material must pass a 100-mesh sieve. Five States have set a requirement of 30 to 50 percent of the total to pass a 60-

mesh sieve. Fineness of lime is emphasized in Northeastern States and Ohio and North Carolina, which gave assistance payments for lime in 1953 only when 40 percent of a limestone passed a 100-mesh sieve. Eleven States had no specifications regarding material finer than 10- or 20-mesh.

Agronomists of several Midwestern States have concluded that limestone ground to pass an 8-mesh sieve is adequate, since it contains considerable fine dust for quick neutralization of soil acidity. Because the distribution of limestone particles in soil is usually far from perfect, they have felt that any advantages of grinding finer than 8-mesh are not great enough to justify the higher price of the finer material.

THE MAIN AIM of liming is to mix lime uniformly with the surface layer of soil. Surface applications, followed by plowing or disking and harrowing, accomplish that aim most easily. Tillage is necessary because calcium from lime applied to the surface moves downward very slowly in most soils. Surface liming of pastures also is a recommended practice, especially before renovation. A few reports have indicated that finely divided limestone applied in the row for crops like soybeans on acid soils increase yields markedly.

Technicians generally recommend that limestone be applied at least 6 months to a year before seeding legumes, especially when a field is limed for the first time because young alfalfa and clover need abundant calcium.

Lime may be applied at any time of the year on land plowed for cultivated crops in the spring where small grains and legumes are to follow; on land plowed for winter grain with a legume to follow; on land following harvest of cultivated crops; on sod ground before plowing for a cultivated crop; and on permanent pasture.

Lime is spread by trucks, two-wheeled lime or fertilizer distributors, and endgate lime spreaders. Most of the lime is spread by custom operators. Trucks equipped with V-shaped beds and centrifugal spreaders at the rear are used for hauling and spreading.

Lime can be applied in that way on plowed ground, but many truckers prefer to spread lime on sod, pasture, or cultivated crops after the harvest. Applications in late summer or fall are usually most convenient, because then the roads and fields are generally in a good condition.

In places where hydrated or burned lime is applied or when lime is shipped in by railroad car and when weather conditions prevent the use of heavy trucks, a two-wheeled, box-type spreader is commonly used. Some equipment, designed for lime or fertilizer, can haul more than 1,000 pounds and apply lime at the rate of 2 tons an acre.

Grain drills equipped with fertilizer compartments can be used to apply small amounts of lime at seeding time or in a separate operation, but they cannot be used for materials high in moisture, such as marl.

The endgate spreader attached to the end of a wagon box has been used to spread lime. Special attachments of this type are available for manure spreaders. Many dairy farmers mix limestone with manure before loading or dump lime on the top or bottom of a load of manure. Up to 200 pounds of limestone to a ton of manure may be spread without a special operation.

MORE THAN 400 million tons of limestone were used in 35 States in the period 1930–1954. The ten North Central States used about 3.5 times as much lime as any other region. Second highest in the use of lime were the East Central States. Next were the Northeastern States and the Gulf States.

The Northeast, East Central, and North Central States increased their limestone consumption 5, 6.5, and 12 times, respectively, from 1930–1935 to 1950–1954, but a 58-fold increase occurred in the Gulf States.

The total tonnage used in Illinois in 25 years was almost double the amount used in any other State. Indiana, Ohio, Iowa, Wisconsin, and Missouri each used 30 million to 40 million tons in 1930–1945. Pennsylvania and Kentucky each used about 21 million tons of limestone.

Assistance payments for liming as a soil conserving practice, together with an improvement in farm income and an intensive educational program, boosted limestone consumption from less than 4 million tons in 1935 to more than 30 million tons in 1947. Between 1940 and 1949, 80 to 95 percent of the limestone used in most States was bought under an assistance program. In 1954 less than 67 percent of lime was purchased through the Agricultural Conservation Program.

The amount used has dropped since 1947; less than 20 million tons of agricultural limestone were used in 1954.

Our agricultural soils still need large amounts of lime. Agronomists of land-grant colleges and universities in 37 States estimated in 1956 that 161 million acres would be improved by liming. They estimated that the lime required for those soils in 1956 on a corrective basis (rather than an annual basis) would be more than 332 million tons, or an average application per acre of slightly more than 2 tons. If the total figure is compared with the 407 million tons of limestone used in 1930–1954, the actual lime requirement for maximum crop production is about 80 percent of the amount used then.

Data compiled by the National Agricultural Limestone Institute indicated that the limestone tonnage for the Nation in 1954 was only 23.5 percent of the annual needs. On that basis, about 80 million tons of lime would be required annually.

Legal regulations control the quality of limestone that is sold. A number of States include restrictions on liming materials in their fertilizer laws. Others group lime with fertilizer, regulating both as agricultural minerals.

About half the States have laws that apply to specific agricultural liming materials and generally list the materials that qualify as lime. Almost all States require the licensing of manu-

facturers, dealers, and importers, and the labeling of their products.

Bagged or packaged materials generally must carry the name, brand or trademark, the name and address of the manufacturer, the minimum neutralizing value in terms of calcium carbonate or calcium oxide, and the percentages of the total material that will pass certain screens.

The purchaser of lot or bulk material usually receives an invoice or waybill bearing such guarantees.

Few States have set up legal limitations as to the purity and fineness of liming materials. Delaware, Maryland, Rhode Island, and Wisconsin have laws establishing required degrees of purity. Alabama, North Carolina, Ohio, Rhode Island, Virginia, and Wisconsin have set up legal standards of fineness for one or more grades of liming material.

The specifications for lime set by the Agricultural Conservation Program have brought considerable uniformity to standards of fineness and neutralizing value. In order to qualify in this program, lime must pass the specifications set up by State committees of the Agricultural Conservation Program. For instance, 15 States have set a minimum neutralizing value of 80 percent for standard ground limestone, 8 States have legalized a minimum level of 85 percent, and 12 States require a neutralizing value of at least 89.2 percent calcium carbonate equivalent.

In States where marl and refuse-lime from sugar beet factories, paper mills, and water-softening establishments are sold, a minimum of 70 percent on a dry basis is commonly accepted. Since these materials are often sold on a volume basis, the ACP specifications of several States require that a cubic yard contain 800 pounds of calcium carbonate. Carbide refuse-lime must have a neutralizing value of 85 percent.

The minimum neutralizing value for blast furnace slag is quite variable in six or seven States where it is distributed. One State accepts slag as low as 70 percent calcium carbonate equivalent.

Trends in Fertilizers

J. Richard Adams

Many changes have occurred in the manufacture and use of fertilizers since 1939. The annual use of fertilizers in the United States reached a peak of 23,412,608 tons in 1953, and declined the next 2 years, although more plant nutrients were applied.

Consumption almost tripled in the period 1939–1953, and increases were recorded each year except 1950. A slight decrease then was followed by further decreases in 1954 and 1955. (Unless otherwise noted, the years cited in this chapter are the 12 months ending on June 30.)

About two-thirds of all fertilizers used since 1939 have been mixed fertilizers. This ratio has remained relatively constant. The annual consumption of mixed fertilizers almost tripled between 1939 and 1953 and then declined the next 2 years.

Farmers in New England (Maine, New Hampshire, Vermont, Massachusetts, Rhode Island, and Connecticut), Middle Atlantic States (New York, New Jersey, Pennsylvania, Delaware, District of Columbia, Maryland, and West Virginia), and South Atlantic States (Virginia, North Carolina, South Carolina, Georgia, and Florida) used more than half the mixed fertilizers consumed in 1945 and slightly less than half in 1955. The drop was due to a decrease in New England and to smaller percentage increases in the Atlantic

Coast regions than in most of the other regions. Annual consumption in the North Central States (Ohio, Indiana, Illinois, Michigan, Wisconsin, Minnesota, Iowa, Missouri, North Dakota, South Dakota, Nebraska, and Kansas) increased 156 percent. The combined increase in the Middle Atlantic and South Atlantic States was 40 percent.

The annual consumption of separate materials—individual products that contain one or more plant nutrients and are applied directly to the soil—reached 7,375,855 tons in 1955. Materials supplying one or more of the primary nutrients—nitrogen (N), available phosphoric oxide (P_2O_5), and potash (K_2O)—accounted for approximately 90 percent of the separate materials. The remaining 10 percent included the secondary and trace nutrient materials. The use of the combined classes of separate materials increased more than 70 percent between 1945 and 1955. The greatest increase occurred in the West North Central and Western States (Montana, Idaho, Wyoming, Colorado, New Mexico, Arizona, Utah, Nevada, Washington, Oregon, and California), while their use in New England and the Middle Atlantic region decreased. Annual consumption in 1954 in the East North Central States (Ohio, Indiana, Illinois, Michigan, and Wisconsin) was more than double the consumption in 1945 and then declined sharply in 1955. Consumption more than doubled in the Pacific region (Washington, Oregon, and California) from 1945 to 1955 and was greater for a number of years than the consumption in any other region.

Use in the United States of separate materials containing primary nutrients increased continuously between 1945 and 1953, after which there was a small drop. Since 1951 the largest tonnage of these materials has been used in the Pacific region. The only other region that used more than a million tons in 1955 was the South Atlantic States. The New England and Middle Atlantic regions were the only ones to show a decrease between 1945 and 1955.

Data on the consumption of secondary nutrient materials are limited to materials supplying sulfur, calcium, or magnesium and refer only to products not containing primary nutrients. The data have been recorded separately only since 1945. (Liming materials, which supply both calcium and magnesium, are not included, as they are considered to be soil amendments rather than fertilizers.) Gypsum was included as a fertilizer material, although most of the tonnage was used to improve alkaline soils, not as a fertilizer. The same was true of sulfur and sulfuric acid.

Between 400,000 and 900,000 tons of gypsum, sulfur, and sulfuric acid are consumed annually. This accounts for almost 100 percent of the tonnage of secondary materials consumed in the United States. The major part of this tonnage is used in the Pacific region. A few thousand tons of magnesium carbonate (mostly in the Pacific region) and smaller amounts of magnesium sulfate (mostly in South Atlantic States) have been used as separate materials. Large additional amounts of these secondary nutrients are supplied in the primary nutrient materials and mixed fertilizers.

The annual consumption of materials supplying manganese, copper, boron, and zinc has never exceeded 25 thousand tons and generally amounts to less than 10 thousand tons. A few thousand tons of borax have been used annually in the United States, mostly in the Coastal States and East North Central States. The major quantities of iron and zinc are used in the Pacific region. The use of manganese is centered in the East North Central States; they and the South Atlantic and Pacific States use most of the copper salts.

THE TOTAL CONSUMPTION of the three primary nutrients almost quadrupled between 1939 and 1955. The increase was continuous for each of the nutrients except in 1954, when there was a slight drop in the consumption of available phosphoric oxide. The rates of increase in use of nitrogen and potash since 1950 were greater than for any previous period since 1939. They exceeded the rate of increase in the consumption of available phosphoric oxide, with a consequent narrowing of the $N-P_2O_5-K_2O$ ratio, which was 1.0–1.9–1.1 in 1950 and 1.0–1.2–1.0 in 1954.

Consumption increases of each of the three primary nutrients, in terms of weight, from 1939 to 1955 were surprisingly uniform. The percentage increases in nitrogen and potash were much greater than that of phosphoric oxide. Total consumption of nitrogen increased 410 percent; potash, 370; and phosphoric oxide, 192 percent.

Mixed fertilizers accounted for almost three-fourths of the increased tonnage of nutrients in 1955 relative to 1939. In that period, a drop occurred in the proportion of nitrogen in mixed fertilizers relative to the total consumption in the United States, and the relative proportion of available phosphoric oxide and potash increased.

REGIONAL TRENDS in the use of primary nutrients exhibit interesting variations. The total consumption more than doubled between 1945 and 1955, brought about by increases in the use of each of the three primary nutrients. The rate of increase in consumption of nitrogen was more than triple that of available phosphoric oxide, while potash consumption increased a little more than twice as fast as the use of available phosphoric oxide.

Farmers in the East North Central region accounted for almost a third of the increased consumption of nutrients in the United States. They used more nutrients in 1953, 1954, and 1955 than those in the South Atlantic region, the leaders in previous years.

Mixtures supplied more than three-fourths of the increased nutrient consumption in the East North Central region, and only a little less than 90 percent in the South Atlantic region. Separate materials supplied more than half the increases in the West South Central, Mountain, and Pacific re-

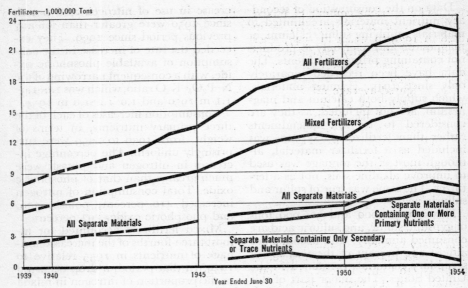

Fertilizers—1,000,000 Tons

All Fertilizers

Mixed Fertilizers

All Separate Materials

Separate Materials Containing One or More Primary Nutrients

All Separate Materials

Separate Materials Containing Only Secondary or Trace Nutrients

1939   1940   1945   1950   1954
Year Ended June 30

1. Consumption of fertilizer in the United States and Territories.

gions. The Middle Atlantic region showed a decrease over the 11-year period in the amount of nutrients distributed as separate materials, but this was more than compensated for by the increased quantity supplied by mixed fertilizers. There was a lower nutrient consumption in New England since the increased consumption of nutrients in mixed fertilizers was not sufficient to offset the decreased consumption of nutrients in the separate materials.

The South Atlantic region used almost 50 percent more nitrogen in 1955 than either the West North Central or East North Central regions. Consumption increased more than 900 percent since 1945 in the North Central States and somewhat more than 70 percent in the South Atlantic region. All other regions used greater amounts of nitrogen in 1955 than in 1945. The consumption in the Territories fell off some after 1951, but increased about 80 percent in the 11 years.

As with nitrogen, the South Atlantic States annually consumed a greater tonnage of available phosphoric oxide than any other region until 1953, when

it was surpassed by the East North Central region. Consumption of available phosphoric oxide has increased more rapidly in the North Central States since 1945 than in any other region. Since 1951, the use of available phosphoric oxide fell off in all regions except the North Central, Mountain, and Pacific. The decrease in New England was sufficient to reduce consumption in 1955 below 1945.

The East North Central and South Atlantic regions consumed almost 60 percent of all the potash used annually in the United States in 1955 and at least two to three times as much as was used in any of the other regions. Annual consumption in the South Atlantic region was greater than in any other region until 1952, when it was surpassed by consumption in the East North Central region. Annual consumption in the East North Central region more than doubled in the 5-year period after 1950.

The content of primary nutrients, or concentration, of fertilizers increased slowly from 19.78 percent in 1939 to 20.06 percent in 1947, and then at an accelerated rate to 26.93 percent in

1955. The nutrient content of mixed fertilizers rose more rapidly, from 19.28 in 1939 to 21.44 in 1947, after which it substantially paralleled the rate of increase in all fertilizers to 27.90 in 1955.

The weighted-average nitrogen and potash contents of all fertilizers increased 78 and 64 percent, respectively, from 1939 to 1955. The content of available phosphoric oxide increased in the 1940's but dropped later, so that the average content in 1955 was less than 2 percent higher than in 1939. Increases were noted in the concentration of each plant nutrient in mixed fertilizers.

The greatest changes in the content of primary nutrients in mixed fertilizers between 1945 and 1955 took place in the North Central States. The concentration in the eastern part of the region increased from 23.78 percent to 34.30, and in the western part from 24.08 to 36.49.

The increases were brought about by increases in each of the three nutrients, but the magnitude of the changes was not the same. The $N-P_2O_5-K_2O$ ratio in the East North Central region changed from 1.0–6.0–4.4 to 1.0–3.1–3.2, and in the West North Central region from 1.0–5.9–4.2 to 1.0–2.4–1.5. The nutrient content of mixed fertilizers increased in all other regions, but to a much smaller extent.

The greatest change in the other eight regions was in the West South Central and the smallest in the Territories. The nutrient ratios show that the mixtures used in the Middle Atlantic, South Atlantic, West North Central, and South Central regions were higher in available phosphoric oxide, followed by potash and nitrogen. Available phosphoric oxide was the predominant nutrient in the mixed fertilizers of the Mountain and Pacific regions, followed by nitrogen and potash. Potash was the major nutrient in mixtures used in New England and the Territories. The mixtures in the Territories were the only ones that averaged less available phosphoric oxide

than either of the other two nutrients.

Changes in nitrogen fertilizer materials have had the greatest impact on the fertilizer industry. Imports of fertilizer-grade sodium nitrate, a material containing approximately 16 percent of nitrogen, supplied 27 percent of the total nitrogen used as fertilizer in the calendar year 1939 and only 6 percent of the total in 1954.

The organic nitrogenous materials supplied approximately 12 percent of the total fertilizer nitrogen in 1939 and only 2 to 3 percent in 1955.

The tonnage of cottonseed meal used as fertilizer dropped from 120,000 in 1939 to 37,000 in 1953. Production increased approximately 42 percent in the same period, but most of the cottonseed meal went into animal feeds.

Annual imports of guano sank from 5,700 tons in 1939 to 68 tons in 1953 and then increased to 8,540 tons in the calendar year 1955.

An expansion of the ammonia industry in the United States since 1945 has more than overcome the previous shortages in nitrogen supplies.

Anhydrous ammonia, a gas at normal temperature and pressure, contains 82 percent nitrogen. It accounted for 25 percent of the nitrogen applied directly to the soil in the form of separate materials in 1955, compared to 7 percent in 1947. Limited amounts of ammonia were used earlier, primarily in California.

Other liquid nitrogen materials have come into widespread use. They are of two types—nonpressure solutions, which develop no appreciable vapor pressure at normal temperatures and pressures, and low-pressure solutions, which do develop pressures of not more than 60 pounds per square inch under normal working conditions. Nonpressure solutions comprise water solutions of ammonium nitrate alone or with urea and contain 16 to 32 percent of nitrogen. The low-pressure solutions are aqua ammonia, which contains approximately 24 percent of nitrogen, and ammoniacal solutions of ammonium nitrate and urea, alone or in combination. These ammoniacal solutions contain 37 to 49 percent of nitrogen.

Almost 30 times more nonpressure and low-pressure solutions were applied directly to the soil in 1955 than in 1947. The low-pressure solutions and anhydrous ammonia probably supplied at least 60 percent of the nitrogen in the mixed fertilizers used in 1955.

Ammonium nitrate fertilizer was an important postwar development. It was first imported from Canada in 1943. The total consumption for use as a separate material in 1943 was 18,200 tons. Much of it was crystalline and unsatisfactory for direct application. Improved processing developed a granular fertilizer-grade material, whose particles are covered with an inert substance to prevent them from sticking together. The material contains 32.5 to 33.5 percent of nitrogen.

Demand for nitrogen in this form has been phenomenal, and 1,115,358 tons of ammonium nitrate were used for direct application in 1955. An additional 500,000 tons of ammonium nitrate in low-pressure or ammoniating solutions has been used in the production of mixed fertilizers or for direct application to the soil.

Another high-analysis source of nitrogen is urea, which contains 42 to 45 percent of nitrogen. It has been used in ammoniating solutions since 1932 and as a domestically produced solid fertilizer since 1935. Its use as a fertilizer has been restricted by limited facilities and an increasing demand from the chemical and animal-feed industries. A greater supply became available in 1955 with the completion of additional producing plants.

A new fertilizer developed in the Department of Agriculture is a urea-form-aldehyde reaction product, which contains 38 percent of nitrogen. Called urea-form, it is the only slightly soluble chemical nitrogen fertilizer that is slowly available to plants. One application will satisfy the nitrogen requirements of long-season crops over the full growing period. It is also a specialty fertilizer for turf and ornamentals.

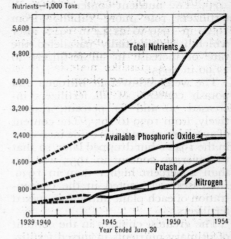

2. Consumption of nitrogen, available phosphoric oxide, and potash in the United States and Territories.

Changes in the supply of available phosphoric oxide have come from the use of more concentrated superphosphates and the introduction of new materials. Normal and concentrated superphosphates were supplemented in the early 1950's by enriched superphosphate, made by treating phosphate rock with a mixture of sulfuric and phosphoric acids. The production of concentrated superphosphate accounted for 17 percent of the available phosphoric oxide produced in the form of superphosphates in the calendar year 1939 and 31 percent in 1954.

The use of ammonium phosphates as separate materials increased from some 19,000 tons in 1939 to 336,300 tons in 1955. Smaller amounts were used in mixed fertilizers. Almost 80 percent of the ammonium phosphates directly applied to the soil were guaranteed to contain 16 percent of nitrogen and 20 percent of available phosphoric oxide. About equal amounts of the remaining material had N–P_2O_5 ratios of 11–48 and 13–39.

A fourth ammonium phosphate came on the market in 1955. It is diammonium phosphate and contains approximately 21 percent of nitrogen and 53 percent of phosphoric oxide.

Another of the newer sources of phosphoric oxide is calcium metaphosphate, which contains about 63 percent of phosphoric oxide. It was developed by the Tennessee Valley Authority. A glasslike material, it is produced by treating phosphate rock with phosphoric oxide vapor. The phosphoric oxide in this fertilizer material is only slightly soluble in water but almost completely available to growing plants. Production increased from about 4,000 tons in 1939 to 56,700 tons in 1954.

Potassium chloride has been the major source of fertilizer potash and has been marketed in 50-percent and 60-percent grades. The 60-percent grade accounted for 82.2 percent of the agricultural potash of American origin in this form in 1939. By 1955, potassium chloride was supplying nearly 94 percent of the total potash for agriculture; most of it was distributed as the 60-percent grade. Nearly all the remaining 6 percent of total potash was in the form of potassium sulfate or sulfate of potash magnesia.

Increasing quantities of liquid mixed fertilizers, containing as high as 32 percent of plant nutrients, have been manufactured in recent years. Consumption of liquid mixed fertilizers amounted to 27,500 tons in 1954. Consumption in California accounted for about three-quarters of the total consumption in the United States.

ADVANCES in the manufacture and processing of materials and mixtures have improved the quality of fertilizers and helped hold down the costs.

A continuous ammoniator developed by the Tennessee Valley Authority in 1954 may be used in continuous processes for the manufacture of mixed fertilizers and in the granulation of mixed fertilizers.

Granulation consists of forming small grains or masses of fertilizer mixtures. The ingredients of the mixture are thoroughly mixed with sufficient moisture to make them semiplastic or sticky. The granules are formed by rolling or

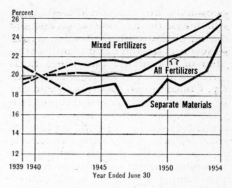

3. Primary nutrient content of fertilizers consumed in the United States and Territories.

tumbling and drying to hard masses.

Granulation processes have been improved and are widely accepted as one means of improving the physical character of fertilizers. Consumer demand for granular fertilizers has increased steadily. Many materials and large tonnages of fertilizer mixtures are granulated because of the greater ease with which they can be handled. They have a lower caking tendency and less dusting loss, and can be distributed more uniformly in the field. The more hygroscopic granular materials may be coated with a conditioning agent—an inert substance used to prevent the granules from sticking together. The granular products are packed in moisture-resistant bags to facilitate storage and handling.

Modern methods of granulation also make it possible to use more ammonia and ammoniating solutions, which are employed to ammoniate superphosphate and to supply a relatively inexpensive form of nitrogen in mixed fertilizers. Formerly their use was limited by the amount of ammonia that could be absorbed by the superphosphate without reversion of available phosphoric oxide.

Modern techniques, however, permit additions of ammonia in excess of this amount because of the simultaneous use of sulfuric or phosphoric acid. The acids neutralize any excess ammonia to form ammonium sulfate or phosphate. The reaction liberates heat, which aids the agglomeration and the drying of the finished product.

New uses for the more plentiful supplies of phosphoric and nitric acids have opened up in the fertilizer industry. Concentrated superphosphate can be manufactured in normal superphosphate equipment by treating phosphate rock with phosphoric acid rather than sulfuric acid. Some phosphoric acid is neutralized with ammonia to make ammonium phosphates. At least two companies have manufactured high-analysis mixed fertilizers by the nitric acid-sulfuric acid or nitric acid-phosphoric acid treatment of phosphate rock. The necessary potash for the finished product is added as a soluble salt to the process slurry.

Ways of handling fertilizers also have changed. The farmer once had to buy and handle bags of fertilizer weighing at least 80 pounds. The use of liquid fertilizers, which can be handled in bulk, has helped to relieve him of some of this chore. Solid fertilizers can be bought in bulk. Shipments of solid fertilizers in this form in 1954 were 8.25 percent of the total shipments of solid fertilizer. Sometimes the mixture is formulated to the farmer's specifications.

Modern techniques in production and handling and the acceptance by the farmer of higher analysis fertilizers have enabled the manufacturer to supply the farmer with fertilizer that is relatively inexpensive in comparison with the other materials he must buy. The index numbers (based on data for 1910–1914 as 100) of the prices paid by farmers for fertilizers were 101 and 155 in the calendar years 1939 and 1954, respectively. Corresponding numbers for feed were 93 and 226; for farm machinery, 155 and 313; and for seed, 92 and 226.

As the demand for fertilizer increases, new problems will arise. The solutions of the problems may lead to more highly concentrated fertilizers, the development of new materials, and better and cheaper methods of manufacturing fertilizers.

Materials and Mixtures

K. D. Jacob

Our known resources of economically usable fertilizer raw materials—already sufficient to meet our domestic requirements for many years—are being augmented constantly by discovery of new supplies and by improvements in the techniques of processing them.

Each of the three great subdivisions of the earth—the atmosphere, the lithosphere, and the hydrosphere—is an economic source of one or more of the nutrient elements supplied in fertilizers. Thus, the atmosphere is the principal source of nitrogen. The lithosphere furnishes nearly all the phosphorus. The hydrosphere gives us potassium.

RESOURCES OF FERTILIZER NITROGEN in the United States comprise the atmosphere, deposits of mineral fuels (bituminous coal, lignite, and oil shale), and natural organic materials.

The atmosphere is a continually renewing, inexhaustible reservoir of nitrogen—about 34,500 tons over each acre of the earth's surface. This nitrogen, present in the elemental form, cannot be utilized by plants, however, until it has been combined with other elements by chemical or biological means. Atmospheric nitrogen is the basis of the great chemical nitrogen-fixation industry, which accounted for about 90 percent of the Nation's production of some 2 million tons of commercial fertilizer nitrogen in 1955.

Huge quantities of atmospheric nitrogen also are made available annually for plant nutrition by the action of biological agencies such as the bacteria in root nodules of legumes.

The country's next most important source of fertilizer nitrogen is bituminous coal, from which ammonia is obtained as a byproduct, chiefly in the manufacture of coke. The nitrogen content of a ton of coal averages about 30 pounds, of which about 4 pounds are recoverable when the coal is processed in modern, byproduct coke ovens. This source annually supplies about 185,000 tons of nitrogen for fertilizer use.

Deposits of many billions of tons of lignite and oil shale, containing about 0.5 to 1.5 percent of nitrogen, occur in the western half of the United States.

These deposits, as yet virtually untapped, may supply substantial quantities of fertilizer nitrogen in the future.

Natural organic materials, such as plant residues, fish products, and animal tankages, accounted for about 90 percent of the Nation's consumption of commercial fertilizer nitrogen in 1900, but only 1.5 percent in 1955.

The proportion may decline still further. That is because production of the natural organic materials is geared to other processes and operations, so that it is not capable of independent expansion, and because many of the products are finding more profitable markets as animal feeds. Also, these materials generally have the disadvantage of low plant-nutrient content and high unit cost in comparison with chemical nitrogen fertilizers.

RESOURCES OF FERTILIZER PHOSPHORUS in the United States are almost entirely in the form of deposits of phosphate rock, which is composed chiefly of one or more complex fluorine-bearing calcium phosphates. Minor sources include bones and other natural organic materials and phosphatic iron ores. Utilization of the latter is confined to the area around Birmingham, Ala., where there is some production of low-analysis basic slag as a byproduct of steel manufacture.

Our phosphate rock resources are mainly in Idaho, Montana, Utah, Wyoming, Florida, and Tennessee. Minor deposits exist in Arkansas, Kentucky, South Carolina, and Virginia.

V. E. McKelvey and his coworkers in the Geological Survey have estimated that the reserves of phosphoric oxide (P_2O_5) in phosphate rock minable under 1956 conditions total 1,545 million long tons—56 percent in the Western States, 43 percent in Florida, and 1 percent in Tennessee.

An additional 12 thousand million long tons of phosphoric oxide are in inferred reserves of phosphate rock that are not minable under present conditions—about 50 percent in the West, 40 percent in Florida, and 10 percent in Tennessee.

The United States in 1955 marketed 13,186,034 long tons of phosphate rock containing 4,179,532 long tons of phosphoric oxide, of which 73 percent of the rock and 76 percent of the phosphoric oxide came from the Florida deposits. The remainder was divided about equally between Tennessee and the Western States (Idaho, Montana, Utah, and Wyoming). Of the total quantity of rock, 83 percent was used within the country—61 percent for fertilizer and other agricultural purposes and 22 percent for industrial uses—and 17 percent was exported.

Some sources of phosphate rock are such that preparation of the material for the market requires elaborate treatments to separate the phosphate from the accompanying impurities. The rock in other places is of commercial grade as it comes from the deposits.

Two notable technological advances have made possible the utilization of huge quantities of phosphate rock that formerly were wasted or were considered uneconomical to exploit.

One of the developments is the separation of phosphate particles from silica grains by flotation processes, which enable greatly increased recovery of phosphate from the Florida deposits and have brought many submarginal deposits into the economic reserve.

The other development is the manufacture of elemental phosphorus directly from lower grade phosphate rock by the electric-furnace process and by the blast-furnace process. The latter has experienced only limited commercial operation. The processes require substantial quantities of silica, and it is often more economical to use directly the lower analysis siliceous phosphate than to smelt high-grade rock with added silica. Thus certain phosphate deposits, especially in Tennessee and the West, that are unsuited for beneficiation to the grades of rock required for acid-treatment processes have been raised to the level of economic reserves.

Further improvements and developments in methods and techniques of mining, beneficiating, and processing undoubtedly will enable the utilization of additional large resources of phosphate rock.

RESOURCES OF FERTILIZER POTASSIUM in the United States include water-soluble minerals, lake and subterranean brines, insoluble minerals and rocks, and natural organic materials.

Sea water contains an average of about 0.04 percent of potassium and constitutes a potentially inexhaustible source of potassium. The technical feasibility of recovering potassium salts from the ocean has been demonstrated in Europe, but the cost is not yet competitive with customary sources.

The Nation's proved reserve of potassium economically recoverable under present conditions is mostly in the Carlsbad, N. Mex., deposits of readily soluble minerals (sylvite and langbeinite) and in the brines of Searles Lake in California and Salduro Marsh in Utah. The reserve in these three sources is estimated to be equivalent to more than 200 million tons of potash (K_2O). An additional large reserve, of unknown extent, resides in the undeveloped deposits of soluble minerals in Utah, Texas, and New Mexico.

Many millions of tons of potassium are present in the deposits of insoluble minerals and rocks—including alunite, greensand, leucite, and certain shales and feldspars—that are widely distributed over the country. The cost of mining and processing these materials, which commonly contain no more than 6 to 10 percent of potash, is such, however, that they generally cannot compete with the brines and soluble minerals as sources of fertilizer potassium.

Tobacco waste, plant ash, dried animal manures, Steffens waste from the beet-sugar industry, and cement-kiln dust are among the minor sources of potassium for fertilizer.

In 1955 the United States produced potassium materials containing 2,064,-808 tons of potash, of which 91 percent came from the New Mexico deposits. Exports totaled 130,226 tons of potash, as compared with imports of 177,052 tons, chiefly from Germany.

RESOURCES OF SECONDARY NUTRIENT elements are abundant and widely distributed in the United States.

Calcium resources are chiefly in the form of limestone, large deposits of which occur in practically every State. Other important resources include deposits of marl, shells, calcium sulfate (gypsum and anhydrite), and phosphate rock.

Magnesium supplies for agricultural use reside largely in deposits of high-magnesium limestone and dolomite, particularly in the eastern half of the country. Additional resources include deposits of magnesite (magnesium carbonate), silicate minerals (olivine and serpentine), soluble salts, and lake and well brines. Magnesium compounds are recovered from sea water on the Pacific, gulf, and Atlantic coasts.

The world's most extensively developed deposits of native sulfur occur in the coastal areas of Louisiana and Texas. Minor deposits are known elsewhere in the country. Additional resources of sulfur, widely distributed among the States, include deposits of iron pyrites and other metallic sulfides, calcium and alkali sulfates, and natural and oil-refinery gases.

The Nation's total known reserve of the materials economically usable as sources of elemental sulfur or sulfuric acid in 1951 was equivalent to nearly 100 million long tons of the element—about half in the form of native sulfur and the remainder mostly in pyrites. The production of elemental sulfur in 1955 was about 6,145,000 long tons.

Vast reserves of potentially usable sulfur reside in the country's deposits of calcium sulfate. Processes for the manufacture of sulfuric acid and cement from calcium sulfate, as well as for its conversion into ammonium sulfate by treatment with ammonia and carbon dioxide, have been developed in several foreign countries.

RESOURCES OF TRACE NUTRIENT elements include more than 14 million tons of boron—probably the world's largest reserve of this element—in deposits and brines in California. The domestic production of boron compounds in 1955 was equivalent to about 91 thousand tons of the element, mostly in the form of sodium borates. The consumption as a plant nutrient probably did not exceed 2.5 thousand tons of boron.

The country's resources of copper, manganese, molybdenum, and zinc are mostly in deposits of sulfide, oxide, carbonate, and silicate ores, from which they are recovered principally by the metallurgical industry. The domestic productions of copper, manganese, and zinc are supplemented by imports, but our productive capacity for molybdenum—chiefly from the Climax, Colo., deposits—exceeds the peacetime world requirements. It is estimated that about 4,500 tons of copper, 3,600 tons of manganese, and 2,000 tons of zinc were consumed for plant nutrient purposes in 1952, for example.

FERTILIZER MANUFACTURING METHODS commonly involve chemical processing of the raw materials to convert the nutrient elements into forms that can be utilized more readily by plants—for example, by combining atmospheric nitrogen with other elements.

Potassium fertilizers, on the other hand, generally are obtained directly from water-soluble sources, and they usually need relatively little chemical processing. Except for their presence as auxiliary constituents of the primary nutrient products, the chemical processing of secondary and trace nutrient materials for fertilizer use is done chiefly by industries whose interests are largely in other fields.

The three commercial methods for chemical fixation of atmospheric nitrogen are the arc, the calcium cyanamide, and the synthetic ammonia processes, of which only the last is operated in the United States.

The arc process involves heating air in the electric arc to produce nitrogen oxides, which are converted into nitric acid and nitrate salts. Formerly operated on a commercial scale, chiefly in Norway, the process is no longer used, mostly because of its high energy requirement. In recently proposed versions of the arc process, the high temperature required for the direct union of nitrogen and oxygen is obtained by a gas flame or by solar energy.

Calcium cyanamide, produced by reaction of nitrogen with calcium carbide, is manufactured chiefly in Europe and Japan. Canada has the only plant in the Western Hemisphere. The usefulness of calcium cyanamide is restricted by its high alkalinity, which severely limits its inclusion in mixed fertilizers, and often by the need for more than average precaution in its field applications. It can be converted into more versatile nitrogen fertilizer materials, but usually with economic disadvantage relative to the same products made with the aid of the direct synthetic ammonia process.

Synthesis of ammonia by reaction of hydrogen with atmospheric nitrogen at high temperature and pressure in the presence of a catalyst is recognized generally to be the most economical of the chemical nitrogen-fixation processes. The hydrogen is produced readily with various carbonaceous substances abundantly available in the United States, including coal, coke, petroleum, and natural gas. Byproduct hydrogen from the manufacture of caustic soda and chlorine, from the processing of petroleum, and from other industrial operations also finds important use in ammonia synthesis.

The country's facilities for ammonia synthesis in 1956 comprised 43 plants in 22 States, with an estimated total capacity of 3,353,000 tons of nitrogen annually. At least seven additional plants were under construction.

Aside from a small amount of phosphorus in the form of basic slag obtained as a byproduct in the steel industry, chemical conversion of mineral phosphates for fertilizer production in the United States is entirely by two types of processes, which involve treatment of the raw phosphate with acids or its smelting with silica and coke in electric furnaces.

Other types of processes include treatment of the phosphate at high temperature with the alkali or alkaline earth compounds, as practiced to a limited extent in some other countries, or with silica and water vapor to produce defluorinated phosphates, such as the fused tricalcium phosphate formerly made by the Tennessee Valley Authority.

Treatment of phosphate rock with sulfuric acid to produce directly normal or ordinary superphosphate provides the greater portion of the country's supply of fertilizer phosphorus.

Of rapidly increasing importance, however, is the manufacture of triple or concentrated superphosphate with phosphoric acid made by the sulfuric acid process. Substantial quantities of ammonium phosphates also are produced with phosphoric acid so made.

Domestic facilities for making phosphorus fertilizers with the aid of sulfuric acid at the beginning of 1956 included 14 triple superphosphate plants, with a total annual capacity estimated to exceed 725,000 tons

of phosphoric oxide, and more than 200 normal superphosphate plants, with a total annual capacity exceeding 3 million tons of phosphoric oxide.

Processes involving treatment of phosphate rock with nitric acid to produce fertilizers containing nitrogen and phosphorus, usually with additions of potassium salts, have had increasing commercial application.

Although elemental phosphorus, the primary product of smelting phosphate rock with silica and coke in electric furnaces, has its principal use in the manufacture of chemicals for technical and industrial purposes, it can be converted readily into a variety of concentrated fertilizer materials such as phosphoric acid, triple superphosphate, calcium metaphosphate, and ammonium phosphates.

TVA once produced nearly all of the domestic output of fertilizers based on elemental phosphorus. Recently, however, other electric-furnace operators have channeled increasing quantities of phosphorus products, mostly phosphoric acid, to fertilizer outlets.

The processes of recovering and concentrating potassium salts from brines and readily soluble minerals, which supply nearly all of the Nation's production of potassium materials, include flotation, evaporation, and crystallization and the application of the principles of base exchange, double decomposition, and the phase rule. The products are chiefly potassium chloride and much smaller amounts of potassium sulfate, sulfate of potash-magnesia, and manure salts. Some potassium sulfate is produced by treating potassium chloride with sulfuric acid.

Domestic facilities in 1955 for producing potassium salts from brines and soluble minerals comprised eight plants with a total annual capacity of approximately 2.1 million tons of potash. Additional annual capacity for 400 thousand tons of potash was under construction or was planned.

FERTILIZER MATERIALS are individual products that contain one or more plant nutrients in forms suitable for use as such or in the preparation of mixed fertilizers. This category includes more or less pure chemical compounds, natural organic substances of vegetable and animal origins, and certain crude mineral materials and inorganic byproducts. Among them are solid materials, aqueous solutions, and liquefied gases.

Ammonium sulfate, ammonium nitrate and its mixtures, sodium nitrate, urea, and ammonium phosphate products are the principal solid nitrogenous fertilizers used in the United States. Widely varying quantities of them are used in mixed fertilizers and for direct application to crops. The ammonium nitrate products and sodium nitrate are employed mostly for the latter purpose, while the greater part of the ammonium sulfate goes into mixtures. Urea (45 percent nitrogen) and fertilizer-grade ammonium nitrate (33.5 percent nitrogen) are the most concentrated of the solid nitrogen materials.

Liquid anhydrous ammonia (a gas at ordinary temperature and pressure), aqueous ammonia, and solutions of ammonia with ammonium nitrate or urea accounted for about 50 percent of the total domestic consumption of fertilizer nitrogen in 1955. The low cost of the nitrogen, compared with that of the element in solid forms, is an important factor in the use of these materials, both for direct application and for addition to mixed fertilizers. Their utility for the latter purpose depends chiefly on the presence of superphosphate in the mixture, whereby the free ammonia is fixed principally as ammonium phosphate.

Liquid anhydrous ammonia is distinguished from the other liquid nitrogen materials by its high content of nitrogen (82 percent) and its high vapor pressure (211 pounds per square inch at 104° F.). Its utilization directly as a fertilizer is by addition to irrigation water and injection into soil.

The nitrogen content of the aqueous nitrogen solution usually is no more than half that of anhydrous ammonia, and the unit factory cost of the nitrogen is substantially higher.

On the other hand, the solutions have much lower vapor pressures (usually below 25 pounds per square inch), require simpler and less expensive equipment for transportation, storage, and field distribution, and present fewer problems in their handling and application to the soil. Those advantages and a smaller hazard are factors in the growing use of the solutions as materials for direct application. They often may offset largely or completely the advantages of the higher concentration and lower factory cost of nitrogen in the form of anhydrous ammonia.

The normal and triple superphosphates furnish about 90 percent of the Nation's production of fertilizer phosphorus. They supply phosphorus in water-soluble forms, generally at a lower cost than other materials. They are satisfactory for use in mixed fertilizers and for direct application to the soil. They are suitable sources of phosphorus for all crops and for nearly all soils. Similar characteristics and utility are shown by the enriched superphosphates, made by treating phosphate rock with mixtures of sulfuric and phosphoric acids.

Other sources of water-soluble phosphorus are chiefly the monoammonium and diammonium phosphates and the ammonium phosphate-ammonium sulfate products, which serve for direct application and for inclusion in mixed fertilizers.

Direct use of liquid phosphoric acid as a fertilizer by addition to irrigation water is practiced to a limited extent in the West. Small but increasing quantities of the acid are used in the manufacture of some mixed fertilizers.

The products obtained by treating phosphate rock with nitric acid contain varying proportions of water-soluble and water-insoluble phosphorus. Their manufacture in the United States involves addition of ammonia and potassium salts and processing directly into predetermined grades of granular mixtures containing all three of the primary nutrients.

The domestic use of fertilizer materials having low solubility of the phosphorus in water includes basic slag, calcium metaphosphate, dicalcium phosphate, and natural products such as bone and ground raw phosphate rock. Dicalcium phosphate is a common constituent of mixed fertilizers prepared with the aid of ammonia or other basic substances.

Potassium chloride supplies about 90 percent of the country's consumption of fertilizer potassium, and approximately 85 percent of the total is used in mixed fertilizers. The rest of the consumption is chiefly in the forms of potassium sulfate and sulfate of potash-magnesia, which, for reasons of crop quality, are applied principally to tobacco. Other crops for which the nonchloride forms of potash are preferred include citrus and white potatoes.

Most of the country's consumption of commercial, plant-nutrient calcium and magnesium is applied in the form of natural carbonates and other soil liming materials. The superphosphates, raw phosphate rock, and mineral calcium sulfates furnish large additional quantities of calcium. The relatively small amount of magnesium supplied by materials other than the natural carbonates is largely in the form of sulfates, especially sulfate of potash-magnesia.

The commercial fertilizers used annually in the United States contain more than 1.4 million tons of sulfur, of which about 90 percent is supplied as a constituent of normal superphosphate and ammonium sulfate. Elemental sulfur and mineral calcium sulfate (gypsum and anhydrite), applied chiefly as ameliorants for alkali soils, account for most of the remainder.

Trace nutrients are used chiefly in the form of water-soluble salts. Thus borax and its modifications furnish nearly all of the boron, but copper, iron, manganese, and zinc are applied mostly as the sulfate salts.

Increasing attention has been given to the utility of insoluble or slightly soluble compounds—for example, colemanite (a calcium borate mineral) and aluminum borosilicate glasses, or frits, containing other trace elements.

Also of growing interest are certain synthetic organic substances known as chelating agents, which have the property of maintaining copper, manganese, zinc, and iron in the nonionized water-soluble condition, so that these trace nutrients may be absorbed readily by plants.

MIXED FERTILIZERS are manufactured in more than 1,250 plants—including more than 100 farmer cooperative facilities—distributed in nearly all the States, the District of Columbia, Hawaii, and Puerto Rico. The capacities of the plants range from a few tons to more than 200,000 tons annually.

The several disadvantages of mixed fertilizers usually are outweighed by the advantages, especially the convenience and the economy in time and labor attending their use, so that mixtures long have occupied a high position in the domestic fertilizer industry. In recent years they have accounted for about 70 percent of the total consumptions of both fertilizers and primary plant nutrients.

The types of mixed fertilizers are many and varied. They include solids and liquids, powders and granules, and a host of specialty products intended primarily for nonfarm use. Their nutrient concentrations and nutrient ratios extend over wide limits. The materials used in their manufacture range from gases and liquids to solids that differ greatly in their chemical and physical characteristics.

As practiced in the United States, the manufacture of mixed fertilizers chiefly involves the relatively simple process of blending the required quantities of solid fertilizer materials—usually with addition of aqueous solutions of ammonia and ammonium nitrate or urea—with other materials such as conditioning and neutralizing agents and with sufficient filler to adjust the concentration of total nutrients to the desired level.

The products commonly are powdery in nature. The operations and equipment for making mixed fertilizers in this way vary considerably from plant to plant. They range from simple types requiring much hand labor to plants that are highly mechanized.

The production of granulated mixtures, which requires the use of special processes and equipment, has been growing rapidly in many parts of the country. When properly done, granulation minimizes segregation of the constituents, reduces caking, cuts loss by dusting, and facilitates distribution of the fertilizer in the field. Together with packaging in moisture-resistant containers, it makes possible the preparation and use of mixtures containing larger proportions of hygroscopic materials, like ammonium nitrate and urea, than otherwise would be possible.

Because the nitrogen materials commonly used in mixed fertilizers have an acidic action on the soil, it is the general practice in some parts of the country to overcome this effect, and at the same time to supply nutrient magnesium, by adding dolomitic limestone to the mixtures. Such use of the limestone serves an important purpose in areas that do not have adequate farm-liming programs, but the objectives usually can be accomplished more effectively by proper liming.

Considerable progress has been made in reducing the use of makeweight filler in mixed fertilizers since 1945. Many mixtures, however, still contain high percentages of such filler, much of which—being technically and agronomically unnecessary—could be eliminated with corresponding increase in the percentage nutrient content of the fertilizer and economy in handling, transportation, and application costs per unit of nutrients.

Liquid mixed fertilizers containing two or more of the primary nutrient elements (nitrogen, phosphorus, and potassium) are gaining much use in some parts of the country. Compared with solid products, liquid mixtures appear to have the advantage of lower capital investment and labor costs for

their production, and the problems of physical condition and uniformity of composition are less difficult.

The requirement of a high degree of solubility in water restricts considerably, however, the choice and availability of nutrient materials, especially those supplying phosphorus, and may increase the cost of some nutrients. Other problems include the low solubility of most of the secondary and trace nutrient elements, crystallization of salts from solution, corrosion of equipment, and the storage of materials and products.

Liquid mixtures have the advantage of convenience in handling and application, but the farmer's choice between liquids and solids will depend chiefly on the applied-to-the-soil cost of nutrients in the two forms.

Incorporation of pesticides in fertilizer materials and especially in mixed fertilizers—to control weeds, fungi, and chiefly insects—is practiced extensively in some parts of the United States. The use of such products has the advantage of convenience and often of economy, as compared with separately timed, individual applications of the fertilizer and the pesticide. The preparation, distribution, and use of fertilizer-pesticide mixtures involve numerous problems in the agronomic, entomologic, regulatory control, and manufacturing phases of the subject, however.

THE CHEMICAL COMPOSITION of a fertilizer, as reflected by the quantity and quality of its nutrients, is the principal criterion of its utility for crop production. Although the commercial value of most fertilizers is based chiefly on their content of nitrogen, phosphorus, and potassium, the presence or absence of other nutrient elements may be a factor in the choice of fertilizers for specific crops, soils, and areas of use.

The composition of a specific kind and grade of fertilizer material usually shows only narrow fluctuations, whereas a specific grade of mixed fertilizer, being made up of several materials and prepared under varying conditions, may contain widely different quantities of nutrient elements other than nitrogen, phosphorus, and potassium.

The quality of the nutrients in fertilizers usually is determined by laboratory methods based on the solubility of the nutrients in specified solvents and under closely defined conditions.

The nitrogen in nearly all chemical nitrogen fertilizers is readily soluble in water. The nitrogen in natural organic materials, on the other hand, is chiefly insoluble in water, and there are no satisfactory laboratory methods for quickly estimating the quality of the insoluble nitrogen, which may vary considerably with the kind of material and the conditions of its use.

Although nitrogen fertilizers commonly are marketed on the basis of total nitrogen content, their evaluation may require, too, determination of the form of the nitrogen—organic, water-insoluble, nitrate, and others.

Phosphorus fertilizers usually are evaluated in the United States on the basis of the quantity dissolved in successive extractions of the sample with water and neutral ammonium citrate solution. The soluble phosphorus determined in this manner is considered to be readily usable by plants and commonly is designated as available phosphorus. Total phosphorus and particle fineness are the principal guides to quality in natural products like bone and phosphate rock.

Solubility in water is the usual criterion of the quality of chemical potassium materials. Because of reactions that result in conversion of some of the potassium to slightly soluble but plant-usable forms, however, the potassium in mixed fertilizers customarily is evaluated with the aid of an ammonium oxalate solution.

THE COMPOSITION of mixed fertilizers, as regards the primary nutrients, is indicated by the grade designations expressed as percentages of the nutrients in the order total nitrogen (N), available phosphoric oxide (P_2O_5), and soluble potash (K_2O). Thus, a 4–16–8 fertilizer contains 4 percent total nitrogen, 16 percent available phosphoric oxide, and 8 percent soluble potash. The nutrients other than these three customarily are not included in the grade designation, but the information thereon may be given in other ways.

More than 1,600 different grades of mixed fertilizers were sold in the continental United States in the year that ended June 30, 1955.

Thirty grades supplied about 79 percent of the total tonnage of mixtures. Only 15 grades accounted for 63 percent.

Many of the States publish lists of the grades recommended by the respective agricultural experiment stations, and several prohibit the registration and sale of nonrecommended grades. Restriction of the number of grades of mixed fertilizers makes for simplification of manufacturing operations, lower production and marketing costs, and more effective utilization of supplies of fertilizer materials. It also aids regulatory operations and simplifies the choice and use of fertilizers.

PHYSICAL CONDITION is a major problem in the manufacture, distribution, and use of solid fertilizers. The problem has been intensified by the trend toward higher-analysis materials and mixtures, but progress has been made in solving it.

Important factors involved in the physical condition of a fertilizer are its hygroscopicity (proneness to absorb moisture from the atmosphere), caking tendency, and particle size. These factors, often interrelated in their effects, markedly influence the utility of the product as regards its storage, shipping, and application in the field.

Many fertilizers readily absorb moisture from the air, which may cause them to become sticky. This is especially true of calcium nitrate, ammonium nitrate, sodium nitrate, urea, and their mixtures with other materials.

Among the materials that have little or no tendency to absorb moisture under the atmospheric conditions prevailing in the United States are monoammonium phosphate, potassium nitrate, potassium sulfate, and the superphosphates.

Serious caking may occur when hygroscopic fertilizers are subjected to pressure, as in large piles or high stacks, or when moisture is lost because of changes in atmospheric conditions.

Caking may result, too, from other causes—as from chemical reactions among the ingredients of mixed fertilizers—and it is encouraged by high proportions of fine particles.

Mixed fertilizers may undergo segregation during shipping and handling because of differences in the specific gravity and the size of the particles of their ingredients.

A solid fertilizer cannot be distributed evenly in the field if it is sticky or caked, if its ingredients undergo segregation, or if its drillability (uniformity of flow) is hindered by its particle size. The drillability of fertilizer is at its best when the particles are dry, uniform in size, spherical in shape, and of such a practical size as to minimize the cohesive forces between them.

Good physical condition in fertilizers is favored by regulation of the initial moisture content; proper curing to insure completion of chemical reactions before shipment; elimination of fine particles; use of the right kind and quantity of conditioning agent to hinder coalescence of the particles; granulation or, with mixtures, use of ingredients having uniform and relatively large particle size; packaging in moisture-resistant containers; protection from extremes of atmospheric temperature and humidity; and storage in low stacks or piles.

Granulation of fertilizers, whereby the particles are converted into spheroids of substantially uniform size, is an especially effective way of promoting good physical condition. Several fertilizer materials, including ammonium nitrate, ammonium phosphate, calcium cyanamide, calcium nitrate, sodium nitrate, the normal and triple super-

phosphates, and urea, are marketed wholly or partly in granular form, and granulation of mixed fertilizers is practiced extensively.

FERTILIZER-CONTROL LAWS have been enacted by all States, but the Federal Government does not exercise similar authority in this field. The laws are revised from time to time as may be necessitated by changed conditions and practices.

In the interest of more uniform legislation among the States, recent revisions have been based largely on a model fertilizer bill developed by the Association of American Fertilizer Control Officials (*Proposed Model State Fertilizer Bill* (11th draft), Association of American Fertilizer Control Officials, Official Publication No. 10, 66–77, 1956).

All the State laws require registration of the various brands and grades of fertilizers before they are offered for sale, sold, or distributed. They also require guarantees of the minimum percentages of each of the three primary nutrient elements—expressed in terms of total nitrogen (N), available phosphoric oxide (P_2O_5), and soluble potash (K_2O)—and they provide penalties for failure to meet the guarantees and for other violations. Guarantees of other constituents are required or permitted in some instances, and it may be necessary for the container or tag to carry certain information relating to filler and to the character of the fertilizer.

Many of the State laws designate the minimum percentage of total plant nutrients that may be guaranteed in a fertilizer. Some States limit the sale of mixed fertilizers to certain specified grades approved by the appropriate agricultural experiment station.

The laws or the accompanying regulations generally include provision for registration and inspection fees; the labeling and identification of packaged fertilizers and of fertilizers distributed in bulk; the periodic reporting (to the control authority by the manufacturer or the distributor) of the quantities of fertilizer distributed; and the inspection, sampling, and analysis of fertilizers and the publication of the data.

Satisfactory operation of fertilizer-control laws necessitates, among other things, the use of standardized methods of sampling and chemical analysis. The development and publication of such methods is a function of the Association of Official Agricultural Chemists. The State laws or the accompanying regulations generally specify the use of the A.O.A.C. methods in official fertilizer inspections.

Variations in certain phases of the fertilizer-control laws among the individual States or groups of States reflect largely the differences in the character of the agriculture and in the soil and crop requirements for plant nutrients. The laws generally afford protection to the consumer as well as to the manufacturer.

IT MAY BE SAID with confidence that fertilizers will play an increasingly significant role in the Nation's agricultural economy and that in the years to come the trend in their production and use will continue markedly upward.

The country is richly endowed with resources of fertilizer raw materials and of their requisites for processing, which are economically usable under present conditions, and far larger resources reside in less favorable situations.

We have extensive facilities for winning and processing the raw materials by modern methods and techniques, all of which constantly are undergoing improvement. For the most part, those facilities are widely distributed over the country.

For the foreseeable future, the problem of adequate supplies of fertilizer for the American farmer appears to be largely one of continuing to expand the productive capacity to keep pace with the demand. But it should be emphasized that great opportunity remains for technological advances in fertilizers and for improving the efficiency of their use in crop production and in other phases of farm management.

New and Better Fertilizers

E. L. Newman and W. L. Hill

Better fertilizers have been coming on the market for years.

New fertilizers are rarely new from the chemist's viewpoint. They generally are composed of known chemical compounds, although the proportions of the compounds actually present may be difficult to determine.

Usually a promising new fertilizer undergoes lengthy development before it is offered commercially. Also, a nutrient-bearing compound often is used as a raw or intermediate material in the manufacture of fertilizers for some years before it may become available to the farmer for direct use. Anhydrous ammonia and phosphoric oxide are two of many examples.

Novelty in a fertilizer must then be regarded as newness to the retail market. In this light, our subject demands a discussion of the things that are likely to influence new or improved fertilizers.

The development of a new fertilizer to market status is a response to the need for some particular quality or set of qualities that are expected to lower the cost, provide easier handling, or supply soil and crop requirements better. Examples are the water-soluble phosphorus of ammonium phosphates, the water-insoluble nitrogen of urea-formaldehyde, the noncaking and dust-free character of granular fertilizers, balanced nutrient contents of polynutrient fertilizers, and the low-cost nitrogen afforded by anhydrous ammonia.

Because needs vary from region to region, reflecting a diversity of soils, crops, climates, and farm practices, the nature of the most suitable fertilizer also differs among the regions. Often the fertilizer is expected to do more than supply additional nutrients.

These circumstances are illustrated by the following specifications for an ideal fertilizer, compiled by T. P. Hignett of the Tennessee Valley Authority, from suggestions by agronomists, farmers, and fertilizer manufacturers:

The ideal fertilizer—Mr. Hignett was advised—should carry high concentrations of the three primary plant nutrients (nitrogen, phosphorus, and potassium), generous amounts of the secondary nutrients (calcium, magnesium, and sulfur), and small amounts of several micronutrients. It should be in the form of hard, round granules, about 0.1 inch in diameter, that are impervious to moisture until placed in the soil, whereupon the nutrients should dissolve immediately, even though the soil be dry, and become completely utilizable by short-season crops. At the same time the nutrients should neither be fixed by the soil nor leached from it, so that a residual effect will extend over a period of years. It should have an alkaline reaction on acid soil, and an acid reaction on alkaline soil. It should be adaptable to manufacture by unskilled labor in whatever equipment happens to be available in the factory. Finally, it should kill weeds and bugs and condition the soil.

Obviously this is an absurd specification and was meant to show the impossibility of achieving the perfect fertilizer. Nevertheless the respective specifications are desirable under certain conditions and must be given proper consideration in the design of improved fertilizers. The specifications can be used also as factors in judging the possibilities of materials yet to come. The several elements of value arise in one or more of three avenues of approach to fertilizer appraisal—character, effectiveness, and cost.

THE CHARACTER OF A FERTILIZER depends largely on such chemical properties as concentration and reactivity of the major nutrients.

Reactivity, as we use the word here, means the tendency of the fertilizer substance to dissolve and become available to plant roots. It can be measured reasonably accurately as solubility.

Among the factors that influence the character of fertilizer are certain physical properties that facilitate handling in storage, transportation, and application to the soil. Emphasis on physical character has increased notably in recent years. Farmers no longer tolerate caked fertilizers. Powdery materials are becoming less acceptable.

The benefits of some high-analysis products have been gaining recognition over a very much longer period. These trends are especially marked in the regions where the use of fertilizer is relatively new. Considerable attention also has been given to the reactivity or solubility of nutrients. Some results along this line are the development of urea-form, a synthetic nitrogen fertilizer of controlled solubility, and recognition of the importance of water-soluble, phosphorus-bearing fertilizers for fast-growing crops.

THE EFFECTIVENESS OF A FERTILIZER is measured in terms of crop response to its use. Responses are determined to a large extent by environmental factors peculiar to the farming region—soil type, climate, and water supply. These conditions must be accepted much as they are, and farming is thereby regionalized. Response is also influenced by cultural practice, in which some noteworthy factors are kind of crop, crop rotation, kind and amount of fertilizer, placement of fertilizer in soil, and time of application. Effectiveness of a fertilizer thus depends not only on its character but also on where it is used and the way it is used.

Experimental evaluation of a fertilizer can be approached from two basic viewpoints. A fertilizer of known character may be tested to find the region and cultural practice that provides the conditions for best performance, or a particular cultural practice may be studied to determine fertilizer characteristics that will induce the greatest response. The sets of conditions under which present-day fertilizers prove effective have been broadly demonstrated experimentally, although in farming practice the choice of fertilizers is not always in line with experiment.

Cost is probably the most important consideration in the consumer's choice of a fertilizer. The farmer's first thought is usually, "How much does it cost?" Only so much can be spent for fertilizer, and he wants the most for his money. This is a proper view, provided he measures cost in terms of the quantity of plant nutrients purchased rather than on the basis of the weight of material received. For example, the Illinois farmer who chooses a 5–10–10 (the numbers indicate percentages of nitrogen, phosphate, and potash, in that order) fertilizer at 59 dollars a ton may not realize that a 10–20–20 fertilizer at 104 dollars a ton is the better bargain. Adding the costs of distribution and application to the purchase price widens the margin, because the same amount of nutrients can be handled and applied more cheaply in the concentrated material.

Prospects for better fertilizers may be gaged on the basis of the criteria for appraisal—character, effectiveness, and cost.

The manufacturer alone can make alterations in fertilizer character, but both manufacturer and consumer can make contributions to effectiveness and lower the cost, especially the cost after application to the soil. The farmer who uses a fertilizer of low reactivity as a starter fertilizer for a fast-growing crop is not getting the best out of the fertilizer. Conversely, a farmer sometimes may integrate fertilizer application with crop rotation in such a way that application of one low-cost major nutrient is required only once in several years. He thus achieves economies in tonnage and cost greater than any price advantage that the manufacturer could provide.

Improved physical character of fertilizers, particularly the polynutrient goods, has been a subject of much research. Great strides have been made toward the development of noncaking, free-flowing fertilizers. Much remains to be done, of course.

For years diluents known as conditioners have been incorporated into fertilizers, either deliberately or incidentally, to prevent caking by formation of a coating on the fertilizer particles or by simple mechanical separation of the particles. The trend to goods of higher analysis has squeezed out diluents to a marked extent and thus has necessitated a search for other ways to keep fertilizers free-flowing.

Physical nature is controlled by one or more procedures—choosing the best-adapted ingredients, selecting favorable proportions of ingredients, granulating the fertilizer, reducing the moisture content, coating the granules with suitable agents, and packaging in moisture-resistant bags.

Each nutrient combination usually presents a special problem, so that considerable research is nearly always required for the development of an economic technique that permits production of the fertilizer in free-flowing form. Despite the many obstacles, the current effort to better the physical character of fertilizers is improving the marketed products.

The difficulty of maintaining a fertilizer in good condition usually increases with the solubility of the nutrients. Highly soluble and concentrated forms of nutrients frequently present major problems. In such cases, one answer to the question of poor physical condition is direct use in solution form. The direct application of liquid fertilizers is a growing practice. The problem here is transferred from the physical condition of a solid to the nutrient level in a liquid. Poor condition is nicely avoided at the expense of nutrient concentration. At the same time, the cost of storage and transportation is increased. Because liquids of higher nutrient content thus become a chief objective of improvement, the problem in this case shifts from physical to chemical character.

CHEMICAL CHARACTER, which includes such properties as concentration and reactivity, is an avenue for the further improvement of fertilizers. The trend toward high-analysis goods persists. It has perhaps approached the practical limit in a few of the newer market areas, but in the old and at the same time heavy-consuming regions the acceptance of higher concentrations is slow. Progress can be made as rapidly as the consumer is convinced of the advantages of higher grades.

Adjustment of nutrient proportions in polynutrient fertilizers, to reach proper balance for crop needs, provides another opportunity for betterment. The manufacturer must look to the agronomist for guidance here.

Continued expansion of the use of anhydrous ammonia and nitrogen solutions for side and top dressings could have a pronounced effect on the formulation of solid fertilizers. Because this practice relieves the need for nitrogen-rich fertilizer at planting time, a part of the nitrogen will likely be dropped from the starter fertilizer and, in the interest of economy and effectiveness, transferred to later applications. The lowered content of nitrogen compounds would alter somewhat the physical and chemical nature of the fertilizer used at planting time. The net effect would probably be improvement.

The choice of nutrient-bearing ingredients of mixed fertilizers to improve character has not received adequate attention. Intimate association of chemical compounds in a mixture may bring about an increase or decrease of nutrient reactivity. High ammoniation of superphosphate reduces its solubility. Favorable effects are to be expected normally from the influence of nitrogen and potassium compounds, which are soluble, on slightly soluble phosphates. The influence is not the same for all soluble compounds. For example, potassium sulfate increases the solubility of dicalcium phosphate to a far greater extent than does potassium chloride. Furthermore, the effect is magnified in intimate mixtures that are granulated. Investigation of this aspect of fertilizers should yield worthwhile information on possibilities of improvement.

We noted the need for raising the nutrient content of liquid fertilizers. This end must be reached by suitable choice of ingredients. Most fertilizer compounds are less soluble at low temperatures than at high temperatures. Hence a liquid fertilizer that is quite satisfactory for summer use, for example, may salt out during cool days in spring or fall. Then the fertilizer may truly be said to be in a poor physical condition. In order to prevent salt deposition as a consequence of normal fluctuations in temperature, the grade of the liquids must be lower than would otherwise be necessary.

Enhancement of the grade of liquid fertilizers will follow systematic studies of the solubility of various ingredients to find combinations that are less susceptible to salt deposition. It is likely also that additives will be found that will inhibit or delay crystallization. The wide interest in liquids has stimulated such studies.

IMPROVED EFFECTIVENESS, as far as the manufacturer is directly concerned, must proceed largely from modifications in the character of fertilizers. The producer can use the most desirable nutrient-bearing substances and proportion them accurately in a recommended ratio. He can process the mixture into a uniformly granular, free-flowing fertilizer. He can add conditioner and package the product in moisture-resistant bags to insure preservation of its good character. He can supervise delivery to the farm. At that point he relinquishes control of the fertilizer. As to its mode of use, he can only recommend, unless he is one of the few manufacturers who also apply fertilizers and can carry out his own recommendations. Some manufacturers have representatives in leading market areas whose chief responsibility is to advise consumers about the choice and use of fertilizers. This growing practice, maintained in accordance with acceptable ethical standards, enhances the prospects for efficient use of fertilizers.

Increased nutrient concentration, exemplified in high-analysis fertilizers, does not necessarily contribute to effectiveness. The trend to high-grade products at first provided incentive for the elimination of inert fillers. Later the squeeze came on the components that bear the secondary nutrients. The extra high grades often contain little or no calcium, magnesium, or sulfur.

The concentrated fertilizers can be effective if the amounts of calcium, magnesium, and sulfur in the soil are adequate to supply crop needs, but they may be unsatisfactory on soils deficient in those secondary nutrients. Potential difficulties of this kind can be avoided by a suitable choice of market areas, so that the products offered in trade contain (although often in insufficient amounts) secondary elements needed for the farming practices of the region. Adequate amounts of secondary nutrients can be provided, however, at less expense by generous application of low-cost separate materials, such as limestone, dolomite, or gypsum, once in several years. The growth of this practice in a region relieves the need for secondary nutrients in the marketed fertilizers and helps prepare the way for products of higher analysis.

The addition of micronutrients, such as zinc, manganese, boron, copper, iron, and molybdenum, to otherwise regular grades of fertilizers often is advantageous and is customary in some areas. Present practice generally provides for one or two micronutrients in fertilizers that move into certain areas or to particular crops. The opinion of some informed persons is that fertilizers generally would give better performance if several of the micronutrients were incorporated in them. Since the manufacturer could expect little if any premium for the additional nutrients, the problem is to find suitable low-cost micronutrient substances for such use. This matter has received attention.

LOWER CONSUMER PRICES for a product usually follow reduction in costs of manufacture and distribution. In the fertilizer industry, basic manufacturing costs are being reduced gradually as a consequence of process integration that eliminates expensive steps formerly necessary. Distribution costs are being lowered by moving manufacturing plants into favorable locations with respect to market areas and by the trend toward fertilizers of higher analysis that permits shipment of more nutrients per freight dollar. In many instances, however, the savings are offset somewhat by the increased cost of processing and packaging the fertilizer, so that it will meet consumer demands as to physical character.

The reduction in price the manufacturer may be able to pass to the consumer depends on the pattern of fertilizer use for the market area. In regions where the dominant preference of the farmer is for low-analysis goods, little can be expected, because the cost is just as much for handling, shipping, and applying a ton of low-analysis material as it is for a ton of concentrate. The marked differences among the use patterns of different regions are shown by consumption figures. Thus, in the region that includes Virginia, the Carolinas, Georgia, and Florida, nearly three-fifths of the tonnage of the 15 dominant grades of polynutrient fertilizer moved as goods containing 16 to 20 percent of nutrients in 1954. But in the region comprising Ohio, Indiana, Illinois, Michigan, and Wisconsin, only 1 percent of the tonnage moved as material carrying as low as 20 percent of nutrients.

The concentrated materials, such as anhydrous ammonia, triple superphosphate, and muriate of potash (potassium chloride) show up as the cheapest fertilizers. Although normally they are the farmer's best bargains, he often prefers a mixed fertilizer at a higher price to save the time, trouble, and expense of mixing it himself.

Nitrogen is the most expensive of the three major nutrients. Such relatively new materials as anhydrous ammonia and ammonium nitrate demonstrate wide margins of cost advantage over the older materials, ammonium sulfate and sodium nitrate. Urea and nitrogen solutions are examples of concentrated and fairly cheap nitrogen fertilizers that are being applied in increasing tonnages. When cost differences are great, a movement toward the cheaper materials is inevitable, barring unusual advantages for an expensive material.

Cost advantages of the concentrated phosphate and potash materials over the lower analysis materials are apparent. Triple superphosphate, though far from a new material and costing more to make than ordinary superphosphate, is much more concentrated and therefore usually has an advantage in final cost.

The cost factor varies less among polynutrient fertilizers than among others but still is definitely weighted in favor of the newer and more concentrated products. For example, in comparing fertilizers of similar ratios, the 4-16-16 grade usually reaches the land cheaper than 3-12-12, and 10-20-20 is more economical than 5-10-10. Liquids are competitive with solids in some localities. Nitric phosphates and ammonium phosphates (especially diammonium phosphate) show economic advantages in some areas.

Cost figures prove that the high-analysis fertilizers are to be preferred to the low-analysis products wherever the more concentrated materials meet agronomic requirements. One of the most beneficial effects of advanced fertilizer technology, as far as the farmer is concerned, is lower final cost. This indicates good prospects for the improved types of fertilizers.

Highly seasonal demand prevails for fertilizer products. Since deliveries reach the peaks during spring and fall plantings and drop to almost nothing the rest of the year, storage and transportation are big problems. Efforts to remedy this situation with lower prices during the off season thus far have met with only modest success. Nevertheless, the future seems to hold promise of progress in this direction. Many fertilizers produced today will hold up in bag storage for several weeks or months; some years ago fertilizers often deteriorated rapidly. If the farmer could be convinced that with reasonable care he can keep his fertilizer in storage on the farm for extended periods without deterioration in quality and if the price inducements were made attractive enough, the peak-season rush would be lightened.

NEW FERTILIZERS will appear from several directions in response to specific needs. The trend toward higher analysis can be expected to bring the extra high grades.

Fertilizer grades such as 5-20-20, 10-20-20, and 14-14-14 are on the market. Still higher grades are realizable. Development work has begun on 17-17-17 and 26-26-0 fertilizers. They are combinations of ammonium phosphates and ammonium nitrate with or without potash, and are termed ammonium phosphate-nitrates. Various ratios can be produced from a variety of ingredients. This class of product is entirely soluble in water.

Other new fertilizers are on the horizon, especially one- and two-nutrient materials with built-in desirable characteristics that meet predetermined specifications.

The compounds used in fertilizers vary in water solubility. All the conventional compounds of potassium and of nitrogen, with the exception of natural organic materials, dissolve to about the same extent as table salt, whereas the natural organic nitrogen-bearing materials and some of the phosphates dissolve scarcely at all. This circumstance hampers adjustment of the nutrient reactivity of fertilizers to specific crop requirements. Adjustment is

216

obtainable only by choosing compounds with either high or low solubilities, or mixtures of the two. There is a need for compounds that possess intermediate reactivities.

A urea-formaldehyde reaction product, termed urea-form and on the market under the names *Urea-form*, *Uramite*, *Nitroform*, and *Borden's 38*, represents a step in the direction of specially designed fertilizer compounds of nitrogen. This high-grade synthetic product is classed as water insoluble and was designed to supply the need for nonleachable nitrogen. It has quickly become competitive with natural organic products on the basis of nutrient cost. Urea-form should be regarded as a prototype of things to come. We envision a whole series of graduated reactivities, intermediate between the extremes now available.

Development work on potassium fertilizers of controlled solubility has started. Noteworthy is a study of the possibilities of fused potassium phosphates. Both potassium and phosphorus of these compounds are of intermediate solubility.

The metaphosphates, particularly the vitreous forms, are of similar type. Calcium metaphosphate, which has been produced as a fertilizer by the Tennessee Valley Authority for more than 15 years, is classed by conventional fertilizer criteria as a water-insoluble phosphate. Nevertheless, the quality of its insolubility differs from that of the common insoluble phosphates, because it can absorb water slowly and change to soluble monocalcium phosphate. The pattern of behavior of this phosphate under soil environments has been placed under close study. The results of this research may point up the possibilities of this type of material in providing an intermediate phosphate reactivity.

Ammonium metaphosphate, analyzing about 17–73–0, is an experimental fertilizer with varying degrees of quick solubility in water. It is under study as a new material offering advantages of high concentration and possible improvements in other characteristics. As an ingredient for liquid fertilizers, it appears to give unusual opportunities for making more concentrated products.

Micronutrient materials for direct use and also for incorporation in mixtures containing major and secondary nutrients have been studied. Much of this work is concerned with adjustment of reactivity to soil environment for the improvement of nutrient utilization by crops. Thus chelating agents (organic complexing compounds) and glasses (frits) are used to control reactivity of micronutrients such as iron, copper, or boron.

Applying Fertilizers

R. L. Cook and Walter C. Hulburt

Plant nutrients differ in the way they may be applied most effectively as fertilizers because of the differences in their chemical properties, the amounts plants need, the chemical and biological activity in the soil, and their solubility, which varies according to their formula and physical condition.

The nitrogen that exists in the soil as organic matter is a basic consideration. Organisms decompose it and release the nitrogen as ammonia. Other organisms change the ammonia to the nitrate form. The organisms themselves use nitrogen to build the tissues of their own bodies.

If the organic matter (such as straw and corn stover) in the soil is high in carbon, it releases too little nitrogen to supply the metabolic requirements of the organisms. Organisms then may compete with crops for soil nitrogen, including the nitrogen that is applied as fertilizer. Thus a deficiency may develop at a time when the growing crop urgently needs nitrogen.

Experiments at Michigan State University showed that 300 pounds of nitrogen an acre applied at planting time was not enough to supply the nitrogen requirement of sugar beets throughout the growing season. But plants that had received the same total amount of nitrogen fertilizer at three different times—one at planting time and two later—were well supplied with nitrogen the whole season. The weight of the crop and an analysis of the beets indicated that only 50 percent of the nitrogen that was applied at planting time could be accounted for. About 70 percent of the nitrogen applied in three parts was accounted for, however, and soil and tissue tests indicated some was still available to the crop at harvesttime.

R. L. Carolus found that potatoes in Virginia required 7 pounds of nitrogen an acre during the first 7 weeks of their growth period. During the next 5 weeks the crop used 53 pounds to the acre.

W. R. Jones and H. A. Huston recorded similar data for corn in Indiana.

During such periods of lesser need, fertilizer nitrogen may be used up by soil organisms or may be leached out of the root zone of the crop.

Rates, methods, and time of application of nitrogen fertilizers should be varied with different soils and crops so that an adequate supply is present at all times for the growing crop.

Usually some nitrogen should be applied in the starter fertilizer. A. C. Caldwell, of the University of Minnesota, learned that ammonium nitrogen in contact with phosphate caused young corn plants to make better use of starter phosphate. Sometimes it is wise to make applications primarily to

feed the organisms that decompose the organic matter.

PHOSPHORUS exists in soil as primary and secondary minerals and as a constituent of organic matter. A small amount is held by clay in an adsorbed state and an extremely small amount is in solution.

Phosphorus combines readily with other elements. It is applied as a constituent of various carriers, the simplest of which is phosphoric acid (H_3PO_4). This acid and several phosphate-carrying salts ionize to form $H_2PO_4^-$, HPO_4^{--}, and PO_4^{---} ions, depending on the soil pH.

PO_4^{---} ions are present only in alkali soils and are not important in plant nutrition. Iron and aluminum hydrated oxides combine readily with $H_2PO_4^-$ in medium to strongly acid soils. The resulting phosphate compounds are so insoluble that they cannot be used readily by soil organisms or higher plants. This fixation is more effective in the more acid soils.

Efficient management of fertilizers is the art of feeding the plant rather than the soil: It is getting phosphorus into the plant without allowing the reactions between soil minerals and phosphorus to take place.

The nature of the plant, the characteristics of the soil, the chemistry of the phosphate carrier, and the amount of capital to be invested are factors to be considered in deciding on methods of using phosphorus fertilizers.

Experiments by Kirk Lawton, James Vomocil, and Lowell Owens and his coworkers at Michigan State University show that fertilizers containing a high percentage of their phosphorus in water-soluble form should be applied differently than those that contain all or most of their phosphorus in insoluble forms.

Broadcasting and mixing soluble phosphates with soil (as with a harrow) or spraying solutions on the soil surface result in maximum fixation and least efficiency as far as the immediate crop is concerned. That is because maximum contact is provided between the particles of fertilizer and the hydrated oxides, which are a part of the soil and with which the phosphate ions readily combine.

Placing the phosphates in bands beside the rows of seeds is a more efficient way to apply them both as to crop yields and the percentage of the phosphorus the plants take up.

Dr. Lawton and Dr. Vomocil showed that soluble phosphorus moves rapidly out of fertilizer granules (much fertilizer is now sold in a granular or pelleted rather than powdered form), but moves slowly away from the granules.

The result is a highly concentrated spherical zone of soluble phosphorus around a granule as long as the soil is not disturbed. Roots may then penetrate that sphere and feed readily on the phosphorus in soluble form.

Dr. Owens and his coworkers found that banding and granulating caused an increase in the intake of fertilizer phosphorus by wheat and sugar beet seedlings but that both banding and granulating were not necessary. In other words, the banding of granulated fertilizers did not result in greater use of fertilizer phosphorus than resulted from the banding of pulverant (powdered) fertilizers.

Fertilizers containing only citrate-insoluble and perhaps citrate-soluble (but water-insoluble) forms of phosphate should be applied in finely powdered form and should not be banded.

Rock phosphate is an example of the materials that should be finely ground and mixed with soil to obtain maximum solution effect. That may be true also of highly ammoniated superphosphates, calcium metaphosphate, and fused tricalcium phosphate.

Producers of high-value crops and greenhouse operators should concern themselves with raising the available phosphorus levels of their soils to a point where this fixing power has been satisfied and there are no longer appreciable quantities of "hungry" minerals to combine with the phosphate ions. Phosphate fertilization then can be a simple matter of maintenance by any convenient method.

The specific recommendations listed later are primarily for those who wish to fertilize their current crops at the least cost to insure top yields.

POTASSIUM exists in soil as primary and secondary minerals, as an exchangeable cation attached to soil colloids, as a constituent of fresh organic matter, and in solution. It leaches from soil rather readily when a large amount is present in exchangeable or soluble form. An equilibrium among mineral, exchangeable, and soluble forms of potassium exists in normal soils.

Plants take in more potassium than they need when it is present in excess of their normal needs. Such luxury consumption is wasteful of soil potassium. Excessive applications of potash salts tend furthermore to drive the potassium equilibrium to the direction of unavailable mineral forms.

The farmer should consider these reactions of potassium in soil and the tendency toward luxury consumption by plants when he chooses the method and time of application of potash fertilizer. Because potash salts are somewhat toxic to germinating seeds and young seedlings, excessive amounts should not be applied with seeds or too close to seeds or young transplants.

Broadcast applications of potash are agronomically sounder than are such applications of phosphorus fertilizers because reactions with soil minerals are unimportant except when the rates are excessive. Small, frequent applications are preferred.

Band applications of potash are better for some crops that need a plentiful supply of potassium from the earliest seedling stage. This is probably true of alfalfa, which has responded well to band seeding.

MINOR AND SECONDARY ELEMENTS generally are applied most economically and effectively as constituents of mixed fertilizers. One reason is that the amounts needed are generally so small that separate applications are difficult, except as they may be applied in solution as foliage sprays. Such methods, though, are more costly unless the crop is to be sprayed for other reasons and the minor element is compatible with the spray material.

Several minor elements (among them manganese and boron) are more efficient when they are applied in bands with complete fertilizers. They are usually needed in alkaline soils, in which they are quickly rendered unavailable when mixed with the soil.

Copper and zinc may be mixed effectively with complete fertilizers or may be applied through spray equipment. This latter method is used on vegetable and fruit crops that are sprayed to control diseases and insects.

LIQUID AND GASEOUS FORMS of fertilizer compete with the solid forms.

The use of liquid and ammonia fertilizers has grown steadily.

Applicator equipment, metering devices, and storage facilities have been perfected and make direct applications of anhydrous ammonia practical. In fact, on many farms anhydrous ammonia may be the most economical form of nitrogen.

Anhydrous ammonia and all nitrogen solutions containing free ammonia must be stored in pressure tanks and be applied by equipment that immediately covers them with sufficient soil to prevent volatilization—usually 5 to 6 inches deep with the anhydrous form. Soil should be friable and neither too dry nor too wet. Dry soil may not close in readily over the ammonia, and there may not be sufficient soil water to effect adsorption. Wet soil may contain so small a volume of air-filled pores that the ammonia gas cannot penetrate enough soil to make adsorption complete.

Nonpressure nitrogen solutions may be effectively applied on the soil surface. Wide-boom equipment can be used; it saves time and costs.

The wide use of phosphoric acid and ammonium phosphates as carriers of fertilizer phosphorus has stimulated the practice of applying complete and mixed fertilizers in solution. Precipitation—salting out—limits the concentration of such fertilizers, especially in regions where temperatures may be low. The formula determines the actual concentration; however, (as an average) 30 units is the top grade that may be used with assurance of a stable solution in Northern States.

Two methods of application of solution fertilizer—broadcasting and banding—generally are possible. Phosphates in solution are ready to unite immediately with such soil minerals as hydrated iron oxides. Because solutions cannot be granulated, it would seem that (to avoid extreme fixation) banding should be practiced unless the farmer has decided to apply enough phosphorus to satisfy the fixing power of the soil and leave some for the currently growing crop.

On a Miami soil in Michigan, several tons of superphosphate to the acre may be needed.

According to F. W. Smith, experiments in Kansas indicated that solution fertilizers may be banded efficiently for small grains. Experiments there and elsewhere indicate further that for these crops neither liquid nor solid fertilizers can be efficiently applied in any other way.

The saving of labor is perhaps the greatest advantage in the use of liquid fertilizers. Anhydrous ammonia may be pumped or moved by its own pressure. Nonpressure liquids may be pumped more easily than they can be carried or moved in bags. Storage, however, may be more costly for liquids than for solids.

IRRIGATION WATER may carry fertilizers to the plants. Such methods of distribution are particularly suitable for supplementary applications of nitrogen, potassium, and some of the minor elements.

A large percentage of the fertilizer used for citrus in California and Arizona is applied through the irrigation water. The amount applied in that way for other crops has been increasing. The possibility exists in humid regions that excessive rains may delay irrigation to the extent that plants may suffer from deficiency of the nutrients that have not been applied. Other methods must be used then.

Phosphorus fixation is at a maximum when fertilizers are applied through irrigation water. Because plants must have a plentiful supply of nutrients during the seedling stage, band applications at planting may be more satisfactory. There is probably no advantage in providing for more than one application of phosphate fertilizer for each crop.

Foliar feeding sometimes is successful. Nutrients—nitrogen, iron, copper, zinc, and manganese—may be absorbed readily through plant leaves. Experiments indicate that part of the phosphorus may also be effectively applied in this manner.

The amounts of the major nutrients required for maximum production makes it impractical for most growers to attempt to use foliar feeding except possibly for occasional supplementary applications.

The trace elements we mentioned, however, are needed in such small amounts (often less than 1 pound an acre) that they can be applied as a foliar spray. Because they are not usually needed as fertilizers during the seedling stages, foliar applications are quite permissible if they fit in with the grower's plans. For tree fruits and certain greenhouse plants, in fact, foliar applications are much more effective than are soil applications.

SPECIFIC CROPS vary in their need for certain nutrients and in the way they react to methods of application.

Some seeds are easily injured by direct contact with fertilizer salts.

Rooting habits and the season (as it affects levels of soil moisture) may have a definite bearing on the response of a crop to a method of application.

A few principles should be considered in deciding which method or methods of application should be followed.

Is the cost of fertilizer a major item in the production of the crop?

If the answer is "No," the broadcast, mixed-in application of maximum amounts of nutrients may be the simplest and best method. Even then, starter fertilizer may be advisable for certain crops—like sugar beets on mineral soils and onions on organic soils.

If the answer to the question is "Yes," as it usually is, a farmer has to choose the method or methods from which he gets greatest efficiency.

Starter fertilizer is essential for most crops—early stimulation usually is advantageous. That means that nutrients should be placed close to seeds.

Nutrients are ineffective in dry soil. They therefore should be placed rather deeply in the soil and in places where roots penetrate. But excessive amounts of fertilizer should not be placed directly under the seeds of plants that have taproots.

Cultural practices should be such that roots may develop freely in the region where the fertilizer is placed. Deeply placed fertilizer is not effective if aeration is poor. Too much compaction around or above the fertilizer may slow up the diffusion of oxygen and thus inhibit the intake of nutrients by the roots.

Nitrogen (N) and potash (K_2O) salts are more likely to be toxic to germinating seeds and young seedlings than are carriers of phosphoric oxide (P_2O_5). Some agronomists describe the safe amounts of fertilizer in contact with seeds in terms of pounds of N and K_2O per acre (10 to 30 pounds) and disregard the pounds of P_2O_5. Such recommendations favor starter fertilizers high in P_2O_5 and relatively low in N and K_2O and provide for applying the N and K_2O in previous or sidedressing operations. The other alternative (if suitable equipment is available) is to use separate band applications for all the fertilizer or for just the N and K_2O.

Fertilizers applied below the surface

are less likely to be lost by erosion. Leaching of N and K_2O is more likely from sandy soils, and heavy, infrequent applications encourage luxury consumption. Recent information indicates that small, frequent applications of K_2O fertilizer are most efficient.

BAND SEEDING of alfalfa, as suggested by J. L. Haynes and L. E. Thatcher of Ohio, and others, is recommended rather widely in the North Central States. It provides for the dropping of the alfalfa seeds on top of the soil directly over fertilizer bands. Combination grain and fertilizer drills are easily adapted to this method of seeding. Sod grassland drills and other placement drills that may handle grasses along with legumes are now available.

Alfalfa may be seeded alone in this manner or as a companion crop with spring grain. Henry Mederski, of the Ohio Agricultural Experiment Station, found that seeds should be directly above the fertilizer band and should be separated from it by at least three-fourths inch of soil. Oats and fertilizer may be mixed together in the band. He suggested that the amount of fertilizer applied in this manner should contain not more than 100 pounds of N or K_2O or both per acre. Heavier applications may hinder germination. Covering chains should not be used. Many research workers advocate that the alfalfa seeds should be pressed into the soil by press wheels to compact the soil below the seed (which has been disturbed by the fertilizer placement) and also the soil around the seed.

If press wheels are not available, rolling the planting with a land roller with packer wheels will firm the soil somewhat but has certain undesirable features—such as a tendency to pulverize the surface of the soil and to favor the germination of weed seeds between the seed rows.

If band seeding is not practiced, alfalfa fertilizers should be plowed under or drilled deeply before or at the time of seeding. The seeds should not be in contact with fertilizers that contain more than 25 pounds of K_2O per acre. If soil tests show that only phosphate is needed, contact application may be permissable, but in no case should the alfalfa seeds be covered to any depth greater than one-half inch.

If alfalfa is seeded in the early spring on fall-sown wheat, a light application of superphosphate or mixed fertilizer containing not more than 25 pounds of K_2O has been recommended in some States. Such fertilizers may be placed in contact with the alfalfa seed by means of a combination grain and fertilizer drill or they may be drilled separately. If soil tests show that more than 25 pounds of K_2O is needed and if nitrogen is also to be applied, contact between seed and fertilizer should be avoided. Press wheels on the drill will insure better stands on many soils if soil moisture is good at the time of drilling.

Agronomists differ as to whether an attempt should be made to build potassium reserves in soil. It may be advisable to make frequent, small applications as topdressings in order to avoid luxury consumption of potassium. Such a system has been practiced successfully in the Eastern and New England States.

Kirk Lawton and Milo Tesar, of the Michigan Agricultural Experiment Station, have shown that alfalfa takes most of its nutrients from the surface soil. The feeder roots of old alfalfa plants are close to the surface—topdressings of fertilizer, even phosphates, therefore are effective in feeding them.

Annual and biennial forage crops should be fertilized in much the same manner as is recommended for establishing alfalfa. However, the adaptation of grain drills for band seeding is not practical for many species, as many of the elongated and fluffy grass seeds cannot be metered successfully with "grass seed" attachments to grain drills. Short-lived legumes may receive all their nutrients at planting time; or, if the rates are to be large, a part of the fertilizer may be plowed under or drilled deeply after plowing.

GRASSES usually need more nitrogen than can be applied safely and efficiently at planting time. Topdressings at rather frequent intervals are recommended.

Solid or liquid nitrogen may be used.

FOR CORN, fertilizer management may be divided into three phases—starter, maintenance level, and supplementary applications.

Starter fertilizer, applied at planting time, should be high in phosphorus because it stimulates early growth. A small amount of nitrogen (probably ammonium) will increase the intake of fertilizer phosphorus. If soil tests reveal a low level of potassium, it also may be used in the starter.

Starter fertilizer, if its use is indicated, should be applied in a band 1.5 to 2 inches to the side of the seed and the same distance below the seed. Relatively large applications of fertilizer applied in that way will not affect germination.

The split-boot applicator does not place corn fertilizer in a safe or efficient location. If such equipment is used, the total amount of N or K$_2$O, or both, should not exceed 40 pounds an acre. Starter fertilizers should be drilled rather than hill dropped.

Maintenance applications of nutrients may be applied in several ways. If corn is grown in rotations with other crops, particularly legumes, most of the minerals the corn needs may be applied for the other crops in the rotation.

If soil tests disclose a need for more fertilizer than can be applied safely as starter, the balance probably should be plowed under. The soil should be left loose after plowing, so that the corn roots may readily reach the plowed-under fertilizer and enough oxygen is in the plowed soil to allow the nutrients to enter the plant roots.

Experiments in a few States have indicated that starter and maintenance fertilizers may be applied at the same time. If soil tests show that a large maintenance application is needed, the fertilizer may be placed in a band somewhat deeper in the soil or in two bands—one-fourth of the fertilizer 1.5 to 2 inches below the seed and the remainder 6 inches below the seed. Large amounts of nitrogen may be safely placed in a deep band at planting.

Corn needs plenty of nitrogen. On fields where legumes have not been grown recently, 120 pounds an acre may be needed for 100-bushel yields. Some of it, perhaps 80 pounds, should be plowed under or applied as a sidedressing. Sidedressing probably means a more efficient use of nitrogen, but many farmers plow the fertilizer under because of convenience.

SORGHUM is like corn in its needs for nutrients. It is more easily injured by high concentrations of fertilizer salts. Because sorghum is planted later than corn, it must produce grain in a shorter season and the starter effect may be more important.

Starter fertilizers should be especially high in phosphorus, and no more than 30 pounds of N plus K$_2$O should be applied through the split-boot applicator.

Many farmers use a combination grain and fertilizer drill to plant sorghum because yields are higher if it is grown in rows 16 to 24 inches apart. Because the grain drill places fertilizer in contact with the seed, the amount of N plus K$_2$O should be reduced to 10 pounds an acre. The P$_2$O$_5$ in the fertilizer will not injure the germination. If more N and K$_2$O are needed, the additional materials should be drilled in or applied broadcast before planting or before plowing.

SMALL GRAINS may be planted and fertilized satisfactorily with the combination drill, which places the fertilizer in contact with the seed. Because grains are planted in rows 6 or 7 inches apart, the amount of fertilizer in each band is not too great, and the contact application is not injurious at medium rates. The close proximity of the phosphorus insures rapid development of seedling roots and no doubt is largely responsible for the success of this method.

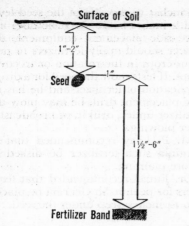

Surface of Soil

1"-2"

Seed — 1"

1½"-6"

Fertilizer Band

The proper placement of fertilizer bands for beans, corn, cotton, peanuts, soybeans, sugar beets, and many vegetable crops.

Wheat planted in relatively dry soil may be injured by the N and K_2O in the fertilizer. F. W. Smith, of Kansas State College, says that it is well to limit the sum of these two nutrients to 30 pounds an acre in Kansas. Somewhat larger rates are permissible in the more humid regions. There need be no limit on the amount of P_2O_5 that can be applied safely. An additional application of K_2O fertilizer may be plowed under or applied as a top-dressing if soils are especially low in potassium.

Wheat usually requires more nitrogen than can be applied safely with the seed. A supplementary application may be made at any time in the early stages of growth. For winter wheat, that is up until the spring growth is well started. Spring wheat (and spring oats) should receive supplementary nitrogen as early as convenient.

Anhydrous ammonia and pressure solutions are applied most effectively before grains are planted to avoid disturbance of the established plants, but other solutions or solid forms of nitrogen may be applied at any convenient time, even when the soil is frozen. The salts readily melt into frozen soil.

Sideband applications of fertilizer for small grains have been tried. They are better for high rates on wheat. The advantage of having the phosphorus in contact with the seed may be sufficiently great to offset the slight injury which may result from contact applications of small amounts of the other two nutrients.

FIELD BEANS AND SOYBEANS should receive fertilizer in a single band 1 to 1.5 inches to the side of the row and 1.5 to 2 inches below the seed level. Applied thus, rates up to 400 pounds an acre are safe and desirable in places where soil tests indicate a need.

The seeds of both these crops are easily injured by fertilizer salts. If side-band equipment is not available and soil tests demonstrate a relatively low nutrient level, the fertilizer should be plowed under or drilled deeply just before planting.

Manganese may be needed. The carrier should be mixed with the fertilizer or sprayed on the foliage. Boron should not be applied.

SUGAR BEETS yield best when fertilizers are placed 1 to 2 inches directly below the seed or in a band 1 to 1.5 inches to the side of the row and 1 to 2 inches below the seed. Either placement has given good results if the rate of application does not exceed 60 pounds of N plus K_2O. Larger quantities should be confined to the side locations and the band should be moved out to a distance of 2 inches from the row.

Not more than 20 pounds of N plus K_2O should be placed in direct contact with sugar beet seeds. A part should be plowed under if soil conditions indicate a need for very heavy applications of fertilizer.

Good soil aeration is especially important for sugar beets. Fertilizer efficiency will be improved if root beds are left loose and if fertilizers are plowed under just before planting time.

It may be advisable to sidedress nitrogen soon after blocking. Locations relative to the row may vary, but it is better to apply the nitrogen at the surface than to disturb the roots by deep placement.

Anhydrous ammonia should be placed in the middle of the row and as early in the season as possible. Applications late in the season are not advisable. Excessively large applications may reduce yields and also the percentage of sucrose.

Beets may need less than 30 pounds of fertilizer nitrogen during the season if they follow alfalfa.

COTTON is even more sensitive than field beans to injury from fertilizer salts. Many experiments in a wide range of conditions lead us to recommend that the fertilizer be placed in a single band 2.5 inches to the side and 2 to 2.5 inches below the seed level. Equal results may be expected when the same amount of fertilizer is placed in bands on both sides of the row.

With side placement machines one can throw up soil to form a bed, smooth the bed, and plant the seed, all in one operation. Without such equipment, several operations may be necessary to mix the fertilizer with the soil, form the bed, and later plant the seed. Instead of that, some agronomists recommend broadcasting and mixing with the soil before planting.

Nitrogen sidedressing may be advisable. J. G. Futral, of the Georgia Agricultural Experiment Station, recommended that on the lighter soils of that State at least one-half of the nitrogen be applied in that way. It is usually done when plants are 8 to 10 inches tall and may be accomplished by use of a sidedressing attachment to the cultivators.

One should be careful to avoid damage to roots, but losses through erosion are less likely if the nitrogen is applied below the surface. Less fertilization of weeds is done when no fertilizer is placed on the surface of the soil. Potash fertilizer may be applied in the same way and at the same time.

FERTILIZER FOR PEANUTS may be applied as for cotton, in one or two bands

2.5 inches to the side of the seed level and 2 inches below it. If he does not have side placement equipment, the farmer should apply fertilizers to previous crops in the rotation or to cover crops. If tests show the need for a direct application of fertilizer and he has no side placement drill, he may plow the fertilizer under, drill it, or broadcast it after plowing.

M. P. Lacy recommended that in Virginia such fertilizer be disked in before planting.

Dr. Futral recommended that fertilizers for peanuts in Georgia be placed 8 to 14 inches deep under the seed.

TOBACCO FERTILIZERS, up to 800 pounds an acre, should be placed in two bands 7 inches apart and about 5 inches below the surface of the soil. The depth should be regulated to be 1 to 1.5 inches below the root crown of the transplant. Care should be taken to avoid placing the roots of transplants in contact with fertilizer.

Where previous cropping history or soil tests indicate a need for more than 800 pounds an acre, the extra amount should be plowed under or broadcast and worked into the soil before the plants are set.

If double band placement equipment is not available, G. R. Mathews, of the Virginia Polytechnic Institute, recommends that in Virginia the first 800 pounds of the fertilizer should be placed 6 to 10 inches deep under the ridge that is to be the row. The ridge should be high enough that the roots of the newly set plants will be 1 to 2 inches above the fertilizer. This method also has been recommended by J. M. Carr, of the Oxford Tobacco Research Station, Oxford, N. C.

Sidedressing is not generally recommended. All necessary nutrients, including nitrogen, may be applied in the bands at the time of transplanting. Supplementary applications of nitrogen and potassium sulfate, however, may be advisable on sandy soils if leaching is a problem. Conventional sidedressing equipment may be used.

VEGETABLE growers apply rather large amounts of fertilizer. With high rates of application, the cost of fertilizers represents a smaller percentage of the total production costs than is the case in the production of crops like wheat or corn.

Many vegetables are short-season crops, and some are planted in cool weather. Starter fertilizers therefore usually are advantageous. The use of foliar sprays and the application of fertilizer in irrigation water might be feasible.

Nutrient levels, as indicated by soil tests, plant tissue tests, and deficiency symptoms, should be considered in deciding the timeliness and extent of supplementary fertilizer additions.

Potato fertilizers, if the rates are not above 1,000 pounds an acre, should all be placed in two bands at each side of the row, except possibly some of the nitrogen. The bands should be 2 inches out from the bottom of the seed pieces and level with or slightly below them. If conditions indicate a need for more than 1,000 pounds an acre, the additional amount should be plowed under or drilled deeply after plowing.

If more than 50 pounds of nitrogen are needed during the season, a portion should be plowed under or applied as a sidedressing at the time of the last cultivation. If the field is irrigated, supplementary nitrogen may well be applied through the system. Nitrogen solutions are well adapted to such a method of application, either through sprinklers or ditches.

SWEETPOTATOES are grown extensively as a field crop. If fertilizer rates range from 400 to 700 pounds an acre, all of it should be applied in bands about 3 inches deep and 3 to 5 inches away from the plants. At the larger rates the bands should be at the greater distance from the plants. Modern transplanters are equipped to apply fertilizer in sidebands.

When sweetpotatoes are grown as a truck crop, rates of 1,500 to 2,000 pounds of fertilizer are common. Then one-third of it should be plowed under or drilled deeply before transplanting or be applied as a sidedressing 2 or 3 weeks after transplanting. Sidedressing applications should be 5 to 6 inches from the row and 3 inches deep.

TOMATOES are a rather long-season crop and should get plenty of nutrients over a period of several months. On sandy soils that means three or four applications. The first portion should be plowed under. A second application should be in bands 3 to 4 inches from the plants at the time of transplanting. One or two additional applications should be made during cultivations or through irrigation water.

Two applications of complete fertilizer, with an additional application of nitrogen, usually have been enough on heavy soils. The complete fertilizer should be equally divided between plow-under and sideband applications unless the total rate per acre is less than 500 pounds. In that case it can all be applied in the sidebands at transplanting time.

Starter solutions are recommended on all soils. Foliar sprays have been used successfully and are recommended where the crop is to be sprayed often to control diseases and insects.

ROOT CROPS AND SPINACH call for different recommendations in various regions. Application in bands 2 inches out and 2 to 3 inches deeper than the seed is generally approved if the rates of application are 500 pounds an acre or less. If the rates exceed 500 pounds, the additional quantity should be plowed under, broadcast after plowing, or applied as a sidedressing. Extra nitrogen, particularly for spinach, should be sidedressed or applied through irrigation water. Complete fertilizers may be successfully applied through some irrigation systems.

Recommendations for sweet corn are not unlike those for field corn. Sweet corn plants are less vigorous and their season of growth is shorter. Starter fertilizers thus become more important.

Perhaps sidedressings should be more frequent. Irrigation water can be used successfully as a medium for applying the fertilizer. Soil and tissue tests may be used to time the application properly.

SNAP BEANS AND LIMA BEANS should be fertilized as recommended for field beans, except that rates are usually greater. For that reason, the sidebands should be 2 to 3 inches out from the row.

If amounts greater than 500 pounds an acre are advisable, the additional quantity should be plowed under or applied as a sidedressing. Under most conditions the plow-under method is preferred. Extra nitrogen may be sidedressed.

Manganese should be mixed with the fertilizer or applied as a foliar spray.

PEAS are easily injured if fertilizer is placed in contact with the seed. It should be in a band 1 to 2 inches to the side and 1 to 3 inches deeper than the seed. Combination grain drills may be used for planting peas, but most of them do not apply fertilizer in sidebands. If peas are to be planted with such a drill, the fertilizer should be plowed under or drilled deeply just before planting.

Bean drills designed to place fertilizer in bands separate from the seed, but in rather widely spaced rows, may be used for peas. Such a method of planting and fertilizing is appropriate for seed production.

CABBAGE, broccoli, brussels sprouts, cauliflower, and celery respond best to fertilizer placed in bands at planting time, 3 inches deep and 2 to 2.5 inches from the row. Fertilizer in excess of 500 pounds should be plowed under or (on light soils) should be drilled deeply just before planting or should be sidedressed.

The need for nitrogen may be determined by plant tests or leaf color. Supplemental applications may be sidedressed or applied through irrigation water or sprayed on the leaves.

Foliar sprays for magnesium on celery are recommended in Michigan, New York, Canada, and California.

ONION FERTILIZERS placed directly under the row have been successful on muck. Where rates are in excess of 800 pounds an acre (16-inch row spacing), it is better to apply the potash broadcast and to place the nitrogen and phosphorus 2 inches under the row.

Onions are sometimes grown in raised beds on mineral soils. Then the fertilizer should be placed 4 inches deep on the shoulder of the bed and 2 inches from the row.

CANTALOUPS, cucumbers, melons, squash, pumpkins, kale, lettuce, and salad greens respond well when up to 500 pounds an acre is placed in a band 2 to 3 inches from the row and 2 inches deeper than the seed.

Deeper placement is recommended in California.

If more than 500 pounds is needed, additional fertilizer should be plowed under or applied in irrigation water. Supplementary nitrogen may be needed and can be applied in the same way or it may be applied as a sidedressing.

FRUIT FERTILIZERS are not commonly applied in bands. Only a small fraction of the total fertilizer applied for fruit can be considered as a starter. Perhaps that is part of the reason why phosphate fertilizers are less important and are largely for the cover crops.

Nitrogen and potash fertilizers, applied primarily for fruit trees and vines, should be broadcast or may be applied through irrigation water. Much of the fertilizer for citrus trees in California is applied in irrigation water. Because furrow irrigation is practiced, the fertilizer is applied between rather than under the trees. Dry fertilizers are dumped into weirs and solutions are metered into ditches.

Deciduous fruits in humid regions and citrus fruits in Florida cannot be so well fertilized through irrigation water because the need for nutrients and water is less well established. Most of the fertilizer is broadcast under the trees or over the entire orchard. If the fertilizers are primarily applied for the trees, as with nitrogen in early spring, it is usually placed under the trees. On the other hand, complete fertilizers are usually broadcast or drilled for use by the cover crop as well as the trees.

Manganese, copper, and zinc are applied more successfully as foliage sprays—especially on citrus in alkaline soils. Frequent applications enable the growers to apply much of the nitrogen through the leaves.

Leaf analysis is used as a means of diagnosing the needs of tree fruits. Soil tests have limited value for this purpose, probably because of errors in sampling. Many horticulturists believe that soil tests may well be used for determining the needs of the cover crops.

NUMEROUS IMPROVEMENTS have been made in equipment used for the application of fertilizer on farms since the resumption of the production of farm implements after the Second World War. In some instances, complete new machines have been made available to the farmer and the grower.

These changes have been brought about by many things, such as new types of fertilizer materials, use of higher analysis fertilizers, increased rates of fertilizer application, and results of research in the application of fertilizer. The research on the effects of placement of fertilizer on crop production has had a definite bearing on equipment design. The following changes are not to be considered a full résumé of improvements of fertilizer machines, but an account of some selected examples to illustrate some of the more important changes since equipment production was resumed after the war.

SEVERAL ROW PLANTERS are now available with deep placement attachments for fertilizer, which is a marked contrast to the split-boot depositor used on planters for several decades. To take care of the increased rates, the hoppers and fertilizer boxes have been made bigger. Many persons, however, feel the large amount of time taken in the field to stop the operation and fill the small hoppers has had considerable bearing on the changes in hopper size. The split-boot never gave good results, but it is even less satisfactory at the high planter speeds and greater rates of fertilizer application that have come into use.

One company is manufacturing a broadcast spreader with three hoppers so that nitrogen, phosphorus, and potassium are applied separately and the ratios can be varied. With the three-hopper broadcaster, a saving in cost of fertilizer should be expected by buying fertilizer materials in bulk quantities in concentrated form. Bulk truck spreaders have come into common use for applying complete fertilizers—a method that requires less handling of the fertilizer materials and reduces costs of application. Compaction of soils under such large concentrated loads, however, is considered a potential problem in some areas. The use of fertilizer in liquid form may be found to be extremely efficient as far as ease of handling is concerned; a minimum of muscular exertion is needed when suitable equipment is provided for this fairly new form of fertilizer.

BETTER PROVISION has been made for cleaning equipment because much of the corrosion is caused by the fertilizer that remains in the machine after use. Many machines now have easily removable bottoms, agitators, and metering mechanisms. Some have hoppers that are removable or can be inverted for removing the residue of fertilizer and cleaning. Some are equipped with corrosionproof plastic hoppers that are reinforced with fiberglass.

Many fertilizer distributors have positive metering devices that can dispense damp and lumpy fertilizers. Improved gage settings assist in making calibrations more accurately and with greater ease. Agitator parts are stronger, and the controls of fertilizer flow are being made sturdier and are adapted to manual and automatic operation.

Fertilizers of higher analysis have brought about a need for machines that apply them more uniformly and more accurately with respect to the seed or plant.

IMPROVEMENT IN THE PHYSICAL condition of solid fertilizers is reflected in the production of more granulated fertilizers, which cake and harden less during storage and can be distributed more easily and uniformly in the field. These free-flowing granular fertilizers continue to flow in many machines after the agitator or metering mechanism has stopped, however, and the hopper opening has to be closed in order to stop the flow of fertilizer. On many machines this is accomplished by closing the bottom of the hopper with the metering plate as the drive is thrown out of gear.

Another method is to have a second plate under the hopper; the plate closes the openings automatically when the drive is disengaged. This arrangement does not disturb the setting of the metering plate when operating in the field—which is often quite important, as resetting an orifice-type opening is very sensitive, particularly at relatively low application rates of fertilization.

TO APPLY LIQUID fertilizers, new machines have come into use. Anhydrous ammonia requires equipment to withstand high pressures and soil depositors to place the material at least 6 inches deep. One high-pressure liquid applicator has rotating shafts in front of the knife-blade openers to open the soil for deposition. The device reduces draft and tends to disturb the soil less so as to have less chance of losing the nitrogen gas.

The mixed liquid fertilizers that contain nitrogen, phosphorus, and potassium may be applied on the surface without loss of plant food. They are more adaptable to close-growing crops when applications are delayed. They can be applied with field sprayers, particularly on pastures and small grains. The development of metering pumps and their use with dribble tubes has improved the ease of obtaining a uniform flow in the broadcast or row application.

The high-pressure metering piston pump has been adapted for low-pressure and nonpressure solutions. A metering hose pump, invented in the late 1930's, was further developed for its adaptation to the nitrogen fertilizer solutions and mixed liquid fertilizers. The refinement of the hose pump was accomplished by research engineers in cooperative research with the North Carolina Agricultural Experiment Station and the Agricultural Research Service of the Department of Agriculture. Through this cooperative research and subsequent field testing, this metering hose pump was made practical for farm use. The metering pump is now being made commercially for use on farms.

Compressors driven by tractor power takeoff are arranged on tractors to maintain constant tank pressure for low-pressure solutions which provides a simple and effective arrangement on many commercial liquid fertilizer applicators. However, the system requires steady forward travel in the field to maintain a uniform application, which is also a requirement of the gravity-flow systems and pump systems of the power takeoff type.

THE RESULTS of research in the application of fertilizer for most efficient use of nutrients has complicated the equipment requirements in some cases. An example in the complication of equipment is in the band seeding of hay lands and pasture crops. Crops in various sections respond differently to fertilizers, and machines have had to be designed with greater flexibility to meet the varied requirements. Attachments have been put on conventional corn planters so that the plant food can be placed to one side and below the seed; the placement can be adjusted conveniently by the operator.

Some planters also have a high and low position for fertilizer bands so that large amounts can be placed deeply and smaller amounts can be put at a more shallow depth as starters. One machine with such a dual-level arrangement has been made to plant row crops in either prepared seedbeds or in sod or stubble land.

Equipment is available for applying fertilizer to the lower soil zones at the time that the subsoiling operations are undertaken.

Several grassland machines have been put on the market for seeding and applying fertilizers on pastures or rough land without destroying the existing crop. Various arrangements of depositors to put seed and fertilizer at different depths are found on the different sod grassland drills and some may be adjusted to vary the amounts of soil left between seed and fertilizer.

The greater response to fertilizer and more efficient use of seeds for pasture and hay land by the band seeding method has brought demands for new machines to do band seeding. The heavy-duty grassland drills may be used for band seeding in prepared seedbeds, but other means are available through conversion kits for fertilizer-grain drills. Some machines for band seeding use the packer wheels of a corrugated land roller for press wheels. They plant the seed in rows, and the fertilizer is placed in bands below the seed.

PROBLEMS HAVE ARISEN in the wake of these changes. A great need is storage facilities on farms for liquid fertilizers and dry fertilizers in bulk. The future of some of the machines mentioned may depend on the solutions to the storage problems. There also has been a need for a single machine that dispenses granulated and pulverized fertilizers in a more satisfactory manner. Corrosion of metal parts has always been a problem with fertilizers, and in some instances it has been greatly intensified with some of the new materials in both dry and liquid fertilizers.

Farm Manure

Myron S. Anderson

Livestock on American farms each year produce a billion tons of manure. It has great potential value, and its organic matter is twice the amount of humus that the soil gets from our grain and cotton crops.

Manure has value in maintaining and improving soil because of the plant nutrients, humus, and the organic substances it may contain.

About 250 thousand tons of dried animal manures, bagged and in bulk, are sold each year in the United States. Four-fifths of it is produced and sold in Pacific Coast States. Near Los Angeles alone, about 5 million bags of manure, with a retail value of 3.5 million dollars, are used annually.

Much of the manure sold in the West is produced by dairy cattle on ranches and farms where little or no feed is grown.

Gardeners in the East apply considerable amounts of dried manures, which originate in commercial dairies and in stockyards. The manures, dried and bagged, often are sold with a guaranteed nitrogen content of 2 percent. Superphosphate is sometimes added before the manures are dried. Such products may have a guaranteed content of phosphoric oxide.

The values of manure on irrigated and on nonirrigated lands vary with the market prices of crops and have

This chapter is based on a chapter by Robert M. Salter and C. J. Schollenberger in the 1938 Yearbook of Agriculture.

been estimated within the range of 2 dollars to 6 dollars a ton when field crops are grown.

If we assume an average value of 2.50 dollars and the recovery of two-thirds of the potential manure production from feeding all crops except wheat grain, the annual value of the manure from 100 acres of land that produces 50 bushels of corn, 40 bushels of oats, 25 bushels of wheat, and 2 tons of hay an acre in rotation would be about 500 dollars.

But only about one-third or one-half of the potential crop-producing and soil-conserving value of the manure actually is utilized. Probably one-half of it is dropped on pastures and uncultivated ground. Of the rest, an enormous loss occurs because of failure to save the liquid portion; improper fermentation and drying, whereby nitrogen is lost; and leaching from storage piles exposed to heavy rainfall.

Even after it is spread on the field, the manure may lose a great deal of ammonia through volatilization before it is incorporated into the soil, and a part of the soluble constituents may be lost in surface runoff.

A final factor in the inefficient use of manure is that it is not always applied at the season, in the manner, at the rate, or to the crop that would give the greatest return.

It is possible to prevent much of this loss if one understands the nature of manure, the character of its most valuable constituents, and how it may be utilized best.

The maximum benefits can be realized by handling and storing the manure properly; using it on suitable soils; applying it at the proper place in a rotation as regards crop or crops; using supplemental fertilization and lime, if needed; installing adequate drainage and irrigation, if needed; using high-quality, well-adapted seed; and observing good tillage practices.

FARM MANURE is a mixture of animal excrements and the soiled bedding that accumulates in stables.

Average farm manure in a damp condition is usually assigned the formula of 0.5–0.25–0.5—meaning, respectively, the percentages of nitrogen phosphoric oxide, and potash.

At least two-thirds of the nitrogen is in slow-acting forms. Commercial fertilizer equivalent to 1 ton of average manure could be bought at retail for about 2.50 dollars in 1957. The expense of applying 100 pounds of 10–5–10 fertilizer is much less than that of applying a ton of manure. On soils in good tilth, the returns from an equivalent amount of fertilizer usually will be greater. Many persons therefore discount the value of manure as fertilizer.

Experiments in Denmark in 1894–1948 compared crop yields from plots treated with farmyard manure and plots treated with equal amounts of plant nutrients as artificial fertilizers. A clover and grass mixture was grown every fourth year and probably supplied enough fresh organic matter to maintain the physical condition of the soil. Higher yields were obtained from the artificial fertilizers. It can be concluded that at least in northern latitudes manure does not provide all of the plant nutrients needed and fails to provide any plant nutrients or growth substances that cannot be supplied by artificial fertilizers.

The chief benefits from manure are indirect. The humus it supplies improves the physical character of the soil by increasing its capacity to take in and hold water, its aeration, and temperature relations. It favors the biological activities of lower organisms that work over the stock of organic residues and plant nutrient-bearing minerals in the soil and make them more usable. The physical properties of soils that are too heavy or too light are improved by an increase in the humus content.

Gardeners and nurserymen who use large amounts of manure know its beneficial effects on the soil. Farmers who apply limited amounts may not see marked changes in the soil. Without a doubt, however, the incorporation of moderate amounts of coarse organic matter into the soil is important. The protection from beating rains and evaporation afforded by manure used as topdressing improves the tilth and reduces erosion.

In an experiment at Zanesville, Ohio, runoff and soil loss were measured from two corn plots, one topdressed with manure and one not, on a 12-percent slope of Muskingum Silt Loam. Erosive rainfall was heavy the first year of the experiment. Soil loss from the untreated plot from late June until harvest was 41 tons an acre. Soil loss from the plot topdressed with manure was 1.4 tons an acre. Runoff loss of rainfall from the topdressed plot was less than half of that from the unmanured plot.

Maintenance of the humus content of the soil is not merely a matter of incorporating organic matter, such as straw and cornstalks, the composition of which differs greatly from that of stabilized soil humus, which results from the accumulation of centuries of biological activity in the virgin soil. Such materials as straw contain relatively less nitrogen in proportion to carbon, in the form of easily decomposed carbohydrates, than does humus; the carbon-nitrogen ratio is about 50 to 1, compared with 10 to 1 for humus.

When unhumified organic matter with a wide carbon-nitrogen ratio undergoes biological decomposition, the organisms that carry on the processes require nitrogen and the other fertility elements, which they build into their cell substance, just as higher plants do. The straw has too little nitrogen to supply what the organisms need to decompose this raw material. Because they must get more nitrogen from the soil, they and the crop compete for it. That explains the bad effect often noted from plowing under straw or fresh manure containing a lot of straw or sawdust. It can be prevented by adding 0.5 to 1 percent of available nitrogen, based on dry weight of straw.

Good manure, however, contains enough quick-acting nitrogen to take care of the decomposition of a normal amount of straw and also furnish some for the immediate needs of the crop. Thus it is necessary to conserve the nitrogen of farm manure, for it is a direct plant nutrient and is essential to the formation of humus.

The reducing action of manure decomposing in the soil aids in making available iron and manganese, present in all soils but sometimes unavailable under excessively oxidizing conditions. The soluble organic matter supplied by manure is believed to aid in keeping iron and phosphates in solution, thus promoting their availability to plants. Some persons believe grain and forage grown with animal manures have greater nutritive qualities than those grown in the presence of mineral fertilizers. Experiments provide no data to justify this hypothesis, however.

MANURE FROM DIFFERENT classes of animals varies in value. Manure from grass-fed animals, growing stock, and milk cows is less rich than manure from animals being fattened or from work animals liberally fed on concentrates. The reason is that the constituents of the excreta are derived from the food. Passage through the animal can add nothing to the total amount of the fertility elements.

Growing animals and milking cows utilize considerably more of the nitrogen, phosphoric oxide, calcium, and so on of their food for flesh, bone, and milk than is retained by mature stock on maintenance rations or fattening. They need liberal feed to get the carbohydrates and proteins necessary to transform energy from food into work or stored fat, but less of the nitrogen and minerals are retained in proportion to the greater amount of food.

The constituents of feedstuffs actually utilized are the carbohydrates and fats for energy, the nitrogenous proteins for energy and tissue building, and the mineral constituents for bone and milk and body processes.

Digestive processes depend on the

action of enzymes, which the animal secretes and which dissolve and break down the complex molecules of feed materials into more simple soluble substances—carbohydrates to sugars, proteins to amino acids, and fats to fatty acids. In this state the food can diffuse into the blood and be carried to all parts of the body.

Some carbohydrates, such as cellulose and nonprotein nitrogen compounds, are not made available by the processes of digestion as such, but can be utilized by ruminants with the aid of bacteria living in the digestive tract. These substances are turned into sugars by enzymes secreted by the bacteria, or they are built directly into the protoplasms of the bacteria and then digested by the animal.

Constituents too resistant to be dissolved in these ways, or insufficiently chewed, or too well protected by indigestible matter simply pass through the animal and are rejected in the feces. The feces then contain little that has really been a part of the animal. They consist of undigested material taken as food and of bacterial cells, living and dead, which make up 20 to 30 percent of the solid excrement and contain half or more of its nitrogen content as proteins.

The most resistant constituent of feedstuffs is lignin, a woody substance, although much cellulose and related carbohydrates also escape digestion. Only about half the protein of timothy hay, a typical low-grade roughage, is digested, compared with 80 percent of the protein in a concentrate like cottonseed meal. Also, as the level of

protein feeding is raised beyond a certain point, the protein is less effectively digested and more of it passes into the feces. Some of the nitrogen compounds of dung are insoluble and have already resisted digestion; hence they are not fully available as fertilizers.

The waste products of carbohydrate metabolism are excreted through the lungs, as carbon dioxide. Those of protein metabolism are excreted through the kidneys, in the form of nitrogen compounds, like urea. Such compounds are readily attacked by microorganisms common in dung and soil. The nitrogen is converted to the ammonium form, in which it is available for immediate use by plants. Urine also contains most of the potash originally in the food, but the phosphoric oxide and calcium are mostly in dung.

The dung of horses and sheep is drier and their urine is more concentrated than are the dung and urine of hogs and cattle. Manure from horses and sheep is not easily compacted. Consequently it ferments or heats more readily than that of hogs and cattle, which is commonly called "cold" by farmers.

The urinary secretion of birds is semisolid and is voided mixed with the feces, so that hen manure is concentrated. The urine of hogs makes up a greater proportion of the total excrement and is notably low in nitrogen and high in phosphoric oxide. These differences are partly physiological peculiarities; they can be attributed in part to the nature and concentration of the food.

BEDDING MATERIAL or litter is necessary to keep stabled stock clean and

Average Daily Amount and Composition of Solid and Liquid Excrement of Mature Animals

Animal	Daily production per animal		Dry matter		Nitrogen		Phosphoric oxide (P_2O_5)		Potash (K_2O)		Lime (CaO)	
	Solid lbs	Liquid lbs	Solid %	Liquid %	Solid %	Liquid %	Solid %	Liquid %	Solid %	Liquid %	Solid %	Liquid %
Horses...	35.5	8.0	24.3	9.9	0.52	1.20	0.30	Trace	0.24	1.50	0.15	0.45
Cattle...	52.0	20.0	16.2	6.2	.32	.95	.21	0.03	.16	.95	.34	.01
Sheep...	2.5	1.5	34.5	12.8	.65	1.68	.46	.03	.23	2.10	.46	.16
Hogs....	6.0	3.5	18.0	3.3	.60	.30	.46	.12	.44	1.00	.09	.00
Hens....	.1	....	35.0	....	1.00	....	.80	....	.40	....	....	....

Characteristics of Litter Materials

| Material | Litter required to absorb 100 pounds of liquid | Nitrogen held per ton of litter [1] | Content of fertilizing ingredients per ton of air-dry material | | | Carbohydrate activity |
			Nitrogen	Phosphoric oxide	Potash	
	Pounds	Pounds	Pounds	Pounds	Pounds	
Wheat straw	45	4. 5	11	4	20	High.
Oat straw	35	7. 1	12	4	26	Do.
Rye straw	45	3. 4	12	6	16	Do.
Chopped straw	20–30	.....	.....	.....	.....	Do.
Cornstalks (shredded)	25–35	5. 3	15	8	18	Do.
Sawdust	25	0	4	2	4	Medium.
Wood shavings	25–45	0	4	2	4	Do.
Spent tanbark	25	.....	10–20	.....	.....	Do.
Leaf litter	25–60	[2] 26. 6	16	6	6	Do.
Peat moss (sphagnum)	10	40. 0	16	2	3	Do.
Peat (sedge and woody)	15–25	60. 0	20–60	2	3	Low.

[1] Fixing capacity for ammonia nitrogen.　　[2] Oak leaves.

comfortable and conserve values in the manure.

The ideal litter should have these characteristics:

It should be easy to get and cheap.

It should have high absorptive power for liquids so it can prevent loss of urine.

It should not be dusty—an especially important point in dairies and poultry houses. It should be as nearly sterile as possible; at any rate, it should be a poor medium for the growth of micro-organisms.

It should be able to absorb ammonia and potash.

Available plant nutrients in the litter add to the value of the manure.

A high content of cellulose and similar carbohydrates easily attacked by micro-organisms is undesirable in one respect—it promotes fermentation and heating, which favor the loss of ammonia by volatilization and its transformation to less available organic forms. With proper fermentation, however, carbohydrates produce acids that tend to increase the production of ammonia and favor its conservation under practical conditions of handling.

The matter should not be so coarse that it detracts from the animal's comfort, reduces absorption, and prevents proper compaction and easy handling of the manure.

Litter should remain well in place and not be too readily kicked aside.

Cereal straws are most used for litter because they are cheap and available on many farms. They do not have a high absorptive capacity unless they are chopped, but then they do not stay in place. They are dusty and fix little ammonia and potash.

Whole corn stover from which the animals have picked the edible parts has only cheapness and available plant nutrients to recommend it. When it is run through a husker-shredder, however, more is eaten, and the rest is considered equal to straw bedding.

Wood products are widely used, but they are poor in absorbing capacity and in available plant nutrients.

Fibrous sphagnum peat, or peat moss, is a good litter if it can be got at low cost. It is unexcelled in absorptive powers. It contains little readily decomposable carbohydrate. In poultry houses, however, it may become too dusty as the birds scratch it about.

A MANURE HEAP, handled in the ordinary way, undergoes profound changes. Fresh manure is an ideal breeding place for myriad organisms because of its high content of vegetable and animal wastes as sources of energy, its supply of suitable salts and water, and its generally favorable temperature and aeration.

The organisms work over the materials, utilizing some and dissipating their energy as heat of oxidation in vital processes. What the firstcomers reject is consumed by others in successive phases of the cycle, until at length there is left only humus and some mineral elements.

The desirability of rotting manure before it is incorporated with the soil is mentioned often. Otherwise it is supposed to be too hot and quick in action. Experience seems to support such a belief. The effect of well-rotted manure applied in large amounts, as to a garden, for example, undoubtedly is better than that of large amounts of fresh manure. One reason is that the rotted manure has lost much of its quick-acting ammonia and so much organic matter that the phosphoric oxide and potash remaining are relatively increased and the fertilizer action is in better balance. But this result is obtained at heavy cost in nitrogen, organic matter, and potash. It would be more economical to use less fresh manure and supplement it with phosphoric oxide and potash, which would result in better utilization of the available nitrogen. Even with very strawy manure, the advisability of rotting may be doubted; supplemental fertilizer nitrogen will enable the organic matter to undergo normal humification in the soil without harming the crop.

LOSSES start with failure to utilize the value of urine in manure because of insufficient bedding, the seepage through stall floors, or drainage from storage.

When animals are kept on earth floors, quantities of litter that otherwise would be ample may not suffice to keep the liquid from entering the earth.

At the Ohio Agricultural Experiment Station, a direct comparison with two lots of steers, one kept on compacted earth, the other on a cement floor, indicated that one-fourth of the liquid excrement was lost with the former, and the value of the manure was reduced by one-sixth. It was calculated that the saving in two feeding periods of 6 months each was enough to pay for the floor.

Leaching by rain may be even more serious, as all of the soluble matter is thus removed. A single rain of 1.5 inches is equivalent to about 1 gallon of water to the square foot, and most of it will percolate through manure in shallow piles and remove a large part of the soluble material in doing so.

Manure that must be stored need not necessarily be under cover. If a high heap is compacted properly on a relatively small base, the rainfall may be just enough to keep the manure properly moist and in good condition for conservation of value if there is no loss by leaching. The manure at the top will be leached, but it will serve as a seal to prevent access of air to lower layers, in which the fertility will be retained. Under such circumstances, protection for the sides of the heap is more important than for the top. A method used in Germany consists of a structure tightly built of boards and usually not roofed; the contents may be covered with about a foot of earth if the pile is to be left undisturbed.

Access of air to the interior of a mass of manure results in too much heating and losses of organic matter and

Percentages of Fertilizing Constituents in Urine of Various Farm Animals and Value in Relation to Total Excrements

Animal	Nitrogen %	Phosphoric oxide %	Potash %	Value %
Horse.....	35	0	58	50
Cattle.....	53	5	71	65
Sheep.....	63	4	86	75
Hogs......	32	13	55	40

Proportion of Fertilizing Constituents and Organic Matter of Farm Manures, Including Litter, that is Soluble in Water

Animal	Organic matter %	Nitrogen %	Phosphoric oxide %	Potash %
Horse.....	5	53	53	76
Dairy cow.	7	50	50	97
Steer......	7	56	36	92
Sheep.....	7	42	58	97

nitrogen. The conditions of fermentation are unfavorable to the accumulation of organic acids to hold ammonia. The ammonia escapes with the air circulating through the mass—if it is not decomposed by nitrification-denitrification reactions.

These losses can be controlled more or less by care in collecting and storing manure, but other precautions are needed.

Fermented manure spread on a field is subject to losses of ammonia by direct volatilization into the air, especially in warm, dry, windy weather. The better the quality of the manure, the greater the possibility of losses in application—therefore the effect of previous care may be nullified from causes too little appreciated.

Workers at the Wisconsin Agricultural Experiment Station measured the rates at which ammonia was lost from fermented cow manure under different conditions. One-half to three-fourths of the ammonia (one-fourth to one-third of the total nitrogen) was lost within 12 hours to 7 days at 68° F. with an 8.5-mile wind—an indication of the importance of air circulation in loose heaps, storage in places exposed to wind, forking over fermented manure, and permitting it to dry before plowing under as causes of losses of nitrogen.

THE ADDITION OF antiseptics to prevent fermentation losses has been proposed, but the antiseptics that are effective generally are objectionable.

Fixing agents for ammonia have been more generally advocated. Gypsum (calcium sulfate) has been used for many years, although probably as much to reduce the ammoniacal odor in stables as to increase the value of the manure. Because the carbonate produced makes the reaction reversible, gypsum and similar salts of calcium and magnesium cannot prevent the loss of ammonia by volatilization in drying.

Similar use of superphosphate, which consists principally of monocalcium phosphate and calcium sulfate, has been advocated by some and has much to recommend it. Manure is deficient in phosphoric oxide and requires supplements in order to get the full value of the nitrogen and potash.

Superphosphate added to manure causes chemical reactions that lead to a decrease in the solubility of the phosphorus in the superphosphate. The less soluble phosphorus compounds formed are less available to plants, especially those growing on neutral or alkaline soils, as are the phosphorus compounds originally present in the superphosphate. On some soils, therefore, the saving of ammonia nitrogen caused by adding superphosphate to manure may be canceled by the decrease in value of the superphosphate.

Most experiments, however, indicate that superphosphate mixed with manure is as effective as superphosphate applied directly to the soil.

Research workers at Cornell University obtained manure in which the phosphorus was tagged with a radioactive phosphorus isotope by feeding radioactive phosphorus to a sheep. In a greenhouse test, in which a silt loam soil of pH 6.2 was used, the phosphorus in the manure was shown to be of about the same availability to ryegrass as that from superphosphate. Superphosphate incubated with manure for 22 days was of nearly the same availability to plants as superphosphate applied directly to the soil.

It is not possible to prevent all losses. Even if it is spread daily, the fresh material lies exposed for some time and permits volatilization of the ammonia that is rapidly developed in the first stages of fermentation. It is inferred from data obtained in a 40-year field experiment at the Ohio Agricultural Experiment Station that losses from daily spreading may average very little less than losses that occur with a good method of storage, spreading under favorable conditions, and plowing under promptly.

Losses can be reduced if the liquid excrements are handled separately and water is used to moisten the dung if necessary. On many American farms, however, the value of the nutrients contained in liquid manure does not offset the investment and labor required to give special handling to liquid manure.

The principle to be applied in storing manure to keep down the losses without using chemical preservatives is simple—compact the manure to exclude air. This prevents heating with its attendant losses, insures acid fermentation, and prevents leaching and drying. The easiest method of compacting manure is to let the animals do it—the well-known deep-stall method of accumulating manure under fattening stock effectively conserves values.

Sanitary regulations applying to the production of market milk prevent the use of the simple deep-stall for dairy cows, but the essential requirement of compacting the manure under cover at the legal distance from the quarters for milk cows may be met.

THE VALUE of manure as a mulching material may be greater than its value as a source of plant nutrients.

In experiments in Ohio, strawy manure used as a topdressing on corn after the first cultivation increased corn yields more than did equal amounts of manure plowed under before planting. The corn crops followed legume or legume-grass meadows in a rotation. The yield differences in favor of topdressed manure have been greater in drier years than in wet years, an indication of the importance of the manure mulch as a moisture conservation measure. Part of this moisture conservation was probably due to the effect of the manure mulch in reducing runoff. Another part was probably due to the effect of the mulch in lowering evaporation of soil moisture.

A surface mulch of manure will reduce soil blowing on coarse-textured soils. The clumps of manure on the surface of the soil break the force of the wind on bare soil. Such mulches are especially valuable in protecting newly seeded crops.

Freshly shaped and seeded grass waterways should be coated with a topdressing of manure whenever possible. It will reduce soil washing within the waterway and promote a better stand of the new seeding by preventing excessive drying of the surface soil.

The value of manure as a mulch is largely due to the bulk and the undecomposed litter material—the nutrient content is less important. Stack bottoms, spoiled hay, and such can be substituted for manure for mulching.

On farms where a critical problem of soil washing or blowing exists and manure is the only mulching material available, first priority on its use should be as a mulch.

Another rule to follow in deciding where to use manure is that the poorer the land, the more valuable the manure. In one experiment in Ohio, an area of soil was desurfaced with scrapers and the topsoil spread over a similar unscraped area of the same size. Each of these two areas and one with normal depth of topsoil were farmed for a number of years with different systems of management, some with manure and some without. The experiment was set up so that the value of manure could be determined on soil with each of the three topsoil conditions. The manure was most valuable on the desurfaced plots and least valuable on the plots with a double thickness of topsoil.

Manure will be of most value on row crops that follow nonleguminous crops. While land is in grass-legume sod, soil aggregation is improved. Soil nitrogen is increased when the legume meadows are turned under. When intertilled row crops follow, the physical condition of the soil usually becomes less desirable, and supplies of available nitrogen diminish. Liberal applications of manure can help to slow down this trend and permit the crops that do not follow legume-grass sods to grow under more favorable soil conditions.

Manure will give greater economic

returns on crops with a high acre value. Thus, applications of manure are likely to be more profitable on crops like corn, burley tobacco, potatoes, and vegetables than on crops like small grain or pasture.

WHEN MANURE is used as a topdressing or mulch to help combat soil washing or blowing, the application should just precede the time of greatest hazard. Often that will mean applying the manure fairly soon after the crop has been planted.

Losses of nitrogen by volatilization of ammonia are sharply cut as soon as the manure is covered by soil. Research in Denmark indicated that if manure spread and plowed under immediately is rated 100 in crop-production ability, manure spread and plowed under 2 days later rates as 71, and manure plowed under 2 weeks after spreading can be rated as 49. Spreading manure just ahead of a tillage operation that will incorporate it with the soil, therefore, is preferred when the manure is not used as a topdressing.

Other research in Denmark demonstrated that manure spread and plowed under just before the crop is planted is more effective than manure spread and plowed under at earlier dates. A farmer who uses such a plan of manure management should keep in mind, however, that factors other than the need for conserving nutrients in manure may be more important in determining the best time for plowing.

When dairy barns of the stanchion type or farrowing sheds for hogs must be cleaned often, a manure carrier or gutter cleaner that empties directly into the spreader saves work. Such a setup frequently makes it convenient to spread manure on frozen or snow-covered ground. Studies in Vermont showed that this practice resembles partial drying insofar as its effect on losses of ammonia through volatilization are concerned. These losses of nitrogen, therefore, will have to be balanced against the labor-saving features of the system.

Composts, Peat, and Sewage Sludge

H. W. Reuszer

Organic materials once were the only fertilizers used by farmers. They were mainly plant and animal products high in protein and were used for their nitrogen-supplying value. The demand for many of them in making feed and the lower cost and greater availability of plant nutrients in mineral fertilizer have led to the replacement of most of them as fertilizer.

Other organic materials, such as composts, peat, and sewage sludge, continue to be used to improve soil. They are called soil amendments rather than fertilizers because of their low content of plant nutrients.

They may be incorporated into the soil or used as mulches. Heavy rates of application are the rule. Thus they have the double effect of contributing some plant nutrients and improving the physical condition of the soil.

Sometimes the amendments represent utilization of materials that otherwise would be wasted. Some have an unusual composition, and special practices are needed to use them successfully.

IN COMPOSTING, a microbiological process, organic materials are partially decomposed by the activity of microbes. Hemicelluloses (the gumlike substances), cellulose (the plant fiber), and lignin, (the woody material) make up

50 to 85 percent of mature plant materials. The lower percentages occur in the leguminous plants, the intermediate ones in nonleguminous crops, and the higher amounts in wood. The rest of the plant is largely water-soluble substances and protein and small amounts of fat and ash.

Microbes readily attack the water-soluble substances, hemicelluloses, and cellulose, which rot quickly.

Lignin is quite resistant to attack. Its nature changes somewhat, but it disappears only slowly.

From the readily decomposable substances, microbes get energy to carry on their activities and the carbon they need for building their cells.

About 20 percent of the carbon in the decomposed part may be synthesized into microbial cells. The remainder enters the air as carbon dioxide and becomes available for photosynthesis by new generations of plants.

About one-half of the total dry matter originally present is decomposed by the time the compost is ready for use. Three-fourths of this loss is represented by a decrease in hemicelluloses and cellulose.

Microbial cells contain 5 to 10 percent of nitrogen. So, if large amounts of energy substances are present, considerable nitrogen is needed for synthesis of cells. The amount of energy available and consequently the amount of nitrogen needed depend on the amount of material susceptible to decomposition by the microbes.

Materials like sphagnum plants and highly lignified wood tissues, which resist decomposition, have low nitrogen requirements. For the usual farm crop residues, a nitrogen content of 1.5 percent is enough for a maximum rate of decomposition. Microbes do not assimilate all the nitrogen in materials that have higher nitrogen values, and the excess is subject to loss by volatilization, leaching, or denitrification. Actually, values of 1 to 1.25 percent of nitrogen are adequate.

Mature nonleguminous plant residues are low in nitrogen and high in substances that supply energy for microbial growth. When they are incorporated into soil, microbes assimilate available nitrogen from the soil and cause a shortage of nitrogen for crop growth.

This nitrogen-depleting effect can be overcome by adding enough available nitrogen to supply the needs of the microbes. The nitrogen may be supplied by commercial fertilizer added with the organic matter if it is turned under directly. If used as bedding for livestock, the feces and urine of animals supply the nitrogen. A third (but more expensive) way to overcome the nitrogen-depleting effect is to compost the material.

Two main objectives are accomplished by composting.

First, readily decomposable substances are removed, and the percentage of nitrogen content is increased. Thus there is no danger that a nitrogen shortage will be induced when composts are added to soils.

Second, the physical nature of the material is changed. The decomposition of cellulose causes the plant material to lose its strength and to break easily. It becomes friable, crumbly, and easier to handle and incorporate into the soil. That is important when hand tools or small tillage implements are used.

With some materials, such as manure or municipal garbage, a third result of composting is the removal of obnoxious odors.

THE COMPOSITION of composts is variable. The moisture content is usually in the neighborhood of 75 percent, but it may be as low as 40 percent. A high moisture content makes the finished compost weigh more than the dry weight of the material originally placed in the heap. That is the basis of statements that 1 ton of plant residues will produce 2 tons or more of compost. Its value, of course, is in the dry matter.

Composts commonly contain 2 percent of nitrogen, but the content may be 1.5 to 3.5 percent in the dry matter.

The phosphorus content of dry composts is about 0.5 to 1.0 percent. Potassium values probably are twice as high. These values will be correspondingly higher if phosphate and potash are added to the compost.

The nitrogen of composts is only slowly available and never approaches that of inorganic sources of nitrogen. Its slow availability lowers the possibility of leaching and extends availability over the entire growing season. Presumably the availability of phosphorus and potassium in composts approaches that of inorganic sources.

Composts are essentially low-analysis fertilizers, and large amounts must be used to obtain adequate additions of plant nutrients to soils.

THE MAXIMUM EFFECTS of composts on soil structure—increased aggregation, pore space, and water-holding ability—and on crop yield usually occur only after several years of use.

Composts increase crop yields as much as do equal additions of manure from the bedding of horses and cattle. Composts should be used in much the same way as manure with regard to amount and method of application and reinforcement. Because compost is like farmyard manure in physical nature, composition, and value, we sometimes call it synthetic manure.

Composts are good to use as mulches in gardens or around shrubbery. Applied 2 or 3 inches deep, they conserve soil moisture, lower soil temperatures in hot weather, help control weeds, and contribute nutrients.

Applications on small areas of large amounts of compost may supply the entire nutrient needs for the successful production of crops. If the composted materials come from a large area, the land from which they come loses its share of organic matter. One can overcome some of that loss by using rotations of sod crops whose roots restore the physical condition of the soil. The amount of organic matter that can be returned to the soil over any large area of land can be no larger than the amount produced on it. Because, furthermore, some is used by animals and man, only moderate rates of compost applications can be attained over any large area.

Before you decide whether to practice composting in practical farming operations, you should compare the soil-improving value of compost and that of the fresh residues from which it is made.

In 12 years of comparisons at the Rothamsted Experimental Station in England, turning under fresh straw to which nitrogen was added gave 10 to 20 percent greater yields of potatoes, barley, and sugar beets than composts prepared from the same amount of straw and nitrogen.

At the New Jersey Agricultural Experiment Station, fresh residues, applied on an equal organic-matter basis, produced double or triple the aggregation of silt and clay particles produced by composts prepared from the same materials.

One must also realize that (since one-half the organic matter is lost in composting) fresh residues applied at the same rate will cover twice the area that can be covered by composts. When it is feasible to do so, one should return plant residues directly to the soil in preference to composting; doing so leads to greater soil improvement and saving of labor. Sufficient nitrogen and other nutrients in the form of commercial fertilizers should be added to meet the needs of the crop.

In some situations, however, composting meets a need and is a highly desirable practice.

The first is in areas where commercial fertilizers are expensive, labor is cheap, and implements are simple. Composts prepared from plant, animal, and human wastes have been used extensively for many centuries in India, Japan, and China. More than one-half the nitrogen and a higher proportion of the phosphorus and potassium returned to the soil in Japan in 1946 were supplied by composts. Composting practices in some countries include the use of town garbage and night soil; a supplementary benefit thus is improved sanitation.

Composts also are used when soil is used intensively as in market gardening, in which frequent tillage and almost complete removal of crops (sometimes even the roots) may lead to soil deterioration. Composts are used to overcome this effect.

Special composts are needed for growing mushrooms. They used to be prepared from horse manure, but more and more they are made from definite mixtures of plant products and commercial fertilizers, which supply nitrogen and potash.

The most prevalent composting in the United States is by gardeners who save garden residues, weeds, tree leaves, lawn clippings, and kitchen wastes.

COMPOST is produced commercially in many places.

A few operations in the United States use manure from stockyards or large dairies. An installation at the stockyards in Chicago uses a mechanized process and can treat 50 tons of manure daily. Plans have been made to compost all of the 75,000 tons of manure produced annually at the stockyards. These preparations command a premium price and are used on gardens and lawns.

A plant at Wyster, Holland, produces 120,000 tons of compost a year from municipal refuse. The annual production of compost is sold at a low price to farmers, and the demand for it is great.

In general, it may be said that commercial production of compost is limited to situations where the cost of assembling the material is not charged to the composting operation itself.

TWO SOURCES of compostable material may get greater—wood residues (from lumbering, woodworking plants, and improvement cuttings in forests) and organic wastes in cities.

The total annual quantity of unutilized wood residues was estimated in 1956 by the Forest Service to be 1.4 billion cubic feet at sawmills and woodworking plants. An almost equal quantity was left as logging residues in the forests. About 700 million cubic feet of the residues at sawmills and plants was fine material, such as sawdust, which requires no further reduction in size for use in soil improvement. A large part of the wood residues accumulate at points remote from possible agricultural use, but in some sections, as in the North Central States, nearly all lumbering operations are on farms. Wood residues are also quite accessible for agricultural use in the Northeast and the South.

The use of these residues has been confined mainly to sawdust and shavings because of their favorable physical form and accumulation in large amounts.

All available supplies of sawdust and shavings in parts of new England are used as bedding for dairy cows. The manure is used on crops. Waste wood is also converted to chips for use as bedding. The cost may be so high, however, that the use of chips may be restricted to localities where supplies of sawdust and other forms of bedding are inadequate and transportation costs make wood chips competitive with other bedding materials.

Wood residues can be incorporated directly into the soil. They also can be composted. Both sawdust and woodchips make excellent mulches for blueberries, strawberries, fruit trees, ornamentals, and garden crops. Because woody plant materials are low in plant nutrients, they need extra nitrogen and phosphate when they are composted or added to soil.

Municipal organic wastes of garbage and street refuse are composted for agricultural use in many European cities and in the Far East. In this country they have been disposed of mostly by land filling, soil burial, or incineration, but there is an increasing interest in the possibility of disposing of them by composting because of the growing scarcity of areas to be filled in, objections to air pollution produced by incineration, and the possibility of reducing costs of waste disposal from the sale of the compost.

The staff of the Sanitary Engineering Research Project of the University of California in 1953 completed a series of experiments on composting municipal wastes. They found that a wide variety of wastes could be composted successfully. Shredding the material (after cans and bottles had been removed) to permit uniform mixing was found desirable. No further modification was found necessary. Turning the heaps every 3 or 4 days meant that finished compost could be produced in 2 or 3 weeks. The composts contained as much plant nutrient as did compost from crop residues. Its value for soil improvement should equal those of manure or composted farm residues.

Almost any natural organic product can be composted with proper care—cornstalks, straw, hay, tree leaves, wood residues, coconut husks, animal and human excreta, garbage, wastes from wineries and breweries, and many more. The microbes are not choosy.

FOR MAKING COMPOSTS, you must provide proper aeration, moisture, nutrients, and temperature for microbial decomposition. Those factors and the nature of the material affect the time required for preparation and the final composition. Composting is usually carried out by piling organic materials into heaps where reasonable control of these factors can be maintained.

Air should penetrate the entire compost heap to allow microbes to act and finish the compost in a minimum of time. Aeration depends on size of air spaces within the heap, the height of the pile, and the moisture content.

The coarse materials, like cornstalks, cause large air spaces, excessive aeration, and rapid loss of moisture and heat from the heap. They should be cut to 6-inch lengths or mixed with finer materials before composting. Excessive aeration can be reduced by compacting the pile and by increasing its height. Fine materials, such as saw-

dust, are hard to aerate and may be mixed with coarser materials or turned oftener. Cereal straws and tree leaves have good properties for composting.

Compost heaps should be built no more than 6 feet high so air can penetrate to the bottom of the pile. Width and length may be adjusted for convenient handling.

Excessive moisture cuts aeration by filling air spaces in the material and by increasing compaction.

Only a slow partial decomposition takes place when aeration is insufficient. Intermediate products of anaerobic microbes, such as organic acids and reduced nitrogenous and sulfur compounds, are formed. Many have offensive odors.

The physical nature of the composting material frequently is altered little under anaerobic conditions, and it remains hard to handle. Poor aeration is overcome by turning the heap.

The best moisture content of the compost heap is between 50 and 70 percent—the weight of the moisture should be 1 to 2.5 times that of the dry organic material. Decomposition is slowed down when the heap is drier than that; anaerobic conditions set in, particularly at the bottom of the heap, when it is wetter. Water is best applied to the layers as the pile is built up.

Many fresh dry plant residues are somewhat hard to wet. They can be wetted best by applying the water in a fine spray. If necessary, water should be added on 2 or 3 successive days at the start of the composting period.

Letting water run out at the bottom of the pile should be avoided because nutrients are lost. Fresh green materials, such as grass clippings, contain too much moisture for proper composting. They should be left to wilt before piling or should be mixed with about one-third their weight of dry material. Rainfall may increase moisture in the heap. If the moisture becomes excessive, it can be reduced by turning and loosening the pile. Small heaps that have a high proportion of exposed surface may become unduly dry. Water should be added to them as needed.

Most plant residues will form composts in time if they simply are put in a heap and kept moist. Sometimes nutrients are added. Mature residues of nonleguminous plants require the addition of about 15 pounds of actual nitrogen per ton of dry material—equal to the nitrogen in 70 pounds of ammonium sulfate or calcium cyanamide, 45 pounds of ammonium nitrate, or 30 pounds of urea. Any of them are satisfactory. Calcium cyanamide and urea give a slightly basic reaction, which promotes rapid decay. If ammonium sulfate is used, an equal amount of finely ground limestone should be added to neutralize the acidity arising from the sulfate anion.

Residues of leguminous plants and young nonleguminous plants may contain 1.5 to 3.5 percent of nitrogen and need no additional nitrogen. Substantial losses of nitrogen occur if such residues are composted directly, because the amount of nitrogen present is in excess of that assimilated by the microbes. Such materials should be mixed with residues of low nitrogen content. Two or three parts of mature, nonleguminous residues mixed with young plants or with leguminous plants give a satisfactory mixture.

Other organic nitrogenous substances, such as cottonseed and soybean meals and dried blood, may be added to composts to give the proper nitrogen content. The cost of nitrogen in these forms is greater than in the inorganic form. Liquid and solid excreta of animals and sewage sludge also may be used to supply nitrogen to composts

The microbes need so little phosphate and potash that ordinary plant residues supply enough for composting. To sawdust or plant residues that become leached before composting, it may be wise to add phosphate and potash—about 20 pounds (or 3 gallons) of superphosphate and 5 or 10 pounds of potassium sulfate or potassium chloride to a ton of residue.

The phosphate and potash increase the fertilizing value of the resulting compost. A complete fertilizer with an analysis such as 10–6–4 may be used to supply nitrogen, phosphate, and potash. The fertilizer should be added to give the proper amount of nitrogen in the beginning compost. Extra care should be taken to prevent leaching. If that cannot be done, it is preferable to reinforce the compost when it is applied to the soil instead of in the pile.

Rotting proceeds slowly at temperatures near freezing. Microbial processes increase at higher temperatures. The rate nearly doubles for every rise of 18° F. in temperature.

Microbes themselves produce heat as a byproduct of the decomposition. They release large amounts of heat in the pile; since it is nearly self-insulating, the temperature of the pile rises. Microbes that grow best at ordinary temperatures initiate the decomposition and carry it on until a temperature of about 115° to 120° is reached. That temperature kills them, and another group of microbes takes over. They are called thermophiles, or thermophilic organisms, because they can carry on at high temperatures. They raise the temperature inside the heap to 140° to 170°. This rise in temperature, which usually persists 2 or 3 weeks, indicates that the composting is proceeding normally. It greatly shortens the time required for the decay of the plant material. The rapid dissipation of heat in small or open heaps may keep temperatures down too low.

The high temperature also kills disease-causing organisms, insects, and weed seeds, except in the outer parts and the bottom of the heap. When the heap is turned, those parts should be turned to the center of the pile so that they also will be subjected to the high temperatures.

Residues of diseased plants should be composted only if they can be completely subjected to the high temperatures in the interior of the heap. That is seldom possible with small piles; if so, they should be burned to avoid spreading disease.

Turning the compost heap hastens the decomposition by increasing the supply of air for the microbes. Heaps may be turned every 3 or 4 days in commercial operations. In some mechanized processes, air is blown continuously through the composting mixture. In farm and garden practices, the compost should be turned at least once about 3 weeks after its preparation. More frequent turning is desirable to assure mixing and more uniform decomposition of the heap. The number of turnings may be adjusted to facilities available and the desired time for completing the compost.

Occasionally some practices are advocated that are not essential. Inoculation with prepared cultures of microbes is sometimes said to hasten the process and lead to a better product.

Experiments at the University of California tested soil, horse manure, partially composted material, and a commercial preparation of selected cultures as inoculants. None had any significant effect on the course of composting. It appears that the materials used in composting have enough of the microbes on their surfaces to start and continue decomposition.

Mixing small amounts of soil into composts is unnecessary, but the soil may help conserve nitrogen and other nutrients. A thin layer of soil on the outside surfaces of a heap will aid in retaining moisture. A shallow pit does the same, but the pit should be in a well-drained place, because accumulation of water in a poorly drained pit will produce anaerobic conditions.

When is the composting process completed? In large, well-prepared heaps, a drop in the interior temperature to values near air temperature and easy crumbling of the materials in the hand indicate completion.

Full composting in small heaps usually requires 3 months under favorable conditions of moisture and temperature. Composts prepared late in the fall in regions of cold winters may not be ready for use until early the next summer. Under commercial conditions, with large heaps and frequent turning, composting time may be shortened to 2 or 3 weeks. With some mechanized processes, only 10 days are required for fresh material, and that may be shortened to 3 days if the beginning material is already partly decomposed.

Bins of simple construction are desirable for home or garden-scale composting. A bin will help to maintain moisture at the edges of the heap and prevent blowing. It should be about 4 feet wide, 5 feet high, and as long as needed to hold the material available for composting. No floor is needed.

It is well to have two bins side by side with one common wall. The compost may be forked then from one bin to the other for turning and mixing. The compost that is ready for use may be kept in one bin while fresh compost is started in the other.

Snow fencing with posts at the corners makes a satisfactory bin. A variety of timbers, arranged in log-cabin fashion, or boards nailed to corner posts provide satisfactory enclosures. Only narrow cracks should be left between the timbers or boards. More permanent structures may be built of concrete blocks or bricks. Small openings should be left near the bottom of such walls to permit penetration of air. One end of the bin should be closed with removable boards to permit access for mixing and removal of the compost.

PEAT is a widely used organic soil amendment. It is made up of plant remains that have accumulated over the centuries under relatively airless conditions in bogs.

Peats may be divided into two main types, according to the kind of plants from which they were formed. One is sphagnum peat—or peat moss, or highmoor peat—which is derived from species of the sphagnum plant. The other, formed from the sedges, reeds, mosses, or trees is called lowmoor peat.

Peat derived from trees is sometimes grouped separately as forest peat, or peat mold. It is intermediate in composition between sphagnum peat and that derived from sedges and reeds. Forest peat contains many finely divided particles of wood and is often used for mulching.

Sphagnum peats on a dry-matter basis have an ash content usually below 5 percent, nitrogen 1 percent or less, and phosphorus and potassium below 0.1 percent. They are very acid, with pH values between 3.0 and 4.5. Fresh sphagnum peats have a high water-holding capacity equal to 15 to 30 times their own weight, but that is cut in half following drying. Cellulose and hemicellulose make up about 40 percent of sphagnum peats, but they are resistant to decomposition by microbes.

Lowmoor peats are more variable than sphagnum. Their dry matter contains 5 to 40 percent of ash, 1.5 to 3.5 percent of nitrogen, and less than 0.1 percent of phosphorus and potassium. They can hold 3 to 8 times their own weight of water. Their pH values range from 3.5 to 7.0. Because most of the cellulose and hemicellulose in them has been decomposed, they have a high amount of ligninlike substances.

Peats improve the water-holding ability of most soils and give better physical structure to fine soils. Heavy applications equal to 25 to 50 percent of the volume of the soil often are made with that in mind. They are used mostly on specialty crops and home grounds.

Undecomposed or slightly decomposed forms of sphagnum, if incorporated into the soil, require small amounts of nitrogen. Acid peats are used for acid-loving plants as a direct growth medium or by mixing into the soil or as a mulch on the place where they are grown. The acidity of such peats may need to be neutralized with ground limestone if they are to be used for ordinary plants.

Peats, especially the coarser grades of sphagnum, are good livestock bedding and poultry litter. In 1950 in the United States an estimated 161,000 tons of peat were used for soil improvement and 31,000 tons for stable bedding and poultry litter.

SEWAGE SLUDGE is the solids remaining from the treatment of sewage in disposal plants. Various methods of digestion and removal of the solids reduce the organic matter in the plant effluent to a safe point. The resulting sludge is filtered off and may be burned or sold or given away for use as fertilizer.

The value of the sludge for soil improvement depends on the method used for treating the sewage.

Activated sludge comes from disposal plants in which aerobic treatment is obtained by bubbling large quantities of air through the digesting sewage. The sludge is then allowed to settle in large settling tanks, drawn off, and filtered. The filtered material still contains 80 to 85 percent of water. If it is to be sold as fertilizer, it is dried by heat to a moisture content of 5 to 10 percent. Activated sludge contains 30 to 40 percent of ash, 5 to 6 percent of nitrogen, and 1 to 3.5 percent of phosphorus.

Digested sludges come from disposal systems in which solids are allowed to settle out and are then digested anaerobically. On a dry-matter basis, they contain 35 to 60 percent of ash, 1 to 3 percent of nitrogen, and 0.5 to 1.5 percent of phosphorus. They are allowed to air-dry on sand filter beds outside or in greenhouses where they are protected from rain. Because of their low content of plant nutrients, they are seldom sold for fertilizer.

Activated sludge has a higher nutrient content, lower moisture, better physical condition, and no odor. Available nitrogen in activated sludge is almost equal to that in cottonseed meal and costs about the same. When it is added to soil, about one-half the nitrogen is nitrified in 4 weeks. More than 50,000 tons of activated sludge are produced annually by the sewage disposal plant of Milwaukee, Wis. There is a wide demand at good prices for this product for fertilizing grass in lawns, parks, and golf courses.

All sewage sludges are low in potassium because compounds of potassium dissolve readily in water. They must then be supplemented with a potash fertilizer when used on soils that have too little potassium. Additional phosphate also is needed on some soils, depending on the amount of sludge used.

Sludges contain appreciable quantities of the minor elements, copper, boron, manganese, molybdenum, and zinc. A few experiments indicate that they are available for plant growth.

Sanitary aspects must be considered when digested sludges are applied. Pathogenic organisms may escape the treatment process. It is not advisable to use digested sludge on root crops or low-growing vegetables that are to be eaten raw. Incorporation into the soil 3 months ahead of planting leads to destruction of the disease organisms. Digested sludges give rise to bad odors, which can be overcome by immediate incorporation into the soil. Activated sludges have no bad odor and microbes are killed in the heat treatment.

Maintaining Organic Matter

W. V. Bartholomew

Soil organic matter is dynamic material. It changes continually through further decomposition, but it maintains a degree of stability in quantity and in quality through the additions of new raw materials.

Organic matter is a temporary product—a stage in a natural cycle of elements. Each increment remains in the soil while it passes through the several slow biological oxidation changes that eventually reduce it to carbon dioxide, water, and mineral elements. As it passes through the cycle, it is replaced by organic matter formed from fresh residues.

Organic matter is formed in the biological decomposition of plant and animal residues. In the decomposition process, some of the plant substances are converted rapidly to carbon dioxide, water, and mineral elements (mineralization), and other substances may be only chemically altered at first.

The microbiological activity is high when fresh plant residues begin to decay. As the micro-organisms consume the more easily decomposable materials, the level of activity gets less and less. When only the more resistant plant substances remain along with the series of new organic materials synthesized by the micro-organisms, the microbial activity becomes slow—akin to a smoldering fire—and is the cause of constant loss of organic matter from soil.

The amount of organic matter in soil at any time hinges on the speed of the microbiological activity and the amount of fresh residue material that is added each year. The principles that regulate microbiological decomposition—which affect mechanical losses of soil and determine the amount and kind of residues returned to the soil—therefore are the principles that govern the level of organic matter in soil.

A number of things affect the speed of activity of soil microbes. We can control some of them. Others depend on the weather. Some are determined by early geological processes and the kind of plant cover that prevailed before man became interested in soil organic matter. Among the factors are temperature, moisture, aeration, acidity, supply of plant nutrients, tillage, and the kind and the amount of crop residues and manures returned to the soil. Cropping systems and soil management exert strong influences on most of these factors.

Microbes are most active in a moist soil. Microbial activity is depressed when a soil is extremely wet or dry. Air is excluded from the soil pore spaces in a wet soil, and the lack of air slows decomposition. Although microbial activity is less when moisture is low, many microbes remain rather active when soil moisture is below the wilting point for crop plants. Decomposition, in fact, proceeds about half as fast at the wilting point for plants as it does when the soil is at field-moisture capacity.

Soil temperature is determined generally by the temperature of the air, but it can be modified by man's use and manipulation of the soil. Operations that influence moisture also influence temperature. Dry soil has a low heat capacity and warms up faster than a wet soil.

Soil temperatures are generally cooler in daytime and warmer at night when the soil is covered by a growing crop. Similar modifications occur when crop residues are on the surface. In fact, under mulch culture in spring, increases in temperature are noticeably lower than those under clean cultivation.

The optimum temperatures for most soil microbes are between 75° and 95° F. The soil temperature seldom goes higher than that unless the soils are bare and dry, but in many areas temperatures often fall far below the optimum. The activity of soil microbes drops as the soil temperatures drop, but the activity of most microbes does not stop completely until the soil freezes. General decomposition of soil organic matter proceeds about two-thirds as fast at 75° as at 90°, and about one-third as fast at 60° as at 90°.

Aeration remains generally optimum for microbiological processes in soils that are not saturated with water.

When the soil pores are filled with water, as when drainage is poor or after a soaking rain, aeration—the exposure to air—limits the general rate of decomposition in that the slower acting anaerobic organisms are stimulated and most of the fast acting aerobic organisms are eliminated. Artificial drainage of wet soils greatly improves aeration and thus tends to speed up microbial activity.

SOIL REACTION may influence microbial activity in two ways. Soil organic matter is slightly less available as food for micro-organisms when the soil is acid than when it is neutral or alkaline. Further, because organisms differ in optimum pH for growth, soil reaction markedly influences the kinds of microbes that predominate in the flora and fauna in the soil. The general range in soil reaction, pH 5 to pH 8, however, has only minor effects on the overall rate of decomposition. When one organism is repressed, another generally arises to take its place.

The plant nutrients, except nitrogen, probably have only minor direct effects on the decomposition of plant residues and the activities of soil organisms. Enough calcium, magnesium, and potassium generally is present in the organic matter, plant residues, and manures to supply the needs of microbes. Phosphorus also is normally sufficient for microbiological activity, but minor elements may not be in some soils.

Nitrogen often influences microbiological activity. Too little nitrogen may occur in many crop residues to provide for the needs of the microbes during the early stages of decomposition. If additional nitrogen is not supplied from the soil or from fertilizer, the speed of decay of fresh plant residues may be lessened.

High rates of loss of soil organic matter have been associated with intensive tillage, particularly with the production of row crops. Stirring and disturbance of the soil seem to stimulate the microbiological population, but the reasons therefor are not known.

The kind of plant or animal residue from which soil organic matter is formed also influences the activity of the microbes, which depend on it as food. Some plant materials resist decomposition. Others decompose quickly. Decomposition of young, succulent grasses and legumes may be almost complete in one season, but the roots of some grasses and sedges may undergo little decomposition in many years.

Decomposition of the soil organic matter can be increased by the addition of easily decomposable substances like green manures. In fact, in soils that have moderate or high amounts of organic matter, green manure may so stimulate the metabolism of soil organisms that the loss of organic matter may more than offset that added from the fresh residues.

Every crop that grows makes a contribution in residues and therefore helps to maintain the soil organic matter. Top growth from some crops is wholly or partly returned to the soil. Only the roots and stubble of other crops may be left.

Because annual crops die each year, both tops and roots may contribute to the organic matter. The contributions from perennials vary with the kind of crop and the conditions of growth. Sod crops harvested for hay contribute only through root residues, but a large part or all of the top growth may be returned to the soil if they are pastured or used as green manure.

The entire root of an annual dies and begins to decompose each season. Some dying and regeneration of roots occurs annually with all perennials, but the amount and proportion of root dieback are greater in some plants than in others. The major parts of the root systems of some grasses perform much like annuals in that they die at the end of each growing season and are replaced by new roots the next.

Plant residue materials, because of differences in composition and structure, vary in susceptibility to decomposition and therefore in the contribution they make to the soil organic matter as they decompose.

Residues of mature plants generally decompose more slowly than immature plants. Roots and stubble rot more slowly than top growth. Nonlegumes rot more slowly than legumes. The residues that decompose most slowly remain longer in the soil and contribute more to the supply of organic matter.

THE INFLUENCE of these principles can be seen by comparing the organic matter contents of different soil areas. The Prairie soils of the Midwest at-

tained high levels of organic matter under virgin conditions. The vegetation was prairiegrass. Fertility was high, and moisture and the growing season were adequate for high production. Decomposition processes were not excessive, because microbial activity during a large part of each season was arrested by cold temperatures. Soil organic matter therefore accumulated to near maximum amounts for arable mineral soils.

Less soil organic matter has accumulated in the Southern States than in the North. Soil temperatures in the South are warm during the growing season, and they remain generally favorable for microbial activity during the winter. The mild, moist climate accelerates soil weathering and causes some loss of plant nutrients. It does not increase plant growth and increments of organic matter as much as it stimulates decomposition by microbes.

The marked influence of high soil temperature in stimulating decomposition of organic materials more than the production of residue is demonstrated in the tropical forest regions. Annual production of residue materials is higher there than under any other current vegetation cover, less residue accumulates on the forest floor, and less organic matter is found in the soil than in forests of the temperate region. The teeming activity of the soil organisms under continuous optimum temperature and moisture more than keeps pace with the high production of organic debris.

A different set of conditions exists in the arid regions. The shrublike vegetation produces little residue, and the annual input of organic residues to the soil is small. The heat and the drought of the hot desert has not arrested the activity of the micro-organisms and the decomposition processes as much as it has curtailed the growth of the plants. Little organic matter has accumulated therefore in or on the hot desert soils.

In cold climates, which have short growing seasons and low annual rain-

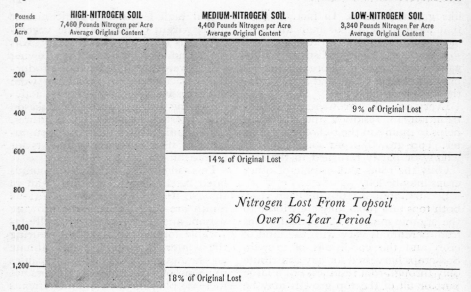

1. *Nitrogen decline related to original nitrogen content. A 5-year rotation on Clarion-Webster soil at Ames, Iowa.*

fall, decomposition is slow; despite the small annual additions, a thin layer of organic debris accumulates on the surface soil.

The influence of crop and of treatment is illustrated in the nitrogen changes in the Morrow plots in Illinois. (The Morrow plots, named for George E. Morrow, who established them, were started in 1876. They are the oldest experimental plots in America.) H. P. Rusk, of the Illinois Agricultural Experiment Station, in 1947 reported a decline of 1,525 pounds of nitrogen an acre—37 percent of the original between 1904 and 1943 from the untreated plot in continuous corn. All top growth was removed at the end of each harvest season. Only roots and stubble were left.

When manure, equivalent to the residues removed, and lime and phosphorus were applied to continuous corn, the decline in organic nitrogen was only 780 pounds an acre, or 19 percent of the original. Reductions in nitrogen in the untreated and treated plots cropped to a corn-oats rotation with a catch crop of sweetclover were,

respectively, 860 pounds an acre (or 21 percent) and 145 pounds an acre (or 4 percent). For the corn-oats-meadow cropping sequence, the changes were 780 pounds of nitrogen an acre (or 20 percent) and 345 pounds an acre (or 7 percent), respectively, on the untreated and treated plots. Returning manure equivalent to the top growth removed and the application of needed lime and phosphorus resulted in 745 pounds an acre less loss of soil nitrogen in continuous corn, 720 pounds an acre less loss in the corn-oats plots, and 550 pounds less loss of nitrogen under corn-oats-meadow.

In longtime cropping systems near Wooster, Ohio, continuous corn plots have had the largest decline in organic matter and nitrogen. Next, in the order of decreasing loss, were continuous wheat, continuous oats, a 5-year rotation of corn-oats-wheat-clover-timothy, and a 3-year rotation of corn-wheat-clover. The conclusion was that the meadow crops added organic matter and nitrogen, but the nonmeadow crops depleted the organic matter supplies. One year of clover in a 3-year rotation was better in conserving nitrogen than 2 years of clover and timothy in the 5-year rotation.

Row crops and fallow induced the largest declines in nitrogen and organic matter in soils of the Great Plains. Small grains caused a smaller decline than row crops. The smallest decline in organic matter and nitrogen occurred when grass or alfalfa was included in the cropping systems.

Manure was effective in minimizing declines of soil nitrogen. In some instances, in fact, soil nitrogen actually was maintained equal to virgin conditions when moderate applications of manure were made to small grain.

K. W. Hill, at the Lethbridge Experiment Station in Canada, found that declines in organic matter were closely related to the incidence of clean fallow. Wheat with alternate fallow caused the largest overall losses of soil organic matter among the cropping systems studied. The least decline in organic matter occurred under continuous wheat. In longtime rotations, which included legumes and clean fallow, the losses in organic matter were intermediate between those in continuous wheat and those found under wheat fallow.

THE DECOMPOSITION of organic matter each year in a particular soil is closely related to the total amount of organic matter contained therein— other conditions being the same.

More decomposition occurs annually in soils high in organic matter than those that have little organic matter. Within the limits of climatic variations, however, additions of crop residue and manure in a soil area and management system tend to be constant.

To see how these principles operate, let us consider a virgin Prairie soil that originally contained 150 thousand pounds an acre of organic matter in the plow layer. When cultivation began, 2 percent of the organic matter underwent complete mineralization each year. The first year, 3 thousand pounds of organic matter were mineralized. Lesser amounts were miner-

alized in each of the succeeding years of cultivation. The level of organic matter in the soil declined because the return of residues and manures under cultivation was too little to produce enough organic matter to offset the initial losses. If the mineralization continued at 2 percent a year and the annual additions were enough to produce 1,500 pounds of organic matter, an equilibrium level would eventually be established at one-half the original level.

Changes in organic matter and nitrogen resulting from the cultivation of virgin soils indicate the trends toward equilibrium in that the declines have generally been greatest immediately after the land was broken.

The magnitude of the annual changes have tended to decrease with additional years of cultivation. Hans Jenny reported that soils in Missouri declined in organic matter about 20 percent from the virgin conditions in the first 20 years of cultivation. They declined another 10 percent the second 20 years of cultivation and underwent a further decline of about 7 percent in the third 20 years. At that rate of decline, an equilibrium level of organic matter of about 50 to 60 percent of the amount present in virgin soil would finally be reached. The change would be about 80 percent complete in 60 years.

The rate of decline of organic matter among cultivated Prairie soils in Canada, as reported by J. D. Newton and associates of the University of Alberta, was more than twice as rapid during the first 9 years of cultivation as it was during the following 10 to 30 years. Declines in organic matter in the Morrow plots were only about 60 percent as fast during the second 20 years of cultivation as during the first 20 years.

Not all experiments show the same trends. Losses of organic matter in a few instances have been as rapid in the later years as in the earlier years of cultivation. In general, however, annual changes have become smaller with increasing time of cultivation, and amounts of organic matter in soils have tended toward levels where the

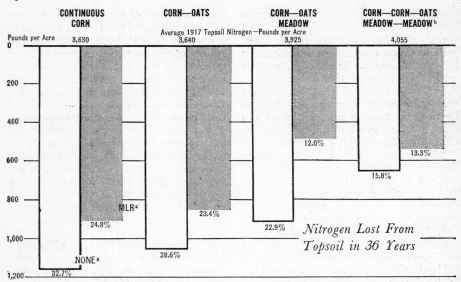

2. Soil nitrogen declines related to cropping system and soil treatment.
a "None" is no treatment. *"MLR"* is manure equivalent to 2 tons an acre a year, lime as needed and moderate applications of phosphate. *b* Rotation was slightly different in crop order before 1942, but the land was in meadows two-fifths of the time.

annual incomes were equal to the amounts lost each year through mineralization. When this steady state is reached under cultivation, the soils will be in balance with their environments, and the organic matter will remain at constant levels despite ceaseless losses and continual replacements.

The steady state largely had been attained under virgin conditions. Cultivation made a new set of environmental conditions. Changes were made in the kinds and amounts of plant and animal residues that were returned to the soil. Tillage operations and the growth of cultivated crops altered the environment for microbiological activity. The tendency for mechanical or erosion losses increased. In consequence, the soil organic matter contents began adjustments toward new equilibrium levels consistent with the new rates of organic matter formation, mineralization, and mechanical loss.

Although the changes in some soils have been marked in the past, further declines in the future are likely to be small. The adjustments from virgin conditions, brought about by cultivation, largely have been made. Although the time necessary to reach complete equilibrium is very long, in view of the rates of change observed in longtime experiments, we can conclude that more than 90 percent of the total adjustment in the content of organic matter from the virgin condition occurs during the first 80 to 100 years of cultivation. Sometimes a steady state appears to have been established in 50 to 70 years.

WHEN THE MAJOR ADJUSTMENTS in soil organic matter accompanying present-day management have been made, some soil areas and systems of soil management will be found to have higher amounts of organic matter than others, although the differences among regions will not be so marked as they were under virgin conditions. The steady state levels will be highest in the Prairie soil regions, just as the native Prairie soils contained initially the highest quantity of organic matter of the normal, arable mineral soils.

Organic matter levels at equilibrium with current cultivation generally will be low in semiarid regions and in the Red and Yellow soils of the Southern and Southeastern States.

Heavy-textured soils will be higher in organic matter than comparable light-textured soils, partly because of higher fertility and of greater water-holding capacity and partly because of the stabilizing influence of mineral soil colloids on decomposition of the soil organic matter.

Levels of organic matter will be higher when meadow crops occur frequently in the cropping system than where row crops predominate. Because the first year of meadow makes a larger contribution to organic matter than succeeding years, the frequent use of meadow in short rotations with non-meadow crops will be more effective in maintaining organic matter than an equal proportion of meadow in longer rotation cycles.

Culture of intertilled crops, particularly those requiring extensive cultivation, will result in less organic matter in the soil than the growth of crops requiring little or no cultivation.

Soils less subject to erosion will be higher in organic matter than those susceptible to erosion.

The losses that have occurred in the contents of organic matter in soils since cultivation began—unless caused by excessive erosion—were the natural consequence of the changes in rates of organic matter addition and decomposition associated with crop production. These losses of soil organic matter represent a depletion of a valuable substance, but the depletion has not been the result of a wanton misuse of soil.

The losses of soil organic matter that have occurred in the past have not resulted from any substantial difference between present-day and earlier practices of crop production and soil management. Current cropping systems and soil management, except for somewhat better control of erosion, if practiced in the past would have altered the rate of decline but little.

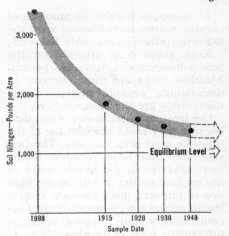

3. *Organic nitrogen approaches new steady state under cultivation of continuous corn.*

Decomposition of soil organic matter provided most of the nitrogen and part of the other plant nutrients that made many of our soils productive for nonleguminous crops in earlier years. In the past, the absence of this source of nitrogen would have required more dependence on fixation of nitrogen by frequently recurring plantings of legumes. With modern developments of technology and facilities for fertilizer production, we are approaching a position in which fertilizer nitrogen can substitute for a large part of the nitrogen once supplied by the decomposition of organic matter.

The maintenance of very high levels of soil organic matter is not compatible with economic use of much of our land. Maintenance at levels adequate for high productivity, however, can be continued or achieved. Some buildup in organic matter can be attained in soils that are below the steady state for the area. Good management of soils that are now above the equilibrium level will arrest the rate of the decline of organic matter.

Organic matter under cropping will be highest in fields where the largest residue returns are made to the soil and mechanical losses and microbial decomposition are kept at a minimum.

To MAINTAIN maximum amounts of organic matter in cultivated soils, the following principles should be followed:

Keep some crop growing on the land whenever circumstances permit. Meadow crops are most effective in maintaining organic matter. Intertilled crops are the least effective.

Use frequent short stands of meadow because they make the best use of the time the land is in meadow. The first year the land is in meadow is the most effective in the maintenance of soil organic matter as well as the fixation of nitrogen if the meadow crop is leguminous. Lesser contributions of organic matter and nitrogen result in subsequent years of meadow.

Follow good soil-management practices to produce high yields of crops. High yields permit the return of large amounts of crop residues and manures.

Return all residues to the soil. Mature residues and animal manures are most effective.

Cultivate no more than necessary, because tillage tends to hasten the biological decomposition process.

Control losses by wind and water erosion, which carries away the lighter organic materials from soil.

Green Manure and Cover Crops

T. Hayden Rogers and Joel E. Giddens

A green manure crop is grown and plowed under for the purpose of improving the soil. A cover crop is grown primarily to prevent or reduce erosion.

Both types of crops often are used for the same purpose, as well as for temporary grazing or for forage or grain. In this discussion of the effects these crops have on the soil and on the following crop, we use the term "green manure crop" to include cover crops. Green manure crops are usually annuals, either legumes or grasses.

Some advantages generally attributed to them: They add nitrogen to the soil for use by the following crop. They increase the general level of fertility by mobilizing minerals and building up the organic matter and the nitrogen content. They reduce losses from erosion. They improve the physical condition of the soil and permit a more efficient use of plant nutrients. They conserve nutrients by cutting down the losses from leaching.

Some disadvantages: A risk is involved in obtaining a satisfactory stand and growth of the crops. The cost of growing them may be more than the cost of commercial nitrogen. An increase of diseases, insects, and nematodes is possible. They may exhaust the supply of moisture. They may adversely affect the stand of the next crop.

Green manuring has been practiced a long time as a way to supplement animal manures. The efficiency of the practice depends on the soil, climate, and the crop.

It is often said that green manuring is not effective in regions with an annual rainfall of less than 20 inches.

In an experiment near Fargo, N. Dak., from 1929 to 1954, sweetclover, plowed early, did not result in an increase of flax as compared to straight fallow. When sweetclover was allowed to stay on the land during a large part of the fallow season, the yield of flax was less than when no sweetclover was used. Moisture was probably the limiting factor.

Green manure crops are grown most extensively in the Southeastern States. Usually they are planted in the fall and turned the following spring before the summer or cash crop is sown. About 13 million acres of green manure crops were grown in the Southeast in 1940. The acreage has since declined.

The rate of decay of the organic residues is determined by conditions for microbial growth. Warmth, proper aeration, and ample moisture increase microbial growth. The decomposition releases carbon dioxide and weak acids, which act on insoluble soil minerals and may release nutrients for plant growth.

The decomposing crop residues also release inorganic plant nutrients in addition to nutrients from insoluble minerals. The chemical composition of the crops affects their value for green manuring.

An increase in potato yields in Maine following green manures was attributed to the nutrients added in the organic materials. Vetch used as a cover crop in North Carolina increased the available nitrogen, potassium, calcium, and magnesium of soil in both cotton-peanut and cotton-corn rotations. The cover crop did not increase the exchange capacity of the soil—the ability of the soil to hold or exchange plant nutrient elements. Alfalfa used as a green manure crop in Ohio increased the availability of residual soil phosphorus.

Some green manure crops with the approximate nitrogen percentages on a dry basis:

Crop	Percentage of N
Alfalfa	3. 0–4. 0
Austrian winter peas	3. 0–3. 8
Clover, Red	2. 8–3. 2
Clover, Crimson	3. 0–3. 3
Cowpeas	2. 5–3. 0
Lespedeza, Common	2. 2–2. 5
Lespedeza, Sericea	2. 1–2. 4
Lupine, Blue	2. 0–2. 5
Vetch, Hairy	3. 0–4. 0
Oats	1. 3–1. 4
Rye	1. 2–1. 3
Ryegrass	1. 2–1. 3

An experiment in progress at Athens, Ga., for 8 years showed no increase in corn yields or in soil organic matter from green manure crops—vetch, Austrian winter peas, and crimson clover—if adequate amounts of nitrogen, phosphorus, and potassium were added.

Experiments in all parts of the country have indicated that if soil nitrogen is deficient, leguminous green manure crops supply the needed nitrogen; the amount of nitrogen they fix depends on the crop and amount of growth.

Green manure crops have little influence on soil organic matter if cultivation is continuous. In cooler sections, green manure increases organic matter and nitrogen somewhat. Such crops in warmer areas have a temporary effect, with little or no overall increase in soil organic matter because only a relatively small amount of plant material actually is grown and returned to the soil by most cover crops and because cultivation speeds up the rate of decomposition. Even soils in forests lose their supply of organic matter rapidly when they are first cultivated.

Perennial sod or cover crops increase soil organic matter and nitrogen.

Four years of cropping to kudzu in Mississippi brought an increase of 43 percent in nitrogen and 85 percent in carbon over the nitrogen and carbon present when corn was grown all the time. A long-term rotation, including alfalfa, in Ohio gave increased yields, but the top yield levels were reached quickly. In a 5-year rotation of corn, oats, alfalfa, alfalfa, alfalfa, no sustained benefit accrued once the first round of the rotation was completed.

Green, easily decomposable organic materials added to soils may speed up decomposition of the soil organic matter already present. F. E. Broadbent and A. G. Norman, at Iowa State College, found by using isotopic carbon and nitrogen that adding young Sudangrass increased the rate of loss of native carbon in soil.

Green manure crops can be expected to have more effect on soil organic matter when the soil clays are the montmorillonitic type (expanding clay with high exchange capacity) than when they are of the kaolinitic (nonswelling with low exchange) type. Proteinaceous organic materials have been shown to react with clays, especially montmorillonitic clays.

F. E. Allison and others at Beltsville, Md., found that more carbon was retained after adding soybean plants and corn stover to sand-bentonite clay mixtures than in sand-kaolin mixtures or in pure sand. Perhaps one reason that soil organic matter is low in the Southeast is that the soil clays are largely kaolinitic.

COVER CROPS prevent leaching of nitrogen and potassium and possibly other elements from soils. Studies throughout the United States have shown that losses from leaching are reduced greatly by soil cover—a matter of great importance when soils are light and sandy.

The time of turning green manure crops under is important from this standpoint. Fall-turned crops may lose most of their nitrogen by leaching before the following crop can utilize it. Soybeans turned into a sandy soil in Alabama in the fall lost 70 percent of the added nitrogen by leaching, but the loss was 38 percent when soybeans were turned in the spring.

Cover crops improve the soil physical properties of aggregation, porosity, bulk density, and permeability. The effects are more pronounced on fine-textured soils than on coarse ones.

Any material that supplies a readily available source of food for soil microorganisms will cause an increase in soil aggregation. Rapidly decomposing organic residues are more beneficial than slowly decaying materials.

G. M. Browning and F. M. Milam in West Virginia showed that cane sugar was more effective in producing aggregation of a Gilpin silty clay loam than alfalfa, rye, and vetch, or wheat straw. Aggregation no doubt is associated with the gums, slimes, and other products of soil micro-organisms, which tend to cement soil particles together. The benefits of decomposing cover crops generally are of rather short duration, because the rapidly decaying materials remain briefly in the soil.

Good ground cover reduces soil erosion. The crops slow down the beating action of rain on soil particles and so lower the runoff and erosion.

Many fall-planted green manure crops, however, make too little growth to check erosion before winter rains set in. Residues from the preceding summer crop and from weed growth might do a better job of preventing soil loss by runoff than plowing and planting a new crop.

Data from the Georgia Coastal Plain Experiment Station indicate that soil loss is greater on land that has an annual winter cover crop than on land on which corn stubble is left on the ground. Seeding without disturbing the surface residues may be the answer.

Because most of the soil loss from cultivated fields by water occurs in June, July, and August, summer crops would be best for controlling erosion. When corn followed a winter cover of rye and vetch in South Carolina, the soil loss was less than when no cover crop was used.

Cover crops can help control wind erosion, but often the crops are not on the land during periods of high winds.

Cover crops increase the rate at which water filters into soils. Leaves and stems catch the rain, and the roots open channels for the water. Improved aggregation, which usually follows green manuring, also allows better penetration. The improved permeability of soils to water does not mean, however, that more nutrients would leach away. The growing crop would absorb a large part of the nutrients.

Deep-rooted crops, such as some of the legumes, help open up soils with restricted subsoils. Crops grown for a short time usually have little effect on heavy subsoils.

Bulk density of soils is lowered and porosity is enhanced in turn by the use of green manure crops. The improved aggregation allows more space between soil particles and therefore less weight of soil per unit volume.

There is little experimental evidence that green manure or cover crops boost the water-holding ability of soils except while growing on the land. Ryegrass, vetch, crimson clover, and Austrian winter peas did not improve the water-holding ability of Onslow fine sandy loam in Virginia. The amount of water held by a soil is increased, however, if the soil organic matter is increased appreciably by a cover crop, such as a perennial grass or legume.

The effect of green manure crops on the yield of corn varies with the crop, the soil, climate, and other factors.

F. S. Arant, of Auburn, Ala., found less damage to corn from the Southern corn rootworm when corn planting was delayed 3 to 4 weeks after the green manure crop was turned.

J. L. Stephens, Tifton, Ga., conducted extensive tests with winter legumes in the Coastal Plain of Georgia. He reported that winter legumes do not furnish an adequate amount of nitrogen for maximum yield of corn and recommended the addition of commercial nitrogen when corn follows a winter legume. The residual effect of hairy vetch and monantha vetch was greater than that of Austrian winter peas.

S. S. Obenshain, Blacksburg, Va., and P. T. Gish, Shenandoah Valley, Va., tested a number of green manure crops in Virginia. Vetch in 8 years gave a greater increase in the yield of corn than any other crop tested. Crimson clover produced the next highest increase. Rye and buckwheat produced less than did the crop without green manure.

Martin Nelson, Fayetteville, Ark., found that the removal of the tops of green manure crops had an appreciable effect on the yield of corn at the Arkansas Cotton Experiment Station. When the tops of burclover were removed, the increase in the yield of corn was less than half of what it was when the entire plant was turned. Of the various crops tested, burclover gave the highest increase in the yield of corn. Crimson clover was second. Oats had no significant effect.

Austrian peas and vetch were compared in a 2-year cotton-corn rotation at Rocky Mount, N. C. Corn following Austrian peas produced 57 bushels an acre. The addition of 80 pounds of nitrogen lifted the yield of corn to 84 bushels. The addition of another 80

pounds of nitrogen had no significant effect. Austrian peas were found to be less valuable for corn production than 80 pounds of commercial nitrogen. Addition of 80 or 160 pounds of nitrogen to corn following vetch did not increase the yield of corn during the 5 years the experiment was continued.

Another experiment conducted for 8 years in North Carolina on Marlboro very fine, sandy loam compared vetch with no cover when no nitrogen and low and high rates of nitrogen were added. The low rate of nitrogen was 60 pounds an acre the first 2 years, 90 pounds the following 2 years, and 110 pounds the last 4 years. The high rate was double the low rate. In the 8 years, the average yield of corn with low nitrogen and no cover was the same as the corn that had vetch and no nitrogen. Vetch and low nitrogen produced 92.9 bushels an acre, or 17.3 bushels more than vetch without nitrogen. High nitrogen and no vetch produced 89.1 bushels an acre.

On the basis of these and other experiments, we can summarize the effect of green manure crops on the yield of corn thus: Of the various green manure crops tested, legumes are superior to nonlegumes. Winter legumes are superior to summer legumes. Hairy vetch is the most dependable green manure crop. The removal of the top growth of green manure crops usually results in a reduction in yields below that obtained when the whole plant is turned. A good growth of a winter legume turned 3 to 4 weeks before planting corn will produce as much corn as 50 to 100 pounds of commercial nitrogen.

Experiments in the hilly section of Mississippi indicate that the value of a winter legume to the following crop of cotton depends largely on the natural fertility of the soil. Winter legumes increased cotton yields about the same as 24 pounds of commercial nitrogen, even when the legume turned under added up to 75 pounds of nitrogen.

In a 14-year comparison of different winter green manure crops preceding cotton on Delta soil at Stoneville,

Miss., hairy vetch was superior to the other crops tested. Hairy vetch turned as a green manure crop produced slightly more than 300 pounds of seed cotton than 30 pounds of nitrogen from commercial fertilizer.

California burclover produced almost as much as hairy vetch. Rye produced less than 60 percent as much.

At two places in Arkansas, cotton responded to 20 pounds of commercial nitrogen after winter legumes were turned. There was no response to 40 or 60 pounds of commercial nitrogen when cotton followed a winter legume.

In another 10-year experiment in Arkansas, the effects of removing and turning the green manure crop were compared. The yield of cotton when hairy vetch was removed was 72 percent as much as when it was turned.

In one of three 6-year studies in Alabama, hairy vetch was superior to no green manure plus 36 pounds of nitrogen—apparently a reflection of the total amount of green material turned. In the other experiments, the residual effect of vetch preceding corn in a cotton-corn rotation was equivalent to 213 pounds of seed cotton.

Annual winter legumes turned as green manure increased cotton yields over the no-cover treatment plus 30 pounds of nitrogen during a 17-year test in Georgia. When no nitrogen was applied, rye produced 313 pounds less seed cotton than Austrian peas.

Several winter annuals were tested as green manure crops on Olivier silt loam in Louisiana. Certain of the legumes were as effective as 36 pounds of nitrogen in the production of cotton. Oats produced approximately half as much cotton as 36 pounds of nitrogen.

Research at the Northeast Louisiana Experiment Station showed that the use of winter legumes as green manure crops increased the yield of cotton from 1 bale to 1.5 bales an acre and maintained the high yield over a period of 23 years. After turning under good growths of winter legumes for 3 years in succession, the beneficial effect extended to the following second and third cotton crop. The application of 30 pounds of nitrogen an acre at the time the green manure crop was turned was profitable.

Studies in North Carolina disclosed that a good crop of Austrian peas or vetch produced as much cotton as 80 pounds of commercial nitrogen. No significant increase in the yield of cotton was obtained from 120 pounds of nitrogen as compared to 80 pounds or when 20 or 40 pounds of nitrogen was added to cotton following Austrian peas or vetch.

Workers at the Pee Dee Experiment Station in South Carolina reported that in 3 years out of 5 difficulty is experienced in obtaining and maintaining the stands of cotton following green manure crops, particularly when weather conditions are adverse.

Results of experiments studying the effect of green manure crops on the yield of cotton may be summarized thus: The beneficial effect of green manure crops is related to the nitrogen supplied by the crop. This tends to eliminate nonlegumes as green manure crops. Annual winter legumes have been found equal to 80 pounds of commercial nitrogen in producing cotton. It often is necessary to delay the turning of a winter legume in order to obtain sufficient growth. This may result in planting cotton too late for maximum production.

Research workers in States in which peanuts are grown commercially usually recommend that green manure crops follow the peanut crop. The Alabama Station compared peanuts in a 2-year and a 3-year rotation for 10 years at two places. The yield of peanuts in the rotation cotton-peanuts was 1,349 pounds an acre. When the rotation was cotton-winter legumes-peanuts, the yield of peanuts was increased 130 pounds. In a 3-year rotation—cotton-winter legumes-peanuts-winter legumes-corn—the yield of peanuts was 134 pounds more than the 2-year rotation without legumes.

Several winter annuals were tested in a cotton-peanut rotation at Rocky

Mount, N. C. Average yields for a 6-year period indicated crimson clover, vetch, ryegrass (plus 18 pounds of nitrogen), and Austrian peas, in that order, were effective in increasing the yield of peanuts. In 2 years out of the 6 years, none of the green manure crops produced a significant increase over the crop without green manure.

The Georgia Coastal Plain Experiment Station has recommended the use of green manure crops in peanut rotations. It is suggested, however, that the green manure crop precede corn, cotton, or some other crop that can use large amounts of nitrogen more effectively than peanuts can.

The evaluation of green manure crops in the production of peanuts can be summed up in this way: The peanut, a legume, can obtain part or all of the needed nitrogen from the atmosphere when it is properly inoculated. Large amounts of nitrogen may be detrimental to peanuts. In order for fruits to be formed, the peanut peg must penetrate the surface of the soil. Measurements made after green manure crops are turned indicate that they made the soil less compact and more easily penetrable. The use of green manure crops preceding peanuts may result in increased damage from diseases, insects, and nematodes.

In considering the influence of green manure crops on tobacco, one must take into account the effect on yield and quality. A 7-year experiment in Maryland showed that the highest yield and the best quality tobacco was produced when tobacco was grown following ragweed turned in the spring. The lowest yield and quality was produced when tobacco followed lambsquarter. Lespedeza produced a fairly satisfactory yield, but it was of low quality.

An experiment in North Carolina compared the effect of vetch, crimson clover, fallow, cowpeas, soybeans, and lespedeza on flue-cured tobacco. Vetch and crimson clover resulted in lower quality and acre value. There were no striking differences in the other.

These and some other experiments are summarized thus: Flue-cured tobacco should not be grown immediately following a leguminous crop. The amount and availability of nitrogen is too difficult to control. Some weeds appear to exert a favorable influence on the yield and quality of tobacco. Others exert an unfavorable influence. Management of the green manure crop will affect its influence on tobacco. Rye turned late may tie up nitrogen during the early part of the tobacco season and release it late in the season, causing an inferior quality of tobacco. Certain green manure crops may result in an increased damage to tobacco from diseases and pests. Crotalaria and velvet beans appear most effective of the legumes tested in reducing damage by nematodes.

GREEN MANURE CROPS often are used in vegetable rotations. The effects of various organic matter additions on yield of potatoes in a 2-year rotation were studied for 16 years in Maine. Green manure increased the yield of potatoes an average of 53 bushels an acre. When the green manure crop was removed, the yield of potatoes was reduced 38 bushels, as compared to turning the crop.

Another experiment in Maine showed that legumes increased the yield of potatoes considerably more than non-legumes. Eighty pounds of commercial nitrogen was applied in both of these experiments.

L. M. Ware and W. A. Johnson, of Auburn, Ala., studied the value of vetch with and without commercial nitrogen. During a 6-year period, they obtained only 3 bushels of snap beans an acre when no nitrogen was used. Snap beans following vetch produced 161 bushels. When 60 pounds of nitrogen was applied, the yield was 144 bushels. Similar results were obtained with lima beans and eggplant. They reported that the average value of the organic treatment on all vegetables studied was 135 dollars an acre above the cost of the practice.

Soil Management and Crop Quality

Kenneth C. Beeson

The term "crop quality" means both marketable quality and nutritional quality of a crop. A potato with yellowish flesh and of small, irregular size can be unusually high in vitamin C. It would have high nutritive value, but the housewife would not be inclined to buy it.

Nature has not always combined two aspects of crop quality in one package, and man has seldom improved matters in his efforts to breed plants and manage soil so as to produce crops that are both attractive and high yielding.

Nutritional quality is hard to define. A crop may be rich in a vitamin or one of the mineral elements, such as iron. The importance of each component in terms of man or a specific domestic animal is not always clear. Each species of animal has a different set of nutritional requirements.

The horse can survive and be healthy on a pasture where cows fail to thrive and reproduce normally. Sheep may not even survive on the same pasture. The difference in the response of each animal in this instance could be due to their different requirements for the mineral element cobalt. Hence, if cobalt is determined in the laboratory by chemical means, the interpretation of the results in terms of nutritional quality must be made with respect to the particular animal involved.

Our knowledge concerning nutritional quality is still quite limited.

First, all of the factors that enter into this entity in crops are not known. Studies in research laboratories attempt to identify some of these unknown factors. One that apparently is required by the chicken and another that the rabbit (and possibly the growing calf) seems to need are two clues being investigated.

Secondly, we recognize that there is a definite and desirable balance among the factors comprising nutritional quality. Thus the nutrition of an animal may be upset if calcium is too high in relation to phosphorus in a forage.

The measurement of nutritional quality by a laboratory method or groups of methods is not possible. Only partial estimations can be made. For this reason, no single unique value can be assigned to a food or a feed to express its nutritional quality. It follows, of course, that no laboratory measurement of the overall nutritional quality of a food or feed has ever been made.

We are not entirely without a handle in dealing with this important matter, however. The animal itself is a good indicator of nutritional quality of the feed it consumes. Certain standards for growth, reproduction, and lactation can be used as bases for evaluating nutritional quality of one food or feed, at least in terms of another. We can compare corn and wheat, clover and timothy, or two sources of timothy by feeding them to a test animal. We can supplement the tests with laboratory determinations of individual nutritive constituents of the crop. These methods have limitations of basic importance, but if we recognize the limitations we can make an intelligent appraisal of the nutritional quality of crops and the factors affecting it.

DIFFERENT CROPS can exhibit different levels of nutritional quality.

Legumes, for example, will contain 2 to 10 times the amount of calcium ordinarily found in timothy or similar grasses when all are grown on the same kind of soil. The legumes contain more protein and cobalt than the grasses.

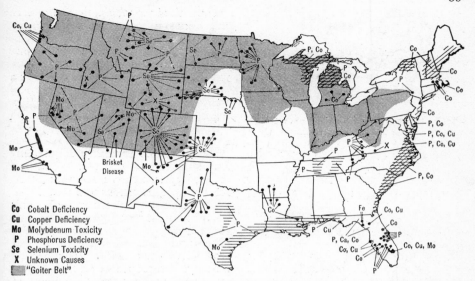

Co   Cobalt Deficiency
Cu   Copper Deficiency
Mo   Molybdenum Toxicity
P   Phosphorus Deficiency
Se   Selenium Toxicity
X   Unknown Causes
▨   "Goiter Belt"

1. Known areas in the United States where mineral-nutritional diseases of animals occur. The dots indicate approximate locations where troubles occur. The lines not terminating in dots indicate a generalized area or areas where specific locations have not been reported.

The content of phosphorus, however, will not differ materially between these two classes of forage crops.

A study of several hundred samples of mixed hay from New York farms illustrates the importance of legumes. If the hay contained 25 percent of a legume, the cobalt content was always high enough to meet the needs of cattle. Timothy from the same farms often failed to supply sufficient cobalt.

The protein of wheat may have a higher biological value for certain animals than does the protein from corn. The iron in spinach may be less available nutritionally than the iron in turnip greens.

Such differences in nutritional quality in different kinds of crops emphasize the importance of producing the kind of crop we want wherever we may need it. To do that requires an understanding of the cultural factors involved.

Alfalfa is one of our best forage crops. Its production in abundance guarantees healthier animals and more animal products, such as meat and milk, for our human population. Alfalfa will not grow satisfactorily on many soils in the Eastern States unless boron is applied to them.

Citrus fruit, a good source of vitamin C, could not be produced in abundance in this country without the help of zinc, copper, and, in some regions, molybdenum.

Potatoes, an important source of energy, vitamin C, iron, and copper, cannot be produced in abundance on many soils unless magnesium is added to the soil.

These mineral nutrients have been especially limiting in crop production because different crops have different requirements for them.

Most crops respond to applications of nitrogen, phosphorus, and potassium to the soil. But not all crops have the unusually high requirements for boron as does alfalfa, for example. Hence, we now recognize that supplements of boron, in addition to nitrogen, phosphorus, and potassium, make possible the production of alfalfa of high nutritional quality where only poor-quality grasses grew before.

The nutritional quality of crops

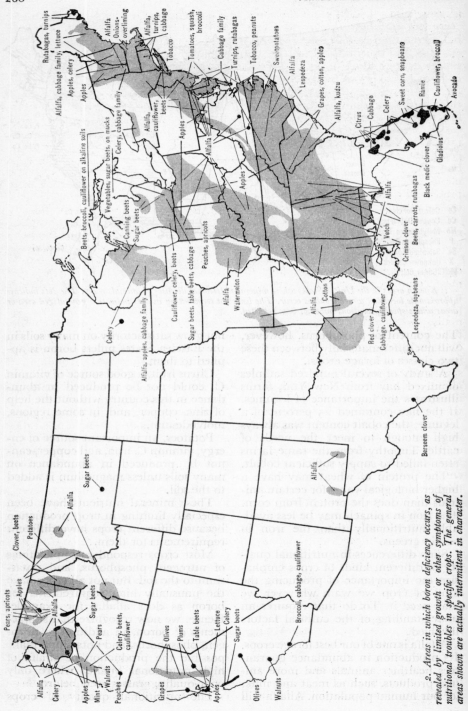

2. Areas in which boron deficiency occurs, as revealed by limited growth or other symptoms of nutritional troubles in specific crops. The general areas shown are actually intermittent in character.

as grown on all soils is not the same.

Some soils do not supply enough cobalt to a forage crop to meet the needs of cattle and sheep. Some soils do not supply enough phosphorus. Others do not supply copper or iodine.

In contrast to these deficiencies, there are soils that supply elements like selenium and molybdenum in excessive or harmful amounts to the vegetation. The management of such soils generally requires a choice of methods best suited to the particular environment, the nature of the farm enterprise, and the nature of the deficiency or toxicity.

Feeding the deficient mineral element directly to the animal is a common method of correction.

In the dairy regions of the Northeast, for example, cobalt is added to most commercially prepared concentrates. Salt with added cobalt can be purchased. In this manner the normally low-cobalt grass, hays, and pasture herbage of this region are adequately supplemented. The mineral form of cobalt is as effective in this respect as is the cobalt in the crop. Only about 0.003 part of 1 ounce of cobalt is required by a sheep in a day. Somewhat more is required by the cow.

This small amount is difficult to work with on the farm where mixing of homegrown feeds is practiced. In New Zealand and Australia, cobalt is commonly added to the fertilizer mixture or to superphosphate, and so it is supplied to the animal through the crop. Cobalt salts have been added directly to the soil in New Hampshire. Salt diluted with sand and applied at a rate equivalent to 5 pounds of cobalt to the acre was effective 7 years later in supplying an adequate amount to the forage crop.

A low content of cobalt in the native forage is an important limiting factor in the utilization of vast acreages in the Coastal Plain. The addition of cobalt to salt or other carriers is not always successful for supplementing the rations of unconfined cattle.

Experiments were started in the Flor-

ida Everglades to determine the feasibility of spraying a solution of cobalt on such pastures from an airplane. The results in increasing the cobalt content of the vegetation have been surprisingly successful, at least for the first year or two following the application. This method of coping with other deficiencies where the usual cultural practices are not possible holds much promise.

MOST NUTRIENT ELEMENTS, except cobalt and iodine, required by animals also are needed by plants. Hence, where soils are supplying insufficient quantities of an element like phosphorus, not only crop yields but the production of more desirable crops may be limited. In such instances there is a double advantage in applying the phosphorus directly to the soil in amounts sufficient to produce a good yield of the desired crop and to increase the phosphorus content of the plant. The productive capacity of rangeland as well as smaller pastures has thus been increased severalfold.

All nutrient elements added to the soil are not readily absorbed by plants. The reasons therefor are not clear.

The copper content of a plant is increased materially only with great difficulty, and it is not ordinarily economical to attempt to apply copper compounds to the soil, except to improve yields. In places where a copper supplement is required by animals, therefore, it is better to supply it directly in salt or a feed concentrate. That is particularly true on alkaline mucks where toxic amounts of molybdenum in the crop are often encountered. Relatively large doses of copper then are required by the animal to counteract the effect of the molybdenum. It is improbable that such amounts of copper can be absorbed by the plant irrespective of the soil treatment.

A plant readily absorbs molybdenum from the soil or from molybdenum salts added to the soil. Molybdenum is required in appreciable amounts by some crop plants, such as alfalfa, and its use

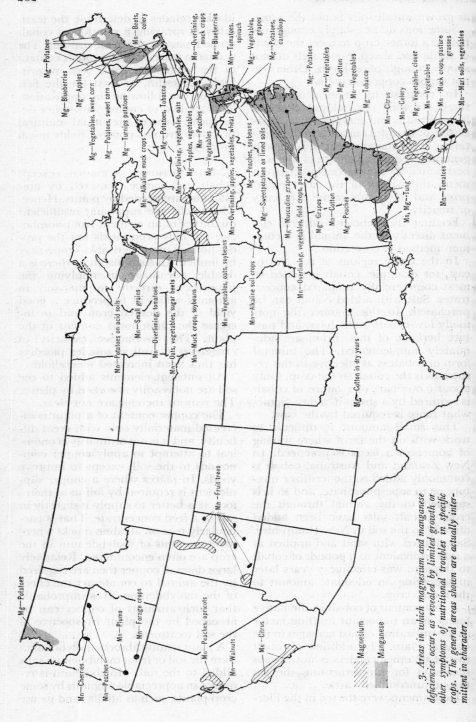

Mg—Potatoes
Mg—Blueberries
Mg—Apples
Mn—Beets, celery
Mn—Overliming, muck crops
Mg—Blueberries
Mn—Tomatoes, celery
Mg—Vegetables, grapes
Mg—Potatoes, cantaloup
Mg—Potatoes
Mg—Vegetables
Mg—Vegetables, clover
Mn—Muck soils, vegetables
Mg—Vegetables, sweet corn
Mg—Potatoes, sweet corn
Mg—Turnips potatoes
Mg—Potatoes, Tobacco
Mn—Apples, vegetables
Mn—Peaches
Mg—Vegetables
Mn—Citrus
Mn—Celery
Mg—Vegetables
Mn—Vegetables
Mn—Marl soils, vegetables
Mg—Tobacco
Mn—Alkaline muck crops
Mg—Overliming, vegetables, oats
Mn—Overliming, apples, vegetables, wheat
Mg—Peaches, soybeans
Mg—Sweetpotatoes on limed soils
Mn, Mg—Apples
Mn, Mg—Tomatoes
Mn—Overliming, tomatoes
Mn—Vegetables, oats, soybeans
Mg—Muscadine grapes
Mn—Overliming, vegetables, field crops, peanuts
Mn—Tung
Mn—Small grains
Mn—Vegetables, oats, soybeans
Mn—Alkaline soil crops
Mn—Grapes
Mn—Cotton
Mn—Peaches
Mn—Oats, vegetables, sugar beets
Mn—Muck crops, soybeans
Mn—Potatoes on acid soils
Mg—Cotton in dry years
Mg—Potatoes
Mn—Fruit trees
Mg—Potatoes
Mn—Cherries
Mn—Plums
Mn—Forage crops
Mn—Peaches, apricots
Mn—Citrus
Mn—Peaches
Mn—Walnuts

Magnesium
Manganese

3. *Areas in which magnesium and manganese deficiencies occur, as revealed by limited growth or other symptoms of nutritional troubles in specific crops. The general areas shown are actually intermittent in character.*

for good yields of this important crop on certain soils is increasing. Caution should be exercised, however, to avoid excesses of the element, since it can upset the normal nutritional processes of the animal, particularly cattle.

AGRICULTURAL SCIENTISTS are studying the extension of spraying practices by the use of certain mineral nutrients. Applications of zinc, copper, and iron have been made by spraying them on trees where applications to the soil have been inefficient. The wider use of sprays containing nitrogen, potash, and phosphate appears promising, but we still have much to learn about improved nutritional quality and the relative costs, effectiveness, and other benefits of spray techniques, soil applications, and direct feeding of the elements to the animal. For some elements, however, spraying seems to be the only practical method of getting them into the plant.

We have reason to suspect that these elements may have some effect on the nutritional quality of the plant other than the presence of the element itself. If that is true, additions of the mineral elements to the soil or plant—rather than directly to the animal as a mineral supplement—is especially desirable.

THERE IS MUCH TO BE LEARNED concerning the effect of fertilizer elements and other mineral elements on the nutritional quality of foods and feeds.

Many of the minor elements are associated in the plants with the vitamins or with enzyme systems and other organic components. If the minor element in the soil is limited in amount, the plant does not grow normally. Such plants are usually less nutritious than normal plants. The supply of a mineral element often exceeds that required for maximum growth of the plant. The excess taken up by the plant may thus improve its nutritional quality.

Phosphate fertilization of a soil producing a crop of soybean hay is an illustration. The Department of Agriculture and the North Carolina Agricultural Experiment Station supplied superphosphate to a soil extremely low in available phosphate. Two levels of phosphate fertilization were used. The smaller application resulted in a substantial increase in the yield of the crop but the higher application resulted in only a slightly higher yield beyond that obtained with the smaller application.

The effect on the nutritional quality is interesting. The best growth in rabbits, used as test animals, was obtained by feeding the crop grown with the smaller application of superphosphate. The poorest growth was obtained from the crop grown without superphosphate. The conclusion is that some optimum level of phosphate fertilization exists, above or below which a less nutritious plant is obtained. The true explanation of the differences is not apparent.

Several other experiments point to the general conclusion that the nutritional quality of crops is influenced by fertilization. In another experiment in North Carolina, soybean hay from a phosphate-fertilized soil again proved to be superior to that from an unfertilized soil. When a phosphate supplement was added to the diets, the rabbits receiving the hay from the unfertilized soils grew better than did those receiving hay from the phosphated soils. The plants from the phosphate-fertilized soils were larger and stemmier and had a smaller proportion of leaves. Some factor other than phosphate apparently became limiting in these plants as they grew larger and produced more dry matter.

That this conclusion appears true is shown by the results of a third experiment. Again two lots of soybean hay were used. One lot was grown with superphosphate and one without. The effect of the fertilizer was reflected in the greater yield of hay. Rabbits fed the hay from the phosphate plots grew better. When a mineral phosphate was added to the diets of the rabbits, growth was the same with both lots of hay. As a third step, casein, a protein,

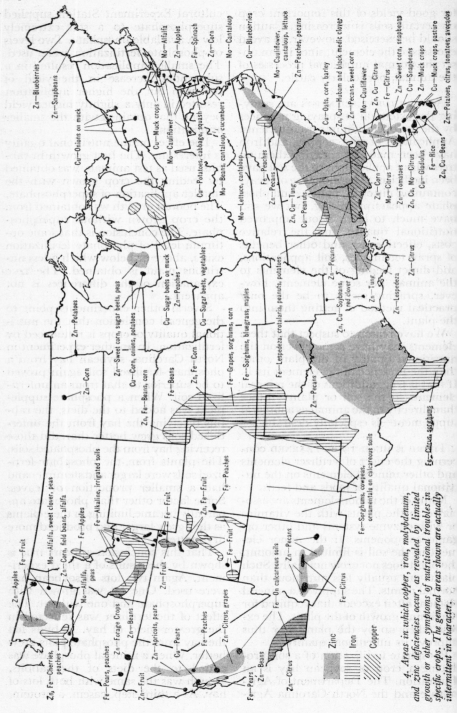

4. Areas in which copper, iron, molybdenum, and zinc deficiencies occur, as revealed by limited growth or other symptoms of nutritional troubles in specific crops. The general areas shown are actually intermittent in character.

was added to both diets. No better growth was obtained with the rabbits fed the hay from the nonphosphated soil. The rabbits fed the hay from the phosphated soil, plus the casein, however, showed a 50-percent increase in weight in 8 weeks. It was concluded that some factor other than phosphorus or protein was limiting in the no-phosphate hay but was present in the hay from the phosphated plots.

All these experiments point to profound effects of fertilization on the nutritional quality of a plant.

To determine their meaning in terms of practical agriculture, we must first identify and measure the growth factors that must be involved. If these factors have never been identified, the task will be exceedingly complicated. It is possible, however, that an imbalance of factors occurs, particularly where the fertilization program is not a balanced one. The task then is less difficult, but still not easy. Finally, we will have to determine the balance of plant nutrients in the soil that will produce a plant of optimum nutritional quality.

Some progress is being made. As the plant grows and develops, many complicated and intricate chemical reactions occur. From relatively simple compounds they produce the complex proteins, the carbohydrates, and other components of food and feed. An example would be the formation of protein from the simpler amino acids.

Experiments in the Department of Agriculture have shown that in cases of a deficiency of a mineral nutrient, these reactions sometimes slow down or fail altogether. Thus, in a plant growing in a soil deficient in potassium, magnesium or manganese, for example, certain amino acids tend to accumulate as such in the plant instead of building up into proteins. The nutritional importance of this point is still to be demonstrated, but the implications are that here is a suggestion for the differences found in the nutritional quality of the forages I have described.

CLIMATE is a factor of great importance in the production of crops of high nutritional quality. Crops grown on two different soils in two climatic regions differ in nutritional quality. Experiments carried on in the Department of Agriculture nearly 50 years ago demonstrated the predominant effects of climate in influencing the nature of protein. Research workers in a group of Southern State agricultural experiment stations have advanced our knowledge concerning the relation of climatic factors to both the organic and mineral components of plants.

The farmer cannot adjust temperature, sunlight, wind movement, or humidity to suit his needs, but in many situations he can supply water when necessary. At various times some effort has been made to evaluate the effects of water on nutritional quality.

Such effects must be profound. Yet to isolate moisture supply and determine the magnitude and direction of its influence has proved to be exceedingly difficult, and few generalizations of value have been discovered. For example, moisture has marked effects on the growth of plants and on the solubility and mobility of the plant nutrients in the soil. No specific recommendations can be made, however, concerning irrigation except as it is required to produce normal yields of food and feed crops.

THE METHODS OF HARVESTING, curing, and storing crops can preserve or destroy most of the effort for better nutritional quality that has gone into their production.

There is no need here to dwell at length on such well-known practices as the best time for harvesting hay. Innumerable reports from the agricultural experiment stations have shown that in the prebloom stage, forages are higher in protein, retain their color better in curing, and hence have a higher nutritional quality than forages harvested in the postbloom stage.

Other practices that preserve nutritional quality include the curing of hay without subjecting it to excessive weathering and techniques that allow the retention of leaves. The latter factor is of great importance, because a high proportion of the protein, vitamins, and minerals is in the leafy tissue.

Management of the potato crop is an example of the effects of time of harvest and storage on quality. The potato is an excellent source of vitamin C, which is essential in the human diet. The vitamin C in the potato tuber increases as the plant matures. As soon as the vine dies, however, the tuber is essentially in a storage condition in the soil. The longer it remains in the soil, the less vitamin C will be found in the potato. That is exactly what happens if the potato is harvested and put into artificial storage, in which, however, some measure of control can be exercised, and more of the vitamin C is preserved.

THE MANAGEMENT OF SOILS that contain toxic amounts of some mineral elements has in no case been clearly defined, but certain simple remedies are known and have been used to counteract some of these toxicities. The basic causes of such troubles must be investigated before sound recommendations can be made.

Selenium toxicity in vegetation in some places in the West is an example of this type of problem. An adequate mapping of the critically toxic areas will provide information necessary for fencing the affected soils. Grazing would be prevented in such areas, but fiber and seed crops could be grown there. Overgrazing of seleniferous areas should be avoided. It is a common observation that cattle will not select the selenium accumulator plants —the plants that tend to absorb and store excessively large quantities of selenium—if other forage is available. Finally, a small amount of arsenic given through the drinking water or in the salt will counteract the effects of selenium. No effective soil treatment in seleniferous areas has been devised.

Soils supplying excessive quantities of molybdenum to plants present similar difficulties. The known remedy, doses of copper sulfate (blue vitriol), is applied directly to the animal. Some control in pasture and forage can be applied through soil management by eliminating legumes from the forage mixture. On the same soil, legumes will absorb and store 2 to 10 times as much molybdenum as will associated grasses. Here, again, no effective soil treatment has been devised.

MUCH HAS BEEN SPOKEN and written about the occurrence of nutritional troubles and other diseases in man and impoverished soils, leached soils, eroded soils, "wornout" soils.

The truth of these relationships is difficult to deny—but confirmation is almost impossible to achieve.

The fallacy of the claims lies in the generalizations that have been made. The reason for this lies obviously in the almost insurmountable complications attendant upon longtime experiments with human subjects.

Isolated communities dependent on their own produce might supply the answer, but in the United States few such communities are available for study. Furthermore, it has not been possible to separate economic and other circumstances from soil conditions as causes of poor nutrition in such communities.

Any sensible approach to the problems of soils in relation to human nutrition must therefore be indirect.

Management practices that produce ample supplies of crops containing maximum amounts of vitamins and minerals will have an influence on human health and welfare. Management practices aimed at the production of better feed for animals—thus supplying the market with animal products such as meat, milk, and eggs—also will help improve human nutrition. An example: The localities where it has not been practical to keep a family cow because of a deficiency of cobalt or possibly copper or phosphorus in the soil could easily be made suitable for cows. I know of few ways better than this to raise the standard of living of some farm families.

An effective system of soil management will aim to provide food and feed crops with an optimum level of all nutrients required by animals and man. Such a system will seek to avoid upsetting nutritional balances simply to provide greater yields. It will be based on the best information available as to all of the requirements for good yields and good nutrition.

The Economics of Fertilizers

L. B. Nelson and D. B. Ibach

The wise use of fertilizers can increase farm returns and help maintain or improve the soil. But potential gains from them are not realized on many farms.

Agronomic, economic, and managerial factors influence the use of fertilizer and must be considered together in relation to the crop to be fertilized and in relation to succeeding crops and the farm as a whole.

Some of these points were discussed in previous chapters. Some we repeat here by way of summary and to emphasize how the factors mesh together.

The starting point in a fertilizer program is to take inventory of the existing nutrient supplies, particularly those obtained directly from the soil.

Some soils may be deficient in one nutrient. Others may lack two or more. Only a few have all nutrients in proper balance for the best plant growth. The nutrient status of the soil differs between fields and within the same field. It changes with time. It

reflects the farm cropping practices.

You can estimate the soil-nutrient status in several ways, although none will give a direct estimate of the exact amount of nutrient to apply to get the best balance.

Soil tests may provide the most useful estimate, but they are subject to error unless samples are properly taken and proved tests are made and interpreted by technicians. Information on the characteristics of the soil, the cropping history of the field, and the results of fertilizer trials conducted in the locality increase the chances that the tests are interpreted properly.

The kind of crop and how fast and how big it grows determine how much nutrients it uses.

A 40-bushel corn crop has one requirement for nutrients. A 100-bushel crop has another. The problem is to estimate the optimum economic level of yield to be reached. Some of the controlling factors are discussed later. But data on the amounts of different nutrients used in producing specified yields of crops can help the farmer select the kind and rate of fertilization.

If one crop uses more of a nutrient than another in producing the yield desired on the same soil, more of that nutrient must be applied for the one than for the other. For example, potatoes, tobacco, and alfalfa use large amounts of potassium. Comparable yields of corn, wheat, and soybeans use less potassium.

The quantities of nitrogen, phosphorus, potassium, and sulfur taken up by a crop are especially useful in estimating the kind and rate of fertilizer to apply. We need not consider the amounts of nitrogen that legumes use because they obtain most of their nitrogen through the activity of bacteria in their root nodules.

Crops recover and utilize in any year only a portion of the nutrients applied. Nonleguminous crops frequently recover 20 to 70 percent of the nitrogen applied. Recovery of phosphorus is lower; usually it may be 5 to 15 percent. Potassium is intermediate.

Phosphorus and potassium not recovered during the year of application may be recovered partly by future crops. At the Rothamsted Experimental Station in England, crops are still utilizing phosphorus from large applications made more than 50 years ago. Nitrogen left over from the year of application except in dry climates or during dry seasons may be lost from overwinter leaching.

The higher the rate of fertilizer application, the lower is the percentage recovered during the year of application. Recovery is less when fertilizers are applied on soils that are well supplied with a particular nutrient. Crop residues also may tie up nitrogen and phosphorus. Some soils more than others hold elements in unavailable forms. Leaching and erosion reduce recovery, as does lack of moisture. Liming acid soils favors recovery of soluble phosphates but lowers recovery of the insoluble forms of that element, such as phosphate rock. Placement of fertilizer markedly affects recovery of the nutrients applied.

TOO LITTLE OR TOO MUCH of a nutrient may affect adversely the yield and quality of a crop.

We could give many examples. Adding certain nutrients sometimes accentuates the deficiency of another nutrient and results in either no increase in yield or a lower yield. Excessive nitrogen may overstimulate the growth of leaves and stems and interfere with the formation of seed.

Plants can grow well under a rather wide range of nutrient conditions, if no one nutrient is in short supply. Thus a farmer has some leeway in achieving nutrient balance and can compensate somewhat for a lack of it by applying fertilizer generously. But he will get better and more economical results if he considers the supplies of nutrients and the need for them before he applies fertilizer.

If soils are seriously deficient in two nutrients, adding one of them affects yields little or not at all.

Results from a field experiment conducted on soil that was very low in nitrogen and phosphorus illustrate this point. With no application of either nitrogen or phosphorus, the yield of corn was only 4 bushels. Adding 40 pounds of nitrogen but no phosphorus resulted in a yield of 12 bushels. Adding 40 pounds of phosphoric oxide but no nitrogen gave a 21-bushel yield. In one instance the increase was 8 bushels; in the other, 17 bushels. But when 40 pounds of each nutrient were applied, the yield was 58 bushels. The gain from the combination was 54 bushels, or 29 bushels more than the sum of the two increases. Thus the two nutrients complement each other. The response from the combination is much greater than from either alone.

OTHER FACTORS affect the response to fertilization. Different combinations of such things as density of stand, water supply, variety of crop, or degree of control of insects and diseases affect the results a farmer hopes to get from fertilizers. Any factors that limit yield must be given attention if potential response from fertilizer is to be realized.

It often happens that a factor that does not limit yields becomes a problem when nutrients are plentiful. An example: A low level of nitrogen may be adequate if a lack of moisture limits the yield of corn to, say, 30 bushels an acre. But when the field is irrigated, the rapidly growing corn might encounter a nitrogen deficiency and the yield might be only 25 bushels. If both nitrogen and water are adequate, however, the yield might be 90 bushels an acre.

Too little soil moisture is probably the greatest handicap to effective results from fertilizer. Plants depend largely on the nutrients in the plow layer. When this layer dries out, the uptake of nutrients is impeded even though there is ample moisture deeper in the root zone. Thus irrigation water applied at the proper time and in the right amounts can greatly increase returns when fertilizer is applied. But care must be taken not to overirrigate.

Excess water leaches much nitrogen and some potassium from the root zone.

A particular variety of crop may not respond as well to fertilizer as another. Some of the old varieties of open-pollinated corn, for example, cannot utilize large applications of nitrogen as can some of the better hybrids. Some hybrids respond more to fertilizer than others do. Crops that are not adapted to a region may not respond profitably to fertilization.

Too few plants to the acre often limit returns from fertilizers on row crops. Some common planting practices were developed under conditions of low soil fertility, so that the number of plants per acre is too low for the higher rates of application of fertilizer now used.

In an experiment with hybrid corn in North Carolina, the yield was 39 bushels when there were 4 thousand plants and 20 pounds of nitrogen were applied per acre. Increasing the nitrogen to 120 pounds an acre resulted in a yield of 63 bushels, a gain of 24 bushels. With 10 thousand plants and 20 pounds of nitrogen an acre, the yield was only 41 bushels, a gain of 2 bushels over the combination of 4 thousand plants and 20 pounds of nitrogen. But when plant population and nitrogen were stepped up to 10 thousand plants and 120 pounds an acre, respectively, the yield was 92 bushels—a gain of 53 bushels over the low plant population and the low nitrogen application. This is an example of complementary effect or of two yield factors working together.

THE RESPONSE—greater yields—is the basis for determining the most profitable use of fertilizer.

Yields of irrigated corn at different rates of nitrogen applied in an experiment at Prosser, Wash., show how information on response is used in estimating the most profitable rate of application. When 12 rates of nitrogen ranging from 0 to 520 pounds an acre were applied, yields ranged from 12 bushels to about 150 bushels an acre.

Additional nitrogen increases yields.

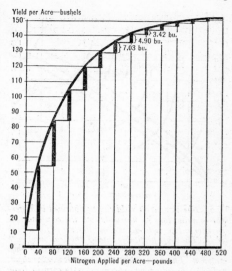

1. The yield response of irrigated corn to nitrogen at Prosser, Wash., shows how the response diminishes with increasing quantities of fertilizer. Such curves are used to estimate most profitable rates.

But with each equal-sized unit of nitrogen added, the increase in yield is less than the increase obtained with the preceding unit. In other words: The additions of extra amounts of nitrogen increase yields less and less. As the maximum yield is approached, additional nitrogen has little or no effect on the yield. In the experiment at Prosser, only nitrogen seriously limited yield. If too little moisture had been supplied or if there had been too thin a stand of the crop, much less response would have been obtained by adding nitrogen. Conversely, something else may have prevented the yield from going even higher. But the results illustrate the principle of decreasing increments in yield with successively higher rates of nitrogen when there are no other important limiting factors.

WE HAVE NOW LAID the groundwork for an important economic determination—the most profitable rate of fertilizer to apply for a specified pattern of response at specified prices of the crop and the fertilizer.

If corn is worth 1.40 dollars a bushel

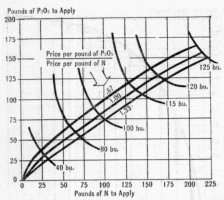

Pounds of P₂O₅ to Apply

Pounds of N to Apply

2. *The same crop yield can be obtained by different combinations of nutrients and the combinations best for a low yield differ from those best for a high yield. The most profitable rate of application of each nutrient also depends on the prevailing costs of each nutrient. These principles are illustrated in the chart, which is based on an experiment with corn in Iowa on soil seriously deficient in both nitrogen and phosphorus. Three nitrogen and phosphorus price relationships are shown—when the price per pound of phosphoric oxide is two-thirds that of nitrogen; equal to nitrogen; and one-third more than nitrogen.*

and nitrogen costs 14 cents a pound, or 5.60 dollars for 40 pounds, the most profitable rate is that at which the last 40-pound unit of nitrogen applied results in an additional yield of 4 bushels of corn. That is, the cost of 40 pounds of nitrogen, or 5.60 dollars, divided by the price of 1 bushel of corn, or 1.40 dollars, equals 4 bushels, and 4 bushels of corn equal in value the 40 pounds of nitrogen.

In our example, an additional yield of 4 bushels occurs somewhere between a 280-pound and a 320-pound application of nitrogen. At the 280-pound rate, the yield was 4.9 bushels more than at the 240-pound rate. But at 320 pounds, the yield was only 3.4 bushels more than at 280 pounds. As determined by direct computation, the most profitable rate was found to be 281 pounds. Response from smaller units, such as 10 or 5 pounds of nitrogen, could be shown graphically on a response curve drawn to a large scale. In this way, a nearly exact graphic reading of the most profitable rate could be obtained.

This illustrates the principle of mar-

ginal returns. As applied to our example, the principle may be stated thus: The most profitable rate (other things being constant) is the amount at which the last unit just pays its way. The most profitable rate is thus determined without knowledge of other costs. At the most profitable rate, returns available to meet other costs are at a maximum.

But that does not indicate profit per acre. If the value of the crop at different rates of application and the total cost per acre (including fertilizer and cost of harvesting the additional yield) were calculated, the most profitable rate would be the one at which the difference between gross value and total cost is greatest. That means that the last increment in value of the crop is just equal to the cost of obtaining it. Thus the highest profit occurs at the rate at which marginal return equals marginal cost.

Agronomic and economic principles operate together in establishing the rate needed to get a specified return per dollar spent for fertilizer. Yield response that shows the rate of decreasing increments in the yield is the foundation for economic interpretation. The principle that marginal return equals marginal cost at the point of highest profit is general. But, as we have seen, many natural factors and many management practices influence yield response and modify the operation of the principle.

RISK AND UNCERTAINTY as to returns from an application of fertilizer keep farmers from applying as much fertilizer as would be profitable if there were no uncertainties as to the result. The future is always uncertain. So is the weather. So are prices.

An analysis like the following, which is based on the experiment at Prosser, will help farmers balance risks against possible returns.

As the calculated most profitable rate of application is approached, increments in yield are small as more fertilizer is added. In the experiment with irrigated corn, yield increments are shown for each additional 40-pound unit of nitrogen costing 5.60 dollars. At the seventh 40-pound unit, or the 280-pound rate, the additional yield was 4.9 bushels, worth 6.86 dollars at 1.40 dollars a bushel. Then the added return per added dollar spent for this unit was 1.22 dollars. Thus, at this rate, the marginal return slightly exceeds the marginal cost. The most profitable rate is just a little more than 280 pounds. The added return from the eighth 40-pound unit would be only 85 cents per additional dollar spent. Application of this eighth unit would therefore be unprofitable. But for the sixth, fifth, and fourth 40-pound units, the additional return per additional dollar spent would be 1.76, 2.52, and 3.64 dollars, respectively.

Many farmers might consider that a calculated marginal return of about 2.50 dollars for each additional dollar spent for fertilizer would allow them about the right margin for risk and uncertainty. That return would occur at the fifth unit, or the 200-pound rate in our example. They would consider the expected marginal returns from the sixth and seventh units too small to offset the risk of unfavorable weather and prices. But applications lower than that represented by the fifth unit probably would result in such reductions in yield that the loss because of applying less fertilizer would be greater than the risk and uncertainty as to growing conditions.

Natural risks are of greater importance than price risks for farmers who are trying to estimate the best practical rate of application. A drop in the price of a crop greatly affects returns per acre. But declines in price after application of fertilizer do not affect returns significantly compared with what the returns would have been if the most profitable rate for the lower price had been applied.

In the experiment we cited, the seventh unit of application is most profitable if corn sells for 1.40 dollars a bushel. If this application is made, and if the price falls to 60 cents a bushel after the fertilizer is applied, the net return per acre will be only about 4.25 dollars below what it would have been if the most profitable rate for the 60-cent corn had been applied. The probability of variations of more than 4.25 dollars an acre from other causes are so great that this amount of reduction associated with more than a 50-percent decline in price is relatively small.

THE COMBINATION OF NUTRIENTS most profitable for a low yield differs from the one used to get a high yield.

The combinations most profitable for different yields are based on the separate rates of response to each nutrient at different levels of application and on the relative costs of the nutrients.

Thus, if a farmer has data about the way a field responds to fertilization, he can establish the different combinations of nutrients that would be most profitable in producing different yields, at different relative costs per pound of nutrients. These combinations would hold true irrespective of actual prices for the crop or actual costs per pound of the nutrients.

For example: Analysis of a corn-fertilizer rate experiment in Iowa showed that the most profitable rate of application of fertilizer was 153 pounds of nitrogen and 135 pounds of phosphoric oxide, with corn at 1.40 dollars a bushel, nitrogen at 14 cents a pound, and phosphoric oxide at 10 cents a pound. Thus the ratio of nitrogen to phosphoric oxide to apply would be 1.0 to 0.88. But if the farmer were to fertilize for an 80-bushel yield only, the ratio of nitrogen to phosphoric oxide would be 1.0 to 1.12. Thus in analyzing fertilizer rate experiments, the results can be put in a form so that the farmer can see quickly the combination that would be most profitable for any level of application and yield that he might choose.

Farmers whose funds are limited may have to apply much less fertilizer and obtain a lower yield than would be most profitable. Such farmers may also tend to apply combinations that contain too high a proportion of nutrient that costs less per pound than another nutrient. For example, if nitrogen costs 14 cents a pound and phosphoric oxide costs 10 cents, the most profitable quantity for a yield of 80 bushels of corn in the Iowa experiment would be 56 pounds of nitrogen and 65 pounds of phosphoric oxide. The cost per acre for this combination would be 14.34 dollars. But the experiment showed that a yield of 80 bushels could also be obtained by applying only 40 pounds of nitrogen if the application of phosphoric oxide were increased to 140 pounds. However, this combination would cost 19.60 dollars an acre, or 5.26 dollars more than the one that contains more nitrogen.

Changes in the fertilizer industry may change the relative cost of plant nutrients to the farmer. With phosphoric oxide costing two-thirds as much a pound as nitrogen, the most profitable combination of these nutrients to produce a 100-bushel yield under the experimental conditions would be 85 pounds of nitrogen and 88 pounds of phosphoric oxide. This is a nutrient ratio of 1 to 1.04. But if nitrogen were to become available to farmers in a form that costs two-thirds as much per pound as phosphoric oxide, the most profitable combination for a 100-bushel yield of corn would be 98 pounds of nitrogen and 74 pounds of phosphoric oxide. This is a nutrient ratio of 1 to 0.76. Therefore the analysis can also show the effects of changes in nutrient cost relationships on the combinations that would pay off best for any yield.

Different combinations of nutrients may be applied to obtain the same yield. If the combination applied does not properly compensate for deficiencies of nutrients in the soil, the soil supply of the nutrients not added in adequate amounts may be drawn on more heavily.

Economic factors may make such an unbalanced application profitable for a time. But eventually the available

soil supply may be reduced to a point at which the continued addition of other nutrients will no longer maintain the yield. As this very critical point is approached, yield response to the nutrient previously withheld will be such that inclusion of large amounts of it in the combination applied will become the most profitable alternative.

Knowledge of different combinations of nutrients that may be applied is particularly useful when shortages of some materials occur. Such information also enables the farmer to make the most economical choice of fertilizers.

IN SELECTING FERTILIZERS, farmers have a wide choice between single-nutrient materials, a few multiple-nutrient materials, and a long list of mixed fertilizers. Their final selection will depend on the kinds of nutrients needed and the proportions needed; comparative costs; availability of the nutrients to plants under local soil conditions; and the physical nature and condition of the fertilizer as related to the method and ease of application.

If only nitrogen is needed, or if it is needed in large amounts in addition to other nutrients, the choice lies among about a dozen nitrogen carriers. Alternatives include solid and liquid sources, low-pressure and high-pressure solutions, nitrate and ammonia forms, and inorganic and the synthetic and natural organics.

Pound for pound, nitrogen supplied by one carrier is about as effective as that supplied by another. Hence the price per pound of nitrogen, including cost of hauling, equipment, and application, is the major factor to consider.

Phosphorus alone is often applied to hay or meadow crops or is applied to raise the phosphorus level of the soil. As there are different grades of superphosphates, the choice depends largely on local prices and on costs of hauling and application. Ordinary superphosphate contains sulfur and has an advantage in some situations. Use of finely ground phosphate rock should be limited largely to acid soils in rotations that include a high percentage of legumes and to places where field trials have demonstrated its benefits. In general, 2 or 3 times as much phosphorus must be supplied in the form of phosphate rock as in superphosphate to obtain equal crop yields. Liquid phosphoric acid, which is used chiefly in irrigation water, is available in some parts of the West. It usually costs more per pound of phosphorus than some other forms. Calcium metaphosphate is about as effective as superphosphate.

The chief potassium sources are muriate of potash, sulfate of potash, sulfate of potash-magnesia, and manure salts. Muriate makes up about 90 percent of the amount sold. The sulfate forms are used largely on tobacco, citrus fruits, and potatoes, for which large amounts of chloride may be undesirable. Manure salts—a low analysis material—contains a large amount of sodium chloride and is sold only in limited quantities. For most farmers, therefore, the choice of potassium for separate application is limited to muriate.

Multiple-nutrient materials contain two and sometimes three major nutrient elements. The decision to use them rests on the need for all the major elements they carry and in approximately the same ratio. These materials include ammonium phosphate, ammoniated superphosphate, potassium nitrate, and potassium nitrogen phosphates. Selection of one of these over one of the ordinary mixed fertilizers of about the same nutrient composition should be based largely on the comparative cost per pound of the nutrients.

In selecting mixed fertilizers, the content of nutrients in the proportions desired is most important. If equal proportions of N, P_2O_5, and K_2O are needed, a 1–1–1 ratio would be selected. Or if no nitrogen, a little phosphorus, and much potassium are needed, a ratio of 0–1–3 or 0–1–4 might be chosen. Within each ratio are frequently many grades. The 1–1–1 ratio might range from a low-analysis 5–5–5 to a high-analysis

14–14–14, or there may be variations, such as 6–8–6 or 7–9–9. It is usually best to pick the grade that costs the least per pound of total nutrients. Often this is the fertilizer of a higher analysis. Such items as physical condition and sulfur content may influence the decision, however. (The three figures refer to the ratio of $N:P_2O_5:K_2O$. For example, a 10–10–10 fertilizer grade is a 1–1–1 ratio.)

Infrequent and large applications of fertilizer resulting in benefits to succeeding crops can be regarded as occasional investments rather than annual expenditures. The large applications, when they are feasible, save annual costs of applying fertilizer and permit the farmer to limit the annual applications to the mobile nutrients, such as nitrogen. Returns on the investment are spread over a period of years. Thus in figuring profits the farmer should discount the expected future returns at a rate of interest that reflects the returns he could get from alternative investments. Then, the discounted value of the future returns must at least equal the initial outlay if the investment is to pay him.

For example, the additional returns the first, second, third, fourth, and fifth years after a large application of phosphorus may be 6, 4, 3, 2, and 1 dollars, respectively. This is a total of 16 dollars for the 5 years. But if the farmer can invest all of his funds without going to enterprises that would probably yield less than a 10-percent annual return, he should discount the first year's return at 10 percent, or 6 dollars÷1.10, which is 5.45 dollars. The present value of the second year's return would be 4 dollars÷1.10×1.10 or 4 dollars÷1.21=3.31 dollars; returns the third year in the future would be 3 dollars÷1.33 or 2.26 dollars the fourth year, 2 dollars÷1.46, or 1.45 dollars; and the fifth year, 1 dollar÷1.61 or 62 cents. The present worth of all of the expected future returns is 5.45+3.31+2.26+1.45+0.62 dollars, or 13.09 dollars. This is the maximum amount the farmer could spend profitably for the initial application if 10 percent is the proper discount rate for him.

Farmers with less money available might consider that they could invest all without going into enterprises that yield less than 20 percent that year. They would discount the same expected future returns from a large application of phosphorus at that rate and could afford to spend only 10.87 dollars, instead of 13.09 dollars per acre for the initial application. This would be true even though the undiscounted returns over the 5-year period amounted to 16 dollars.

Large initial applications of fertilizer or lime for residual benefits on rented farms present problems of sharing the investment and paying a vacating tenant for investments he has made.

A basic principle of good leasing is that the owner and tenant share the annual costs in the same proportion as they share the returns. So long as the tenant remains on the farm, the problem is only to estimate the returns and establish the proper division of costs.

If owner and tenant share the costs as they share the returns, the same rate of application of fertilizer will be equally profitable to both. That is true whether it is a matter of a large application to give residual benefits or an annual application designed to benefit one crop. But the shares of residual benefits may be altered if the tenant leaves, unless he is reimbursed.

Solution of the problem requires an estimate of the future annual residual effects on yields because the financial benefits are based thereon. The problem also exists of recovery from the oncoming tenant of the benefits purchased by the owner. Meeting the first problem is a matter of obtaining local experiment station data that show residual yield effects of different investments in soil fertility.

An oncoming tenant regards unexhausted soil conditions in the same way that he regards the serviceability, design, and condition of farm buildings. An owner who has good buildings and a built-up soil to offer can get a higher rental and a better class of tenant than can the owner of a rundown farm having an exhausted soil. If the managerial abilities of the new and the old tenants are equal, however, the problem is to make a satisfactory adjustment for the compensation the owner has made to the previous tenant. If a direct cash payment is not feasible, arrangements might be made to have the new tenant make contributions to soil improvement in addition to those that might reflect his normal share.

When fertilizers are applied annually and in small amounts primarily to benefit the immediate crops, the problem is only one of sharing in the cost of fertilizer in the same proportion as landlord and tenant share gross returns. But if the tenant pays for harvesting the whole crop, a slight adjustment is needed to take care of the harvesting cost of the owner's share of the additional production that resulted from the application of fertilizer. Otherwise the tenant will get a smaller share of the return over the cost of fertilizer than he would obtain from the unfertilized crop.

This discrepancy would be more serious if the cost of the fertilizer itself were not shared as are the gross returns. The principle involved is that the costs of fertilizer should be shared in a way that will provide equal incentives to owner and tenant to apply the most profitable rate after allowance is made for risk and uncertainty.

Owners and tenants may have different ideas of risk, or their capital positions may differ so that one of them may be unwilling to apply as much fertilizer as would be most profitable. Their ideas also may differ as to expected response. A simple field trial with a few selected rates of nutrients and competent interpretation of tests of soil samples should be particularly useful in such instances.

THE FARMER'S CAPITAL POSITION— the amount of money he has or can borrow to spend for fertilizer—also influences his decision about using fertilizers. If funds and credit are unlimited, the farmer may wish to apply the most profitable rate on all acres of all crops. That is not usually the case, however, and the problem becomes one of the most profitable distribution of a specified amount of fertilizer in the farming system.

Results from use of fertilizer at different rates on corn, oats, and hay in the Corn Belt help to illustrate this problem. The most profitable rates involve an expenditure of about 33 dollars an acre for corn, 15 dollars for oats, and 9 dollars for hay. A typical farm organization in the area from which the results were obtained is 70 acres in corn, 42 acres in oats, and 25 acres in hay. If all the crops are fertilized at the most profitable rates, the total cost of fertilizer is 3,165 dollars. If each crop is fertilized so that the marginal return per dollar spent is 3 dollars, the total cost of fertilizer would be 1,693 dollars. The assumption here is that 1,693 dollars is all the farmer has or can obtain to spend for fertilizer. What is the effect of distributing this expenditure differently among the three crops?

To get the most profit from a limited expenditure, the distribution must be such that the marginal return per dollar spent is the same on all crops—3 dollars, in this instance. If the fertilizer is distributed in this way, the return above the cost of fertilizer for the acreages of all crops on the farm is 10,270 dollars. But if all the fertilizer is put on corn at the most profitable rate, only about 52 acres can be treated. Thus 18 acres of corn and all acres of the other crops are left untreated. The return above the cost of fertilizer for the farm is 8,185 dollars—a reduction of 2,085 dollars from that obtained when fertilizer is used so that marginal returns are the same on all crops.

The response of different crops to fertilization influences the kind of rotation that would be most profitable.

On soils of medium to low productivity, inclusion of some forage in the rotation usually results in production

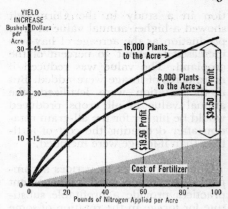

3. An example of increase in corn yields from applications of nitrogen fertilizer on a nitrogen-deficient soil as influenced by the number of corn plants per acre. Management practices and nutrient availability influence the amount of fertilizer to apply. (With 8,000 plants an acre, 60 pounds of nitrogen an acre was the most profitable rate showing a profit of 19.50 dollars an acre; with 16,000 plants an acre, 95 pounds of nitrogen an acre was the most profitable rate showing a profit of 34.50 dollars an acre.)

of more grain per 100 acres of cropland than if an all-grain cropping system were followed. As the percentage of cropland in forage is increased, however, a point is reached after which use of more of the cropland for forage will reduce the total production of grain from the rotation. At that point, grain production and forage production become competitive. More forage can be produced only at the sacrifice of grain. The relationship on productive soils may be competitive from the start—that is, the use of any of the cropland for forage will result in the production of less grain from the land included in the rotation.

Moderate to high rates of fertilizer, particularly nitrogen, usually increase yields of grain more than they increase yields of forage crops commonly used in rotations. As more of the cropland is used for forage in well-fertilized rotation, therefore, more grain is sacrificed per pound of forage gained than when more forage is included in the same rotation without fertilization.

For example, an unfertilized rotation in a study in the Corn Belt showed a higher annual value of crop production as the acreage of hay was increased to about 30 percent of the cropland. The value was reduced if more acres of forage were added. But if the rotation were fertilized, the annual value of all crops produced would be higher for the all-grain rotation after deducting the cost of fertilizer than if forage were included.

GOOD FERTILIZER PRACTICES accompanied by other good management practices provide a profitable substitute for forage in the rotation of some soils. More specifically: Nitrogen provides a profitable substitute for legumes when crop residues are properly handled on soils where slope and soil physical characteristics permit sustained high yields without inclusion of legumes or grasses in the rotation.

The effect of using fertilizers on the production relationship between grain and forage has been shown. But the decision as to the substitution of nitrogen for legumes is also influenced by the price of forage crops in comparison with the price of grain. The production relationship and the price relationship are considered together in making the decision, when more forage production can be obtained from the rotation only at the sacrifice of grain. Then the most profitable combination of grain and forage acreage is that at which the amount of grain sacrificed to obtain a pound of forage is equal to the ratio of the price of forage to the price of grain. For example: At the highest profit grain-forage acreage combination, pounds of grain sacrificed divided by pounds of forage gained is equal to price per pound of forage divided by price per pound of grain.

If a pound of forage is worth one-third as much as a pound of grain, it would be unprofitable to increase the acreage of forage beyond the point where more than one-third of a pound of grain is sacrificed to obtain a pound of forage. In a well-fertilized rotation,

loss of one-third of a pound of grain per pound of forage gained would probably occur at a lower acreage of forage than if the rotation were unfertilized.

In deciding whether to substitute fertilizer for forage crops in a rotation, one has to consider also the nature of the soil and the type of farming. Some soils need certain types of cropping to maintain physical condition that will permit profitable response from fertilizer. Also, the structure of some soils may require occasional legumes or grasses to keep them in good tilth. A tendency of a soil to excessive erosion also needs to be considered unless erosion can be controlled by other methods. Then, some farmers can get more than market value from forage and other feed crops by efficient livestock operations.

Fertilizers can aid in making profitable changes in farming. Farmers can reduce unit costs and increase the margin of return over total cost by increasing rates of application of fertilizer on principal cash and feed crops. This puts them in stronger position to make investments in soil conservation and soil improvements often needed when shifting acreage from surplus crops to other uses. Many cotton-livestock farms were once cash-crop farms. For many farmers, however, making this shift involves a substantial net cost that presents a major problem in efforts to adjust to changes in supply-demand relationships.

The first farmers to adopt new improvements that result in higher yields gain most from advancing technology. As adoption becomes more general, total production is increased. Some of the increases may occur more rapidly than the market can absorb them at prices profitable to most farmers. This brings a need for changes in farming, and the transition problem becomes difficult, particularly for farmers who do not or cannot adopt the new methods. Individual farmers who can do so, adopt them and thereby increase their net returns.

Soil Care

Principles of Tillage

W. A. Raney and A. W. Zingg

The purposes of tillage are three: To change the structure of the soil, to kill weeds, and to manage crop residues. Modification of the soil structure often is required to facilitate the intake, storage, and transmission of water and to provide a good seedbed and environment for the roots of plants.

Eradication of weeds is necessary to eliminate competition for water, nutrients, and sometimes light.

Crop residues must be managed in order to provide suitable conditions for seeding and managing a crop.

In the process of producing a crop, the planting, cultivating, and harvesting operations, though highly necessary, usually work in the direction of destroying the structure of the soil. Practices associated with the preparation of the seedbed therefore are of paramount importance. They give opportunity to create a desirable structure.

A desirable soil structure is one in which large, stable pores extend from the surface to the water table or drains.

Such pores ensure rapid infiltration and drainage of excess or free water and enhance the aeration of the subsoil. The retention and storage of moisture are associated with small pores. The small pores should ramify the soil between large pores and hold a considerable amount of water against drainage and for the use of plant roots. A combination of large and small

277

pores gives both adequate moisture-holding ability and satisfactory water intake and transmission. The combination exists in soils, with granular structure, where the small pores within the granules provide moisture storage and the large voids between the granules or aggregates facilitate rapid water movement throughout the soil.

Theoretically the best sizes of aggregates range from 1 to 5 millimeters. Soil composed of the smaller size is less well drained and is desirable under dry conditions. The larger sizes are preferred for moist conditions.

The soil texture and the change desired in size of aggregates determine the procedure for preparation of the seedbed. On coarse-textured soils any increase in aggregate size depends mainly on tillage. The size of aggregates is increased by tilling the soil at a moisture content that will just permit the particles to slip over one another. This moisture corresponds to a situation in which only the small pores are full of water. If the moisture content is higher or lower than this ideal, tillage makes smaller aggregates.

Fine-textured soils tend to have clods, which need to be broken into smaller units by weathering and machines. The power requirements for cutting wet clods or shattering dry ones into smaller units by tillage alone tend to be prohibitive. A slow, drizzling rain causes such clods to develop planes of weakness, which allow them to be broken easily with implements. It is therefore wise to reduce the size of clods mechanically only after they have been moistened in such a way that planes of weakness exist throughout their mass.

DEEPENING the root zone is necessary for many soil profiles. A soil horizon or layer of high density and low porosity reduces the rate of downward movement of water, limits the amount that is stored during periods of heavy rainfall, and reduces the intake of irrigation water.

Because roots do not grow in dry soil, the zones that limit moisture storage may reduce the rooting depth of a crop. Unfavorable aeration in zones of poor internal drainage also limits the development of roots and prevents the use of water in the subsoil that plants might otherwise utilize.

Compact soil layers may occur naturally. They also may be caused by tillage, notably in loam or silt loam soils that have been continuously in row crops.

A tillage pan, if it is present, occurs just below the zone disturbed by normal tillage. It is similar in texture and chemical properties to material immediately above and below it.

This kind of layer occurs more and more frequently as mechanization is increased. It is best shattered when the soil is relatively dry, usually in the fall. Water from rainfall or irrigation after the shattering operation will supply moisture for storage in and below the shattered zone for later crops. If dry conditions prevail after shattering, water loss by evaporation will be greater than from untreated areas, and the yield of the subsequent crop may be reduced.

If aggregate size is satisfactory, preparation of the seedbed is no more than the eradication of weeds and the management of residues.

If the field is weedy, it is usually economical to plow under both crop residues and weeds in order to cut subsequent cultivation costs. This should be done far enough ahead of seeding to allow the residues to decompose partially so as to minimize the temporary reduction of plant nutrients, particularly nitrogen.

In humid sections where erosion is not a problem, crop residues (such as oats straw) that are primarily cellulose often are removed before plowing if another crop is to follow immediately. Such residues supply practically no plant nutrients when they rot, and the products of decomposition may contain little structure-stabilizing materials. On erosive sloping lands such materials should be left on the surface to maintain the infiltration rate and help the soil surface resist erosion.

THE MOISTURE CONTENT of soils and compaction from the use of heavy tillage implements are related. Moisture acts somewhat like a lubricant and allows soil particles to slide over one another. The result is a decline in the ability of soil aggregates to withstand implement traffic as the moisture increases. When the moisture in the surface soil is best for tillage, the subsoil moisture may be higher and best for compaction. Tractor tires then may compact the soil below normal tillage depths. No more tillage than necessary should be done when the subsoil is moist enough to compact easily.

Soils can bear most weight and are least susceptible to compaction at the end of the cropping season when the moisture in the soil is depleted. That is the best time to use the implements necessary for turning under the residue or for undercutting it with sweeps if mulches are to be left on the soil.

Deep-rooted crops improve the soil structure in places where a packed subsoil does not restrict growth of roots. Compact subsoils can be shattered by tillage, but often they remain shattered only temporarily, because compact layers are basically unstable. Often tillage and the wise use of deep-rooted crops together are needed to improve the structure.

The use of cropping systems that involve the least amount of tillage may have merit, because intensive tillage destroys structure a great deal. Cropping systems that offer maximum protection to the tilled surface in the form of mulches and protective cover tend to keep raindrops from breaking down the surface soil structure.

WEED CONTROL is only partly effective unless consideration is given to all the circumstances of their propagation, growth, and destruction. Because weeds have about the same requirements as crop plants for germination, emergence, and growth, their control is influenced by tillage practices associated with preparing the seedbed.

Some control of weeds is obtained by tillage that leaves the middles between the crop rows loose and cloddy. When a good seedbed is provided only in the row or close to the place crop seeds are planted, the seeded crop can become established ahead of the weeds. Plowing with a moldboard plow buries the weed seeds, retards their sprouting, and tends to reduce the operations needed to control them.

If weed infestations are particularly bad, they may be reduced somewhat by undercutting them with subsurface sweeps—a method particularly effective in fallowing. Some weeds, like pigweed, which produce thousands of seeds that stay viable for many years, are hard to get rid of. If soil layers restrict the downward movement of water, spring rains may drain away slowly and delay cultivation and intensify the weed problem.

Chemicals for weed control, which have given some measure of success but which need further development before they are adapted to many variable situations, may reduce the number of tillage operations for a crop.

Because the amount and distribution of rainfall seldom coincide with the needs of a crop, effort must be made to store as much soil moisture as possible during periods when crops are not grown. From the standpoint of soil moisture, any tillage practice that does not control weeds and at the same time result in increased moisture intake and retention during the storage period is unnecessary or undesirable.

Excessive tillage breaks down the structure of the soil and leaves it susceptible to crusting. The small pore sizes associated with surface crusts impede water intake, increase runoff, and reduce the amount of moisture stored for crop use. Improper use of machinery often results in reduced water intake. For example, the disk harrow, improperly used, may reduce the aggregate sizes of surface soil excessively, increase susceptibility to crusting, and compact the subsoil immediately below the depth of surface working.

Intensive cropping systems, especially vegetable production in warm climates, tend to cause poor soil structure. In extreme circumstances, where three different crops may be grown on the same land each year, tillage practices may accomplish no more than to loosen the seedbed. Such cropping systems in time break down the soil into an almost single-grain structure and may bring problems of surface cementation, crusting, and poor aeration.

Regardless of the implement used for tillage, the soil mass generally is compressed, lifted, or moved in a manner that will change the structure of soil.

PLOWING, the standard method of breaking land, consists of cutting loose, granulating, and inverting a slice of earth and turning under organic litter. The furrow slice is cut loose by the edge and shin of the plowshare. The crumbling or granulating action takes place at the plow surface and at right angles to the moldboard throughout its length. The loosening and granulating actions of plowing are structure-improving practices, if the plowing is done when the soil has the correct moisture content. Lifting and inverting the furrow slice and turning under organic litter take place throughout the length of the moldboard. Inversion of the furrow slice and burial of residues are not always desirable. In many instances it is advisable to leave a trashy surface.

A stable soil structure is difficult to attain on some soil formations, such as loessial deposits in the lower Mississippi Valley. Tillage there is a destructive process and increases susceptibility to erosion. Such soils should be left in sod or trees. If they are cropped, they should be tilled no more than is absolutely necessary.

Several types of tillage have been classified as minimum tillage.

Seeding small grains in sods that have had little or no prior disturbance is one type. It consists of cutting narrow slits in the sod and placing seed and fertilizer in the breaks formed in the sod. Soil normally subject to erosion thus can be planted to small grains while maintaining the beneficial effects of the sod. Seeding in sod has been used successfully in preparing winter grazing for livestock in the Southeast.

Breaking the land and planting without any other preparation of the seedbed is another type of minimum tillage. One way is to break land and plant seeds in the tractor tracks—the weight of the tractor crushes the clods and permits plantings in a firm seedbed.

Another method consists of mounting a planter behind the plow and planting without further traffic. That leaves a rather loose seedbed and is satisfactory in places in the Northeast, where rainfall after planting may be heavy.

In the Pacific Northwest, where winter rain often comes soon after wheat is drilled, a rotation of wheat-peas has worked well. The field is rough-plowed after canning peas are harvested. Fall wheat then is drilled directly in the rough-plowed land.

All these methods require a minimum of expense and land preparation before a crop is seeded. They tend to leave the soil in a rough condition so that water intake is increased and runoff and erosion are reduced.

Mulch tillage was developed primarily to protect the soil surface from erosion. Crop residues are left on the soil surface and subsurface tillage is employed so as not to disturb the mulch. In dryland areas of the Great Plains as much mulch material as possible is left on the surface. It is usually better in more humid sections to bury some of the residue. Planters with disk openers, which go through several inches of mulch without clogging, are used for seeding.

If one is to make the most of the benefits of sod or mulch protection in subhumid and humid areas, one should apply extra plant nutrients, particularly nitrogen; otherwise, the microbes that decompose the residues may deprive crops of nutrients. The mulch lasts longer if fertilizer is placed below the mulch rather than on the surface with the mulch.

Intercrops are used to extend the protection that surface mulches give against erosion. They are usually small grains or the sod crops that are grown between the rows of the field crop. Crimson clover is excellent in the Southeast for such a crop between rows of a field crop. It reaches maturity shortly after the field crop has been established and furnishes a mulch cover for an extended period. Alfalfa has been used successfully in the Midwest for this purpose. Because of the competition for water, the use of an intercrop is limited to rainy sections.

Planting furrows usually are prepared 2 to 4 weeks before seeding time when intercrops are used. The furrows usually are made by using a small subsurface sweep or other implement to undercut a section of the intercrop. Disk hillers may be used to till the furrow further before planting with conventional equipment. If growth of the intercrop tends to compete with the main crop for moisture and nutrients, that growth may be killed at seeding time or shortly thereafter by undercutting it with sweeps or blades.

In areas of low rainfall or where much of the rain comes in intense storms, every effort must be made to conserve rain for crop production. In southern districts, a lister or middle-buster has been used to ridge land to impound water and insure its infiltration into the soil. A general practice is to bed the land and then to rebed with the lister just before planting time. It takes less time than a number of other methods of seedbed preparation, but the depth of tillage is shallow and seldom varied. In humid regions, where tractor tires may compact the subsoil, shallow tillage might cause hardpans.

Crops such as tobacco, which are sensitive to soil aeration, are grown occasionally on poorly drained soils. To provide better drainage, the crop is planted on rather high ridge rows or beds, which allow excess water to drain from the zone where sensitive roots are.

Subsoiling (breaking of compact subsoils without inverting them), chiseling (one method of subsoiling), and deep breaking (breaking of compact subsoils with inversion of the soil) have been praised and condemned. Limited experiments years ago showed a favorable crop response from breaking the soil deeper than normal, and the practice was applied widely with little regard for the reasons for the response. It was soon discredited by many.

Now we know that deep breaking may be effective on soils with compact layers that restrict the downward movement of water and roots. The layers must be shattered when the soil is relatively dry, and the tillage operations must give a continuous shatter to the layer for maximum effect. If deep breaking is done when the soil is moist, the compact layer will not be shattered, and the problem of compaction may be made worse. Breaking when dry requires a tremendous amount of power when pans are near the surface.

Deep tillage may not increase crop yields if there are enough showers and cloudy days during the succeeding growing season to prevent deficiencies of soil moisture in untreated areas. It is impractical in dry localities to add irrigation water often enough to prevent deficiencies in soil moisture if roots are restricted to the surface 6 inches of soil, where they would be if the soil contained a plowpan.

Deep chiseling on the contour increases the rate of recharge of soil moisture reserves in parts of the western Corn Belt, where rainfall is low in amount but high in intensity. Subsoiling also reduces runoff from spring snowmelt and increases subsoil moisture in the Northwest. There the total capacity of the soil to hold water is not affected—only the rate of recharge.

Deep plowing may be used to improve soil structure in alluvial soils where clay or sand was deposited on top of the soil during overflow periods.

Saline and Alkali Soils

C. A. Bower and Milton Fireman

Saline and alkali conditions lower the productivity and value of large areas of agricultural land in the United States—an estimated one-fourth of our 29 million acres of irrigated land and less extensive acreages of nonirrigated crop and pasture lands.

Saline and alkali soils are soils that have been harmed by soluble salts, consisting mainly of sodium, calcium, magnesium, chloride, and sulfate and secondarily of potassium, bicarbonate, carbonate, nitrate, and boron.

Salt-affected soils are problem soils that require special remedial measures and management practices.

Soluble salts may harm soils by increasing the salt concentration of the soil solution and by increasing the percentage saturation of the soil adsorption complex with sodium.

The second effect occurs when sodium salts predominate. It is more permanent than the first because adsorbed sodium usually persists after most of the soluble salts are removed.

Saline soils contain excessive amounts of soluble salts only. Alkali soils contain excessive adsorbed sodium. Because leaching may have occurred previously, alkali soils do not always contain excess soluble salt. They are designated as nonsaline-alkali or saline-alkali soils according to their content of salts.

Salt-affected soils occur mostly in regions of an arid or a semiarid climate.

Under humid conditions, the soluble salts originally present in soil materials and those formed by the weathering of minerals generally are carried downward into the ground water and are transported ultimately by streams to the oceans.

In arid regions, leaching and transportation of salts to the oceans is not so complete as in humid regions. Leaching is usually local in nature, and soluble salts may not be transported far. This occurs because there is less rainfall available to leach and transport the salts and because the high evaporation and plant transpiration rates in arid climates tend further to concentrate the salts in soils and surface waters.

Weathering of primary minerals is the indirect source of nearly all soluble salts, but there may be a few instances in which enough salts have accumulated from this source alone to form a saline soil. Saline soils usually occur in places that receive salts from other locations; water is the main carrier.

RESTRICTED DRAINAGE usually contributes to the salinization of soils and may involve low permeability of the soil or the presence of a high ground-water table.

High ground-water tables often are related to topographic position. The drainage of waters from the higher lands of valleys and basins may raise the ground-water level near to the soil surface on lower lands. Low permeability of the soil causes poor drainage by impeding the downward movement of water. The impedance may be the result of an unfavorable soil texture or structure or the presence of hardened layers, called hardpan.

Salt-affected soils occur extensively under natural conditions, but the salt problem of greatest importance in agriculture arises when previously productive soil becomes salt-affected as a result of irrigation.

Irrigated lands are often located in valleys near streams; because they can be irrigated easily, the lower and more level soils usually are selected for cultivation. Such soils may be adequately drained and nonsaline under natural conditions, but the drainage facilities may not be adequate under irrigation. Irrigation waters may contain from 200 pounds to as much as 5 tons of salt per acre-foot, and the annual application of water may amount to 5 acre-feet or more an acre. Considerable quantities of soluble salts thus may be added to irrigated soils in a short time.

Farmers who bring new lands under irrigation often have failed to recognize the need for establishing artificial drains to care for the additional water and the leaching required to prevent the accumulation of soluble salts. As a result, the water table may rise from a considerable depth to within a few feet of the soil surface in a few years.

During the early development of irrigation projects, water is frequently plentiful, and there is a tendency to use it in excess. This hastens the rise of the water table. When the water table rises to within 5 or 6 feet of the surface, ground water containing more or less dissolved salt moves upward into the root zone and to the soil surface. Ground water, as well as irrigation water, then causes the soil to become saline.

ALKALI SOILS CONTAIN excessive amounts of adsorbed sodium.

Because of the presence of negative electrical charges at their surfaces, soil particles adsorb and retain cations, such as calcium, magnesium, and sodium. While the adsorbed cations are combined chemically with the soil particles, they may be replaced or exchanged by other cations that are added to the soil solution. Each soil has a reasonably definite capacity to adsorb and exchange cations, and the percentage of this capacity that is taken up by sodium is referred to as the exchangeable-sodium-percentage. The exchangeable-sodium-percentage of alkali soils is usually 15 or more.

As cations adsorbed on soil particles

can interchange freely with those in the soil solution, the proportions of the various adsorbed cations are related to their concentrations in the soil solution. Calcium and magnesium are the principal cations in the soil solution and on the particles of normal, productive soils of arid regions. When normal soils come in contact with irrigation or drainage waters containing a high proportion of sodium, this cation becomes the dominant one in the soil solution and replaces part of the original adsorbed calcium and magnesium. As a consequence of the adsorption of sodium, alkali soils are formed.

THE ACCUMULATION of soluble salts and adsorbed sodium by soils impairs their productivity in several ways.

Because of the presence of considerable dissolved salt and the absence of significant amounts of adsorbed sodium, saline soils generally are flocculated. Their tillage properties and permeability to water therefore are equal to or higher than those of similar nonsaline soils. The abnormally high salt concentration of the soil solution of saline soils, however, reduces the rate at which plants absorb water; consequently growth is retarded. The retardation of growth is almost directly related to the total salt concentration of the soil solution and is largely independent of the kind of salts present.

The salinity status of soils is appraised in terms of effects on crop growth by measuring the electrical conductivity of the solution extracted from saturated soil paste. The electrical conductivity of a solution is a good measure of its total salt concentration, and the water content of saturated soil is related to the field-moisture range. Thus the electrical conductivity of the saturation extract is directly related to the total salt concentration of the soil solution under field conditions.

The effects of salinity on growth are largely negligible when the electrical conductivity reading (expressed in millimhos per centimeter) is less than 2.

At readings in excess of about 16, only a few very salt-tolerant crops yield satisfactorily. The yields of very salt-sensitive crops may be restricted at readings as low as 2; moderately salt-tolerant crops grow satisfactorily below readings of 8; only salt-tolerant crops grow satisfactorily when readings range between 8 and 16.

While the primary effect of soil salinity on crops is one of retarding growth by limiting the uptake of water, certain salt constituents are specifically toxic to some crops. Boron, for example, when present in the soil solution at concentrations of only a few parts per million, is highly toxic to many crops.

Alkali soils remain flocculated and their properties usually are similar to those of saline soils as long as considerable amounts of soluble salts are present. If the excess salts are removed by leaching, however, saline-alkali soils generally become nonsaline-alkali soils, and their physical properties deteriorate markedly.

As the concentration of the salts in the soil solution is lowered by leaching, the adsorbed sodium present causes undesirable characteristics to develop. The soil may become strongly alkaline (pH readings above 8.5), the particles may disperse, and the soil may become unfavorable for the entry and movement of water and air and for tillage. Adsorbed sodium also may be toxic and cause various nutritional disturbances in plants.

There are two principal aspects of the salt problem in irrigation agriculture. One is the improvement (reclamation) of soils that are salt-affected under natural conditions or have become salt-affected because of mismanagement. The other aspect is the management of productive or slightly salt-affected soils so as to prevent increases in the soluble salt and adsorbed sodium contents and thus prevent reduction in crop yields.

SALINE SOILS are improved by establishing artificial drains if a high ground-water table exists and by subsequent leaching with irrigation water to remove excess soluble salts. The improvement of alkali soils involves (besides drainage and leaching) the replacement of adsorbed sodium by calcium or magnesium and the use of practices that develop good soil structure.

Adequate drainage is essential for the permanent improvement of saline and alkali soils. Leaching operations and the application of amendments for the replacement of adsorbed sodium will be largely ineffective unless the ground-water table remains deep enough to prevent appreciable upward movement of water.

The permissible depth to the water table in various types of soils under irrigation and drainage requirements and methods are discussed in the chapter on soil drainage, page 378.

SOILS CAN BE LEACHED by applying water to the surface and allowing it to pass downward through the root zone. Leaching is most efficient when it is possible to pond water over the entire soil surface.

Water can be ponded on nearly level land in shallow basins formed by the construction of earthen dikes or borders 2 to 4 feet high. The dimensions of individual basins depend on the slope of the land. Normally the difference in elevation at the high and low points of the basin should not exceed 6 inches. It is wise to construct dikes on the contour where possible, especially if the land slopes very much. Overflow gates or spillways placed in dikes between adjacent ponded areas facilitate the control of water and allow a number of basins to be kept full simultaneously.

Either continuous flooding or periodic applications of water may be used for leaching. Periodic drying usually helps maintain infiltration rates. When the topography is such that ponding is not practical, moderately effective leaching can be accomplished through frequent applications of excess irrigation water in furrows, between border strips, or by sprinklers.

Except in climates where the soil

freezes, it is often convenient to conduct leaching operations during the winter, when water may be more plentiful and the water table and drainage conditions may be more favorable than during the regular irrigation season.

If the soil is only moderately saline, crops that withstand flooding, such as rice, sesbania, and Bermuda-grass, may be grown while leaching is in progress. Care must be exercised in hot weather, however, because holding water on some plants too long may cause scalding. The permeability of most soils declines markedly during prolonged leaching with water of very low salt content. The decrease in permeability is not so marked if the leaching water contains a moderate amount of salt and has a calcium plus magnesium to sodium ratio of 1 or more.

THE AMOUNT of water required to leach saline soils depends on the initial salinity level of the soil and the final salinity level desired.

When water is ponded, about 50 percent of the salt in the root zone can be removed by leaching with 6 inches of water for each foot of root zone; about 80 percent can be removed with 1 foot of water per foot of soil; to remove 90 percent of the salt, 2 feet of water must be used for each foot of soil that is to be leached.

For example, if the average salinity reading in a 3-foot depth of soil is 40 millimhos per centimeter and it is desired to reduce this 80 percent, or to about 8 millimhos per centimeter, then 3 feet of water should be applied.

If water is not applied to the entire soil surface, somewhat greater amounts will be needed to accomplish the same degree of leaching. In estimating the amount of water required for leaching, losses of applied water by evaporation and transpiration should be taken into account.

THE REMOVAL of excess soluble salts is not enough to restore alkali soils to productivity. Most of the adsorbed sodium must be replaced with calcium or magnesium and usually soil structure must be improved.

Some alkali soils contain calcium sulfate in the form of the mineral gypsum. When such soils are leached, the gypsum dissolves, and the replacement of adsorbed sodium by calcium takes place concurrently with the removal of excess salts.

When alkali soils do not naturally contain gypsum, soluble calcium or magnesium must be supplied. Some waters, when used for irrigation, supply appreciable amounts of calcium and magnesium, but it is usually necessary to apply a chemical amendment to restore alkali soils to productivity in a reasonable length of time.

CHEMICAL AMENDMENTS for the replacement of adsorbed sodium are of three types: Soluble calcium salts (calcium chloride and gypsum); calcium salts of low solubility (limestone); and acids or acid-formers (sulfuric acid, sulfur, and iron and aluminum sulfate).

The suitability of the various types of amendments is governed primarily by their solubility and by the lime content and pH reading of the soil.

Any of the soluble calcium salts or acids or acid-formers may be used on alkali soils containing lime, but the addition of limestone will be of no value. Acid and acid-forming amendments react with the lime in the soil to form gypsum. The addition of acids and acid-forming amendments to soils containing no lime tends to make them acid. When the amount of acid or acid-forming amendment needed would make the soil excessively acid (pH 6 or less), the choice of amendment is limited to soluble calcium salts, unless limestone also is applied. The application of limestone alone to lime-free alkali soils tends to be beneficial, but its effectiveness is not great unless the pH reading is 7 or less.

The selection of an amendment is influenced generally by cost considerations and the time required for its reaction in the soil. The cheaper amendments are slower to react. Because of its high solubility in water, calcium chloride is probably the most readily available source of soluble calcium, but it is seldom used because of its high cost. Sulfuric acid and iron and aluminum sulfates, which decompose readily in the soil to form sulfuric acid, also act quickly. Sulfuric acid is often cheap enough for field application, but the use of iron and aluminum sulfates is usually too costly. Because of their relatively low cost, gypsum and sulfur are most commonly used.

The rate of reaction of gypsum is limited only by its solubility, which is about 0.25 percent. Under field conditions, the application of 3 to 4 acre-feet of irrigation water is required to dissolve 4 or 5 tons of the high-grade agricultural gypsum. As sulfur must first be oxidized to sulfuric acid by soil micro-organisms before it is available for reaction, it is slow acting.

Limestone is a relatively cheap amendment, but only occasionally is it useful, as most alkali soils already contain lime. Unless the soil is decidedly acid, the reaction of limestone is slow. Particle size is an important factor affecting the rate at which limestone (as well as sulfur and gypsum) reacts in soils. The finer the particle size, the faster the reaction.

Because the application of chemical amendments usually is expensive, chemical tests should be made on soil samples to determine the kind and amount needed. It is worthwhile to get the advice and help of a county farm adviser or Soil Conservation Service technician.

Chemical amendments, such as gypsum, sulfur, and limestone, normally are applied broadcast and then incorporated with the soil by means of a disk or plow. Thorough incorporation is especially important when sulfur is used to insure a satisfactory rate of reaction. Because of hazards in handling, special equipment is used to spray sulfuric acid on the soil surface.

Except where sulfur is employed, alkali soils should be leached immedi-

ately following the application of amendments. Leaching dissolves the amendment and carries it downward. Leaching also removes the soluble sodium salts that form as the adsorbed sodium is replaced by calcium.

When sulfur is applied, 2 or 3 months should be allowed before leaching so that the amendment may oxidize and form gypsum. The soil should be kept moist, however, as water is essential for the oxidation of sulfur.

If the structure of saline-alkali soils is good originally, it will tend to remain good during the removal of excess salt and adsorbed sodium if soil disturbance is kept at a minimum and adequate soluble calcium is supplied. In this case tillage should be reduced, and the use of heavy machinery should be avoided during the improvement process.

If the alkali soil is relatively free of salt, its structure usually is poor. Here, the improvement process may be facilitated by loosening the soil to a considerable depth with a subsoiler or deep plow before applying amendments and leaching. The value of subsoiling and deep plowing alkali soils is questionable, however, unless an amendment is applied. Even after the removal of adsorbed sodium, soil structure may remain poor. The rearrangement and aggregation of soil particles, so as to improve structure, is facilitated by alternate wetting and drying, by alternate freezing and thawing, and by the action of growing plant roots and organic matter.

A SATISFACTORY and sustained crop production on nonsaline irrigated land generally requires the use of special soil-management practices to prevent the excessive accumulation of soluble salts and adsorbed sodium.

Often it is not practical to reclaim completely salt-affected soils or even to maintain conditions of very low salinity and adsorbed sodium (alkali) in irrigated soils. The reasons may be high costs of the amendments, difficulty in providing adequate drainage, use of irrigation water of inferior quality, or inherently low permeability of the soil. If the soil cannot be reclaimed completely, farmers can often live with the salinity or alkali by adopting suitable management practices.

MANAGEMENT PRACTICES for the control of salinity and alkali include: Selection of crops or crop varieties that will produce satisfactory yields under moderately saline conditions; use of land-preparation and tillage methods that aid in the control or removal of salinity and alkali; special planting procedures that minimize salt accumulation around the seed; irrigation so as to maintain a relatively high soil-moisture level and at the same time allow for periodic leaching of the soil; maintenance of water conveyance and drainage systems; and special treatments, such as additions of chemical amendments and organic matter, and growing sod crops to improve structure.

The quality of water used for irrigation and the soil texture determines to a large degree the kind and extent of management practices needed. In judging the quality of irrigation waters, primary consideration is ordinarily given to the salinity and sodium hazards involved in their use.

The total salt content of the water, as measured by its electrical conductivity, is a good index of the salinity hazard. Waters whose electrical conductivity is less than 0.25 millimhos per centimeter can be used for the irrigation of most crops on most soils with little likelihood that soil salinity will develop, but in only a few locations can water having an electrical conductivity in excess of 5 millimhos per centimeter be successfully employed. The greater the electrical conductivity of waters, the greater the care that must be taken to prevent the accumulation of salts. Moreover, the salinity of the irrigation water may limit the choice of crops that can be grown.

The alkali or sodium hazard of an irrigation water is an index of its tendency to increase the adsorbed sodium content of soils upon application. The alkali hazard is more difficult to evaluate than the salinity hazard. It is determined largely by the proportion of sodium to calcium plus magnesium present, together with the total salt content. As the salt content of the water increases, the permissible ratio of sodium to calcium plus magnesium decreases. Under some conditions, the bicarbonate content of the water as related to its content of calcium plus magnesium may influence the alkali hazard. It should also be recognized that irrigation waters may contain toxic amounts of boron.

For more detailed information on water quality, publications such as Circular 969, *Classification and Use of Irrigation Waters*, of the Department of Agriculture, should be consulted.

We know of no economically feasible method for reducing the salt content and, thus, the salinity hazard of irrigation waters.

The alkali hazard of waters can be lowered or nearly eliminated by lowering the ratio of sodium to calcium plus magnesium through the addition of gypsum (calcium sulfate). Reducing the alkali hazard of waters is most practical when the total salt content is low because smaller amounts of gypsum are required and the resulting increase in the salinity hazard is less. Special equipment for adding gypsum to water is available. A simple method of application consists of placing a cloth bag of gypsum with the side slit open at a place in the irrigation system where the water has considerable turbulence.

The control of salinity and alkali is accomplished, in general, most easily in coarse-textured soils, which usually are quite permeable and are less susceptible to deterioration of the physical condition upon the accumulation of adsorbed sodium than the soils of finer texture. Medium- and fine-textured soils have the advantage of a greater water-holding capacity and ordinarily present no great problem from the standpoint of salinity control if they have good structure and are underlain by a sand or gravel aquifer which facilitates the removal of drainage water. Prevention of salt accumulation is most difficult in soils consisting of fine-textured, slowly permeable material that extends to a considerable depth.

WHERE SALINITY CANNOT be entirely eliminated, the judicious selection of crops that can produce satisfactory yields under moderately saline conditions may mean the difference between profit and loss.

In selecting crops for saline soils, particular attention should be given to the salt tolerance of the crop during germination, because poor yields frequently result from failure to obtain a satisfactory stand. Some crops that are salt-tolerant during later stages of growth are quite sensitive to salinity during germination.

The tolerances of many crops are listed in Agriculture Handbook No. 60, *Diagnosis and Improvement of Saline and Alkali Soils.*

Among the highly tolerant crops are barley, sugar beets, cotton, Bermudagrass, Rhodesgrass, western wheatgrass, birdsfoot trefoil, table beets, kale, asparagus, spinach, and tomato. Crops having low salt tolerance include radish, celery, beans, and White Dutch, alsike, red, and Ladino clovers, and nearly all fruit trees.

CAREFUL LEVELING of land makes possible a more uniform application of water and better salinity control.

Barren or poor areas in otherwise productive fields often are high spots that do not receive enough water for good crop growth or for leaching purposes. Lands that have been irrigated 1 or 2 years after initial leveling often can be improved by replaning to remove the surface unevenness caused by the settling of fill material. Annual crops should be grown after the first leveling, so that replaning can be performed without disturbing the crops.

Soils containing appreciable amounts of adsorbed sodium are especially subject to puddling and crusting. They should be tilled carefully. They should not be tilled when moist. Heavy machinery should not be moved over them. More frequent irrigation, especially during the germination and seedling stages of plants, tends to soften surface crusts on alkali soils and helps to get a better stand.

FAILURE TO OBTAIN a satisfactory stand of furrow-irrigated row crops on moderately saline soils is a serious problem in many places. The failures usually are due to the tendency of soluble salt to accumulate in raised beds that are moistened by irrigation water moving from the furrow. Modifications in irrigation practice and bed shape may alter considerably the tendency of salts to accumulate near the seed. Preemergence irrigation in special furrows placed close to the seed often is done to reduce the soluble salt concentration around the seeds and thus permit germination. After the seedlings are established, the special furrows may be abandoned and new furrows made between the rows.

The tendency of salts to accumulate near the seed during irrigation is greatest in single-row, flat-topped planting beds. Sufficient salt to prevent germination may move laterally and concentrate in the seed zone, even if the average salt content of the soil is relatively low. With double-row beds also, most of the salt is carried into the center of the bed, but that leaves the shoulders relatively free of salt and satisfactory for planting, especially if the soil is only slightly saline.

Sloping beds are best on saline soils because seed can be safely planted on the slope below the zone of salt accumulation. The salt is carried away from the soil around the seed instead of accumulating in it. Planting in furrows or basins is satisfactory from the standpoint of salinity control but is often unfavorable for the emergence of many row crops because of crusting or poor aeration.

The method and frequency of irrigation and the amount of irrigation water applied are of prime importance in the control of salinity.

The main ways to apply water are flooding, furrow irrigation, sprinkling, and subirrigation.

Flooding, in which water is applied to the entire surface, is preferable from the standpoint of salinity control if the land is sufficiently level and the crop can be flooded.

Furrow irrigation is well adapted to row crops and is also useful if the land is too steep for flooding. This method allows salts to accumulate in the rows, but plowing and mixing the entire surface soil periodically usually will prevent serious increases in the salt content of the soil. If excess salt does accumulate, a rotation of crops and a change to irrigation by flooding is a possible salinity-control measure.

Irrigation by sprinkling allows a close control of the amount and distribution of water. Sprinkling often is used in places where the slope is too great for other methods. One tends to apply too little water by this method, and leaching of salts beyond the root zone is not accomplished without special effort.

Subirrigation, in which the water table is maintained close to the soil surface, is not suitable when salinity is a problem. Even under the most favorable circumstances, this method is not suitable for longtime use unless the water table is lowered periodically and leaching is accomplished by rainfall or by surface applications of water.

As soluble salts retard plant growth in almost direct relation to their total concentration in the soil solution, the moisture content of saline soils should be maintained as high as practicable, especially during the stage of vegetative growth. With a given amount of salt in the soil, the salt concentration in the soil solution drops as the moisture content of the soil increases. A high moisture level is maintained by irrigating oftener than would be the practice for similar nonsaline soils.

BECAUSE ALL IRRIGATION waters contain dissolved salts, some water in addition to that required to replenish losses by plant transpiration and evaporation must be applied occasionally to leach out the salt that has accumulated during previous irrigations.

The additional irrigation water required for leaching is called the leaching requirement and is defined as the fraction of the applied irrigation water that must be leached through the root zone to control salinity at any predetermined level. The leaching requirement therefore depends on the salt content of the irrigation water and on the maximum salt concentration permissible in the soil solution. This maximum concentration in turn depends on the salt tolerance of the crop.

For salt-sensitive crops, the maximum concentration of the soil solution in the root zone should be 3 to 4 millimhos per centimeter. For moderately salt-tolerant crops it should not exceed 8 millimhos per centimeter. For highly salt-tolerant crops, it should not exceed 16 millimhos per centimeter.

If there is no rainfall and no removal of salt by the crop and if drainage is adequate and no salt becomes insoluble in the soil, the leaching requirement is simply the ratio of the electrical conductivity of the irrigation water to the electrical conductivity of the drainage water, expressed as a fraction or as a percentage.

For example, where an electrical conductivity of 8 millimhos per centimeter can be tolerated in the soil solution of the root zone and the irrigation water has a conductivity of 2 millimhos per centimeter, the leaching requirement will be 2 divided by 8, or 25 percent. That means that if crop use and evaporation amount to 30 inches of water during the growing season, 10 extra inches should be added—a total of 40 inches that enter the soil. Because of the assumptions involved, the 10 extra inches are a maximum value. Care must be exercised in estimating the leaching requirement by this method, especially if leaching due to rainfall has taken place. In any event, the method is useful as a concept of what must occur in the root zone of the growing crop.

Unless the soil is well drained, the application of irrigation water in considerable excess over that required for the crop and for leaching can be as detrimental from the standpoint of salinity control as underirrigation.

Overirrigation increases the amount of water that the drainage system must convey; if the capacity of the system is exceeded, the water table will rise to an unsafe level. It is apparent therefore that a proper relation between irrigation, leaching, and drainage is of utmost importance in preventing soils from becoming salt affected. The amount of water applied should be sufficient to supply the crop and satisfy the leaching requirement but not enough to overload the system.

EXCESSIVE LOSS of irrigation water from canals constructed in permeable soil is a major cause of high water tables and salt accumulation. Seepage losses can be reduced by lining canals with cement, buried asphalt membranes, or more commonly with earth of low permeability. The maintenance of drainage systems is also important and usually involves nothing more than keeping tile lines in repair or open ditches clean and excavated to grade.

A gradual decrease in soil permeability is a common cause of declining productivity in land under irrigation. Without satisfactory soil permeability, crops cannot be kept adequately supplied with water and the leaching of salts is not accomplished. Soil treatments for the maintenance of permeability are the same as those we discussed for improving soil structure.

To meet the demand for agricultural products, it will be necessary to utilize salt-affected soils and irrigation waters of inferior quality more and more fully. Thus it can be assumed that the improvement of salt-affected soils and the management of productive soils so as to prevent the excessive accumulation of soluble salts and adsorbed sodium will grow in importance.

Erosion on Cultivated Land

B. D. Blakely, J. J. Coyle, and J. G. Steele

To protect soil from erosion and to hold as much of the rain as possible in a place where crops can use it are a big part of modern soil management.

We cannot avoid all risks of erosion when we lay a soil bare by cultivating it. Neither can we hold all the rain where it falls in humid or subhumid areas. But we need to know the risks and control them the best we can.

Erosion is slow wherever the soils are covered by trees or grass. Near Zanesville, Ohio, scarcely any loss of soil could be measured in 9 years from a woodland watershed of 2 acres. A nearby pasture lost soil during the same period at an average rate of one-tenth ton an acre a year, or about 1 inch in 1,500 years. A similar watershed cropped to a 3-year rotation of corn, wheat, and hay lost an inch of soil in the 9 years.

The rate of erosion in any storm depends on the force with which raindrops stir up soil and the amount and speed of the runoff water. Other factors affecting erosion include kind and amount of cover, kind of soil, and steepness and length of slope.

To judge the erosion hazards in a particular situation, we need to look at more than one rain and consider the pattern of rainfall for a whole year or for several years.

We need to study the location by looking uphill to see how much water is likely to cross the field and by looking downhill to see where the runoff water and the soil it carries are likely to go.

We need to look at the cover that the cropping system provides each season, especially if a crop must be planted at a time when hard storms are likely to occur.

We need to study the whole soil profile to find out the effect of layers that lie beneath the surface.

We need to know what recent tillage practices have done to the structure of the surface soil and how much protection we can get from mulches.

Having appraised these hazards, we need to plan the cropping system and supporting conservation practices for the field to offset them.

Short-time changes other than erosion also are important in the management of soil and water. Nutrients may be depleted through leaching and removal of crops. Changes in soil structure can have great effect on the supply of water in the root zone available to plants. The nutrients can be replaced by fertilizers, but changes in soil structure are harder to correct.

Structure of surface soil affects intake of water and air. Whenever the surface layer becomes puddled by a hard rain or compacted by heavy machinery, the danger of runoff and erosion increases and the intake and storage of water decrease. Structure is likely to break down as organic matter becomes oxidized.

Tillage pans, also called plowpans or traffic pans, are formed in some soils as they are cultivated. A tillage pan is a thin, dense layer that develops just under the plow layer. It restricts root growth and can seriously reduce crop yields. Many silt loam and loam soils are subject to formation of tillage pans.

Structure of subsoil is important because we need the full capacity of a soil to furnish plant nutrients, water, and air. Many farmers have found that their soils drained well at first but needed more drainage after they had been farmed a few years and the crevices and root channels in the subsoil began to be filled.

We need good management of water for crops to get the full benefits of controlling erosion, improving fertility, and maintaining soil structure. Most soils contain either too little or too much water during at least part of each year.

Although drainage of wet lands and irrigation of arid land are major operations, they affect only part of the total cropland, probably less than one-third. Irrigation is increasing in humid areas but will continue to be limited by water shortages, high costs, and other factors.

Farmers who can reduce runoff from upland fields and who can increase the amount of water taken in and stored for use by plants during the growing season have a good chance of increasing their crop yields. Such management of water on most of our cultivated land where neither drainage nor irrigation is involved may produce greater benefits than the more spectacular measures.

A cover of vegetation is the first defense against erosion and runoff.

A soil protected by the right kind and amount of sod or forest litter is not likely to erode, no matter how hard or how long it rains. A soil so protected readily absorbs the rainfall. Its good structure permits the water to move freely through it, and heavy runoff seldom occurs unless rock or impervious layers near the surface block the downward movement of water.

Occasionally there are exceptions. Concentrated water may start a gully, or a cloudburst can saturate an entire slope and unleash a landslide. Long rains may overrun the water-storage in the soil and cause streams to rise.

The protection cultivated crops give is intermediate between none at all, as on a newly plowed field, and the nearly complete protection of thick sod or forest litter.

Some hay crops are almost as good as pasture sod. Others, like alfalfa and sweetclover, can allow much washing if the spaces between plants are not filled in with grasses or mulched by dead stems and leaves. Small grains offer only partial protection, and that only after they have made considerable growth. Intertilled crops are little better than bare fallow unless the rows are on the contour. Crops that must be dug, like potatoes and peanuts, leave the soil ready for erosion by the next hard rain.

To judge the risk of erosion in a cropping system, we need to know the chances of erosive rains whenever the soil is cultivated or cover is thin. In a 4-year rotation of corn, grain, and 2 years of hay, the soil is plowed twice and is cultivated two or three times after the corn is planted. The risk of erosion-producing rains at those times is high in most corn-growing areas.

As many farmers know, a rotation of fallow, wheat, and kafir leaves soil exposed to erosion for most of a year and also part of the spring in which kafir is planted. A rotation of wheat 1 year and alfalfa mixed with bromegrass for 3 years gives protection most of the time and allows both crops to be planted when the risk of erosion is low.

Much can be done to reduce erosion by matching the crops grown to the erosion hazards of each field. Certain crops also can be used to keep or to restore fertility and good structure.

Green manure crops, which return large amounts of organic matter to the soil, are needed in humid and subhumid areas to keep good tilth in the topsoil. In drier farming areas, crops that leave heavy mulches on the surface may serve better.

Deep-rooted legumes, such as sweetclover, improve subsoil structure. We need legumes in cropping systems on many soils to keep the subsoils porous enough so that water, roots, and air can get through them.

TILLAGE METHODS, as well as the crops grown, affect soil conditions and therefore runoff and erosion.

Corn, cotton, and soybeans for many years have been considered the most soil-depleting crops. Much of the damage resulted from overtillage in preparing seedbeds, controlling weeds, and attempting to get more nitrogen from decomposing residues.

New cultural practices and tillage implements now available will overcome some of the hazards of clean tillage. Agronomists are studying mulch tillage, rough seedbeds, sod seedbeds, and many other practices to determine their effects on crop yields, erosion, and control of weeds and crop diseases.

Ten years of study in the Southeast showed that mulch tillage permitted less runoff and erosion and resulted in higher corn yields than clean tillage.

Rough seedbeds prepared with a field cultivator in the Midwest lost about half as much soil as plowed fields.

Contour listing of corn in western Iowa reduced water losses about 50 percent and soil losses 73 percent from those where the crop was surface planted on the contour.

Minimum tillage that keeps crop residues on or near the soil surface, used with nitrogen fertilizers and living mulches, has proved successful in many places. More research is needed to adapt these methods to all sections.

A farmer usually can choose different combinations of soil-saving and water-saving practices to use with the crops he wants to grow.

The land capability classification is a useful guide in matching conservation practices with the cropping system or type of cover on each field.

On a soil of a certain capability, for example, the cover needs to be hay or pasture two-thirds of the time if no extra practices (such as stripcropping or terracing) are used to support the protection given by the rotation. If the field is stripcropped, hay or pasture is needed half the time. Sod is needed only one-third of the time if it is terraced.

This is only one example of the many choices that can be made. In general, whenever sloping soil is to be cultivated and exposed to erosive rains, the protection offered by sod or close-growing crops in the rotation needs to be supported by practices that will slow the runoff water and thus reduce the soil it can carry.

The most important of these supporting practices for cropland are waterways, contour tillage, stripcropping, terracing, and diversion terraces.

WATERWAYS (as used in soil and water conservation work) are natural or manmade depressions on sloping land. Waterways can carry specified amounts of water without erosion and serve as outlets for terraces, diversions, and contour rows. They are needed often as passageways for water that enters a farm from other land.

Waterways are the most important single item in the control of runoff water from cultivated land. If they fail, all other parts of the system may fail.

The best locations for waterways usually are the natural drainageways of the landscape. Natural depressions require a minimum of shaping to be able to carry the expected runoff. Soil and moisture are favorable for good growth of protective vegetation. The topography usually allows free discharge of water into natural drainages from terraces, diversions, and rows. Manmade channels near field boundaries or fence lines can be made to work, but they are never so satisfactory as the natural locations.

Waterways need to be large enough to carry the runoff from the watersheds they serve without overflowing during heavy storms. Usually this means designing them to carry the runoff from the heaviest rainfall to be expected once in 10 years.

The waterway needs to be shaped and smoothed to remove irregularities that would cause turbulence in flowing water. If the site is in a natural depression, this usually can be done with ordinary farm equipment. If there is a small wash or gully down the center of the depression, it should be plowed in and the soil compacted by repeated trips over the filled area with a tractor. The shape of the waterway should keep water from concentrating to a great depth at any point. A dished, or parabolic, shape is best. A V-shape is satisfactory if the sides of the V are laid back so that the top width is at least 10 times the depth.

It is desirable to establish a dense vegetative cover as soon as possible. Since the waterway will carry rather heavy flows at times, the seeding and fertilizing rates normally used for pasture are not sufficient. A good rule is to double these rates—or more—when seeding a waterway. In sodding, the sod pieces should be closely spaced and should be well fertilized.

Grasses that form a dense turf are best for waterway protection. Where they are not adapted, bunch grasses like the bluestems and gramas, or lespedeza sericea and many other plants do a satisfactory job if the depth of flow is kept shallow and the slope is not steep. Kudzu is good in places where it is adapted. If kudzu is used, the size of the waterway must allow for the bulky growth of the plant. Reed canarygrass is good in wet places.

CONTOUR TILLAGE is one of the simpler practices for reducing soil and water losses. It is effective and inexpensive in the right places. Its effectiveness depends on the ridges, made by tillage implements, to retard the flow of water. Contour cultivation alone protects the soil on the flatter slopes during the less intense storms but is of little benefit at times when the rains are intense.

Contour tillage is most effective on 2- to 8-percent slopes not more than 300 feet long. Here the practice reduces soil loss to about half that with tillage up and down the hill. On slopes greater than 8 percent, the ridges retard the flow less, and soil loss is reduced only 20 to 40 percent.

On a 7-percent slope near Guthrie, Okla., contour tillage reduced losses of soil about 50 percent and losses of water 12 percent (as compared to farming up-and-down the hill) on land planted to cotton with wheat as a winter cover. In Missouri, on a soil having a rather tight subsoil, contouring re-

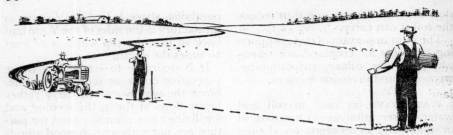

duced soil losses 52 percent and runoff 20 percent on land planted to corn.

Contouring alone is not sufficient protection for soils that are severely eroded or have hard clay subsoils, for the excess runoff may break through the rows. Other practices such as terracing are needed when those conditions exist.

Contouring can increase yields of row crops as much as 50 percent; increases of 5 to 10 percent are common. The effect is greatest in years when rainfall is scant during the growing season.

To be able to plow and plant on the contour, a farmer needs one or more key contour lines marked on each field. These are level lines across the slope to be followed in tillage operations.

On short, uniform slopes, one key contour line about halfway down the hill is enough. If the slope is long or irregular, several lines are necessary. It is important to have enough lines to guide farming operations, taking into consideration a convenient width of land for plowing or planting.

Anyone with a little experience and a helper can stake out the key contour lines, using an inexpensive hand level.

First, determine which part of your helper's body is level with your eyes (e. g., hair, face, or shoulder) when you are standing together on level ground. Then, when you sight through the hand level and see the crosshair against this part of his body, you are both standing at the same elevation.

Next, decide where the first key contour should be. Set a stake at any point on the proposed line. Stand at this stake while your helper walks about 100 feet (or not so far on sharp curves) around the slope as nearly on the level as he can. When he stops, sight through the hand level and signal for him to move up or down the hill as necessary until the crosshair again strikes the part of his body previously determined. When you signal that he is on the level with you, he drives a stake.

Move to the new stake while your helper moves on, and repeat the process. When you have crossed the field in this manner, you will have a line of stakes all on the same level. The line can now be marked with a plow.

When the entire field is contoured and planted to a single crop, odd-

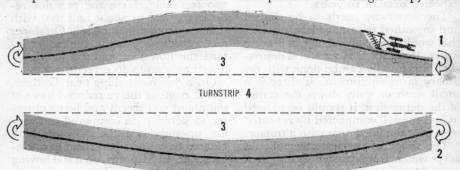

TURNSTRIP 4

shaped areas may cause some difficulty in plowing. The sketch shows how to avoid turning on loose plowed ground.

Use each contour line as a backfurrow and plow around areas 1 and 2. Plow area 3 next until the remaining land is just wide enough to turn the tractor. Then plow the turnstrip (4).

IN STRIPCROPPING, close-sown crops alternating with strips of other crops slow down the flow of water.

Stripcropping combined with contour tillage is more effective than contouring alone. On experimental areas in Missouri, Ohio, and Wisconsin, contour stripcropping (compared to up-and-down farming) reduced soil losses about three-fourths on slopes that were less than 12 percent and one-half on steeper slopes.

There are three types of stripcropping: Contour stripcropping, field stripcropping, and buffer stripcropping. The type to use depends on the kind of soil, the crops grown, and the topography.

Grassed waterways are essential in a stripcropped field wherever excess runoff water accumulates.

Contour stripcropping is adapted to well-drained cultivated soils on sloping land where rainfall causes erosion. This type of stripcropping is effective on 2- to 12-percent slopes that are not longer than 400 feet.

Where both erosion and wetness are

problems, strips can be laid out with a grade of 1 to 2 percent to lead the water into grassed waterways.

Steepness of slope, kind of soil, the usual amount and intensity of rainfall, and the size of the farm equipment are factors to consider in determining the width of the strips. In many localities, strips are made 100 feet wide on slopes of less than 6 percent, 80 feet on slopes of 6 to 10 percent, and 50 feet on slopes of 11 to 16 percent.

When the system is laid out so that both the upper and lower edges of the strips are on the true contour, all strips are irregular in width, as shown in the sketch below.

Strips are narrow where the slope is steep and wide where it is gentle. As a result, some rows in uneven-width strips do not go all the way through the field. Since these short, or point, rows occur on the more gentle slopes where the soil is usually best, most farmers prefer to plant these areas to the regular crops in rotation, despite the difficulty of cultivating them. Others, however, prefer to plant them to perennial hay crops or to close-growing annual crops to eliminate the point rows.

Another common method is to lay out two or more even-width strips from one key contour line, as shown at the top of page 296. When the topography of the field changes, a new contour line should be laid out as a guide for addi-

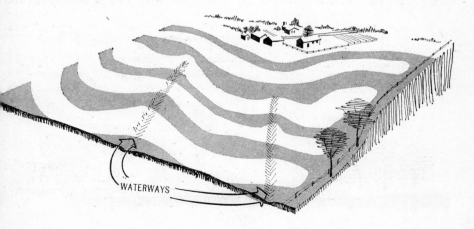

WATERWAYS

tional strips of even width. This results in an irregular correction strip between the two sets of even-width strips.

A third method provides for even-width strips alternating with irregular strips. From the first contour line, an even-width strip is measured. A second contour line is staked two strip widths above or below the first, and an even-width strip is measured from it. This process is repeated until the entire field has been laid out.

If the fields are large—160 acres or more—contour maps are helpful in laying out the system. Uniform-width strips separated by irregular-width strips can be located on the map in relation to the contour lines. Minor variations can often be made so that a minimum of land is devoted to the irregular strips. These irregular strips often are planted to perennial grasses.

Field stripcropping is used when slopes are so irregular that contour strips would be hard to till. Field strips are uniform in width and are laid out across the general slope instead of on the true contour. This method is less effective than contour stripcropping in reducing soil and water losses. A good crop rotation and cultural treatments are necessary therefore to provide the major protection to the soil.

Buffer stripcropping consists of narrow protective strips alternating with wide cultivated strips.

The location of the protective strips is determined largely by the width and arrangement of adjoining strips to be cropped in the rotation and by the location of steep, severely eroded areas on slopes. Buffer strips usually occupy

WATERWAY

the correction areas on sloping land. They are seeded to perennial grasses and legumes. This type of stripcropping is not so effective as contour stripcropping but will serve as a temporary measure until a more adequate system is established.

Some extra precautions are necessary in farming the stripcropped fields. For ease in handling farm equipment, we need to have two types of crops in each group of strips: A row crop may alternate with a sod crop or a grain crop with a sod crop.

Plowing should be varied to prevent ridges at the edges and deep dead-furrows in the centers of strips. Two-way plows are often used to prevent formation of ridges and dead furrows.

When planting uniform-width strips, the farmer can start at the top or bottom edge and continue across the entire strip. If the strips are irregular in width, many farmers prefer to plant the row crops from both sides. Then the greatest number of rows are on the contour, and all the point rows are in the center of the strip.

TERRACING has long been used to protect cultivated land against erosion and to make best use of available water.

We now usually use the word "terrace" to mean a ridge, or a combination of ridge and channel, built across the slope on a controlled grade or on the level, depending on its purpose.

Terraces intercept the flow of water down the slope before it attains enough velocity to damage the land. Graded terraces lead this water off the field at nonerosive velocities. Level terraces hold back the water until it can soak into the soil.

Not all soils and slopes can be terraced successfully. It is nearly impossible to maintain terraces on deep sands. The cost of construction and the difficulty of maintenance make them unsatisfactory on stony soils and on shallow soils over rock or over tough, heavy subsoil.

Terraces are impractical on moundy fields or fields where direction or steepness of slope changes every 100 feet or so. A tillable row pattern cannot be worked out on them.

The difficulties of constructing, cultivating, and maintaining terraces increases with the steepness of slope. Satisfactory waterways are also harder to establish on the steeper slopes. For slopes of more than 8 to 12 percent (even less for some of the tighter soils), we might better consider land uses or cropping systems that will give adequate protection without terraces.

The first problem to be solved in terracing a field is how to dispose of the water that cannot be taken into the soil. If graded terraces are used, or if the ends of level terraces cannot be blocked, a waterway must be provided. Level terraces with ends blocked present no problem of water disposal.

An area covered with a dense sod of permanent grasses is a safe place on which to spill the water from terraces. A good pasture next to the field provides a readymade solution to the problem if the terraces can be run onto it. If no such area exists, one must be developed or a waterway must be established. If the terraces will bring more water to the location than had been coming there before, the vegetation needs to be established before the terraces are built.

Level terraces are used mainly in areas where the average annual rainfall is less than 30 inches. If the soil is able to take in water at a rate of at least one-half inch an hour, the ends of the terraces may be blocked, and the runoff from all but the most intense rains can be made to enter the soil. If the rate is much less than that, the ends are left open or only partially blocked. Otherwise, the impounded water may damage small grain by causing uneven ripening or difficulty in harvesting. For row crops, such as grain sorghum, slower water intake is not always objectionable.

Where the average annual rainfall exceeds 30 inches, it is generally best to give terraces grade or fall to allow the surplus water to drain from the field. The grade must be gentle enough that the water will flow at low speed. It should not exceed 3 inches per 100 feet on soils that are easily eroded. On others it may be as much as 6 inches or more per 100 feet.

The spacing of terraces usually varies, inversely with steepness of the field slope—that is, as the steepness increases, the distance between terraces decreases.

Two basic spacing formulas are used: In the Northern States, $V. I. = \frac{S}{3} + 2$; in the Southern States, $V. I. = \frac{S}{4} + 2$. $V. I.$ stands for vertical interval in feet, and S for slope of the land in feet per 100 feet. The vertical interval is converted to horizontal distance by multiplying by $\frac{100}{S}$.

The way the soil is managed is about as important as steepness of slope in determining the correct spacing of terraces. If good soil-management practices are used, the spacing indicated by the formulas can be increased as much as 50 percent or more on some of the deep, permeable soils. If little attention is given to soil management, the spacing should be narrowed.

The more nearly two terraces parallel each other, the easier it is to farm the space between them. Irregular spaces mean that some rows do not run the full length of the terraces, so that equipment has to be turned in the planted part of the field when row crops are grown, and fields of odd shapes have to be drilled and harvested when drilled crops are grown.

IRREGULARITIES in the space between two terraces result from changes in land slope along the terrace line, the extension of terraces across natural depressions, or the grading of terraces so they drain across ridges or hogbacks.

These irregularities can be reduced by grading the terraces to drain each way from all ridges and to discharge into the first depression reached. On

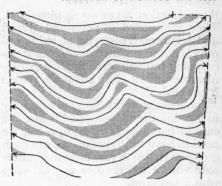

A terraced field with terraces extended across depressions and ridges to reach waterways along field boundaries. Shaded portion shows area in point rows. Equipment must be turned in the planted area.

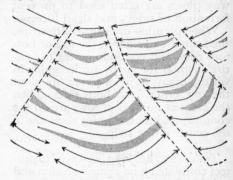

The same field with waterways in natural depressions and terraces graded each way from ridges. This permits adjustment in alinement at ridges. Sharp bends at depressions are eliminated. Note reduction in point rows. Similar results could be achieved by cutting and filling but cost would be more, wet areas would exist above fills, and subsoil would be exposed.

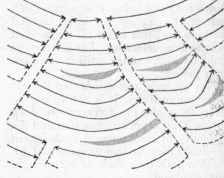

The same field shown in first two sketches. By careful planning, several sets of parallel terraces were worked out. Note the small area in point rows.

some fields this may call for several waterways, and on first thought the farmer may object to them. Experience has proved, however, that the inconvenience of raising tillage tools to cross waterways is less bothersome than farming the additional short rows that result when terraces are built across them.

The sketches on the preceding page illustrate the advantages of using the waterways in natural locations.

THE INCONVENIENCE of farming terraces can be reduced by using parallel terraces. Actually, it is seldom possible to have all terraces in a field parallel, but the ideal can be approached by care in laying out the system according to the following suggestions:

First, locate all ridges and depressions in the field. All terraces will be graded to drain from the ridges toward the natural depressions.

Next, stake a key terrace on the grade recommended for the soil; adjust the staked line to ease sharp curves as much as possible. All stakes moved in making the adjustment must be rechecked with the level to be sure that the grade from ridge to depression is continuous and not excessive.

Stake a trial line above or below the key terrace and parallel to it. That is done by having one man walk along the line of the key terrace carrying one end of a tape. A second man, holding the tape at a point marking the proper distance between terraces, keeps pace with the first man, setting stakes to mark the trial line. This line is then checked with the instrument. The location is accepted if the grade is not excessive or does not reverse anywhere along the line. Repeat the procedure for each new line.

When the grade of the new line becomes excessive or reverses, lay out a new key terrace a distance of two or more terrace intervals from the last acceptable line.

This gives two sets of terraces, all those in each set being parallel to each other. The only short rows will be in the small adjustment area between the two sets of terraces. Some fields may require several sets of parallel terraces.

A comparison of the bottom sketch with the other two illustrates the advantages of this system.

Two requirements govern the dimensions of the individual terrace.

First, the terrace must be large enough (either in ridge size or channel capacity) that it will seldom be overtopped. The usual recommendation is that a terrace be built to carry the runoff resulting from the heaviest rain normally expected to occur on an average of once in 10 years.

Second, the terrace should be shaped so that mechanized farming equipment can be used without undue difficulty.

Two SKETCHES show dimensions generally recommended for the two types of terraces most commonly used.

Adequate terraces can be constructed with almost any type of equipment that will move soil.

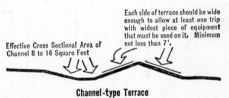

Effective Cross Sectional Area of Channel 8 to 16 Square Feet

Each side of terrace should be wide enough to allow at least one trip with widest piece of equipment that must be used on it. Minimum not less than 7'.

Channel-type Terrace

Generally used in humid and sub-humid areas where removal of excess water is the problem. Usually given a grade.

The typical shape and dimensions of channel-type terrace.

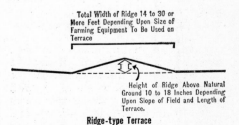

Total Width of Ridge 14 to 30 or More Feet Depending Upon Size of Farming Equipment To Be Used on Terrace

Height of Ridge Above Natural Ground 10 to 18 Inches Depending Upon Slope of Field and Length of Terrace.

Ridge-type Terrace

Generally used in low rainfall areas to impound water until it can be absorbed by the soil. Usually level.

The typical shape and dimensions of ridge-type terrace.

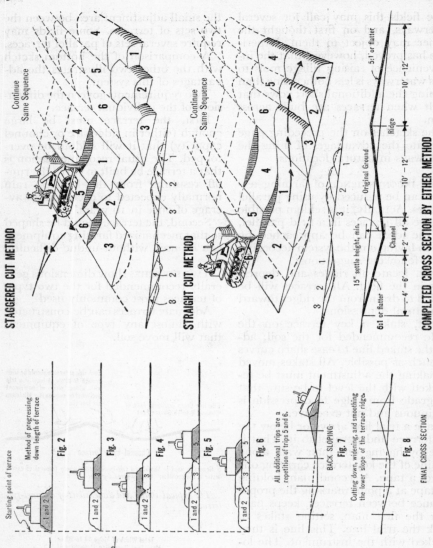

STAGGERED CUT METHOD

Continue
Same Sequence

STRAIGHT CUT METHOD

Continue
Same Sequence

COMPLETED CROSS SECTION BY EITHER METHOD

Terrace construction with a bulldozer.

CONSTRUCTION PROCEDURE

Starting point of terrace

Method of progressing
down length of terrace

Dozer at end
of first trip

Level

Fig. 1

Fig. 2

Dozer at end of
second trip

Field Slope

Fig. 2

Fig. 3

Fig. 4

Fig. 5

Fig. 6

All additional trips are a
repetition of trips 5 and 6.

BACK SLOPING

Fig. 7

Cutting down, widening, and smoothing
the lower slope of the terrace ridge

FINAL CROSS SECTION

Fig. 8

A. Scarify, chisel, rip, or plow a 20-foot strip
8 or 10 inches deep on channel excavation
area. This step must not be omitted.
Loose soil is required to build an adequate
terrace section in two trips as shown.

B. Method of placing earth in cross section
of terrace is shown above, figures 1 and 2.

C. Sequence of construction down the terrace
is shown at right, figures 2 through 6.

D. Back slope of terrace must be built while
bulldozer is moving forward down length
of terrace, as shown at right in figure 7.
A motor patrol grader can be used to widen
the back slope if the bulldozer operator is
not skilled in keeping a smooth path of
forward travel.

E. Resulting terrace, figure 8 at right, averages 15.6 square feet in ridge, 20 to 22
feet in base width, and 14 square feet excavation in channel.

F. In easy moving soils a gap equal to half the
width of the dozer blade may be left between trips (1 and 2) and 3, and the same
gap left between 3 and 5. This results in
faster construction.

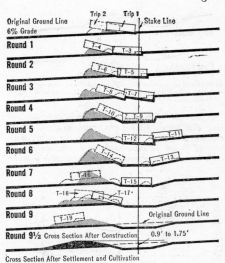

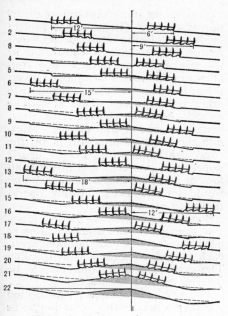

Terrace construction with 4-foot disk tiller. The number of rounds, or trips, required to build a terrace depends on the size of the terrace desired, the effectiveness of the equipment, and the condition of the soil.

Progressive steps in constructing a channel terrace with a 10-foot blade terracer. The terrace is constructed from the upper side.

Terrace construction with a motor grader.

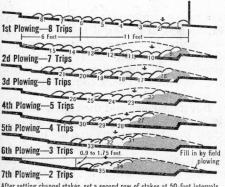

After setting channel stakes, set a second row of stakes at 50-foot intervals (closer on sharp curves) 11 feet below channel stakes. This row marks first plowing.

Drawing is based on use of a two-bottom 14- or 16-inch plow. Use sharp shares. Maintain enough speed to turn furrow slice completely over. Remove crop residues and disk heavy sod well before plowing.

Construction of channel-type terrace with two-way plow. This plow permits building terraces from one side—an advantage in terracing steep land. It is a valuable tool for carrying out maintenance operations. It turns all the furrows down hill. It is also used on the flatter lands, when the furrows can be turned up hill.

Four sketches show construction methods applicable to some types of equipment.

Keeping the terraces built up to their original size is important. This requires attention to maintenance every year. The job consists of removing silt bars that may have formed above the terrace; inspecting terrace ends to see that they are fully open (if they are supposed to be open) or properly closed (if that is the plan); building up low sections in the terrace ridge; and plowing to maintain adequate size of ridge or channel.

Having terraces on a field often calls for changes in farming operations. The problem is simple where most of the terraces are parallel. If that is impossible, one of the systems shown in the sketches on the next page will be helpful.

A DIVERSION TERRACE (also called diversion ditch) is like a field terrace in shape. The main difference is that it is designed to handle larger flows of water. Diversion terraces usually are considerably larger than field terraces.

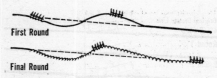

First Round

Final Round

Rounds should be spaced so that width of plowed area below terrace is ⅓ more than width of plowed area above terrace. This calls for overlapping the rounds above the terrace.

A method of maintaining channel-type terraces with disk plow. This method tends to clean out the channel and move the soil up onto the ridge. This method is not recommended for continuous use. It may be used occasionally in rotation with a motor grader.

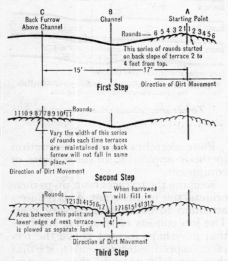

C
Back Furrow
Above Channel

B
Channel

A
Starting Point

Rounds— 6 5 4 3 2 1 1 2 3 4 5 6

This series of rounds started on back slope of terrace 2 to 4 feet from top.

|— 15' —|— 17' —|

First Step   Direction of Dirt Movement

Rounds
11 10 9 8 7 7 8 9 10 11

Vary the width of this series of rounds each time terraces are maintained so back furrow will not fall in same place.

Direction of Dirt Movement

Second Step

Rounds
12 13 14 15 16 17

When harrowed will fill in
17 16 15 14 13 12

Area between this point and lower edge of next terrace is plowed as separate land.

|— 4' —|

Direction of Dirt Movement

Third Step

A method of maintaining channel-type terraces with moldboard plow. By starting with a back furrow at the terrace ridge, as shown in step 1, and ending with a dead furrow in the channel (step 3), the farmer can keep the terrace at the desired capacity.

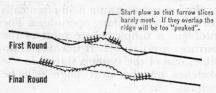

Start plow so that furrow slices barely meet. If they overlap the ridge will be too "peaked".

First Round

Final Round

Vary width of land each plowing so dead furrow will not fall in same place repeatedly. Plow area between terraces as a separate land.

NOTE: If terrace should become peaked, start back furrow on back slope, one plow width from top of ridge.

A method of maintaining ridge-type terraces with disk plow. This method is adapted for the gentler slopes where level terraces are used in areas of low rainfall and the conservation of water is vital.

Some of the important uses of diversion terraces or ditches are to protect fields from hillside runoff; divert water from a gully to assist in controlling it; increase or decrease the amount of runoff water entering a farm pond; divert water from points of concentration to other nearby areas where it can be spread and used; protect terrace systems from runoff that originates outside the terraced area; break up the concentration of water on long, gentle slopes; and intercept and divert shallow, or perched, subsurface water that would interfere with farming operations and plant growth.

Because diversions are used to intercept the runoff from drainage areas of a few acres up to several hundred acres, each must be designed to fit the site. The grade and dimensions should be determined by a technician.

The need for adequately protected waterways and outlet areas is just as important for diversions as for field terraces. Special structures of concrete or other permanent materials often are required to protect the outlet ends of diversions that intercept the runoff from large drainage areas.

ONE OF THE GOALS in conservation farming is to keep soil losses down to something like the natural rate in the undisturbed landscape. It is often impossible and impractical to use farming systems that will completely prevent all soil losses.

But the farmer and the conservationist need to be aware of the rate of loss their practices permit and to plan to keep erosion within allowable limits.

This section presents a method of estimating soil loss as a guide to conservation planning in the Corn Belt. The principles could be used in other sections where experimental data are available to give reliable values for the various factors involved.

The first question to be answered is: What is "allowable soil loss"—that is, how much soil can be removed annually per acre, on the average, without damaging the land or causing excessive

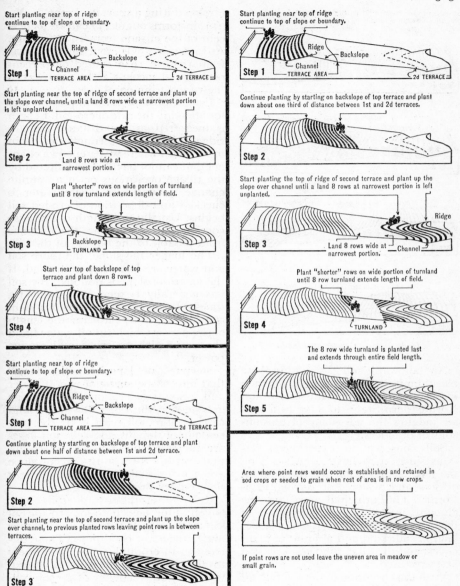

Four methods of planting row crops on terraced land.

silting on lower lying fields or in streams and reservoirs?

More effective erosion-control practices are needed on shallow soils than on deep ones on similar slopes. Conservation practices for cropland in the Corn Belt should keep average annual soil losses below 4 to 5 tons an acre on deep soils and 2 to 3 tons an acre on shallow ones. Soil washing, gully formation, and silting are not excessive at those rates.

Harvest row crops in reverse of the way the field was planted. The illustrations below show how to harvest corn where the turnland was planted between the terraces.

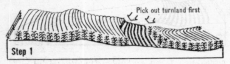

Pick out turnland first

Step 1

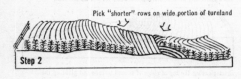

Pick "shorter" rows on wide portion of turnland

Step 2

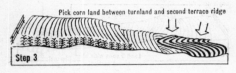

Pick corn land between turnland and second terrace ridge

Step 3

Pick all corn above turnland to field boundary.

Step 4

Harvesting corn on terraced land.

An "allowable soil loss" within these broad limits has been assigned for each important soil in the Midwestern and Northeastern States to serve as a goal for judging the adequacy of erosion-control practices.

Soil conservation experiment stations since 1929 have been studying the factors that influence the amount of soil and water lost during rainstorms. The principal ones are the amount, intensity, and distribution of the rain; length and steepness of slope; kind of soil; kind and amount of plant cover; and the tillage and conservation practices used.

With the exception of the rainfall, all of these factors can be influenced to some extent by what the land operator does. It is important therefore that he consider all factors when he develops a conservation plan for his farm.

Usually once each year a rain will fall faster and in such amount that the soil will be unable to absorb it. Usually a few hard rains cause most of the erosion during a year. At Arnot, N. Y., 21 rainstorms out of 177 caused 65 percent of the erosion from 1935 to 1943. At La Crosse, Wis., four storms a year from 1940 to 1943 caused 95 percent of the total soil loss and 84 percent of the runoff from cornland.

Length of slope is an important factor affecting the rate of erosion. Length is measured as the distance from a ridge or crest where runoff can begin to the point where water enters a channel that cannot be filled and altered by the tillage operations or to a definite change in steepness where water is checked and deposition of eroded soil begins. Usually the length of slope, so considered, is less than the distance from the top to the bottom of the hill.

The longer the slope, the more soil and water are lost when cultivated. If the length of slope is doubled, the soil loss generally is increased about 1.5 times. Terraces and diversions help control erosion by reducing the length of slope over which runoff water has a chance to pick up speed and erosive power.

Steepness of slope is another factor that affects the speed of runoff water and amount of erosion. As the slope gets steeper, the water flows faster and carries more soil with it. If the percentage of slope is doubled, soil losses are increased 2.5 times. This means that soil losses on a 16-percent slope are 2.5 times those on an 8-percent slope, other things being equal.

Relative erodibility of soils vary widely. One field may lose 10 tons of soil an acre while another loses 15 tons under the same conditions. These differences in erodibility are due largely to the ability of the soil to absorb water and the tendency of the soil particles to stick together.

To reflect the comparative rates at which different soils will erode, soil scientists have assigned erodibility factors based on measurements at conservation experiment stations. A factor of 1.0 is given to deep Prairie soils such as Marshall, Parr, and Tama. Other soils, such as those developed

On land that slopes less than about 6% terraces are built wide enough to let you cross them with machinery at almost any angle you choose. Thus you can cut such fields by going 'round and 'round them just as you always do. On steeper slopes, where terraces can't be built wide, it is probably better to harvest the grain with the terraces. The three drawings below showing a windrower in operation illustrate how this may be done.

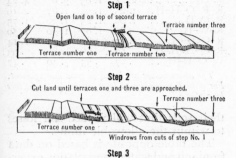

Step 1

Open land on top of second terrace

Terrace number three

Terrace number one   Terrace number two

Step 2

Cut land until terraces one and three are approached.

Terrace number three

Terrace number one

Windrows from cuts of step No. 1

Step 3

Cut around the area left above, and including, terrace number one.

Terrace number one

Harvesting grain on terraced land.

under a forest cover, have a factor of 1.25, meaning that they erode 25 percent faster than those having a factor of 1.0. For slowly permeable soils and some sandy soils, the factor is 1.5. Soils with tight, nearly impermeable subsoils have a factor of 1.75.

Conservation practices like terracing, contour stripcropping, and contouring materially reduce losses of soil and water. Each has its limitations and needs to be used in its proper place. For example, terraces are not generally constructed on steep slopes, contour stripcropping is most effective on slopes that are not more than 400 feet long, and contouring alone is most effective on 2 to 6 percent slopes that are not more than 200 feet long.

Measurements show that contouring reduces soil losses about 50 percent from those occurring with up-and-down-hill cultivation, contour stripcropping reduces losses about 75 percent and terracing even more, depending on length and steepness of the slopes involved.

Tillage and crop-management practices modify the erosion-control effectiveness of crops they are used with.

Corn, cotton, and soybeans long have been considered soil-depleting

crops. Most of the damage associated with them was due to overtillage in attempting to prepare fine seedbeds, control weeds, and get more nitrogen from decomposing organic matter. Improved cultural practices and new tillage implements have helped overcome some of the hazards of clean tillage.

In the Midwest, seedbeds that were prepared with a field cultivator lost about half as much soil as plowed ones.

Contour listing in western Iowa reduced water losses about 50 percent and soil losses 73 percent from those on fields planted on the contour.

Leaving the crop residues, such as cornstalks or grain straw, on the surface of the soil will reduce soil losses as much as 50 percent.

The kind and amount of plant cover have a major influence on the rate of erosion. On cropland this varies with different crops and their sequence in the rotation. Measurements at experiment stations have shown the relative amounts of soil losses from different crops in various rotations. These are shown below in comparison to a standard 3-year rotation of row crop (R), spring grain (O), and hay (H)—that is, R–O–H has the index number of 100.

	Percentage of R–O–H
Row crop, spring grain, hay (R–O–H)	100
Continuous row crop (R)	422
Row crop, spring grain catch crop (R–O$_x$)	242
Row crop, row crop, spring grain, hay, hay (R–R–O–H–H)	125
Row crop, winter grain, hay (R–W–H)	86
Row crop, spring grain, hay, hay (R–O–H–H)	65
Row crop, spring grain, hay, hay, hay (R–O–H–H–H)	52
Winter grain, spring grain, hay, hay (W–O–H–H)	27

The relative values of individual crops in different sequences have also been found.

Conservation workers in the Corn Belt and the Northeastern States have used tables of soil-loss factors reflecting these variables to evaluate conservation cropping systems. The tables serve as guides to help farmers select combinations of rotations and practices for

Average Annual Soil Losses in Tons per Acre a Year, Using a Rotation of R–O–H Having a Soil Factor of 1.0

Length of Slope

Slope (Percent)	No Practices 100'	200'	300'	400'	Contouring 100'	200'	300'	400'	Stripcropping 100'	200'	300'	400'	Terracing
2	1.7	2.4	3.0	3.4	1.0	1.4	1.7	2.0	0.5	0.7	0.9	1.0	0.6
4	3.3	4.6	5.7	6.6	1.7	2.3	2.9	3.3	0.8	1.2	1.4	1.7	0.8
6	5.3	7.6	9.3	10.7	2.7	3.8	4.7	5.4	1.3	1.9	2.3	2.7	1.2
8	8.0	11.2	13.7	15.8	4.7	6.7	8.2	9.5	2.4	3.4	4.1	4.7	2.0
10	11.0	15.5	19.0	22.0	6.5	9.3	11.3	13.1	3.3	4.7	5.7	6.6	2.7
12	14.5	20.5	25.0	29.0	8.7	12.3	15.0	17.3	4.4	6.2	7.5	8.7	3.5
14	18.5	26.0	32.0	37.0	14.8	21.0	25.5	30.0	5.5	7.5	9.1	10.5	
16	23.0	32.0	40.0	46.0	18.0	26.0	32.0	37.0	6.7	9.5	11.0	13.0	

R–corn, O–spring grain, H–hay.

Combined Soil-Loss Factors for Different Rotations and Soils

	Soil Factor			
Rotation	*1.0*	*1.25*	*1.50*	*1.75*
R–O$_x$	2.42	1.85	3.6	4.24
R-R–O–H–H.	1.25	1.55	1.87	2.19
R–O–H	1.00	1.25	1.50	1.75
R–W–H	.86	1.07	1.30	1.50
R–O–H–H	.65	.81	.97	1.14
R–O–H–H–H.	.52	.66	.80	.93
W–O–H–H	.27	.33	.40	.47

The above values are based on good management. For a high management level, multiply the factors by 0.7.

their soils that will reduce soil losses to within the allowable limits.

The table opposite is based on data from soil and water conservation experiment stations in that region. It shows the average annual soil losses from the standard 3-year rotation (R–O–H) on soils have an erodibility factor of 1.0 with different slopes and practices.

The table above presents combined soil-loss factors for common rotations on soils of different erodibilities. When the basic soil losses in the first table are multiplied by these factors, the results are the estimated soil losses from corresponding slopes and practices with different rotations on different soils.

For example, to estimate the soil loss from an R–R–O–H–H rotation on a soil that has an erodibility factor of 1.25 and a 6-percent slope 300 feet long that is contoured, first find the basic soil loss figure in the first table for the slope and practice specified. It is 4.7 tons per acre. This figure multiplied by the combined soil loss factor from the second table (1.55) gives 7.3 tons an acre as the expected average annual soil loss under the conditions described.

If the allowable annual soil loss for this soil is 4 tons an acre, this rotation with contouring is not an adequate conservation system. Either a more effective rotation must be used or the land must be stripcropped or terraced to bring the expected soil loss down to the allowable figure. Other calculations with the two tables will indicate which combinations of crops and practices will do that.

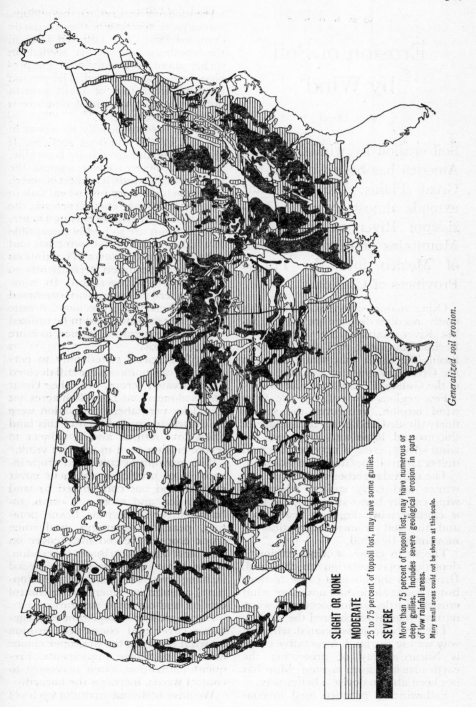

Generalized soil erosion.

SLIGHT OR NONE

MODERATE
25 to 75 percent of topsoil lost, may have some gullies.

SEVERE
More than 75 percent of topsoil lost, may have numerous or deep gullies. Includes severe geological erosion in parts of low rainfall areas.
Many small areas could not be shown at this scale.

Erosion of Soil
by Wind

W. S. Chepil

Soil erosion by wind in North America has been worst in the Great Plains, the area that extends almost from the Mississippi River to the Rocky Mountains and from the Gulf of Mexico into the Prairie Provinces of Canada.

Other major regions subject to this costly, needless damage are the Columbia River plains, some parts of the Pacific Southwest and the Colorado Basin, the muck and sandy areas in the Great Lakes region, and the sands of the Gulf and Atlantic seaboards.

Few regions are entirely safe from wind erosion. Wherever the soil is finely divided and bare, the surface of the ground loose and dry, and the wind strong, erosion may be expected unless control measures are adopted.

The most dangerous seasons are late winter and early spring, when the wind usually blows strongest, the land is clothed with the least vegetation, and the soil is most susceptible to movement by wind.

The main cause of wind erosion is depletion of vegetation on the land. Drought is the obvious cause of that, but drought alone does not cause wind erosion. Little erosion occurred when natural vegetation covered the land.

The problem is associated with the way we use the land. Vegetative cover is Nature's way of protecting the earth's surface from erosion. Man has not been able to devise a better way.

Fallowing, a practice used to conserve moisture in dry-farming regions, leaves large acreages of bare or partly denuded land. The fallowed land in the northern sections is seeded in spring about 20 months after the previous crop was harvested. The ground must be kept free of plant growth during those 20 months if moisture is to be conserved.

Fallow is sown usually to wheat in the fall in the southern sections. If germination and growth are favorable, a good protective cover against the next spring's winds is almost assured. But if the land is dry and wheat fails to germinate or make enough growth, the danger of wind erosion becomes acute.

Some lands are so highly susceptible to wind erosion that fallowing has had to be abandoned in favor of continuous cropping or returned permanently to grass or other vegetation. In some places where fallowing was attempted and wind erosion broke loose, drastic emergency measures had to be utilized to check the spread of erosion to more valuable lands.

Large acreages suited only to permanent grass or forests are still devoted to cultivated crops. In the Great Plains alone about 14 million acres not suited for permanent cultivation were cultivated in 1955. Much of this land offers low returns and is subject to severe erosion even in average years.

The growing of cultivated crops incapable of providing sufficient cover on the land has contributed to land denudation and erosion. Cotton, tobacco, sugar beets, peas, beans, potatoes, peanuts, asparagus, and some truck crops leave too little cover on the land and contribute to erosion. When those crops are grown, special farming systems (such as stripcropping) are almost imperative to control erosion and conserve moisture.

Another cause of depletion of a vegetative cover and consequent erosion by wind has been the improper choice and use of tillage implements. Frequent cultivation, often necessary to control weeds, increases the hazard. We have had some irregular cycles of severe wind erosion, which reflect the cycles of the weather. Recurring periods of drought and high winds have worsened the erosion.

High temperatures also have been a factor. High temperature usually is linked with dry years and low temperatures with wet years. The variations in the amount of precipitation and intensity of winds are based on a probability law like the one concerning floods. We can predict the general frequency of occurrence of periods of high wind and low precipitation from past records, but we cannot predict the time when they will occur. Constant preparedness for periods of high winds and low precipitation therefore is essential if erosion by wind is to be controlled.

Essential also is the establishment of practices that prevent wind erosion. Too many of us begin to worry about erosion after it has started. Then it is usually too late to prevent damage to crops and soil. It is much more practical to adopt permanent measures than it is to delay and then depend on emergency methods.

The wind erosion process has several major phases: Initiation of movement of the soil and its transportation, sorting, abrasion, and deposition. Each phase is influenced by the condition of the air, the ground surface, and the soil.

THE WEATHER causes considerable loosening and structural disintegration of the surface soil. Alternating wetting and drying and freezing and thawing tend to break down the soil aggregates to granules that are highly erodible by wind. The effects of weathering are greatest at the surface and diminish rapidly with depth. Vegetation and vegetative residues usually protect this granulated surface material from erosion by wind. Tillage tends to bury both the erodible surface material and the residues. We have no implements that can bury the surface soil and at the same time retain the crop residue on the surface. Implements for this dual purpose need to be developed.

Improper tillage is another cause. When he tries to eradicate weeds or create a favorable seedbed, a farmer often unavoidably loosens and pulverizes the soil so that wind can carry it away. Light rains may end temporarily the danger of soil drifting because the fine particles (if the soil is not very sandy) tend to cement the soil mass together to form clods and a surface crust that resist the force of wind. But heavy rains tend to smoothen the soil surface and to leave a few loose grains of sand or water-stable soil grains on the surface. The topmost grains, as soon as they are dry, may be moved—the first stage of erosion.

THE MOVEMENT BEGINS with the most erodible grains on the most exposed positions of the surface. The direct force of the wind against the soil particles dislodges them from their perches. They move a short distance along the surface and then suddenly shoot upwards in a jumping movement known as saltation. The height of the jumps varies with the size and density of the soil particles, the roughness of the soil surface, and the velocity of the wind. The largest particles do not jump at all, but roll and slide—surface creep—along the surface.

Some particles jump a short distance. Others jump a foot or several feet, depending on the initial velocity of rise from the ground. As they rise and fall through the air, they gain considerable momentum from the pressure of the wind against them and continue to gain velocity until they strike the ground, when they either rebound and continue their movement in saltation or lose most of their energy by striking other particles, which they cause to rise upward while they themselves come to rest or form part of the movement in surface creep.

Movement of grains by surface creep is induced primarily by impacts of particles in saltation. The interchange of movement in saltation and surface creep is constant.

Most of the particles kicked up by

jumping grains are fine grains of dust. They rise high, travel far, and drop to earth only when rain washes them down or when the wind subsides.

The movement of fine dust in suspension is the most spectacular mode of transport. But fine dust itself is extremely resistant to movement by direct force of wind against the ground—partly because it coheres to the surface and partly because it is submerged below the turbulent flow of air. The dust clouds are only a show.

Dust clouds are a result of impacts of grains moving in saltation, the force that primarily brings them into the airstream. Dust is raised in a like manner by vehicles, animals, and other objects traveling along the ground.

Once kicked up in the air, dust is lifted high in the atmosphere by the upward velocity of eddies of turbulent wind. The upward velocity of eddies of erosive wind is at least 2 or 3 miles an hour—enough to lift particles of the size of clay, silt, and very fine sand.

The erosive wind is turbulent at all heights except in a paper-thin zone among the surface projections. Its average forward velocity is zero somewhere among the irregularities of the surface. From this level upward, the average forward velocity increases rapidly. The rate of increase of average velocity with height—the drag velocity—is governed by the driving force of atmospheric wind.

The actual velocity and turbulence of the wind near the ground depend on the nature and height of irregularities of the surface.

The degree of turbulence varies directly with the roughness of the ground and inversely with height. The wind near the ground, in fact, is characterized by eddies of extremely variable velocity moving in all directions. On the surface of a sand dune, for example, the maximum eddy velocity is about twice the average forward velocity.

This eddying, or turbulence, is what makes the soil erode. Erosion of soil by nonturbulent flow of air has never been recorded.

Turbulence of the atmosphere has a considerable tendency to increase the surface velocity and hence the momentary frictional force of the wind against the ground. Atmospheric turbulence cannot be controlled by presently known means. The surface velocity and the force of wind against the ground can be modified substantially, however.

AFTER SOIL MOVEMENT has started, the impacts of saltating particles against the ground provide the bulk of the driving force in the erosion process.

That is because the velocity of wind some distance above the ground is much greater than the velocity at the ground. The magnitude of movement of soil by wind therefore depends primarily on the velocity of the wind up to the height of saltation.

Natural variations in air density, as affected by variations in temperature, pressure, and humidity, have little effect on the rate of soil movement. Natural changes in air viscosity—stickiness—also have little effect on the erosive force of wind.

Little can be done to reduce turbulence, but the surface velocity can be reduced by various measures. Even a slight reduction in wind velocity near the ground produces a relatively great reduction in the possible amount of soil erosion, because the force of the wind varies as the square of its velocity. Reduction of surface velocity therefore should be one of the main principles of control of wind erosion.

The concentration of soil particles carried by wind is greatest at the surface of the ground and decreases rapidly with height. The coarse particles tend to move closer to the ground than the fine ones. Granulated soils, such as sands or clays, usually drift closer to the ground than the medium-textured soils containing a large proportion of dust. Usually 90 to 98 percent of the particles in saltation are carried below a height of 1 foot.

The proportion of the three types of movement varies greatly for different soils. Between 50 and 75 percent of the weight of the soil is carried in saltation, 3 to 40 percent in suspension, and 5 to 25 percent in surface creep.

The height to which particles in saltation rise has an important bearing on the effectiveness of different methods of controlling wind erosion. The height of rise is in definite ratio to the horizontal length of grain path. The ratio is about 1:7 for a rise up to 2 inches; 1:8 for a rise of 2 to 4 inches; 1:9 for 4 to 6 inches; and 1:10 for heights above 6 inches.

The ability of stubble or ridged strips to trap moving soil (and hence to reduce wind erosion) is governed by the height of jump of particles in saltation. The height of the jump varies somewhat with type of soil and drag velocity. The receptiveness of stubble or ridges to trap saltation also is an important factor. The traps must be wide enough to prevent the particles from jumping over them. They also must be wide enough to allow a sufficient reservoir for the trapped soil.

When soil material comprises only erodible particles, such as dune sand, the rate of soil movement varies as the cube of the drag velocity. When the soil contains a mixture of erodible and nonerodible fractions, as most cultivated soils do, the rate of soil movement is never constant.

The intensity of erosion on a small isolated area, such as a narrow strip at right angles to the direction of the wind, is rapid at first, diminishes with duration of exposure, and ceases as soon as the height and number of nonerodible soil fractions become sufficient to shelter the erodible fractions from the wind.

Erosion on large areas, once it has started, usually increases in intensity, especially on the leeward side of the area. Here the increase in the intensity of erosion with duration of exposure is due mainly to an increase in the amount of erodible fractions produced by abrasion, or wearing away, of nonerodible clods and surface crust by impacts of saltation. The shorter the length of the eroded area, the less is the amount of abrasion and hence the lower is the rate of soil movement.

Thus the intensity of erosion increases with time. It also increases with distance across a large area.

When the surface of the eroding area is composed only of erodible fractions, such as in sands, the maximum rate of movement is reached at a distance of about 30 feet downwind. But on most cultivated fields the rate of soil movement increases all the way to the leeward side or, if the field is extremely large, for 500 yards or more, depending on the condition of the soil.

The acceleration in the rate of soil movement with distance across a cultivated field is due to three main factors: Sorting and progressive accumulation of erodible particles toward the leeward side of the eroded area; a progressive increase in degree of abrasion of surface crust and nonerodible soil fractions by impacts of saltation; and a gradual decrease in surface roughness resulting from the leveling process of the wind, which works against the roughening effects of tillage implements.

The rate of increase of intensity of erosion across eroding fields varies with the type of soil. The rate of increase on medium-textured soils usually is gradual for 500 yards or more. On highly erodible sandy soils and granulated clays, the rate of increase is extremely rapid the first 100 yards or so and then slows down as the concentration of transported particles approaches the possible maximum for a given wind. At 100 yards from the windward edge, the intensity of erosion on medium-textured soils seldom exceeds 25 percent of the possible maximum intensity, but on the extremely erodible soils it is usually more than 60 percent at the same distance to the leeward edge.

It is therefore evident that the effectiveness of a system of trap strips separating erodible strips of, say, 100 yards in width is much greater on slightly and moderately erodible soils than on highly erodible soils.

ERODIBILITY of soil by wind is influenced primarily by soil structure and stability of structure in a dry condition. This structure is usually referred to as the dry aggregate, or the clod structure.

Erodibility is influenced specifically by the proportion, size, and bulk density of the erodible soil particles. It is convenient to relate erodibility with the equivalent diameter of the particles. The equivalent diameter is equal to $OD/2.65$, in which O is the bulk density of the particles and D is their diameter.

The most erodible soil particles are about 0.1 millimeter in equivalent diameter. Particles larger and smaller than that are more resistant to movement by wind. This diameter is also an approximate dividing point between the two ways the particles are moved by wind. Particles smaller than 0.1 millimeter, known as dust, are moved mostly by suspension, and those larger than that are moved by saltation and surface creep. The impact action resulting from saltation of the most erodible particles causes the movement of the larger and the smaller ones.

Soil fractions larger than the size of a wheat kernel or a bean, depending on their bulk density and on wind velocity, are nonerodible.

The smallest nonerodible clods are most effective in protecting the erodible fractions because they have more protective surface in proportion to their weight. Large clods are not so effective as the smaller ones.

Often a farmer has no choice but to use a tillage implement that will bring to the surface as many clods as possible, even if the clods are not of an ideal size.

A crude but simple index of soil erodibility is the proportion of soil fractions greater than about 1 millimeter in diameter, as determined by dry sieving. This diameter is an approximate dividing point between the erodible and the nonerodible fractions. Soils resistant to movement by wind contain at least two-thirds by weight of nonerodible fractions.

The surface crust is another phase of clod structure that influences erodibility by wind. Usually some crusting of the surface is caused by rain or melting snow. The crust offers a degree of resistance, depending on how thick and hard it is and on the amount of soil grains that can be loosened off its surface by the wind. A high wind velocity usually is necessary to initiate perceptible soil movement on a crusted surface. Once the erodible particles are loosened and the crust is worn through by impacts of saltation, erosion may be started later by a much lower wind.

The sorting action of the wind causes accumulations of dune materials that require a much lower threshold velocity than the unsorted material of a noneroded field. The threshold velocity for dry dune material is the lowest possible and varies little with soil type.

Unconsolidated dune materials—that is, accumulated materials not yet wetted by rain—usually are started in motion when wind reaches 13 to 15 miles an hour at a height of 1 foot. These materials contain little of the fine fraction, or dust, necessary to bind the eroded grains together when they are wetted. Once a field has been eroded by wind, therefore, rains do little good, for if wind continues to blow, erosion is resumed as soon as the topmost grains have barely dried.

The resistance of soil structure to various disintegrating forces is important in maintaining stability against wind. These forces are mechanical agents, such as tillage machinery; the abrasive action of windblown soil material; and the forces of the weather.

Resistance to breakdown by mechanical forces is mechanical stability.

Mechanical stability also varies in direct proportion with resistance to abrasion by impacts of material.

Mechanical stability varies greatly for the different structural units of the soil. It is highest for the water-stable aggregates, followed in order by that of dry secondary aggregates or clods, the surface crust, and the weakly consolidated material among the clods.

The stability of all structural units varies directly with the fineness of texture—that is, with the percentage of clay they contain. The proportion and stability of clods increase with depth in the soil, because the elements of the weather tend to soften and break down the aggregates in direct proportion with their proximity to the surface.

Clay aggregates have a high degree of resistance to breakdown by mechanical forces and abrasion but a low degree of resistance against the forces of weather, particularly freezing and thawing.

The relative importance of degree of cloddiness and stability of clods varies with conditions. If the field subject to erosion is small, the amount of abrasion is also small, and the amount of erosion is influenced primarily by the proportion of erodible fractions. If the field is large, the stability of clods is the more important factor. In such a case, if the clods lack mechanical stability, the presence of even a small amount of loose, erodible particles on the surface is usually enough to disintegrate the clods by abrasion from particles moving in saltation and ultimately to cause intense erosion over the whole field.

A ROUGH GROUND SURFACE is more resistant to wind erosion than a smooth one: A rough surface slows down wind velocity and tends to trap whatever particles might have been dislodged from its more exposed parts.

Vegetation and vegetative residues act as a protective cover as well as a rough surface does. Generally they have a greater capacity to trap the moving soil than does a ridged or a cloddy soil surface. Thus, in addition to providing roughness, cover in itself is likewise important in reducing erosion by wind. The two factors therefore are inseparable in many cases.

The first addition of vegetative cover reduces the amount of erosion most. Each addition is proportionately less effective. How much vegetative material is required to protect the soil from wind depends primarily on surface roughness, degree of cloddiness, size of field, and strength of the wind. Often one-fourth ton an acre (air-dry basis) of wheat stubble is sufficient on slightly erodible soil, 1 ton on moderately susceptible soil, and at least 4 tons on the most erodible dune material.

Tall stubble is more effective against wind than an equal weight of short stubble because it reduces the surface velocity of the wind more.

Stubble is more effective than straw because the crowns are heavier and less subject to removal by wind. Sorghum stubble is less effective than an equal weight and height of wheat stubble because it has less protective surface.

Grass makes one of the best covers because it has a relatively great protective surface above and below the ground and because it is well anchored.

THE BASIC FACTORS that influence clod structure, stability of structure, and erodibility by wind are varied.

Soil texture—that is, the relative proportion of sand, silt, and clay—is one factor. The coarsest and often the finest textured soils are more erodible than the medium-textured soils because they have a less well developed clod structure. The coarse-textured soils lack sufficient silt and clay to bind the erodible sand grains. The fine-textured soils have too much clay, which, especially under freezing and thawing, causes the soil clods to disintegrate into a finely granulated, erodible condition. The cloddiest and least erodible soils have a clay content of 20 to 30 percent and a silt content as high as possible. Silt ranging from 0.005 to 0.01 millimeter produces the greatest degree of cloddiness and resistance to erosion by wind.

The water-stable particles greater than about 1 millimeter in diameter, whether they are single grains or aggregates, are highly resistant to movement and abrasion by wind erosion.

Many dryland soils contain relatively small amounts of these particles but contain a considerable proportion of the fine, water-stable particles smaller than 0.02 millimeter in diameter. These fine particles are partly responsible for the formation of clods large enough to resist the force of wind.

Free calcium carbonate, or lime, in excess of 1 percent and not above 10 percent by weight, in soil reduces cloddiness and mechanical stability of clods and increases erodibility by wind. These influences are amplified in soils containing a high percentage of decomposed organic matter.

The organic matter has a variable effect on soil structure and erodibility, according to its degree of decomposition. Undecomposed vegetative matter is highly effective as a soil cover and binder. Decomposing vegetative matter increases soil aggregation and reduces erodibility. Decomposed organic matter, which usually gives the soil a characteristic black color, often facilitates erosion by wind.

In a sense, the decomposed organic matter, or humus, induces aggregation in that it causes the soil to aggregate into small granules. In dryland regions especially subject to the effects of freezing and thawing, the granules generally are too small to resist the force of wind. Some soils with much organic matter are coarsely granulated and not readily eroded by wind except under exposure to extreme influences of freezing and thawing.

THE EFFECTS of wind erosion are serious and extensive. Many farmers have lost entire crops, and the fertility of the soil has been greatly reduced. But those effects are less serious than the loss of fine soil fractions (silt, clay, and organic matter) gradually sorted from the sands and carried to distant places, where they may be of little or no use to anyone.

The wind acts on some soils like a sieve that removes the fine fractions and retains the coarse ones. The coarse mechanical fractions are infertile and are no more than a skeleton of the soil. The remaining sand often is much more erodible than was the original

soil and usually is a serious threat to better surrounding lands. Extensive areas of aeolian (wind-deposited) soils in this country do not show this type of sorting action. All of the material to the depth of plowing is known to have been removed in some instances from these soils in a single season. Crop yields in some areas have been much lower for many years after serious erosion by wind occurred. Sometimes the land seems to have been injured permanently.

Wind erosion is bad in other ways. Railways and highways have been buried under drifted soil. Traffic accidents have been common during severe soil drifting. Insects and weed seeds are blown far and wide with drifted soil. Fences, hedges, and shelterbelts have been buried and ruined. Shrubs and trees may be smothered under the accumulated soil. Farmsteads may be blocked and farm buildings ruined by soil drifts. Duststorms are disagreeable and sometimes unbearable to the farm family. People in towns and cities also suffer.

THE DECISIVE FACTOR of duststorms is depletion of vegetative cover on the land.

One of the methods of wind erosion control obviously should be to protect the soil by vegetation and crop residues. But this should be only one of the methods.

All of the major factors that influence wind erosion can be modified by various practices.

The principles of the control are fourfold: Protect the soil surface with a cover (the best of which is vegetation); roughen the surface to slow down wind velocity and trap drifting soil; produce stable soil aggregates large enough to resist the force of wind; and place barriers, such as crop strips, ridges, or shelterbelts, in the path of the wind to trap the drifting soil and keep it from spreading.

The principles are applicable everywhere, but their importance varies with the conditions.

How To Control a Gully

C. J. Francis

A system for disposing of water is essential on all farms on which runoff occurs. It will control the runoff and erosion so that gullies will not form. The natural processes of erosion have created natural drainage patterns. The runoff from fields and within fields is collected in these drainageways and carried to the mainstream channels.

Natural waterways are selected to carry runoff from individual fields and farms. The waterways are shaped where necessary to provide a channel having sufficient capacity to carry the expected runoff at nonerosive velocities.

The channels are maintained in grass. During the plowing and cultivation of fields, equipment is raised when crossing the waterways so as not to damage them or reduce their capacity. Grass seed and forage may be harvested from the waterways. Often they can be grazed to good advantage.

A good conservation plan put into effect before an extensive system of gullies has formed insures protection against gullies. It also will transform many gullies into good vegetated waterways and increase farm values.

Gullies that have developed can be stabilized or improved to serve as adequate water disposal systems. The cost of repairing a gully generally is proportional to its size. Some gullies have been allowed to advance to the point where it does not pay to repair them.

A small gully is considered to be less than 8 feet deep, a medium gully less than 8 to 15 feet deep, and a large gully more than 15 feet deep. The drainage area—that is, the area draining into a gully at any given point—also affects the type of control that may be used. Gullies whose drainage areas cover less than 50 acres are considered to have a small drainage area. Drainage areas of 50 to 150 acres are considered medium sized. Drainage areas greater than 150 acres are large.

Small gullies with small to medium drainage areas are the ones that can best be improved and controlled by the farmer.

The measures used to control, improve, or obliterate gullies depend on the size of the gully and its drainage area.

ONE OF THE SIMPLEST and cheapest ways to arrest the advance of small- to medium-sized gullies having small drainage areas is to fence them and exclude livestock—a common procedure in areas that are gullied badly and cannot feasibly be restored to cropland.

The fence should completely enclose the area to be controlled. It should be placed far enough from the banks of the gully to allow a good growth of vegetation to form. A good rule is to set the fence back from the edges of the banks a distance approximately equal to twice the gully depth.

Once the area is fenced, natural revegetation often will give adequate protection, but natural revegetation usually is a slow process. Grass, shrubs, or trees used separately or in combination give good results. If natural growth does not give adequate control or if the farmer wants a particular type of vegetation, the gully should be planted.

When trees are used, the process of control can be speeded up by planting adapted species.

It is hard to give a complete list of adapted species to cover all sections and conditions, but the following list is suggestive:

Northeast: Eastern redcedar, Scotch pine, red pine, pitch pine.

Middle Atlantic States: Eastern redcedar, red pine, Scotch pine, Virginia pine, shortleaf pine, pitch pine.

Southeast: Shortleaf pine, Virginia pine, eastern redcedar, loblolly pine.

Northern Great Plains: Red pine, eastern redcedar, willow, elm, poplar.

Southern Great Plains: Eastern redcedar, incense-cedar, poplar, willow.

Northwest: Ponderosa pine, Scotch pine, Douglas-fir, poplar.

Southwest: Ponderosa pine, incense-cedar, poplar, pinyon.

Mountain States: Ponderosa pine, Douglas-fir, Scotch pine.

When a gully is planted, it may be necessary to do some bank sloping to permit successful planting or seeding of steep areas. Usually a satisfactory growth can be established without extensive sloping.

When a gully is to be retired to woodlot or grass and if stabilization is the primary factor, only little bank sloping should be done.

DIVERSION OF RUNOFF from a gully is an effective control measure.

The use of diversions is limited to small drainages because of the difficulties in handling large volumes of water. A diversion can be used only at sites where a satisfactory outlet exists. If the outlet is subject to erosion, the water should not be diverted. No advantage comes from diverting water from one gully if there is danger of forming another.

Diversions are best used in connection with small gullies in pastures in which satisfactory outlets are commoner.

The areas above a diversion should be in grass or woods to reduce siltation in the channel. Diversions below cultivated fields may silt rapidly and create maintenance problems. The diversion should be set upstream from the head of the gully a distance not less than 3 to 4 times the depth of the gully.

The diversion is like a terrace, except that it normally has a larger cross section. Its capacity should be suffi-

cient to carry the runoff from the heaviest storm that is likely to occur about once in 10 years. A velocity of 4 to 6 feet a second normally will protect the channel from erosion when a good stand of grass is established. A grade of 6 to 12 inches per 100 feet usually is safe. By diverting water from a gully, natural revegetation may provide adequate control. Diversions also are used to provide protection to vegetated waterways during the period that vegetation is being established. The diversion is removed when vegetation is established.

IN PLACES WHERE LEVEL TERRACES or contour furrows are used, runoff into gullies may be reduced to the extent they will become stable through natural revegetation.

Level terraces and contour furrows should be applied to the major part of the area draining into the gully. The spacing of level terraces to control erosion and conserve water will reduce runoff enough to provide for gully control. The spacing and water-holding capacity of contour furrows depend on their purpose.

Contour furrows built solely to improve range or pastureland may not store enough runoff to be wholly effective in controlling gullies.

DEVELOPMENT OF STOCKWATER in range sections or pastures may help to solve gully problems. A dam built near the head of a gully or in a gully may store a large part of the runoff. The storage of water behind a dam reduces runoff downstream, and the reduction in runoff may permit natural revegetation to control erosion for a reasonable distance below the dam.

The development of a water disposal system for a farm requires the use of most of the natural drainageways. The drainageways that are gullied or have an improper cross section can be improved to carry the runoff safely.

A practical way to transform a gully into a satisfactory waterway is to shape it and seed it to adapted species of grasses. This method is best adapted to small and medium gullies that have small to medium drainage areas. A properly shaped earth channel with good vegetative cover will carry the runoff from the average farm or field without causing erosion.

If a vegetative waterway is to function effectively, the velocity of flow should be about 3 to 6 feet a second, depending on soil type and grasses used. The channel cross section should be broad and flat to keep the water spread uniformly over a wide area.

Usually the depth of flow in a vegetated channel should be about 6 to 18 inches, depending on the slope in order to keep velocities within reasonable limits. The slope of the channel—that is, the drop per unit of length—normally should not exceed 10 feet per 100 feet. Steeper slopes usually cause the water to flow too fast to maintain a good vegetative cover.

One cannot give a simple rule for determining the velocity of flow for a specific cross section and given slope. However, one point to remember is: As the slope of the channel increases, the depth of flow must decrease to maintain velocities in reasonable limits.

Because vegetated channels cannot be constructed to precise dimensions, it is hard to maintain flow at shallow depths uniformly over wide areas. Therefore the maximum width of waterways rarely should exceed 50 feet. It is advantageous to divide the waterway into two parallel channels when greater widths are required. That can be done easily by constructing a small ridge of earth down the center of the proposed channel. Each waterway is then planned and built as one unit.

Vegetated waterways carry runoff without erosion when the runoff lasts a relatively short time and flows at reasonable velocities.

A waterway should not remain wet over long periods. Continued wetting may kill desirable vegetation. It softens the soil to the extent that the vegetation is not effective in protecting the soil when stronger flow occurs.

As the size of the drainage area increases, the duration and volume of flow increases. Therefore vegetated waterways having drainage areas larger than 150 to 200 acres usually are not successful. Melting snow and resultant runoff in northern sections may cause flow for long periods and should be considered in planning a waterway.

Because natural waterways occur at elevations below the level of the adjoining field, seepage may cause the area to be wet and boggy. A tile drainage system may then be required. A proper system of drainage will remove ground water to the extent required to dry up the waterway and make it work.

A GULLY that is to be changed into a waterway should first be shaped to the cross section needed to carry the runoff. A direct relationship exists between the size of the drainage area and the amount of runoff that occurs when rain falls.

Gullies can be shaped with heavy earth moving equipment or with the power equipment that is available on the farm. Small gullies can be shaped with a farm tractor and plow. They can be filled gradually by plowing around the gully, starting near the edge of the bank and working the earth toward the center. A series of rounds, as is used in building a terrace, by working the earth toward the center of the gully, gives good results. Considerable working of the soil may be required to provide for a smooth, regular cross section. A blade, scraper, or harrow are good pieces of equipment for doing that. A little experience soon develops the plowing pattern that gives best results.

Heavy earth moving equipment—especially the track-type tractor and bulldozer and the motor patrol—is well suited to filling gullies. Either unit can push the dirt into the channel efficiently. The blade, an integral part of each unit, is suited to finishing operations. The heavy equipment packs the earth during filling operations and reduces settling to a minimum. Uncompacted earth settles; in deep gullies it might settle enough to distort the shape of the channel in time. Compaction also increases the erosion resistance of the earth in the channel—an important item particularly during the time vegetation is being established.

A firm seedbed should be prepared when the gully has been shaped to the desired cross section. The channel area should be fertilized, because much of the topsoil may have been removed in filling operations. A good mulch cover is helpful in obtaining a good stand.

Grass then is seeded in the usual way. Some of the grasses best adapted for use in waterways are: Midwest and Northeast—bromegrass, redtop, and bluegrass; reed canarygrass (well suited for wet waterways); tall fescue adapted to southern one-third to one-half of area. Southeast—tall fescue, Bermudagrass, and Pensacola Bahiagrass. Great Plains and Northwest—intermediate wheatgrass, western wheatgrass, buffalograss. Southwest—switchgrass, Indiangrass, bluestems, western wheatgrass, buffalograss; tall fescue and Bermudagrass in the more humid parts.

As the channel may erode during the period of establishing grass, a temporary diversion should be built to divert water away from it. Later it can be removed with a plow or scraper. If it is difficult to keep water out of the channel, a companion crop should be planted to give protection during the establishment stage.

Waterways used to carry water from terraces and diversions should be shaped and seeded, and a good growth of vegetation should be established before the terraces or diversions are built.

Vegetation cannot be used to stabilize all types of gullies. The determination of where vegetative measures become unsatisfactory and structural measures are required can only be made after a careful study of individual site conditions. Structural measures consist of dams of varying design constructed for the purpose of stabilizing the grade and halting further erosion. Properly installed structures will trans-

form an unstable gully into a satisfactory waterway.

Many types of temporary structures—brush dams, log dams, wire dams, rock dams—have been used to stabilize gullies while vegetation is being established. They involve much hand labor and are relatively costly to construct. Their value is doubtful. Temporary structures therefore are not generally recommended.

PERMANENT STRUCTURES usually are built of reinforced concrete, masonry, or of earth utilizing concrete or steel pipe spillways.

Permanent structures generally are used in medium to large gullies with medium to large drainage areas. Vegetation usually is not successful in controlling such gullies. Structures require the use of materials that must be purchased. Often special equipment and skilled labor must be used to build them. Permanent structures therefore are relatively costly. They should be built only after engineering studies and adequate plans have been made.

The main purpose of a permanent structure is to halt the advance of the vertical overfall at gully heads, stabilize the grade so the gully can be used as a waterway, and to reduce the flow downstream when spillway storage is provided. In stabilizing the grade of a gully, structures trap sediment and eventually cause filling of the gully. If one wants to speed the filling process, the raw gully banks above and between structures can be shaped at the time of construction.

Three basic structures are employed in stabilizing gullies: The drop inlet, drop spillway, and chute. Each is adapted to specific site conditions, and the selection of one or another can be determined only by an engineer after examining the site and deciding which will satisfy the requirements best.

Because the permanent structures must have a stable grade downstream, it often is necessary to build several structures in a reach of gully to stabilize it. A stable grade exists when the channel is neither agrading or degrading. Stability depends on the velocity, the kind and amount of vegetation in the channel, and the material of which the channel is composed. A dam in a gully traps most of the sediment that would normally pass downstream. This loss of sediment may cause a grade that seems to be stable to start eroding, particularly when the channel is in sandy soil.

A structure built to protect head erosion must be located so that the grade from the crest of the spillway to ultimate lip of the gully will not exceed the silting grade. The safest procedure is to build the dam high enough to make the crest of the spillway level with the lip of the gully. The silting grade depends on the nature of the soil and is best determined by investigating the grade of existing gullies in the area that appear stable. As a general rule, the silting grade should be kept within the limits of 6 inches per 100 feet.

The most important factor affecting the safety of the structure is the capacity of the spillway. The spillway should safely discharge the runoff from the heaviest rainfall that can be expected once in 25 to 100 years, depending on the estimated life of the structure. For example, if the structure is estimated to have a life of about 25 years, the spillway should be designed to pass a flood that will occur once in 25 years.

THE DROP INLET is ideally adapted to installation for grade stabilization or control of advancing gully heads when the gully is more than 10 feet deep.

It consists of an earth dam having a spillway of concrete or metal pipe. The spillway has a vertical section on the upstream side of the dam, called the riser, which is connected to a culvert or barrel passing through the earth dam. The crest of the riser is set at the elevation required to stabilize the grade upstream or protect the gully head.

Usually an earth emergency spillway is built around one end of the dam to take the infrequent or high flood flows. The use of an emergency spillway incorporating provisions for temporary flood storage where possible will reduce the size and consequent cost of the drop inlet structure. The cost of passing the total flood flow through a drop inlet may result in costs that may make the structure uneconomical.

The emergency spillway should have a good cover of vegetation, a uniform cross section, a gradual slope to the channel downstream, and no abrupt turns. It is primarily for the purpose of safeguarding the structure under extreme flow conditions at a reasonable cost. The elevation of the two spillways should be established to permit the drop inlet to discharge at its rated capacity before the emergency spillway functions.

The outlet of the drop inlet is placed at or slightly above the elevation of the grade established below the structure. A propped outlet is generally used. The pipe is extended about 8 feet below the toe of the dam and is supported by piling or a concrete pier. The support is placed 6 to 8 feet from the end of the pipe to protect it from the scour hole that will form. The advantage of the propped outlet is its low cost and its ability to discharge water far enough downstream so as not to endanger the safety of the structure. If the grade lowers excessively downstream from the outlet, the outlet can be extended and lowered at a reasonable cost. A propped outlet permits installation of structures at locations where the grade downstream is not considered completely stable.

As a general rule, a drop inlet with a propped outlet should not be built where the grade downstream averages more than 1 percent. In places where grades are steeper, supporting structures should be built downstream to a point where the resultant grade is less than 1 percent.

The preparation of the foundation and placement of earth fill for drop inlet structures is carried out in accord with standards covering the construction of earthen embankments. These standards, which are based on long experience, can be obtained from the local office of the Soil Conservation Service.

THE DROP SPILLWAY, or notch spillway, is built of reinforced concrete, masonry, or steel sheet piling. It is like the old mill dams built in small streams to serve as a source of power. Because dams in dry draws are not subject to continuous flows, the drop spillway is simpler in design and of lighter construction. It can be designed for almost any height, but it is best adapted to drops of 10 feet or less. The total storm runoff usually passes over the crest of the drop spillway. Emergency earth spillways are rarely used in connection with drop spillways.

Drop spillways require careful design of the apron or floor, on which the water falls, to dissipate the energy before passing to the channel below. Improper apron designs cause scour of the channel immediately below the structure. Excessive scour immediately downstream endangers the safety of the structure. Drop spillways therefore are used only at places where the grade downstream from the structure has been carefully studied and determined stable. Earth fills are used to connect the structure with the earth abutments.

CHUTES ARE USED in combination with earth dams to drop water farther than is ordinarily feasible with drop structures. They are built of reinforced concrete.

Chutes are constructed on foundations on original ground or on fill that has been carefully compacted under controlled conditions. The chute is susceptible to movement because of frost action or other causes. Closely spaced expansion joints are required to relieve the structure of stress that would cause cracking. Chutes are individually designed to fit specific site conditions.

STRUCTURAL IMPROVEMENT of gullies usually requires the service of an engineer to insure an economical, safe job.

The sizes and costs of the structures required to control a gully or system of gullies vary widely. Structural improvement of waterways generally requires a sizable outlay of money.

Standard plans have been developed and can be used successfully when properly adapted to site conditions. The plans are usually confined to drop spillways that have a height of 5 feet or less and to small drop inlets that have a total height of fill less than 15 feet.

These small structures can usually be built by the farmer with technical assistance. Whenever structural or vegetative control of a gully is considered, it is advisable to get in touch with the Soil Conservation Service or the Extension Service to ascertain the technical services that are available.

Most vegetative control measures can be wholly or largely carried out by the individual farmer. For structures, an engineering survey must be made, detailed plans must be prepared, and construction must be carried out by skilled individuals under careful supervision. Good materials and safe designs are essential for satisfactory permanent structures.

Uncontrolled gullies might continue to advance to the point where they cut up fields and whole farms so they must be abandoned. The sediment from eroding gullies is deposited on bottom lands and may destroy their value. The sediment trapped in reservoirs and deposited in stream channels creates an economic loss. Gullies lower the water table and may drain areas to the extent that crop production is reduced. The cost of maintenance of highways, railroads, pipelines, and other public utilities is increased by gully erosion and resultant sedimentation.

Gullies occur in every State. The extent to which they create damage depends on climate, topography, geology, soil type, and land use. Over the ages gullies have developed through the process of natural or geologic erosion. Their formation and resultant effect on the general configuration of the land is considered a normal part of the processes of erosion.

Stabilizing Sand Dunes

A. D. Stoesz and Robert L. Brown

To many of the millions of Americans who see them each year, the large sand dunes of our country are mounds and ridges of great beauty. To many others the dunes mean terror, when the shifting sands threaten to cover and destroy homes; a menace, when they make highways unsafe; an economic danger, when they make farms and ranches worthless.

Sand dunes in the United States occupied an area one-tenth as large as that of the agricultural land in 1957.

Inland dunes occur in geologic lakebeds, old beach lines and deltas, glacial outwash, along rivers, and in deserts and midgrass areas, where they are formed by wind action.

The second major group of sand dunes includes the ones on the Atlantic and Pacific coasts and the shores of the Great Lakes. They are developed naturally as coastwise currents take sand from the rivers where they enter the ocean or as coastal headlands are eroded. Winds take the sand as it is deposited on the beach and dunes form as the sand is blown inland.

Sand dunes may become unstable at any time because the vegetative cover is destroyed by fire, by overgrazing with livestock, by jetties at the mouths of rivers, and by the construction of buildings and roads, wearing of trails, and cultivation.

406157°—57——22

Dunes lack a soil profile because they are unstable and undeveloped. Water percolates through the sand freely. Because the sand has no organic matter, it does not retain very much moisture for plants. The fertility level is low. The sand is fine, loose, and easily moved by wind. It is abrasive and destructive to plants when it moves.

The basic problem in stabilizing a dune is to still the sand as near as possible to its source of origin or the point of disturbance and to establish and maintain permanent vegetation on it. A renewed supply of fresh sand is continually being washed up on coastal dunes by the waves. On inland dunes new material is not added, and the movement of sand is caused by the disturbance or destruction of the existing vegetative cover.

Once the sand is stilled, a plant cover can be established.

Sand dunes can be stilled temporarily by vegetation or by artificial barriers.

VEGETATION used on the sand must thrive in shifting sand and survive inundation or keep pace with the sand.

The plants generally have coarse, stiff stems that resist sand blasting. They should be unpalatable to livestock, because any grazing will be detrimental to dune control. They will have to grow fast on practically a starvation diet, or their nutrients will have to be supplied in fertilizers. Plants seldom provide a complete cover.

Grasses of primary importance for stilling sand in the Pacific Northwest are European beachgrass (*Ammophila arenaria*), a naturalized grass used to control coastal sand dunes since 1896; American beachgrass (*Ammophila breviligulata*), a native of the Great Lakes dunes and of the Atlantic coast as far south as North Carolina; and Volga wildrye (*Elymus giganteus*), a strain developed by Soil Conservation Service nurseries from a grass from Siberia.

The primary sand-stilling grass on the Great Lakes dunes and on those of the Atlantic coast north of North Carolina is American beachgrass.

The Carolina dunes are stilled most effectively by plantings of sea-oats (*Uniola paniculata*) and sea panicgrass (*Panicum amarum*).

Inland dunes of the Great Plains are anchored effectively by seeding the dunes to such fast-growing plants as broomcorn (*Sorghum vulgare, var. technicum*), Sudangrass (*S. vulgare var. sudanese*), and Black amber cane (*S. vulgare var. coffrorum*).

The seed heads are clipped before they mature to prevent reseeding the following year. The high stubble is left standing. It makes a protective mulch in which to seed a permanent cover.

Seeding these rapid-growing species as sand-stillers has not been successful on the inland dunes in the Western States because of the Mediterranean (rather than continental) climate. Seeding for initial sand-stilling is not successful on any of the coastal dunes because of the continual wind, whose velocities exceed 15 miles an hour.

Sand-stilling grasses such as the American and European beachgrass and Volga wildrye are planted as clones or culms rather than by seeding, because the winds cause the sand to shift too much to permit the establishment of seedlings. (A clone is a single stalk taken from a clump; it can produce a new clump.)

Plantings on coastal or lake dunes will usually start if a foredune (or "barrier" dune) that will stop the sand is established as near the water line as possible rather than let it continue to blow inland.

Planting on these dunes is in spaced hills rather than as a broadcast planting. Spacing of hills and number of culms to a hill vary. When the sand slopes to be planted are gentle, spacing of hills should be 18 by 18 inches, with 5 culms to a hill. On steep slopes, road cuts, and on the foredune, spacing should be 12 by 12 inches, with 3 culms to a hill. On protected, flat areas, a spacing of 24 by 24 inches, with 5 culms to a hill, will be close enough. Wider spacing will cause the planting to scour out, and loss will

occur. Culms must be planted 12 to 14 inches deep for good survival and effectiveness against wind.

An example of the costs of planting stock and the planting operation is the rates paid in the Siuslaw district of Oregon in 1956. Planting stock of European beachgrass cost 1.75 dollars for 1 thousand culms (95 thousand culms are used to an acre for an 18 by 18 inch planting of 5 culms to a hill). Planting by hand was contracted at 80 dollars an acre for 18-inch planting. Planting by machine has required approximately 18 man-hours and 3 tractor-hours an acre, compared to 80 man-hours for hand planting.

Good, vigorous, clean, and carefully graded stock is essential. All dead trash should be cleaned from the culms. Underground stems are broken back to one or two nodes. The long tops should be cut off, for they serve no useful purpose and cause excessive evaporation. The culms should be about 20 inches long when ready for planting.

In trials and field plantings at Warrenton, Oreg., maximum temperature and not precipitation determined the survival of European beachgrass. Survival of plants in 50 percent or more of the hills was always obtained when maximum temperatures for the 72 hours following planting did not exceed 55° F. Survival was always less than 50 percent when maximum temperatures exceeded 60°. Between the two temperatures survival was erratic. A survival of 50 percent or more is necessary for stilling eroding dune sand.

AMERICAN BEACHGRASS is much less sensitive to environmental factors than the European beachgrass. Successful dune plantings on the Pacific coast can be made with American beachgrass any time between early fall and late spring. Volga wildrye should be planted when maximum temperatures are under 55°.

The best survival of these plants on the Great Lakes and Atlantic coast dunes was when they were planted between the time the grass matures in the fall and the ground freezes. The period of planting may be extended until growth starts in the spring in places where the ground does not freeze.

Plantings for sand stilling should be fertilized as soon as growth starts in the spring. Nitrogen at the rate of 40 pounds an acre must be applied to insure success. Inorganic fertilizers, such as ammonium sulfate, have been more successful than organic fertilizers.

Seedings for sand stilling on the inland dunes in the Great Plains are made with regular farm equipment at the same time as regular crop seedings of the same species are made.

ARTIFICIAL BARRIERS can be used to stabilize temporarily the dune sands that cannot be planted effectively. The barriers include oil, clay, gravel, picket fence, brush, and hay.

Emulsified asphalt has been used in emergencies by several State highway departments. The North Carolina State Highway and Public Works Commission used AE-5 emulsified asphalt cut to 25 percent asphalt emulsion and 75 percent water and applied at the rate of 0.4 gallon the square yard. The application penetrated the sand 1 inch and did not crust. Heavier concentrations of asphalt crusted. Seedings made under the lighter application germinated and grew, but they failed under crusts.

The concentration of the emulsified asphalt depends on climatic conditions. The higher temperatures require lighter concentrations for penetration without crusting. A danger exists of burning seedlings in sands treated with asphalt because sand and asphalt become extremely hot from the rays of the sun. Hot crude oil sprayed on the unstilled sand has been used as a temporary stilling agent in several of the arid or semiarid dune areas.

Clay is effective, but it is expensive. Blankets of clay 4 to 6 inches thick are spread over the unstable dune sand. Permanent seedings or plantings can then be made.

Gravel or crusher waste was used by the Corps of Engineers on a railroad relocation near McNary Dam in Oregon and Washington. Sand dunes with slopes flatter than 1 to 3 can be stabilized with relatively small amounts of material. The important thing is to make complete coverage with materials not subject to movement by the wind. A 2-inch cover was used on 1:3 slopes. A 4-inch cover should be used on steeper slopes. This work cost 400 to 645 dollars an acre.

Picket fences have two primary uses. Located approximately at right angles to the prevailing winds, they cause temporary deposits of sand. Located at a tangent to the prevailing winds, they direct the sand-laden wind and may cause sand scouring.

Picket fences were used on the Clatsop Plains dune area at the mouth of the Columbia River in Oregon to build up a foredune. Two parallel lines of fence 30 feet apart were needed to get proper and stable shape in the dune. (This distance between fences may not be the same in other localities; the size of the sand particles and the velocity of the winds determine the spacing.) The pickets were 4 feet long and made from 1 x 4-inch lumber. The openings between pickets was equal to the width of the picket. A smaller space caused scour along the fence. A greater space allowed the wind to move sand through the fence unstilled. The top of the picket fence should be even, because unevenness at the top causes the dune to be uneven.

Commercial snow fence of the picket type can be used if it does not cause the dune to be higher than the fence before planting. Snow fence is almost impossible to raise because all pickets are wired together in 50- or 100-foot lengths.

Brush matting sometimes is used to stop sand blowing. A surface mulch on the sand serves as a temporary check against sand movement. Brush was used in Michigan and Vermont on small blowouts when beachgrass was not obtainable. Rows of brush are laid with the butts toward the prevailing wind. Tops are laid over the butts of adjoining rows, like shingles. Permanent plantings of trees are set into the brush mat.

Brush mats have been of little value on dunes on the Pacific coast because winds have velocities of 40 to 50 miles an hour or more. Scouring or deposition of sand takes place as soon as the mat begins to deteriorate.

Hay can be used as a temporary mulch on blowouts or small areas of dune sand at road cuts, around dwellings, and in other disturbed areas. Permanent seedings or plantings must be made as soon as the weather is suitable because the hay mulch deteriorates very rapidly. The hay provides some organic matter, which is critically needed for successful dune plantings. Fire is a hazard when mulches are used.

Artificial barriers are only temporary measures.

THE ESTABLISHMENT of permanent vegetation is the final objective in the stabilization of dunes. The climax species of plants or species in common use in the area are best for the purpose. If grasses are the climax vegetation, a mixture of the right grasses will do the best job. If woody plants are the climax, the adapted species of trees and shrubs, properly managed, will provide the best permanent cover. The best adapted native species are found near the area of use and should therefore be considered for plantings.

Successful establishment of permanent vegetation is begun after the sand has been stilled.

Trees can be planted safely on Cape Cod 2 or 3 years after beachgrass is established. Various species of pine 3 to 5 years old and spaced 3 x 3 feet apart have been successful. They are Scotch pine (*Pinus sylvestris*), Mugho pine (*P. mugo*), Austrian pine (*P. nigra*), and pitch pine (*P. rigida*). The two native shrubs that have been transplanted successfully are southern bayberry (*Myrica cerifera*) and beach plum (*Prunus maritima*).

At Cape Hatteras in North Carolina,

after moving sand dunes were stopped by planting them to sea-oats, beachgrass, adapted shrubs, and trees were planted for permanent cover.

At Fort Macon, N. C., a fair to good cover of sea-oats, sea panicgrass, broomsedge (*Andropogon virginicus*), hoary milkpea (*Galactia mollis*) and trailing wildbean (*Strophostyles helvola*) was reported 2 years after planting.

On the gulf coast of Texas, seacoast bluestem (*Andropogon littoralis*), weeping lovegrass (*Ergrostis curvula*), and Veldtgrass (*Ehrharta calycina*) gave good stands when seeded in mulched dunes.

Stilled sands in the Great Lakes region are planted to jack pine (*Pinus banksiana*), Scotch pine, or pitch pine, spaced 4 x 5 feet, or to common pasture grasses, such as smooth brome (*Bromus inermis*) and orchardgrass (*Dactylis glomerata*), depending on the choice of the farmer.

A permanent cover is established on the inland dunes of the Great Plains by seeding into sorghum stubble such native grasses common to the area as Indiangrass (*Sorghastrum nutans*), switchgrass (*Panicum virgatum*), Canada wildrye (*Elymus canadensis*), sand bluestem or "turkeyfoot" (*Andropogon hallii*), big bluestem (*A. gerardi*), little bluestem (*A. scoparius*) and side-oats grama (*Bouteloua curtipendula*).

The best seeding time is in spring when soil moisture and rainfall are favorable for germination and growth.

Mowing is necessary to eliminate competition with weeds.

Along the west coast at the mouth of the Columbia River in Oregon and southward, a combination of native and commercially available species was used for final control. Tall fescue (*Festuca elatior var. arundinacea*) and Clatsop fescue (*F. rubra*), a local strain developed from native stands of red fescue, provided the sod cover. Hairy vetch (*Vicia villosa*) aided in the establishment of grasses by protecting them from sand blast and drying winds. Purple beachpea (*Lathyrus japonicus*) provided the long-lived legume in the mixture needed for furnishing nitrogen to the grasses. Seedings were made in the early fall when moisture was favorable and the temperatures were moderate.

More lasting protection can be provided along the west coast by planting stabilized dunes to adapted shrubs and trees. Mixed plantings are recommended in order to safeguard against the complete destruction of the tree cover from an epidemic of disease or insect pests. The one shrub that is most commonly used for this purpose is Scotch-broom (*Cytisus scoparius*). It provides good protection, adds beauty to the landscape, and, being a legume, supplies nitrogen to the soil. Two species of pine are planted for final control as 2-year seedlings spaced 8 x 8 feet alternating with the Scotch-broom. Monterey pine (*Pinus radiata*) is planted on the California coastal dunes. Shore pine (*P. contorta*) is planted on the coastal dunes of Washington and Oregon.

CAREFUL MANAGEMENT is necessary when stabilized sand-dune land is used. The erosion hazards are many, and the damages resulting from misuse come about quickly and usually are severe. Delays in making prompt repair of breaks in the protective vegetative cover, whether grass or trees, can be costly.

We list seven uses and cite the precautions for each.

Recreation: Trails and roads leading through loose sand should be covered with gravel, crushed rock, or blacktop in order to prevent a serious break in the sod or other ground cover that would subject the area to blowing. Provision should be made for adequate parking, camping, and bathing facilities to prevent undue wear and destruction of ground cover.

The entire area requires protection from fire by building fire trails and by restricting smoking and fires to camp areas. Containers should be provided for disposing of papers, trash, and other material that may otherwise increase the fire hazard. Promiscuous cutting of vegetation is not permitted.

Wildlife: It is essential that an adequate cover of good food plants be maintained in order to attract wildlife. Such cover provides the needed shelter and food under which wildlife thrives. One should prevent fires and maintain trails and roads to provide access to all parts of the area for fire control.

Homes: Homes should not be built on unstable sands, such as foredunes where sand is being blown in.

When homes are being built in dune sand, proper precautions should be taken to prevent undue disturbance of existing ground cover. Access roads or trails should be surfaced promptly in order to avoid sand removal and deposition around buildings. Breaks in the sod should be repaired at once.

Woodlands: Woodlands on dunes provide fuel, posts, and pulpwood. Dunes with a good understory furnish Christmas greenery, such as salal, swordfern, cascara, huckleberry, and bearberry.

If seed trees of climax species do not occur nearby, they should be included in the composition to assure greater permanence by supplying the necessary seed for reproduction. One should give them proper protection by preventing fires, building trails, and regulating the cutting of trees.

Watershed cover and storage: The open texture of dune sand permits the ready intake of water without serious runoff. Stabilized dunes therefore act as reservoirs. Thus the Sandhills of Nebraska, for example, regulate streamflow by supplying water for domestic and irrigation use steadily throughout the growing season. The maintenance of a good cover prevents clogging stream channels with sand and debris and facilitates the infiltration of water.

Special crops: The growing of special crops can be considered only on azonal soils where the soil profile has begun to develop—a condition that exists only in dune troughs or the more level lowlying flats between the stabilized dunes. This use is not recommended, but the pressure for land may be such that these lands are used for growing such crops as bulbs, cultivated blueberries, and cranberries.

Green manure crops help to maintain the organic matter and productivity of the soil. They also protect the soil during the time of year when the crop leaves the ground bare. To get high yields and enough cover to keep the surface from eroding, green manure crops should be fertilized. One should cultivate only as necessary to control weeds. Rotations for other than bog crops should include grasses and legumes in rotation. Windbreaks are necessary for adequate soil protection if such lands continue in cultivation.

Grazing: Pastures and ranges on dunes must be grazed carefully in order to keep the surface protected at all times. Every good pasture and range management practice is necessary to keep the range or pasture in good condition. Proper attention should be given to stocking rates, rotation and deferred grazing, and the placing of salt to avoid concentration of livestock at watering places and to aid in better distribution. Trailing to water and salt on the dune ranges should not be permitted.

The blow areas should be repaired promptly before they get larger and spread. The bottoms of haystacks or hay cut when the seed is ripe are used as mulch for stabilizing such danger spots; they should then be covered with brush to keep livestock out.

STABILIZED DUNES are managed primarily for recreation and for their esthetic value and for the protection of more valuable agricultural land, including forests, highways, harbors, military installations, resorts, towns, and cities.

Sand dunes must be stabilized and properly managed in order to control shifting sands permanently. Without proper management, there is grave danger of losing all the money and effort that has been invested in stabilization. For the most part, they should remain in ownership that provides for the enjoyment of the greatest number of people and without damage to the vegetation on them.

Soil Management and Insect Control

Walter E. Fleming

Insects are the chief rivals of man for the available food of the world. Intensive agriculture, in which a few kinds of plants may occupy the land in nearly pure stands, provides abundant food and a favorable environment for the insects that attack those crops.

Many insects pass part of their life in the soil. The damage they do to plants by chewing or sucking on the roots and underground parts of the stems may not be noticed until the crop has suffered.

The noxious insects in the soil may be divided into four general groups on the basis of the time they spend in the soil and the kinds and parts of plants they attack.

Examples of these groups are:

1. The white grubs and wireworms that live in the soil for 1 to 3 years and chew the roots and underground stems of a wide variety of plants during the growing seasons.

2. The pale western cutworm and the glassy cutworm, which appear in the spring and attack nearly all plants, except those with hard, woody stems.

3. The root and the seed maggots that appear in the field after the crop is planted but generally are quite restricted in the kinds of plants attacked.

4. The plum curculio, the flea beetles, the sweetclover weevil, and the grasshoppers that spend much of the year below the surface of the soil but

do part or all of their damage by feeding aboveground.

The management of soil to control many kinds of insects must be based on a knowledge of their life history and habits. An operation that is effective against one kind of insect might be useless against a closely related kind because of the differences in their cycles of development or behavior.

Tillage, crop rotation, time of planting, fertilization, irrigation, and field sanitation help in our fight against noxious insects. Good husbandry reduces the possibility of infestation by soil-inhabiting insects but does not always control it. A good soil insecticide also may be necessary.

CROP ROTATION often helps reduce damage by insects that attack only a few kinds of plants.

Growing plants of any given kind on the same land year after year produces a condition favorable to the insects that attack that crop.

Chinch bugs are controlled by planting legumes or other immune crops in place of corn, wheat, barley, oats, or rye. A rotation to avoid two successive crops of corn on the same land will do much to prevent injury by the corn root aphid, the seed-corn maggot, the northern corn rootworm, the southern cornstalk borer, and the sugarcane beetle. A 4-year rotation of corn, soybeans, small grain, and clover is recommended in the North Central States to control the European corn borer.

Planting pastureland the first year of cultivation to crops other than corn, rice, or potatoes tends to prevent damage by sod webworms, whitegrubs, wireworms, and cutworms.

A cropping system of wheat following wheat favors an increase in infestation by the hessian fly, the false wireworm, the winter grain mite, the wheat jointworm, the wheat stem sawfly, and the wheat strawworm. This cycle of wheat may be broken by planting oats, buckwheat, corn, or sorghum in fields infested by the hessian fly.

Legumes or sorghum are recommended to break the cycle for the false wireworm; corn, sorghum, cotton, or clover for the winter grain mite; rye, barley, oats, or buckwheat for the wheat jointworm; and barley, oats, flax, corn, or mustard for the wheat stem sawfly. Since wheat is apparently the only host of the wheat strawworm, any other crop will break its cycle.

Peanuts, soybeans, velvet beans, and crotalaria provide good food and cover for the adult white-fringed beetle and its grubs. The grasses, including corn and the small grains, are poor foods for the adults. When the succession of crops is a legume followed by oats, corn, and cotton, the population of grubs in the soil does not increase to the extent that much damage is done to susceptible crops.

The native white grubs and those of the Japanese beetle, the European chafer, the Asiatic garden beetle, and the oriental beetle feed on a wide range of garden and field crops and grasses and nursery plants, but they do not thrive in plantings of whiteclover, red clover, alsike clover, sweetclover, alfalfa, soybeans, buckwheat, or orchardgrass.

The proper use of legumes in the rotation cycle in cultivated fields, or in combination with grasses in pastures, reduces damage by white grubs.

The habits of wireworms differ in the various sections of the United States. In the irrigated areas of the Pacific Northwest, the wireworms increase in abundance in cultivated land on which truck crops are grown and in fields of sweetclover, red clover, or small grains. Pasture, if maintained for several years, is detrimental to them. Growing potatoes in short rotation with clover or grain is undesirable.

The best rotation for keeping these wireworms at a low level is 3 or 4 years of alfalfa followed by 1 year of potatoes, and 1 or 2 years of other truck crops, such as sugar beets, corn, beans, or peas. In regions east of the Rocky Mountains, wireworms thrive in land devoted to hay crops or small grains. They are best controlled by rotations that include legumes (alfalfa, sweet-clover, red clover, or soybeans) by not planting susceptible crops two successive years and by clean cultivation.

THE TIME OF PLANTING corn has a great influence on its infestation by some insects. Early-planted corn is damaged less by the corn earworm in the North Central and the Northeastern States, but in the Southern States early corn is more apt to be infested than corn planted later because other attractive plants, such as cotton, are not then available to the moths.

In the North Central and the Northeastern States, corn planted early is usually more severely infested by the European corn borer, but late corn is likely to be damaged by the second brood of the borer. Planting corn in the Southwest as late as is consistent with good agronomic practice is one of the best methods for controlling the southwestern corn borer.

In the Southeast, corn should be planted in April and May, when the southern corn rootworm is the least active. In areas where the southern cornstalk borer is common, planting somewhat later than usual may be a good way to reduce the injury it does.

Early plantings of corn and sugarcane in the Southern States are injured less than late plantings by the sugarcane beetle and by wireworms. In parts of Louisiana where sugarcane is subject to severe damage by wireworms, planting the cane as early as practical in August gives better stands than plantings made late in September or October.

Beans, corn, peas, and melons may not get past the sprouting stage if the seed-corn maggot is in the fields. Because damage by maggots occurs usually in early spring and in cool, wet soils, it is wise to delay the planting so that the seeds do not sprout until the maggots are no longer active.

A practical and effective way to avoid infestation of wheat by the hessian fly is to delay the seeding in the fall until most of the fall brood of the

fly has disappeared. By delaying the sowing, considerable damage by false wireworms, the wireworms, and white grubs also is prevented.

Early-seeded crops make considerable growth before grasshoppers hatch and withstand feeding by grasshoppers better than late-seeded crops. Well-advanced crops are less attractive to the hoppers. Barley, oats, and wheat that have headed can withstand considerable defoliation without serious reduction in the yield of grain.

The early planting of all cotton within a given area and during a short period enables the crop to attain maximum growth and fruit before some insects multiply and spread afield.

PLANTS GROWN IN FERTILE SOIL are usually hardier, healthier, and more resistant to insects than those in poor soil. Barnyard manure, green manure crops, and commercial fertilizers are of value in assisting plants to outgrow damage by insects. The fertilizing of field crops often is recommended in combating infestations of the corn root aphid, the southern corn rootworm, the hessian fly, the white-fringed beetle, the wheat stem sawfly, the sugarcane beetle, and white grubs.

An important means of controlling the bronze apple tree weevil, the shot-hole borer, the greater shot-hole borer, and the flatheaded apple tree borer is to keep the trees growing vigorously by proper cultivation, fertilizing, spraying, and pruning.

PLOWING UNDER the residues of field crops and other trash is a good practice. Plowing under infested stubble may not kill many European corn borers, but the borers subsequently crawling to the surface cannot find shelter and are killed by exposure to the weather and by natural enemies.

Plowing under remnants of sugarcane, sorghum, and corn in fall or winter in the Southern States will prevent many moths of the sugarcane borer and the southern cornstalk borer from emerging. In southern Arizona, turning the stubble under to a depth of at least 4 inches in the fall and thoroughly topworking the land keep most moths of the southwestern corn borer from emerging.

Fewer than 1 percent of the rice stalk borers live through the winter in stubble that is plowed properly in the fall.

Plowing under wheat stubble as early after harvest as practicable and destroying volunteer growth in the summer and early fall does much to destroy the hessian fly, the wheat jointworm, the wheat strawworm, the wheat stem sawfly, the black grain stem sawfly, and the European wheat stem sawfly.

Plowing under volunteer and second-growth wheat before April and seeding of quick-maturing varieties of spring wheat are recommended in Oregon in years when an outbreak of wheat stem maggot is threatened.

The destruction or killing of cotton plants as early as possible before the first killing frost by mechanical or chemical methods aids in the control of the boll weevil and the pink bollworm. Plowing under the crop residue after the stalks are cut further reduces the numbers of the pink bollworm.

TILLAGE may destroy insects in the soil when they are in a vulnerable position or stage of development.

Plowing fields in which grasshoppers have deposited their eggs may bury the eggs so deeply that the newly hatched hoppers cannot reach the surface. Plowing also may bring the eggs to the surface, where they are killed by exposure to sun and wind. Tillage also loosens the soil so that it is not suitable for grasshoppers to lay their eggs.

The pupae of wireworms, native white grubs, Japanese beetles, white-fringed beetles, the European chafer, and the sugarcane beetle are fragile and easily killed mechanically. Plowing fields that have been in small grains or early truck crops between July 15 and August 15 kills many of the pupating wireworms.

Plowing pastures in late August or early September in Virginia and earlier in areas farther south will destroy many pupae of the sugarcane beetle.

Thorough disking of the soil at 10-day intervals in June and July will kill a large proportion of the pupae of the white-fringed beetle, the Japanese beetle, the European chafer, and native white grubs.

Thorough cultivation of alfalfa fields in Arizona in the fall and winter will cover many seed pods that contain the overwintering larvae of the clover seed chalcid. The covering of the seed and the exposure to moisture causes infested seed to rot, and the hibernating larvae are destroyed.

Disking the soil in orchards at weekly intervals during May and June in Georgia and at later times farther North will kill many pupae of the plum curculio.

The injury by the hickory shuckworm to pecans can be reduced by cultivating the orchard during July and August to keep the infested nuts that drop covered with soil. The decay of the nuts in the soil prevents the larvae from developing fully.

Cultivation of vineyards in the spring to bury the overwintering cocoons of the grape berry moth with at least 1 inch of soil reduces the number of emerging moths and facilitates the control of the insect by spraying.

The corn root aphid depends on ants for its welfare. Stirring the soil before planting disturbs the colonies of ants and scatters and kills the aphids so that corn and cotton may make substantial growth before the ants and the aphids can become reestablished. Infested fields that are to be replanted to corn should be plowed and disked after March 15 in the latitude of central Indiana and Illinois. Plowing and disking in the fall kills many of the aphids, destroys weeds upon which they live, and prevents ants from forming new colonies. The number of aphid eggs carried over the winter is reduced considerably thereby.

Elimination of food plants by tillage controls some insects.

Young orchards containing alfalfa or clover as cover crops are subject to attacks by several species of treehoppers, among which the buffalo treehopper, the green clover treehopper, and the dark-colored treehopper are the most injurious.

Clean culture in the orchard is the most obvious and practical method for controlling these treehoppers. In the Red River Valley, the prairie grain wireworm can be starved out by summer fallowing at least once in 4 years. Summer fallowing tends also to reduce injury caused by false wireworms.

Injury by the southern corn rootworm and the sugarcane beetle can be reduced by practicing clean tillage of fields.

Clean culture that reduces the grassy areas along roadsides and swales may help to prevent injury by several kinds of cutworms. The pale western cutworm, a serious pest of small grains in the Great Plains, dies quickly after hatching in the early spring if, as soon as it has had a little time to feed, the newly sprouted vegetation is killed by thorough cultivation.

MOST INSECTS cannot endure prolonged drying of the soil, but only in a few sections of the country can this procedure be used as a control measure.

In the irrigated fields west of the Rocky Mountains, most of the wireworms can be killed by allowing the soil to become very dry for several weeks in the summer.

If heavily infested fields can be dried once every 5 or 6 years, the populations of wireworms can be kept below the number that will cause commercial damage.

FLOODING at the proper time is a practical method for protecting cranberries from attack by some insects. Flooding the bogs over winter and holding the water until May controls the cranberry fruitworm, the southern red mite, the fall armyworm, the red-striped fireworm, and the yellow-headed fireworm in Massachusetts and New Jersey. This overwinter flooding kills the eggs of the gypsy moth laid on the bog the previous year, but to kill any caterpillars that invade the bog after the water is withdrawn, the bog is reflooded for 24 hours in late May.

After the overwinter water is withdrawn from the cranberry bogs, infestations of other insects are controlled by reflooding. Infestations of the blackheaded fireworm, the cranberry blossom worm, the green cranberry spanworm, the armyworm, the fall armyworm, the black cutworm, and the spotted cutworm are destroyed by reflooding for 10 hours. Flooding for 24 hours when the blossoms open controls the cranberry spittle bug and the cranberry black bug, but submersion for 30 hours is necessary to control the spotted fireworm. Flooding for 1 week in the fall before the worms form their cocoons will eliminate the cranberry girdler. The cranberry root grub, native white grubs, and grubs of the Japanese beetle can endure the overwinter flooding, even when the water is held until June. If the winter water is withdrawn early in the spring and the bog allowed to dry, reflooding early in May and holding the water until the middle of July usually kills most of these white grubs. The flooding will destroy the current crop, but the crop the following year usually is large enough to make up for it.

Insects on other crops can be controlled by flooding the fields in areas where irrigation is available. Most of the alfalfa caterpillars and many of the young clear-winged grasshoppers are killed in alfalfa fields in the Southwest by flooding after harvesting the crop.

Flooding sugarcane fields after harvest will reduce infestations of the sugarcane beetle and the sugarcane borer. Submerging stubble fields for the winter will kill many overwintering rice stalk borers.

Continuous submersion for 2 weeks in the summer or for a month during the winter will practically eliminate the garden centipede. Flooding infested fields in the Northwest for 6 or 7 days with 1 inch of water in extremely hot weather will kill nearly all the wireworms, but in the Everglades of Florida, flooding for periods up to 2 weeks in April, August, or September is of little value against wireworms.

It is not always possible even with the best agronomic practices to control noxious insects in the soil. It is well for the farmer to be on guard and to be prepared to supplement the cultural practices with soil insecticides.

Soil insecticides are of two main groups—fumigants, which kill insects quickly but do not persist in the soil, and the residual insecticides, which may remain in the soil for some time.

FUMIGANTS are chemicals that give off poisonous vapors. The vapors of many chemicals will kill insects, but only a few of them are of value as soil insecticides.

Among the chemicals that have shown some promise as fumigants against soil-infesting insects are carbon disulfide, chloropicrin, dichloroethyl ether, methyl bromide, a mixture of dichloropropylene and dichloropropane (D-D mixture), ethylene dichloride, and ethylene dibromide.

Carbon disulfide once was used widely as a soil fumigant, particularly against wireworms, native white grubs, and grubs of the Japanese beetle. It is seldom used now because of its explosive hazards and its low toxicity.

Chloropicrin is a highly effective fumigant against many soil-inhabiting insects, but it is intensely irritating.

Dichloroethyl ether is of value against wireworms in cultivated soil and against sod webworms in lawns. It has been applied by southern growers to the ground around peach trees to control the plum curculio.

Methyl bromide is highly toxic to many kinds of insects, but its use as a soil fumigant has been limited because in most instances a fumigation chamber or tent is required. It is used to treat soil of nursery stock infested by the Japanese beetle or by the white-fringed beetle.

The dichloropropylene-dichloropropane mixture is of value against the root-knot nematode in Hawaiian pineapple fields. It has been used to control wireworms in irrigated lands of the Pacific Northwest.

An emulsion of ethylene dichloride is applied to the ground about peach trees to control the peach tree borer. Emulsified ethylene dichloride is used also to kill grubs of the Japanese beetle in the soil about the roots of ornamental nursery stock.

Ethylene dibromide is the most effective fumigant yet found for the control of wireworms in the irrigated lands of the west coast States. One thorough, timely application of ethylene dibromide usually prevents damage by wireworms for 2 years.

A practical method of controlling the chestnut weevil is to kill the larvae in the soil by injecting ethylene dibromide. Emulsified ethylene dibromide is effective in killing Japanese beetle grubs in grasslands and in eliminating those grubs and those of the European chafer in the soil about the roots of ornamentals.

Some of the fumigants are effective in killing insects in the soil at the time of application, but they do not prevent reinfestation and are usually too costly to be of general use. Entomologists have tried for many years to develop a relatively cheap insecticide of such persistence that a single application is effective in soil for several years.

LEAD ARSENATE was the first residual insecticide to be used in the United States to control a soil-inhabiting insect. Since 1929 this arsenical has been applied as a topdressing to lawns and golf courses to prevent injury by the Japanese beetle, the Asiatic garden beetle, the oriental beetle, and some native white grubs. The treatment usually protects turf at least 5 years.

Lead arsenate is applied also to the soil about ornamental nursery stock to satisfy the requirements of the Federal quarantine on the Japanese beetle. Lead arsenate is a slow-acting insecticide. Since arsenicals poison the soil and impair its fertility, lead arsenate has never been popular as a general soil insecticide.

Topdressing lawns and golf courses with DDT protects them from damage by the Japanese beetle, the Asiatic garden beetle, the oriental beetle, the European chafer, and some of the native white grubs for 5 to 10 years. When DDT is mixed with the upper few inches of soil, the treatment is a basis for certifying nursery stock subject to the Federal quarantines on the Japanese beetle, the European chafer, and the white-fringed beetle. This treatment will clean up infestations of the Pacific coast wireworm in the irrigated lands of the Western States and will prevent reinfestation for at least 5 years. Most of the cutworms are controlled by disking DDT into the soil. Applying DDT in the furrow before planting apple seedlings, or in bands on the surface of the ground on either side of the planted stock, may control the woolly apple aphid.

Lindane and BHC are highly toxic to several soil-infesting insects, among which are the Japanese beetle, the European chafer, native white grubs, wireworms, the seed-corn maggot, and the southern corn rootworm. The use of these materials in the soil is limited because they spoil the flavor or impart a bad odor to such root crops as potatoes, sweetpotatoes, carrots, and beets.

Toxaphene has been used to a limited extent to control soil-infesting insects. Applied as a topdressing, it will protect lawns and golf courses from damage by the Japanese beetle, the Asiatic garden beetle, and the oriental beetle for 7 years. Late plantings of sugarcane in Louisiana are protected from injury by wireworms, centipedes, millipedes, springtails, and bristletails by applying toxaphene in the planting furrow. Toxaphene disked into the soil will control most cutworms. Placing the insecticide in bands along rows of corn is an effective control measure for cutworms in Iowa.

Chlordane kills insects faster than DDT or toxaphene but it may not remain effective so long in the soil. A single topdressing of chlordane will protect lawns and golf courses for 5 years from damage by the Japanese beetle, the Asiatic garden beetle, the oriental beetle, and the European chafer, and for 2 years against the imported fire ant. Crops are protected from damage by the imported and native white grubs, wireworms, and cutworms by mixing chlordane with the upper few inches of soil. Good control of the clover root curculio on alfalfa is obtained by applying chlordane before seeding the crop or late in the fall. An application of chlordane will control the cabbage maggot, the onion maggot, and the southern corn rootworm. Applying chlordane in the planting furrow is effective in controlling wireworms, centipedes, millipedes, springtails, and bristletails in fields of sugarcane, and gives promise of controlling the woolly apple aphid on the roots of young apple trees.

The insecticides developed more recently—aldrin, dieldrin, and heptachlor—are more toxic to insects than chlordane, and only very small amounts are needed to control many soil-infesting insects, among which are the Japanese beetle, the European chafer, the Asiatic garden beetle, the oriental beetle, the white-fringed beetle, native white grubs, wireworms, the false wireworm, the onion maggot, the cabbage maggot, the seed-corn maggot, the sugar-beet root maggot, the plum curculio, the clover root curculio, the sweetpotato weevil, the southern corn rootworm, the northern corn rootworm, the mole cricket, the imported fire ant, the corn root aphid, cutworms, and the grape colaspis.

The direct application of the new chlorinated organic residual insecticides to soil is advantageous in that as much as needed can be applied to control the noxious insects present or anticipated.

The promiscuous use of these materials is to be avoided, however, because excessive amounts may impair the fertility of the soil and damage the crop. The insecticide may be broadcast in cultivated fields and worked into the soil, placed in the planting furrow, or applied as sidedressings to row crops, using it in the form of a dust, or granulated formulation, alone or in combination with a commercial fertilizer, or as a dilute emulsion. The row treatments give protection to the crop but are not so effective as the broadcast treatments in the overall reduction of the insect population. The various formulations, pound for pound of insecticide, appear equally effective in the soil, when properly prepared and used.

The treatment of seed with a residual insecticide before planting is relatively new. A wide variety of seeds, including corn, cotton, small grains, beans, beets, onions, cucumbers, tomatoes, lettuce, and peas, have been treated with dusts and slurries of the new chlorinated organic insecticides. These treatments are of value in protecting the seed from injury by such insects as the seed-corn maggot, the seed-corn beetle, false wireworms, and wireworms, but they probably afford little protection to the roots of established seedlings.

Although most crops seem to endure the insecticidal treatments and do not take up readily from the soil at least some of the chlorinated organic insecticides, the Food and Drug Administration has not established tolerances for many crops grown in soil treated with these materials. Until these tolerances are established, the only safe policy for the grower is to assume that no residue is permitted on or in the crop at harvest.

Under the circumstances, farmers should follow carefully the recommendations of their county agricultural agent and their State agricultural experiment station in the use of the chlorinated organic insecticides for the control of noxious insects in the soil.

Farmers can depend also on the recommendations on the labels of the formulations in interstate commerce because these are approved by the Department of Agriculture.

Soilborne Plant Diseases

Francis E. Clark, William J. Zaumeyer, and John T. Presley

Many parasitic micro-organisms live below ground. They destroy about a billion dollars' worth of crops annually. The root rots and wilts of cotton alone cause yearly losses estimated at more than 100 million dollars. All major agricultural crops are at times seriously damaged by root diseases.

Some fungi that attack plant roots can grow only on the roots of their appropriate hosts. Others can grow in the soil even in the absence of a living root. Many of the root-inhabiting fungi can remain alive in the soil in a resting or dormant condition, sometimes for years, after the death of their host, even though they cannot multiply in the soil.

Fungi that can grow in the absence of roots are termed soil inhabiting. Usually they are not highly specialized parasites. Many of them grow readily on many kinds of organic debris. They are best known for their role in the damping-off of seedlings and as the agents responsible for plant wilts.

Identifying the causal organism or parasite is one step in dealing with a soilborne disease. You also must determine the relation of the parasite to its soil environment and the extent to which you can manage the soil to destroy the organisms that cause plant diseases.

Control measures for soilborne root

rots are of two main types—those that attempt to fortify the resistance of the plant to attack and those that attempt to inhibit or destroy the parasite.

The most economical and permanent method of controlling microorganisms that attack plants above or below ground is to develop plant varieties that resist them.

Plants resistant to many root diseases have not been discovered. Good farming practices then are valuable control measures. The judicious use of fertilizers has helped to cut down losses.

WELL-FED PLANTS usually are less susceptible to soilborne organisms than are poorly nourished plants. Good fertility may so enhance the resistance of the host plant that the parasite cannot successfully attack the roots.

Sometimes fertilizer reduces the damage by increasing the root-forming ability of the plant. In such instances the parasite readily enters and destroys individual roots, but meanwhile other roots are formed and they in turn support plant growth.

It is not always true that a fully nourished plant is less susceptible than a poorly nourished one. Crop damage by some diseases is increased by fertilizer treatment. The fertility practices required for root disease control vary so markedly for different parasites and for differing soil and farming conditions that they must be defined individually and regionally for each soilborne disease.

Nitrogen fertilization reduces the severity of some root rots and increases the severity of others. The increased resistance of sugar beets to root rot after fertilization with nitrogen seems to be associated with an excess consumption of the element and not simply with the correction of any nitrogen deficiency. The addition of nitrogen is almost as effective in fields of high nitrogen fertility as in fields with less nitrogen. The *Aphanomyces* root rot of peas also is controlled by nitrogen fertilization.

The *Pythium* root rots of cereals and sugarcane, the *Fusarium* rot of gladiolus, and the *Verticillium* wilts of many plants are aggravated by applications of nitrogen. That may be due partly to the occurrence of more turgid and thinner walled plant cells after nitrogen application and their greater susceptibility to parasitic invasion. Also involved is a disturbance of the normal nitrogen and phosphorus ratio in the plant. The nitrogen fertility of the soil needs to be kept in balance with that of phosphorus, at least as far as the *Pythium* root rots are concerned.

Phosphorus fertilization usually helps control seedling and root diseases of cereals. The more vigorous development of new roots in phosphate-fertilized plants permits the plants to escape destruction. In many places where the take-all disease of wheat is severe, good response to phosphate fertilization is sometimes obtained. Phosphates also are beneficial in controlling both *Fusarium* yellows and black root in sugar beets.

A deficiency of potassium makes many diseases more severe, presumably because plant sugars accumulate in the cells in the absence of potassium instead of being built into new tissue.

Among the few diseases that are suppressed by potash deficiency are the crown and root galls, the clubroot of cabbage, and (in some soils) the *Verticillium* wilt of cotton. Potash fertilization helps control tomato wilt, cabbage yellows, the *Fusarium* wilt of cotton, the powdery mildew of cereals, and wildfire of tobacco.

The lack of trace elements, or micronutrients, in the soil, particularly boron, copper, iron, manganese, molybdenum, and zinc, often causes abnormalities, which are known as mineral-deficiency diseases. Sometimes the plant symptoms caused by shortage of a trace element can be mistaken for symptoms caused by a parasitic organism. Usually, however, the symptoms are sufficiently unique to be recognized. Nutrient deficiencies sometimes permit damage to roots by otherwise harmless soil organisms.

The heart rot and dry rot of sugar beets, caused by too little boron in the soil, are common in parts of the United States. A breakdown of the fleshy root is the primary symptom. It is followed by the formation of a root canker, where secondary organisms may enter. A similar breakdown of the roots of table beets is called internal black spot. The disease can be controlled in most soils by disking in 12 to 20 pounds of borax an acre before the crop is planted. Soils that are neutral to slightly alkaline and high in organic matter require 40 to 60 pounds an acre. Other boron-deficiency diseases are crack stem of celery, internal brown spot of sweetpotato, internal cork of apples, top sickness of tobacco, and root necrosis of radish. Cabbage and cauliflower are also susceptible to boron deficiency.

Plant abnormalities can be listed for each of the other micronutrients. To mention a few: The typical chlorosis in many plants due to iron deficiency; chlorosis and necrosis, such as gray speck disease of oats and Pahala blight of sugarcane, due to manganese deficiency; whiptail of cauliflower, due to molybdenum shortage; and little-leaf, due to lack of zinc.

The amounts of fertilizer or spray material needed for correction in most instances are small. In some alkaline soils all one has to do is to create a neutral or slightly acid reaction by adding sulfur or an acid-forming fertilizer. Accurate diagnosis is important. An excess of any one of several nutrient elements causes toxicities, and you cannot always distinguish clearly between deficiency of one element and excess of another, particularly because the lack of one element may lead to excess accumulation in the plant of some other element.

GOOD MANAGEMENT PRACTICES are especially important in controlling a group of seedling diseases known as damping-off. The organisms that cause damping-off are widely distributed in the soil, but usually it is only in the presence of unfavorable environmental factors that their damage becomes significant.

Excessive soil moisture or an unfavorable growing condition, such as an unsuitable temperature, poor lighting, or excessive soil acidity, commonly increases the susceptibility of seedlings to the damping-off fungi. Under identical soil conditions, seedlings from seed of low vitality are more susceptible to damping-off than those that develop from good seed.

Influences of any one environmental factor may differ with the crop. Sugar beet seedlings are less susceptible to damping-off at soil temperatures below 60° F. than at 75° or 80°, but tomato seedlings are more susceptible. In common bunt of wheat, the greatest infection occurs at soil temperatures of 40° to 60°. If fall wheat is planted early in northern Idaho and eastern Washington while warm soil temperatures still prevail, the wheat seedlings largely escape infection. To the extent that marketing considerations and the length of the growing season permit, the date of seeding for each crop should be chosen to take advantage of a favorable soil temperature.

Drainage or bedding-up to eliminate excessive wetness reduces the damping-off losses of a number of field and vegetable crops. The use of soil that is well drained controls the *Aphanomyces* seedling rot of peas in the North.

Conditions of soil moisture that are ideal for plant growth also favor the fungus of the *Rhizoctonia* seedling disease of cotton. Allowing the soil to become dry at the surface simply causes the fungus attack to occur an inch or more below the surface. In extremely wet soil, the fungus causes only negligible damage. In irrigation farming, where the soil moisture can be regulated, the fungus can be controlled by planting the cotton in dry ground and then irrigating.

Water management also can be used to influence soil temperature. *Verticillium* wilt of cotton, which causes severe losses in the irrigated Southwest, is favored by low soil temperature. Incidence of the disease has been reduced by planting the crop on high ridges or cantaloup-type beds and irrigating every other middle.

Treatment of seeds with fungicides is a widely used and practical way to control damping-off. Because only the seed is treated, the cost is reasonable. A number of seed protectants are on the market. Among them are the organic mercuric formulations, such as Ceresan and Panogen; the nonmercuric organic formulations, such as Arasan, Phygon, Captan 50–W, Spergon, Dow 9B, and Vancide, 51; and the metallic inorganic compounds, such as basic copper carbonate.

Because nearly all soils are infested with the damping-off fungi, the need for protectants probably will continue or increase. Attachments for the seeding shoe that permit spraying a fungicide on the temporarily open faces of the seeding furrow are a means of providing additional protection for the emerging seedling without the expense that would be involved in drenching the entire soil.

The vascular wilts are diseases caused by free-living members of the soil flora. Soil-inhabiting fungi are commonly involved. They enter the root system, grow into the water-conducting tissues, and choke off water movement or induce excessive loss of water.

Many wilt fungi can grow on organic residues in the soil. They usually are restricted in their parasitic growth to single or closely related species of higher plants. This specificity often extends to individual varieties of plants, and outstandingly successful control of many wilts has been obtained by selection of varieties and breeding wilt resistance into them. Plant wilts can be measurably reduced in many soils by fertilization and soil-management practices, but by themselves these practices do not seem adequate to control most wilts.

The use of wilt-resistant varieties offers the most promising approach.

Good farming provides supplementary or secondary control measures.

IT IS OFTEN POSSIBLE to destroy parasitic micro-organisms in the soil. A simple and effective way is to sterilize the soil when the host plants are not growing on it. Sterilization with chemical fumigants or heat nearly always is too expensive to use in the field, but it is practical for planting beds, greenhouses, and nurseries. Treatment of field soil with chemical fumigants or with heat in amounts sufficient to kill pathogenic fungi costs up to a thousand dollars an acre, depending on depth of treatment.

Some chemical fumigants have enough lethal activity for specific parasites to effect a reasonably complete killing at dosage rates costing 100 dollars or less an acre. Fungicides and bactericides, although commonly used for direct application on seeds, cuttings, and plants, almost without exception are too expensive for direct application to soil.

A less direct, less expensive, and less efficient way to destroy parasites is to work the soil to provide such unsuitable conditions as unfavorable moisture, aeration, or reaction. Separated from plant roots, many parasitic fungi survive less well in extremely wet soil than in dry soil. Flooding sometimes can be used to promote destruction of plant parasites. The addition of sulfur to increase soil acidity or liming to produce alkalinity are sometimes useful. In some instances these practices are impractical or inadequate.

Adjusting the soil reaction provides control of some diseases. The organism that causes potato scab can persist in the soil almost indefinitely, but its development is reduced when the soil acidity reaches or exceeds pH 5.2, at which potatoes can produce a normal crop. In noncalcareous soils, such as those along the Atlantic seaboard, scab is controlled by using an acid fertilizer, such as ammonium sulfate, or by applying the proper amount of sulfur.

Development of excessive acidity is

The purposes, methods, and results of good management of soil pertain not only to owners of large acreages; they apply also to the person who tends a lawn, a backyard garden, a geranium in a pot on a window sill. Soil erosion means trouble. To the farmer, it can mean loss of soil productivity, reduced income, and crop loss—even sometimes, the need to abandon fields. To the home gardener, soil erosion means mud at the bottom of the plot, washed-out plants, little gullies where the lawn mower will get stuck, and several wheelbarrows of new soil to repair the damage. The soil conservationist would suggest that good management of land could have prevented the trouble.

The farmer has a choice of many implements with which to turn the soil and prepare the seedbed. When the weather warms, he must work fast. He must be precise in his tillage and planting so as to protect the land as much as he can. The gardener likewise stirs the soil, and where the soil slopes, he, too, will keep his rows on the contour.

The home gardener may envy the farmer who can spread manure on his fields. In the city, one has to buy fertilizer in small amounts from the hardware or seed store. Nitrogen, phosphorus, potassium, and other elements needed by growing plants must be supplied from chemical or organic sources. The farmer fertilizes to maintain the level of plant nutrients in his soil as required by the growing crop. His soil has been analyzed, and he knows how much fertilizer to apply; unfortunately many city gardeners guess. But they, too, can get their soil tested.

Good crops can be grown on hills. They do not flood out from winter storms, and the creeping cold of an early frost does not rise up so readily to kill the tender plants. We have learned to farm the slopes by plowing and planting across them. Water is caught in each contour and sinks gently into the earth, or it is led slowly across the face and released safely into waterways. Hill farming is risky but rewarding to the smart farmer and backyard gardener who understand good soil management.

Water must be brought to the soil by mechanical means in dry parts of the West. Tremendous quantities of water are applied to irrigated fields and orchards in the United States during each crop season.   The irrigation farmer builds a complex system of dams, canals, and field ditches.   Water is measured, sold, and used as a precious commodity. Only the home gardener can turn the faucet and sprinkle his plants when the urge moves him and the garden looks wilted—better still, before the plants start to wilt.   But when the rains fail and the city restricts the amount he can use for sprinkling, he, too, realizes how precious water is.

Good topsoil is full of life. Worms, insects, bacteria, and microscopic organisms live and die within the soil and enrich it with their bodies. Their food comes mostly from plants. Many farmers turn back into the soil a leguminous crop to supply nitrogen and improve tilth. They call it green manure. The city dweller collects the leaves that gave him summer shade and builds his own little soil kingdom in a compost pile that will help nourish his garden next year.

Productive surface soil cannot exist for long without protection. Uncover it, and the wind and rain may blow or wash it away. Keep it covered, and you will lose less of it and less of the moisture in it. The farmer mulches with grain straw and other material left after harvest. The gardener must buy his straw or find some suitable substitute. In his little plot, he spreads the mulch around the growing plants to keep the earth cool, save moisture, and keep weeds in check.

It is easy to touch a match to stubble in the autumn to get a clean, bare field for plowing. But a farmer, when he does that, may be creating his own little dust bowl. The city dweller, who has an urge for neatness and a liking for the smell of burning leaves, does not always recognize the value of the organic materials he is destroying. These protective coverings and soil improvers, so freely given, cannot be purchased in a store.

undesirable and harmful to some plants that follow potatoes. In limestone soils the cost of developing the acidity is prohibitive, and the changed soil reaction is unfavorable for growing other crops normally grown thereon.

In some soils in Louisiana that have a pH reaction of 5.6 or above, the soil rot disease of sweetpotato often causes severe losses. Adding enough sulfur to such soils to lower the reaction to pH 5 practically eliminates the losses.

Southern bacterial wilt has been controlled in Florida by acidifying the soil. The wilt often causes heavy losses to potato, pepper, eggplant, and tobacco in subtropical and tropical regions. The causal organism is controlled when the soil is made extremely acid (pH 3) by the use of sulfur. Such acidity is maintained during the summer when no crop plants are present. The soil is limed to about pH 5 in the fall. Liming to pH 5.5 is necessary if tomatoes or eggplants are to be grown.

The control of clubroot of cabbage, turnips, and other crucifers by liming has been practiced for a long time. Plant infection is retarded if the soil is maintained at pH 7.0 or above. The causative fungus, capable of surviving in the soil for years, forms free-swimming spores, which first infect the roots and root hairs of crucifers, readily in acid soils but not in alkaline soils.

Other diseases favored by acid soils and therefore reduced by addition of lime to the soil are the *Pythium* rots of sugar beet and alfalfa; the *Fusarium* wilts of tobacco, tomato, and cotton; and powdery scab and black wart of potatoes.

Flooding the soil destroys some soilborne parasites. Flooding *Sclerotinia*-infested fields in Florida for 6 to 8 weeks in the summer destroys the fungus. In the absence of flooding it remains viable in the soil for many years. *Sclerotinia* causes root rots of many vegetable plants.

Other agents of disease, including the virus of common tobacco mosaic, survive longer in flooded than in nonflooded soil. Flood irrigation must be avoided in the growing of safflower—otherwise the plants succumb to *Phytophthora* root rot. Subirrigation, or sprinkler irrigation carefully controlled to prevent waterlogging of the soil surface, can safely be employed.

Overirrigation must also be avoided in growing avocado on *Phytophthora*-infested soils. The lack of oxygen in extremely wet soil is more injurious to the plant roots than to the parasite.

Certain tillage methods influence the severity of rot disease by reducing the amount of contact between plant roots and disease-infested soil. In the *Rhizoctonia* disease of potatoes, which causes cankers on the tubers and stems, the lesions on the stems can be reduced by shallow planting. The tubers are placed in furrows of regular depth but are covered only lightly until plant growth is well started. The soil is then thrown to the plants. In fields where the surface soil becomes heavily infested with root parasites, an unusually deep plowing reduces plant infection.

In a field in Indiana in which wilt had previously caused almost complete loss of mint crops, nearly perfect control was obtained by means of heavy machinery that inverted and buried the *Verticillium*-infested surface soil to a depth of 30 inches. In some row crops, parasitic organisms are spread along the rows during intertilling for weed control. Sometimes it is feasible to use weedicides in place of plowing, and in such instances there is less mechanical spreading of root diseases.

CROP ROTATION is commonly used for controlling root diseases. In the absence of their host plants, root-dwelling fungi tend to die out in the soil, but they tend to build up in the presence of susceptible plants. Failure to employ crop rotation at times has led to severe losses from parasitic fungi as well as from nematodes and insects.

Crop rotation has been the management practice most widely and most successfully used in many farming systems to achieve soil sanitation. Its relative importance seems to have declined in recent years as resistant plant varieties and specific nematocides and insecticides have been developed. Alternative procedures tend to replace crop rotation when they permit the growing of economically desirable crops at shorter intervals. Some diseases whose control depends on crop rotation make it necessary to grow the susceptible crop only once in 5 to 8 years.

Some farmers believe that growing an annual crop for a number of years on the same land hurts the soil. That is not always true, because certain annual crops, such as onions or tobacco, produce as well or better in continuous culture in some localities. Nor is it invariably true that crop rotation will control all soilborne diseases.

Pathogenic organisms that can grow in the soil even in the absence of susceptible plants are little affected by crop rotation. The fungi that cause damping-off, vascular wilts, and potato scab exemplify this group. Other diseases not amenable to control by crop rotation are caused by parasitic fungi, which cannot grow in the soil in the absence of their host roots but can persist almost indefinitely in the soil because of their ability to form dormant or resting bodies like spores or sclerotia. Examples are the *Sclerotinia* that cause rots of vegetables and the clubroot parasite of crucifers.

Crop rotations are especially useful in controlling the fungi that cannot long survive in the soil in the absence of their host plants. Such organisms as those causing bacterial bean blight, anthracnose of beans, and blackleg of cabbage are controlled by 3- or 4-year rotations with other crops that these organisms do not attack.

Rotations often have been widely used to combat root diseases of tobacco—rootknot, or nematode root rot, black shank, Granville wilt, and *Fusarium* wilt—the nematode root diseases of many plants, and a miscellany of other soilborne diseases on vegetables, including black rot of carrot, *Phoma* rot of celery, black leg of crucifers, *Fusarium* wilt of watermelons, *Fusarium* basal rot of onions, *Fusarium* root rot of peas and beans, and *Verticillium* wilt of strawberries.

ANTIBIOSIS—the inhibition or destruction of one micro-organism by another—is important in the control of several root diseases. The soil teems with microscopic organisms, some of which are beneficial to plants because they make nutrients more readily available or favorably affect soil tilth. Others have no such direct effects on plants.

As these nonparasitic organisms multiply in the soil, they exert a natural biological control on many of the parasitic organisms responsible for soilborne diseases of plants. Most root parasites survive longer in soil that has few nonparasitic micro-organisms than they do in soil containing an abundant microflora. When a parasite and its host plant are introduced experimentally into a sterilized soil, the severity of disease is much greater than when ordinary members of the soil microflora are added with the parasite.

Recognition of the competitive and associative effects that micro-organisms exert on one another has led to the discovery and widespread use of antibiotics and to the development of management practices based on the intensification of microbiological interactions in the soil.

This approach is also one of parasite destruction by natural forces, the distinction being that instead of physical factors (such as heat, light, flooding, or drying), less tangible biological factors are involved.

Soil organisms check the activity of plant parasites in several ways. Sometimes they attack and consume the plant parasites. Sometimes they produce destructive toxic materials or antibiotics. In still other instances they compete more successfully for oxygen and nutrients and thus cause suffocation or starvation of the parasite. When fresh organic material, such as green manure, is added to the soil, the nonparasitic micro-organisms multiply rapidly, and whatever ill effects they exert on parasites are intensified. The significance of antibiosis in soil came to be recognized generally only a generation ago. L. H. Pammel, of the Texas Agricultural Experiment Station, who investigated Texas root rot of cotton, discovered the value of stable manure or other organic materials in controlling the disease.

Biological control has become the method of choice in dealing with the cotton root rot. Practical control of the disease is achieved in irrigated sections of the Southwest by incorporating large amounts of organic matter into the soil. The land is irrigated well before planting time. Control is achieved in nonirrigated areas by growing (and turning under) legume crops in rotation with cotton. The legumes may be grown as winter green manure crops and followed immediately by cotton, or they may be grown to maturity and the residues turned under in summer. The use of early maturing varieties of cotton and early fall plowing are recommended. The latter destroys the remaining live cotton root and so deprives the parasite of its favorite environment.

The take-all disease of wheat is susceptible to biological control if the antibiosis is accomplished during the time the soil is free of wheat. Because it is not feasible to grow green manures in many wheat areas, the application of biological control has to be limited. The take-all disease, however, can be checked in most soils by providing a balanced fertility.

The potato scab organism in heavily infested soil has been reduced by plowing under soybeans, but turning under rye, clover, peas, or barley has not been effective.

Strawberry root rot has been eliminated by incorporating several crops of soybeans, but red clover used in a similar manner has had little effect on the severity of the disease.

In the Columbia River Basin of eastern Washington, the *Fusarium* root rot disease of beans often is serious in virgin soils where beans are one of the first crops planted and are grown in consecutive years. Other fields in the same area that have been under cultivation for a number of years and on which hay or other crops have been grown for several years before beans are planted produce bean crops practically free of root rot. Such soils presumably develop microbiological properties unfavorable to the organism that causes root rot.

Copies of the following publications of the Department of Agriculture can be obtained from the Superintendent of Documents, the United States Government Printing Office, Washington 25, D. C., at the prices given: *Grass*, the 1948 Yearbook of Agriculture ($2.00); *Trees*, the 1949 Yearbook of Agriculture ($2.00); *Water*, the 1955 Yearbook of Agriculture ($2.00); Handbook 18, *Soil Survey Manual* ($3.50); Information Bulletin 99, *Conquest of the Land Through Seven Thousand Years* (15 cents); Farmers' Bulletin 1797, *Implements and Methods of Tillage To Control Soil Blowing on the Northern Great Plains* (15 cents); Information Bulletin 27, *How To Recognize Erosion in the Northeast* (15 cents); Circular 982, *Tests for Salinity and Sodium Status of Soil and of Irrigation Water* (15 cents); Handbook 60, *Diagnosis and Improvement of Saline and Alkali Soils* ($2.00); Technical Bulletin 1013, *The Occurrence of Barium in Soils and Plants* (15 cents); Handbook 61, *A Manual on Conservation of Soil and Water* (60 cents); Leaflet 394, *Facts About Wind Erosion and Dust Storms on the Great Plains* (10 cents); Information Bulletin 106, *Our Productive Land . . . We Can Conserve and Improve It While Using It* (10 cents); Leaflet 328, *Your Soil . . . Crumbly or Cloddy?* (10 cents); Circular 757, *Methods of Soil Analysis for Soil-Fertility Investigations* (15 cents); Farmers' Bulletin 1997, *Stubble-Mulch Farming To Hold Soil and Water* (10 cents); Farmers' Bulletin 2002, *For Insurance Against Drought . . . Soil and Water Conservation* (15 cents); and Farmers' Bulletin 1982, *When Drought Returns to the Great Plains* (5 cents).

Conserving Soil Moisture

Chester E. Evans and Edgar R. Lemon

Conserving the soil moisture is mostly a matter of preventing drought. But drought, like so many other natural phenomena, is a subtle process, a stubborn problem for those who seek to understand it, an occurrence that baffles exact definition.

Farmers and agronomists, to be sure, have devised methods of combating it. Even the obvious solution of adding irrigation water is empirical, for it is based more on observation and experience than on science, and the theories differ as to when and how much water should be used to prevent drought.

We all associate a deficiency of rainfall with poor crops. Some men have defined drought in terms of the number of days without rain. But 10 days without rain (or irrigation) in the humid East is not the same as 10 days without rain in the Great Plains.

Carrying the definition of drought one step farther, some have emphasized the available water in the soil and used it as a yardstick. Yet here again the amount of available water in the soil for one crop at a given location does not have the same effect as an equal amount of available water upon the same crop or a different one in another place.

We really need to ask the crop how it is feeling! Is it taking up water fast enough from the soil by its roots to satisfy the demands for water in the leaves, from which it passes into the atmosphere?

If the demand for water in the leaves is greater than the supply from the roots, then basically we have drought. The extent of the lag between supply and demand within the plant is the true yardstick of drought. It is this lag that determines the plant's efficiency in manufacturing food. Plants differ in their sensitivity to drought, but still, for any given crop, drought is basically the lag between the water uptake from the soil and evaporation of water from the leaves. We can conclude that too little soil moisture invariably prevents plants from realizing full efficiency in their growth.

The subject of conserving soil moisture must necessarily concern itself therefore with the accumulation and saving of soil moisture for efficient crop production. And to understand soil moisture conservation as a means of minimizing drought, one needs to look into the distribution and transport of water—the hydrologic cycle.

A portion of the total precipitation that reaches the ground is returned to the oceans as runoff. The remainder is returned to the atmosphere by evaporation, either directly from the earth's surface or through plant transpiration.

The soil acts as a reservoir; at any given time some water is in storage in the soil. Considerable time may elapse before this water in storage flows underground to the streams or is returned to the atmosphere by evaporation. Eventually, however, the water in storage in the soil enters the hydrologic cycle even though the amount of water in storage increases with precipitation and decreases with evaporation and transpiration. Thus conservation of soil moisture deals with the balance among precipitation, runoff, and evaporation.

IN A CASUAL OBSERVATION of the average annual rainfall distribution over the United States, one notices a gradual decrease from east to west until the Rocky Mountains are reached. Westward, a complex of humid mountain and arid intermountain patterns extends almost to the west coast. A narrow region of high rainfall is encountered along the west coast.

Nearly all of the rainfall east of the Rockies is caused by the interaction between the great cold airmasses arising in the vast Canadian Arctic and the warm airmasses arising over the Gulf of Mexico. When the Arctic air, moving southeastwardly, meets the maritime Gulf air, the cold dry air forces the warm moist air to rise and yield some of its moisture as precipitation.

The Gulf air characteristically takes a semicircular path across the Gulf up through the Mississippi Valley and out through the St. Lawrence Valley, covering the eastern United States but falling short of the Great Plains.

The dry tropical airmasses that normally flow northward across the Great Plains arise in Mexico and yield little water when they meet the Arctic air. Occasionally, however, an especially strong Gulf mass veers westward into the Great Plains, bringing brief, violent rainstorms.

These incursions are rare and erratic. Their frequency nonetheless seems to be associated with long-term variations in solar activity. People living in the Great Plains know about the higher rainfall periods of the early 1900's, the 1920's, and the 1940's and the droughts in the 1930's and 1950's. Meteorologists have observed that longtime, large-scale migrations of rainfall into the Great Plains occur during periods of high solar radiation and that migrations to the East occur when radiation is low.

Precipitation west of the Rocky Mountains usually is the result of moist Pacific airmasses rising and cooling over mountain ranges. Between the mountain ranges, however, precipitation generally is low, and irrigation is necessary to produce crops.

Average rainfall figures, we know, are deceptive. Year-to-year and month-to-month variations from the normal are the rule, not the exception. Nevertheless, normal figures have to be used as a yardstick to tell us in general what

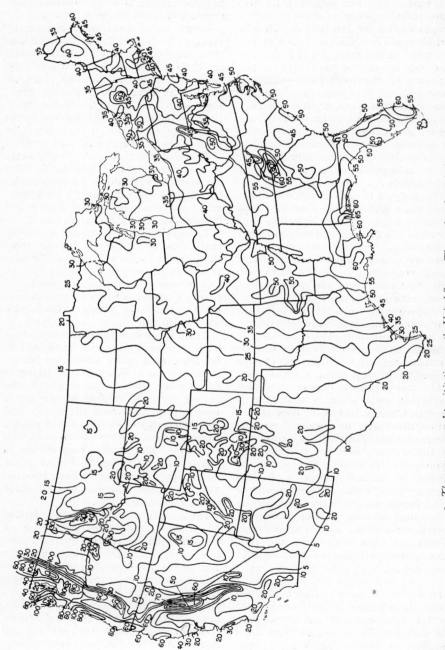

1. The average annual precipitation over the United States. The numbers denote inches.

type of climate a region has. We need also to know the variations that are included in the normal.

Probably the relative variations from normal rainfall determine to a large degree the importance of soil moisture conservation. In the arid West, for instance, the farmer knows what to expect and plans accordingly by developing irrigation. In the humid East, variation in rainfall is relatively small.

Here, too, the farmer can plan with fair assurance and can even use irrigation. Farmers of the subhumid and the semiarid regions, however, must expect wide departures from the "normal" rainfall. It is in this region of erratic rainfall that conservation of soil moisture often means the difference between a crop and a crop failure.

OF THE RAINFALL that reaches the ground, the amount that enters the soil is important. We are still limited in our ability to modify rainfall. We still have to take it as it comes. Infiltration and runoff are highly responsive to management.

For runoff to occur, rainfall must exceed in intensity and volume what the soil, vegetation, and land surface will absorb and retain. The slope, the nature of the soil, its depth and condition, the nature of the cover, the nature of the storm, and the season in which it occurs determine the amount of water taken into the soil.

The soil characteristics that play a major role in infiltration are the size of pores, the total volume of space unoccupied by water, and the stability of the pores during a storm. The size of the pores largely depends on the size and arrangement of the particles that make up the soil. The size and arrangement of the soil particles we call structure. Soils with large pores and good structure have a rapid infiltration rate if they are not filled with water.

A soil that during the early stages of a storm has large pores and a favorable structure for rapid infiltration may lose its favorable structure during the course of the storm by the melting or slaking down of the particles. Closing the pores during this process obviously does not favor infiltration. One has to take into account the prior history of tillage and cropping systems in order to evaluate the infiltration response in terms of stability of soil structure. The cover that is on the land also has a marked influence on the deterioration of soil structure and infiltration.

The characteristics of the individual storm and the season in which it occurs influence infiltration and runoff. Certain combinations of intensity and amounts of rainfall are important in this respect. The size of the raindrops and their impact upon the ground affect infiltration and runoff. The form of precipitation, either as rain, snow, or hail, is important, too.

Perhaps the season when precipitation occurs determines the success of saving and storing soil moisture more than any other factor. Soil temperatures are important. Less water will enter the soil when it is cold than when it is warm. Wet, frozen soils have low infiltration rates. You should not conclude, however, that rain that comes during the warm months is stored more efficiently. For instance, torrential storms yielding high runoff occur in warm months. Rapid evaporation in the southern Great Plains in the summer takes a heavy toll; winter precipitation is more efficiently stored.

A farmer can take action in three general ways in order to maximize infiltration to his best advantage. He can alter the surface of the soil to increase infiltration rates as the rain falls. He can provide more time for water to infiltrate during and after precipitation by mechanical measures. He can manage his cropping system to take advantage of the seasonal rainfall distribution. These we discuss in detail later.

THE LOSS OF WATER from the soil through direct evaporation or plant transpiration depends on two related phenomena—the water available in the soil and the evaporative demand created by meteorological environment.

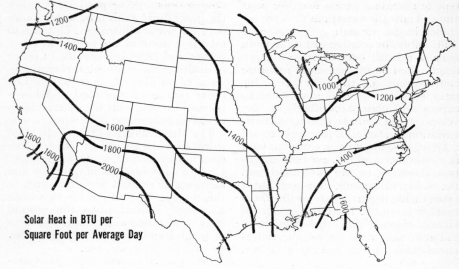

Solar Heat in BTU per
Square Foot per Average Day

2. The distribution of solar energy over the United States.

In the transfer of liquid water in the soil to water as vapor in the atmosphere, two conditions have to be met. Energy has to be supplied to convert water from a liquid to a gas, and there has to be a mechanism of transfer. Let us consider the energy relations first.

The sun is the original source of energy involved in the conversion of liquid water to a vapor. The drawing illustrates the distribution of solar energy over the United States for an average day.

Not all this incoming radiant energy is absorbed. A part of it is reflected back to space. Snow, for instance, reflects a large part of the sun's energy. Darker surfaces, such as green leaves, may absorb as much as 80 percent. Soils absorb somewhat less.

Even though most crops have visible differences in color, they all absorb about the same percentage of the radiant energy supplied by the sun. After we deduct the energy that is reflected and radiated back to space, the absorbed or net radiation is then divided into three parts. The energy absorbed in the plant tissues or the soil surface can go toward heating the air, heating the soil, and evaporating water. It is

the apportioning of the net radiation absorbed by the surface in question that is the critical part of the energy budget.

The manner in which this absorbed energy from the sun is divided among heating the air, heating the soil, and evaporating water depends on how much water is available for evaporation. This partition of the net radiation then depends indirectly on rainfall and irrigation, but more directly on the ability of the soil to offer up water for evaporation and transpiration.

If rainfall is low and, as a consequence, soil moisture is not readily available for evaporation and transpiration, a large share of the absorbed energy goes toward heating the air and a much smaller part toward heating the soil. On the other hand, if rainfall is high or soil moisture is readily available for evaporation and transpiration, a large share of the energy available will go toward converting liquid water to a vapor and a very much smaller amount will go toward heating the soil.

The third diagram demonstrates the way in which the available energy absorbed by a growing crop is primarily apportioned as the available moisture in the soil decreases.

As the soil dries, the percentage of net radiation going toward evaporation gradually falls. Because only a minor part of the heat budget involves heating the soil, most of the energy that does not go toward evaporation will go toward heating the air. As a result, air temperatures will rise as the available soil moisture decreases.

Normally during the daytime, the air is heated somewhat, even when evaporation is high. That means that the energy being used for evaporation is somewhat less than the available energy coming from the sun. That will not always be true, however, where "oases" are created by irrigation or by local rains. Then we have a wet area surrounded by a dry area. Evaporation will be low in the drier surroundings, and heating of the air will be considerable. When such hot, dry air reaches the wet area—the "oasis"— some of the heat in the air will be used for evaporation where water is available. Then the air will be cooled as it passes over the freely transpiring crop or wet soil. Now the energy used for evaporation exceeds the energy absorbed from the sun, since additional energy used in evaporation is gained from hot air transported from another region.

The fourth illustration shows the apportionment of energy used for evaporation within an oasis as the soil outside the oasis dries. The extent of the "oasis" effect would depend on differences in available soil moisture inside and outside the oasis as well as the size of the oasis. You can well imagine that this phenomenon can apply to areas of considerable size.

Two conditions have to be met in the evaporation process: Energy has to be supplied, and some mechanism of transfer has to be provided. We have already discussed the sources of energy and their relation.

The transfer of water can best be considered now in two parts. First, water in the liquid or gaseous form has

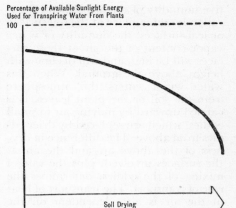

Percentage of Available Sunlight Energy Used for Transpiring Water From Plants

3. The relationship between dryness of the soil and the percentage of available sunlight energy used for transpiring water from plants.

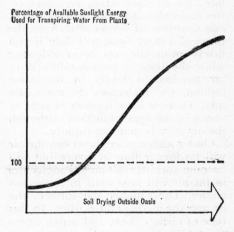

Percentage of Available Sunlight Energy Used for Transpiring Water From Plants

4. The relationship between dryness of the soil outside an oasis and percentage of available sunlight energy used for transpiring water from plants growing within an oasis.

to be transported from the soil reservoir directly to the soil surface or indirectly through the crop to the leaf surfaces. The water vapor then has to be transported from these surfaces into the atmosphere. Let us consider the latter phenomenon first.

Besides the energy aspects—sunlight and temperature—evaporation also is influenced by the wind and the relative humidity of the air. When evaporation is taking place at the soil surface or leaf surfaces, the humidity or water vapor content of the air at those surfaces will be high and will decline with height above the ground. When this water vapor enters the atmosphere from the soil or the plant leaves, it is carried upward by moving air in small eddies, which are replaced by drier eddies from above. The difference in dryness of the above air and the air at the surfaces involved, plus the rate of mixing of the eddies, determines the rate of transport. The transport of heat in the air is also dependent on the mixing of the eddies. Before leaving the subject of eddie transport, a few additional words should be given to its mechanism of operation.

If wind is flowing over a smooth surface, an airplane wing, for instance, the molecules of the air will slide over one another in layers—much as the pages of a large book will slide if you firmly push the top cover sideways while the book lies on a table. With air moving in layers in the same fashion, the molecules do not easily mix. There is little transfer of heat or vapor in this type of airflow, although the air may be moving rapidly.

On a rough surface, however, the air will no longer flow in layers, but will become turbulent. The gas molecules in the air will now swirl in numerous eddies. The rougher the surface, the greater the mixing and swirling. In this type of airflow, heat and water vapor are readily transferred, even though the wind speed may be fairly slow. Theory of turbulent transport predicts that the change in wind speed with height above a surface determines this rate of mixing. Thus the rate of transport of water vapor from the soil or plant leaves should depend on the surface roughness of the soil or the height that a crop extends above the soil. We have meager field information concerning this phenomenon.

So far we have concentrated on the meteorological aspects involved in evaporation and transpiration. The transport of liquid and gaseous water in the soil and the plant is subject, of course, to plant and soil characteristics. These, too, then have an important part in governing evaporation and transpiration.

If we return now to the third illustration, we can see the manner in which plant transpiration drops as the soil dries out. The exact shape of this curve and the numerical quantities involved depend on a host of soil and plant characteristics, as well as meteorological ones.

The rate of drying of a soil where plants are growing depends on how widely the plant roots explore the soil, the amount of water in the soil, and the ability of the soil to give up that water to the roots.

Sandy soils, for instance, have a low water-holding capacity but release most of that they do hold fairly easily. Soils with more clay have a higher ability to hold water but release a greater portion of it less readily. Often the wider distribution of roots in sandy soils offsets to some extent their lower water-holding capacity. Shallow soils, soils that have compacted layers, or soils in otherwise poor physical condition will restrict root exploration and thus will offer only a limited water supply as far as the plants are concerned. Many cultural practices encourage greater root exploration by improving soil structure.

Our understanding of the suppression of direct evaporation from the soil leaves much to be desired. Despite many statements about saving soil moisture by slowing evaporation, we have little substantial proof that any practices we now use are effective in slowing down direct evaporation of soil moisture.

Let us take a brief look at what we know now about the process of direct evaporation of moisture from the soil.

The fifth illustration demonstrates the way in which the evaporation rate at the soil surface decreases with drying. In the first stage of drying (the level portion of the curve), the pores

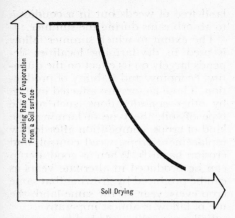

5. *The relationship between rate of evaporation from a soil surface and the dryness of the soil.*

between the soil particles are essentially full of water, and loss of moisture results in thinning of the water films separating the soil particles. In this stage, capillary flow of liquid water to the surface is enough to meet the evaporative demand of the aboveground meteorological conditions. The first stage ends when the soil begins to develop a distinct dry layer at the surface. This critical point appears as a distinct break in the curve. The mechanisms of soil moisture flow become more complex in the second stage of evaporation of soil moisture. Here the aboveground conditions are no longer so important, while soil factors assume a dominant role in governing the slower rate of moisture flow to the surface.

Experiments have demonstrated that the faster the drying during stage one, the further to the left the critical point falls. This mechanism appears to be a natural one for conserving moisture where evaporation rates are high.

Rapid drying of the surface creates a "self-mulching" and lowers subsequent evaporation. With subsequent drying after reaching the critical point, it is believed that the simple liquid flow due to capillarity gradually gives way to vapor flow in the empty pores as a mechanism of transport. Vapor flow is much slower than liquid flow.

A variety of management practices that have special significance in making better use of precipitation for maximum sustained production of crops has evolved from research studies and farmers' experience. Not all practices, even though gaining widespread acceptance at one time, have been successful in conserving soil moisture. A notable example is the dust mulch.

THE DUST MULCH was an early misconception of a way to conserve moisture in the soil. It was assumed that a finely pulverized surface soil condition, created by tillage, would greatly reduce the loss of moisture by evaporation. Cultivation of the soil was advocated after every rain to prevent movement of the moisture to the soil surface, where it would be lost by evaporation. Lending support to the theory were the experiments of F. H. King in Wisconsin about 1890, which showed that water would rise in a tube filled with soil in contact with water in a pan.

A more complete understanding of the factors involved in moisture movement in soils led to the abandonment of the dust mulch as a moisture-saving practice. The observation that soils of the drier areas in the Great Plains did not contain a water table had a definite bearing on discounting the dust mulch. In the absence of a water table, King's classic concept of water rise was no longer applicable, because the soil was not in contact with "water in a pan." Moreover, in soils without a water table, moisture moves downward into the drier subsurface layers as readily as it moves upward into dry surface soils.

When it was shown that evaporation losses from surface soils occur at rapid rates following precipitation and (for all practical purposes) cease before the soil becomes dry enough to permit cultivation, working the soil after each rain had little merit except to control weeds.

The dust-mulch theory had indirect support in that the cultivation necessary to form a finely pulverized surface also was an effective way to control weeds. The moisture saved by eliminating weeds was erroneously credited to the dust mulch. Although S. Barnes in western Canada in the summers of 1931 and 1935 found that 29.5 percent of the rainfall was conserved where a soil mulch was maintained, as compared to 26.4 percent without mulching, he concluded that the type of surface condition left by a tillage machine is not so important from a moisture conservation standpoint as is its efficiency in controlling weeds.

A fuller knowledge of the several factors involved has led to a reduction in the number of cultivations required for preparing the soil for growing crops. Pulverizing the surface soil is not very effective in reducing evaporation losses. A finely divided surface soil seals over under the impact of raindrops, thus causing a lowering of water infiltration and a consequent increase in runoff and soil loss. Cultivation breaks down clods, which resist wind erosion. The increasing use of chemicals for weed control has lessened the need for cultivating soils for that purpose. Probably the best reason favoring fewer cultivations is that of lowering production costs.

Although surface mulches of dust are no longer recommended, other practices that came into prominence about the same time as the dust mulch have gained full acceptance and have become an essential part of farming systems in areas of limited and highly variable precipitation. Probably the most important is the specialized moisture storage practice known as summer fallow.

SUMMER FALLOW as applied to dry-farming areas refers to keeping the land free of vegetation during one crop season in order to store moisture for crop production the following season. The commonest method of handling fallow is to permit the stubble from a crop to stand over winter, to till the soil in the spring before weeds have removed much water, and to keep the land free of weeds but in a condition to absorb rains during the summer.

The extent to which summer fallow is used in dry-farming localities depends largely on its effect on the quantity, economy, and stability of production. Those factors are affected in turn by other considerations, such as the type of soil, the type of farming, the kind of crops, competition afforded by replacement crops, weed control, and erosion hazards. When as good a crop can be produced in alternate years as can be produced by growing that same crop every year on the same land, the use of fallow is almost imperative.

Fallow is still a desirable practice when considerably less than equal total production is attained, because it is cheaper to keep part of the land in fallow and part in crop than to grow a crop on all of the land.

The use of fallow has other advantages. Production tends to be stabilized in that complete crop failures under a fallow system of farming are less frequent, even though production totals may be unaffected. Weeds, plant diseases, and insects usually can be controlled more effectively under a system of farming when land is fallowed periodically. Erosion by wind and water, on the other hand, is more likely in the crop-fallow system, as compared with continuous cropping. The danger of erosion can be lessened by keeping as much vegetation as possible on the surface of the land. The safest method for land susceptible to erosion is to use subsurface tillage implements of the sweep or blade types and delay the first operation until the spring following harvest.

Examined in another light, summer fallow becomes necessary when other management practices fail to provide sufficient moisture for sustained economic production of crops. In this sense, then, summer fallow is a practice by which moisture is stored in soils for later use by plants. Although some moisture storage above plant requirements is possible when the crop is growing, most of the additions in the dryland area occur during the periods when the crop is not on the land.

Although summer fallow is a means of storing moisture in the soil for later use by crops, it is very inefficient in conserving moisture. Usually only about one-quarter of the rainfall that comes during the fallow season is stored in the soil for future crop use. Water losses by evaporation from clean-tilled fallow land are high. Small amounts are lost by runoff. Water losses by transpiration by weeds often are large.

THE EFFICIENCY of the summer fallow practice in storing moisture varies with soil and environment. For example, S. Barnes at Swift Current, Saskatchewan, found the efficiency of moisture storage during the summer fallow period to be 29.7 percent. As this experiment was conducted in tanks, there was no runoff. The weeds were pulled from the soil by hand, and the soil surface was kept in the best possible condition to absorb moisture.

On field plots at the same location where the same positive control of weeds, runoff, or deep percolation was not exercised, W. J. Staple and J. J. Lehane reported a moisture storage efficiency of only about 21 percent. Swift Current is in the spring wheat area. The fallow period starts after wheat harvest in August and continues until wheat seeding time in April, some 20 to 21 months later. Although this fallow period is somewhat longer than that experienced at more southerly locations, and as such would not favor high storage efficiency, the prevailing cooler temperatures are more favorable for moisture storage.

At the Northern Great Plains Field Station near Mandan, N. Dak., where the average annual precipitation of about 16 inches is about 1 inch higher than that at Swift Current, J. C. Thysell reported a moisture storage efficiency during the summer fallow period of 20 percent as an average for a 19-year span ending in 1934. The length of the summer fallow period was about the same as that at Swift Current, since here again spring wheat was the crop grown in alternate years. The gently sloping land on which the field experiment was conducted permitted little or no runoff. Small losses of water by runoff and the possibility of percolation of water below sampling depth, however, may have been responsible for a lower moisture storage efficiency at Mandan than in the tank studies at Swift Current. The most efficient storage was during the first winter when the stubble was present to catch snow.

Moisture storage efficiency of only 15 percent was measured at the Fort Hays, Kans., station over a 40-year period. Winter wheat was grown in alternate years. The fallow period therefore was from July of one year until September of the following year—about 15 months. Storage efficiency was highest in fall, winter, and spring. It was considerably lower in summer. The mean annual temperatures in Kansas are considerably higher than those in North Dakota.

The greater evaporative demand associated with the higher temperatures accounts in large measure for the lower efficiency of moisture storage in Kansas, even though the summer fallow period is some 5 months shorter than in North Dakota. Other factors contribute to this lowered efficiency. The average annual rainfall at Fort Hays is about 23 inches—about 7 inches higher than at Mandan. The heavier rainfall and the occurrence of storms of higher intensity favor higher runoff and lower storage. Moreover, the soil-root zone is filled to capacity oftener under the higher rainfall at Fort Hays. These conditions do not favor a high moisture storage efficiency during the summer fallow period.

The rainfall distribution pattern has a marked effect on the efficiency of storing moisture during the summer fallow period. Rainfall is highest in summer in the Great Plains. The period of heaviest rainfall therefore coincides with the months when temperatures are also highest. Evaporative demand for moisture is greatest at this time and accounts for the relatively low efficiencies for storing moisture in fallow.

In contrast, A. F. Bracken and P. V. Cardon at Nephi, Utah, reported a moisture storage efficiency of about 31 percent. The period of highest rainfall there is in winter, when temperatures are lowest. Averages in 15 years (1918–1933) showed a moisture storage efficiency of 60.5 percent the first winter after harvest, for the undisturbed wheat stubble caught snow and held it on the land. The summer period that followed spring plowing had a negative efficiency of 8.4 percent, even though 4.7 inches of rain fell during this period. The moisture storage efficiency reached 25.8 percent during the winter after emergence of winter wheat.

This is an example of storing considerable moisture while a crop is growing, a situation that occurs infrequently in semiarid or arid regions. The summer period at Nephi stresses the point that an actual loss of moisture often occurs when periods of low precipitation and high temperature coincide.

Although summer fallow is inefficient in storing moisture, the relatively small amounts of moisture stored take on special significance in that crop production then becomes possible in areas otherwise too arid for growing crops successfully. Considerable data are available showing that unless a given amount of water is stored in the soil, no crop can be grown.

The minimum amount varies with the soil and environmental conditions. For example, O. R. Mathews and Lindsay A. Brown in studies with winter wheat in the southern Great Plains area of southeastern Colorado, southwestern Kansas, and the Panhandles of Oklahoma and Texas, found an average of 7.4 inches of water were required before any wheat could be realized and that each additional inch of water produced about 2 bushels of wheat. They defined inches of water as the amount of water used during the

life of the crop; that included water removed from the soil plus precipitation from seeding to harvest.

On this same basis, Dr. Staple and Mr. Lehane found that about 5 inches of water were required before any wheat grain was produced in southern Saskatchewan. Each additional inch of water used increased the yield at the rate of 3.4 bushels an acre.

Results from the two studies demonstrate the wide difference that exists in the efficiency with which stored and seasonal moisture is used by wheat and illustrate the effect environmental conditions have on efficiency of water use.

Moisture storage is the primary function of summer fallowing. Effecting more complete and positive control of weeds is also a highly important reason why the practice is widely used. Considerable saving of moisture can be accomplished if weeds are kept down.

Experiments of L. J. Briggs and H. L. Shantz of the Department of Agriculture in 1914 on the relative water requirements of plants showed that weeds require as much water to produce a pound of dry matter as other common crops adapted to the dryland conditions of the Great Plains.

A profuse growth of weeds on summer-fallowed land defeats the very purpose of leaving the land idle. Weeds continuously transpire moisture that otherwise would be stored for subsequent crops. Volunteer growth of a crop during the summer-fallow season also uses stored moisture.

WEED GROWTH often begins soon after harvest of the crop. Late summer or fall tillage would seem to be indicated to prevent weeds from using moisture. All tillage operations, even those of the subsurface blade or sweep types, however, tend to bury stubble and destroy its effectiveness in controlling wind and water erosion and in holding snow.

As a general rule, the moisture gain in preventing weed growth by cultivation in the fall is more than offset by loss of moisture from snow. The benefits in the control of wind and water erosion, as well as the savings occurring from fewer tillage operations, usually favor delaying the first tillage until the following spring.

Weed growth in spring on land to be summer fallowed, however, should be prevented, since (as we said) the winter immediately following harvest is the period primarily responsible for storing the highest percentage and normally the highest quantity of moisture. The 3-year (1951–1954) results from Swift Current, given in the table, demonstrate the effect of controlling weed growth by early spring cultivation of summer-fallow land on moisture conservation and the yield of the following wheat crop.

Treatment	Water stored in soil	Comparative wheat yield	
		Total crop	Grain
Weed growth prevented.............	Inches 5.1	100	100
First cultivation May 15..........	4.5	89	88
First cultivation June 15..........	3.6	75	78
First cultivation July 15..........	1.9	43	47

Control of weeds on summer-fallow land by chemical and mechanical measures or combinations of both has been studied by O. K. Barnes and his coworkers at Sheridan, Wyo. First-year results and previous experience showed that chemical control of weeds on summer-fallow with 2,4-D was generally unsatisfactory because only the broad-leaved weeds were affected and the fallow became weedy with such grasses as cheatgrass, barnyard grass, foxtail grass, and volunteer grain. Complete weed control was obtained in 1954 with 2,4-D and dalapon, which is a newly developed chemical effective in controlling grassy weeds.

It is important to obtain positive weed control and to maintain a surface condition on summer-fallow land that readily absorbs intense rains.

At the end of the fallow season, wheat stubble at Sheridan either remained standing or was partly decomposed as a surface mulch on land treated with chemicals for weed control. The straw was practically covered with soil on land where four operations with the subsurface sweeps were required to control weeds satisfactorily. All straw was covered on moldboard-plowed fallow.

Using artificial rainfall applicators, the investigators found that plowed land absorbs water rapidly at first but that in a short time the cloddy surface breaks down and seals over and then water infiltration becomes very slow. The land with good cover over the surface continued to absorb water for a much longer period. During the second 30 minutes of the 1-hour period of application of rainfall, the chemical fallow with the stubble-mulched surface absorbed water at a rate more than double the rate when the residue had been worked into the surface with subsurface sweeps.

These results on comparative infiltration rates are evidence that we must consider many factors in evaluating various measures for control of weeds on summer-fallowed land. The cost of chemicals is a major consideration. The chemical fallow operation allows faster coverage of the land with lighter equipment. Stubble undisturbed by the chemical operations protects the soil against erosion.

Weeds sprayed with 2,4-D are not killed immediately and appear to use moisture for an indefinite period. The tests in Saskatchewan showed that in order to conserve the greatest amount of moisture, weeds should be sprayed during the early stages of growth. Weeds sprayed for the first time during the bloom stage used about 60 percent as much water during the first week after spraying as weeds not sprayed. The use of water by weeds following the spraying operation decreased as the time of applying the first spray treatment came nearer the seedling stage of growth.

Weeds growing with a crop also reduce yield. A companion weed growth competes with the crop for moisture, space, and nutrients.

In studies with cereals and weeds under dryland conditions in western Canada, T. K. Pavlychenko and J. B. Harrington enumerated several characteristics that favor a high competitive capacity of plants for moisture. They include earliness and uniformity of germination under adverse moisture conditions, a large absorbing root surface during the early seedling stage, a root system with a large mass of fibrous roots close to the surface, and a main root that penetrates deeply into the soil. Among the cereals, barley, rye, wheat, oats, and flax, were listed in that order in their ability to compete. Wild oats (*Avena fatua*) and wild mustard (*Brassica arvensis*) were the most vigorous of the weeds.

Timely cultivation, proper use of chemical weed killers, and keeping the land free of weed seed are the best methods to use to control weeds.

SUBSOILING, or deep plowing, to shatter or disrupt subsurface horizons that restrict the downward movement of water may reduce runoff losses and thus increase the amount of water stored in the soil. Their effectiveness depends on the kind of soil and the amount of water to be stored.

Some soils with tight layers do not respond to subsoiling. Experiments in Kansas begun in 1952 and concluded in 1955 on soils varying from a fine sandy loam with a distinct plowpan to a silty clay loam with a tight subsoil showed that subsoiling had no effect on the infiltration rates of water, moisture storage, or wheat yield. The results support findings in 1909–1916 of the negative value of subsoiling and deep tilling of soil at some 12 places in the Great Plains. Results at most places showed no measurable responses in the form of increased crop yields. The effect at a few places was to lower yields. In any one year, a combination of conditions favorable to subsoiling occurred at a few stations. When crop yields were increased by subsoiling,

however, the increases were too small to be profitable.

Deep tillage, either by a subsoiling implement or a plow-type implement, to improve the permeability of subsurface layers to water has shown favorable results under certain conditions.

Harley A. Daniel, at the Wheatland Conservation Experiment Station near Cherokee, Okla., used a chisel and deep plow for breaking of the plowpan of a fine-textured soil in 1952. As compared with untreated areas, both the chiseled and deep-plowed treatments reduced runoff from three storms in 1953. Again, during the second year after treatment (1954), runoff from seven storms was still substantially less on the deep-plowed land than on either the chiseled or untreated areas. In each of the two seasons, runoff from the deep-plowed plot was approximately one-half that from the untreated area. In 1955, the third season after treatment, runoff losses from 10 storms were practically the same from the chiseled, deep-plowed, and untreated areas. The 3-year period was abnormally dry, and runoff losses from all plots were strikingly below normal.

Increased moisture storage has also been attributed to the use of subsoiling implements at St. Anthony, Idaho. Areas subsoiled in the fall of 1951 produced higher yields of spring wheat in 1953 than summer-fallowed areas not subsoiled. Soil samples in March 1953 showed 1.38 inches of additional moisture stored in soils that received fall chiseling or subsoiling in comparison with no fall treatment. The previous year, 1951–1952, a comparable figure was 3.43 additional inches of moisture in the profile. A part of the increased moisture storage was due to snow accumulations on the rougher fall-tilled areas. The furrows or channels left by the chisel tools hastened intake and were a temporary reservoir to hold the water from melting snow.

Because of the higher power requirements, the cost of subsoiling or deep plowing is greater than the costs of normal tillage operations. Thus a sizable increase in moisture storage and subsequent crop yield must be realized to offset the cost of the operation.

Another factor not favoring deep tillage is that any operation that stirs the soil, particularly those that expose subsurface layers, accelerate evaporation losses of water already stored.

CONTOUR CULTIVATION effectively conserves moisture when it is used with other good farming practices. Farming on the contour reduces the velocity of runoff water below that on the same slopes if the land were cultivated up and down. Ridges and trenches resulting from planting and cultivation of crops form a series of small basins for water that otherwise would run off the field. The major factor is detention of water on the surface. A greater chance of infiltration results. The capacity of the soil to absorb water is enhanced by impounding water in the basins of the irregular surface made by the contour operations.

The effectiveness of contour cultivation in increasing crop yields, reducing runoff, conserving moisture, and preventing loss of soil is influenced by such factors as soil type; rainfall intensity, distribution, and amount; and land slope, length, and intensity.

In the semiarid regions where conservation of moisture is so vital, contour cultivation should be used in most circumstances. Although the problem of conserving all available moisture for use by crops is less acute in the more humid areas, contour cultivation has widespread application as an aid to the orderly disposal of surplus water during wet periods and to the conservation of moisture during the drier periods in the growing season.

Considerable experimental data are available as to the higher yields of crops on contoured fields than on fields cultivated up and down the hill. A summarization of data by J. H. Stallings from some 37 places in 12 States indicated that contouring accounted for an increase in corn yields of about 11 percent on a weighted average ba-

sis. Comparisons of wheat yields, computed on the same basis, showed increases due to contouring to be better than 20 percent. Yield increases in favor of contouring also were reported for soybeans, potatoes, sorghum, cotton, beans, and hay.

At Spur, Tex., results of C. E. Fisher and Earl Burnett bear on the value of contouring in growing cotton continuously since 1927 on land with a slope of 0.5 percent. As an annual average, contouring reduced runoff from 2.75 inches for up-and-down farming to 1.95 inches and increased the yield of cotton 29 pounds an acre.

The water saved by contour cultivation often is relatively insignificant in terms of increased available moisture in the root zone. Small increments of additional water at critical stages during the growing season, however, often give substantial increases in crop yields.

IN STRIPCROPPING, different crops are grown in long, narrow strips on the same field. Strips of intertilled row crops, usually on the contour, alternate with strips of close-growing vegetation; or in the drier wheat-producing regions where summer fallow is practiced, slopes are broken by strips of close-growing crops, such as small grains, or hay and pasture crops. A general guide for stripcropping is that the more critical the runoff problem, the narrower the strips should be.

Close-growing crops tend to catch and hold the water from the strips of intertilled crops or fallow. The close-growing crop tends to slow down the rate of flow of water and, if infiltration opportunity is present, give it time to enter the soil.

In the Pacific Northwest, strips of undisturbed wheat stubble have been effective as a device for intercepting and spreading runoff water from melting snow during the spring months when unprotected fall-seeded winter wheatland is frozen. The standing stubble lowers the velocity of runoff water and protects the soil from becoming frozen as deeply as bare or poorly protected soil. Several measurements of soil moisture have shown larger amounts stored in the undisturbed stubble strip land.

TERRACES are combinations of low ridges and shallow channels laid out nearly on the contour of sloping land. Terraces are built to catch the water running across fields and divert or hold it. Graded terraces are used in humid regions or on steeper sloping land in the dryland regions as a means of diverting runoff to protected waterways and thus controlling erosion. Level terraces are used almost exclusively in semiarid or arid regions. They are designed to catch runoff water and give it an opportunity to infiltrate into the soil. Level terraces at times are ridged at the ends or at intervals along their length and thus serve as catchment basins for normal runoff.

As shown by data (given in the table) of C. E. Fisher and Earl Burnett, closed-end, level terraces on land of 0.5-percent slope at Spur, Tex., have been instrumental in collecting and storing larger amounts of available moisture in the upper 5 feet of soil than other practices. During the test period, 1937–1952, no runoff occurred from the closed, level-terraced area. The water so saved increased the yield of lint cotton an average of 41 pounds an acre a year. Planting and cultivating on the contour must be credited with its rightful share of the increase in moisture storage and yield brought about by terracing because contour tillage is almost always associated with a system of terraces on farm fields.

Type of practice	Average available moisture in upper 5 feet of soil on May 20 Inches	Yield of lint cotton per acre Pounds
Rows with slope	3. 06	130
Rows on contour	3. 33	165
Rows on contour supplemented with closed level terraces	3. 72	206

Results of Harley A. Daniel for the 10 years, 1942 through 1951, at Cherokee, Okla., also demonstrate benefits from terracing. The precipitation lost in runoff from land cultivated with the slope was 15 percent; the amount lost from terraced and contour cultivated areas was only 9.7 percent. The greatest saving of runoff water was when contour cultivation and terraces with vertical spacings of 3 feet were used on a land slope of 1.7 to 3.0 percent. Terraces with vertical intervals as great as 8 feet, when supplemented with contour cultivation, reduced runoff losses, however.

The prevention of all runoff under a system of closed-end, level terraces does not mean that water movement over the soil between terraces is eliminated. Observations on the distribution of moisture in a terraced field invariably indicate that water moves from areas between terraces and is concentrated over terrace channels. Consequently the soil in the terrace channel often serves as a storage reservoir or catchment basin for runoff water.

The water storage capacity of the narrow channel area of level, closed-end terraces is limited, and percolation of water below the root zone often occurs. Also, runoff water is not distributed over a great enough area to infiltrate rapidly and add to the moisture supply over an area of much consequence to crop production. Often it is impounded in the channels to a considerable depth and for periods long enough to cause crop damage.

A new study to test the feasibility of altering the configuration of the land to intercept and spread surface runoff on contour benches was initiated by A. W. Zingg at the Southwestern Great Plains Field Station near Amarillo, Tex., in the spring of 1955. The new practice, called conservation benching, departs radically from the usual terrace system in an attempt to retain the water and erosion control benefits of terraces and at the same time hold all surface runoff on the field and utilize it for subsequent crop production.

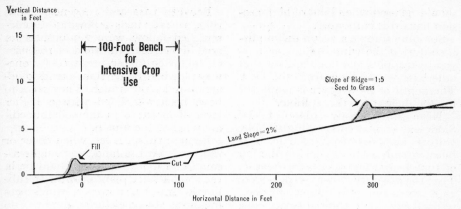

6. *Diagrammatic cross-sectional sketch of conservation benches.*

A diagrammatic sketch in cross section of a conservation bench is shown in the drawing. Since no runoff has occurred after construction of the benches, further study is needed to gain an insight into their possibilities.

Another practice that may have promise on gently sloping dryland soils is to level contour strips and construct border dikes around the leveled areas. That would prevent runoff from the treated areas.

WATER SPREADING, another method of conserving water normally lost in runoff, is the collection and diversion of runoff water from higher land for use by crops in another field or area.

Water spreading has limitations imposed by configuration, relief, and type of land. The area on which the water is to be spread must be level or gently sloping and near the higher land from which runoff occurs. The soils in the spreading area should be deep and moderately permeable. Systems of level or graded diversions or terraces usually are laid out in such a way as to collect, convey, and spread the water. Grassed waterways for conveying the water sometimes are necessary.

A water-spreading system comprising a 1,200-acre watershed area and 120-acre spreading area was set up by R. E. Dickson and his coworkers at Spur, Tex., in 1930. Nineteen rains in

9 years (1931–1939) produced runoff, which was diverted to the spreading area. The water caught and held on the upper half of the spreading area averaged 3.73 inches an acre annually, and that on the lower half was 2.41 inches. Those added quantities of water represented increases of 19.3 and 12.5 percent over the annual rainfall in the locality. The high yields of sorghum and Sudan produced on the land were valuable supplements to the short feed supplies in drought years.

In an evaluation of conserving runoff water by spreading near Cherokee, Okla., diverted runoff water practically doubled the yield of alfalfa in 1948 and increased it 29 percent in the extremely wet season of 1949 and 22 percent in 1950.

Spreading water is a good way to conserve moisture and improve production on pastures and ranges.

ADEQUATE COVER—either as growing crops or vegetative residues on the surface of cultivated lands—helps to conserve moisture. Proper management of vegetative materials makes unnecessary the mechanical measures we mentioned for adequate control of runoff and erosion on deep, permeable soils of moderate slope. Vegetative and mechanical measures in proper combination give more positive control of runoff and soil loss and therefore should be used when land of high erosion hazard is cultivated.

Standing stubble serves a useful purpose during the winter following harvest by trapping and holding snow that otherwise would blow from the field. The depth of snow cover is regulated by the height of the stubble.

Near St. Anthony, Idaho, F. H. Siddoway compared standing stubble, cutting and removing stubble, and burning stubble treatments in the fall of 1952 before the 1953 fallow season. The 1954 winter wheat yields were 25.1, 20.4, and 15.9 bushels an acre, respectively, for the three treatments. Differences were attributed directly to the relative amounts of snow held on the plots during the winter of 1952–1953 by the three stubble treatments.

F. L. Duley and J. C. Russel, at Lincoln, Nebr., studied the effects of mulches of crop residues on Marshall silt loam soil with a heavy subsoil and a slope of about 5 percent. The total accumulation of moisture under different methods of fallow was for the season between April 23 and September 8, 1938, when 17.9 inches of rain fell. The moisture saved in soil on which 2 tons of straw were applied was more than 2.5 times that on plowed land. On plowed or disked land, however, straw that was only partly buried gave some protection and reduced runoff.

Treatment [1]	Rainfall conserved Surface inches	Rainfall conserved Percent	Depth of water penetration, feet
Straw, 2 tons disked in	6.92	38.7	5
Land disked, no straw	3.49	19.5	4
Straw, 2 tons on the surface	9.72	54.3	6
Straw, 2 tons plowed in	6.12	34.2	5
Land plowed, no straw	3.71	20.7	4
Decayed straw, 2 tons plowed in	3.12	17.4	4
Basin listed	4.95	27.7	5

[1] A second application of straw was made to these plots on Aug. 9, 1938.

Between 1942 and 1953 near Amarillo, wheat yields following stubble-mulched fallow were 2.3 bushels an acre higher than the yield of 16 bushels following fallow prepared by one-way plowing. Better stands tend to develop under the mulch. They seem to have been associated with a higher level of moisture in the soil immediately below the mulch.

Because runoff is less when cover or residue is on the land, you might assume that more moisture would be in the soil for later plant growth. In subhumid regions, however, differences measured by moisture sampling do not seem to be of the magnitude indicated by the lower runoff values on stubble-mulched land.

In experiments with soil columns in cylinders, Mr. Russel found at Lincoln that the major effects of mulches on evaporation persist about 2 days after a rain. Evaporation declined about 0.1 inch during the first 24 hours after wetting the soil columns. More than 2 tons an acre of residue did not improve the control of evaporation.

The surface of unmulched soil seems to dry faster after a rain than does the soil surface under the mulch. If another rain wets the mulched soil before it dries out, more moisture from the first rain will be saved under the mulch than under the bare soil condition. But if the period between rains is long enough to allow evaporation to proceed until the surfaces of both mulched and bare soils are dry, the evidence points toward slightly higher total evaporation from the mulched soil.

Mulches of straw or other residues sometimes can reduce losses from evaporation. In North Carolina, for example, mulches applied at the time of the last cultivation increased yields of corn 21 bushels an acre in eight experiments conducted under droughty conditions and 5.4 bushels an acre in 10 experiments conducted under normal or abnormal moisture conditions. A part of the increase in the dry years was due to the effect of the mulch in controlling evaporation of moisture from the soil. The value of the mulch in controlling evaporation may depend on the length of the dry period. Very likely the mulches provide control of evaporation in short droughts, but mulched soil may lose as much water by evaporation as bare soil during long droughts.

CROPS AND CROPPING SYSTEMS differ as the soil and environment change. Maximum efficiency in the utilization of all available moisture is usually the goal in selecting the crop or cropping system. This guide is particularly important in regions of limited precipitation. In order to realize maximum utilization of moisture in dry areas, selection of a crop from the standpoint of its seasonal moisture requirements, timeliness of seeding, and cultivating at the proper time are important.

Crops best adapted to dry land are those that make maximum growth when climatic conditions are not too severe. The general displacement of spring wheat by winter wheat in the dryland areas where both are adapted is an example. Winter wheat is usually mature before the hottest part of the summer. Spring wheat, being somewhat later, often completes its development under much more severe conditions of temperature and transpiration.

Grasses and legumes have not been able to compete on an economic basis with wheat and other grain crops on cultivated dryland soils. Legumes and grasses leave the soil in a dry condition and have a high water requirement, which limits their use and adaptation to dry-farming systems. For example, Arthur C. Dillman found in western South Dakota that 430 pounds of water were needed to produce 1 pound of dry matter of spring wheat. Alfalfa required 798 pounds of water to produce 1 pound of dry matter.

The amount of water available to a particular crop may be augmented somewhat by growing it after a crop that does not exhaust the water supply of the soil. Row crops, such as corn and potatoes, usually do not utilize all of the available soil moisture; crops that follow therefore are favored by this residual moisture. Grasses and legumes, as we said, leave the soil dry to great depths; crops that follow them often suffer for lack of moisture.

Findings at several places in the Great Plains show that the yield of the first grain crop following a legume or grass is depressed well below the second or third grain crop after the sod crop. In most instances, this decline occurs on land fallowed for a year following the plowing of the sod crop. At North Platte, Nebr., and St. Anthony, Idaho, legumes such as sweetclover or alfalfa caused greater declines than grass. Overstimulation due to higher soil nitrogen often occurs after legumes, and grain yields are depressed when moisture becomes the limiting factor before the crop matures.

Grasses help greatly to keep the soil in place and make it receptive to water. Because of their fibrous root system, grasses use all available water within their rooting depth. In experiments at North Platte and Havre, Mont., yields of grass tend to increase until 2 or 3 years after the date of their establishment and then decrease with increasing age of the sod. These declines have been due to depletion of subsoil moisture and thinning stands.

Deep-rooted crops make effective use of stored moisture in deep soils. Alfalfa and coastal Bermuda-grass are examples. If the nutrient status of lower depths is adequate, they can utilize soil moisture at depths of 10 feet or more. If the storage capacity of the soil can be recharged in seasons of heavy rainfall, these crops resist drought on deep soils.

Sorghums and cotton can withstand dry periods and then resume rapid growth when it rains. They yield more if their growth is not interrupted by drought, but they are not total failures in years when dry spells occur. Sorghum has a greater ability to withstand drought than corn. This is attributed to a better developed absorbing system as compared to the transpiring system. The primary root area of the two crops is similar, but the secondary root area of sorghum is much larger than that of corn.

One way you can reduce water losses by transpiration is to seed fewer plants to the acre. In the drier areas, that is commonly done by planting crops in wider rows. Lowering the number of plants in the row is a second possibility. The net effect is to give each plant access to more moisture. The yield from each plant is increased, but usually the acre yield is less. A reduction in yield often is acceptable in that a more thickly planted crop might fail to mature.

Research done in the southern High Plains between 1945 and 1954 disclosed that plant population and not row spacing determines the yield of grain sorghum. Regardless of plant population, narrower rows (20 inch) tended to yield more than wider rows (40 inch) in years of above-normal precipitation. The reverse was true in the drier years.

The crop or cropping system can have a controlling influence upon the amount of runoff and hence moisture storage occurring on sloping land.

For example, G. M. Horner observed that the cropping system employed on the land had a profound effect on runoff losses at Pullman, Wash. During a 30-day period beginning January 9, 1953, rain amounted to 9.23 inches. Wheatland, after alfalfa and grass, yielded 0.9 inch of runoff. Wheat after fallow in a wheat-fallow system yielded about 3.1 inches of runoff. Subsurface-tilled land following sweetclover green manure yielded about 2.6 inches; when moldboard plowing was done, the runoff was 5.6 inches.

ADEQUATE FERTILITY is essential for the efficient use of soil moisture. Symptoms of deficiency of plant nutrients—especially those associated with insufficient nitrogen—have been wrongly diagnosed as drought injury.

Proper distribution of adequate amounts of all essential nutrients in the soil permits plants to make more effective use of limited moisture supplies in surface soil and also to extend their roots into subsoils for stored moisture.

In experiments at the Missouri Agricultural Experiment Station in 1952–1953, Dwight D. Smith found root development under fertilized crops was greater and penetrated deeper than without fertilization. Corn receiving a complete fertilizer yielded 79 bushels an acre and required 16 inches of water. Corn grown without fertilizer produced only 18 bushels and required about 14 inches of water. The fertilized corn not only extracted more moisture from the soil; it used the extracted water more efficiently. Each inch of water used by the fertilized plants produced about 5 bushels of grain, but each inch of water extracted by plants that did not receive fertilizer yielded only 1.3 bushels of grain.

PROPERLY FERTILIZED crops help conserve moisture in another way. Of the small amount of rainfall received at McCredie, Mo., in 1953, nearly 1 inch was lost as runoff from the unfertilized corn plots. The loss was only one-fourth this amount on fertilized corn land. In the previous 6 years, when precipitation in the crop season averaged nearly 20 inches, 3 inches of runoff occurred under corn without fertilizer. In contrast, fertilized corn in a 2- and 4-year rotation yielded slightly less than 1 inch and one-half inch of runoff.

Crop production in the Great Plains is curtailed oftenest by limited moisture but periodically by inadequate amounts of nitrogen. Wide fluctuations in moisture resulting from climatic variations create difficult and complex problems in adjusting nitrogen to the moisture available at any one time. An overabundance of available nitrogen in relation to moisture can cause marked reduction in yields. Not only is the total supply of nitrogen important; the timing of its availability in relation to moisture availability and stage of plant development is critical.

That the balance between supplies of moisture and nitrogen is important in the efficiency of moisture use by winter wheat was demonstrated in 1954–1955 by R. E. Ramig at North Platte, Nebr. In each season, 5.75 inches of available moisture in the soil at seeding time was best from the standpoint of efficiency of water use. The efficiency, however, varied widely in the two years and with the rate of nitrogen fertilization. In 1954, a year when seeding-to-harvest precipitation measured only 8.9 inches, the highest efficiency of 1.85 bushels per inch of water used was realized when 40 pounds of nitrogen fertilizer was applied to the acre. In 1955, when precipitation during the crop season was 17.1 inches, the top efficiency was 2.3 bushels per inch of water used, but that occurred when 80 pounds of nitrogen an acre was applied. In both years, as the applied nitrogen rate was reduced from those giving the highest efficiencies, the grain produced per inch of water used also was less. Without nitrogen fertilizer, only 0.9 bushel in 1954 and 1.1 bushels in 1955 were produced per inch of water. Each year, the efficiency of water use was approximately doubled by adjusting the nitrogen supply to a level that made possible the best use of stored and seasonal moisture.

Lack of other nutrients also lowers the efficiency of water use by plants. C. O. Stanberry and his coworkers in a study at Yuma, Ariz., in 1949–1952 showed that the combined 4-year yield of alfalfa varied from 25.8 to 50.0 tons an acre, depending on the quantities of irrigation water and phosphorus fertilizer applied. Efficiency of water use varied nearly 100 percent among different phosphorus treatments. It was 7.8 acre-inches per ton of hay when 800 pounds of P_2O_5 per acre were applied during the 3-year period and 14.2 acre-inches per ton when only 100 pounds of P_2O_5 were applied. The results substantiate the importance of adequate soil fertility in achieving the goal of maximum conservation of soil moisture.

Irrigation in Arid Regions

Wayne D. Criddle and Howard R. Haise

A farmer has to bear six factors in mind when he plans to irrigate his land. They are: The adequacy, reliability, and quality of the water supply; the control and conveyance of water; water requirements, including consumptive use, effective rainfall, net irrigation requirement, and irrigation efficiency; application of water; drainage for removal of both surface and subsurface excess water; and institutional arrangements.

Existing rights and uses must be respected. The fact that water flows past a man's farm does not necessarily give him the right to divert the waters and use them for irrigation. Downstream users may have established rights to the waters in accordance with State laws. If the flow is insufficient to meet all needs, the first appropriators may be entitled to receive their water first. Domestic and municipal uses also may have first priority. Irrigation, power, industry, navigation, wildlife, and recreation may have lower priorities.

The source of irrigation water usually is the rain and snow that falls on the watershed above. It may flow down to the valley in surface streams that can be stored or diverted for use, or it may travel underground and have to be pumped up. Occasionally the source is the ground water reservoir under the cropped land. Seldom in the arid West does the surface water supply fully coincide with the irrigation needs. Because peak streamflows from melting snows usually occur in the spring or early summer, storage works must be developed to control the flow of the streams and make the water available as needed.

Only a relatively few holdings can be served with individually developed water supplies. Most farmers must work out agreements with their neighbors as to the use of their water rights and the development of facilities to divert, convey, and distribute the water. Such arrangements usually are needed to insure that each farmer contributes his proportion of the costs of development and operation of irrigation and drainage systems. Each, furthermore, must receive his share of water at a set time and in a way that he can use it.

The quality of the water is highly important. Foreign material, whether dissolved or in solid form, may be objectionable. Excess silt, moss, sand, brush, small insects, or other debris in the water may make special treatment necessary. The treatment may consist of simple screening or may require the use of expensive sand or debris traps, depending on the kind and amount of material the water carries and the method of irrigation.

Heavy concentrations of dissolved salts are objectionable. Their total amount and kinds and the characteristics of the crops, soils, climate, and irrigation practices must all be considered in appraising water quality.

Various physical controls and structures are needed after a suitable water supply for irrigation is found. A way to control the supply and deliver it economically from the point of origin to the point of use on the farms must be made. It may include storage and diversion dams on the streams; canals and laterals to carry water to the farms; farm distribution systems; and other structures as canal linings, pump-

ing plants, headgates, drops to control erosion, measuring devices, pipelines, siphons, check dams, and spiles.

This part of irrigation is largely engineering. It is not specifically related to the crops that are grown, except that the capacity must meet their needs. It is related to the soils only as the soils affect the stability of structures, seepage losses, and so on. Surface and underground storage reservoirs must be developed to make the natural flow of the streams correspond directly with the irrigation needs of the crops.

Preparation of irrigated land is necessary for efficient and uniform application of water regardless of the method of irrigation.

Sprinkler irrigation usually requires the least preparation, although considerable leveling is sometimes done. For good surface and subsurface irrigation, land leveling is essential. Greater efficiencies of application, more uniform distribution, ease in farming, increased production, and savings of water are among the advantages.

LAND LEVELING usually is done by tractor-drawn equipment. Some farmers prefer to do their own leveling with scrapers and levelers that can be pulled with medium-sized farm tractors, even though that takes more time than leveling by contractors who use heavy equipment.

The carryall is an efficient machine that scrapes, spreads, and transports soil. Bulldozers, graders, terracers, and maintainers are sometimes used for rough grading, but the cost of using them is higher than when a carryall is used, and only skilled operators can use them efficiently.

After the fields are rough leveled, smoothing equipment such as levelers, floats, or land planes are used to establish the final grade and finished surface. Land planes usually are more than 60 feet long and are supported at the corners by swivel wheels. A combination scraper-bucket in the center of the frame can scrape high spots and carry enough dirt to fill in low spots. Smaller levelers, usually about 30 feet long, are pulled by medium-sized farm tractors and can be used for additional smoothing operations.

Because a certain amount of soil settling always occurs on newly leveled land, it is advisable to grow a small grain or similar crop with border irrigation or a row crop with furrow irrigation after the first leveling. After harvest, the high and low spots can be releveled before a perennial crop, like alfalfa, is established.

Land leveling sometimes lowers the productivity of soils. Moving heavy equipment across fields compacts soils, especially if they are wet, and often creates a condition that is not easily remedied.

Rebuilding structure damaged by leveling operations is difficult in places where freezing and thawing do not occur. Deep-rooted legumes and grasses have been used in the Lower Rio Grande Valley of Texas to loosen surface soils and increase intake rates after fields were leveled. Rough or minimum tillage operations with alternate wetting and drying and applications of organic materials also help improve the intake rate of soil whose structure has deteriorated.

Land leveling may remove topsoil and expose subsoil. The problem is worse in the sections of higher rainfall (where soil profile development has progressed more) than in the arid regions (where cutting 1, 2, or even 5 feet into deep alluvial soils often is considered feasible). Soils with a marked development of profile often present a physical or chemical problem, or both, when the organic layer is removed in the leveling process.

When newly irrigated lands were leveled for irrigation in the Columbia River Basin, deficiencies of nitrogen, phosphorus, and zinc occurred when subsoils were exposed. Symptoms of zinc deficiency were noted first on corn and beans, but the deficiencies were found later to affect 14 other crops. On areas where surface soils were re-moved, fertilizers containing nitrogen, phosphorus, and zinc were applied, and production jumped from 280 to 2,280 pounds of field beans an acre.

Symptoms of a deficiency of zinc have been noted in North Dakota on corn growing on Gardena subsoils that were exposed by leveling operations. Additions of 180 pounds of nitrogen and 100 pounds of P_2O_5 with and without 15 pounds of zinc sulfate an acre increased corn forage yields 5,390 to 6,420 pounds, respectively. When no fertilizers were added, yields were 1,480 pounds an acre, compared to 7,940 pounds when those rates of nitrogen, phosphorus, and zinc, and 20 tons of manure were applied.

In a long-time experiment in Colorado, topsoil was removed to varying degrees. Liberal applications of nitrogen and phosphorus restored the productivity of Fort Collins subsoil equal to that of the original surface soil. Yields of sugar beets on check plots averaged about 7 tons an acre, compared to 20 tons on fields that got nitrogen and phosphorus. The ease with which stands were established indicated also that within a relatively short time the physical condition of the soil was as good as that of the natural surface soil.

In some localities of shallow topsoil underlain by sand or gravel, farmers have found it feasible to remove and save the topsoil, which is spread over the field again after the subsoil is leveled. This practice takes money and work, but the farmers believe many dollars can be spent to make poor land (which may nevertheless sell for 500 dollars an acre if it can be irrigated) into good land.

Leveling of land to be irrigated is not something that can be done once and then forgotten. Normal farming operations, erosion by wind and water, silting from some water supplies, and other factors tend to get the land out of level. For efficient irrigation, the grade must be uniform. Therefore some periodic floating or smoothing usually is desirable and should be considered in planning the farm operations and equipment needs.

Because a smooth land surface is desirable for spreading water over the field, some farmers tend to overtill their fields. Soils high in silt soon lose their structure under continuous tillage. The density of soil is increased by running tractors over it. Although maximum compaction might be obtained by working the soils while wet, working some soils when dry forms a dust, which lowers the intake rate. Most irrigated soils therefore should be tilled no more than absolutely necessary to prepare the seedbed, control weeds and insects, and ready it for irrigation. All other tillage merely costs the farmer money, makes it harder to get water into the soil, and lowers production because it impedes movement of soil water and air.

THE THREE GENERAL METHODS of applying water to cropland are surface irrigation, sprinkler or overhead irrigation, and subsurface irrigation.

Whatever the method, the aim is to apply adequate water to the soil uniformly over the field with no harm to the crop or the soil and with a minimum of water and labor.

In surface irrigation, the water may completely cover the surface (commonly called flood irrigation) or it may flow in furrows or small ditches. Either method may be used on sloping or relatively flat lands.

Flood irrigation includes border irrigation (running water downslope between dikes), and basin irrigation (quickly ponding water on a level area), and flooding downslope from the contour ditches.

For border irrigation, the slope of the land down the strip generally should not be less than 0.1 percent and not more than 2 percent, although slopes exceeding 6 percent have been used for narrow border strips planted to grass or dense cover crops. If crops are to be established on steeper slopes, sprinkler irrigation should be used to prevent erosion unless rainfall is adequate to start the crop. Cross slope within the strip is not permitted.

In basin irrigation, water is applied quickly to a flat area surrounded by dikes. A relatively large stream is used. The water is ponded on the basin area and continues to percolate into the soil some time after the stream has been turned off.

Level basin irrigation for both close-growing and the row crops has been gaining favor in the Lower Rio Grande Valley. Farmers who have invested approximately 100 dollars an acre to install such systems say that increased production has repaid the investment in 2 or 3 years. Greater production has come from more uniform distribution of water and control of excess salts.

With level basin irrigation, each plant in the row receives its share of the water applied. Less labor is required. The amount of water applied can be more easily controlled. Because no runoff occurs, knowing the size of irrigation stream and the duration of application makes possible efficient applications without detailed knowledge of soil intake rates which is necessary for efficient irrigation on graded land. Also, more of the precipitation falling on the area may be retained and made effective in meeting the water requirement of the crop.

Considerable interest has developed in level contour bench irrigation on land slopes up to 5 percent in the High Plains of Texas. This system allows for more efficient use of limited supplies of ground water through maximum utilization of rainfall without surface runoff. Impounded water remains on the level strips laid out on the contour until it is absorbed by the soil or (in case of excess amounts from heavy storms) is removed by surface drainage facilities.

One farmer remarked, "My land will be ready for productive dry-farming when the irrigation well is dry." From the standpoint of maximum utilization of rain, his statement is no doubt correct.

Level contour bench systems have

been studied at Mitchell, Nebr., as a possible way to prevent severe erosion on irrigated slopes adjoining river bottom lands. Severe damage to irrigation and drainage structures has occurred in western Nebraska from runoff that accumulates in small watersheds above the irrigated project. Attention also has been given to a method of removing and storing topsoil for subsequent replacement on the leveled benches.

Flooding from contour ditches has been used a great deal on rather steeply sloping lands. The water is allowed to flow as a sheet downslope between field ditches that are closely spaced and on the contour. The ditches distribute the water through frequent openings and also capture runoff from the field above and redistribute it. This method is not considered efficient in the use of labor or water.

Both the border and the basin methods require the use of farming practices that leave the dikes intact so the boundaries of the strips need not be changed frequently. Once the land is leveled to meet the requirements for the type of irrigation chosen, the farmer will not want to unlevel the land by improper tillage practices. Also, because good irrigation depends on storing needed water in the soil, he will not want to use practices that will change greatly the structure and intake rate of his soil.

The soil is not only the moisture storage reservoir. Under surface irrigation it is also the channel that conveys water from the upper end to the lower end of the field. Intake rates that are too slow or too rapid therefore are not suitable for surface irrigation.

Proper irrigation and efficient use of water is difficult to attain when soils absorb water at rates less than 0.1 inch an hour. Irrigation by surface methods becomes impractical when rates of intake exceed 3 inches an hour. The usable water-holding capacities of these soils with high intake rates are often so low, however, that the soils are too droughty for most agriculture.

Sprinkler, or overhead, irrigation is adapted to most soils and crops. It provides excellent control of the water and can be turned off when the soil has absorbed the required amount. The rate of application should be no greater than the amount the soil can absorb without surface runoff. Such good control of water makes it possible to use sprinkler irrigation for a number of special purposes, such as to establish new seedings on steeper lands or on permeable soils that will be irrigated later by another method.

Sprinkling requires less land smoothing. Less care is needed to keep the surface level. On the tighter soils or those readily compacted or puddled, care must be taken to see that the farm operations do not compact the soil until the intake rate is reduced below the rate at which sprinklers apply the water.

In subsurface irrigation, an artificial water table is created and maintained at a predetermined depth below the surface within reach of plant roots. Moisture is supplied to the plant roots through upward capillary movement. The depth to water must be controlled carefully; otherwise the depth can become too small or too great and may retard or stop root growth.

Certain special management practices seem necessary where subirrigation is practiced in the West. Special provisions—the temporary use of sprinklers or local surface irrigation—may be required to get seed germinated and the seedlings started. Also, when the underground water contains appreciable quantities of salts and fluctuates regularly in a soil, an impervious layer, or lens, of salt tends to develop and may retard the movement of the water. The lens is usually just a little below the level at which the "sub" (water table) is generally maintained. Deep chiseling to shatter the lens may be desirable.

When precipitation is light, an annual surface irrigation during the period when the water table is low may be necessary to leach out the salts. Since the soil must be highly permeable for satisfactory subsurface irrigation, careful management of fertilizers may be necessary, especially if precipitation is heavy in winter or if excessive surface irrigation is practiced for leaching purposes or to get the crop started.

Surface irrigation may be 50 to 90 percent efficient. Efficiencies of sprinkler applications normally are 70 to 80 percent. Thus more irrigation water must be made available to the farm than will actually be consumed by the crops. The amount of excess will depend on the efficiency with which the water can be applied.

EFFICIENCY OF IRRIGATION is affected by topography and soil and crop conditions.

The design of the irrigation system, the degree of land preparation, and the skill and care of the irrigator, however, probably have the greatest influence on the efficiency and total amount of water that must be delivered to the farm headgate.

Efficiencies of 100 percent in applying irrigation water are not possible with present irrigation facilities and practices. More water is applied at some spots in the field than in others. Some water is usually lost by deep percolation. Frequently some surface runoff occurs. This is not entirely undesirable, however, because some excess water must move downward through the soil to prevent a harmful accumulation of salts near the surface of the land. The amount of deep percolation required for this purpose seldom exceeds 15 to 20 percent of the water.

The factors that govern the selection of an irrigation system should be considered not only as they exist at the time the system is planned but as they will be modified under improved management practices.

Some irrigation systems are better adapted to growing certain types of crops than others. Close-growing crops, such as alfalfa and pastures, are usually flood irrigated. Row crops, like corn, cotton, and sugar beets, are furrow irrigated. Rotation from row crops to cover crops is common, and plans should be made to irrigate by several methods. Seldom nowadays is land planted to a single crop year after year.

Topography and slope greatly influenced the choice of irrigation method in the past. New earth-moving equipment now makes it feasible to modify land surfaces to almost any condition desired. Consideration must be given, however, to cost and benefits in relation to soil conditions and crops to be grown before modification of the land surface is made and the method of application selected.

The most important soil characteristics that influence the choice of irrigation are the usable depth of water that can be stored in the root zone of the crop and the erodibility and the intake rate of the soil. Each of these factors can be changed greatly by the type of soil management. For example, deep plowing to disrupt a plowpan, combined with minimum tillage operations, will usually increase intake rates and depth of root penetration.

Water supply also is important in choosing a system of irrigation. Small, constant-flow streams may be more adaptable to sprinkler irrigation, but large, intermittent streams, particularly if storage facilities are not present, often can be used better by surface irrigation methods.

Intensity of rainfall must be considered in the design of irrigation systems.

In the Northwest, where rains are gentle, little attention need be given to erosion from irrigated fields because of rain. In the Southwest, where cloudbursts occur, rainfall must be taken into account in laying out irrigation systems and fields.

The irrigation system may be used only once or twice a year if summer precipitation is heavy. Certainly this will affect the choice of methods. Also, in areas of heavier precipitation it is often found desirable to level the land so that excess waters can be removed in the winter and early spring. Once the land is properly leveled for drainage, little extra effort or expense is needed to prepare it for various methods of surface irrigation.

Removal of excess irrigation water from irrigated lands usually is necessary. High water tables are caused by losses that occur in storage and conveyance of water to the point where it can be utilized; by the relatively low irrigation application efficiencies resulting from deep percolation losses and runoff; and from excess water applications required to maintain a favorable salt balance in the surface soil.

Subsurface drainage is required if soils become waterlogged. Root development is restricted because of inadequate aeration. Soils are slow to warm up in the spring. Seed germination is delayed. High water tables can result also in the accumulation of excess salt in the surface soil. That adversely affects soil structure and reduces intake rates and the availability of moisture to the plant.

The water table must be held low enough to provide adequate removal of water from the crop root zone and prevent upward movement of salts into the root zone from the more saline ground water. Since soil is farmed to greater depths in the West than in the East, drains must be installed deeper. It is not uncommon therefore to have open ditches or tile drains as deep as 8 to 10 feet in many western irrigated projects to accommodate crops with deep roots. Roots of the same crops grown in humid areas usually are restricted to the upper 2 or 3 feet because of poorer subsoil conditions.

Excess water on higher land may waterlog the lower lands. An extensive system of drains may be necessary to correct that. Lands once waterlogged often are never fully productive again. On the field itself, poor distribution and inefficient use of water sometimes show up in poor yields at the top and bottom of the field and fairly good yields at the center: The upper end gets too much water and loses plant food by leaching and erosion, and plants at the lower end get too little water for proper growth.

Good surface drainage is also essential for top crop yields. Most crops will not live very long in standing water, especially during hot weather. Whether the water comes from rainfall or irrigation, the results are the same— excess water must be removed quickly and safely.

Not all irrigated lands are readily subject to damage from ponded surface waste water. The coarser textured flat lands absorb water rapidly. On the tighter and steeper lands, however, irrigation without surface waste by any method is difficult, and most of the rain that falls may be lost in runoff.

High water tables or accumulation of excess salt have occurred in parts of nearly every irrigated project in the West. Development of drainage systems concurrently with land development of an irrigated project usually prevents trouble.

Another serious problem in the West is how to apply irrigation water to crops without washing away soil. Anything done to improve the structure of the soil usually increases the rate at which the irrigation water is absorbed. An increase in the rate of intake means that larger irrigation streams must be delivered to the fields.

Even though the erodibility of the soil may be reduced somewhat by proper soil management, the effect of the larger streams more than offsets any gain in stability of the soil. Although an improvement in soil structure usually makes necessary a larger irrigation stream, increasing the effective depth of the root zone tends to allow the use of smaller streams.

Water applied to soil immediately after plowing or cultivation causes breakdown of clods and filling of larger pore spaces with soil particles lubricated and made buoyant by water. Water thus tends to settle, or compact, the soil and to increase its density. Gradual consolidation of the cultivated surface continues for several irrigations, after which it becomes more or less stable. With further irrigation, increased intake rates can occur because plant foliage and crop residues usually reduce the velocity of flowing water and increase the wetted areas.

Investigations at Prosser, Wash., have shown that an eightfold variation of furrow intake rates occurred within a given season. This is in addition to variations that occur from season to season, depending on previous crop history, the crop irrigated, moisture content of soil, cultivation, and stream.

Irrigation water applied improperly also causes segregation of the soil particles. The smaller particles are moved downslope and tend to increase the intake rate at the upper end and seal off the lower end of the field. Uniform irrigation throughout the field thus is harder to achieve. Proper irrigation and soil management will help prevent particle segregation.

Uncontrolled irrigation water can cause erosion. It can strip soil from bare sloping fields at an alarming rate: The very water that is so essential to crop growth can also be the means by which the land is ruined.

Changes in absorption rate of soil during the cropping sequence must be kept in mind when the system is designed. Obviously, water need not be in contact with the soil for as long a time when the absorption rate is high as when it is lower to store the same amount of water.

Thus, for the more permeable soils, irrigation streams should be large but should be applied for a short time. Thus the irrigator can get the water across the field rapidly so that no more is absorbed than is desired for good irrigation.

Also (since the rate at which the soil absorbs water declines with time), the shallower the irrigation, the larger the stream needed but for a shorter period of time. Thus, the faster the intake rate of the soil and the less depth applied each irrigation, the larger the stream must be.

When sprinklers are used, the intake rate of the soil governs the size of the stream only as far as the maximum intake rate of the soil is concerned. If water is applied faster than the soil will absorb it, losses of water will occur by surface runoff.

Equally important is the management of irrigation water for good crop production after it has reached the farm. When to irrigate and how much water to apply are questions that continually confront the farmer.

Excessive use of water often can aggravate a drainage problem and reduce yields by allowing deep percolation and leaching of soluble nutrients below root depths. Proper scheduling of irrigations to maintain soil moisture conditions for continuous growth of the plant is important.

To do a good job of irrigating, a farmer needs to know something about how much water is needed to grow a crop; the amount of water that can be stored in the soil-root reservoir; how much of the stored water that can be used before reapplying water; the amount of water withdrawn by the crop at the time he irrigates; and the length of time that water must be in contact with the soil to replace the amount used.

The farmer can eliminate some of the guesswork involved in water management by using the irrigation guides of the Department of Agriculture.

The formulation of irrigation guides requires information about the amount and the rate that crops use water. This phenomenon is referred to as consumptive use or evapotranspiration—the water transpired and evaporated from a given area—and is an important element in the hydrologic cycle of water movement from the time it falls on the land until it returns to the atmosphere or reaches the ocean. It is the best index of how much water will be needed to produce good crops.

Measurements of consumptive use of water by various crops and natural vegetation have been made under many different physical and climatic conditions. Methods have been developed to estimate consumptive use for a given locality, based on a correlation of climatological data with actual measurements. These methods give the total consumptive requirement of the crop regardless of the source of the water.

In areas where ground water is not a major contributor, the amount of water that must be supplied by irrigation depends on how much precipitation can be utilized to meet the consumptive needs of the crops. The contribution may vary from practically nothing (as at Yuma, Ariz.) to all crop needs.

How nearly precipitation meets the needs of the crops depends on the annual amount of precipitation and on the time and way it occurs. It also depends on how much water can be stored as soil moisture in the root zone of the crop at any time. The usable amount varies from place to place and with crop and soil conditions. The more precipitation the root zone of the crop absorbs and stores, the less irrigation water will be required. Thus the consumptive use of the crop minus the effective rainfall gives the net irrigation water requirement.

Values of normal consumptive use of water by each of the major crops and effective rainfall are available for each irrigated area of most States of the West through publications of the State experiment stations or the Soil Conservation Service.

The depth of water required in each irrigation depends on how large the soil moisture reservoir is and how nearly it can be emptied between each irrigation. A medium-textured soil normally stores about 2 inches of usable water per foot of depth of soil. Not all of that water should be removed before irrigating again, however. Usually not more than about 1 inch is removed if the crop is to grow most rapidly. Thus, if the root zone of the crop is 3 feet deep, about 3 inches of water should be stored each irrigation. A farm efficiency of 75 percent would require that 4 inches of depth or 4 acre-inches per acre should be delivered to the farm headgate for the irrigation. Assuming a medium rate of use of water by the plants of 0.2 inch a day, the 3 inches

stored would last 15 days, or the irrigation interval would be every 2 weeks.

The time required to apply an average of 4 acre-inches per acre would depend upon the size of the stream delivered to the farm and the acreage to be irrigated. A stream of 1 cubic foot a second (1 c.f.s.) is approximately equivalent to 1 acre-inch of water an hour. Thus, if the irrigating stream is 4 c.f.s., an average depth of 4 inches could be applied to an acre each hour. At 75 percent efficiency, 3 inches of depth or more would be stored in the crop root zone.

Plants do not withdraw moisture at equal rates from all depths of the root zone. Much of the greatest use is from the top half of the root zone depth. When all available moisture is extracted from any appreciable part of the root zone, growth slows down. Thus irrigation often is considered desirable while 35 percent to 50 percent of the total available moisture is still left in the root zone. An example: A 4-foot root zone that could store 2 inches of usable water per foot of depth would mean that irrigation should start when about 4 inches (or not more than 5 inches) had been used by the crop.

The amount of available moisture that a soil can store for plant use influences the frequency, size of streams, size of farm laterals, and other elements of design. In general, inches of available moisture that can be stored in a foot of sand range from 0.25 to 0.75; loamy sands, 0.75 to 1.25; sandy loams, 1.00 to 1.50; fine sandy loams, 1.50 to 2.00; clay loams, 1.75 to 2.25; and clays, 2.00 to 3.00.

Some plants go deeply into the soil. Others have shallow roots. If the roots can extract water from as deep as 6 feet, instead of only 3 feet, it will be more efficient to apply more water at each irrigation and the irrigations will be less frequent. With the greater depths of water applied at each irrigation to the deeper rooted crops, lengths of irrigation run can be greater or the size of irrigation streams may be smaller and still give efficient irrigation.

Irrigation
in the East

T. H. Quackenbush and M. D. Thorne

The irrigated acreage in the 31 States in the humid region in 1954 was 70 percent greater than that in 1949, according to the 1954 Census of Agriculture.

The increase probably occurred as a result of successive years of severe drought and the realization of production increases that can be achieved by irrigation under such conditions.

Many think this "emergency" increase in irrigation is only a natural consequence of the unusual weather and that if a period of years of "normal" rainfall occurs again, the irrigated acreage in the East will be reduced markedly.

Others contend that farming practices have so changed that farmers can no longer afford the risks associated with unfavorable rainfall distribution in any year. They reason that production costs of some crops have increased so much that a further investment for irrigation is necessary to insure production every year.

In order to examine accurately the probable future of irrigation in the humid region, we need to know what the normal situation is with regard to moisture supply for crops and the frequency and extent of the departures from normal that are to be expected. Then we need to know what increases in yield we may expect if we eliminate these periods of moisture deficiency by means of irrigation. We need to know how much water will be required and whether we can obtain this amount of water with legal right to use it for irri-

gation. Also, we need to know the best methods and the resulting costs of developing the supply, conveying it to the farm site, and applying it to the crop. We need information about the effect of an irrigation program on the other farm operations, such as drainage, fertilization, tillage, and cropping.

Many of the basic principles of irrigation developed through 100 years of experience and 50 years of research in the drier Western States can be applied to the humid areas. In order to take full advantage of this information and adapt it properly to humid conditions, it is important to know the following basic principles that make irrigation in humid climates different from irrigation in the West.

1. Good yields of farm crops can be obtained without irrigation in many years. The margin of profit from irrigation is much smaller while installation costs are comparable. Maximum utilization of equipment and labor therefore is needed to keep irrigation on a sound economic basis.

2. Provisions must be made in humid climates to dispose of surplus rainfall. This requires additional precautions against soil erosion and provisions for adequate drainage.

3. Farm crops generally do not root so deeply as in the arid areas. Winter rain and snow can be relied on in most years to replenish the soil moisture that is used from greater depths. This requires lighter and more frequent irrigations and the off-season irrigations (before planting or after the harvest) will not be required.

4. Seasonal requirements of irrigation water are not so great. Short-time, peak-use requirements may be nearly as large, however.

5. It should be kept in mind when considering surface irrigation that a large part of the benefits obtained from land leveling can be charged to the better surface drainage provided.

6. Soils underlain with fine-textured subsoils, which modify root depths, moisture-holding capacities, intake rates, and land leveling operations,

are more widespread in the areas being irrigated.

DROUGHT PROBABILITY in the humid region can now be predicted fairly accurately. For example, we can predict that over a great many years an average of 2 years out of 10 will have droughts of a stated severity. We can calculate the probability that a drought of any specified duration will occur during any month of the growing season of any crop. We can also calculate the amount of irrigation water likely to be needed to alleviate this drought. Because assumptions have to be made in this procedure, the results are not completely accurate, but they are probably good enough for most uses for which they are intended.

A drought day, for this purpose, is considered to be any day when the available soil moisture in the root zone has been depleted. Separate computations are then made for various values of available soil moisture—1 inch, 2 inches, 3 inches, and so on.

The rate the crop uses moisture is calculated from weather data, such as sunlight, humidity, and wind, for the desired location. These moisture-use data are then balanced against the actual rainfall recorded at the location in a sort of bookkeeping procedure.

We do this for as many previous years as we have weather records available and establish the patterns, which can be used to predict probability of occurrence of the drought periods in the future.

The equations used to compute moisture use from weather data are being checked continually by actual field measurements under a variety of conditions and probably will be improved further in the coming years to increase the accuracy of prediction. It is not possible, however, to predict when the drought years will fall or when during any one year a drought period will come.

This procedure is adapted particularly to the humid region, where the soil root zone is at field capacity when the growing season begins. Computations of this sort are not so simple for an arid region and probably are not so essential where droughts are to be expected every year and where rainfall may contribute only a minor portion of the water needed for the crop.

A drought survey of this type has been completed for North Carolina, and similar studies have been started for some other Southeastern States. It is planned to extend the studies to cover all the region where the technique is applicable.

The user of this type of information must know the moisture-holding ability of his soil and the depth of rooting of his crop in order to decide which level of available moisture he should use in his situation. Then he can predict with fair accuracy the probability that he will have droughts of varying frequency in the years to come.

Again, it must be emphasized that a study of this type will not tell him which years the drought will come, but only what are the longtime chances of having droughts.

Also, if his chances are 3 out of 10 that at least 20 drought days will occur in July and he has just had 3 successive years with July droughts of this severity, his chances that the coming July will have 20 or more drought days are still 3 out of 10, a fact that often is not realized.

The study in North Carolina shows, for example, that all sections of the State may expect at least 17 drought days in June and July in 2 out of 10 years if the storage capacity for moisture in the soil available to plants is 2 inches. The Coastal Plain can expect a minimum of 34 drought days on the same basis. All parts of the State would require at least 8 inches of irrigation water to overcome the drought that may be expected during the growing season in 9 out of 10 years, with a moisture storage capacity of 2 inches. Except for the mountain regions of the State, the probability that any day in June will be a drought day is at least 30 percent for a moisture storage capacity of 2 inches; however, the probability of a drought day in June is insignificantly low, except for the lower Coastal Plain.

Information of this type for the entire humid region will help put irrigation planning and practice on a much sounder basis.

CROP RESPONSE to irrigation must be known in order to plan an irrigation program if it has been determined that the probability of drought occurrence is such as to indicate appreciable deficiency of water for the crop.

Many determinations of this response have been made, both under experimental conditions and in irrigation practice in the field.

Many of these investigations in the humid region were made to explore the possibilities of irrigation under local conditions. Consequently the data may have only limited application.

At Blacksburg, Va., in 1954, for example, 3 inches of water applied during tasseling and through the milk stage increased corn yields 38 bushels over the nonirrigated yields of 65 bushels an acre. Three additional inches applied before tasseling increased the yield 55 bushels an acre over the unirrigated plots. Full-season irrigation increased the yield 64 bushels an acre over the controls but required 10.5 inches of water. In each instance, water was applied whenever available soil moisture was 50 percent depleted during the specified period.

Information of this sort is valuable to those interested in irrigation in the immediate vicinity. The information given, however, would tell us little about how frequently we could expect this magnitude of response to the same treatments at this location. Nor does it tell us whether we would have measured the same response if the treatments had been applied to corn on another soil type in the vicinity that same year.

Increases in yield from irrigation are more meaningful when we know the frequency of occurrence of the drought condition encountered and when we have a measurement of the moisture conditions of the soil or plants in units that permit us to reproduce them on other soils and in other environments.

Current thinking is that drought surveys will provide the former and that irrigation treatments specified according to moisture stress or moisture tension will provide the latter.

Moisture stress and tension are terms that refer to the energy with which moisture is held in the soil. It is believed they give a good measure of the work that plant roots must do to get the moisture—hence of the degree of availability of the moisture.

The percentage of available moisture gives no general indication of the degree of availability. The data from Virginia would thus have much greater applicability when the moisture stress corresponding to the 50-percent available moisture were determined.

Yield results from more than one level of irrigation are required in order to determine the true value of irrigation. Sometimes the conclusion has been drawn that irrigation does not pay in the humid region because only one irrigation treatment was tried and this was an unprofitable one—but another rate or frequency of application might have been much better.

Some data in the humid region provide the information in this form.

An example is the determination of the response of cotton to various levels of irrigation at the Mississippi Delta Branch Station in 1952, 1953, and 1954. Unirrigated plots yielded an average of 2,700 pounds of seed cotton an acre. Plots irrigated when the soil was at wilting point (15 atmospheres tension) averaged 3,030 pounds an acre. Plots irrigated when half the available moisture was depleted (4 atmospheres tension) averaged 3,340 pounds an acre. Plots irrigated when one-quarter of the available moisture was depleted (1 atmosphere tension) averaged 3,380 pounds an acre. The research men concluded that irrigation at about 4 atmospheres moisture tension (50 percent depletion of available moisture for their soil) was about optimum under their conditions.

A separate study at that location had shown that the moisture deficiency encountered was likely to occur in at least 11 out of 22 years in June; 17 out of 22 years in July; and 21 out of 22 years in August.

At the experiment station in Oxford, N. C., in 1951, an increase in gross income from irrigation of tobacco of about 150 dollars an acre was measured. Two rates of irrigation gave about the same yield and value. The drought encountered might be expected to occur about 4 out of 10 years, on the average.

A study at the same location in 1952 under weather conditions expected 7 out of 10 years showed an increase of gross return of only 80 dollars an acre if the regular planting density, 6,800 plants to the acre, was used. When the plant population was increased to 10,500 the acre, the gross income was about 250 dollars an acre greater than unirrigated with regular spacing.

Potato yields at the New Jersey Agricultural Experiment Station were increased in 1953 and 1954 by each of three irrigation treatments in comparison with no irrigation. Irrigation at 0.8, 1.2, or 2.5 atmospheres maximum moisture tension had no significant differential effect on the yields. The irrigation study was conducted from 1946 through 1954, and yield increases were obtained every year. The greatest increases came in 1953 and 1954, however, because they were the years with greatest moisture deficiency.

Studies conducted at Ithaca, N. Y., by the Department of Agriculture and the Cornell University Agricultural Experiment Station in 1950, 1951, and 1952 showed that the forage yield on nonirrigated "high fertilization" plots was consistently greater than yields on irrigated "normal fertilization" plots —a good indication that often the maintenance of high fertility alone will increase yields more than will irrigation coupled with low fertility.

The University of Illinois completed a 5-year study on the irrigation of pasture for beef cattle. The results showed that irrigation did not pay. Yields from the irrigated pasture were consistently more than those from the nonirrigated pasture, but the increase in beef production was not enough to pay the cost of irrigating. In the analysis of the results of the test is the statement: "It is reasonable to expect pasture irrigation to be economically feasible when better fertility treatments and better grazing management practices are used."

The difference between profit and loss in this case was management and fertility—a good example that water alone will not do the job.

Irrigation, properly used, eliminates the drought hazard from farming, but you should remember that soil management (fertility, tilth, and aeration) will replace soil moisture as the major limiting factor in crop production.

THE AMOUNT of water to apply at any particular irrigation should be the depth of water, expressed in inches, required to bring the moisture content of the desired portion of the soil profile up to field capacity plus the depth required to overcome unavoidable losses. Stated another way, it is the depth of water to be replaced in the profile divided by the estimated efficiency of irrigation.

An example: Assuming an irrigation efficiency of 70 percent and the depth of water required to refill the soil profile as 1.8 inches, the total depth of water that would be applied would be 1.8 divided by 0.70, or 2.6 inches.

In determining the required depth of water application at any given time, the irrigator is faced with the problem of first estimating or measuring the amount of available moisture remaining in the soil profile within the predetermined irrigation depth.

After the soil moisture remaining in the profile has been determined, the difference between it and the total available water-holding capacity of the profile is the amount to be replaced by irrigation. The actual depth of application is determined by dividing the amount to be replaced by the anticipated irrigation efficiency.

MEASURING OR ESTIMATING the available soil moisture can be done in several ways. Each has advantages and limitations. We mention five of them.

Soil samples are taken at desired depths at several places in each soil type encountered in the field. The samples are weighed, dried in an oven, and weighed again. The difference in weight can be converted readily into percentage or inches of available water remaining in the profile.

Measuring instruments for measuring soil moisture are available commercially. The results obtained with them are not so accurate as those obtained by the sampling and drying procedure. They are being improved, and their use may result in more efficient water application if they are used carefully and with a realization of their limitations. Most of the instruments are of one or two general types—the tensiometer and electrical conductivity measuring devices.

Moisture accounting, or accumulated consumptive-use values, have been used to maintain a daily inventory of the soil moisture remaining in the profile.

Starting at a time when the moisture level in the soil profile is known to be at or very near field capacity, a "bookkeeping" system is set up whereby the computed consumptive use is subtracted daily from the total available moisture in the profile. When the daily balance has reached a predetermined level, usually 50 to 60 percent of the total, the time to commence irrigation has been indicated.

The daily consumptive-use values are average values computed from climatological data for monthly periods. The values must be adjusted from the computed values as temperature, humidity, sunshine, and wind velocities vary from normal. The effective

rainfall also must be measured and added to the daily balance as it occurs.

This procedure has the obvious advantage of requiring no equipment or field labor. Its accuracy depends on the accuracy of the computed daily consumptive-use rates and on the irrigator's judgment in evaluating the climatological departures from normal and his adjustment of these rates.

The feel and the appearance of soil samples taken from various depths give an estimate of the amount of available moisture in the soil profile. Samples are taken at several places in a field with a soil auger or shovel. Their feel and appearance are compared with a table or guide sheet prepared for the soils in the area, and the soil moisture level is estimated. This method is not accurate, but with experience the irrigator should be able to estimate the moisture level within reasonable limits of error.

Irrigation guides, developed by employees of the Department of Agriculture and experiment stations in the humid area, contain the best local information about soils, crops, and their treatment under irrigation.

The guides give estimates of the water-holding capacity and the intake rate of a particular soil type. Peak moisture-use rates and recommended depth to irrigate are shown for the different crops. Frequency of irrigation for periods of peak moisture-use rates and probable efficiencies to be expected from the system are listed.

WATER SUPPLIES for irrigation in the humid eastern areas come from three general sources—perennial streams, reservoirs or lakes, and ground water.

Regardless of the source, the water supply should be dependable, adequate to meet the requirements of the acreage of crops to be irrigated, of suitable quality, and legally available.

Perennial streams in the humid areas depend for their flow almost entirely on rainfall. As a rule their rates of flow fluctuate widely throughout the year. The flow in streams, particularly the smaller ones, is usually lowest during long dry periods when the requirements are greatest.

The rate of dependable flow required when irrigating directly from a stream depends on the size of the area irrigated, the moisture requirements of the crops during periods of peak use, the efficiency of the distribution system on the farm, and the time allotted for finishing one irrigation.

This required rate may be determined using the formula $Q=\dfrac{453\ AD}{FH}$, in which Q is the required flow in gallons per minute, A is the irrigated area in acres, D is the gross depth of application in inches, F is the number of days required to complete one irrigation, and H is the actual operating hours per day.

If losses occur in the farm distribution system, the required flow, Q, must be increased to the extent of the losses. There will be no losses in pipelines and almost negligible losses in lined ditches, but the losses in unlined ditches may be large.

For example: If a farmer requires 2.4 inches of water on a 40-acre field in 6 days, irrigating for 12 hours a day, his required stream flow would be 600 gallons per minute, computed as follows:

$$Q=\frac{453\times 40\ \text{acres}\times 2.4\ \text{inches}}{6\ \text{days}\times 12\ \text{hours}}=$$

600 g. p. m.

OFTEN THE FARMER can increase the acreage irrigated by a given rate of flow by storing the overnight flow in an excavated pit or reservoir.

Except for the larger streams whose adequacy of supply is obvious, the dependable flow in dry weather must be determined. If the stream has not been gaged by the United States Geological Survey or some other Federal or State agency, arrangements should be made to measure the flow during a dry period.

The quality of water in streams in the humid areas is generally satisfactory for irrigation purposes, but cau-tion is needed wherever pollution from industrial or mine wastes may occur.

The mouths of streams along the Atlantic and gulf coasts are influenced by tidal fluctuations and often contain excessive amounts of salt. A remedy is to install automatic tide gates, which open to permit the flow of fresh water at low tide and close to keep out sea water at high tide. Tidal streams may also be used for irrigating only at periods of low tide, when fresh water is running in them. Tidal streams should be used for irrigation only after chemical analyses have shown that their waters are suitable.

The rights of a farmer to use water from streams in most States in the humid area are governed by the riparian doctrine. Under the rules of common law, a riparian owner is entitled to have the stream flow through or past his land undiminished in quantity and unimpaired in quality except for use by upper riparian owners for domestic purposes. The courts in many States have not determined whether irrigation constitutes domestic use. In such instances the farmers' rights to use water for irrigation are in doubt.

STORAGE RESERVOIRS used for irrigation purposes usually are of the impounding type, developed by constructing an earth dam across an intermittent or spring-fed stream. The reservoirs should be located as near to the irrigated fields as possible.

The acreage of crops irrigated from a farm reservoir must be limited to the acreage for which water will be available as required throughout the growing season.

The required storage capacity of a farm reservoir used for irrigation is determined after considering the maximum seasonal requirements of the crops to be irrigated, the effective rainfall expected in the growing season, the application efficiency of the method of irrigation, the unavoidable losses from seepage and evaporation, and the volume of dry-weather flow. An allowance for anticipated sedimentation in the reservoir should usually be made.

The amount of runoff to the reservoir that can be expected annually from a given watershed acreage depends on many interrelated climatological and physical factors that vary widely over the States in the humid area. These factors must be duly considered for each watershed before an estimate of expected annual runoff can be made. It is often possible, however, to estimate the adequacy of the contributing watershed by observing and studying other nearby reservoirs with watershed areas having similar runoff-producing characteristics.

Offchannel storage is sometimes provided in reservoirs constructed on sites where the watershed area is relatively small but where water can be pumped or diverted from a nearby stream during the rainy seasons and stored.

The farmer's right to impound surface runoff for irrigation purposes is not ordinarily questioned if he owns the entire watershed area and all runoff is from his land. He may impound runoff from lands owned by others only if he does not damage owners below him by depriving them of their riparian rights to such water.

In most States in the humid area a permit to impound water must be obtained from a designated State or county agency.

GROUND WATER or water stored beneath the surface of the ground in layers of saturated sand and gravel is available in many localities. Not all of this water can be recovered, and the water table in all areas is not close enough to the surface to be within the economic limit of recovery. If conditions are favorable, however, ground water becomes the most dependable source of irrigation water.

The most feasible method of recovering this water is by pumping from wells. The required rates of flow from wells are computed in the same manner as we gave for perennial streams. The capacity of wells sometimes can be augmented by storage facilities.

In many localities water can be obtained near the surface from shallow water-bearing strata. They usually have low specific yields, and a single well may not yield the required flow. It is advisable then to consider a battery installation. Of the several types of shallow wells, the drilled well and the driven-point well are used most commonly. The drilled well generally is more expensive than the driven-point well but is better suited for irrigation purposes in that yields usually are greater.

The quality of ground water in the humid States generally is good enough for irrigation purposes. Near the Atlantic and gulf coasts, however, salt intrusion has affected deep aquifers in many places to the extent that their waters are unfit for irrigation. Well water of questionable quality should be tested before it is used.

The rights of a farmer to the use of ground water for irrigation are not clearly defined in most Eastern States. The rule of reasonable use applies in many States to ground water, and it may be used for irrigation if other users are not affected adversely. In some States and in many counties a permit is required to develop ground water supplies.

APPLICATION of irrigation water can be done by three general methods: Sprinkler irrigation, surface irrigation, and subirrigation. The choice of method depends on the climate, the characteristics of the soil, the topography of the land, the water supply, the crop to be irrigated, and the availability of labor. No one method fits all conditions.

In sprinkler irrigation the water is sprayed into the air and falls on the land in a uniform pattern at a rate that is less than the intake rate of the soil.

The sprinkler method has a number of advantages. It is adapted to most soils that can be irrigated and is particularly adapted to sandy soils. It can be used on all major crops except rice. Sprinklers can be used on level land

and steep slopes on land subject to erosion. They can be used with the necessary erosion control and drainage measures, and require little or no land leveling. Light applications for new seedings and small plants can be made efficiently. Farming operations are not hindered by field irrigation ditches and dikes. Sprinklers can make efficient use of small streams of water. Soluble fertilizers can generally be applied and controlled economically and efficiently. Frost can be controlled on certain fruit and truck crops. Most of the equipment can be moved from field to field and has a resale value.

Some limitations: A sprinkler system usually requires the highest initial investment, except in places where extensive land leveling is necessary for surface methods. Wind causes uneven water distribution. The power requirements are high because of high pressures required to operate the sprinklers. Sprinklers require clean water relatively free of sand and debris. Water cannot be applied efficiently at low rates on hot, windy days. Labor requirements may be high.

IN THE FURROW IRRIGATION, small streams are run in furrows between the crop rows. The water soaks into the soil and spreads out into the crop root areas between furrows.

The furrow system is adapted to all field crops planted in rows, including truck crops, tree fruits, small fruits, and vineyards.

The land to be irrigated should have enough depth of productive soil to permit necessary land leveling without exposing harmful amounts of subsoil. The water intake rate should not be much less than 0.3 inch an hour or more than 4 inches an hour.

The loams and clay loams are best adapted because of their high water-holding capacities and intake rates, which are generally within the range given above. Very sandy soils are ordinarily not adapted to furrow irrigation because of their high intake rates, which necessitate short row lengths.

Topography should be smooth and relatively uniform. Irregular topography increases leveling costs and work.

Water should be available at the rate of at least 10 gallons per minute an acre to be irrigated. The supply must be sufficient to satisfy the requirements of the crop acreage to be irrigated and overcome all losses.

Furrow grades in humid areas normally should not exceed 0.3 foot per 100 feet so as to prevent erosive action resulting from high intensity storms. Furrow grades up to 0.5 foot per 100 feet are permissible if the lengths of run are reduced to prevent the accumulation of a volume of water that will cause erosion. A minimum furrow grade of 0.05 foot per 100 feet should be provided to help surface drainage.

The slope of the land surface at right angles to the direction of irrigation, often called the cross slope, should not exceed 2 feet per 100 feet where the furrow depths are maintained at 6 inches or more. If furrow depths less than 6 inches are maintained, the cross slope should be less than 2 percent, and it may be necessary to shorten the length of run to prevent accumulation of enough water to cause overtopping of the furrows.

The moving of equipment across wet and muddy areas of the field is not required in furrow irrigation. If land leveling is not excessive, initial investment is low because the furrow normally developed in row crop cultivation is used.

Uniform water distribution and relatively high efficiency can be obtained with a proper design and operation. The water does not wet foliage and wash off insecticides. The required land leveling provides excellent surface drainage. Small streams of water can be used efficiently.

Furrow irrigation has several limitations. Its use is confined to the soils and topographic conditions we mentioned. Land leveling usually is required to make the system function properly—water must travel the entire length of the row without ponding. That means that all high and low spots must be removed and the land given enough slope to let the water flow down the furrows. The leveled grade must be maintained from year to year. Some water is lost from the furrow ends.

BORDER IRRIGATION applies water to a field that has been divided into several strips bounded by low earth ridges or border levees. Water is flooded over the strips between the ridges, which confine the water to a specified area until the required amount has entered the soil or has fulfilled the purpose for which it was applied.

Two types of border irrigation are recommended for use in humid climates—contour and graded borders.

IN CONTOUR BORDER systems, earth dikes are placed on the contour to hold water on gently sloping land. The method is used commonly to irrigate rice. It also is well adapted for irrigating improved pasture and hay crops. Sometimes it can be used to irrigate row crops such as corn and cotton.

The water is spread rapidly over the area between dikes at a rate that is considerably above the intake rate of the soil. It is retained in place by the dikes and (except on rice) is drained off as soon as the desired depth of application has soaked into the soil. The excess water is used to irrigate a similar area lower down the slope.

Soils should be of a medium or heavy texture. They should have an available water-holding capacity of not less than 1.5 inches per foot of depth or not less than 3 inches for the root zone depth of the crop. The intake rate should not exceed 0.5 inch an hour. When it is used for rice, the soil profile must contain a restricting layer just below the root zone. The permeability rate of this layer should not exceed 0.01 inch. The topography should be smooth and reasonably uniform. The maximum slope should not exceed 1 foot per 100 feet. If slopes in relatively small parts of a field exceed 1 percent, land leveling or grading is necessary.

Enough water must be available to permit rapid flooding of each border strip (the area between the dikes). A minimum of 225 gallons per minute per acre in the largest border is recommended. Since one man can irrigate a relatively large acreage in a day, larger irrigation streams than those specified may be desirable in order to utilize labor efficiently.

Advantages of the contour border method are: Efficient and uniform distribution of irrigation water is easily obtained, maximum utilization can be made of rainfall, adequate drainage facilities are easily provided, operation of the system is simple and easy, initial installation costs are low, and operational costs are relatively low.

Limitations are: The contour borders are restricted in use by the required combination of soil characteristics and topographic conditions we mentioned, land smoothing is required, relatively large irrigation streams are usually required, and the maintenance of ditches and structures is a problem.

The surface of the area to be irrigated should be smoothed by two or more passes with a landplane. The number of passes depends on the relative smoothness of the existing surface.

Smoothing tends to permit better alinement of the levees and a more uniform application of water and provides for more effective drainage.

GRADED OR PARALLEL BORDER irrigation systems have parallel strips of land separated by low earth ridges on fields that have previously been leveled to a desired grade. The strips are transversely level between borders and normally run down the predominant slope. If the land has been leveled in benches, the strips run perpendicular to the predominant slope.

A large stream of water is introduced at the head of the border strip. A sheet of water, confined by the ridges or borders, is advanced down the slope. It enters the soil as it goes. The desired amount of the water is applied to the strip, usually before the sheet has reached the lower end. The water is then cut off; when the receding sheet of water has reached the lower end, the entire strip has been irrigated.

The graded border method is adapted to most soils whose profile and topography permit the required leveling at a reasonable cost and without lasting reduction in productivity.

It can be used efficiently on all soils except those that have extremely high or extremely low intake rates. Soils with high intake rates require excessively large irrigation streams and very short strips if losses from deep percolation at the upper ends of the strips are to be kept within reason. Soils with low intake rates require relatively small irrigation streams, and it is hard to avoid excessive runoff from the lower ends of the strips and to get adequate coverage over the land.

This method is recommended for the irrigation of close-growing crops that are not damaged by temporary flooding. It is used primarily for irrigating hay crops, pastures, and small grains.

The topography of land to be irrigated by this method must be flat to very gently sloping. The slopes should be sufficiently uniform to permit land leveling within reasonable and economic limits. Slopes should ordinarily not exceed 2 feet per 100 feet.

The method has a number of advantages. The initial investment is relatively low, because the border ridges can be constructed with ordinary farm implements. The greatest initial expense is for land leveling; if that cost can be kept low, the total initial investment will be modest. With a properly installed system, one man can irrigate a relatively large acreage. Labor costs thus are relatively low. If pumping is involved, this cost will be low, since the system does not operate under pressure. Uniform distribution and resulting high water-use efficiencies may be obtained through proper design, layout, and operation. Relatively large irrigation streams may be used efficiently. Operation of the system is simple and easy. Properly graded border strips give excellent surface drainage if adequate outlet facilities are provided.

On the other hand, a more precise land-leveling job is required for graded borders than is needed for other surface methods. Relatively large irrigation streams are needed—usually in excess of 900 gallons per minute. Light applications, less than 2 inches deep, cannot ordinarily be made without difficulty and without sacrificing efficiency. Difficulties often are encountered on soils that tend to bake or crust after becoming wet. The border ridges present a maintenance problem and may hinder the use of machines.

A precise land-leveling job is a normal prerequisite to successful irrigation by the graded border method. The land should be graded to a slope of not more than 1 foot per 100 feet (in the direction of irrigation) for hay crops and small grains. Slopes up to 2 feet per 100 feet are permissible for irrigating permanent pastures.

If the crop to be irrigated is to be rotated with row crops irrigated by the furrow method, the permissible slopes for furrows in the direction of irrigation will be applicable.

The border strips should be transversely level if possible. The cross slope should never exceed 0.10 foot in the width of one strip.

The width, or distance between border ridges, is largely governed by the slope of the land and the size of the irrigation stream that is available and can be safely turned into the head of the strip. The selected border strip width whenever possible should be a multiple of the width of the least flexible farm implement to be used.

SUBIRRIGATION is a method of applying water beneath the ground surface rather than on the surface.

Subirrigation is accomplished usually by controlling the water table and maintaining it at some predetermined depth below the surface. Moisture then reaches the plant roots through capillary movement upward.

This method has several major advantages. Subirrigation can be used effectively on soils that are difficult and expensive to irrigate by other methods. Except where water is introduced through tile drains, the installation costs are low. Labor requirements are low. Subirrigation is adaptable to a large variety of crops and does not interfere with tillage practices.

Subirrigation also has limitations. The main one is the unusual combination of natural conditions required. Only water of good quality may be used. Soils may become saline unless careful control is exercised. High levels of fertility may be hard to maintain.

Several conditions must be met. An adequate supply of water relatively free of salts must be available throughout the growing season. The topography must be nearly level and comparatively smooth. Land leveling or smoothing is required in most cases for best results. A layer of soil must exist immediately below the surface soil, which is sufficiently permeable to permit the free and rapid movement of water both laterally and vertically. A barrier against excessive losses through deep percolation must exist in the soil profile. This barrier may be in the form of a relatively impervious layer in the substratum or a permanently high natural water table on which an artificial table can be maintained. An adequate drainage outlet is needed.

Relatively few places exist in the humid area where all these conditions occur together. The use of subirrigation therefore is limited. Among the more well-known areas where subirrigation is practiced are the Everglades of southern Florida, the Flatwoods of the Florida Coastal Plain, and smaller, scattered localities with organic soils in Michigan, Indiana, Minnesota, Wisconsin, and Ohio.

The principles of subirrigation are the same in all areas, although the means of introducing water into the soil profile may differ. The controlled water table is usually 12 to 30 inches below the surface.

Drainage Problems and Methods

T. W. Edminster and Ronald C. Reeve

Good management of the land means good management of the water. Excess water in the soil interferes with crop growth and the timely performance of tillage, seeding, cultivation, and harvesting. Poor drainage also abets the accumulation of salts in soils of arid regions.

The source of the excess water determines the severity of drainage problems and the ways to solve them.

The problems are: Periodic flooding of lands by overflow from streams or by tidal action in coastal areas; overflow of low-lying flat lands from hillside runoff or return-flow seepage on sloping land; accumulation of too much water in soils when subsoil drainage is restricted; accumulation of excess water in depressions or low-lying areas, such as old ponds and lakebeds; buildup of a high water table as a result of applying excess irrigation water; buildup of a high water table from seepage losses from irrigation canals; and the development of a high water table because of the movement of artesian water.

Lands are drained primarily to insure agricultural productivity and increase efficiency of farming operations.

There are other beneficial effects. Poorly drained areas require large expenditures annually to build and drain highway subgrades and to prepare construction sites. Mosquitoes and some disease problems may be related to poor drainage.

About 103 million acres of land, encompassing nearly 2 million farms, were in organized district and county drainage enterprises in 1950. These public projects were in 40 States and covered areas from less than 100 acres to more than 1 million acres. The average enterprise covered about 7 thousand acres.

The annual cost of constructing, operating, and maintaining public drainage projects was about 32 million dollars in 1949. It was estimated in 1956 that some 15 million acres were still too wet for cultivation and that crop losses were frequent on an additional 10 million poorly drained acres.

The Soil Conservation Service in 1955 estimated that more than 20 million acres would require drainage by means of group drainage facilities.

An estimated 15.5 million acres of land have been drained through private projects. Soil Conservation Service in 1955 estimated that 67 million acres still required drainage improvement through individual activity.

The development of a drainage system will embrace three basic points: The drainage requirements, the water transmission properties of soils, and physiographic features.

THE DRAINAGE REQUIREMENTS involve the adequacy of drainage—whether there is too much water on or in the soil—and the amount of water to be drained.

In humid regions, where rainfall supplies most of the moisture for crops, the drainage requirements are related to the oxygen status and the soil-water relationships that will influence crop growth. The optimum moisture content of the soil for farming is particularly important.

The drainage requirement usually is referred to as a drainage coefficient and is expressed in terms of the time required to remove a given depth of water—for example, a drainage coefficient of three-eighths means that the drainage system would permit the removal of three-eighths inch of water from the soil surface in 24 hours. The drainage requirement may be adjusted to the susceptibility of the crop to damage by exposure to excess water or to the cost of delaying farm work.

The salinity factor alters greatly the drainage requirements in arid regions. Irrigation water contains soluble salts, which are concentrated in the soil by evaporation and transpiration. To keep the salts in the soil solution from becoming so concentrated that they hurt crop growth, excess water must pass through the root zone and flush away, or leach out, soluble salts.

Information concerning the consumptive use—the amount of water lost by evaporation and transpiration—helps one to estimate the amount of water that must pass through and beyond the root zone to provide the required amount of leaching. That amount is determined on the basis of the salt content of the irrigation water and the salt concentration that can be permitted in the drainage water.

The leaching requirement is an estimate of the fraction of the surface-applied water that must be leached through the root zone to control soil salinity at any specified level. The total amount of water to be drained will be greater than the leaching requirement by an amount equal to the losses in conveying and applying the water to the land, plus the water from other sources, such as management waste and artesian waters.

The amount of water that must be removed from the land may be expressed as a rate of flow per unit area of land. One must also establish a minimum allowable water-table depth to prevent damage to crops, either from excess water in the root zone or from the concentration of salts in the soil by upward flow.

The minimum depth is governed by the crops to be grown, the soil conditions, and the salt content of the drainage water. The main requirement in any case is that the depth to the water table must be such that the upward movement of salts from ground water into the root zone can be conveniently controlled.

If an adequate water-table depth cannot be maintained, irrigation and management practices can sometimes be altered to allow crop production. Improvement of irrigation efficiencies and more uniform application of water are examples of ways by which drainage conditions can be improved and a net movement of salts maintained.

Irrigation efficiency, losses in conveyance and distribution, regulatory losses, rainfall, the amount of salt in the irrigation water, and salt tolerance of crops all enter into the problem of determining drainage requirements.

The ability of soils to transmit water has primary importance in the drainage of farm lands. The rate at which water enters a soil after a rain or after an irrigation and the rate that water tables can be lowered and excess waters drained away are directly related to the rate at which water can move through the soil. Of the factors that govern the flow of water in soils, the transmission properties are the hardest to evaluate, primarily because soils vary so much.

THE PHYSIOGRAPHIC FEATURES bear strongly on drainage design. The topography, stratigraphy (or the vertical arrangement of strata or layers of different types of soil), and location of outlets and sources of water must be considered in the design.

Topography is important when excess water originates as an application on the land surface, either as rainfall or from irrigation. The location of drains depends largely on topography.

Stratigraphy must be considered in subsurface drainage. The occurrence of permeable layers, such as sands or gravel, within the soil profile at a convenient depth to be tapped by open or tile drains may permit a wider spacing of drains and thereby reduce the total number of drains. On sloping hillsides or at the bottom of a slope, interception drains may drain relatively large acreages, but on relatively level lands a large number of ditches or tile drains may be required to control the water table.

The effectiveness of drainage structures is related directly to their location with respect to subsoil layers. Water that enters the soil in one area from rainfall or deep percolation from irrigation may come to the surface in a nearby area or may appear as a seep on a hillside, according to the path of flow through the subsoil. The drains should be located to remove water from the more permeable soil layers through which such flow occurs.

Highly permeable layers may discharge excess water from an area or may conduct excess water from one area to another. Impermeable soil layers may intercept conducting layers and block the free movement of ground water away from the farmland.

Proper orientation and placement of the drains with respect to stratigraphy may be the most important single factor in the design of a good system.

In general, the most effective method of drainage for the control of ground water tables is one that takes advantage of the most permeable materials in the profile for intercepting, collecting, and discharging excess waters from the land.

Crops may be affected in a number of ways by high water tables or excess soil moisture. Some affect root development—aeration and temperature of the soil, nutrient uptake, and plant disease. Salinity problems may also develop and affect crop growth in arid soils where water tables are just under the surface.

The roots of most cultivated crops will not penetrate saturated soil areas. When a rising water table inundates a root, there is usually an early change in the appearance of the crop, reflecting changes in the ability of the root to function properly.

POOR SOIL AERATION is a primary factor in this adverse response of roots and crops. Gas diffusion drops rapidly if the larger pore spaces are filled with water. The oxygen level declines and the carbon dioxide level rises as organic matter decomposes when the soil is saturated. Oxygen, which helps convert insoluble plant nutrients into a soluble form, also is a critical agent in the decomposition of organic materials. It is essential for seed germination and the development of root hairs. When the oxygen supply is cut off to roots of most cultivated plants, the root suffocates and dies, the intake of water and plant food is lowered, and the plant wilts and dies.

Plants that normally grow on well-drained and aerated soils usually are most sensitive to the lack of oxygen. Even plants, such as cranberries, which can remain covered during a long dormant period, however, will suffer from poor aeration in summer when the plant uses more water and nutrients. Plants that can withstand long periods of little oxygen have special tissues in their stems and roots that can conduct the oxygen to the roots.

Because carbon dioxide rarely occurs in the soil in amounts sufficient to harm the roots, the reduction in the oxygen level is the most critical result of soil saturation.

The gaseous balance changes more rapidly under higher temperatures because of greater biotic activity—one reason why flooding in summer often is more damaging than flooding in winter. A second reason is that the reduced plant growth in winter places fewer demands on the injured and unhealthy roots that may occur under winter flooding.

Poor aeration also affects the nutrient uptake by plants. In studies of the influence of restricted aeration on the growth and absorption of nutrients by corn, K. Lawton, while working in Iowa, reported that the order of reduction of absorption was potassium >calcium >magnesium >nitrogen >phosphorus. Ferrous iron was highest when the soil was moist. When it was saturated, higher concentrations of reduced iron and manganese may injure the plant roots. Hydrogen sulfide gas may

reach toxic levels when organic matter decomposes in saturated soil. Denitrification proceeds faster when the supply of oxygen is low. An upsetting of the nitrogen balance in saturated soils has been reflected in the lower content of crude protein content in plant tissues under such conditions.

SOIL TEMPERATURE is affected by exposure, amount of shade, radiation from the sun, moisture, and the rate of retention and movement of moisture in the soil.

Well-drained soils warm up faster than saturated soils. The specific heat of water is 1.000 at 15° C. The specific heat of dry mineral soils averages 0.20. That means that raising the temperature of a unit volume of water 1 degree requires 5 times the heat units required to raise an equal volume of dry mineral soil the same amount. The higher the moisture content of the soil, therefore, the greater is the amount of heat required to raise its temperature. The rapid evaporation of water from a saturated soil also has a cooling effect—it takes 580 calories of heat to transform 1 gram of water from the liquid state to a gaseous state.

This effect of excess moisture on soil temperature is particularly serious during the period when seeds germinate. Germination and root growth rates of most species increase slowly with an increase in temperature through a range of 20° to 25° C. from minimum to optimum temperature for normal growth.

Low soil temperatures usually restrict the branching and development of the fine roots. They also affect the period of dormancy and the rate of after-ripening and subsequent germination. The absorption and synthesis of organic materials, translocation of food materials within the root system, and respiration all depend on temperature of the soil.

The power of root cells to accumulate various nutrient ions is related directly to temperature. Low temperatures due to saturated soil do not appear to retard seriously the absorption of nitrogen, but they do affect the rate at which the roots reduce or assimilate the nitrate and convert it into organic forms.

Low soil temperatures similarly reduce the rate of absorption of water, even to the point of causing wilting if rapid transpiration creates considerable moisture stress. One or more factors may cause that: Retardation of root elongation; a lower rate of movement of water from the soil to the root; greater viscosity of water and of the root protoplasm; and decreased permeability of the root cells.

When low temperatures accompany poor aeration, plant roots lack the vigor necessary to resist infection. Tobacco root rot and onion smut are examples of infectious organisms that flourish when temperatures are low and moisture is excessive. Disease is usually most severe at temperatures that are otherwise unfavorable to the seedlings.

SOIL STRUCTURE—the arrangement of soil particles—can suffer from too much water. When soil is saturated, normal biotic activity and root development are reduced. If saturation continues, the normal wetting and drying cycles, with attendant shrinking and swelling action, are absent. Many persons have noted an improvement in soil structure after drainage. The low rates of water movement through poorly drained soils improve after drainage.

Soil structure also is destroyed or harmed when tillage, planting, and harvesting are done when the soil is too wet—notably when only a part of a field is poorly drained. Rather than delay farm operations on the well-drained parts of the field, the operator will go through the wet places and cause puddling. Imprudent pasturing of saturated meadows may cause similar destruction of soil. This breakdown of structure complicates the drainage problem later. Adequate drainage eliminates these hazards and permits the use of soil-improvement practices.

The accumulation of excess salts in the root zone of soils in drier localities often is associated with high water tables and inadequate drainage. When the water table rises near the soil surface, the rate of water movement upward to the surface is accelerated. As water is lost by evaporation and transpiration, the salts are left behind. If the process continues, salts soon accumulate in the soil root zone and the increase in salinity of the soil solution causes a reduction in crop growth.

Salts affect the growth of plants in two ways: By reducing the amount of water that the plants can take from the soil as a result of the increase in osmotic pressure, and by causing toxic effects. As the roots take up water, leaving most of the salt behind, the soil solution becomes saltier. The osmotic pressure, which is an expression of the salt content of the soil solution on an energy basis, increases as the salts build up. Retardation of growth is related directly to increases in the osmotic pressure of the soil solution and is largely independent of the kind of salts.

Chloride, sodium, boron, and bicarbonate may be toxic to some crops. Most fruit trees are susceptible to this kind of injury. A characteristic leafburn develops, leaves fall off, and the trees may die when harmful amounts of sodium or chloride are accumulated. Most field, forage, and truck crops may have much larger amounts of sodium or chloride in the leaves without developing visible symptoms of injury. Boron and bicarbonate are toxic to all species of plants, but the level of tolerance may vary among crops.

The installation of adequate drainage facilities before water tables rise close to the surface and the application of proper irrigation and management practices are necessary to prevent the deterioration of farmlands and reduced crop yields due to salt accumulation.

Surface drainage is the collection and removal of excess water from the surface. The movement of water downward through the soil and its discharge from the area by natural means or into deep open or tile drains is subsurface drainage. Subsurface drainage facilities are installed primarily to control the water table. Deep drains, open and closed, often are designed to perform both functions.

EFFECTIVE SURFACE DRAINAGE is particularly important in humid regions where excess surface water is a major problem. Surface drains are used to a lesser extent in irrigated areas. In arid regions, however, they have several applications in relation to effective soil- and water-management practices. Surface drainage facilities are designed to meet two objectives: Effective collection and discharge of excess surface waters into main drainage outlet channels and prevention of land inundation because of overflow from lands at higher elevation, streams, or tidal action.

These objectives are accomplished by the use of such practices as land forming or grading, bedding, drainage-type terraces, field ditches for surface water removal, random ditches, uniform or parallel ditches, and deep ditches to control the water table.

Land forming or grading provides simple primary drainage by removing the dead furrows, headlands, spoil banks, depressions, and ridges that restrict the rapid and orderly flow of water from the field to the collection and outletting ditches. It may be used in extremely flat places to create a positive grade towards an outlet ditch. Land forming is an effective supplementary practice in tiled areas when it is used to remove depressions that might otherwise overload single lines.

Bedding—turning furrows to the middle of a cut to form a ridge that gradually slopes towards deep furrows or field collection ditches—often is of limited value because of poor outlets.

Bedding is used primarily on slowly permeable soils having moderate depth and on slopes ranging from zero to 1.5 percent. Bed width is determined by the type of crop, field slope, soil permeability, and the adaptability to the farming operations.

Beds are generally wider under cultivated crops than under pasture and forage crops. Flatter slopes and soils with low infiltration and permeability rates require narrower beds. Bedding systems generally are hard to manage with high-speed farm equipment, because the ridge often is too dry for effective tillage before the interbed furrows are dry enough for machine cultivation. In most instances, bedding systems should be replaced by good land-forming practices supported by carefully designed field ditches.

Drainage terraces, sometimes referred to as cross-slope ditches, are particularly effective for shallow soils underlain by an impermeable subsoil. The drainage terrace is constructed with a top width of 15 to 25 feet and is 6 to 10 inches deep. The excavated material is used to fill depressions between the terraces. Farming operations are parallel to the terrace. Care must be taken to avoid dead furrows and other tillage scars that trap surface water. The smooth, flat 10:1 side slopes make this type of drain highly compatible with mechanized agriculture, and they are replacing conventional field ditches on sloping land.

Field ditches include random field ditches and uniform or parallel field ditches. One type has a single flat V-shaped channel, in which the excavated material is used to fill depressions.

Another design has twin-type channels, sometimes referred to as W-ditches, in which the surplus excavated material is placed between the channels to form a raised separation. This type is particularly good on flat land and on land that slopes to the drain from two directions. It provides for ready entrance of row drainage. Both types are designed with 8:1 to 10:1 side slopes, so that farm machinery can cross them.

Random field ditches are used to advantage in draining fields that have a few depressions that are too deep or too large to fill in by grading and smoothing. They are used to connect several depressions and then convey the excess water to a suitable outlet.

When farm implements must be moved across these ditches, side slopes should be no less than 8:1. If operations are parallel, side slopes of 4:1 may be used. Used with tile systems, they frequently eliminate need for costly surface inlets. Random ditches should not become a substitute for the more effective and efficient land-forming practices and drainage-type terraces.

Uniform or parallel ditches are used on relatively flat, poorly drained soils of too variable a topography to permit surface drainage by land forming or the other systems. They are laid out so that crop rows will lead to the ditches with a grade of 0.1 to 0.2 percent. Their spacing depends on the slope, the erosivity of the soil, and the cross-sectional capacity of the rows.

Ditches to control the water table are used on moderate to highly permeable soils and on organic soils where surface water must be removed and the water table must be lowered. These ditches are deeper than conventional ditches and have moderate to steep side slopes, depending on the type of soil material through which they are constructed. They must be carefully designed to assure sufficient carrying capacity when the water is high. When water-control structures are installed in the ditches, it is possible to control the position of the water table by lowering it in periods of excess and raising it during dry periods.

SURFACE DRAINAGE in arid regions where irrigation is practiced is a fundamental part of overall water management. Although the ideal irrigation system uniformly applies and stores enough water in the root zone for crop needs without wasting water, practical considerations in the application of water to lands makes the ideal hard to achieve. Consequently surface drainage facilities often are required.

On sloping lands, irrigated by the usual furrow and border methods, it is impractical to apply just enough water to wet the root zone uniformly over the entire length of run. To insure proper application at the end of the run, some water usually is wasted, and provisions must be made to collect and remove the runoff. The usual practice is to intercept the water with shallow ditches and discharge it into natural channels or deep drains. In areas where water supplies are limited, waste water is sometimes collected at the lower end of the field and pumped back to the upper end of the field for reuse. Surface drains are not needed then.

The level border method of irrigation is an effective way to attain high irrigation efficiencies on flat land. Water is impounded and allowed to penetrate the soil uniformly in long, narrow, level basins. If rainfall is heavy, surface drainage is necessary if this system is to succeed. If provision is not made to drain the basins, untimely rains might flood crops.

IN SUBSURFACE DRAINAGE, water moves into and through the soil and is discharged through natural drainage channels or through deep open or closed drains, which convey the water away from the field. The planning and design of subsurface drainage systems require knowledge of the drainage requirements of crops and the water-transmitting properties of the soil.

Surface drains are designed to remove ponded water and thus reduce the amount of water that enters the soil profile, but usually they are installed to maintain ground water tables at a sufficient depth to prevent waterlogging of the root zone. Adequate control of the water table in arid regions also prevents the accumulation of salts.

Tile drains, one of the five major types of subsurface drains, are hollow cylinders that are 4, 6, 8, or more inches in diameter and have a wall thickness of about one-twelfth their inside diameter. Usually they are made of burned clay or concrete. Clay tiles are commonly made in 1-foot lengths; 2-foot concrete tiles often are used. Water enters the tile drain through the space or joint between each tile. The tile line is surrounded with a gravel filter in arid regions to prevent the inflow of soil sediments.

Mole drains are a cylindrical channel formed in the soil by pulling a ball or bullet-shaped device through the soil at the bottom of a narrow blade.

Mole drains are similar to the tile drains in shape and function, but are unlined and unstabilized. They depend on the stability of the soil to maintain an open channel. They often have a dual role; they remove excess water during wet periods and are a conveyance system for subirrigation in dry periods. The life expectancy of mole drains is related directly to the stability of the soil in which they have been formed.

Perforated pipe or tubing—long sections of perforated conduits of metal, plastic, or bituminous-fiber—may be placed in a trench and covered or pulled into a mole channel behind a mole plow—a technique that eliminates the need for digging a trench. This system is effective in draining or crossing quicksand pockets that do not provide adequate stability for conventional tile systems.

Deep open drains or channels, which are dug to depths of 5 to 12 feet or more for the purpose of controlling the water table, actually function as a subsurface drain. Frequently they serve as main outlet channels for other drains.

THE TYPE OF SUBSURFACE system used depends on the nature of the drainage problem. In treating localized drainage problems, such as small depressions and waterways, and in intercepting wet-weather springs and seeps, subsurface drains are placed where needed without regard for a uniform pattern. In draining extensive uniform areas that are essentially flat, however, a definite pattern usually is established, with laterals at more or less uniform spacings discharging into main outlets. These patterns are sometimes called gridiron or herringbone layouts.

In any system, careful attention must be given to the design of the outlet drain to assure that it is of adequate capacity, especially if the outlet is a

closed drain. If a free-gravity outfall cannot be obtained, a pump outlet may be used.

DRAINAGE PRACTICES in arid regions resemble those in humid areas in many respects. We mention two important differences. Because of the salinity factor, the water-table depth that is required for favorable conditions for plants is considerably greater in arid soils than in soils in humid regions. The drainage needs in arid regions are closely related to irrigation practices, which are subject to control, but in humid areas drainage needs depend largely on natural rainfall.

To maintain water tables at depths sufficient to control salt accumulation in arid regions, drains are commonly installed to depths of 6 feet or more. Depths of 2.5 to 4 feet are considered adequate in many humid areas. If salinity is not involved, a shallow water table may be advantageous in that it serves as a source of water for crop use.

In the Netherlands a water table held at a constant depth of about 24 inches is desirable, and many crops are grown under constant water-table conditions. The natural rainfall there is in excess of 20 inches, approximately the minimum total required to keep the soils leached and at the same time to provide sufficient water for crop use.

Good drainage practices must be accompanied by sound irrigation and soil-management practices if maximum benefits are to be obtained.

It is essential that management of excess water be integrated with other soil-management practices in order that the overall farm operational program may be successful. In addition to water management, such practices as tillage, replenishment of organic matter, proper fertility practices, insect and disease control, and good irrigation practices are essential. Improved irrigation practices and other farming procedures which control the use of excess water will considerably lessen in most cases the need for costly drainage installations.

Cropping Systems and Soil

W. H. Allaway

Some of the first agricultural experiments in these United States consisted of comparisons of different cropping systems. Their results convinced many agricultural leaders that crop rotations that regularly included a legume sod crop were needed for lasting production.

But a Mississippi 4–H Club boy in 1955 raised 304 bushels of corn an acre, a new record, on a field that had been in corn for at least 6 consecutive years and had never produced more than about 15 bushels an acre before 1950.

Corn has been grown continuously on the Morrow plots at the University of Illinois alongside a 3-year rotation of corn, oats, and meadow since 1876. The results from these comparisons formed one of the cornerstones of the belief that rotations were essential to the maintenance of soil productivity.

But liberal amounts of nitrogen, phosphate, and potash fertilizers and lime were applied in 1955 to part of each plot in this experiment. Where this fertilizer was applied, the 79th consecutive crop of corn yielded 86 bushels an acre. It made 36 bushels an acre without the fertilizer. Corn on plots that had been in a corn-oats-meadow rotation with no soil treatment for 79 years made 63 bushels an acre without the fertilizer and 102 bushels where the nitrogen, phosphate, potash, and lime had been added in 1955. Plots that had been receiving regular treatments of manure, lime, and rock phosphate since 1904 yielded 79 bushels an acre without the extra fertilizer in 1955 and 98 bushels when they were liberally fertilized.

Corn plots of the corn-oats-meadow rotation, treated since 1904 with manure, lime, and rock phosphate, made 100 bushels an acre without the added fertilizer in 1955, and 101 bushels with the added fertilizer. Thus, on the Morrow plots, differences in soil productivity built up by 79 years of different cropping systems were reduced by one application of chemical fertilizer.

Other crops also produce well in continuous culture. Most of the sugarcane and much of the wheat, cotton, and rice raised the world over are grown on the same soil year after year.

On the other hand, crop rotations that include a legume or legume-grass sod at frequent intervals have contributed to the productivity of our soils and to the permanence of American agriculture. To be convinced of this, you need only to look at some of the fine general farms in Pennsylvania and Ohio, where rotation with clover or a grass-legume mixture has been used for many years. Today these farms are more productive than ever.

All this points up the fact that to maintain productivity many farmers can choose their rotation or cropping system from among many possibilities. The decision as to which method to choose is often of critical importance in determining farm income. In considering the choice, one should distinguish between a cropping system and a soil-management system.

A cropping system is the kind and sequence of crops grown on a given area of soil over a period of time. It may be a regular rotation of different crops, in which the crops follow a definite order of appearance on the land, or it may consist of only one crop, grown year after year on the same area. Other cropping systems may include different crops but lack a definite and planned order in which the crops follow one another.

A soil-management system includes the cropping system plus the other practices, such as the use of fertilizers, terracing, irrigation, and drainage, that accompany the cropping system. When it comes to maintaining productivity, the effect of the cropping system may depend on what other practices are used with it in making up the system of soil management.

What effects might each crop have on the properties of the soil? Will any particular one of these crops make the soil better or worse for the next crop?

Some plants add to the supply of nitrogen, an important plant nutrient. Inoculated legumes can get a good share of the nitrogen they need by fixing uncombined nitrogen from the air. Nonleguminous crops must depend on chemically fixed sources of nitrogen— from decomposition of the soil organic matter, manure, or chemical fertilizers. When a legume like alfalfa or a clover is grown and at least part of the crop is plowed under for the next crop, the supply of available nitrogen in the soil will be increased.

The amount of nitrogen a legume adds to the soil depends on its kind and the way it is managed. Soybeans are a legume, but most of the nitrogen they have taken from the air is carried off in the form of the proteins in the seed when the beans are harvested.

Alfalfa, sweetclover, red clover, and Ladino clover are among the more effective legumes for building up nitrogen. As a general rule, the more top growth turned under when a legume field is plowed, the more nitrogen is added to the soil. The amounts of nitrogen added to a field soil by legumes is not accurately known because they are hard to measure. Very likely a perennial such as alfalfa may add 100 pounds an acre of nitrogen to the soil if some of the top growth is turned.

Legumes often are grown with grasses. When such a mixture is plowed for the next crop, the organisms that decompose the carbonaceous residues of the grasses utilize the simple nitrogen compounds that the decomposing legume residues liberate. The net effect is to prolong the release of simple nitrogen compounds for use by the next crop. It may help to prevent losses of the legume nitrogen by leaching and provide some of the nitrogen requirements of nonlegume crops.

In most experiments with crop rotations, yields of grains have been higher when they were rotated with legumes than when they were grown steadily, without rotation. In many of the experiments one could not determine exactly the extent to which the increased yields were due to the nitrogen the legume added to the soil and the extent to which the increases were due to improved soil structure or fewer insects and diseases.

Sometimes nitrogen fixed by legumes can meet most of the requirements for the other crops grown. In some instances it may be best to depend largely on nitrogen fertilizers or manure. In a few soils, high in organic matter, the release of nitrogen by decomposition of the native organic matter may meet most of the requirements of the crops.

Some crops cause marked declines in available nitrogen. If the part of the crop harvested and removed from the soil is high in nitrogen, the removal by itself may represent a critical depletion of the supply of nitrogen. If the crop is one that leaves a large carbonaceous residue and the residue is returned to the soil, the organisms decomposing it will temporarily tie up most of the simple compounds of nitrogen in the soil. This nitrogen will be kept in forms unavailable to succeeding crops until carbonaceous residues decompose.

Crops have different effects on the supply of mineral nutrients. Some crops can feed better than others on the less available forms of some of the mineral nutrients. When these strong feeders are grown, turned under, and decomposed, the minerals they took up are converted to readily available forms for the following crops.

E. E. DeTurk, of Illinois, discovered that sweetclover takes up phosphorus from rock phosphate more readily than

corn and wheat do. When sweetclover was turned under, the supply of readily available phosphorus in the surface soil was increased. In addition to their ability to convert relatively insoluble phosphorus minerals into forms more readily available to other crops, sweetclover, alfalfa, and some other deeprooted legumes tend to bring phosphorus up from the deeper soil layers and deposit it on or near the surface of the soil if not all of the top growth is harvested.

Buckwheat also can feed on difficultly available forms of mineral nutrients and convert them to more readily available forms.

A system—"a bush-fallow"—of alternating food crops with forest is practiced on many areas in tropical countries. A great deal remains to be learned about the mechanisms involved in it, but at least part of the beneficial effect seems to come from nutrients the forest trees transfer from deeper horizons to the surface soil.

Obviously the effect of plants upon the availability of nutrients in soil is different in different soils. Thus, Dr. DeTurk reported that sweetclover had markedly improved the available phosphorus status of soil in some of the Illinois experiment fields but had relatively little effect on other fields.

Heavy and frequent applications of available nutrients in the form of fertilizers on some soils has made less urgent the need to include one of the "strong feeder" crops in the rotation in order to make sparingly soluble minerals available.

DIFFERENT CROPS have different effects on soil structure. The way soils take in water and permit it to move through the profile depends on the way the soil particles are arranged into granules or aggregates. The storage of water in the soil, use of this water by plants, and the exchange of gases between the soil pores and the atmosphere also depend on soil structure.

Conditions that provide large pores within the soil mass for rapid movement of water and air, combined with small pores for the storage of water are desirable, in general. The grouping of individual soil particles into aggregates, which resist the slaking action of water and resist crushing during tillage operations, is an essential feature of good soil structure.

When an intertilled crop is grown, the stirring of the soil in preparation of the seedbed and cultivation tends to break down the structure of the soil, destroy many of the aggregates or granules, and reduce the proportion of large pores.

Because decomposing organic matter provides substances that help to cement soil particles into stable aggregates, the crops that return large amounts of organic residue usually have a beneficial effect on structure.

The roots of certain crops also affect the structure of the lower horizons. The thick taproots of crops such as kudzu, sweetclover, and alfalfa penetrate some soils to considerable depth. When they die and decompose, they leave a channel or pore through which excess water can drain from the profile and down which the roots of the next crop can grow more easily.

The perennial legumes and grass-legume mixtures meet most of the requirements I mentioned for improving soil structure. Because the soil is not stirred by tillage implements while perennial sods are being grown, aggregates and pores, once developed, tend to persist. The amounts of organic matter returned to the soil through the extensive root systems and plowed-under top growth are greater for perennial top sod crops than for most others.

Intertilled crops such as peanuts, potatoes, cotton, tobacco, sugar beets, and vegetables are detrimental to soil structure because they require many tillage operations, return but little organic residue to the soil, and generally have small, shallow root systems. Intertilled crops such as corn, grain sorghum, and sugarcane are less detrimental to soil structure than the ones I listed, because if they are prop-erly managed they provide considerable organic residue for return to the soil and require less tillage.

The percentage of water-stable aggregates and the percentage of large pores in the soil almost always are greater after the grasses, legumes, or grass-legume mixtures than they are after any other crop.

We need long-term experiments designed to permit evaluation of the effects of the changes in structure associated with cropping systems on crop yields, separate from the effects of the systems on nutrient supplies.

One experiment that met those requirements and showed positive effects of the soil structural changes brought about by one crop upon the yields of the following crops was conducted in Mississippi by H. V. Jordan and his coworkers. These men grew kudzu for 4 years on a soil (Loring silt loam) with a moderately dense siltpan subsoil. Other plots in the same experiment were kept in corn the 4 years. Corn was grown on all plots after the fourth year. Part of each corn plot received 160 pounds of nitrogen an acre during the later period. Because that amount of nitrogen should be well in excess of the requirements for maximum corn yields, any differences in the yield of corn following 4 years of kudzu (as compared to corn following 4 years of corn) are undoubtedly due to some factor other than differences in nitrogen supply. Liberal additions of phosphorus and potassium fertilizers were made to all corn plots in the fifth and later years.

The results of the experiment are summarized in the table. Corn following 4 years of kudzu outyielded corn following corn even though liberal amounts of nitrogen, phosphorus, and potash were applied as fertilizer. Furthermore, the effect of kudzu on corn yields carried over through the fourth corn crop after the kudzu was plowed.

Mr. Jordan and his associates measured the amount of water and radioactive phosphorus taken up by the corn from different depths in the soil. The

Effect of Four Years of Kudzu on the Yield of Subsequent Corn Crops on Loring Silt Loam [1]

| | Fertilizer applied to corn each year after 4th year (lbs./A) | | | Yield of corn | |
Previous cropping	N	P₂O₅	K₂O	5th year	8th year
	N P₂O₅ K₂O			5th year	8th year
4 years of kudzu—tops turned............	160–80–80			66. 4	70. 1
	0–80–80			61. 4	41. 6
4 years of kudzu—tops removed..........	160–80–80			60. 9	82. 2
	0–80–80			53. 4	43. 9
4 years of corn........................	160–80–80			51. 8	60. 1
	0–80–80			19. 8	22. 3

[1] From Jordan, H. V., Crockett, S. P., and Bardsley, C. E., Jr.: "Some Effects of Kudzu Versus Continuous Corn on Soil Properties and Crop Yields." Soil Science Society of America, Proceedings; volume 20, 225–227, 1956.

measurements made it plain that the roots of corn following kudzu were more extensive in the subsoil than were those of corn following corn. The greater utilization of subsoil moisture, made possible through the changes in soil structure brought about by the 4 years of kudzu, undoubtedly was a major factor in the improved yields when corn followed kudzu.

J. B. Page and C. J. Willard have described an experiment conducted on the Paulding clay of northern Ohio. They compared rotations of alfalfa, alfalfa-bromegrass mixtures, and sweetclover with continuous corn and cornoats. Paulding clay is a fine-textured, poorly drained soil.

Dr. Page and Dr. Willard found times when the plots of the rotations that included deep-rooted legumes were in good condition to plow, while excess water was still standing on the surface of the plots used for continuous corn. Corn yields were lower when corn was grown continuously than when corn was rotated with deep-rooted legumes. Annual application of 30 pounds of nitrogen an acre to the continuous corn did not increase continuous corn yields to the level of those obtained in rotations with legumes.

Although this amount of nitrogen probably did not entirely meet the requirements of the continuous corn, it nevertheless seems likely that differences in soil structure were largely responsible for the differences in corn yields observed in the experiment.

O. R. Neal, of the Department of Agriculture, has reported experiments conducted on the Coastal Plain of New Jersey. The inclusion of 1 year of a mixture of alfalfa, clover, and timothy in a 3-year rotation of vegetable crops brought higher yields of tomatoes and sweet corn, as compared to cropping systems without a grass-legume sod crop. The vegetable crops were fertilized uniformly according to recommendations for each crop. Since the amounts of fertilizer used on vegetable crops in the area are ordinarily quite high, differences in soil structure very likely accounted for some of the differences in yield.

SOILS ERODE more under some crops than under others. Experiments comparing the amounts of erosion and runoff from plots kept in continuous row crops with the losses from plots kept in a rotation of row crops and sod were started at most of the soil erosion experiment stations soon after they were established. In every instance more runoff occurred from the row crops than from the sod crops, and the soil under row crops grown in rotation with sod showed less tendency to erode than did the plots where row crops were grown continuously.

Crops can be grouped according to their effects on erosion. Peanuts, potatoes, tobacco, cotton, sugar beets, some of the vegetables, and similar row crops that need frequent cultivation and leave little residue after harvest are most likely to permit serious erosion. Next in order come the row crops, such as corn, sugarcane, and grain sorghum, which require few tillage operations and leave considerable plant residue after harvest. The small grains, such as wheat, oats, barley, and rye, ordinarily permit less erosion than the row crops, other factors being equal. The perennial sod crops ordinarily offer the best protection from erosion of any of the regularly grown field crops. Among the sod crops, grasses or grass-legume mixtures are more effective than pure stands of legumes, such as alfalfa or sericea.

Deep soils whose subsoils have favorable physical properties usually are less seriously damaged by erosion—if gullies do not form—than are soils with unfavorable subsoils. It is generally true that cropping systems that tend to control erosion usually also tend to give better yields than systems that permit excessive erosion. For one thing, more water is available for plants to use, other factors being equal, when runoff is less. Also, erosion depletes the plant nutrient content of the soil. The soil material washed away usually is 2 to 5 times richer in plant nutrients than the surface soil of the eroding field.

SOME CROPS draw heavily on subsoil moisture. As they use up available water in the surface soil, some plants can send roots deep into the subsoil. When the roots penetrate the soil and the material beneath and rainfall is low, the amount of water the deep-rooted plants use in one season may exceed the amount the rains add. The subsoil and deeper layers then dry out and the next crop will have to depend entirely on current rainfall.

Sweetclover and some of the deeper rooted perennial grasses can exhaust subsoil moisture, but tend to do so less than alfalfa. Crops that have long growing seasons and continue their growth during the summer usually leave the soil drier than do shorter season crops.

The relation of cropping systems to soil moisture is demonstrated by an examination of cropping systems from the eastern front of the Rockies to the center of the Corn Belt.

The first cropping on nonirrigated lands east of the Rockies often consists of alternate wheat and fallow; moisture stored in the soil during the fallow period is used by the following crop. Fallowing is done less farther east, and continuous cropping to grain crops predominates in the Central Plains. East of the Central Plains short-lived legumes are included in many cropping systems. In places where alfalfa or alfalfa-grass mixtures are used, the cropping system frequently provides for a long period of grain cropping between periods when deep-rooted sod crops are grown. In the central Corn Belt, where annual rainfall commonly exceeds the water used by crops, deep-rooted legumes often are used in regular rotations, such as corn-small grain and 2 years of alfalfa. Here, the water alfalfa removes from the subsoil is ordinarily replaced during the winter and early spring, so that each season the crops start with the soil profile filled to field capacity with water.

Winter cover crops deplete the soil moisture supply on some soils to the extent that the subsequent summer crop may be damaged by drought. The use of winter cover crops between seasons when corn or cotton is grown generally is most successful in the more humid parts of the country, where moisture used by the winter cover crop is ordinarily replaced by rain before the time when the summer crops are making their heaviest drafts on soil moisture supplies. Turning under the winter cover crop in early spring lowers the possibility that the winter and summer crops will compete for moisture, but it also reduces the soil-improving effects of the winter cover crops.

CHANGING THE CROP changes the problem of weed control. Some weeds are harder to control in some crops than in other crops. For example, because cockleburs have a life cycle like that of corn, they can sprout and grow in corn fields unless one uses cultivation or control practices specifically aimed at the cockleburs. But the periodic mowings of a hay meadow usually catch the cockleburs before the seed matures. Cockleburs therefore tend to become more troublesome in fields that are in corn for many years.

Growing hay crops on the infested fields will not simplify all weed problems. Some weeds become prevalent faster in meadows than in intertilled crops. Quackgrass, for example, tends to increase in hay meadows in the northern part of the Corn Belt.

The control of weeds is simplified in other instances by keeping the same crop on the same field year after year. Johnsongrass is a serious weed in cottonfields in parts of the South. Once a field has been cleaned of Johnsongrass, however, it may be easier to keep it from becoming reestablished by keeping the field in cotton than by rotations with corn or soybeans.

Cropping systems that call for continuous use of the land for small grains have encountered difficulties because of weed infestation. On some of the plots at the Rothamsted Experimental Station in England, weeds became so prevalent that it was necessary to include fallowing at regular intervals.

The rapid advances in the use of chemical herbicides have helped solve many weed problems, which in many instances no longer are the dominant factor in planning a cropping system. A consideration of the problem and alternative methods—herbicides, tillage, and crop rotation—should nevertheless be a part of the planning.

CROP YIELDS are affected by many soil properties. Some of the properties can be enhanced by growing certain kinds of crops on the soil. No crop exists that improves all soil properties, and in most cases the growing of a specific crop is only one alternative method of making a desirable change.

In planning a cropping system for a particular field or farm, the first question is, "What properties of the soil in this field or farm require the most careful attention in order to insure efficient production over a period of years?"

Also: "What are the different ways of controlling these critical soil factors and how much of the desired control or improvement can be achieved by the different alternative methods? How can different practices be fitted together to form alternative systems of soil management, each one of which will insure continued or increasing efficiency in farming?"

On the better soils, this sort of analysis shows that a choice can be made from among many systems. As the soil becomes steeper, or has poorer physical properties, or moisture becomes more of a limiting factor, or any other feature becomes less desirable, the number of systems from which to make a selection becomes fewer.

ROTATIONS with a legume-grass sod are based on the fact that growing a perennial legume, grass, or grass-legume mixture usually brings about an improvement in several of the important properties of the soil. A rotation in which periods of legume or legume-grass mixtures alternate with intertilled nonlegume crops therefore provides for periods of soil improvement alternating with (and at least partly counterbalancing) periods of soil depletion. In the more humid sections where the water used by the sod crop is replenished during the cool season, rotations with grass-legume sod are popular.

The 3-year rotation of corn, oats, red clover, and timothy sod has been used for many years in the Corn Belt. The 4-year rotation of corn, soybeans, oats, and clover and the 5-year rotation of 2 years of corn, 1 year of oats and 2 years of alfalfa-bromegrass are other examples of sod-based rotations used in the Corn Belt.

Cotton, wheat, lespedeza, and corn, cotton, oats, followed by one or more years of fescue-clover are examples of sod-based rotations that have been coming into common use in the South.

Rotations of potatoes with redtop or the 3-year rotation of potatoes, oats, and red clover are used in New England.

Rotations of sugar beets, field beans, potatoes, and barley with several years of alfalfa are common on the irrigated lands of the West.

The number of possible sod-based rotations, including different kinds of sod crops and different kinds of small grain and intertilled crops, is large. The grass-legume crop may be used for hay or pasture, or it may be left unharvested and all the growth turned under. There is scarcely a single type of soil or location in the United States where some sort of sod-based rotation is not adapted.

Success in the use of sod-based rotations depends on producing a good stand of a vigorously growing sod crop. The requirements of a legume or legume-grass mixture for lime, phosphorus, and potash will need to be met to do that. No rotation, however good in theory, can result in high yields if mineral nutrients are lacking.

A sod crop or sod mixture in a rotation must be one that is easily established and also can be readily killed or controlled when the time comes to rotate the field into some other crop.

Finally, sod-based rotations must be fitted to the soil where they are to be used and supplemented with other practices as necessary. Each crop in the rotation must be adapted to the soil. Because the beneficial effects of the sod crops persist for different lengths of time in different soils, different ratios of sod crops to intertilled crops and different lengths of the period in each kind of crop will be needed for different soil conditions. In places where the slopes are steep and the erosion hazard is severe, the proportion of sod relative to row crops in the rotation should be high or other erosion-control practices, like terraces, contouring, and stripcropping, should be used along with the rotation in order to control erosion.

MONOCULTURE—the practice of growing the same crop year after year—has been looked down on as a way of using soils. But, as I pointed out, advances in the science of farming are causing us to take another look at monoculture. Actually, there are a few time-honored examples of successful monoculture, but in the more humid States the comparisons of monoculture with rotations were conducted almost always under conditions where lack of nitrogen soon limited yields of continuously grown nonlegume crops. Since the Second World War, nitrogen fertilizers have become abundant and relatively low in cost and have been a reason for reevaluating monoculture.

The fact that successful monoculture may be possible is in itself not enough to justify its existence as a practice—there must also be some other advantages to monoculture as compared to rotational cropping systems. Consider a general farm, where for reasons of business organization it is desirable to produce several different kinds of crops—what are the advantages, as far as maintaining productivity is concerned, of the practice of growing each one of these crops on the same land year after year?

For one thing, if different kinds of soil exist on the farm, a monoculture system may permit each crop to be grown on the best suited soil. Thus the steep soils, where erosion is a hazard, can be kept in a close-growing forage crop, while the intertilled row crops occupy the better soils with gentle slopes all of the time. Slowly drained areas can be used continuously for crops that do not require early spring field operations; droughty soils can be used for drought-resistant crops, such as sorghums or winter small grains.

Second, the fertility level of the soil can be adjusted to fit one crop more readily and precisely than it can be adjusted to fit all the crops in a rotation. In order to grow alfalfa, for example, the soil should be limed to about pH 6.5, but it is not necessary to use this much lime in order to get satisfactory yields of crops like corn or small grains. For a few crops, such as potatoes, this degree of liming actually may be detrimental. In order to produce maximum yields of corn, a high level of available nitrogen is required. The level must be higher than is actually used up by the corn crop in a year. A residue of available nitrogen will be left after corn is harvested; that is an advantage when corn follows corn, but it may bring about lodging when small grain crops follow corn.

Where continuous cropping is practiced, and the forage crops are perennials, regular reseedings, each one accompanied by a possibility of stand failure, are avoided.

Finally, systems based on continuous cropping generally offer greater flexibility in planning the cropping system to meet year-to-year changes in the need for various crops. Part of the acreage can be shifted from one crop to another without upsetting the cropping plan over the whole farm.

The requirements for successful monoculture are stricter and demand greater management skill than do the requirements for successful use of sod-based rotations.

The entire nitrogen requirement of the nonlegume crops must be met with nitrogen from fertilizers or farmyard manure when monoculture is used. Because the nitrogen in fertilizers is subject to loss from the soil through leaching, careful attention must be paid to the timing of applications of nitrogen fertilizers in order to meet crop requirements.

Successful monoculture requires close attention to erosion control, except for the special case of perennial sod.

Problems of soil structure may become severe when one grows crops that require frequent tillage operations and return little organic residue to the soil. The exact kinds of soil that will stay in satisfactory physical condition under continuous cropping with each

of the different crops are not definitely known. The best course for a farmer to follow is probably to watch the water relationships of the soil. If he sees a growing tendency for water to stay ponded on the surface or to run off more readily from sloping areas, the soil-management system should be changed to provide greater returns of organic residues, less frequent tillage, and perhaps more deep-rooted crops. Poor physical conditions in the soil will be more evident in seasons that are too wet or too dry.

Users of monoculture will be completely dependent on chemical insecticides, disease-resistant varieties of plants, soil fumigation, and similar methods of controlling insects, plant diseases, and other pests. The severity of this problem varies from crop to crop, from one locality to another, and even from time to time.

Chances for the successful monoculture of different crops vary widely with the characteristics of the crop and the diseases and insects that attack it. On one end of the scale are the continuously grown perennial sod crops, which are successful almost everywhere. On the other end are the intertilled crops, such as peanuts, potatoes, and bright leaf tobacco, which rarely are grown successfully by monoculture and then only on soils of naturally good physical properties. Continuous wheat or alternate wheat and fallow has been successful over relatively large areas in the Western States and Canada. Soybeans have been grown continuously on some of the flat claypan soils of the southern Corn Belt. Continuous sugarcane is the rule rather than the exception in areas where it is grown.

The use of the newer insecticides and tillage methods and nitrogen fertilizers has opened up new possibilities for successful production of continuous corn. Continuous cotton has been successful in some of the nearly level soils of the South and on irrigated areas in the Southwest, although special subsoil tillage operations may be required to break up compacted soil layers.

One-year cropping systems, in which a winter crop alternates each year with a summer crop, tend to resemble monoculture systems in their advantages and requirements. Among these systems are those in which a close-growing winter cover crop (such as rye, ryegrass, crimson clover, vetch or a mixture like rye and vetch) alternates with a summer row crop (like corn, cotton, or tobacco). The winter cover crop is not ordinarily harvested but is turned under as a green manure crop. The use of the close-growing winter cover crop protects the land from erosion for at least part of the year and tends to decrease problems of soil structure maintenance. The range of soil conditions upon which intertilled crops can be successfully grown each year is increased by adding a close-growing winter cover crop to the monoculture systems.

Another 1-year system with two crops consists of winter grain followed by annual lespedeza. Here the winter grain is the harvested crop, and the lespedeza contributes to the system primarily through its effect in maintaining available nitrogen in the soil.

Systems where two harvested crops are grown each year are found in some of the vegetable producing areas, where the growing season required for each vegetable crop in the system is short.

In the Southern States, winter grain and soybeans, both crops being harvested for seed, is a promising 1-year, 2-crop system. Similar systems found in irrigated regions of the Southwest include winter grain and cotton.

An important fact to keep in mind concerning these 2-crop annual sequences is that there must be enough water for both crops. The use of these systems therefore is confined to the more humid States and to irrigated areas with long warm seasons.

Crop sequences without a legume or other sod crop are used on cash-crop farms, expecially in subhumid sections. The sequence in which the crops follow one another frequently varies from cycle to cycle, depending on conditions

of soil moisture and the demand for the different crops. As far as maintenance of nitrogen and soil structure are concerned, these nonsod rotations resemble monoculture systems.

THE CHOICE of a cropping system that will provide for the longtime maintenance of soil productivity involves many factors.

The pattern of different kinds of soil on the farm must be considered. If the soil on the farm is quite uniform and is subject to hazard from erosion, a cropping system that involves fairly regular use of grass-legume sods, rotated over all the cropland on the farm, should be given serious consideration.

On the other hand, if the farmer has several different kinds of soil, a monoculture system with each crop grown continuously on the soil where it is best adapted may be most satisfactory.

The agronomic characteristics of the forage crops to be grown are also important in determining the cropping system. Forage crops which are relatively easy to establish by seeding but which tend to decline in yield as time goes on are best used as a component of fairly short sod-based rotations. Red clover and timothy mixtures are a good example. If the preferred forage crop is rather slow or difficult to establish, but when once established remains productive over a long period, continuous use of the same field for this crop may be desirable. Birdsfoot trefoil is an example of a desirable forage crop that is well suited to continuous production on the same soil.

Every plan of a cropping system should provide for flexibility, in order to permit changing the acreage of crops from year to year to adjust to changes in demand and farm organization. Provision for alternate crops for use on areas where the intended crop is destroyed by weather, insects, or diseases early in its growing season is also needed. As a general rule, regular rotations are best adapted to regions where annual rainfall is less subject to extreme variations.

Soil Classification and Surveys

Guy D. Smith and Andrew R. Aandahl

Soil maps are a basic tool for selecting a system of soil management. The maps show the kinds of soil in a field and farm— essential knowledge for selecting from the various available soil-management practices the combination of practices that is best suited to the soil and to the resources, skills, and desires of the farmer and rancher.

If they know the effect of a given practice on a field, whose kind of soil also is known, they can foresee the effect of that practice on other fields with the same kind of soil. Just as they can predict the behavior of a particular variety of hybrid corn, so can they predict the response to management of a particular soil.

Soils are classified and named, just as plants and animals are. Plants are identified by such characteristics as the structure of the flower and the form of the leaf. Soils are identified by such characteristics as the kinds and numbers of horizons, or layers, that have developed in them. The texture (the relative amounts of stones, gravel, sand, silt, and clay), the kinds of minerals present and their amounts, and the presence of salts and alkali help distinguish the horizons.

Most of the characteristics that identify soils can be determined in the field. A few can be determined only in the laboratory, but even without labora-

tory tests you often can get an accurate knowledge of them from standard works on soils and geology. For example, you can estimate the amount of sand in a soil from its feel when you rub it between your fingers, but for an accurate knowledge you would have to depend on laboratory analyses.

THE TYPE is the smallest unit in the natural classification of soils. One or a few types constitute a soil series. These are the common classification units seen on soil maps and survey reports.

A soil series is a group of soils that have horizons that are essentially the same in the properties used to identify soils, with the exception of the texture of the surface soil and the kinds of layers that lie below what is considered the true soil.

The names of soil series are taken from the towns or localities near the place where the soils were first defined.

The soil type, a subdivision of the soil series, is based on the texture of the surface soil. Stones, gravel, sand, silt, and clay have been defined as having the following diameters: Gravel, between 0.08 inch and 3 inches; sand, between 0.08 and 0.002 inch; silt, between 0.002 and 0.00008 inch; and clay, less than 0.00008 inch.

The full name of soil type includes the name of the soil series and the textural class of the surface soil equivalent to the plow layer—that is, the upper 6 or 7 inches. Thus, if the surface of an area of the Fayette series is a silt loam, the name of the soil type is "Fayette silt loam."

The soil phase is not a part of the natural classification. It can be a subdivision of the soil type, series, or one of the higher units in the classification.

Phases shown on soil maps commonly are subdivisions of soil types and are based on characteristics of the soil significant to its use for agriculture.

Phases shown on large-scale soil maps generally have reflected differences in slope, degree of erosion, and stoniness, but other bases for defining phases include drainage and flood protection, climate, and the presence of contrasting layers below the soil. (A comparable subdivision in the classification of animals might be classes according to their age, such as old animals, old cows, or old Holstein cows.)

The legends that accompany soil maps generally include such names for the units on the map, as "Sharpsburg silty clay loam, eroded rolling phase," or "Fayette silt loam, 8–14 percent slopes, eroded." Those names identify the soil series, the soil type, and the phase. They represent names of the most specific kinds of soil, comparable to the name of a practical subdivision of a variety of a plant, such as old Jonathan apple trees.

The word "Fayette" in the second soil name we mentioned is the name of the soil series. This name, plus the words "silt loam," identify the soil type, and the phase is identified by the words, "8–14 percent slopes, eroded." In this name, the word "phase" is not used but is understood.

Higher units in the classification system include families, great soil groups, suborders, and orders. They are seldom used on any but small-scale soil maps.

Soil series, types, and phases do not occur at random in the landscape. They have an orderly pattern of occurrence that is related to the land form; the parent material from which the soil was formed; and the influence of the plants that grew on the soils, the animals that lived on them, and the way men have used them.

On a given farm, the different kinds of soil commonly have a repeating pattern, which is associated with the slope.

The relationships between the soils and landscapes vary in details in different parts of the country, but the relationships generally exist. Anyone who is familiar with the soils can visualize the landscape from a soil map; or, if he sees the landscape, he can predict where the boundaries are.

A SOIL SURVEY includes finding out which properties of soils are important, organizing the knowledge about the relations of soil properties and soil use, classifying soils into defined and described units, locating and plotting the boundaries of the units on maps, and preparing and publishing the maps and reports.

The soil survey report consists of a map that shows the distribution of soils in the area, descriptions of the soils, some suggestions as to their use and management, and general information about the area.

Reports usually are prepared on the soils of one county, although a single report may cover several small counties or only parts of counties.

Soil surveys are made cooperatively by the Soil Conservation Service of the Department of Agriculture, the agricultural experiment stations, and other State and Federal agencies. Plans for the work in any area are developed jointly, and the reports are reviewed jointly before publication.

Soil maps have many uses, but generally they are made for one main purpose—to identify the soil as a basis for applying the results of research and experience to individual fields or parts of fields. Results from an experiment on a given soil can be applied directly to other areas of the same kind of soil with confidence. Two areas of the same kind of soil are no more identical than two oak trees, but they are so similar that (with comparable past management) they should respond to the same practices in a similar manner.

But many thousands of kinds of soil exist in the United States. Research can be conducted on only a few of them. The application of the research results must usually be based on the relationships of the properties of the soil on which the experiment was conducted to the properties of the soils shown on the maps. This can be done best by the soil classification system.

The significant properties that can be known from the soil maps include physical properties, such as the amount of moisture that the soil will hold for plants, the rate at which air and water move through the soil, and the kinds and amounts of clays, all of which are important in drainage, irrigation, erosion control, maintenance of good tilth, and the choice of crops.

Some important chemical properties can be known from the soil maps. The ability of a soil to convert phosphate fertilizer to forms unavailable to plants is an example. Generally speaking, however, the ability of a soil to supply nutrients needed by plants cannot be known with precision from the soil map alone, for the supplies of the nutrients are changed when a farmer applies fertilizers.

Soil tests on individual fields are becoming more and more important. Considered in relation to the kind of soil, they form the most reliable background for recommending the application of fertilizers.

THE SOIL MAP shows the distribution of specific kinds of soil and identifies them through the map legend. The legend is a list of the symbols used to identify the kinds of soil on the map.

The most common soil units shown on maps are the phases of soil types, but other kinds of units may be shown.

The soil bodies, areas occupied by the individual soil units, generally range from a few acres to a few hundred acres. Often within one soil body are small areas of other soils—series, types, or phases. If the included soils are similar in nature, they are generally not identified unless they represent more than 10 or 15 percent of the soil body in which they are included. If the properties of the included soils differ markedly from those of the rest of the soil body, they usually are indicated by special symbols.

But occasionally the individual parts of a unit are so small and so mixed with other units that they cannot be shown. Then the legend will indicate the area occupied by the intricate mixture as a soil complex if all of the included units are present in nearly every area.

A complex may consist of two or more phases of a soil type, but commonly it consists of two or more series.

The names of complexes may carry a hyphen between the names of two soil types or phases, as "Barnes-Buse loams." If several series or types are included in the complex, the names of one or two of the most important series or types will be followed by the word "complex," for example, "Clarinda-Lagonda complex."

Two other kinds of units are common on soil maps—the undifferentiated group and the miscellaneous land type.

Two or more recognized kinds of soil that are not regularly associated in the landscape may be combined if their separation is costly and the differences between them are not significant for the objective of the soil survey. This kind of undifferentiated group is shown in the legend with the names of the individual units connected by a conjunction—for example, "Downs or Fayette silt loams."

The miscellaneous land types are used for land that has little or no natural soil. The map units then are given descriptive names, such as "steep, stony land," "gullied land," and "mixed alluvial land."

The relationships between the units that appear on the maps and legends and the use and management alternatives are explained in the text that accompanies the soil survey report.

The Department of Agriculture began making soil surveys about 1900. The purposes of the work were the same then as now, but there was no body of knowledge of how soils are formed or how nutrients become available to plants. The early definitions of the soil series therefore failed to take into account some important properties and overemphasized some of the more obvious but less important ones, such as color.

As scientists have learned more about the relationships between soils and plants, ideas have changed about the importance of the properties originally used to distinguish between soil series and types. The first soil series was split into two or more series. They in turn have often been subdivided. Consequently many of the names shown on the older maps have been changed. Changes will continue to be made as long as we continue to learn new things about soil-plant relationships.

Soil maps are made by experienced soil scientists who are graduates of the State agricultural colleges or other colleges that offer courses in soil science. After graduation, the soil scientists usually receive several months of intensive training. They work in the field. First they observe the techniques of an experienced soil scientist. Then they practice, and their mistakes are pointed out by their supervisor. Finally, when they prove their ability, they begin work.

Ordinarily the soil scientists use aerial photographs as a base for plotting the soil boundaries. The scientist goes over the land and digs with a spade or auger as often as necessary to determine and evaluate the important characteristics of the entire profile. He identifies the kind of soil, locates its boundaries in the field, plots the boundaries, and places the identification symbol of each soil mapping unit on the map.

In making detailed maps, he follows or sees the boundaries between the kinds of soil through their entire length. In making reconnaissance surveys, he may not see the boundaries over their entire length; he merely identifies one when he crosses it and draws the boundary through to his next traverse, or crossing, on the basis of the information he can get from the aerial photograph.

The soil scientist makes simple chemical tests in the field to determine the degree of acidity and the presence of lime, salts, and a few toxic compounds. He measures slopes with a hand level. He usually takes samples of a few representative soils during the survey and sends them to the laboratory for detailed study.

All stages of the work from the mapping to the contents of the report are reviewed by the supervisors and representatives of the cooperating agencies.

Soil maps often are used before they are published. Each cooperator of the soil conservation districts is furnished a copy of the soil map of his holding.

County assessors and other users sometimes buy copies of such maps to use in their work before the publication of the completed survey. The local soils handbooks, available for reference at the Soil Conservation Service offices, give information needed to use and interpret the map.

Photographic copies of unpublished maps may be purchased through the Soil Conservation Service offices. These offices are usually located in county seats. Prices for the maps are fixed to cover the cost to the Government.

Soil maps are published by the Soil Conservation Service for all States except Illinois; in Illinois, the University of Illinois Agricultural Experiment Station publishes them.

Copies of available published maps and reports may be obtained through the State Extension Service or Soil Conservation Service offices. Files of unpublished maps are maintained in the Soil Conservation Service offices and may be examined there.

Interpretations of soil maps are physical and economic analyses of the alternative opportunities available to the users of the land. They indicate capabilities of the soils for agricultural use, adapted crops, estimated yields of crops under defined systems of management, presence of specific soil-management problems, opportunities and limitations for various management practices, and problems in nonagricultural use.

The main bases for interpretations are yield estimates, related to specific combinations of practices for soils in their climatic setting. Yield estimates for a soil are predictions of the average production of specific crops that a group of farmers could expect during the following 10 or 15 years if they followed the defined system of soil management. Yield estimates apply less closely to individual farmers, whose skills are variable, than to averages of groups. Sources of information are the results of research, the experiences of farmers, ranchers, and others who grow plants, and observations of plants growing on different kinds of soils.

The definitions and descriptions of the kinds of soil shown on maps provide information on their characteristics. We use these to infer the qualities of soils such as productivity and erosion hazard. We are able to make predictions about a soil whose behavior is unknown by comparing its characteristics with those of the soils about which we have basic information on behavior. Basic principles of soil management are another tool used to help us extend our predictions of soil behavior and responses to all kinds of soils.

Soil survey reports include a number of interpretations, especially the more permanent ones that concern soil qualities. New and additional research, new weeds or insects, changes in relative prices, new crops, new machines, and other changes in agricultural arts require us to revise interpretations from time to time. The interpretation of the soil units shown on soil maps is a continuing task if we are to make full use of available knowledge on the use and management of soils. Interpretations can be no more static than our civilization. Yet soil maps, with accurately plotted boundaries of carefully defined soils, can be reinterpreted as the situation demands in future years.

To go back to a specific kind of soil we cited earlier, some alternatives for Fayette silt loam, 8 to 14 percent slopes eroded, which will result in sustained production now and in the future are:

(1) Permanent pasture, which permits several choices of legumes and grasses, lime, varying amounts and kinds of fertilizers, and varying systems of grazing;

(2) Woodland;

(3) A 4-year rotation of corn-oats-alfalfa-alfalfa with contour cultivation, lime, and fertilizers; and

(4) A 3-year rotation of corn-oats-red clover with contour strips, lime, and fertilizers.

Estimates of the yields of woodland, pasture, forage, and grain under these alternative uses permit the confident selection of the best management from the viewpoints of the desires of the operator and the conservation of the soil. If new crops, new pests, or new techniques of farming appear, the present "best management" may become undesirable. Yield estimates can be revised at that time, and will again provide the basis for selection of a suitable management.

The Use of Soil Maps

A. M. Hedge and A. A. Klingebiel

Soils may be grouped into land capability classes, subclasses, and units to help us use them properly. Of the eight classes, which normally do not all exist on any single farm or ranch, classes I through IV are suited to cultivated crops, pasture or range, woodland, and wildlife.

Classes V through VIII are suited to pasture or woodland and wildlife and are not generally recommended for cultivation. Some kinds of soil in Classes V, VI, and VII may be cultivated safely, with special management, however.

Because several kinds of soil often occur in the same capability class on the same farm or ranch, the classes are divided into subclasses.

Four kinds of problems are recognized in the subclasses and are indicated by symbols: (e)—erosion and runoff; (w)—wetness and drainage; (s)—root zone and tillage limitations, such as shallowness, stoniness, droughtiness, and salinity; and (c)—climatic limitations. The subclass therefore provides more specific information about the kind and the degree of limitation for the use of soil than does the capability class.

The land capability unit is the most detailed and specific soil grouping of the capability classification. Soils that can be used in the same way and will give about the same crop yield are grouped into a capability unit. It is used most commonly for planning in specific areas, as it is a grouping of soils that are nearly alike in features that affect plant growth and in response to management.

Other interpretative soil groupings also are used in conservation planning. In extensive range areas, the mapping units are grouped into range sites, which give information about the kind and amount of vegetation the area will produce when it is in its best condition. This grouping, together with range condition, provides the basis needed for sound range planning.

On farms or ranches that are to be used for woodland, range, or pasture, and cropland, the soil map is interpreted to show the suitability of the land for those uses. For areas that are to be planned as woodland, the mapping units are grouped into woodland sites and interpreted in terms of kinds and amounts of wood crops that can be produced.

Many land capability units are adapted to a number of alternative uses and treatments. For example, on some deep, well-drained, sloping soils in the humid section of the country, the same results in conservation often can be achieved by a 3-year rotation with terraces, by a 4-year rotation with contour stripcropping, or by a 5-year rotation with contouring.

The operator therefore has three equally satisfactory choices of rotations and accompanying practices to control erosion. If he is short of good cropland and has plenty of land suitable for hay and pasture, it would be advantageous for him to choose the 3-year rotation with terraces. If he has enough good cropland to produce all

the cultivated crops he needs and can utilize more hay or pasture, he may want to follow the 5-year rotation with contour cultivation.

Comparative costs will also be an important factor in choosing between the alternatives available in this example. It would be a wise choice if the cost of constructing and maintaining terraces with proper outlets can be avoided without sacrificing conservation of the soil or production of feed for the livestock. Other alternative uses include growing grass or trees.

A number of alternative systems of soil management are usually available on capability units composed of soils that are level, deep, moderately permeable, and well drained but have adequate soil moisture. The maintenance of adequate fertility and the control of weeds and insects are the major problems.

On these soils one level of management may include a 3-year rotation, consisting of 1 year of grass-legume hay. When the crop residues are returned to the soil, a green manure crop is plowed under, necessary plant nutrients are added, and sound cultural practices are followed, however, high crop yields can be expected even under a continuous cropping system. The more level productive soils on a farm may be used more intensively so that the steeper and more erosive soils can be utilized less intensively.

Some capability units consist of level or nearly level soils that require drainage for the successful production of cultivated crops. The decision to drain such soils must take into consideration the cost of the drainage and the potential crop production after drainage, as compared to the possibility of producing hay, pasture, or woodland on the undrained land.

Usually a number of alternative crops can be grown, if the land is drained for cultivation. Of course, the cropping system selected must maintain adequate tilth to insure good air and water movement in the soil.

Many capability units consist of

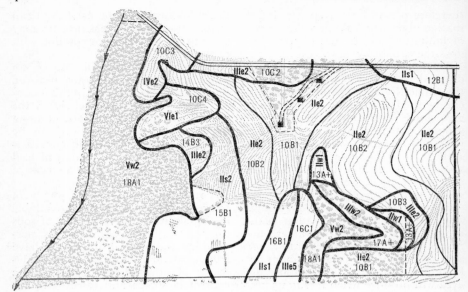

1. A map of the soil and its capability. The symbols pertain to various aspects of soil and topography. For example: 10B1 refers to the kind of soil; the number 10 refers to the soil type; the letter B to steepness of slope; and number 1 to degree of erosion. The symbol IIe2 refers to the land capability unit; II designates the land capability class; e indicates the subclass; and 2 indicates the unit. Heavy lines on map indicate boundaries of a capability unit. See explanation in text for specific definitions.

well-drained sandy soils, some of which are droughty and subject to wind erosion. Sandy soils in the less humid areas often have a wind erosion hazard in addition to the problem of maintaining organic matter and fertility at a high level. Fortunately, the same management practices—such as the return of crop residues, cover crops, and manure to the soil and the use of high rates of fertilizer—help meet the needs for maintaining organic matter and fertility levels as well as offering protection against erosion hazards.

In areas of low rainfall where irrigation is contemplated, the land capability units reflect those soil differences that influence the frequency of irrigation, amount of water applied, length of runs, as well as the kinds and amounts of crops that can be grown.

To illustrate how the technology of conservation farming can be used by farmers, a conservation farm plan from a Southern State is presented. The two maps pertain to it.

CLASS II LAND has some limitation that reduces the choice of use or requires some conservation practice to keep it productive. It can be used for cultivated crops, pastureland, woodland, or wildlife land.

IIe2—These soils are gently sloping, deep, and are slightly to moderately eroded. They are well drained and water moves through them easily. Soil erosion and soil fertility are the main soil problems to overcome. These soils are suitable for growing all crops commonly grown in the area.

10B1—Tifton sandy loam, gently sloping, slightly eroded phase.

10B2—Tifton sandy loam, gently sloping, moderately eroded phase.

IIs1—Soils in this group are deep, sandy, and droughty. Water moves through these soils easily, and the maintenance of soil fertility is difficult.

12B1—Tifton loamy sand, gently sloping, slightly eroded, thick surface phase.

16B1—Norfolk sandy loam, gently sloping, slightly eroded, thick surface.

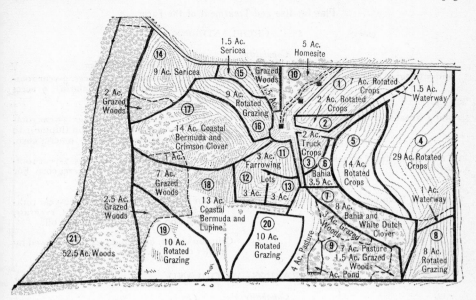

2. *A conservation plan map. The decisions made by the farmer concerning the use and management of the land, together with the field unit arrangement, are recorded on this map. These decisions were based on the soil and capability map shown on the opposite page. Needs of the farmer relative to his farm enterprise were also considered.*

IIs2—These are sandy, droughty soils through which water moves rapidly. Most crops commonly grown in the area are adapted to these soils. However, they often suffer from lack of moisture and fertility.

15B1—Lakeland loamy sand, gently sloping, slightly eroded, shallow surface phase.

IIw1—These soils occur in draws or depressions and are moderately well drained. Water from surrounding higher land often runs on these soils. If properly protected from overflow or seep water, they are suitable for growing many different crops.

13A1—Ochlockonee sandy loam, local alluvial phase.

CLASS III LAND has more natural features that restrict its use and when cultivated requires more careful management than Class II. It can be used for cultivated crops, woodland, pastureland, or wildlife land.

IIIe2—These soils differ from those described in IIe2 largely in that they are steeper and more eroded. Erosion and fertility are the major soil problems. These soils require careful management to deal successfully with these problems. They are adapted to all crops commonly grown in the area.

10B3—Tifton sandy loam, gently sloping, severely eroded phase.

10C2—Tifton sandy loam, sloping, moderately eroded phase.

IIIe5—These well-drained sloping soils are subject to some erosion and are somewhat droughty. They require careful management for safe cultivation. However, most crops adapted to the area can be grown successfully.

16C1—Norfolk sandy loam, sloping, slightly eroded, thick surface phase.

IIIw2—These soils are level and often moderately wet. Water moves through them slowly; when undrained, they are best suited to trees or grass. Some clean-tilled crops may be grown if properly drained.

17A1—Lynchburg sandy loam.

Plan for Use and Treatment of the Farm

CROPLAND

Field No.	Capability unit	Conservation plan
1 and 5 (rotated crops; 21 acres).	IIe2	Contour cultivation with terraces. 3-year rotation: 7 acres tobacco (crotalaria); 7 acres corn; 7 acres oats.
2 and 4 (rotated crops; 31 acres).	IIe2	Contour cultivation with terraces. 3-year rotation: 11 acres peanuts or cotton (lupine); 10 acres lupine for seed (Milo); 10 acres corn.
16 and 19 (rotated grazing; 19 acres).	IIe2 IIs2	Contour cultivation with terraces. 2-year rotation: 9 acres oats (lupine); 10 acres corn. For hog grazing.
8 and 20 (rotated grazing; 18 acres).	IIe2 IIs1	Contour cultivation with terraces. 2-year rotation: 8 acres corn; 10 acres oats, ryegrass, and crimson clover. To be grazed off.
11, 12, and 13 (rotated grazing; 9 acres).	IIe2	Crimson clover, oats, and ryegrass followed by millet each year. Farrowing lots.

GRAZING—WOODLAND

Field No.	Capability unit	Conservation plan
6, 7, and 9 (22 ½ acres）........	IIe2 IIs2 IIw1 IIIw2	Bahiagrass and giant whiteclover. Fertilize and manage pond for fish production.
17 (14 acres)................	IIe2 IIs2 IIIe2 VIe1	Coastal Bermuda-grass and crimson clover.
18 (13 acres)................	IIe2 IIs2 Vw2	Coastal Bermuda-grass and lupine or crimson clover.
14 and 15 (10½ acres)........	IIe2 IIIe2 IVe2	Sericea. Add rescue or ryegrass after sericea is well established. Crimson clover may be added. Plant multiflora rose along south border of field 14.
9, 18, and 19 (14 acres)........	IIe2 Vw2	Grazed woodland. Harvest trees as they mature. Keep enough trees for shade.
21 (52½ acres).............	Vw2	Woodland. Protect from fire. Harvest mature trees. Make stand improvement cuts.

Note.—All grazing land should be limed and fertilized as needed. Mow to control weeds. Topdress annually and rotate grazing.

Class iv land has definite restrictions that reduce the choice of use or require very careful management. The number of years that are favorable for cultivated crops is often limited. It can be used for cultivated crops, pastureland, woodland, or wildlife land.

IVe2—These are well-drained, sloping, severely eroded soils. They differ from the IIIe2 soils in that they are steeper or more severely eroded. These soils are suited for grass or trees, but can be used for cultivated crops if soil-management practices are good.

10C3—Norfolk sandy loam, sloping, severely eroded phase.

CLASS V LAND has natural features that generally restrict its use to pastureland, woodland, or wildlife land. The soils in this class are nearly level and often wet, overflowed, or stony, or have a climatic limitation. Pastures can be renovated. The major limitation is the kind of plants that can be grown. Vw2—These are wet, level soils. They are generally best suited to woodland but, if drained and fertilized, they are good for pastureland. 18A1—Rains sandy loam, thick surface phase.

CLASS VI LAND is suited to pastureland, woodland, or wildlife land but generally not for cultivated crops. Soils in this class have pronounced features such as steep slopes, severely eroded, stony, shallow, or wet condition, or low water-holding ability. These soils usually can be renovated and good pastures are obtained with careful management. VIe1—These soils are sloping and very severely eroded. They are generally too steep or eroded for safe cultivation and are best in grass or trees. 10C4—Tifton sandy loam, sloping, very severely eroded phase.

Expense and Receipts [1]

Cash expense

Feed and fertilizer	$3,277
Machinery repair and operation	1,000
Hired labor	1,500
Capital improvements	1,750
Miscellaneous	1,005
	8,532

Cash receipts [2]

Tobacco, 9,800 lbs	3,920
Peanuts, 1,300 lbs	1,430
Hay and seed	860
Hogs, 150	6,000
Beeves, 16	2,700
	14,910

[1] The 1954 estimated net cash income of $6,378, resulting from installation of the conservation plan on this farm, was calculated by Arthur H. Kautner, Federal Reserve Bank of Atlanta, Ga.

[2] The condition of the woodland in 1954 was such that a harvest cutting cannot be made for several years.

THE PRINCIPLES of planning ranches are the same as for planning farms. On ranches, however, relatively more attention must be given to the condition of the range, the rainfall, and past use of the vegetation. The abilities of range sites to produce various kinds and amounts of forage are affected by these factors as well as by the kind of soil.

Before one starts to make a conservation ranch plan, he needs an inventory of the physical resources of the ranch—the soil, water, and vegetation. Some parts of the ranch may be fertile bottom land, while other parts may be infertile, steep, or rocky. Some of it may be wet, with other portions well drained. The soils may vary from clays to sand. There are likely to be several range sites on a ranch, each one capable of producing different kinds or amounts of forage, and range conditions may vary from poor to excellent.

Grading ranges according to site and condition will help in planning the ranch so as to get the highest production while further improving the range. The grasses that thrive best and occupy each range site in its top condition are known as the climax grasses for that site. The different kinds of climax grasses help identify the sites.

In conservation planning the vegetation on each range site is graded into four range-condition classes: Excellent, good, fair, and poor. A range site in excellent condition has 75 to 100 percent of its vegetation composed of original or climax grasses; in good condition, it has 50 to 75 percent; in fair condition, 25 to 50 percent; and in poor condition, 25 percent or less.

Usually nothing can be done to improve a range site. The soil, rainfall, topography, and other factors that determine the range site were put there by Nature. The objective, however, is to obtain the greatest production from every range site by keeping it in the best forage condition possible. On three different range sites west of Fort Worth, Tex., yields roughly doubled when the range forage was improved from poor to excellent condition.

These differences show up in the land, in the plants, and in the livestock as conditions of the range forage improve. The condition of each range is wholly under the operator's control; his management determines what kinds and how much forage his land produces.

As the ranch plan is developed, an estimate should be made of the returns from the ranch after the basic conservation plan is put into effect. Such a conservation plan should insure that the soil and plant resources are being maintained and improved, that the crop and timber yields and livestock production are sustained and increased, and that the ranch will continue to be a stable provider. Once the plan is headed in this direction, yearly operations can be aimed at the greatest annual earnings.

When the operator has decided what use is to be made of the land, the conservation practices needed for range and cropland should be considered. This involves examining the condition of the ranges; evaluating the tame pasture resources and feed supplies; and determining the kind, class, and approximate number of livestock that can be grazed and fed under the conservation ranching program.

The operator will decide on the miles of new division fences required and where they are to be located, and the areas needing pitting, seeding, or brush control. Cropland fields will be selected to cultivate on the contour or in strips. If any cultivated fields are wet, the operator decides which ones are to be drained. He also decides which fields are to be terraced, and where to construct ponds and plant grassed waterways. Special attention may be given to wildlife areas such as the marshes, ponds, streams, springs, and the other areas needing habitat improvement.

Once the operator has decided what he wants to do, he can then decide when and how. What kind of grass to plant and when to plant it on fields, meadows, and waterways is up to the operator—as well as determining the best season to graze ranges and tame

pastures, and to use feed crops. He must decide the best time to construct new fences, if these are needed, and when to change old field and pasture boundaries.

How best to construct the ponds, terraces, and other water conservation structures needed as well as the best time to build them is planned.

The operator has to estimate what all these things will cost and what he will get out of them. The ranch conservationist can give many good suggestions, but the rancher must make the final decisions.

After all the details of what the rancher wants to do and when he wants to do it have been decided, the ranch conservationist will put these decisions in writing. The conservation plan will be illustrated with aerial photographs showing the ranch layout and information on the land use, soils, and vegetation.

A conservation ranch plan should serve as a reliable guide for ranching operations for a long time. When changes in weather, market prices, or other conditions make it desirable to change the plan, the soil conservation district will provide the technical help needed to make the necessary changes.

An example of a conservation ranch plan developed this way is shown in the map on the next page as follows:

CLASS I is very good land from all points of view. It is nearly level and does not wash or blow readily. The soil is deep and easy to work. It holds water well and is at least fairly well supplied with plant food. You can use it safely in most any way you choose, such as for cultivated crops, pastureland, woodland, or wildlife land. Good soil-management practices are required.

20A1—Denton clay loam.
4A1—Catalpa clay.

CLASS II land has some limitations that reduce the choice of use or require some conservation practices to keep it productive. It can be used for cultivated crops, pastureland, woodland,

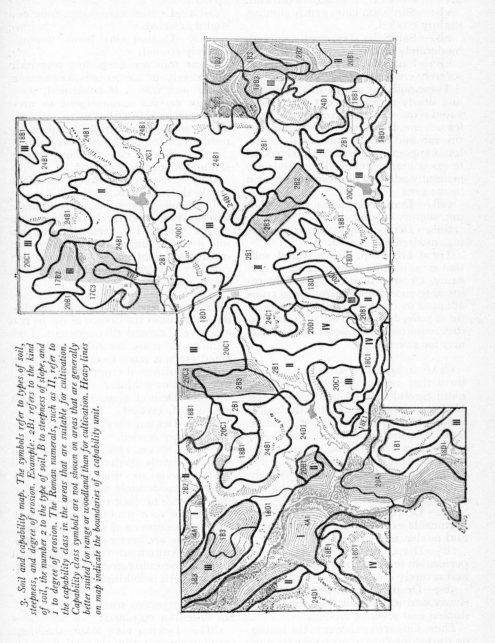

3. *Soil and capability map. The symbols refer to types of soil, steepness, and degree of erosion. Example: 2B1 refers to the kind of soil, the number 2 to the type of soil, B to steepness of slope, and 1 to degree of erosion. The Roman numerals, such as II, refer to the capability class in the areas that are suitable for cultivation. Capability class symbols are not shown on areas that are generally better suited for range or woodland than for cultivation. Heavy lines on map indicate the boundaries of a capability unit.*

or wildlife land. The limitations in use are not great or the practices difficult.

2B1—San Saba clay, gently sloping, slightly eroded.

2B2—San Saba clay, gently sloping, moderately eroded.

2B3—San Saba clay, gently sloping, severely eroded.

These soils are deep, fine textured, and slowly permeable but when cultivated require erosion control measures for safe use. Deep-rooted crops improve the air and water movement in the soil. Crops grown on these soils respond to good management. These soils are generally adapted to most crops grown in the area.

20B1—Denton clay loam, gently sloping, slightly eroded.

20B2—Denton clay loam, gently sloping, moderately eroded.

These are deep, fine-textured soils that air and water move through rather easily. Crops grown on these soils respond to good management. Most crops adapted to the area can be grown on these soils; however, when cultivated they require some erosion control measures for safe use.

CLASS III land has more natural features that restrict its use or require more careful management than Class II. It can be used for cultivated crops, woodland, pastureland, or wildlife land. The limitations in use are more severe than Class II and the problems more difficult to overcome.

1B1—Deep, fine-textured, very slowly permeable soils that are gently sloping and slightly eroded.

1B2—Deep, fine-textured, very slowly permeable soils that are gently sloping and moderately eroded.

1B3—Deep, fine-textured, very slowly permeable soils that are gently sloping and severely eroded.

5B3—Deep, medium-textured, very slowly permeable soils that are gently sloping and severely eroded.

These soils are often wet in the spring or during prolonged wet periods and require very careful management if used for cultivated crops.

2C1—Denton clay, sloping, slightly eroded.

20C1—Denton clay loam, sloping, slightly eroded.

20C3—Denton clay loam, sloping, severely eroded.

These soils are deep, fine textured, and slowly to moderately permeable to air and water. If cultivated, they require careful management to prevent serious damage due to erosion. These soils are generally adapted to most crops common to the area.

17B2—Denton clay, shallow, gently sloping, moderately eroded.

18B1—Denton clay loam, shallow, gently sloping, slightly eroded.

These soils are shallow, fine textured, and slowly to moderately permeable to air and water. The shallowness of the soil material limits the capacity for storing soil moisture, thus reducing the capacity for production of crops and pasture.

CLASS IV land has definite restrictions that limit the choice of use or require very careful management. The number of years favorable for cultivated crops is often limited. It can be used for cultivated crops, pastureland, woodland, or wildlife.

17C1—Denton clay, shallow, sloping, slightly eroded.

17C3—Denton clay, shallow, sloping, severely eroded.

18C1—Denton clay loam, shallow, sloping, slightly eroded.

These soils are fine textured and slowly to moderately permeable to air and water. The lack of soil depth favorable for root penetration and soil moisture storage is a major problem. These soils are better suited for range than for cultivated crops; however, they can be cultivated if very careful management is followed.

THE FOLLOWING SOILS are generally not suited for cropland:

18D1—Denton clay loam, shallow, strongly sloping, slightly eroded.

18E1—Denton clay loam, shallow, moderately steep, slightly eroded.

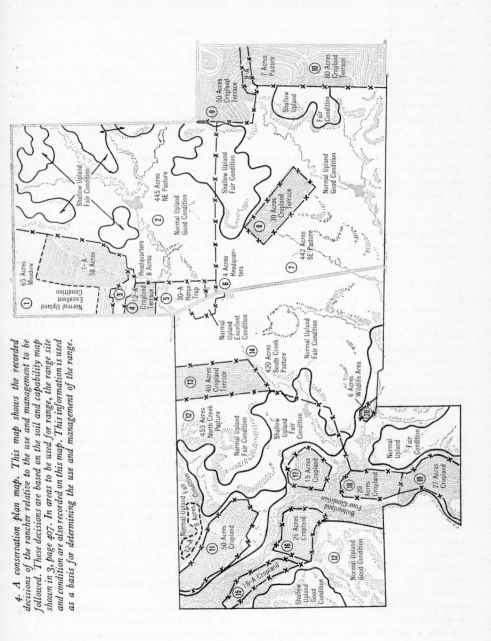

4. A conservation plan map. This map shows the recorded decisions of the rancher relative to the use and management to be followed. These decisions are based on the soil and capability map shown in 3, page 407. In areas to be used for range, the range site and condition are also recorded on this map. This information is used as a basis for determining the use and management of the range.

Because of the shallowness of soil and steepness of slope, these soils are better suited to range use than to cropland use. These soils are classified as Ordinary Upland for range use and are moderately productive if proper grazing management is followed.

24B1—Brackett gravelly clay, gently sloping, slightly eroded.

24C1—Brackett gravelly clay, shallow, sloping, slightly eroded.

24D1—Brackett gravelly clay, shallow, strongly sloping, slightly eroded.

These soils are classified as Shallow Upland for range use. They are very shallow and gravelly or stony and droughty. They are the least productive soils on the ranch.

Here is a description of the range sites on this ranch:

Bottom Land—This is the most productive range site on the ranch. Soils are deep, fine textured, and nearly level to gently sloping. They are subject to occasional overflow.

Normal Upland—This site is productive and well drained. Soils are fine textured, over 20 inches deep, and gently sloping to undulating.

Shallow Upland—This site is the least productive on the ranch. Soils are shallow, fine textured, droughty, and undulating to steep.

A CONSERVATION RANCH plan, as shown on page 409, would be:

General Practices—Tame pastures and new seedings will be mowed in June and July. Fire lanes will be maintained along public roads and other hazardous areas. One hundred to 2 hundred pounds of phosphate are to be applied each year to sweetclover fields. Terraced fields will be cultivated on the contour.

Field 1—65 acres—will be used for native hay meadow and will be protected from fire and grazing—the same as for Field 1–A. Stubble of 4 to 6 inches will be left when mowed.

Field 1–A—58 acres—will be seeded to native bluestem mixture and used as hay meadow.

Field 4—12 acres—will be used for

production of Hubam sweetclover for temporary pasture and will be terraced, with water emptied on pasture to the east.

Pasture 12—453 acres—65 acres of bottom land will be cleared of trees and undesirable brush and seeded to Bermuda-grass, burclover, and rescuegrass. Dam and pond spillway will be sodded and fenced and the pond stocked with fish. Two hundred rods of fence will be constructed between pastures: 110 rods around Field 16; 100 rods on side of Field 11; and 50 rods around stock pond. Pasture will be grazed in winter until seedings along creek bottom and in Field 12–A are established.

Field 12–A—8 acres—will be seeded to native bluestem mixture for grazing.

Fields 9, 10, 11, 15, 16, 17, 18, and 19—286 acres—will be used under 4-year crop rotation for oats, wheat, and corn, with the small grain overseeded with Hubam sweetclover. Fields 9 and 10 will be terraced after pasture outlet strip is established. Pasture strip of 170 rods will be fenced.

Field 20—6 acres—will be fenced and protected from grazing to serve as wildlife area. K. R. bluestem will be planted to control erosion in the gully.

Pastures 2 and 7—887 acres—dams and spillways of the two stock water ponds will be repaired, sodded, and fenced.

Pasture 9–A—7 acres of tame pasture will be shaped for terrace outlets and seeded to Bermuda-grass and K. R. bluestem.

Fields 8 and 13—70 acres—will be used under 3-year crop rotation: Hubam sweetclover for seed, oats-Hubam sweetclover and cane for hay. Land will be terraced. Water from Field 8 and Field 13 will be diverted on pasture. Diversion terraces will be constructed above both fields.

THE GOAL OF MANAGEMENT will be to improve ranges to high, good, or excellent condition. Grazing use of the bluestems and side-oats grama will be about half the annual growth.

About 1,500 pounds of hay will be

fed per animal unit during cold weather and during the early spring calving period. Salt will be fed year long, and a salt-cottonseed meal mixture will be fed on the range during February and March. Salt and cottonseed meal will be fed in portable boxes or feed bunks and moved to undergrazed areas to equalize grazing.

Fall-planted small grain will be lightly grazed in winter in conjunction with native range. Grain fields will not be grazed after March 15—grain crops will be harvested.

Pasture 12 will be grazed only in winter until a new stand of native grass in Field 12-A is established.

Livestock will be moved between pastures to facilitate herd management and to improve the grass. Both current use and trend in condition will be used to fix the stocking rate.

Three Farming Systems

E. L. Langsford, Charles P. Butler, C. W. Crickman, and Trimble R. Hedges

An analysis of representative farms in three parts of the country illustrates some of the economic problems of farming and ways by which a farmer can determine which alternative is most profitable for him.

For these illustrations we selected a family-size cotton farm in the Southern Piedmont, a typical 160-acre Corn Belt farm in western Iowa, and an irrigated cotton farm of 160 acres in the San Joaquin Valley of California. We made a comprehensive budget analysis of alternative soil-management systems on each of them. Although each farm represents a different set of problems, many parallels to them can be found.

Labor is abundant in the Piedmont area. Cotton provides an opportunity for profitable use of more labor than small grains and other alternative enterprises. The development and improvement of pastures, permanent cover for terrace outlets, correction of soil acidity by using lime, and increased rates of fertilization are a few of the physical changes that will result in better conservation of resources and greater profits. The addition of livestock to the farm organization would help the operator of a typical family-operated cotton farm in this area to use his resources more fully. Little additional capital would be needed for changes that would mean increases in profits and stability.

Several alternative adjustments in practices and land use that would assure the same degree of conservation of the soil are available to operators of typical 160-acre farms in the Corn Belt. They include crop rotations that contain more acres of forage crops; a combination of improved rotations, terraces, and contour tillage; and a combination of improved rotations, terraces, contour tillage, and use of fertilizer. There also are several alternative methods of utilizing the crops produced. They may be utilized in fattening cattle or by the dairy or beef cows or they may be sold. Based on 1955 prices, there are significant differences in estimated net farm income from the various alternatives. A herd of beef cows (together with improved rotations, terraces, contour cultivation, and application of fertilizer) provides the largest income, but it also requires the greatest increase in investment over the organization of the farm in 1955.

The high-cost land and water in the upper San Joaquin Valley demand intensive farming, high gross receipts per acre, and efficient methods if the farm operation is to be successful. A farmer on a 160-acre irrigated farm uses resources valued at approximately 100 thousand dollars, and his annual cash expenses are one-fourth to one-third of that amount. A farm operator who earns profits and remains in business must take these facts into consideration in developing soil-management plans and cropping systems.

COTTON, the main cash crop in the Southern Piedmont, is adapted to intensive use of unskilled labor. Farms adapted to the labor resources of one family therefore are more prevalent than farms of any other size. The income of most of these family-operated cotton farms is low.

Because the expense of maintaining the soil often can be deferred, it is one of the first to be eliminated when other needs press for income. Muddy streams and eroded fields on such farms give evidence of soil losses resulting from continued neglect of conservation.

Soils in the area tend to be acid. They consist of sandy and clay loams, which may be subject to severe erosion under the continuous system of row-crop farming that has been practiced many years. Special practices, such as terracing and rotation of row crops with grasses and legumes, are among the soil-management practices generally prescribed for most of these soils.

The farm selected for illustration in this area has 96 acres—66 acres of cropland, 2 acres of permanent pasture, 26 acres of woods, and 2 acres in the homestead. It had 13 acres of cotton, 9 acres of corn, 34 acres of small grain, and 10 acres of idle cropland in 1955. Annual lespedeza followed grain on 5 acres. The farmer had 2 mules, 2 milk cows, 4 hogs, and 50 hens.

The limited pasture meant that he had to depend on harvested crops for most of the feed he needed. The farm had a tractor and tractor-drawn plow, disk harrow, and combine. Mules and mule-drawn equipment were used in planting and cultivating cotton and corn.

An analysis of the soil resources revealed that the cropland was not adequately terraced. An inadequate

water-disposal system for terrace outlets resulted in severe erosion in part of the field. Soils were moderately to severely acid. Supplies of available nitrogen, phosphate, and potash were low.

Practices recommended for the farm included building broad-base terraces on cropland; establishing permanent sod crops in terrace outlets and adjoining eroded areas that are idle; adopting a 4-year rotation, with 2 years of row crops and 2 years of small grain; interplanting annual lespedeza with small grain; correcting soil acidity by applying limestone; and increasing the rates of fertilization in order to restore fertility and increase yields.

Changes from the organization and operation were needed to permit the operator to utilize his resources efficiently and to profit from the adoption of the improved soil-management practices. These changes included: Selling the mules and buying a tractor-drawn planter and cultivator; adding more productive livestock; providing more forage; extra fencing to permit the use of additional acreage for grazing; increasing rates of fertilizing crops and pastures; using hybrid corn and improved varieties of other crops, and bringing forest areas under improved management by thinning and culling undesirable trees and by making annual cuttings for sustained yields.

Information about the characteristics and organization of resources on the farm provides the basis for developing detailed plans for alternative farming systems whereby the recommended conservation practices can be integrated with the recommended reorganization of resources.

The land-use map for 1955 and the land capability map on the next page are useful in the planning process.

What are the economic factors that limit the adjustment opportunities on this farm?

First, the operator's income is low. His cash reserves are small, and he does not want to increase his indebtedness. This limitation restricts the kind of conservation practices and the sys-

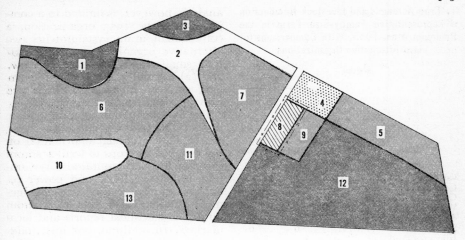

Field Number	Acres	Use	Conservation Need
1	2.5		
3	1.5	Woods	Thin and cull, cut annually for sustained yields.
12	22.0		
4	2.0	Farmstead	
5	5.0	Cotton	
11	8.0		Build up broad base terraces.
7	9.0	Corn	Rotation that would not have row crops on same land more than 2-years in succession.
9	2.0	Wheat	Apply lime and fertilizer according to needs.
13	7.0		
6	25.0	Oats	
2	5.0	Idle cropland	Establish permanent sod crop—grass or Sericea, lime and fertilizer.
10	5.0		
8	2.0	Bermuda pasture	Lime and fertilizer.

1. Land use on a cotton farm, Southern Piedmont, 1955. 2. (Below) Its land capability map.

tem of farming. For example, reforesting part of the cropland would accomplish the conservation and in the long run might be the most profitable adjustment. But because of his financial needs, the operator cannot make this longtime investment.

Second, row crops provide an opportunity for greater use of family labor than would more extensive systems.

Third, agricultural programs impose acreage limitations on cotton and wheat. The operator and his family probably could handle 15 to 20 acres of cotton, but his 1956 allotment was limited to 11 acres.

Many alternative adjustments could be made on this farm. This budget

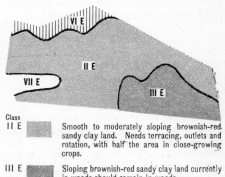

Class		
II E		Smooth to moderately sloping brownish-red sandy clay land. Needs terracing, outlets and rotation, with half the area in close-growing crops.
III E		Sloping brownish-red sandy clay land currently in woods should remain in woods.
VI E		Steep brownish-red sandy clay land with slight erosion. Best use sericea, pasture, or woodland.
VII E		Very steep and rough, severe limitations for grazing or forestry. Best use sodded waterway, sericea, or permanent pasture.

1. Crop Acreages and Livestock Numbers on a Representative Family-Size Farm in the Piedmont Area, 1955, With Comparisons for Two Alternative Organizations

| | 1955 organization (cotton-small grain) | Alternative organizations | |
| | | A Cotton-small grain-beef cattle | B Small grain-beef cattle |
Item			
	Acres	Acres	Acres
Cotton..........	13	11	.....
Corn............	9	9	.....
Oats............	25	24	44
Wheat..........	9	9	9
Annual lespedeza.	5	24	44
Sericea..........	.....	6	6
Idle cropland....	10	.....	.....
Total..........	71	83	103
Double cropped.	5	24	44
Total cropland.	66	59	59
Permanent pasture.	2	9	9
Homesite........	2	2	2
Woods..........	26	26	26
Total land.....	96	96	96
	Number	Number	Number
Work stock......	2	.....	.....
Cows...........	2	6	6
Calves 1–2 years..	.....	5	5
Calves less than 1 year..........	2	5	5
Hogs............	4	4	4
Hens............	50	50	50

2. Average Capital Investment on the Same Farm, and Alternative Organizations

| | 1955 organization (cotton-small grain) | Alternative organizations | |
| | | A Cotton-small grain-beef cattle | B Small grain-beef cattle |
Item			
Land...........	$5,760	$5,760	$5,760
Improvements [1]..	.....	541	541
Buildings........	6,592	6,592	6,812
Fence...........	100	311	311
Machinery.......	2,280	2,430	2,185
Livestock........	475	1,605	1,605
Total..........	15,207	17,239	17,214

[1] Cost of establishing permanent pastures and perennials.

analysis, however, is limited to a comparison of the 1955 organization, a cotton-small grain system, with two alternative organizations: (1) A cotton, small-grain, beef-cattle system, and (2) a small-grain, beef-cattle system, as given in table 1. Either will provide for adequate conservation.

The data we used in computing these budget analyses we got from many sources. We obtained information on the response of crops to fertilizer from experiments and appraisals. We obtained data on labor and power requirements from several farm-management studies. Price data came from published statistical reports and local markets. In addition, our own judgment is reflected in the analysis of the alternatives.

Alternatives A (cotton-small grain and beef cattle) and B (small grain and beef cattle) embrace the recommended land-management practices. A requires more labor than B. B, in which all of the cropland is in close-growing crops, might permit somewhat more conservation than A, but it would be less profitable.

Establishing the permanent sod crops in the fields, as recommended, would cost an estimated 541 dollars. The cost of additional fence was estimated to be 211 dollars for each alternative system. Investment in machinery would be somewhat higher for alternative A because of the need for a row planter and cultivator. Selling the work stock and buying the additional cattle would result in an increase from 475 to 1,605 dollars in the average inventory value of livestock. The total investment for alternatives A or B would be about the same, but it would be about 2 thousand dollars more than the total investment for the 1955 organization, as shown in the second table.

Based on normal yields and 1955 prices, the farm could have had a net return to the operator and his family of 247 dollars from the 1955 organization. Under this system, crop sales would account for 75 percent of the

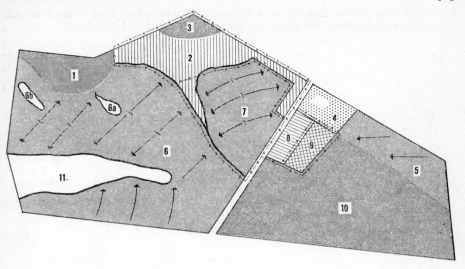

Field Number	Acres	Recommended Use	Recommended Land Management
1	2.5	Woods	Thin and cull, cut annually for sustained yields.
3	1.5		
10	22.0		
2	5.0	Coastal Bermuda and Crimson Clover	Construct fence; lime and fertilizer as determined by soil analysis.
8	2.0	Common Bermuda and Crimson Clover	Lime and fertilizer.
9	2.0	Fescue and Ladino Clover	Construct fence; lime and fertilizer as determined by soil analysis.
4	2.0	Farmstead	
6a	.5	Sericea Lespedeza	Establish permanent sod; lime and fertilizer.
6b	.5		
11	5.0		
6	39.0	Rotation cropland	Build up terraces, establish 4-year rotation of small grain with row crops.
7	9.0	Rotation cropland	Fence to permit grazing small grain, build up terraces, lime and fertilizer as needed.
5	5.0	Rotation cropland	Build up terraces, establish 4-year rotation of small grain with row crops, lime and fertilizer as needed.

3. Recommended land-use and land-management practices on a cotton farm in the Southern Piedmont.

gross receipts (the third table). Returns to the operator and his family were estimated to be 1,753 and 772 dollars, respectively, from alternatives A and B, based on the same price level. These estimates were based on the assumption that the family would do all the work. The increases in income from the alternative systems would result from higher yields and from fuller use of the resources.

The choice of alternative farming systems that provide adequate soil protection on the family-operated cotton farms depends largely on the family labor supply. Ordinarily when family labor is available, alternative A, with the cotton enterprise, would be more profitable than alternative B, because more hours of labor could be utilized profitably. If the operator is a part-time farmer, however, the family labor

3. Estimated Income and Expenses on a Representative Family-Size Farm in the Piedmont Area for 1955, and Alternative Organizations Based on 1955 Prices

		Alternative organizations	
Item	1955 organization (cotton and small grain)	A Cotton-small grain and beef cattle	B Small grain and beef cattle
Cash receipts:			
Crop sales...............................	$2,864	$4,118	$3,083
Livestock and product sales..............	584	1,478	1,478
Forest products sales.....................	....	91	91
Custom machine work..................	100	100	100
Total receipts........................	3,512	5,787	4,752
Cash expenses:			
Crop (includes hired custom work).........	1,002	1,468	1,239
Livestock..............................	106	130	130
Tractor expense.......................	169	291	319
Machinery expense.....................	91	118	145
Feed purchases........................	131	85	219
Building repair........................	75	92	97
Fence repair..........................	10	16	16
Insurance and taxes...................	82	82	82
Total expenses.......................	1,668	2,282	2,247
Net cash receipts........................	1,844	3,505	2,505
Depreciation............................	685	718	701
Returns to capital, labor, and management.....	1,159	2,787	1,804
Interest on investment [1].................	912	1,034	1,032
Returns to operator's family labor and management...........................	247	1,753	772

[1] Interest is based on 6 percent of the total average investment shown in table 2.

supply probably would be inadequate for a cotton enterprise. Alternative B would better fit the needs of the operator in such situations.

The beef cattle enterprise fits in well with either alternative by utilizing profitably the forage and grazing crops needed for soil protection. The beef cattle enterprise also helps to spread the production risks among additional enterprises.

Our analysis illustrates the need to consider the whole farm and the family labor resources in planning and choosing alternative systems that will meet the needs of both operator and land.

The two alternative organizations show that the good land-management practices will pay operators of cotton farms in the Piedmont, and that the initial cost will be a good short-term and long-term investment when prop-

erly balanced with other needed adjustments in organization and operation.

A TYPICAL CORN BELT FARM exemplifies a method of comparing relative returns from three systems of soil management. It is in western Iowa, just back of the Missouri River bluffs, where slopes are steep and long. The soils are Ida-Monona and associated soils. Ida-Monona soils are the more coarsely textured of the loessial soils, and the subsoils are highly permeable. Runoff from even moderate rainfall erodes these soils rapidly when they are farmed intensively with the intertilled crops without protective practices. Gully and sheet erosion is serious.

On the 160-acre farm we selected as typical, a broad ridge of gently rolling Monona silt loam crosses diagonally from west to east and constitutes about

60 percent of the farm. Flanking it are about 16 acres of steeply sloping Ida silt loam. At the foot of the slopes in the northern corners of the farm are about 42 acres of level Napier and Hornick silt loams.

Erosion on the slopes has been severe, but the owner has kept big gullies from forming by filling and packing earth in many small ditches. With a cropping system that includes 62 acres of corn, 53 acres of oats, and 41 acres of hay and pasture, the annual loss of soil was estimated in 1956 to be about 27 tons an acre.

The owner has several choices of methods by which to protect his soil against further losses. Agronomists estimate that if the average annual soil losses are held to about 5 tons an acre, permanent deterioration is not likely to occur.

That can be achieved on this farm by using any one of three different soil-management systems: Crop rotations that contain more acres of forage crops; a combination of improved rotations, terraces, and contour tillage; and a combination of improved rotations, terraces, and contour tillage and the use of fertilizer. By any of the systems it is thought that erosion can be reduced to an acceptable level. Each can be combined with a cash-grain or various livestock systems of farming.

The farmer's economic or management problem is to decide which method, when fully established, would be most profitable.

Use of rotations alone—a separate rotation for each field outlined in the fifth map—to control erosion would limit the acreage of grain to 51 acres of corn and 37 acres of oats—a reduction of almost 25 percent in the acreage of grain.

The increased production of forage on the larger acreage in hay and pasture, however, would provide the basis for cattle enterprises.

A soil-management system built around improved rotations, terraces, and contour tillage would include 60 acres of corn, 40 acres of oats, and 56

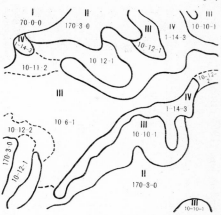

4. Land capability map. The Roman numerals show the capability of each part of the farm. The three-part symbol of Arabic numbers shows soil type, dominant percentage of slopes, and degree of erosion. Boundaries of the capability classes are outlined by heavy lines and those of soil-slope-erosion areas by broken lines. Soil type key: 1—Ida silt loam; 10—Monona silt loam; 70—Hornick silt loam; 93—Shelby silt loam; 170—Castana Napier silt loam. Erosion key: 0—none; 1—slight; 2—moderate; 3—severe.

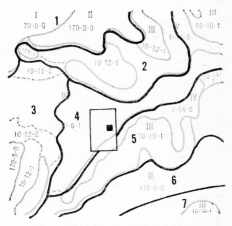

5. Map of field boundaries for the conservation farm plan.

acres of hay and pasture. Terraces would be put on all land with slopes of more than 4 percent or less than 12 percent. About a mile and a half of terraces would be needed in field 4. When terraces are used to reduce erosion, more of the land may be in grains, and conservation depends to a lesser

4. Data on Present and Alternative Systems of Farming on a Typical 160-Acre Farm in Western Iowa (1955 Prices)

Item	1955 organization	Improved rotations and fattening cattle [2]	Rotations, terraces, contouring, and fattening cattle [2]	Improved rotations, terraces, contour cultivation, and fertilizer			
				Fattening cattle [2]	Dairy cows	Beef cow herd	Cash-grain
	Number	*Number*	*Number*	*Number*	*Number*	*Number*	*Number*
Livestock: [1]							
Dairy cows	5				20		
Beef cows						27	
Steers fattened	7	32	30	29			
Hogs raised	117	79	119	165	181	222	50
	Dollars	*Dollars*	*Dollars*	*Dollars*	*Dollars*	*Dollars*	*Dollars*
Receipts:							
Crops	1,288	191	326				3,560
Livestock	8,389	12,083	12,836	13,998	12,363	11,435	3,369
Total	9,677	12,274	13,162	13,998	12,363	11,435	6,929
Cash expenses:							
Crop	1,613	1,541	1,518	1,893	1,893	1,893	2,052
Livestock	1,960	1,877	2,115	2,373	2,595	2,551	1,343
Feeder cattle bought	803	3,672	3,443	3,328			
Hired labor					1,260		
Other [3]	1,134	1,134	1,134	1,134	1,134	1,134	1,134
Total	5,510	8,224	8,210	8,728	6,882	5,578	4,529
Net cash farm income	4,167	4,050	4,952	5,270	5,481	5,857	2,400
Depreciation	1,197	1,216	1,305	1,392	1,396	1,372	1,022
Interest on investment	305	173	181	215	390	256	82
Net farm income [4]	2,665	2,661	3,466	3,663	3,695	4,229	1,296
New investments needed:							
Livestock		1,523	1,567	1,777	858	4,289	
Buildings, fence and equipment		2,621	2,358	2,792	4,411	3,726	
Terraces			275	275	275	275	275
Fertilizer				375	375	375	375

[1] All systems include hogs, 300 hens, 500 chickens.
[2] Fattening cattle are yearling steers bought in the fall, wintered, pastured in spring and summer, and finished on grain in drylot for the fall market.
[3] Real-estate taxes, electricity, fence repairs, and farm share of automobile expense.
[4] Returns to land, other capital, and to labor and management of operator and his family.

5. Use of Land and Production of Feed With Present and Alternative Soil-Management Systems on a Typical 160-Acre Farm on Ida-Monona Soils in Western Iowa [1]

Item	Unit	Soil-management system			
		1955 organization [2]	Improved rotations	Improved rotations, terraces, and contour cultivation	Improved rotations, terraces, contour cultivation and fertilizer
Cropland:					
Corn.................	Acre........	62	51	60	60
Oats.................	....do......	53	37	40	40
Hay and pasture.......	....do......	41	68	56	56
Other land.............	....do......	4	4	4	4
Crop yield per acre:					
Corn.................	Bushel......	51.0	51.0	54.8	61.2
Oats.................	....do......	34.5	34.5	36.2	41.6
Hay and pasture [3].....	Ton........	1.2	1.7	1.8	2.2
Production of feed:					
Corn.................	Bushel......	3,162	2,601	3,288	3,672
Oats.................	....do......	1,828	1,276	1,448	1,664
Hay and pasture.......	Ton........	49	116	101	123

[1] Based on soil map in the first drawing and data in appendix tables B–1 and B–2 in Iowa Agricultural Experiment Station Research Bulletin 429, June 1955.
[2] Based on an average of previous years.
[3] Yield of pasture was estimated in tons of hay equivalent.

extent on a large acreage of forage crops. Terraces lower the rate and (to some extent) the total amount of runoff. The retention of some extra moisture by terraces is beneficial to crop yields during dry periods in western Iowa. This second alternative would produce more feed than is now produced on the farm.

The third possibility—a combination of improved rotations, terraces, and contour tillage and the use of fertilizer—would produce considerably more feed after the conservation system had been used long enough to reflect the yield-increasing potentialities of the improved practices. Heavy applications of fertilizer tend to offset temporary reductions in income that otherwise would accompany a shift of part of the cropland from grain to forage.

Each of the soil-management systems would produce more forage. The additional forage could be used as green manure, but feeding the forage to livestock and returning the manure to the land will give better returns. A livestock system requires further investments in livestock, buildings, and fences, besides the added investments in terraces and fertilizer. The owner of this farm has ample capital, however, and he can choose the method of utilizing forage crops that is likely to give him the highest average returns over a period of years.

He therefore compares the projected costs and returns of the several possibilities for conserving his soil and utilizing the additional forage produced in the different cropping systems. He estimates the changes that would be needed in his system of farming, the additional capital and labor required for these adjustments, and the effects of the changes on net farm income.

He finds from the comparative budgets that the change from the 1955 organization to some of the alternative systems of farming would have been profitable at 1955 prices.

The system that features improved rotations, terraces, contour tillage, and use of fertilizer, in combination with a livestock system that includes hogs and beef cattle, would be best.

Compared with a net farm income of about 2,665 dollars (at 1955 prices) from the system used in 1955, the hog-beef system would return about 4,229 dollars; a dairy-hog system, about 3,695 dollars; yearling steers bought in fall, wintered, pastured in spring and summer, and finished on grain in drylot for the fall market, about 3,663 dollars; and a cash-grain system, about 1,300 dollars. If the farmer does not apply fertilizer, the system of farming that includes hogs and yearling steers (wintered, pastured, and fed grain in drylot) would return about 3,465 dollars—about 200 dollars less than if fertilizer were used. If improved crop rotations were the only soil-conserving measure used and if the forage was utilized in fattening yearling steers, the net farm income would be about 2,660 dollars—more than 1,000 dollars less than with the use of terraces and fertilizer.

If this farmer chooses a system of farming that includes more hay and pasture, terraces, contouring, and fertilizer, and uses beef cows to market the additional forage, he would need to make an additional capital investment of 8,675 dollars at 1955 prices. Of this total, about 275 dollars would be for terraces, 375 dollars for fertilizer, 3,726 dollars for alterations to buildings and fences and additional equipment, and 4,289 dollars for livestock (cattle and hogs). If he chooses a cattle-fattening enterprise, the additional investments would be 2,792 dollars for alterations to buildings and fences and additional equipment, and 1,777 dollars for livestock.

These larger net farm incomes from the soil-conserving systems would not be forthcoming immediately. For 3 or 4 years during the transition from the old to the new system of farming, his incomes would be lower than with the present system. But as the additional capital and labor that are used in the farm business become productive through yield-increasing rotations and other soil-management practices and through more livestock, the net in-

comes would increase. (The sequence of net farm incomes can be measured by budgets for each year in the transition period.)

The accumulated net income from the conservation system in a few years would exceed the net income that would accumulate from the present system. The period in which this would occur would be even shorter if allowance were made for the slow but continuous decline in yields of crops that will result if the annual loss of 27 tons of soil an acre continues.

COTTON DOMINATES the use of alluvial irrigated lands in the upper and central San Joaquin Valley. The individual soil classes lie in reasonably large and relatively homogeneous bodies, and there is little interspersing of varying grades of soil on a farm.

Most soils in the valley floor are highly productive and are suited to continuous production of cash crops. They impose few restrictions on cropping practices. Neither the Soil Conservation Service nor the University of California has made specific recommendations as to rotations or soil-management practices to maintain or improve the soils. Farm operators generally do not select crops or follow definite rotations to attain specific soil-management objectives.

Before allotments of acreages in cotton were in effect, farmers kept well over half of their irrigated acreage in cotton and potatoes. Under the allotment programs of 1954 and 1955, farmers obtained higher yields of cotton than in preallotment years when a higher proportion of the total cropland was in this crop.

The water situation here imposes more limitations on soil management than soils do. Water tends to be in short supply in many localities. To the extent that water tables drop further, this situation will become worse and will affect more farms. The quality of the water also presents problems in some places. The chemical content of underground water, in conjunction with soil types, tends to slow the penetration of water and thus to lessen the effectiveness of irrigation.

Government regulations and profit potentials for various crops have more to do with soil management and cropping systems in the San Joaquin Valley than physical soil and water conditions.

Our analysis evaluates the influence of economic factors of this kind. In doing so, we compared experience before the 1954 acreage-allotment program on cotton with conditions after allotments were in effect. We used data from a cotton-adjustment study in the upper San Joaquin Valley to estimate normal prices for preallotment and postallotment conditions. The prices used for the preallotment period are averages based on records and selling prices. Prices with allotments were estimated according to certain assumptions regarding Government price support levels, general price levels, and market outlets.

We selected a 160-acre farm (the modal size in the area) in Kern County for the analysis. Three possible cropping systems were considered: Cotton-barley, cotton-potatoes, and cotton-alfalfa-potatoes. In each, cotton is the chief source of income and occupies more land than any other crop.

Acreage allotments are important in determining cropping systems on farms in Kern County. The cotton acreage allotments in force there in 1955 were about 45 percent lower than the cotton acres planted in 1953. Potato growers have undertaken at various times to restrict acreage through marketing agreements. Growers of sugar beets were also subject to acreage allotments for the 1955 and 1954 crops.

Many crops will grow well in Kern County, but farmers allocate most of their crop acreages to a few. Cotton is the most important. Potatoes and seed crops come next. Feed crops, including alfalfa hay, barley, and milo, account for most of the rest. Farmers who depend on cotton as the chief crop usu-

6. Land Use and Investment on a 160-Acre Irrigated Cotton Farm, Under Preallotment and Allotment Conditions, Kern County, Calif.

	System of farming					
	A		B		C	
Item	Cotton-barley		Cotton-potatoes		Cotton-alfalfa-potatoes	
	Preallotment	Allotment [1]	Preallotment	Allotment [1]	Preallotment	Allotment [1]
Land use:	Acres	Acres	Acres	Acres	Acres	Acres
Cotton	100	55	100	55	100	55
Potatoes			35	28	20	17
Alfalfa seed	15	30				
Alfalfa hay				20	28	45
Barley	33	63				
Milo			13	45		
Field corn						31
Noncropland	12	12	12	12	12	12
Total acres	160	160	160	160	160	160
Farm investment:	Dollars		Dollars		Dollars	
Undeveloped land	40,000		40,000		40,000	
Land improvement	24,000		24,000		24,000	
Well and facilities	12,000		12,000		12,000	
Buildings	3,250		3,250		3,250	
Machinery and equipment	18,000		18,000		18,000	
Total	97,250		97,250		97,250	

[1] Preallotment represents the 1951–1953 period; allotment represents the 1954–1955 period.

ally grow one or more of the other principal crops.

Cotton yields in Kern County are the highest in California. They averaged about two bales an acre in 1955. Early potatoes also yield well. Cotton yields were considerably higher in 1954 and 1955 than in 1953, the last preallotment year. There is evidence, too, that yields of other crops that farmers planted on diverted acres were also higher than in 1953. This information for cotton and the alternative crops was considered in preparing the normal yields used in this analysis.

Relatively favorable market outlets and prices are available to Kern County cash-crop farmers for their products. Government price supports and premium staple length resulted in favorable prices for cotton in 1952–1955. Early potatoes are subject to sharp year-to-year price fluctuations, which reflect production conditions in both Kern County and other parts of the country. The Los Angeles milk-producing area provides a market for most of the alfalfa hay, but the market for alfalfa seed has been less attractive. Prices of grain usually have been favorable because California is a deficit producer of feed grains.

A farmer who operates 160 acres in Kern County and pumps his irrigation water from underground must invest (at 1956 prices) about 44,000 dollars to develop his farm for irrigation. This does not include the value of the undeveloped land. The well and equipment will cost about 12,000 dollars or 75 dollars an acre, and the distributing system 8,000 dollars or 50 dollars an acre. Leveling may cost 24,000 dollars or 150 dollars an acre. If undeveloped land is valued at 250 dollars an acre, the resulting 40,000 dollars brings the total for land and irrigation facilities to 84,000 dollars. Minimum buildings and operating facilities would represent another 3,250 dollars of initial costs. Power and machinery is valued at 18,000 dollars. These add to a total investment of 97,250 dollars.

The annual fixed costs on this farm are about 72 dollars an acre. These costs include interest on all farm capital investments—investments in undeveloped land as well as improvements.

The amount of total fixed costs per acre indicates the importance of obtaining high gross receipts and efficiency in the farm operation. Water costs, including costs of distribution and pumping, are 9 dollars an acre-foot.

The same per acre water costs for cotton were used for each of the three systems, and the same basic potato and alfalfa data were used for both systems B and C. The data on costs for the latter crops were adjusted for the effects of varying acreages between the two systems.

In order to make an effective comparison among the adapted crops, we included interest on investments with costs of production. Management income, therefore, represents for these particular organizations the relative profit potential of the crops listed, considering all costs outlined within the analytical framework.

Cotton and potatoes were about equally profitable before allotments. These two crops ranked far ahead of other alternatives. The closest competitor was alfalfa hay. Alfalfa seed, milo, and field corn were the only other crops that returned a profit. These facts speak for themselves in explaining the cropping plan under preallotment conditions.

Normal allotment cropping patterns, yields, and prices differ from those before allotments. Farm operators, therefore, must make their soil management and crop decisions under a different set of conditions.

Acreage allotments for cotton that require almost a 50-percent cut in cotton acres represent the dominant fact regarding the cropping systems.

A drop in potato prices that reduces the relative profitability of potatoes as compared with cotton also is important to operators whose soils are adapted to this crop and who are equipped to produce it.

Alfalfa hay has gained in relative

7. Yields, Prices, Gross Receipts, Expenses, and Management Income per Acre, by Crops, 160-Acre Irrigated Cotton Farm, Under Preallotment and Allotment Conditions, Kern County, Calif.

| | | | | | Average per acre | | | |
| | | | | | | Expenses | | |
Crops	Unit	Yield	Price	Gross receipts [1]	Fixed	Variable	Total	Management income
			Dollars	Dollars	Dollars	Dollars	Dollars	Dollars
Preallotments (1951–53):								
Cotton lint [1]	Lbs	875	0.342	334	83	141	224	110
Potatoes [2]	Cwt	290	2.16	626	62	453	515	111
Alfalfa seed	Lbs	550	.347	191	65	116	181	10
Alfalfa hay [3]	Tons	7.0	27.50	192	72	101	173	19
Barley	Cwt	21	2.93	62	44	34	78	−16
Milo [4]								20
Barley and milo								−11
Field corn	Cwt	45	3.91	176	60	109	169	7
Allotments (1954 and 1955):								
Cotton lint	Lbs	1,050	.30	346	106	158	264	82
Potatoes	Cwt	290	2.00	580	64	453	577	63
Alfalfa seed	Lbs	600	.30	180	66	119	185	−5
Alfalfa hay	Tons	7.5	27.50	206	67	99	166	40
Barley	Cwt	25	2.30	58	45	35	80	−22
Milo								4
Field corn	Cwt	50	3.15	158	58	111	169	−11

[1] Gross receipts from cotton include sale of cottonseed.
[2] Noncash and total fixed costs for potatoes on system C; preallotment $61 and $70, allotments $63 and $72 per acre, respectively.
[3] Noncash and total fixed costs for alfalfa hay on system B; allotments $67 and $75 per acre, respectively.
[4] Net income from milo on system B; preallotments $20, allotments $4 per acre, respectively. Net income from barley and milo double-cropped on system B; allotments, −$11.

profitability because of increases in both price and yields. Because of a price decline, alfalfa seed shows less profit under the conditions with allotments, despite higher yields.

Barley, field corn, and milo also are less profitable under the normal prices with the allotments than before—again because of price declines. Milo, however, continues to show a slight excess of gross receipts over total costs; the management income was 20 dollars an acre before allotments and 4 dollars after allotments.

Total farm returns reflect the full effects of these changes in number of acres, yields, prices, and gross receipts; in total costs; and in management returns per acre. Total farm income under allotment conditions for systems B and C is about half that under preallotment conditions. These changes, however, had more drastic effects on the earnings of system A; they cut total management income by more than two-thirds.

Sharp drops in management income on 160-acre farms in Kern County largely reflect the restrictions on cotton, although reduced profits from potatoes also contribute to the decline. Farm operators have available no other crop of comparable earning capacity to plant on the acres diverted from

cotton. This problem is made worse for potato growers because only by reducing the number of acres planted to this crop can they avoid sharp price drops.

Barley in system A showed a net loss under both preallotment and allotment conditions, considering all fixed and variable costs of producing it.

Barley nevertheless was included in system A, because no other crop with a comparably broad market and low water requirement offers better earnings performance for some farms where the cost of water is high and the grade 3 soils are not adapted to economical production of alfalfa and potatoes. Total management incomes on these farms would be greater with barley than without it.

The explanation for this earning effect of barley on some farms lies in a comparison of gross receipts and costs of production. Under allotment conditions, barley grosses 58 dollars, which exceeds variable expenses by 23 dollars. This amount fails to cover all fixed costs by 22 dollars—hence the net loss. But the operator would have most of these fixed costs even without barley.

The cut in cotton acreage affects net income relatively more severely for farmers on the grade 3 land, particularly the operators that have relatively high water costs. As we indicated, these

8. Estimated Management Income From Three Systems of Farming on a 160-Acre Irrigated Cotton Farm Under Preallotment and Allotment Conditions, Kern County, Calif.

	Systems of farming					
	A		B		C	
	Cotton-barley		Cotton-potatoes		Cotton-alfalfa-potatoes	
Crops	Preallotment	Allotment [1]	Preallotment	Allotment [1]	Preallotment	Allotment [1]
Cotton..................	$11,000	$4,510	$11,000	$4,510	$11,000	$4,510
Potatoes................	....	....	3,885	1,764	2,060	935
Alfalfa seed............	150	—150	....	....	....	....
Alfalfa hay.............	....	....	....	640	532	1,800
Barley.................	—528	—1,386	....	....	....	....
Milo...................	....	....	260	180	....	....
Field corn.............	....	....	....	....	....	—341
All crops..........	10,622	2,974	15,145	7,094	13,592	6,904

[1] Preallotment represents the 1951–1953 period; allotment represents the 1954–1955 period.

operators have fewer alternatives than those with lower water costs and a larger percentage of grades 1 and 2 soils. Even alfalfa seed shifts from a slight profit to losses under allotment normals, leaving only cotton to earn profits under system A.

Considering soils alone, if other conditions were favorable, farmers would have little difficulty in selecting a farming system that would return a relatively high level of profit. Preallotment conditions approximated this situation on farms with adequate water supplies under existing price levels. In the late 1940's and early 1950's, these conditions apparently reflected a combination of unusual and temporary circumstances.

Kern County farmers may need to make decisions as to soil-management and cropping systems for some time in the future within a physical and economic context similar to that represented by the estimated allotment normals we use in this analysis. They need to plant somewhat fewer acres of cotton and potatoes than before allotments, and they may face lower prices for them. Some improvement in the profitability of alfalfa hay and a less favorable profit performance by feed grains are indicated also. These conditions favor some expansion in acreage of alfalfa that should both help to support income and contribute to improved soil management.

Both favorable and unfavorable factors may cause future conditions to differ from the estimated norms. Water costs are rising on most farms. On some farms, both costs and supplies were nearing the critical point in 1956. System A, which includes barley, a crop that has a low water requirement, indicates what this trend means to soil management, crop organization, and farm earnings. Unless additional water can be brought in, or better use can be made of existing supplies, many more farmers will find themselves in similar or even less favorable situations.

As we indicated, barley serves to absorb some of the fixed costs for system A. Operators on larger farms in Kern County and in the western San Joaquin Valley commonly fallow a sizable fraction of their cropland each year. Too high costs or drastically reduced quantities of irrigation water will force farmers on the 160-acre units to follow the practice.

Increases in demand and in prices for farm products would represent the most favorable future development for farmers in Kern County, if they can solve their irrigation problems. For cotton and potatoes, this might take the direction of broader outlets, thus permitting farmers to plant more acres at prices similar to normals we used.

Growers of alfalfa seed, on the other hand, need higher selling prices for profitable operation. Price rises, which may come ultimately as a result of growing population and increased demand for livestock and livestock products, would help producers of alfalfa hay and feed grains also. It would lift these crops into the profitable category. Thus farm operators would have a wider range of choice in making their decisions as to soil management and crop organization.

Soil management has been enhanced by technological advancements of science pertaining to soils, agronomy, forestry, and engineering. The combinations of practices that have been developed and tested for specific kinds of soils to establish their effects on yields, quality of plants, and longtime productivity are the products of research and experience. But conservation of the soil and its fertility is something more than throwing up defensive earthworks against the physical forces that attack land. It means dealing with human resources. Often it pits public against private interest, and shortrun against longtime gains. Economic pressure on farmers must be relieved before farmers can ease the pressure on land. Fortunately, soil management can be designed to fit the needs of individual operators as well as the needs of individual parcels of land.

Economics of Cropping Systems

Earl O. Heady

Two sets of forces determine the most profitable rotation or cropping system for a farm: Physical considerations, which determine crop yield possibilities, and economic considerations, particularly the prices and costs of the products.

The physical considerations determine the enterprise relationship among the various crops and how each fits into the overall management plan.

The economic considerations weigh the relative advantage of each crop and service in the selection of a rotation to increase the profits of the farm.

The best system of crops or rotations cannot be selected with one of these types of information alone. Even though the effects of soil type, fertility level, and climate on the yield of different crops are known, deciding on the most profitable system of land use requires the use of economic principles. But even though we know the price and cost ratios, we cannot specify the optimum cropping plan until crop production possibilities have been predicted from the relevant information as to soil and crop yields.

The importance of price in determining the best rotation depends on whether the enterprise relationship is one in which crops compete with one another.

The physical characteristics of the soil and the indirect effects one crop has on yields of the other determine these enterprise relationships. Two of them, the competitive and complementary relationships, are of particular importance in crop combinations and in determining how crops should be grown together. A third relationship, the supplementary relationship, determines how well the crop program fits in with the livestock program and the overall plan of the farm.

The main advantage in combining crops into a rotation occurs when they complement each other—when the output of one on a given acreage also leads to an increase in the output of the other. As an example, suppose a field of 100 acres has been planted continuously to corn; the yield is 30 bushels an acre; the total production is 3 thousand bushels from the 100 acres. A switch to a rotation of corn-corn-corn-oats-meadow gives yields of 50 bushels an acre of corn, 40 bushels of oats, and 2 tons of hay or meadow. The 100 acres now produce 3,800 bushels of grain (or 3,400 bushels of corn equivalent, if a bushel of oats is considered to be worth one-half bushel of corn) and 40 tons of hay. Thus the shift of land, labor, and capital from corn to hay brings about more production of both grain and forage. In this sense, the two crops go hand in hand. They are complementary.

The complementary relationship exists only when one crop, or a soil-management practice associated with the crop, provides a nutrient or service required by the other crop. Thus, grasses and legumes may serve in a complementary capacity to grains or row crops when the grasses and legumes furnish nitrogen, control erosion, eliminate diseases and pests, and maintain or improve soil structure to an extent that a greater production of grains or row crops comes from fewer acres.

Grains and row crops also can be complementary to grasses and legumes. In zonal locations such as the Northern Chernozem soils from North Dakota to Kansas and the Prairie soils in the western Corn Belt, continuous production of deep-rooted legumes depletes subsoil moisture to an extent that yields deteriorate with time. Forage production from a given acreage consequently may be augmented if the sod is frequently plowed up and the land is planted to corn or other row crops until it is returned to forages.

Similarly, in regions of greater rainfall, such as New England, or irrigated lands of the West, or parts of the Southeast, forage stands may deteriorate from winter killing, disease, or grazing to a point where a year of grain or other crops in the rotation allows an improved stand and greater total production of forage as the land is returned to grasses and legumes. Fallow land is complementary to wheat and other small grains over much of the Great Plains.

A rotation of fallow and wheat in places where moisture is sufficiently limited increases the yield of wheat to the extent that a greater total production is possible from fewer acres.

Examples of complementary crops can be found on many soil types. Yields from the Morrow experimental plots at the University of Illinois indicate that 100 acres of Drummer silt loam devoted to continuous corn would have produced 2,433 bushels of corn in the period 1904–1949. A similar plot of 100 acres devoted to a corn-oats-clover rotation would have produced the equivalent of 2,677 bushels of corn (1 bushel of oats is figured to be worth one-half bushel of corn) and 21.7 tons of hay.

After continuous treatment from 1915, continuous corn on Webster silt loam in Iowa would have produced at the rate of 3,220 bushels of corn on 100 acres in the period 1945–1949. In the same period, 100 acres in corn-corn-oats-clover would have produced 3,881 bushels of corn equivalent and 44.5 tons of hay.

Experimental data from Fort Hayes, Kans., for the period 1918–1949 show that 100 acres devoted to continuous wheat would have produced 1,460 bushels. A rotation of fallow-wheat-wheat-wheat would have produced 1,538 bushels and the year-to-year output would have been more stable.

Data from Aroostook County, Maine, are such that we could predict 1,320 bushels of potatoes from 100 acres cropped continuously to potatoes. In the same period, 100 acres devoted to a potato-oats-clover rotation would have produced 1,275 bushels of potatoes and some oats and hay.

The complementary relationships between crops extends only over a limited range of crop combinations, however. They finally cease and give way to the competitive relationship. Complementarity ends because of the physical law of diminishing returns—equal additions of moisture, nitrogen, and organic matter, improved soil structure, and disease or pest control that are furnished by one crop to another adds less to the acre yield of the second. Eventually the reduced acreage of the second crop more than offsets increases in yields. Then a further shift of land from one crop to the other allows production of the first to increase only at the expense of the second. The presence or absence of complementarity between crops has particular implications in determining whether monoculture or crop rotation is more profitable on a particular soil.

Two CROPS are competitive with each other when an increase in the acreage and output of the first crop causes the acreage and output of the second to decline on a given acreage. Even when one crop (or the soil-management practices associated with it) provides enough nutrients or services to cause complementarity with a second, this complementary relationship always merges into a competitive relationship.

In the examples I cited, a further increase in forage, as represented by a corn-oats-clover rotation, on 100 acres of Webster silt loam causes the corn equivalent to drop to 2,968 bushels, while hay increases to 48.4 tons. Compared to a corn-corn-oats-clover rotation, more hay is produced only with a sacrifice in total grain production, and the relationship is one of competition. (Between continuous corn and a corn-

corn-oats-clover rotation, the hay served in a complementary capacity with grain.) At Fort Hayes, Kans., a wheat-fallow rotation reduced wheat production on 100 acres to 1,190 bushels.

When the range of crop competition follows after a range of complementarity, the yield of one crop ordinarily can be increased only with increased sacrifices of the other.

For example, experiments on Canfield-Wooster soils in Ohio showed that in 1937–1943 the 20 percent of land acreage devoted to hay in a corn-corn-corn-wheat-alfalfa rotation, as compared to a continuous corn rotation, was complementary to corn. As the same three crops were combined into a rotation with 33 percent alfalfa, however, each pound added to total hay production caused a sacrifice of 0.19 pound in total grain production. With an increase in alfalfa acreage to 40 percent, each pound added to total hay production caused total grain production to decline by 0.22 pound. With an increase of alfalfa to 50 percent of the acreage in rotation, each pound added to total hay production caused a sacrifice of 0.53 pound in total grain production. These sacrifice or substitution ratios between crops and the price ratios for them determine the economically efficient combination or rotation.

Two crops that have similar requirements of moisture and nutrients and are grown in approximately the same season are almost always competitive. Competition is almost always at a constant rate.

Barley and wheat, for example, are similar crops in most of the Great Plains. Neither furnishes a nutrient or service particularly needed by the other if they are grown in rotation. In the allocation of a given land area between the two, therefore, an increase in one will always cause a constant sacrifice in the other: If the yields are 20 bushels of wheat and 30 bushels of barley an acre, each addition of 1 bushel to total wheat production ne-

cessitates a 1.5-bushel sacrifice in barley—regardless of whether the land is devoted entirely to wheat, one-half each to both crops, or three-fourths to one and one-fourth to the other.

Aside from considerations of uncertainty and livestock feeding, combinations or rotations of crops that compete or substitute at constant rates are never profitable.

In schematic manner, the crop enterprise relationships I outlined can be summarized in the accompanying graphs. The curves or lines within the graphs represent all combinations of the two categories of crops which can be produced from a given land area and under specified techniques or soil-management practices. In the first graph, both categories of crops are complementary to each other over some range of combinations.

Starting from point A, representing continuous grain cropping, an increase in hay production also increases grain production; up to point B, where more hay can be produced only at the expense of grain. Starting from the other extreme, point E (representing a continuous hay cropping), an increase in grain output increases total hay production from a given acreage; up to point D, where competition between the crops again is encountered. For any rotation that produces crop outputs within the range B and D, a shift in acreage from one crop to the other allows output of the first to increase but it causes a diminution in production of the other.

In the second graph, complementarity is one way; a rotation of forage and grain will increase total output of grain, as compared to grain monoculture. Hay grown continuously will produce a greater output only at the expense of grain, but hay cannot be increased by using some land in rotation with grain.

In the third graph, one or both categories of crops furnishes some nutrients or services to the other, but in insufficient quantities to cause a complementary relationship. Hence the crops are competitive and substitute for each other at increasing rates. Increased

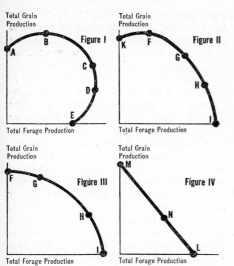

A schematic representation of the enterprise relationships between crops grown in combination or rotations. While relationships are indicated as between grain and forage, similar possibilities may exist within particular categories, such as row crops, grains, vegetables, and others.

sacrifices of one are necessary in adding equal increments to total output of the other, as is denoted by the curvilinear nature of the curve of crop production possibilities.

In the fourth graph, the two categories of crops are competitive and substitute for each other at constant rates, as is denoted by the linear crop production possibility curve. The latter relationship characterizes much of the Podzolic and Dark Brown Prairie soils, where rainfall is the limiting factor in crop production and soil erosion is not a threat under grain.

The relationships illustrated in the graphs are basic in determining (for given techniques) where monoculture or crop rotations represent the economic soil-management system. They also indicate the particular proportions that are best for crops grown in rotation, when rotation is more efficient than a single crop.

An important challenge in agronomic research is to determine the nature of production possibilities for particular soil types and to indicate to which of the general families of the first graph they belong. Single-crop rotations represent separate points on the production possibility curve; such as *B*, *C*, and *D* in the first graph or *G* and *H* in the second and third graphs. Combinations of alternative rotations on a given soil area allow representation of crop production possibilities in the manner of the continuous functional relationships in the graphs.

THE CONCEPTS of crop production possibilities can be related to price ratios in indicating whether monoculture—complete specialization in one crop—should be practiced or whether cropping systems or rotations should be employed. They also are the basis for determining which rotation, if one is to be employed, is best.

Little or no attention need be given to prices when crops are complementary. The acreage of the crop that provides the nutrients and services of benefit to another should be extended as long as the complementary relationship prevails. The price of the complementary crop or the net return from it can be as low as zero; it is still profitable as long as its beneficial effects in fertility improvement, erosion control, or disease and pest prevention are great enough.

Stated another way: A complementary forage crop or fallow will add to profit, even though its price or return is zero, as long as its acre cost of production is equal to or less than the cost per acre of the crop with which it is combined. The complementary crop increases the value of the crop with which it is grown. It reduces total costs if its cost of production is less per acre than the cost of its companion crop. Net income thus must increase.

The cost of producing an acre of hay, for example, generally is lower than the cost of producing and harvesting grain or row crops with which hay is commonly combined for rotational purposes. While the cost of producing and harvesting hay may exceed the same costs for other crops, it can be left unharvested or can simply be plowed under as green manure.

The complementary relationship ordinarily is expressed only as crops are grown in sequence over time. An exception is oats grown as a nurse crop to new seedings in some places. Frequently the seedings get benefits immediately, as well as later, in having the grass crop for shade and weed control. Sometimes, however, the small grain merely serves in a supplementary or independent capacity; neither contributes to or benefits from the legume seeding.

Grain must follow hay to utilize any nitrogen and improve soil structure provided by the latter; or it must follow fallow to utilize any moisture conserved in a preceding season.

Hence the operator who will be on his farm long enough to realize complementary effects will generally increase profits by producing the crop that provides these services. Because complementarity is expressed mainly through a time sequence of crops, however, a tenant operating under leases extending a single year can plan crops only in a competitive framework. If he expects to move at the end of the year, a current investment in forage will not allow him to gain from the yield benefits of later grain crops. Improved cropping programs on a great many of the rented farms in the United States can be brought about only if the leasing and the tenure system is changed to correspond with crop production possibilities.

PRICE AND COST RATIOS are just as important as crop-yield relationships in determining optimum cropping systems when crops are competitive.

Two ratios then determine the most efficient cropping program. One is the substitution or sacrifice ratio I outlined. When the competitive relationship is of a straight-line or linear nature, such as that represented in the fourth graph, the ratio of yields per crop provides the substitution ratio and

can be compared directly with price and cost ratios in determining the most profitable crop system.

When substitution or sacrifice ratios change between rotations, as I explained for Canfield-Wooster soils, or as illustrated by the part of the crop production possibility curve between B and D in the first graph or between F and I in the second and third graphs, the ratio of substitution or sacrifice between crops is not identical with the per acre yield ratio. The curvature of these lines is an indication of the degree of interaction between crops grown in the rotation.

Unless the crop production possibility curve has a portion with a positive slope denoting a complementary relationship, or unless the negatively sloped competitive portion is curved, there is no economic basis for growing a combination or rotation of crops.

For combinations that denote competition between crops, the best rotation is defined by the condition of equation (1a) below. In this equation $\triangle$ means change in quantity.

(1a) $\dfrac{\triangle A}{\triangle B} = \dfrac{P_b}{P_a}$ (1b) $(\triangle A)(P_a) = (\triangle B)(P_b)$

(2a) $\dfrac{\triangle A}{\triangle B} > \dfrac{P_b}{P_a}$ (2b) $(\triangle A)(P_a) > (\triangle B)(P_b)$

(3a) $\dfrac{\triangle A}{\triangle B} < \dfrac{P_b}{P_a}$ (3b) $(\triangle A)(P_a) < (\triangle B)(P_b)$

Hence, $\triangle A$ is the change in quantity of crop A, and $\triangle B$ is the change in crop B. Thus, the ratio $\dfrac{\triangle A}{\triangle B}$ is the substitution or sacrifice ratio of the nature explained for Canfield-Wooster soils. It shows the amount of crop A sacrificed, as land is shifted from A to B, for each one unit gain in crop B. For Canfield-Wooster soils these ratios were 0.19, 0.22, and 0.53 pound of grain sacrificed for each pound of hay gained, as land was successively shifted from grain to a greater proportion of hay. This ratio must approximate the net price, $\dfrac{P_b}{P_a}$ for the crops, if the optimum cropping system or rotation is to be determined. In equation (1a), P_b refers to the net price (the market price per unit less the per unit variable costs of production) of crop B, and P_a is the same quantity for crop A.

If the condition of equation (2a) exists, the rate at which crop A substitutes for crop B (that is, the amount of A sacrificed for each unit of B gained) is greater than ($>$) the price ratio, then this fact is obvious, as illustrated by the corollary condition of equation (2b): The net value (quantity times price) of crop A sacrificed is greater than the value of B gained. Hence, profit is reduced by selecting a rotation that includes a relatively larger acreage of B and a relatively smaller acreage of A. In fact, the rotation should be changed to include an increasing proportion of crop A, until the condition of equation (1a), and its corollary in equation (1b) is close.

If the crop planning results in the condition of equation (3a), a substitution ratio of B for A, which is less than the inverse price ratio, then the condition of equation (3b) will hold true—namely, the value of A sacrificed is less than ($<$) the value of B gained, as the cropping system is shifted to include a relatively greater acreage of B.

Crop B should be grown at the expense of crop A, until the crop substitution or sacrifice ratio is pushed approximately up to the net price ratio, as indicated in equation (1a).

The principles I have given provide the foundation upon which optimum cropping rotations for particular soil and climatic situations are based.

The optimum cropping program for many soils seldom includes a crop combination falling in the competitive range. If the substitution or sacrifice ratio is constant, as indicated by the linear relationship in the fourth graph and as suggested for arid and semiarid places, specialization in a single crop almost always provides a return equal to or greater than a combination of crops. (Returns are equal to specialization only if the substitution or yield ratio is equal to the net price ratio.

Returns from a crop combination can never exceed returns under specialization in a single crop.)

For soils and climatic situations where crop production possibilities are curved as in the first, second, and third graphs, it is sometimes most profitable to select a crop combination or rotation which falls within the competitive range (in contrast to the situation in the fourth graph). However, whether the optimum rotation will fall at the point of departure between the complementary or competitive range (as B and D in the first graph or F in the second), at some intermediate point (as C in the first graph or F, G, and H in the second and third graphs) or at an extreme of specialization (as point I in the second and third graphs) depends on the relative magnitude of the crop substitution or sacrifice ratios and the price ratio.

Over most of the Corn Belt, the price of hay (or the value derived from it in a livestock-feeding program) is low relative to the price or value of grain. Hence, while there are exceptions for particular soils and yield ratios, the optimum cropping program ordinarily falls near the peak of the complementary range (as F in the second graph).

Summer fallow has no value in its own right in the Great Plains. Hence the optimum amount of fallow, in terms of the highest possible income, always is the one that fixes the limits of complementarity of fallow in relation to production of grain in subsequent years. Similarly, in much of New England and in some irrigated areas near centers of population, forage for dairying has a relatively high value as a crop. Frequently it limits the size of the dairy enterprise and cannot be imported at a price as favorable as can grain. In situations such as this, grain crops fit in only to the limits of their complementary effects in allowing sods to be reestablished. The limit of profitability of grain in the rotation then falls at a point such as D in the first graph. In any case, however, the optimum cropping system depends finally on the nature of crop production possibilities—

that is, the substitution or sacrifice rates between crops, and price ratios.

The principles of cropping systems I outlined referred to land or soil area as the given factor against which decisions were to be made. The same basic principles apply when other resources are limited and more than two types of crops are concerned.

The labor supply on many farms limits the selection of an enterprise. On even more farms, capital is a restricting force. The best cropping program then can be defined only if it considers labor and capital and land.

The basic enterprise relationships of complementarity, competition, and supplementarity must then be determined for those resources in combination. Improved budgeting and planning procedures are available for specifying the best cropping system for the farm as a whole, in the light of different types of crops and all farm resources.

Research in Iowa illustrates how the best cropping system varies with capital and labor and with the characteristics of the soil. On Clarion-Webster soils, an owner-operator with enough capital and a typical livestock program gets the highest returns with a rotation including 50 percent corn, 25 percent oats, and 25 percent hay. A tenant on the same farm, but with much less capital, achieves the best returns with a fertilized, corn-soybeans sequence. With somewhat more capital, the same tenant can keep livestock; and a rotation including 40 percent of corn and 20 percent each of soybeans, oats, and hay maximizes returns. The hay comes into the program to allow hogs and feeder cattle to increase income and allow a more efficient utilization of labor. Soybeans come into the program partly to lessen the restrictions of labor during periods of peak labor requirements. Increased availability of agronomic information and econometric procedures can allow greater use of this type of detailed planning to fit the conditions of unique soil situations and to mesh cropping programs with the managerial, labor, and capital situations of the individual farm.

Optimum cropping programs cannot be determined apart from other soil-management practices. As I indicated at the outset, commercial fertilizer often can be used as a substitute for the complementary nitrogen furnished by legumes to row crops or grain crops. The large amount of crop residue resulting from heavy rates of fertilizing such crops as corn also may serve as a partial substitute for organic matter provided by grasses and legumes. If the substitution alternatives are great enough, the nature of crop relationships, and hence the best crop combination, is changed.

For example, nitrogen fertilizer has the effect on some soils of eliminating the complementary range, such as the portion of the curve between K and F in the second graph. The possibility curve then is changed from the nature of the one indicated in the second graph to the curve indicated in the third graph. In this instance, the problem is to determine whether the fertilizer adds more to returns than costs; the principle of equation (1a) should be applied in determining whether a single crop should be grown or the best combination, if a sequence of crops should be grown.

On some farms, cropping systems are chosen to produce the combination of feeds that will sustain a maximum livestock output from a given land area. The principles are the same as the ones I have outlined. The only change is that the ratio at which one feed substitutes for another in livestock production should replace the price ratio as the final criterion in choice of a cropping system.

If, for example, 1 pound of forage substitutes for 0.5 pound of grain in the livestock ration, the cropping program should be shifted to include more hay if less than 0.5 pound of grain is sacrificed in crop production for each pound of hay gained. If a shift of land in the rotation causes a sacrifice of, say, 1 pound of grain, for each pound of hay gained, livestock output will be reduced by growing more hay. The rotation then should be shifted in the direction of grain.

A FINAL CONSIDERATION in selection of cropping systems is variability of prices and yield, and hence uncertainty of income. Since this threat is great in areas of limited rainfall, crops may be grown in combination even though they compete at constant rates, as illustrated in the fourth graph. Crop combinations or diversification can accomplish little to reduce income variability if the correlation coefficient between crop yields and prices nears 1.0.

The combination of crops which gives the lowest variance of income can be determined as follows: The total income variance, V_t, from producing two crops, A and B, can be defined as in equation (a), where V_a refers to the variance of income for crop A, B_b is the variance of income for crop A, q is the proportion of land devoted to crop A, $1-q$ is the proportion devoted to crop B, and r is the correlation coefficient between incomes of A and B. The magnitude of q, the proportion of land planted to crop A, then is equal to the quantity shown in equation (b); and is a function of the correlation coefficient and the individual variance.

(a) $\quad V_t = q^2 V_a + (1-q)^2 V_b + q(1-q) r \sqrt{V_a V_b}$

(b) $\quad q = \dfrac{V_b - r \sqrt{V_a V_b}}{V_a + V_b - 2r \sqrt{V_a V_b}}$

In the wheat example I cited, the figures based on experimental data for Fort Hayes, Kans., predict q to be about 0.75, with A defined as grain sorghum and B defined as wheat.

For the lower correlation coefficients, however, combinations of crops may give more stable incomes than specialization, although the greater stability of income often comes at the expense of level of income. Ordinarily some particular combination of crops will give lowest income variability, just as an-

other combination will give greatest profit.

While grain sorghums may help offset some of the variability of income from wheat in western Kansas, for example, greatest income stability is not necessarily attained from growing grain sorghum alone. Over some range of combinations of acreage, sorghum tends to offset fluctuations in yields and prices of wheat. As sorghum acreage is extended far enough at the expense of wheat, however, its variability begins to predominate and may cause income fluctuations to rise above the minimum defined by the optimum combination, as to income stability, of the two crops.

Factors of Income

Orlin J. Scoville

Farmers try to select soil-management practices and systems that will give them the highest sustained net income. Usually they are interested in maximum income over a period of years.

Circumstances sometimes may cause them to discount future incomes rather heavily in favor of high immediate income. Conversely, farmers are willing under some conditions to forego maximum short-run income to enhance annual returns at some future time.

An important economic principle that affects soil management is the diminishing returns relationship, which applies to the amount of product obtained from successive increments of a variable resource applied to a fixed amount of some other resource.

As more of a resource is applied to a given amount of a fixed resource, a point is reached beyond which the additional product obtained per unit of the added resource declines. Each additional unit applied gives a little less additional product than the preceding unit. With very heavy application, additional amounts of the resource may give no increased production, or they may actually reduce the amount of product obtained.

The fertilizer response curve illustrates the working of this principle. The management problem that arises from this relationship is concerned with the determination of the amount of fertilizer to be applied per acre for a given crop to give maximum profit. If there is no uncertainty as to the yield to be obtained, and if unlimited capital and an abundant supply of fertilizer are available, the optimum rate will be that amount at which the last pound of fertilizer applied produces just enough product to be worth the additional cost. If there is uncertainty as to the expected yield, or if capital or the supply of fertilizer is limited, the optimum rate of application will be somewhat less. These special problems, however, I discuss later.

The diminishing return relationship applies also to yield responses from such management practices as the rate of applying irrigation water, number of cultivations, and rate of seeding.

The principle of diminishing returns is presented most simply in terms of varying the amount of one resource applied to one or a group of fixed resources. It can also be thought of in terms of a group of variable resources applied to one or a group of fixed resources. If the amounts of all the resources used in producing a crop were increased without varying the proportions among them, production would increase at a constant rate. Farmers always have some resources that are fixed in amount, however. Usually the supplies of land and management and often the supply of capital are limited.

An important economic problem with which farmers must deal in making their production plans has to do with the choice of crops to be grown. A farmer must determine how much of each resource available to him should be used in producing each possible alternative crop and livestock enterprise adapted to his locality. As far as soil management is concerned, the economic relationship that is basic to solution of this problem is that of substitution among products, or the rotation relationship.

If the use of resources in production of each crop were independent of the use of resources in the production of other crops, a farmer might simply figure for each crop the amount of resources needed in growing 1 acre, subtract the cost of these resources from the expected value of the crop, and produce only the crop that gives the highest net returns an acre, at least to the extent possible without damaging the soil. But production of one crop may influence the production of another, and knowledge of the rotation relationship is important.

An analysis of rotation experiments shows that sometimes the maximum quantity of grain is not produced by an all-grain farming system. The introduction of a legume or other forage crop may increase acre yields of grain enough to result in a higher total production of grain. As the proportion of acreage devoted to forage is increased further, a point is reached at which total production of grain declines.

Aside from any differences in the costs of production, the most profitable rotation depends on the relative prices of grains and forages and the effects on production that result when grains and forages are substituted for each other in the rotation.

As long as a forage crop can be substituted for a grain crop in the rotation with an increase in total production of grain, the rotation relationship between grain and forage crops is said to be complementary. Substitution of forage for grain is almost certain to be profitable within this range. Beyond this range, as the further substitution of forage reduces total production of grains, it is necessary to compare the reduction in total production of grain and the associated increase in production of forage with the ratio between prices of grain and prices of forage. The most profitable rotation will be the one at which the ratio of substitution in production is inversely proportional to the ratio between prices. In other words, $\frac{fbg}{itf}=\frac{ptf}{pbg}$. In the equation, fbg means fewer bushels of grain; itf means increased tons of forage; ptf means the price of a ton of forage; and pbg means the price of a bushel of grain.

Besides the competing and complementary relationships among crop enterprises, there is a supplementary relationship. A crop is said to supplement others when it can be added to a rotation without affecting the production of the other crop: It uses resources not used by the other crop or uses them at a time when they are not being used by other crops. Small grain seeded with a grass or legume seeding sometimes may be supplementary. In double-cropping, the two crops grown on the same piece of land in the same year are supplementary.

Livestock enterprises enter into the production plans of most farmers. Selection of the most profitable rotation for a livestock farm should not stop with an analysis based on market values of forage and grain crops. Further consideration should be given to the additional value of these crops when processed through livestock.

The analysis of the rotation relationships I mentioned might be considered a first approximation of the most profitable rotation for such farms. Later analysis of the most profitable crop and livestock system for the whole farm might mean some modification of the rotation. The analysis can be made by farm budgeting—that is, by setting up alternative systems and calculating the expected costs and returns to the farm as a whole from each system.

Having chosen the enterprises to be produced, a farmer has a further choice as to method of production. His resources need not necessarily be combined in fixed proportions to produce a crop. He can use more land and less labor and fertilizer per 100 bushels (extensive farming), or he can use less land and more labor and fertilizer (intensive farming). Viewed in this way, labor, fertilizer, and irrigation water can be thought of as substitutes for land in the production of a given quantity of a crop.

THERE IS NO ONE "best combination" of land, labor, and capital for production under all conditions.

A drop in the price of fertilizer in relation to the price of land will make it profitable to substitute more fertilizer for land. An invention that makes it cheaper to pump water will make it profitable to substitute more irrigation water for land. As with the rotation relationship, the rates at which production resources substitute for each other vary.

With an initial application of fertilizer to a particular soil, it may require only 50 pounds to give production equal to the production that could be obtained from an unfertilized acre. The next 50 pounds might replace or substitute for only three-fourths of an acre of land. The third 50 pounds might replace only one-half acre. As with the substitution of one product for another, the rule is that production resources should be substituted for each other until the rate of substitution is inversely proportional to the ratio of their prices.

This relationship assumes a free market for all kinds of resources—a condition that often does not prevail. Farmers often cannot increase or reduce at will the acreage of land they farm. Farmers tend to regard land as a fixed resource, at least in the short run. But a farmer can still combine resources in varying proportions in producing a crop. He can add land and nonland resources together in proportions that make their marginal rates of substitution inversely proportional to their prices.

The nature of the substitution relationship of nonland resources (such as fertilizer and irrigation water) for land is obviously of importance in connection with land-retirement programs. The extent to which it pays to substitute other resources for land will largely determine the effectiveness of such programs in controlling total farm production.

If farmers had abundant capital and perfect knowledge concerning the productivity of farm practices and if they were not confronted by uncertainty as to the growing season and future prices, they would adjust their cropping systems and soil-management practices according to these general principles. They would adjust the cropping system by substituting one crop for another until they had maximized returns; they would substitute resources for each other in the production of each crop to maximize net production per dollar of resources used; and they would invest resources in production until the last dollar's worth used just paid for itself.

Farmers' resources, however, are limited. The capital resources a farmer owns plus the amount that he can borrow do not permit him, as a rule, to invest in production up to the margin at which the last dollar he invests just pays for itself.

For farmers with limited resources, the important principle for the application of resources to alternative production purposes is the principle of equimarginal returns. This means that each dollar's worth of resource should be applied to a particular purpose so long as the added return from the resource is equal to or greater than the return that could be realized in any alternative use.

Thus a farmer would apply enough fertilizer to corn so that an additional dollar's worth would result in an expected return of 1.25 dollar only if enough capital would be left to permit other crops also to be fertilized to the point at which an additional unit applied would also bring a return of 1.25 dollar. Similarly, a decision as to the total amount to be spent for fertilizer should be based on an attempt to equalize the expected return from an additional or marginal unit of fertilizer and an additional or marginal outlay for some alternative purpose—for instance, for insecticides or purchased feeder livestock.

THE APPLICATION of these economic principles in the development of cropping systems is conditioned by the objectives of individual farmers.

The overall objective of most farmers is to manage farm resources in a way that will return maximum income, but that aim varies among individuals in a number of ways. Farmers differ as to their needs for immediate income and the extent to which they tend to discount anticipated returns.

A young farmer who is in debt and has a growing family is likely to be under heavy pressure for immediate income. His farm program may include exploitative cropping practices that will increase income now with a sacrifice of productivity in the future.

A farmer with less pressing needs for immediate income may have an economic goal of sustained annual income, or he may wish to follow a cropping system that will build up the soil to enhance his income in later years. He will not, however, want to carry this so far as to give up more present income than the present value of the increased future income. That is, he will discount the dollar value of anticipated future returns and he will discount a remote return more heavily than one that is to be received in the next year or so.

An additional consideration that enters into farmers' cropping plans has to do with risk and uncertainty. Farmers' attitudes toward risk vary. Some farmers will pay a high premium to avoid or minimize risk. Others are willing to accept risk; they are interested only in making certain that the anticipated returns will be adequate to compensate them for the risks taken.

For some, there may be an element of satisfaction in taking a chance.

Farmers' attitudes toward risk vary with their financial positions. A man whose reserves are meager cannot afford to take risks that might put him out of business.

Farmers are confronted by problems of uncertainty that arise from weather, prices, conditions of health and family affairs, and changes in Government programs. With long-term investments in buildings, equipment, and orchards, there is risk of obsolescence. Not all the hazards of farming are insurable. The degree of uncertainty varies among farm enterprises and tends to increase with the length of the production process.

RISK AND UNCERTAINTY affect the choice of farm enterprises. Recommendations for diversification often are based on ways to reduce risk.

But diversification does not always reduce risk; if it results in lowered average income, it may not be the most economical way to solve the risk problem.

If diversification is to be effective in reducing risk, there should be little or no positive correlation in fluctuations in yields among the crops grown. Negative correlation would be even better. As a rule, though, yields of all crops on a given farm tend to fluctuate together.

E. N. Castle, in an analysis of fluctuations from 1914 through 1941 at the experiment station at Garden City, Kans., found a correlation coefficient for yields of wheat and milo of 0.247. The correlation between wheat and kafir grain was 0.544, and between wheat and kafir forage it was 0.438. Yields of milo and of kafir grain were closely correlated with a coefficient of 0.922, and the relationship between kafir grain and kafir forage was 0.802. With these relationships, diversification of enterprises would reduce the variability of yield substantially, if milo were added to a straight wheat program. Diversification would be somewhat less effective for the other combinations I listed.

Diversification is often recommended also as a protection against price risks. Again, however, prices tend to rise and fall together, and the protection thus obtained is only partial.

According to Dr. Castle, fluctuations in prices of Kansas wheat and milo from 1926 through 1949 were rather closely associated. The coefficient of correlation was 0.794. When price and yield were combined as gross income, the correlation between changes in incomes from wheat and milo was 0.526.

The question as to whether diversification would be worthwhile as a protection against risk would have to be judged according to the amount of protection gained, the effect of the diversified program on average income, and the cost of alternative means of reducing the hazards of uncertainty. These would include crop insurance and the carrying of financial reserves. Other reasons for diversifying may include the more efficient utilization of labor and equipment because of supplementary relationships among enterprises, and, when livestock are included, the possibility of increasing the scale of operation without increasing acreage.

CLOSELY RELATED to the management of risk problems is the objective of flexibility, which farmers often take into account in setting up their cropping systems.

Flexibility here means that an attempt is made to postpone decisions until later information is available or to have a cropping system that permits the revision of plans as circumstances change or one gets new information.

Cropping programs in hazardous areas of the Great Plains frequently contain elements of flexibility. Often farmers do not set aside a definite acreage for spring-sown crops because they want to take a chance on getting a stand of winter wheat on as large an acreage as possible. Then if the stand of wheat fails, they plant all or part of this land to barley or oats. If soil moisture conditions in spring are not satisfactory, they may defer planting until summer and try a sorghum crop.

Land that has been prepared and seeded to wheat, and on which the wheat has failed, is not so well prepared for seeding a spring crop as it would have been had it originally been intended for spring sowing. The soil moisture will have been depleted, and spring planting may be delayed beyond the optimum date. This kind of "opportunity" program involves a deliberate sacrifice of potential yield of a spring-sown crop in the hope of getting a more profitable wheat crop. The reduced yield may be thought of as a cost of maintaining flexibility.

Farm enterprises vary among themselves in opportunities for flexibility. As economic conditions change, it is easier to change a program based on annual crops than one that includes perennials, particularly the longstanding sod crops. It is even more difficult to alter a tree-farming program.

Reserves of various kinds also can be used to give flexibility to a farming system. A livestock farmer, for example, can increase his freedom to vary his acreage of feed crops from year to year by maintaining larger reserves of hay and grain. Or he might accomplish the same objective by maintaining a cash reserve for emergency purchase of feed.

The way in which farmers apply economic principles depends on a number of factors and forces that condition their management decisions. These include tenure, availability of capital, size of farm, extent of knowledge, tradition, weather, uncertainty as to price, and the nature of Government agricultural programs.

Land tenure influences the decisions of farm operators in a number of ways. Expectations of the operator as to the number of years that he may operate a particular farm are closely related to his tenure conditions.

These expectations may be influenced as much by conditions outside the written rental agreement as by the stipulations of the lease. Farm rental agreements in the United States are usually for a year. Often they are unwritten. Tenants usually do not stay on the same farm more than a few years. Even owners often do not have longtime occupancy. It is estimated that in the Midwest the average period of owner-operation is only 16 years.

Uncertainty as to the length of occupancy of a farm influences the choice of cropping system. Numerous studies have shown that tenant farming is associated with the more exploitative land use practices, except for tenants who are related to their landlords. In Iowa, for example, owners and related tenants reported 56 percent of their cropland in corn and soybeans, compared with 66 percent for unrelated tenants. Owners had 21 percent of their cropland in grass and legumes, compared with 23 percent for related tenants and only 15 percent for the unrelated tenants.

Choice of cropping systems on rented farms frequently is influenced by the inadequacy of buildings and equipment for livestock. As a result, further encouragement is given to cash-cropping systems and to short-term production plans.

Various provisions of farm leases influence cropping systems. With the usual crop-share lease, the landlord does not share in the returns from livestock production. Therefore he is likely to be interested in maintaining a high acreage of cash crops.

When the investment in farm buildings is high or when there is a considerable acreage of hay and pasture, the crop-share-cash lease is a common type. This type of lease permits a greater range of choice in production plans if the share of rent and the amount of the cash rental accurately reflect the relative contribution of landlord and tenant. These arrangements are often set by the custom of the community, and when rental payments on a particular farm are out of line with the productivity of the resources of that farm, a less than optimum cropping program is likely to develop. Too high a pasture rental, for example, will tend to drive pasture out of the crop rotation. Conversely, too low a cash rent for buildings will discourage maintenance of barns and other livestock facilities by the landlord and will lead to emphasis on cash-crop farming.

Availability of capital influences the choice of the cropping system on many farms. Lack of adequate capital has the general effect of encouraging short-run production plans, with emphasis on cash crops and short rotations. A farmer whose capital, including what he can borrow, is limited, is likely to choose the livestock enterprises that are most liquid and hence most easily financed.

Financing generally is most readily obtained for enterprises that are suited to the use of short-term credit. Various feeding-out enterprises are notable examples, provided the farmer already has the needed buildings and equipment and grows most of his feed. Enterprises that involve the maintenance of breeding herds or the acquisition of the equipment needed for establishing a new livestock enterprise of almost any kind are less easily financed. This is of particular significance in connection with efforts to change systems of farming in the direction of increased emphasis on livestock.

The size of the farm influences the choice of cropping system. Small farms tend to have more intensive rotations than the larger farms because of the greater pressure for immediate income. The small farm problem represents a special kind of capital limitation. Insufficient land is available in some communities and areas to permit the enlargement of farms to obtain adequate economic units. Making available additional credit for purchase or rental of additional land will help, but other steps are needed also. These include reduction in the pressure for farm income in such areas by development of additional farm and nonfarm resources and adjustments in manpower resources through migration.

EXTENT OF KNOWLEDGE, attitudes, and traditions influence cropping systems and often cause them to deviate from those that would appear to be most profitable.

Often farmers do not know the results that would follow from a change in the rotation or from the introduction of a management practice. Information based on experiments frequently is not available to indicate the productivity of improved practices.

It takes time to disseminate the results of experiments. A study in Iowa in 1949 reported that one-fourth of the farmers interviewed thought that contour farming of fields with slopes of 4 percent or more would not pay, although research studies indicate that this practice is profitable. This study also revealed that the farmers interviewed did not have adequate knowledge of the relative profitability of alternative livestock enterprises under stated conditions. Limitations of knowledge and skill are especially important with respect to situations in which a change in farming systems is needed.

In addition to knowledge, the personal preferences of farm operators influence their choice of cropping systems. Some farmers do not grow forage crops because of an aversion to being "tied down" to the care of livestock.

GOVERNMENT PROGRAMS influence cropping systems by altering price relationships among enterprises. Acreage allotments usually are tied to a historical base, and farmers sometimes try to maintain the acreage of a crop in order to have a favorable base.

Economic conditions change over time, and the changes affect the profitability of rotations and cropping systems. Improvements in varieties have been greater for some crops than for others. The increased use of commercial fertilizers has put inorganic nitrogen in direct competition with legume crops as a source of nitrogen.

Improvements in the mechanization of crop production have reduced labor and power requirements for grains more sharply than for forage crops. During the First World War, about 34 man-hours an acre were used in the production of corn. Producing an acre of hay took about 13 man-hours. Now only about 13 man-hours are needed for an acre of corn and 6.5 hours for an acre of hay. Labor used per acre has declined about 60 percent for corn and 50 percent for hay. Yields of corn have increased much more than have yields of hay, and the decline in man labor per bushel of corn has been 74 percent compared with only 56 percent per ton of hay. But the increase in price of corn over this period has been greater than for hay.

These changing production relationships and altered price conditions have changed the rotation that is most profitable. The rotation that is most profitable today has more grain and less hay in it than was the case 30 years ago.

I have discussed the economic principles that affect soil-management systems in terms of farmers' decisions and farmers' profits. The same principles apply to national decisions and national welfare.

IN APPLYING THE PRINCIPLES to the formulation of national policies, it is necessary to think in terms of a time span that runs over many generations rather than within a single generation or less. Because of the longer term outlook, and the lower interest rate at which the governments can borrow money, the rate of discount of future incomes is lower. It is sometimes held that a national government should not discount future incomes from resources, as a Nation views its own life as perpetual. Ordinarily, however, societies do discount the future because they are confronted continually by pressing short-run demands for use of resources, and emergencies arise that call for all-out immediate production.

Risk also may be viewed differently from the national viewpoint. A country can take an actuarial view of ordinary vagaries of weather, as geographic, seasonal, and cyclical fluctuations in yields tend to average out. These fluctuations can be dealt with more easily at the national or regional level than at the individual level, as is easier to maintain reserves for an area than for an individual farm.

From the standpoint of national policy, three important elements of risk and uncertainty must be taken into account.

The first is the uncertainty of future food and fiber requirements.

Second is the risk of allowing permanent, irreversible soil erosion to impair future potential productivity to such a point that future needs for food cannot be met cheaply.

Then there is the uncertainty that a continuing stream of new technological improvements can be maintained.

These problems are interrelated. Advancing technology may make less arable land necessary to feed a given population, but abundant uneroded land may make future technologies more productive than would otherwise be true.

From the national and the individual viewpoints, the application of basic economic relationships to soil-management problems will improve farm incomes and assist in maintaining a productive agriculture.

Economic principles help farmers choose soil-management practices and systems that will help them reach their objectives.

An understanding of the economic principles involved helps to explain why farmers follow certain soil-management systems and why some of them adopt recommended practices more rapidly than others.

Economic principles also reveal the ways in which changing economic and technological conditions have altered the profitability of soil-management systems over time. These principles are helpful also in shaping the land-use policies and programs of public agencies.

Longtime Investments in Soil Management

M. L. Upchurch

A farmer occasionally has to decide whether he should make a longtime investment to improve the soil on his farm. He finds that installing a drainage system, building terraces, and leveling land are costly. He can recover the costs only over a period of years.

Investments in such major improvements therefore require a kind of management decision that is different from the decisions he makes regarding his year-to-year operating practices.

He may make major soil improvements to increase yields, permit changes in his cropping system or use of land, prevent a decline in yields, or reduce his operating expenses.

Whatever the reason, the improvement should bring him a higher future net return from the land: A prudent longtime investment in a soil improvement must return enough to pay for the improvement itself over the years and enough to pay more for the improvement than for any other use that he could have made of the funds.

How does he decide whether to make the investment?

Incomes and costs may be viewed in terms of "flows" over a period of years when considering longtime investments. A farm or a field will require an inflow of funds for operating expenses year after year into the future and will produce an outflow of product.

Both the inflow and the outflow must be put in terms of money, for comparisons between hours of labor or gallons of tractor fuel and bushels of corn or tons of hay cannot be made unless all are expressed in dollars. The difference between the outflow and the inflow is profit, which also may be considered as a flow that will occur repeatedly in the years ahead.

CHANGES in the volume of flow of operating costs, incomes, and profits may be made in many ways. One way is to invest in a soil improvement, the aim of which is to increase the flow of expected profits. That may be accomplished by increasing incomes more than costs, increasing incomes without changing costs, increasing incomes and reducing costs, reducing costs without changing incomes, or reducing costs more than incomes.

Suppose one field needs drainage. Without it, the farmer can expect a flow of costs and incomes about like that shown by lines A and B in the first chart. Now suppose that a drainage system is installed in 1960, and the use of the land is changed from hay and pasture to rotation hay and crops. A new volume of flow for costs, incomes, and profits is established. The difference in the volume of profits expected without the drainage and that expected with the drainage is available to pay for the investment in the drainage system. In this example, both

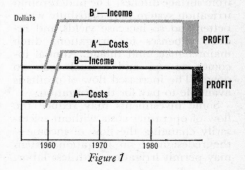

Figure 1

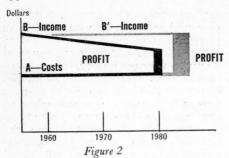

Figure 2

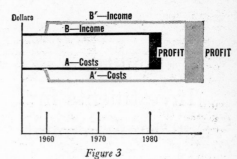

Figure 3

expected costs and incomes would be increased by the investment in the soil improvement.

A field that is eroding badly may produce a declining flow of income, as shown by line *B* in the second figure. The same crops may be continued, so that expenses will remain substantially unchanged, as in line *A*. Terraces are built in 1960 to arrest the erosion and maintain productivity. Again a changed volume of flow of income is established. Although the investment does not increase the flow, the flow is not permitted to drop, as it might if no investment were made. The difference in the expected flow of profit with the terraces, compared with the expected flow without them, is available to pay for terracing.

An investment in a soil improvement may raise incomes and at the same time lower operating costs. Such a situation might occur when an underground irrigation system is installed, as is shown in the third diagram. Lines *A* and *B* may represent the flow of costs and incomes from a field irrigated from surface ditches. The underground irrigation system may distribute water better and so increase yields and reduce expenses for irrigation, ditch maintenance, and tillage. Annual incomes go up, and annual costs go down. The increased flow of profits is available to pay for the irrigation.

Some investments may reduce the flow of operating costs without necessarily changing the flow of income— the redesign of an irrigation system may permit irrigation with less labor.

This situation may be illustrated by lines *A* and *A'* in the fourth diagram. Again the added flow of profits is available to pay for the redesign of the irrigation system.

An investment in a land improvement could result in lowering the flow of both operating costs and income when a change in land use is involved. Suppose the longtime use of a field is changed from crops to pasture. Establishment of the pasture sod may be viewed as a longtime investment. Income may be reduced, but operating costs may be reduced still more: For example, hired labor and machine operation might be eliminated. In the fifth figure, line *A'* represents the changed flow of costs, and line *B'* represents the changed flow of incomes. The increased flow of profits would be available to pay for the investment.

Physical measurement of the effects of a soil improvement is the first requirement for evaluation. What actually is the result of installing tile drainage, building terraces, putting in underground irrigation, or any other major land improvement?

Conditions vary so widely across the country that I can make no generalization. Conditions vary even from field to field on the same farm to such an extent that estimates of the probable effects of any contemplated practice must be made in each instance.

Estimates must be made also of the probable life, requirements for upkeep, and the trend in productiveness of the soil improvement. The facts in each instance are needed to evaluate the

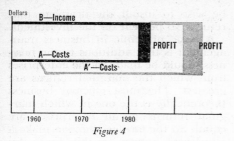

Figure 4

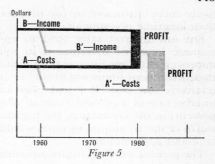

Figure 5

improvement and to arrive at a decision regarding it.

Time distinguishes an investment from an ordinary operating expense because all individuals discount future incomes whether or not they are conscious of doing so. A dollar is worth more today than the prospect of a dollar next year or 10 years from now.

The extent to which farmers discount future incomes varies between individuals. It depends on the degree of need for income now compared with needs in the future, the degree of uncertainty in the planning period, the expected incomes from funds invested in other enterprises, and other factors. Generally, however, the minimum discount rate on future incomes is the going rate of interest on money.

A farmer who has money to invest in land improvements wants to get from those improvements at least as high a return on his money as he could expect by lending it to someone else. Frequently, of course, farmers would rather invest in their own businesses than lend their money to others to invest. The rate of return that can be gained on loans nevertheless should be used to evaluate alternative investments of comparable risks.

A farmer who must borrow money to make land improvements must expect the improvements to result in a net return at least as high as the interest rate on the money he borrows.

An illustration of the kind of figuring that must be done to decide on a longtime investment is furnished by tile drainage. Suppose a 20-acre field needs drainage. It now produces hay and pasture worth 800 dollars a year.

Operating costs run about 400 dollars a year. Net income from the field therefore is about 400 dollars a year without the drainage.

Let us say an adequate drainage system for this field will cost about 2,000 dollars, and it is decided that the investment is to be amortized fully in 10 years. Drainage of the field will permit grain and other more intensive crops to be grown. Annual operating costs therefore may increase to about 600 dollars in the future. Productivity of the field is increased also, and the gross return is expected to be about 1,300 dollars a year instead of the 800 dollars expected without drainage. An extra 300 dollars a year net return is available to pay off the cost of the drainage system. Is this 300 dollars a year for the next 10 years enough to justify investing 2,000 dollars now?

The present worth of a series of 10 annual incomes of 300 dollars is about 2,300 dollars at an interest rate of 5 percent. Under these assumptions, the investment in drainage would be wise.

Higher interest rates tend to discourage longtime investments in land improvements. Higher interest rates simply mean that people generally are willing to pay relatively more for money or income now than later.

If a 10-percent instead of a 5-percent interest rate is used in the illustration I gave, the present worth of the 10 annual incomes of 300 dollars would be only 1,840 dollars, or 160 dollars less than the investment. Short-term investments then (or other activities that yield immediate income) are relatively more attractive to the investor than longtime investments.

But low interest rates tend to encourage longtime investments in soil improvement. Low interest rates mean that investment funds are available at relatively low cost. If I had used an interest rate of 3 percent (instead of 5 percent) in the illustration, the present worth of the 10 annual incomes would be about 2,560 dollars.

The present worth of future amounts can be obtained from mathematical tables or it may be calculated from the equation $P = \left[\dfrac{1}{(1+i)^n} \right] x$—in which P is present value, i is rate of interest, n is the number of years, and x is the amount anticipated in the future. The present value of a recurring income, such as used in the example, is

$$P = \left[\frac{1 - (1+i)^{-n}}{i} \right] x.$$

What rate of discount should be used in calculating the present value of future returns from a longtime investment in soil improvement?

Several factors are involved, but the minimum rate would be at least comparable to the going rate of interest on longtime first-mortgage loans. Individuals may want to use higher rates depending on their own circumstances. Farmers who need ready cash to meet operating and family living expenses place a higher discount on future income than those who have idle funds to invest.

RETURNS from alternative uses of investment funds also place a limit on discount rates.

An example: A farmer may have 2,000 dollars to invest in his business. If he can make a 20-percent return on this sum by feeding steers, he would not want to use his money for a drainage system that would return only 10 percent on the investment, assuming comparable risks and uncertainty. But if his next best use of additional investment is for a machine shed that will return 5 percent of the funds, he will

be wise to install the drainage that returns 10 percent on the investment.

A basic principle in business management is that additions to the business should be made in the enterprises from which the marginal returns are greatest. The most efficient business theoretically is the one in which marginal returns to all enterprises are equal. So the farmer who can make a 20-percent return on his funds by additional investment in one enterprise must use 20 percent as his discount rate in considering an alternative.

Uncertainty—the degree of doubt that exists about the future—has a significant effect on longtime investments. An increase in the degree of uncertainty about the future is associated with an increase in reluctance among farmers to make longtime commitments and, therefore, an increase in the discount rate used to evaluate future income.

Uncertainty may be involved in the soil-improvement practice itself. Will it work? Will it increase yields as expected? Will it be damaged by unusual storms?

Or uncertainty may occur with respect to outside factors. What prices are likely to prevail in the next 10 years? What changes may occur in assessments for tax purposes or in depreciation rates allowed for income tax purposes?

Risks—the possibility of losses in the future—involved in a major improvement also may tend to increase the discount rate on expected future income. Pasture development in the Great Plains, for example, is accompanied by more than usual risk—risk of soil blowing during the seedling period, risk of getting a stand, and risk of drought and low production. Relatively high returns on the investment are required to compensate the farmer for taking such risks with his investment funds.

SHIFTING COSTS between the present and the future is an additional aspect of longtime investments.

Funds invested in longtime improvements are "sunk" and become part of the capital structure of the farm business in the same way as the original cost of the land, costs of buildings, and other rather permanent investments.

Sometimes fixed costs can be substituted in part for variable costs or operating costs. For example, the installation of an underground irrigation system is a fixed investment. Interest on the funds invested and depreciation on the system become fixed costs. The effect of the system, however, may be to reduce the annual labor and other expenses required to do the irrigating. Operating efficiency is increased to the extent that total costs can be reduced by shifting annual operating costs to fixed capital costs. Again, this shift is encouraged by relatively low interest rates, low degree of uncertainty and risk, and an expected increase in price levels. Such a shift is discouraged by high interest rates, high risks, and uncertainty with respect to future production and prices.

PROPER INTEGRATION of a major land improvement into the total farm business is an important aspect of evaluation. Farming generally is a combination of several related enterprises. A successful farmer is one who manages each enterprise efficiently and who achieves and maintains the most profitable combination and balance in his crop and livestock activities.

A major soil improvement may affect the balance between farm enterprises materially and may provide the opportunity for changes in farm organization. Tile drainage may permit a shift in land use from pasture to grain. This in turn may indicate a change from stocker cattle to a beef-fattening enterprise. Additional facilities and perhaps a change in the other farm enterprises will have to be made to fit the beef-fattening enterprise into the total farm business most profitably.

Changes in other parts of the farm business that are implemented by the improvement in question often may be profitable in themselves. Tile drainage may not pay if the land continues to be used for pasture. Terraces may not pay without associated practices that permit them to be as productive as possible. The additional product that results from a soil improvement must be used fully and evaluated fairly in the appraisal of the improvement itself. At the same time, care should be taken not to attribute to the soil improvement added profit that comes from changes in some related enterprise.

CAPITAL OR INVESTMENT FUNDS often are limited in agriculture for all purposes, including soil improvements. Some farm economists call this limitation "capital rationing." Part of this limitation rests in the uncertainty that exists with respect to the future. In reality, this rationing generally limits the investment of funds in farming to a point below the point that would give the highest marginal rate of return. In effect, capital rationing makes shorttime investments relatively more attractive than longtime investments.

Credit for soil improvements may be especially important. If a farmer has no funds of his own, the terms on which he can borrow may determine his willingness to undertake the improvement.

I mentioned scarcity of investment funds and effects of the rate of interest in evaluating investments. A further factor is the relation of the timing and terms of loan repayment to the timing of income from the investment.

Longtime investments usually are financed by loans secured by mortgages on real estate. The period of the loan is longer, and the rate of interest usually is lower for this type of financing than for other types of loans. Commercial banks often are reluctant to grant loans for periods long enough to be useful for financing soil improvements unless the loans can be repaid from more immediate sources of income. Many banks, however, make special efforts to finance conservation work and other types of investments in the productive capacity of farmland.

Land tenure, or the way in which a farmer holds his land, influences any consideration of a longtime investment in soil improvement. My discussion so far has assumed full ownership and operation of the farm by the one who makes the decision. When ownership and operation are divided between individuals with different goals and discount rates on future income, a new set of factors enters the decision.

Tenants who have annual lease contracts are not likely to be interested in making longtime investments in the land. An exception is when provision is made in the lease to compensate the tenant for unexhausted improvements upon termination of his occupancy. Even so, the difficulties of appraising unexhausted improvements and the uncertainty generally associated with tenancy tend to discourage longtime investments in the farm by tenants. Frequently associated with this are differences between landlord and tenant in goals and in relative needs for immediate versus future income.

Landlords themselves may not be encouraged to undertake longtime investments in soil improvements under customary types of lease contracts. An investment that only substitutes fixed costs for operating costs certainly would not be attractive to a landlord under ordinary share leases, in which the tenant usually pays all or most of the operating expenses.

An investment that increases output also might not be to the advantage of the landlord when he gets only a share of the crop with which to meet the costs of the improvement unless some change in the shares compensates him for his extra costs. Full productiveness of the improvement also might not be realized on tenant-operated farms, especially if associated changes in farm organization and management are needed to achieve maximum benefit from the investment.

Landlords and tenants may have to share the costs as well as the added returns from a major land improvement before investments of this kind become attractive to either. This sharing may require a departure from customary rental arrangements as to the length of time provided in the contract, provisions for dividing expenses of production, distribution of the product, or all three combined.

Annual leases ordinarily discourage investments in soil improvements for both landlord and tenant. Longer leases would encourage investment.

LONGTIME INVESTMENTS in land improvements must be considered carefully to avoid any costly mistakes, as money spent in this way usually can be recovered only over the years.

In this consideration, here are some questions that must be answered:

What will this improvement cost?

Is the money available?

Can this money be used to better advantage for some other purpose?

If money must be borrowed, can a loan be made on terms that will permit repayment from the returns?

What will this improvement do in terms of increasing yields, reducing operating costs, or permitting changes in land use?

What other changes will be needed in the farm to realize its full potential in the way of increased livestock, additional machinery, extra labor, or other investments?

How uncertain is the outcome of this investment?

Will this investment reduce future operating costs?

If land is rented, can satisfactory arrangements be made between landlord and tenant?

What assistance is available for planning and financing the land improvement?

Is the present worth of the expected returns from this investment more than its cost or more than the present worth of returns from some other use for these funds?

THESE AND PERHAPS other questions should be weighed carefully before longtime investments are made.

Financing Changes in Soil Management

J. H. Atkinson and Lowell S. Hardin

Profitable changes in soil management often cause the farm's capital requirements to snowball. The first changes brought about by the first investment may not pay off for a year or more, and extensive changes, such as establishing new or improved meadows, may actually reduce farm income for the period of development.

This is the first step in the snowball effect of improvement programs—the investment itself plus possible temporary reduction in cash income.

The second big need for dollars comes when the changes start to bear fruit. If new crops are produced, new types of machines or more machinery and farm buildings may be needed. If the farm plan calls for livestock to eat the new crop or larger production of an old crop, added investment in stock and housing for them may be needed.

Further, a growth period of many months may elapse before the livestock or livestock products are sold. Thus the waiting time between the start of a series of changes in soil management and cashing in on them through sale of livestock products may be 1 to 5 years or more. A farmer needs to know in advance the eventual size of the "snowball" if he is to plan for adequate financing. Some farmers have lined up too little credit and have discovered too late that they could go only part way.

Changes in soil management are difficult to finance if the return from the change amounts to only 5 or 6 percent on the extra investment. Such a return may be enough if you have the dollars and have no better place to invest them.

Suppose the change cost a thousand dollars and 10 percent a year was earned on the investment after the first 2 years. If you borrowed the money, you would need about 20 years for earnings to repay principal and interest at 6 percent. Most farmers prefer to invest first in changes or in enterprises which pay off faster.

If you are out of debt you may find a certain change desirable on your farm. If you are heavily in debt, you may properly omit the same change on your farm because you must invest where the payoff rate is expected to be rapid. Your debt position, therefore, often influences your decision.

If you go through the thinking and budgeting process already outlined and the changes appear profitable for you, several methods of financing are available. Financing is a greater problem for the farmer who needs to borrow than for the farmer who has his own funds to invest.

The rest of this chapter deals with methods of financing by borrowing once the decision is made to go ahead with the program.

Here the budget again comes into use. Amounts needed by certain dates should be worked out carefully. A schedule of payments, dates, and amounts should be developed. They will have to be estimates. Weather, prices, health, and other factors may upset any budget, but a budget does help your plan.

With your needs and repayment schedules budgeted, you are in a position to talk with lending agencies. Interest rates generally are lower on longer term loans secured by mortgages on real estate than on shorter term loans secured by chattel mortgages on personal property (livestock, machinery, stored crops, and the like).

448

The longer loan usually provides the borrower more flexibility than a loan that runs 6 months or 1 to 3 years. If income is lower than expected, pressure to repay may be less on the long-term financing plan.

This suggests that you decide whether you want to borrow for a short period or for a longer period. Short-term loans are usually for a year or less. Frequently they are obtained with the understanding that they may be renewed in full or in part one or more times.

Intermediate loans generally are for periods of 1 to 5 years. Such lending plans are a rather recent development. They are made for various types of farm improvements, including drainage, soil conservation, and related programs. Adequate security, often real estate, usually is required.

Long-term loans are almost always secured by real-estate mortgages and are usually written for periods of more than 5 years. A definite repayment plan and provision for prepayment in good years are desirable. On farms already covered with a first mortgage it may be necessary to refinance one's entire debt structure to use this alternative. If the original borrowings have been reduced, such a refinancing plan may be desirable, but care should be taken not to increase the interest rate on outstanding debt if it can be avoided.

When you have determined the time period that appears well suited to your farm, you should prepare a total financial statement. You need to place all the facts before the lenders when you seek advice and funds. It is well to shop for funds, just as it sometimes pays to get prices from several dealers when you buy a tractor. With the financial statement and proposed budget for the loan requested in hand, you can determine rather quickly where you can get your "best buy" in credit. Terms, service, understanding, and interest rates should be considered in coming to a decision. Variation in those items do exist among lenders.

Actual credit sources that should be considered are outlined below. All of them may not be available in a particular community.

COMMERCIAL BANKS lend funds that are deposited in checking accounts. Most of their loans therefore are for short terms. Banks are a major source of short-term credit for agriculture, however. They also make farm real-estate loans for terms up to about 15 or 20 years; the maximum period is determined by State or National law. Banks have become increasingly interested in making intermediate-term loans to farmers.

Bankers in general want to encourage soil-management practices that increase incomes. Many banks are so interested in servicing farmers that they employ men trained in agriculture. These farm representatives promote profitable changes in agricultural production by advising with farmers and serving as loan agents.

The Nation's 20 thousand banks are located throughout the country, and few towns are without one or more banks. Banks generally are locally owned and managed. All conform to State and Federal regulations. Their interest rates may vary, however, from bank to bank and farmer to farmer because of differences in size of loan, collateral, credit rating, and bank policy. Some banks deal largely in agricultural business. Others lend almost entirely for nonfarm business and needs.

IN THE EARLY DAYS of agricultural development in the United States, dealers and merchants were major sources of short-term credit. They still furnish substantial amounts of credit in some areas and in certain enterprises. But most dealers and merchants are not in the credit business as such; rather, they furnish credit as an aid in making sales.

The cost of credit among dealers and merchants usually is high compared to credit from other sources. The charge for credit may be included in the "time price" for goods, or an interest charge may be made. It should be remembered, however, that credit does cost money and that a merchant who furnishes credit usually recovers the cost from his customers.

The merchant who extends credit is interested in making sales, but in extending credit he should be interested in the soundness of the loan and prospects of repayment. Dealers and merchants, in order to make a sale, therefore, may extend credit without full regard for the soundness of the investment. Losses then may be high—a reason why the cost of credit from dealers and merchants is often higher than from other sources.

THE PRODUCTION CREDIT ASSOCIATIONS are cooperative intermediate- and short-term lending agencies. Within the legal framework created by Federal Farm Credit Acts, they are locally owned and controlled. These cooperatives were formed with capital stock furnished by individuals and the Federal Government. Most of the Government capital has since been repaid, and most of the associations are owned by farmers. The associations formerly made loans for a year or less, but in 1955 they were given authority to make intermediate-term loans with repayment periods up to 3 years.

Interest rates within an association (which usually serves several counties) are the same to all farmers, although some associations charge graduated fees, which make the cost per dollar of credit higher for smaller loans.

Funds for lending by the associations are obtained from central discount banks (Federal Intermediate Credit Banks). These banks, in turn, obtain funds from the investing public by issuing short-term bonds secured by farmers' notes. Thus the system provides a means of tapping the money market for funds for farm uses.

The associations are locally owned and managed. You usually get in touch with the secretary-treasurer or fieldman in his area if you are interested in getting a loan. Their interest rates

are usually competitive with those of other lenders. Budgeted loans are tailored to the farmer's expected needs over the period involved. Borrowers buy stock in their local association equal to 5 percent of the sum borrowed. Some hold this stock after their loan is repaid, but that is optional with the borrower.

Cooperatives other than Production Credit Associations may also be important sources of short-term credit in some localities. For the Nation as a whole, however, they supply a minor part of the short-term credit.

Individuals—businessmen, farmers, professional men—lend more long-term funds to farmers than does any single lending group.

Individuals also are a source of short-term credit, especially when families help relatives to become established in farming. Landlords, retired farmers, and farmers who have surplus funds often prefer to make agricultural loans rather than invest elsewhere.

Interest rates, length of term, and conditions of repayment vary widely among individuals who furnish farm credit. A possible disadvantage in borrowing from individuals is that their supply of funds for lending is limited. If additional funds are needed, the borrower may have to use some other source. It is important to remember that credit obtained from individuals, even from close friends or relatives, should be handled in a businesslike way. Interest rate, repayment plan, length of term, and security should be spelled out in a proper, written credit instrument.

INSURANCE COMPANIES are a major source of long-term credit for farmers. Insurance companies have concentrated their operations in areas that have large farms and stable production, but this source of credit is available in most areas. One should get in touch with representatives of an insurance company only if he is interested in financing or refinancing a loan secured by a real-estate mortgage. Local real-estate brokers often are contact points between interested borrowers and appraisers for insurance firms.

Competition in the farm mortgage lending field has kept interest rates rather uniform among insurance companies. Interest rates do vary, of course, even in a given company, because of location, size of loan, and risks.

National Farm Loan Associations are local cooperative agencies that service farm mortgage loans made by the Federal Land Banks. The Federal Land Bank system was started with the use of Government capital, all of which has been repaid by farmer borrowers.

Funds for Federal Land Bank loans are obtained by issuing bonds, which are bought by the investing public. Farmers' mortgages are security. Cost of this credit to the farmer may vary slightly among the 12 banks in the Nation, but the same rate applies to all farmers in a given locality.

The contact point for loans through the Federal Land Bank is the local National Farm Loan Association secretary-treasurer. He will discuss terms, take loan applications, and have the farm appraised by a Federal Land Bank appraiser who knows the area. Repayment plans are specified in the loan. Interest rates are competitive. Borrowers buy stock in the local National Farm Loan Association equal to 5 percent of their loan. Dividends may be paid on National Farm Loan Association stock in line with the earnings of the cooperative.

The Farmers Home Administration is a Government agency created to lend funds to eligible farmers. For the most part, borrowers must show that they cannot obtain credit on reasonable terms elsewhere. Local offices are available in only some of the counties. It may be necessary to write the State Farmers Home Administration office to make initial contact with this agency.

Farmers Home Administration makes short-, intermediate-, and long-term loans to farmers. Its funds are obtained both from direct Government appropriations and from other sources by means of Government-insured mortgages. The amount of money Farmers Home Administration has available to lend in any year may be limited.

This agency can make loans for most soil-improvement needs. The length of the loan can be fitted to the borrower's needs. Close supervision and assistance in planning, using, and repaying the loan are provided. Interest rates are low. This source of funds, it must be remembered, is available only to those whose needs cannot be provided for by other lending agencies.

SOME FURTHER suggestions:

One should evaluate his financial position and determine whether the project can be financed with his own funds. A financial statement should be prepared showing items owned, their value, and outstanding debts. This statement plus an estimate of expenses and income can guide one in determining whether soil improvements should be self-financed or credit should be used.

In addition to the interest rate, other charges in obtaining a loan should be considered as a part of the cost of credit. The method of figuring interest also affects the cost of loans. Interest is sometimes taken out in advance, thus increasing the cost per dollar of credit used. In other cases, interest is paid for a stated time whether or not funds are actually used.

Terms and conditions of the loan should be clearly spelled out. This includes costs, repayment dates, and collateral for securing the loan. Renewal provisions should be stated.

The lender should be kept informed about progress of the project and the whole farming operation. Many lenders welcome an annual financial statement from borrowers. If payments cannot be made as scheduled, the lender should be informed in advance of the date payment is due. In a sense, lender and borrower are partners. Mutually beneficial decisions can be made only if both parties know the important facts about changes in soil management.

Soil Management in Regions

Carleton P. Barnes

To discuss more easily soil-management problems and opportunities presented by the different conditions found in the United States, we have divided the country into 16 regions.

Each of the regions has a combination of climate, soils, and agriculture that tends to give it soil-management problems different from the others.

Few countries have such a great diversity of soils and climates as ours. Our farming is carried on in subtropical climates, where frost seldom occurs, and in areas where frost occurs practically every month of the year.

Several thousand different kinds of soil have been found in our nationwide soil survey. Not all of them are greatly different from one another, but several hundred are unique and must be managed differently to be fully productive.

If all this diversity occurred in random fashion, as though some giant had strewn the different soils and climates around, there would be little point in using regions in discussing soil-management problems and practices. But our soils and climates follow definite regional patterns, each region having within it a distinct pattern of soils and climates. The climates of our Pacific coast differ from those of our Atlantic coast, and each is different from those of the interior of the country. These differences result from latitude, elevation, and the worldwide movement of airmasses across the continent.

Soils likewise have regional patterns. They result from the climate under

451

which the soils have developed rather than from the geologic material from which they came.

There also are local differences in soils which are due to differences in parent rock, topography, and drainage. One could not, however hard he tries, find a soil in North Dakota just like one in Florida, or one in Delaware just like one in Nevada. This regional arrangement of climates and soils—and therefore of crops—makes it convenient to divide our country into regions to discuss soil management.

This is not to say that soils or climate are uniform within a region. Every farmer knows that soils may differ within a distance of a few feet. These are the local differences in soils due to geology, slope, or drainage. The different parts of a farm and even parts of a field may need different treatment. But the two or three kinds of soil on a farm in the Central Valley of California will not be the same as the three or four on a farm in Iowa, or Alabama, or New York. And in many ways they will be like soils elsewhere in the Central Valley—even elsewhere in California.

Each of the 16 regions, therefore, has within it many different soils and local differences in climate. But the combination of conditions within a region generally is different from the combination of conditions in other regions.

We must realize that in passing from one region to another we often find a gradual rather than an abrupt change from the conditions of one to those of the other. But when we show the regions on a map we have to draw a line between them, implying thereby that on one side of the line we find one thing and on the other side we find something quite different.

Climate is one of the main characteristics that distinguish one region from another, but it is not the only one. Climate sets limits on the kinds of crops that are advantageously grown and that largely determine the kinds of soil-management systems and problems. Climate determines the soil moisture regime that is to be expected, and

a large part of soil management is aimed at providing crops with the right amounts of moisture.

Because of the importance of climate, for example, we treat the North Pacific coastal valleys as a distinct region. No other part of the country is quite like it. We separate the winter wheat region of the Great Plains from the spring wheat region, and we separate the regions where cotton is an important crop from those where it is too cold for cotton—because of climate, we can say, but actually because of differences in the whole complex of climate, crops, types of farming, and soils that make the problems of soil management different.

The boundaries of the regions are not all determined by climate. Where we have a great region with a soil pattern strongly different from surrounding areas, like the lower Mississippi alluvial valley, or Delta, such a region is marked out for separate discussion even though its climate may not sharply contrast with neighboring regions. A regional boundary has been drawn along the eastern edge of the major Texas Blackland. This is a soil boundary primarily, although it also serves to separate a more humid region to the east from a less humid one to the west. The soil boundary, however, is the sharper and more easily recognizable of the two and therefore was used. Wherever practical, regional boundaries are drawn to coincide with recognizable topographic or soil breaks, even though the principal difference between the adjoining regions may be a climatic one. This procedure has the advantage of putting the whole of a soil or topographic area into one region, instead of splitting it.

On our maps here, the regional boundaries are smoothed—that is, a boundary as shown does not try to follow the detailed position of the actual, on-the-ground boundary where, for example, it zigzags around interfingering mountains and interspersed narrow valleys. Instead, it strikes a general course approximately separating the two kinds of regions. This practice avoids having boundary delineation more detailed than is justified by the diverse character of the regions.

Let us see what these regions are like and how they differ.

1. THE NORTH PACIFIC VALLEY REGION is the humid region of cool summers and mild winters west of the Cascade Mountains in Washington and Oregon and the northwestern corner of California. Except for a narrow strip along the California coast, it is our only region where it is cool in summer yet mild in winter. We call it humid because the yearly moisture received is fairly large, but there is a pronounced dry season, usually in July and August. This makes irrigation advantageous in some places, especially where the soils have a low moisture-storing capacity. Actually this region, as shown on our map, contains large areas of rough, mountainous, forested land.

This region differs from region 2 in being much moister and in having much cooler summers than all of region 2 except a narrow strip along the coast. It differs from region 4 in being moister and milder in winter.

2. THE DRY MILD-WINTER REGION is our only region with mild winters and low moisture supply. The mountains of the California coastal ranges are exceptions to the generally dry climate, but they cannot be placed conveniently in any other region.

The part of the region in southern Texas differs from the rest in that most of its rainfall is in spring and summer instead of in winter.

The region includes the lower, western foothills of the Sierra Nevada but not the forested higher parts. Most of the region is hot in summer. Only the mountains and a narrow strip along the California coast are cool. This is the region of all-irrigated production of citrus and other subtropical crops and of long-season, intensive, irrigated agriculture.

This region differs from region 4 primarily in its warmer winters and longer frost-free season. On the whole, it also is hotter in summer.

3. THE PACIFIC NORTHWEST WHEAT REGION is the largest dryland farming region west of the Great Plains.

It differs from the dryland farming regions of the Great Plains in that most of the moisture comes in winter.

It differs from region 4, which surrounds it, in having mainly fertile soils that have good moisture-supplying characteristics. They were developed under grass from wind-blown material.

4. THE GRAZING-IRRIGATED REGION has three principal components: Arid grazing land; mountain forest land, most of it also used as range; and irrigated cropland. There is also some dry-farmed cropland. All of these elements occur intermingled with one another in large and small bodies throughout the region. Each has distinctly different sets of soil-management problems.

This region differs from regions 5, 6, and 7, which adjoin it on the east, mainly in its more arid character (except for its mountains), which makes it mostly too dry for nonirrigated farming. It has many forested mountains.

5. THE NORTHERN GREAT PLAINS includes the northern and colder part of the Great Plains, a region of rather low and irregular rainfall, in which special practices to conserve soil moisture usually are needed. Winters in the Northern Plains generally are too cold for fall-sown wheat, and spring wheat is the main crop. Large areas of this region have such steep, broken topography or soils with such poor moisture-supplying capacity that they are used mainly for grazing. In the region are a number of isolated, forested mountain ranges, like the Black Hills.

The large Nebraska Sandhill area has also been included, not because it is much like the other parts of the region, but because there seemed to be no better place to put it. If we were dividing the country into 40 or 50 regions instead of only 16, the Nebraska Sandhills would certainly be a region by itself. It is a great area of deep, sandy soils and dunelike topography, used largely for grazing.

The Northern Plains region differs from region 6 in its lower winter temperatures and shorter frost-free season and from regions 9 and 10, which adjoin it on the east, in its less humid climate.

6. THE WINTER WHEAT AND GRAZING REGION, a part of the Great Plains, is intermediate in winter temperature between region 5 (on the north) and region 7 (on the south). Its climate permits growing winter wheat, which is its main farm enterprise. As in other parts of the Great Plains, the moisture supply here is rather low, and the amount of precipitation in a particular year is unpredictable.

The bluestem grazing area of eastern Kansas—the Flint Hills—is included.

Region 6 differs from region 7, which adjoins it on the south, in its lower winter temperatures and shorter frost-free season. The boundary between them approximates the northern limit of cotton production. Region 6 is less humid than regions 9 and 11, which adjoin it on the east. Because of this drier climate, sorghum, rather than corn, is the main feed crop.

7. THE SOUTHERN PLAINS is a part of the country that gives us particular trouble in deciding which areas to put together to make a good-sized region. We could take the southern part of the Great Plains, where the climate permits cotton production, and call it a region. But between it and the humid, forested parts of eastern Texas and Oklahoma lie several beltlike areas that are considerably different from either and also quite dissimilar among themselves.

Region 7, as shown on our map, contains the nonforested or lightly forested subhumid areas in Texas and Oklahoma, where the climate is mild

enough for cotton. It extends from semiarid regions 2 and 4 on the west to the humid regions 8 and 12.

We draw its eastern boundary so as to include within it the Texas Blackland Prairies, except the poorly drained prairie along the coast. In Oklahoma we include the Crosstimbers and their intermingled prairies, but exclude the Ozark and Ouachita Mountains.

8a and 8b. THE MISSISSIPPI DELTA AND COASTAL PRAIRIES differ from their neighbors in having predominantly low-lying, naturally poorly drained soils. They contain the bottom lands and terraces of the lower Mississippi Valley and the wetter Coastal Prairies of Louisiana and Texas. They include the soils on which rice is grown outside of California. The soils mostly are fertile, although poor drainage and (in some places) floods limit their productivity.

9. THE MIDLAND FEED REGION combines productive soils, gentle relief, and moderate rainfall over a wide area. Summers are warm, but winters are cold. Nearly all rural land is farmed, and a higher percentage of the total land area is cropped than in any of the other regions. Steep slopes or poor soils in some localities interrupt the generally productive areas that characterize the region, but they are much less extensive than in the other regions.

Feed crops predominate. All but the northern part is in the Corn Belt. Most of the feed is fed on the farms where it is produced, but some areas specialize in growing feed to sell.

Region 9 is more humid than regions 5 and 6. It has a longer frost-free season than region 10 and generally more productive soils. It has a shorter frost-free season than region 11, fewer areas of steep slopes and poor soils, and much more land that requires drainage. Region 14, which touches region 9 on the northeast, differs from region 9 in having a much greater amount of stony, shallow, steep, or otherwise poor soils, and in having somewhat less sunshine and greater humidity in summer.

10. THE NORTHERN PART OF THE LAKE STATES has cool summers, cold winters, moderate moisture, and diverse soils. It sometimes is called the Lake States Cutover region. In contrast to region 9, its neighbor to the south, most of the land has not been converted to farming but remains in forest.

Poorly drained soils, some of them peat bogs, are widely distributed.

These and deep sands, stony soils, shallow soils, and productive, well-drained soils are more or less intermingled in region 10. Parts of the region have soils and climate similar to some parts of region 14, but the two regions are physically separated, have different complexes of physical features, and therefore lend themselves to separate consideration here.

11. THE EAST-CENTRAL UPLANDS comprises a moderately warm, humid region north of the Cotton Belt and south of the Midland feed region. Diversity of soils and relief is characteristic. The diversity is more extreme than that of its neighboring regions 9 and 12.

Its soils range from the highly productive, phosphatic, limestone-derived soils of the Blue Grass and the Nashville Basins to the steep, stony soils of the southern Appalachians. The region has warmer and more open winters than regions 9 and 14, which adjoin it on the north. It is colder and has a shorter frost-free season than region 12 to the south; the boundary between them approximates the cold limit of cotton production. It lacks the extensive areas of wet or swampy soils, found in region 15 to the east, and also lacks the sandy soils found in parts of that region. It is more humid than region 6, which touches it on the west.

12. THE SOUTHEASTERN UPLANDS REGION has a warm, humid climate, generally well-drained soils, and gentle to moderate slopes. It is split by the Mississippi Delta (region 8). It differs from region 11 in that its climate permits cotton to be grown, and from regions

8, 13, and 15, in lacking the extensive poorly drained areas found in those regions. It is more humid than region 7 and has much forest land.

The ridges of the Ouachita Mountains in the northwestern part of the region are an exception to the generally gentle to moderate slopes.

13. THE FLORIDA PENINSULA AND ADJACENT COASTAL FLATWOODS REGION is a humid region of mild winters and long, frost-free seasons, which permit the production of subtropical and early-season vegetables. It is characterized also by a preponderance of low-lying, poorly drained soils, although most of the intensive farming is not on these soils, but on the better drained soils. This predominant poor drainage further distinguishes this region from the Southeastern Uplands (region 12).

14. THE NORTHEAST, as we have delineated it here, is probably distinguished from its adjacent regions more by its predominant type of farming than anything else, although it is cooler than regions 11 and 15. Dairying is its most important farming enterprise, and we have drawn its boundaries approximately along the line where other types of farming become more important.

A soil boundary suitable for separating this region from region 11 is hard to find, although the soils gradually change in some of their characteristics as we pass from one region to the other.

15. THE MIDDLE ATLANTIC COAST, the Atlantic Coastal Plain from Long Island to South Carolina, is used mostly for intensive, high-value crops, like vegetables, tobacco, and peanuts. It contains large areas of poorly drained soils and some deep, dry sands, which are largely in forest. It differs from region 14 in its lack of stony soils, its gentler relief, and its frost-free season; from region 11 in its large amount of poorly drained soils; and from region 12 in its greater prevalence of poorly drained soils and in the predominance of other enterprises than cotton.

The North
Pacific Valleys

H. B. Cheney

Several unusual characteristics influence soil management in the North Pacific valleys.

They are: Land forms; abundant, low-intensity winter rainfall, but summer drought; a narrow range in temperature, with relatively warm winters and cool summers; a long frost-free period; moderately leached to highly leached, acid soils; abundant water for irrigation and power; a large number of adapted crops; concentration of crop production in the valleys; and rapid expansion of urban population.

The relief is varied and strong. The crest of the Cascade Mountains, an effective boundary on the east, averages 5 thousand to 8 thousand feet. Many peaks, most of them of volcanic origin, are higher.

Lower mountains occur along the entire coast. Except for the Olympic Mountains in northwestern Washington, they are less than 4 thousand feet.

The Willamette-Cowlitz-Puget lowlands, between the coastal mountains and the Cascade Range, extend 350 miles from west-central Oregon to Canada and are 20 to 70 miles wide. They are primarily stream valleys that contain alluvial terraces and (in the Puget lowland) glaciofluvial gravel. Many smaller valleys and alluvial terraces occur near the coast and along the Rogue and Umpqua Rivers in Oregon.

The marine influence predominates, but the coastal mountains and the Cascade Range modify it.

The highest precipitation in agricultural areas occurs along the coast, where the annual average is 50 to 100

inches. Precipitation is even higher in the coastal mountains, but it drops sharply in the valleys east of them. The average precipitation near Puget Sound is 20 to 40 inches a year; in the Willamette-Cowlitz Valleys, 35 to 50 inches and in the Rogue and Umpqua Valleys, 16 to 30 inches.

Typically, half of the precipitation falls in winter. Less than 5 percent falls in July and August. Low-intensity rainfall usually falls 16 to 20 days a month in winter, but a total of 0.5 to 1.5 inches is typical in July and August.

Temperatures are remarkably uniform in the farming areas. The average January temperatures are 35 to 45° F. The average July temperatures are 55 to 70°. The small change from winter to summer reflects marine influence.

The frost-free period is more than 200 days in most of the agricultural areas. The Rogue River Valley and some localities in the interior valleys have a shorter growing season.

The soils along the coast are highly acid and low in bases. The soils in the interior valleys are slightly to strongly acid. Soils formed from recent alluvium generally are less acid than soils in the nearby uplands.

Trees—notably Douglas-fir—are the natural vegetation of the region. In the areas of higher rainfall in the mountains and along the coast, hemlock, western redcedar, and alder also occur. Redwood grows along the coast in California. In the areas of lower rainfall, the Oregon white oak, ponderosa pine, sugar pine, California black oak, madrone, grasses, manzanita, and poison-oak are typical of the natural vegetation. Grasses, along with

CROPLANDS
Irrigated
Nonirrigated
Other Lands

1 Puget Sound Lowlands
2 Willamette and Western
   Washington Valleys (Lowland Areas)
3 Willamette and Western
   Washington Valleys (Upland Areas)
4 Rogue and Umpqua Valleys
5 Coastal Areas

shrubs and trees, occur naturally on many of the alluvial soils.

Only 19 percent of the total land area is in farms. About one-third of the 6.6 million acres in farms is cropland. The rest is pasture and woodland.

Practically all cultivated land along the coast is in forage crops. The remainder of the region grows many crops, among them a host of horticultural crops, small grains, and grass and legumes for seed.

An abundance of water resources provide water for irrigation, power, and navigation.

The use of sprinkler irrigation has increased rapidly since 1945. Additional storage reservoirs have been planned to provide the water needed in summer.

The economy is dominated by forestry and agriculture and the processing and manufacturing industries that are associated with them.

Population densities—both urban and rural—are high in the Puget Sound and Willamette Valley zones.

The increasing population has several effects on soil-management programs. Local markets for dairy and poultry products, fruits, vegetables, and nuts have increased. Many farms are small and have intensive operations. The utilization of additional land for urban and other nonagricultural purposes has heightened the pressure on the remaining agricultural land and has caused some of the best farmland to be shifted to other uses.

AMONG THE COMMON soil-management problems are inadequate drainage and flooding, because much of the farm production is on alluvial soils.

Total rainfall is adequate, except in the southern interior valleys, but summer drought limits production of many crops throughout the region.

Soil acidity is a problem in many places. All the soils are acid, but some are not excessively acid for the crops that are grown.

Nitrogen, phosphorus, potassium, sulfur, magnesium, boron, and other trace elements are insufficient for maximum yields on many soils. Soil tests or plant analyses are used as aids in determining the fertility status of specific soil areas.

Soil erosion is a serious problem on some slopes but is less prevalent than one might expect. Most of the sloping soils are protected by close-growing vegetation. Rainfall is usually of low intensity, and the sloping soils are fairly resistant to erosion. Moreover, a high percentage of the cultivated crops is grown on nearly level alluvial soils. Flooding causes serious erosion damage on the recent alluvial soils unless proper precautions are taken.

Problems of tillage and soil structure are variable and have not been studied extensively. Most of the upland soils (but not some of the alluvial soils) have desirable structure.

Specific soil-management problems and programs are discussed for each of five zones in the region.

ZONE 1 consists of the lowlands around Puget Sound in Washington.

Dairying, poultry, and horticultural crops provide its three main sources of income. Forage crops for use as pasture, hay, and silage are important. Grain is shipped into the area for the poultry industry.

Many of the wide range of horticultural crops are sold locally—all types of fresh vegetables, small fruits (such as strawberries, raspberries, blackberries, and loganberries), potatoes, bulbs, nursery stock, and vegetable seed.

Continued urban expansion has taken many acres of fine agricultural land out of production.

More efficient systems of soil management must be adopted in the future in order to meet the increasing demand for agricultural products here.

Most of the soils used for agricultural purposes have been formed from some type of glacial material. The soils—except the younger alluvial soils—are highly leached and are moderately to strongly acid.

The key soil-management problems in the Puget Sound lowlands are: Inadequate drainage, droughtiness, poor structure or tilth, excessive acidity, inadequate fertility. The magnitude of the problems varies on different soils, with different management systems, and on different crops.

Much of the land originally was poorly drained. Many acres still have restricted drainage. They are used for timber and pasture.

Many pastures and haylands have been improved through drainage. This permits the use of high-producing species and the effective use of other desirable management practices, such as the application of fertilizer and lime.

Open-ditch drains have been used extensively in some sections. Further improvement can be obtained through the installation of tile drains on some soils. Improved drainage would increase the yield of crops now grown and might permit a shift to more intensive high-value crops.

The ability of the soil to store available moisture has a marked effect on productivity. Because summer rainfall averages only 3 to 4 inches, unirrigated crops must utilize stored moisture to a large degree during the summer. Soils that have gravelly substrata or are shallow have a low moisture-holding capacity and are droughty and poorly adapted to growing cultivated crops. Even deep-rooting alfalfa is not well adapted to such droughty soils unless irrigation can be provided. The use of fertilizers, manure, and lime usually is not profitable on such soils where moisture is such a limiting factor.

Even on soils that hold moisture well, irrigation is desirable during the summer for the main crops. The irrigated acreage more than doubled between 1950 and 1955, when about 25 thousand acres were irrigated. Very likely most of the suitable soils for which water is available will be irrigated in time.

Nearly all irrigation has been by sprinklers. Vegetables, small fruits, and the forage crops are the main irrigated crops.

Most soils in this zone naturally have desirable tilth, which is favorable to crop production. In the absence of research results, we can only speculate about the effects of cultivation on their physical properties: It is possible that tilth may become a limiting factor first on the alluvial soils that have been cultivated intensively for years.

Soil fertility problems have received major attention in the research programs of this zone. At the Western Washington Experiment Station at Puyallup and the Northwestern Washington Experiment Station at Mount Vernon, studies have been made of the proper use of fertilizers, particularly on horticultural crops. Increased attention has been given to forage crops in a new testing program.

The characteristically low content of available nitrogen in these soils must be raised before they can be successfully farmed. The total nitrogen content is low in the light-colored soils of the uplands. The total nitrogen content of many of the other soils is reasonably high. Yet in practically all soils the available nitrogen supply from organic matter decomposition is not adequate for maximum crop production unless it is improved through management practices.

Among the factors that contribute to the slow release of nitrogen from soil organic matter are the cool summer temperatures, moderate to high soil acidity, poor aeration, insufficiency of nutrients, such as phosphorus, and inadequate soil moisture in summer.

"Homegrown" nitrogen has been an important source of additional available nitrogen on many farms here—the legumes grown with grasses for hay, pasture, or silage on dairy farms, and the barnyard and poultry manure that is returned to the land.

Commercial nitrogen fertilizers have been used in increasing amounts, primarily on the high-value crops like vegetables and small fruits.

Recommendations for the use of nitrogen fertilizers on field crops usually range from none to 60 pounds of actual nitrogen an acre. For horticultural crops the rates recommended are usually considerably higher.

Most of the soils in the region require applications of phosphate fertilizers to produce maximum yields. The need for phosphorus is particularly great for vegetable crops and small fruits, but legumes also need it on many soils.

The Western Washington Experiment Station has conducted an extensive program of research on the use of fertilizers on vegetables and small fruits. The results indicate that yearly applications of phosphate fertilizers are required for vegetable crops and that there is no visible carryover of phosphate from one year to the next. A great response to phosphate is obtained with vegetables on soils at the station that have received as high as 800 pounds of available phosphoric oxide (P_2O_5) over a 10-year period.

Best results with row crops are obtained when the applied phosphate is banded at the time of planting.

Phosphates with a high degree of water solubility—such as ordinary superphosphate, concentrated superphosphate, and ammonium phosphates—generally have been superior to the less soluble ones.

The need for potassium varies throughout zone 1. Potash is included in the recommended mixed fertilizer used on horticultural crops but is recommended less often for field crops. Forage mixtures that include legumes do respond to potash on some soils.

Results of research have indicated a response to magnesium on some soils. Most of the soils here are acid—pH 5.0 to 6.0—yet relatively little limestone has been used. Limestone is recommended in places where alfalfa is to be seeded on the strongly acid soils.

Farmers in the area will achieve maximum yields only by utilizing a combination of all necessary soil and management practices. Many soils are so deficient in phosphorus, for example, that applications of nitrogen, irrigation, or other practices will do little to increase yields if phosphate fertilizer is not applied also. Likewise, the most effective use of fertilizer is obtained only when moisture is adequate and the soil is effectively drained.   .

ZONE 2, the Willamette and western Washington valleys, is a lowland area of 2 million acres. Its soils developed from alluvial materials at elevations of 30 to 500 feet above sea level. Most of it is in the Willamette Valley of Oregon, but lowlands along the Columbia River and along the Cowlitz, Lewis, and Chehalis Rivers in Washington are included.

The soils have been formed largely from three general groups of parent material—older alluvium, or valley fill material; recent alluvium; and organic materials. Some soils in the valleys of Washington have been developed on mixed gravelly materials of old terraces and so are more thoroughly leached and lower in fertility than the soils that are typical of the area.

The soils are moderately acid. The dominant pH range is 5.4 to 6.3. The soils developed on recent alluvium are the least acid and usually are above pH 5.7. A medium amount—about 2 to 4 percent—of the organic matter is in the surface soils. Soils developed on the older terraces exhibit a distinct profile development, but little horizon differentiation exists in the soils formed on recent alluvium. Well-recognized drainage series have developed in both the terraces and the recent alluvium.

Approximately one-half of the soils naturally are imperfectly or poorly drained. Most of the rest have good drainage. Only small areas are excessively drained.

A large number of different crops grown in zone 2 include grains; forage crops for hay, pasture, and silage; grass and legume seeds; vegetables; berries; tree fruits; nuts; and many horticultural specialty crops. A single farm may grow 10 to 15 different crops.

About 8 percent of the cultivated land is irrigated.

The dominant soil-management problems in zone 2 are inadequate drainage, summer drought, stream flooding and erosion, low fertility, soil acidity, and poor tilth.

Inadequate drainage at one time restricted crop production on one-half of this lowland area. Probably one-fourth of the area would still benefit from additional improvement in drainage.

The use of open ditches and tile systems for drainage has increased since 1945. Because drainage outlets are inadequate, many of the drainage programs must be planned and executed on a community basis to be successful.

Most of the ryegrass seed produced in the United States is grown on poorly drained soils in the Willamette Valley.

The Dayton soil, a Planosol, is well adapted to growing ryegrass with but little improvement in drainage. As long as the production of ryegrass seed continues to be the most profitable use of this soil, there will be little incentive to improve drainage, install irrigation, and grow more intensive crops.

The droughty condition in summer

presents a problem, although total annual rainfall is 40 inches. The average in July and August is less than 1 inch.

Many crops, including grass seeds, fall- and spring-planted small grains, and vetch are grown without irrigation, but irrigation is essential if the land is to be used intensively.

The development of sprinkler irrigation brought a great expansion in irrigation—81 thousand acres were irrigated in 1949 and 153 thousand acres in 1954. Sprinklers are used on nearly all of this acreage. The Water Resources Committee of Oregon State College in 1955 estimated that by the year 2000 the irrigated acreage in the Willamette Valley may be five times greater than in 1955.

Vegetables, small fruit, pasture, and mint are the principal crops irrigated. They are not grown extensively without irrigation.

The new irrigator has the problem of learning what good irrigation practices mean and how to reorganize his farming business. Some farmers have started to use moisture measuring devices to determine when to apply water. Oregon State College initiated a service to measure soil moisture tension as a further aid to efficient application and use of irrigation water.

Individual farmers have carried out most of the irrigation development. It has been concentrated on recent alluvial soils where water was readily available from streams or shallow wells. Water has not been so readily available on the higher terraces.

A marked expansion of irrigation will involve more than individual effort. Water storage and distribution systems must be built to supply water to the irrigable land. The greatest possibilities for expansion are on the soils developed on the old alluvium. It is hoped that the water control and development plan of the Corps of Engineers will eventually provide the needed additional water. The plan was about one-third complete in 1957. It includes construction of reservoirs with adequate storage capacity to supply water

for all the land considered suitable for irrigation development.

Some of the most productive alluvial soils often are flooded in winter. A protective cover of plants during the fall and winter is an essential part of the management program on these soils. Winter cover crops must be seeded early enough to provide a good growth by the time the floods start, or serious erosion may occur. Barriers of trees and brush can also be used effectively to slow up the water.

Nitrogen is the plant nutrient that is most likely to be deficient. Applications of 80 to 120 pounds of nitrogen an acre for crops of grass seed and vegetables are needed for optimum yields. Smaller amounts are used on small grains or are needed when legumes are grown in the rotation.

Fall applications of nitrogen generally are not recommended, except on perennial grass crops and strawberries. Since the soil rarely freezes and rainfall in fall and winter usually exceeds 20 to 25 inches, nitrogen applied in the fall leaches readily. Much of the nitrogen for vegetable crops is applied in the irrigation water.

Sulfur should be applied regularly in the fertilizer program, especially for legumes. The sulfate form from gypsum or other fertilizers is preferred to elemental sulfur, which has acidifying tendencies.

Most of the soils are well supplied with available phosphorus and potassium for field crops. Soil tests occasionally show some soils low in available phosphorus or potassium.

The Planosols, used largely for the production of ryegrass seed, commonly are deficient in available phosphorus. Applications of phosphate along with the needed nitrogen will help to increase yields of ryegrass seed on such soils. These soils also are relatively low in exchangeable potassium but have enough for crops of grass seed.

Growers of vegetables generally apply fertilizers containing nitrogen, phosphate, potash, and sulfur in a band by the row at planting time. Rates of 60 to 100 pounds of P_2O_5 and K_2O an acre are fairly common. Phosphate fertilizer, even on soils comparatively high in available phosphorus, has increased the yield of pole beans and sweet corn.

The response of vegetables to potash has been less certain. Some soils appear to have too little available potash, but many are well supplied.

The application of boron generally is recommended for forage legumes, such as alfalfa, vetch, red clover, subclover, and peas. Boron also is used on walnuts, beets, cauliflower, and broccoli. Some crops, such as beans, are extremely sensitive to excesses of boron and may be injured if grown on soils that have previously grown beets that received heavy applications of boron. Other trace elements are required in addition to boron on the small areas of organic soils.

Soil acidity is not yet a major problem on many of the soils in zone 2. The soils formed on recent alluvium are mostly only slightly acid, usually above pH 5.7. Soils on the terraces are more acid. Lime can be used to advantage on the more acid soils when legumes (such as alfalfa) that are less tolerant of acidity are to be grown. The response of many crops on these soils to lime is not known.

The Planosols are strongly acid, but because of their poor drainage they are not adapted to crops that respond well to applications of lime.

Some of the recent alluvial soils are used to grow vegetable crops nearly continuously. Pickers go over the bean fields 7 to 12 times during the season and pack down the soil, which usually is wet from frequent irrigation. The compaction by pickers reduces aeration slightly, but so far no effects on yields have been demonstrated.

Research is needed on the relationship of soil physical properties, as modified by management practices, on crop growth, particularly when intensive cropping under irrigation is practiced. The use of cover crops and sod crops grown in rotation with vegetable crops or small fruits is encouraged.

ZONE 3, the Willamette and western Washington valleys, is an upland area, which consists of the low hills throughout the alluvial plain of zone 2 and the adjacent upland soils in the foothills of the coastal and Cascade Mountains.

The soils are strongly leached and acid. They have a strong granular surface structure with spherical concretions. They are relatively high in iron and aluminum oxides. Most of the upland soils are well drained, but some soils along the lower slopes and in depressions are subject to seepage conditions and have poor drainage.

The soils are derived largely from basic igneous or sedimentary rocks, but some are formed from loess and volcanic ash. Their depth varies, but soils used for agricultural purposes are generally at least 3 to 4 feet deep.

Farm woodlots and commercial timber production occupy much of the land in zone 3 and the steeper slopes in the adjacent mountains.

The dominant agricultural uses include general farming and the production of pasture, grass seed, hay, small grains, strawberries, cane berries, nuts, and tree fruits.

One type of soil may be used to grow a wide variety of crops, including forest trees, unimproved pasture, small grain, hay, grass seed, tree fruits or nuts, cane berries, and strawberries. Rapidly changing economic conditions and methods of production of some of the crops have contributed to this diverse and changing cropping pattern.

The dominant soil-management problems in this zone are soil acidity, low fertility, summer drought, and erosion. Inadequate drainage is a problem in some places. Deteriorating tilth and declining soil organic matter need consideration on intensively cropped soils.

Crops mostly must utilize stored moisture in summer. The total rainfall in July and August averages 0.75 to 1.5 inches. Rainfall in May, June, and September also usually is insufficient to meet crop requirements.

This summer drought limits both the kind of crops that are suitable to the area and the yield of those that are grown. Soil moisture characteristics and soil depth therefore are important.

Most of the soils can hold a good supply of available moisture—sometimes 2 or 3 inches of usable soil moisture per foot of depth. The ability to hold water varies, however, and needs to be considered in a management program.

Effective depth also affects the storage of usable soil moisture. Effective soil depth varies from a few feet to many feet. The most productive agricultural soils have at least 4 to 5 feet of usable depth. Even deeper soils are needed for the best production of walnuts (8 or 10 feet) and deep-rooted perennial crops.

Annual and winter annual crops, such as wheat, barley, or oats and vetch, if properly managed, produced well on soils with less stored moisture than is required for the perennials, since they mature on stored moisture during a drought period.

Perennial legumes and grasses are grown extensively, but their growth drops markedly in the dry summer.

Irrigation cannot be the answer to the midsummer drought problem on most of these upland soils. Even though many of the soils are suitable for sprinkler irrigation, water for irrigation is available on only a few scattered acres. Irrigation undoubtedly will be expanded on the upland soils wherever it is feasible, but in nearly all the area farming will have to be without irrigation.

Several practices have been followed in order to make the most effective use of the available moisture supply.

The crops must be adapted to the moisture-supplying capacity of the soil. For example, deep-rooted orchard trees are most successful on soils with 8 to 10 feet or more of permeable, usable soil depth. Deep-rooted perennial legumes, such as alfalfa, also require relatively deep soils. Crops like vetch and oats, which complete much of their growth during the rainy season, can be produced successfully on the shallower soils.

Although usable moisture sets a limit on production, the available moisture has not been utilized with greatest efficiency because other factors also limit crop growth. Use of improved fertilizers and reduction of soil acidity through liming would help make possible a more efficient use of available moisture on most of the soils.

T. L. Jackson, of Oregon State College, has shown that yield of small grains on infertile soils 3 to 5 feet deep can be increased 25 to 100 percent by proper use of fertilizers and that low fertility has been more limiting on many soils than inadequate moisture.

More effective use of available moisture also is accomplished through practices that increase production during the rainy season in the fall, winter, and early spring. Among them are proper grazing and fertilization of pasture.

Another way is to shift to deeper rooted crops. The growing of alfalfa on deep, permeable upland soils appears to be a promising method of increasing hay for silage production on deep soils. Alfalfa has not been grown extensively on upland soils in the past because of inadequate fertility and strong acidity. Experience, demonstrations, and research indicate, however, that alfalfa can be grown on many upland soils.

Yields of spring-seeded crops may be increased by early planting on a well-prepared seedbed.

In orchards, cover crops should be worked into the soil in early April and the stored soil moisture saved for tree growth. The control of weeds conserves moisture for desirable species.

The regular use of commercial fertilizers is essential if maximum yields of crops are to be obtained on the upland soils. Deficiencies of nitrogen, phosphorus, potassium, boron, and sulfur commonly occur.

The total content of nitrogen in the soil is reasonably high, but the supply of available nitrogen rarely is adequate for maximum production except during or immediately following vigorous legumes, such as red clover, vetch, and alfalfa. Subclover has increased production amazingly on hill pastures.

The use of nitrogen fertilizers has increased rapidly since 1940. The growers of horticultural crops and grass seed crops adopted the use of nitrogen rapidly once its value was demonstrated. Wheat, barley, oats, and grass pastures generally are not adequately supplied with available nitrogen, however. Both commercial nitrogen and vigorous legumes can be used effectively to supply nitrogen needed for maximum yields.

Legumes respond to regular additions of sulfur. Gypsum, or land plaster, for many years was the only fertilizer or soil amendment used extensively. Considerable sulfur has been added in phosphate and nitrogen fertilizers. The yields of barley and other crops are improved by additions of gypsum on land that has not had sulfur applied recently. The sulfate form of sulfur is preferred on these acid soils over the elemental form.

The available phosphorus supply in the upland soils of zone 3 is generally low or very low. Phosphorus fixation is high. This results in low available phosphorus in the soil, even though the total phosphorus content is comparatively high.

A more efficient use of phosphate fertilizers can aid greatly in increasing yields on these soils. Phosphate fertilizers, except on small fruit crops, have not been applied on many of the phosphorus-deficient soils. The application of phosphate fertilizer in bands rather than by the usual broadcast method should increase its efficiency.

Potash fertilizers have not been used widely on these soils except for horticultural crops. Response to potash fertilizers on field crops has been rare. Research has demonstrated a wide variation in the potassium-supplying power of these soils. Additional field research has been started to define the need for potassium. Most of the soils probably are supplied adequately with potassium for field crops, but it is thought that more potash fertilizer will be needed, especially as improved management programs are adopted.

Many of the soils are deficient in available boron for crops such as alfalfa, broccoli, and walnuts, and the application of boron for them is considered good insurance.

Limestone has been applied for many years, but its use is far below estimated needs, largely because of its high cost. Good limestone has cost about 12 dollars a ton, delivered and spread—2 to 4 times the cost in the Midwest. The cost of 2 to 4 or more tons of lime an acre appears prohibitive to many farmers, even though part of the cost may be shared by the Agricultural Conservation Program. All of the high-quality limestone must be shipped in.

Inadequate liming undoubtedly has been one of the factors that has deterred the increased use of alfalfa. Other forage legumes also respond to application of lime on acid soils.

Applying the full requirement of lime at the start gave better results than small applications every 3 to 4 years at the Red Soils Experiment Station, Oregon City, Oreg. The maintenance application there was 1 ton of high-quality limestone in 7 years.

Multiple deficiencies of nitrogen, phosphorus, potassium, sulfur, boron, and possibly other trace elements, as well as strong soil acidity, may occur in zone 3. Field experiments have shown that the application of one or even several of the deficient elements may give poor results if all are not supplied in adequate amounts and in proper balance. The lack of a full understanding of this fact along with the inadequate information on the precise combination of fertilizer nutrients to use may well have contributed to the reluctance of farmers to use lime and fertilizer extensively.

Erosion in the upland area of the Willamette and western Washington valleys of zone 3 is a serious problem only on a limited acreage, even though the slopes often are steep and long. A high percentage of the land is in forest trees or grass, which provide a protective cover. Intensity of rainfall is usually low. The soils are generally permeable and fairly resistant to erosion.

Considerable erosion has occurred on some cultivated land, however, and a few areas are severely eroded. The most critical situations where erosion has occurred are in clean-cultivated orchards and cane fruit plantings; in strawberry plantings, where the rows run up and down the slope; and on land where small grain crops fail to provide cover during fall and winter. The use of winter cover crops in orchards will aid in protecting the soil during the period of greatest erosion hazard. Contour planting and cultivation will aid in reducing erosion losses. Grassed waterways and contour diversion ditches help control gullies.

All practices that are helpful in maintaining a good vegetative cover during the fall, winter, and spring aid in reducing erosion. The growing of sod crops in rotation with the intertilled crops that are grown also help to maintain good tilth and reduce susceptibility to erosion.

The maintenance of desirable tilth and levels of organic matter is not difficult in most of the area where grass or grass-legume mixtures are grown. These soils are generally well aggregated and reasonably high in total organic matter. When clean-cultivated crops are grown intensively, as they are on some farms, the problem of maintaining desirable tilth and a supply of actively decomposing organic matter becomes important. Grass seed and hay and pasture crops can be grown in the rotation successfully with such clean-cultivated crops as strawberries. Winter cover crops can be used in orchards, and animal manures can be applied wherever they are available.

Inadequate drainage, although not considered a major problem in the upland area, does limit production and choice of crops on a sizable acreage. Side-hill seepage areas and wet waterways can often be improved by the use of intercepting tile placed across the slope above the wet area.

ZONE 4, the Rogue and Umpqua Valleys, is in southwestern Oregon.

These valleys get less rain than the rest of the area. Average annual rainfall is 16 to 30 inches on the floor of the Rogue Valley and 30 to 40 inches in the Umpqua Valley. The soils generally are somewhat lower in organic matter and less acid in reaction and have less strongly developed and less stable structure than the soils in the rest of the region.

These valleys contain about 500 thousand acres of cropland and pasture. Somewhat more than two-fifths of the area is cropland, which is largely the terraces and flood plains.

The Rogue Valley is noted for its pears. Many other crops are grown. Hay, pasture, and small grains occupy most of the cultivated lands. Sheep and dairy and beef cattle are raised to utilize the large amount of roughage.

The soil-management problems in the Rogue and Umpqua Valleys include those arising from insufficient rainfall, inadequate drainage, low fertility, erosion, and soil acidity.

Irrigation is necessary for the type of agriculture practiced in most of the Rogue River Valley and is highly beneficial in the Umpqua Valley.

Gravity irrigation is used on most of the 85 thousand irrigated acres, but the use of sprinkler irrigation has been increasing. Additional storage dams are needed to supply supplemental water on about one-half of this acreage and to supply water for irrigation on other soils suitable for irrigation.

Improved irrigation practices will help to extend existing supplies of water and will aid in alleviating the drainage problems that result partly from overirrigation.

As in most irrigated districts, especially where flood irrigation is practiced, the drainage problem is serious in parts of the zone. Often the Grumosols, or "sticky soils," are nearly impermeable to water. The underlying strata range from coarse gravel and sand to fine, sticky clays. Excess water in one area may move in underground aquifers for a considerable distance before it causes a high water table.

The fertility problems of these valleys have not been defined clearly.

The need for both nitrogen and sulfur is widespread. Nitrogen will aid in increasing the yields of tree fruits, grasses, grains, and vegetables—in fact, all crops except legumes. The soils are low in available sulfur. Sulfur therefore is recommended, especially for legumes, grains, and vegetables, unless a sulfur-carrying fertilizer was applied in the previous year.

Some soils respond to applications of phosphorus, potassium, and boron. Soil tests are used in making recommendations for applying them.

Spray applications of iron chelates are made to correct the chlorotic condition found on pear trees in the Rogue River Valley.

The soils of the Rogue and Umpqua Valleys are less acid than those in the rest of the North Pacific area. Most of the soil samples from the Rogue Valley, which were tested at Oregon State College, have been above pH 5.8. Many soil samples from the Umpqua Valley are less than pH 5.7 and typically have lime requirements of 1.5 to 2 tons an acre. Little lime has been used in the area, and additional research is needed to determine its effects. Limestone is recommended on the basis of soil tests.

Because most of the sloping land is in pasture or forest, erosion is not a widespread problem. The greatest erosion problem occurs on nonirrigated sloping land devoted to grain crops and on slopes where gravity irrigation is used for cultivated crops. Accelerated erosion following logging operations is an overall problem in the area.

ZONE 5, the coastal areas, extends from Puget Sound in the north along the entire coast of Washington, Oregon, and the two northernmost counties of California—nearly 500 miles.

This zone has higher rainfall, cooler summers, and warmer winters than the rest of the area. Agriculture is confined largely to alluvial soils along the coast and coastal streams. The adja-

cent uplands mostly are covered with forest.

The organic matter in the surface of most of these soils is high or very high (4 to 12 percent or more). The soils are usually very acid—commonly about pH 5. They are severely leached of bases.

The soils on the upland and terraces usually are well drained. The alluvial soils typically are poorly drained. Many are perpetually waterlogged. The wetter soils often are mottled in the surface, with gleying in the subsoil.

Forage crops occupy nearly all of the cultivated land in the coastal zone. They are used mainly for pasture, but some grass silage and hay also is produced. The pastures consist largely of grass species, but red clover, alsike clover, lotus major, Ladino clover, New Zealand whiteclover, and subclover also are used in improved pastures and meadows.

The principal income is derived from dairying, but poultry and sheep are important in some parts of the zone. A limited acreage is devoted to small grains, such grass seed crops as bentgrass, lily bulbs, and cranberries.

The soil-management problems in the coastal areas include inadequate drainage, insufficient summer rainfall, high acidity, and low fertility.

Drainage by diking, ditching, and tiling has been the means by which most of the tideland, river bottoms, and terraces on which forage crops are grown have been brought into profitable production. The easiest jobs have been done. Much remains to be done if farmers are to achieve maximum production. Clearing of timber and brush is needed in many instances, as well as drainage. Many localities will require community action to solve their drainage problems.

Even with drainage improvement, the soils may be wet or flooded from November to April. The average rainfall is 6 to 12 inches a month in winter in most of the coastal zone. Forage crops must be adapted to such conditions.

Rainfall in the summer is not enough for the best forage production. The average rainfall in July and August is 0.75 inch in the southern part and as high as 3 inches along part of the Washington coast.

Rainfall in June and September also is low in the southern part. Irrigation is essential for maximum forage production in summer. Irrigation has been increasing and will likely continue to expand as long as suitable soils and available water can be combined for profitable production. Marked improvements in irrigation practices are possible on many farms in this zone.

Inadequate available nitrogen limits the production of grass. The total nitrogen content of the soil is high, but the nitrification rate is quite low. The cool soil temperatures throughout the year, often poor aeration, high acidity, and low fertility all contribute to reduce the rate of release of nitrogen from soil organic matter in these soils.

Applications of nitrogen fertilizers can be made throughout the season to increase the growth of grass, especially if moisture is adequate.

The soils along the coast have a high requirement of lime. More than two-thirds of the samples tested in the Oregon State College soil-testing laboratory showed a lime requirement of more than 4 tons an acre. It will take 12 to 16 tons of high-quality limestone to raise many of the soils to pH 6.5.

Results of soil tests in this zone indicate that most of the soils are deficient in phosphorus and some lack potassium. Phosphorus and potassium have been recommended for legumes when soil tests indicate a low level in the soil.

It is expected that the needs for potassium will increase in this area. The grasses compete strongly with the legumes for the available soil potassium, and frequent applications of potassium may be needed on many soils if legume stands are to be maintained in connection with the grass.

Many of the soils in zone 5 contain quite low amounts of exchangeable magnesium.

The Dry Mild-Winter Region

D. G. Aldrich

More than 200 commercial crops are grown in the dry mild-winter region of the Far West, which includes most of the farmlands of California, most of southwestern Arizona, the Rio Grande plain south and west of San Antonio, and the lower Rio Grande Valley.

Production estimates based on preliminary reports from the 1954 Census of Agriculture indicate that it produces more than 90 percent of the almonds, lemons, olives, dried figs and prunes, walnuts, and apricots in the United States; 50 percent of the asparagus, pears, and tomatoes; 40 percent of the peaches; 33 percent of the oranges; about 25 percent of the sugar beets, beans, hops, and rice; more than 15 percent of the grapefruit; 10 percent of the alfalfa and cotton; and 30 percent of 21 of the 27 major vegetables grown for the fresh market.

The soils, natural vegetation, and cropping practices in the northern coastal valleys of California, where the annual rainfall is 30 to 60 inches, differ from those of the southern coastal valleys, where rainfall averages 10 inches.

Similar but smaller differences exist as to soil, vegetation, and crops in the Great Central Valley of California, where annual rainfall is 20 inches in the north and 5 inches in the south, and the desert valleys of southern California and Arizona, where the annual rainfall is 3 to 12 inches.

Probably the most noteworthy variation in climate in region II is that California and Arizona receive rain mainly in the winter months, but rainfall in southwestern Texas is concentrated in the late spring and early fall. Temperatures in winter are mild. There are 200 to 300 frost-free days. Seasonal rainfall is so limited that most crops require irrigation.

THE SOILS of the region may be divided into six general categories.

The valley lands consist of alluvial flood plain or alluvial fan soils that are developed in rainfall zones ranging from a high of 60 inches in the north coastal area of California to a low of less than 3 inches in the desert regions of southern California and Arizona. The upland soils, developed from loosely consolidated water-laid material and found in the Winter Garden area of the lower Rio Grande Plain, are in this category.

The valley lands of wind-modified sandy soils are in zones of intermediate and low rainfall.

There are also valley basin lands which are imperfectly drained and may be high in organic matter, salinity, or alkali.

The gently sloping to undulating terrace lands vary in reaction from acid to alkaline and are underlain by clay subsoils or iron cemented hardpans.

The rolling to steep uplands consist of acid to alkaline residual soils of different depth and are found in rainfall zones varying from high (timberland soil) to moderate (grassland) to low.

The sixth category includes unmapped soils in the desert.

The valley lands include the best agricultural soils of the region. Properly cultivated, fertilized, and irrigated, they produce most of the field crops, vegetable crops, fruits, and berries in the region. Valley soils in the high-rainfall zone are productive of berries, vegetables, and apples. Large irrigated acreages of alfalfa, potatoes, sugar beets, carrots, corn, lettuce, apricots, peaches, and walnuts are grown in the zone of intermediate rainfall. Climatic conditions permitting, citrus, avocados, grapes, and cotton are also produced extensively on these soils. The valley soils in low-rainfall zones are in the desert and semidesert areas. With adequate irrigation, they are valued highly for such crops as alfalfa, cotton, flax, sugar beets, melons, and lettuce. The wind-modified sandy soils of the valleys range from acid to calcareous, depending on rainfall. All of these soils are subject to wind erosion, are low in organic matter, have a low water-holding capacity, and are somewhat deficient in at least one plant nutrient. Properly leveled, fertilized, and irrigated, these soils produce many of the special crops, such as grapes, watermelons, dates, and grapefruit.

The valley basin lands are in the lowest parts of the valleys and are nearly flat and usually poorly drained. The peat and muck soils of the Delta area of California are among them. It is one of our largest bodies of continuous peat soils. It was formed from the decomposition of tule beds and is acid in reaction and low in bases. Most of these soils have been reclaimed and protected from floods and tidal overflows by an extensive series of levees. They are drained by open canals and pumps. Irrigation is necessary because these soils exist in an area of moderate rainfall. Managed properly, they produce great yields of asparagus, celery, onions, potatoes, and sugar beets.

The imperfectly drained valley basin soils of predominantly mineral origin generally are dark-colored clays and have a high water table or are subject to overflow. Under dry-farming condi-

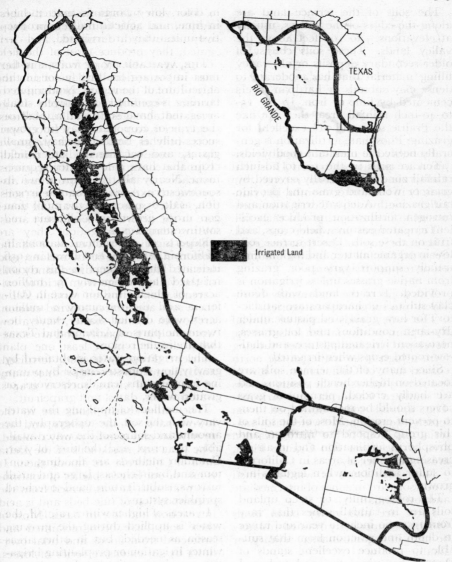

Irrigated Land

tions, these soils are used for wheat, barley, and native pastures. Supplied with adequate irrigation water, they are used extensively for irrigated pasture and rice. They are not adapted to orchard or vineyard culture because of their poor drainage, very fine texture, and susceptibility to frost damage.

The saline, alkali, or saline-alkali soils in the various basins throughout the region generally are unsuitable for cropping until they are reclaimed by leaching if they are saline or by chemical treatment and leaching if they are saline-alkali soils. Partly reclaimed soils produce such salt-tolerant crops as barley, rice, and flax. Completely reclaimed soils produce excellent yields of a wide variety of field, vegetable, and fruit crops.

The soils of the terrace land are along the edges of the valleys, usually at elevations 5 to 100 feet above the valley lands. These soils consist of older secondary deposits or old valley filling material that has moderate to dense clay subsoils or hardpan layers cemented by lime or iron. In the 15- to 40-inch rainfall area, they are like the Prairie soils and are excellent for grazing. Phosphate fertilization is generally needed to maintain good yields.

Terrace soils in the 10- to 20-inch rainfall zone are generally covered by grass or woodland grass and provide fair grazing. Adequate irrigation and nitrogen fertilization produce excellent irrigated pastures, field crops, and fruit on these soils. Desert terrace soils low in organic matter and high in lime usually support very poor grazing from native grasses unless irrigation is provided. Terrace lands with dense clay subsoils or hardpans are satisfactory for hay, grain, and pasture under dry-farm conditions and for grasses, permanent irrigated pasture, and shallow-rooted crops when irrigated.

Since many of the terrace soils are located on higher bench positions and are badly eroded, permanent grass covers should be maintained on them to prevent erosion. Most of the soils of this group respond to nitrogen and phosphorus fertilization and in an increasing number of areas in California to sulfur additions when legumes are grown.

The rolling, hilly, or steep upland soils are in rainfall zones that vary from 10 to 60 inches a year and range in depth and reaction from that suitable to produce excellent stands of Douglas-fir, pine, fir, and redwood (35–60 inches of rainfall, moderately to strongly acid soil, 3 to 6 feet deep, and overlying bedrock) to that suitable only for grazing (10–20 inches of rainfall, slightly acid to neutral in reaction, and of shallow depth).

The unmapped desert soils are in the Mojave and Sonoran Deserts, where annual rainfall seldom exceeds 3 inches. These soils are generally light in color, low in organic matter, high in lime, and agriculturally unproductive unless they are irrigated.

THE AVAILABILITY OF WATER is the most important limiting factor in the agriculture of the region. Nonirrigated farming is confined to relatively small areas that have sufficient rainfall or the type of crop that may be grown successfully is limited to hay, small grains, and occasionally other field crops that have a low water requirement. Nearly all the crops grown in southwestern Arizona require irrigation, as do 85 percent of the more than 200 crops grown in California and southwestern Texas.

Reports of experiment stations in California, Arizona, and Texas in 1956 indicated that farmers in this region irrigated approximately 9 million acres, of which 7 million were in California and the remaining 2 million acres were divided about evenly between the parts of Arizona and Texas that are in the region.

The irrigation water is obtained by gravity flow from streams or by pumping from streams, canals, reservoirs, or ground water.

The methods of applying the water vary with the soil, the topography, the amount and source of the water available, the crop, and the time of year. Common methods are flooding, contour and basin checks, large and small furrows, subirrigation, and overhead sprinkler systems.

In areas of higher winter rainfall, the water is applied during the growing season as needed, but in other areas winter irrigation or preplanting irrigation may be practiced and supplementary water is applied during the growing season.

Since rainfall occurs mainly in winter in most of the region, the streams carry the least water when it is needed most for irrigation. Storage of water for use in summer and fall thus has become necessary. Large irrigation reservoirs and extensive and costly canal systems have been built in many places.

In areas where surface waters cannot be impounded and delivered during seasons of greatest demand, irrigation water is obtained by pumping from underground supplies. As the acreage irrigated from this source expands, however, care must be taken to avoid depletion of underground supplies beyond the average annual natural recharge. Lowered water tables as a consequence of excessive drafts on underground supplies result in increased pumping costs and often produce irrigation water of inferior quality.

The adoption of methods to speed up the recharge of underground water by reducing runoff, increasing infiltration, and by spreading floodwaters over porous bodies of soil is practiced extensively in several areas of the region. Other techniques of water spreading are being investigated.

Because irrigation water of poor quality from pumped and surface sources provide a constant threat to irrigated agriculture in many areas of the Far West, farmers may expend considerable time, energy, and resources combating salinity. On the basis of research conducted by Federal and State scientists, management practices have been developed for correcting or remedying adverse cropping conditions associated with excessive amounts of salt in soil and irrigation water. The practices involve proper land leveling, provision for adequate drainage and leaching of soluble salts if necessary, selection of suitable crops, proper planting and bed shaping techniques, and appropriate application of irrigation water.

There is also a vast drainage and overflow problem. High water tables and spring floods periodically threaten the agricultural use of large areas of fertile valley lands. Extensive drainage projects in many valleys have been developed to lower water tables enough to permit crop growth and reduce the danger of salt accumulation from evaporating ground water. Projects of the Bureau of Reclamation now control spring floods and overflows of major streams that in the past have presented

agriculture with some of its most serious problems. It was estimated that successful completion of irrigation and reclamation projects contemplated in 1957 would add 6 million acres to the 9 million acres of irrigated land.

Evidence is available throughout the region that faulty tillage practices have caused enough deterioration of soil structure to reduce crop yield. Estimates have indicated that in California about 2 million acres of land are affected economically through loss of yield or increased operation expense, and that 2 million acres more are approaching this condition.

Various factors have contributed to the problem of soil structure deterioration, which occurs throughout the region and is not confined to a particular soil class or series—increased specialization in cropping, particularly in cotton, sugar beets, and vegetables; less rotation; heavier machinery and more intensive traffic in fields; reduced supply of organic supplements; and generally accelerated farming operations.

To prepare the seedbed for many irrigated crops, many growers plow, chisel, or subsoil in late fall or early winter or (in the warm interior valleys) in the early spring. The soil is worked several times with such implements as a disk, a landplane, a harrow (spring tooth, spike tooth, or both), a roller, a clod smasher, and a float until the seedbed is finely pulverized and smooth. Most growers also cultivate three times or more during the growing season to control weeds and to reform and reshape irrigation furrows and planting beds.

Experiments at Davis, Calif., indicate that much plowing, chiseling, and subsoiling on deep, well-drained soils is unnecessary if shallow cultivation kills all the weeds. In soils containing hardpans, plowpans, or plowsoles, however, deep tillage or plowing may be necessary. Such layers in the soil interfere with the penetration of irrigation water and restrict root development. When it is necessary to break up such a layer, the work should be done while the soil is relatively dry; otherwise, fracture of the compacted layer does not occur to any great extent, and a deeper plowsole may be produced.

Research at the Arizona Agricultural Experiment Station has produced a soil-preparation program for reducing structural deterioration and improving the production of field and vegetable crops. The program consists of applying irrigation water immediately after plowing and subsoiling or chiseling, without the smoothing or pulverizing operations that usually are done before irrigation. As soon as the surface soil is dry enough after irrigation, a light drag is used to break up the remaining lumps or clods of soil and smooth the surface for planting. This means the soil has been prepared for planting alfalfa or small grains in one operation—rather than several—following irrigation. For row crops such as corn, cotton, and sorghums, a light harrowing after dragging is recommended to facilitate seed placement at the proper planting depth. The cost of seedbed preparation is reduced by this practice, and less structural deterioration occurs.

To prepare a seedbed for vegetables, some modifications in the procedures proposed for field crops are necessary in view of the methods used in planting and irrigating the small vegetable seeds. It is important in producing vegetable crops that the raised seedbeds used in planting be free from irregularities and as level as can be obtained without excessive working of the soil. This prevents the irrigation water from flooding the bed surface, insures more accurate fertilizer placement, and reduces injury to roots by cultivation equipment during the growing season. To accomplish this, it is suggested that after the preplanting irrigation the land be given a single deep disking. This will hasten the drying of the soil in preparation for furrowing or listing, destroy germinating weed seeds, and allow for removal of the border used in preplanting flood irrigation.

When the surface soil has had a chance to become sufficiently dry, it is floated or dragged at an angle different from the angle to be used in planting, furrowed or listed, seeded, and then irrigated for seed germination.

There is a trend away from deep tillage in the management of orchard soils. Heavy disks that penetrate the soil deeply cut too many feeder roots. Disk harrows now have depth-control devices, which permit setting the disk at an appropriate angle to cut all the weeds, yet prevent penetration to a depth of more than 3 or 4 inches.

Tillage in many orchards has been eliminated completely from the soil-management program. Two methods are used: In one, a permanent cover crop is maintained and controlled by periodic beating, shredding, or mowing, and irrigation water is applied by flood irrigation or by sprinklers. In the other, cover crop or weed growth is eliminated, and the soil remains more or less bare at all times. In orchards operated under this system the weeds are destroyed by oil spray or some other suitable herbicide. Irrigation water is applied in permanently established broad furrows or by sprinklers, especially where crop residues, straw, waste from cotton gins, or wood shavings are used as a surface mulch. Many advantages are claimed for the nontillage method of soil management, but the most important is an improvement in soil structure.

MANY TECHNOLOGICAL IMPROVEMENTS have been made in soil- and water-management practices, irrigation and drainage system designs, and in machinery for more economical and effective earth moving, land leveling, and the construction of irrigation and drainage lines.

These advances have brought increased irrigation efficiency, improved or corrected faulty drainage conditions, and increased crop production on many irrigated acres of the Southwest. Better land-leveling practices alone have contributed significantly to the increased efficiency and effectiveness of applications of irrigation water.

Most land preparation for irrigation in the region is done in such a way that slope is practically eliminated. This removes the danger of erosion and permits larger flows of water. The trend toward the use of larger flows and shorter runs makes for higher efficiency and less labor. Long irrigation runs, with small heads of water, lower efficiency, because water penetration into the soil is about proportional to the time the water is in contact with the soil. Leaching losses of water thus occur at the start of the irrigation run, where the water is in contact with the soil for the longest time.

In many areas of the region where water supplies are limited, farmers are installing underground pipes, or gated, aboveground surface pipes and hose in an effort to avoid the losses of water that occur from open irrigation ditches. To reduce losses from open ditches, farmers are urged to destroy the weeds in them or to line the ditches if seepage losses are high. Much water is being saved in Arizona through the extension of concrete ditch lining and the laying of concrete tile. Nearly one-third of the irrigation delivery facilities in Arizona in 1956 were of this type—nearly 3 thousand miles of irrigation line, compared to about 200 miles in 1949.

In the lower Rio Grande Valley, the most concentrated irrigated area of Texas, seriously reduced surface supplies of water originating from the Rio Grande River have forced farmers to develop water supplies from groundwater sources. The amount of land irrigated from these sources increased from 23 thousand acres in 1951 to 160 thousand acres in 1954.

The diversion of rich valley lands to homesites, industry, cities, and superhighways also has had a pronounced effect on irrigation trends in the Southwest. As rising land costs and taxes force farmers to move from the deeper, more level valley soils up on to the coarser, shallower, undulating terrace and foothill soils, land leveling for the usual surface methods of irrigation becomes so difficult and expensive that farmers have had to turn to sprinkler irrigation. Frequent light applications of water by sprinklers on these coarser textured, shallower soils, however, enables the farmer to increase his irrigation efficiency and control erosion more effectively than if he applied the water by conventional surface methods.

Two other developments that have contributed to the improvement of soil use and management in this region pertain to irrigated pastures and fertilization of nonirrigated rangeland.

I mentioned the vast acreage of valley basin and terrace soils in the region. These soils frequently are heavy or shallow and may be underlain by dense clay subsoils or cemented hardpans. Because the irrigated pasture plants that are used generally have a shallow root system, they can produce profitable yields of forage on these soils. Ladino clover is a key factor in the development of the irrigated pasture acreage in California, for it produces abundantly on heavy soils and those underlain by impervious subsoils. Relatively efficient water use is obtained because the fine texture and impervious subsoils reduce water percolation below the root zone of the shallow-rooted plants. The irrigated pasture was estimated in 1957 to be 600 thousand acres, about half of which has been seeded since 1945. An increasing number of farmers are using irrigated pastures in their rotation systems. It has been estimated that more than 8 thousand acres of riceland are rotated with pastures.

A spectacular development in improved land use in the region involves some of the 10 million acres of nonirrigated rangeland that lies above the cultivated valleys in California. Early experiments on range fertilization indicated that pronounced increases in the production of native clovers could be obtained on some range soils by the application of sulfur and phosphate fertilizers. Many areas of range did not respond to this treatment, however, and estimates published in 1950 indicated that only 27 thousand acres of dryland pasture or range in California were fertilized.

Experiments with range fertilization conducted since 1950 revealed why the earlier attempts to improve production on a wider number of range soils failed. The solution to the problem apparently involved larger amounts of fertilizer and the introduction of new species of grasses and clovers that are more responsive to the applied fertilizers than the native range plants. The grasses are Harding, smilo, Veldt, orchard, and tall fescue. The clovers are rose, crimson, and subterranean (or subclover). In the fall of 1953 at the Hopland Range Station of the University of California, the application of 500 pounds of a 16–20–0 fertilizer an acre increased the acre yield of dry matter from 240 pounds on the unfertilized plot to 2,420 pounds on the fertilized plot. Just how many more acres of rangeland will respond thus to treatment is unknown, but estimates by the experimenters indicate that significant increases in forage should be expected on most of the 10 million acres.

As more irrigation water becomes available in California through the development of its water resources program, significant expansion of irrigated pastures and other shallow-rooted field crops on the terrace soils that have been devoted to nonirrigated range can be expected. The effective development and management of these soil resources is of vital importance to California agriculture, for it is one means of replacing the soils lost annually in the valleys to urban and industrial developments.

AMONG ALL THE SOIL MANAGEMENT regions in the United States, probably none is more seriously affected than this one by the pressure of urban development and industrialization.

Out of a total of about 17.5 million acres of tillable land, California has lost more than 2.75 million acres to nonagricultural use, according to a 1956 estimate of the Soil Conservation Service. More than 800 thousand acres of this diversion has taken place since 1942. Average annual figures for 1952–1955 indicate that it is being lost at the rate of 100 thousand acres a year.

California is not the only State in the region that is losing its most productive agricultural lands. A 1956 report of the Arizona Agricultural Experiment Station indicated the Salt River project has lost one-fifth of its acreage to subdivisions or other nonagricultural use. When it was first developed in 1917, this project of 240 thousand acres was the second largest irrigation project in the United States.

As farmers are forced by higher land prices, operating costs, and taxes to move from the more fertile, well-drained valley lands on to the poorer valley basin lands and terraces, they will be confronted with the task of achieving, maintaining, and increasing present levels of production on inherently less productive lands.

Since adequate supplies of irrigation water must be available to the new areas, additional sources of surface and ground water must be developed. Better irrigation methods will have to be used to conserve water and to avoid creating drainage problems from over-irrigation. Valley basin lands currently unproductive because of high water table will have to be drained; those affected by salt and alkali will have to be reclaimed.

Successful management of the terrace lands above the cultivated acreage will require more economical land-leveling techniques, improved irrigation methods, better cropping, and better rotation systems to reduce erosion.

The development of new irrigated acreages in the region to replace those diverted to nonagricultural use will require the adoption of the best soil-management and conservation practices available. To increase production in this area is a challenge for every agricultural scientist and farmer, for present techniques must be improved and new ones developed.

The Pacific Northwest Wheat Region

G. M. Horner, W. A. Starr, and J. K. Patterson

Many variations exist in the amount of rainfall and snowfall, length of growing season, topography, and soils in the Pacific Northwest wheat region. Systems of farming and the problems and production potentials vary accordingly.

The amount of precipitation is the chief factor that divides the region into the annual cropping zone and the summer-fallow zone, which can be divided into the "dry" farm (or low-precipitation) area of 8 to 12 inches of annual precipitation and the area of intermediate precipitation, 12 to 18 inches.

The annual cropping system commonly is used in the zone that receives 18 to about 25 inches of precipitation annually. Thus, in the areas of lower rainfall, crops are grown under a moisture stress; in the 18- to 25-inch belt, the lack of moisture seldom is a major factor in crop growth.

Humid winters and dry summers characterize the region. About 60 percent of the annual precipitation occurs in the five months from November through March. Only 20 to 25 percent of the moisture is received during the active growing season of April, May, and June. July and August are the driest months. Moisture stored in the soil in winter therefore strongly influences crop production.

Relatively low intensities of rainfall permit the infiltration of most of the precipitation into the soil. Total precipitation of 1 inch in 24 hours is unusual. Most of the winter storms at Pullman, Wash., have intensities of less than 0.15 inch an hour. The intensities of storms in late spring and summer are about double the intensities of storms in winter.

The amount of snow is much greater at the higher elevations in the northern sections than in the southern areas, which have low elevations. This variation in snowfall influences runoff and erosion. Runoff may be increased by rapid melting of snow, especially when the soil is frozen. Runoff may be reduced when the precipitation falls as snow instead of rain. A slow rate of melting of the snow allows increased infiltration and reduces runoff.

The topography varies from nearly level to steeply sloping. The more gently sloping land usually is in the low-precipitation zone. The more steeply sloping land is in areas of higher rainfall. Some of the cropland has slopes of 50 percent or more.

The main soils are the Brown soils in the low-precipitation zone and the Chestnut, Chernozem, and Prairie soils in areas of increasing precipitation. These soils vary from rapidly permeable and well drained to slowly permeable and poorly drained. Most of the soils are deep enough to store moisture adequately. Some areas have shallow soils with inadequate storage capacity.

The soils have a very fine sandy or silty texture in the zone of low precipitation. They become finer in texture

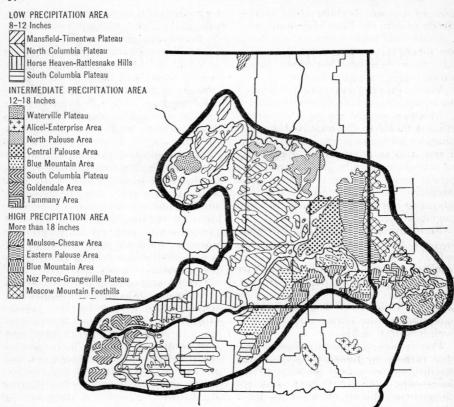

LOW PRECIPITATION AREA
8–12 Inches
Mansfield-Timentwa Plateau
North Columbia Plateau
Horse Heaven-Rattlesnake Hills
South Columbia Plateau

INTERMEDIATE PRECIPITATION AREA
12–18 Inches
Waterville Plateau
Alicel-Enterprise Area
North Palouse Area
Central Palouse Area
Blue Mountain Area
South Columbia Plateau
Goldendale Area
Tammany Area

HIGH PRECIPITATION AREA
More than 18 inches
Moulson-Chesaw Area
Eastern Palouse Area
Blue Mountain Area
Nez Perce-Grangeville Plateau
Moscow Mountain Foothills

in the high-precipitation zone, where most surface soils are silt loams with silty clay loam or clay loam subsoils.

Soil organic matter also varies with the amount of precipitation and ranges from about 1 percent in the dry sections to 4 percent or more in areas of high precipitation.

Winter wheat is the chief crop. Soft white wheats, suitable for pastry flour, comprised about 90 percent of the total wheat production in 1955. The hard red wheats are grown to a limited extent in the low-precipitation areas.

Wheat is practically the only crop grown in places where precipitation is less than 18 inches annually. No satisfactory substitute for wheat has been found in this drier zone. Sod and legume crops are difficult to establish and do not produce well. Wheat is gener-

ally grown in alternate years with summer fallow.

In areas that have more than 18 inches of precipitation, several crops are grown in rotation with wheat—peas, barley, oats, clovers, alfalfa, and grass. The acreage of these crops, in relation to the amount of wheat, increases in the sections of higher rainfall.

One of the more satisfactory rotations includes a sod crop of sweetclover or alfalfa plowed under as a green manure. Other cropping sequences commonly used include wheat-peas and wheat-fallow. The production of clover and grass seeds is important in the Moscow Mountain foothills and Nez Perce-Grangeville Plateau areas.

The crop second in importance is peas. They are grown primarily as dry peas in the eastern Palouse and Moscow Mountain foothills areas and as green peas in the Blue Mountain area.

Cattle and other livestock are raised on many farms, especially those that are near rangeland or grow forage crops in the cropping system.

Wheat production may be limited by moisture or plant nutrients or both.

Moisture nearly always is the determining factor in the zone that gets less than 12 inches of precipitation a year. Even with summer fallow, the supply of moisture usually is too small for wheat yields of more than 30 bushels an acre. Yields sometimes drop to about 10 bushels in years of subnormal precipitation.

Plant nutrients, especially nitrogen, have a more dominant influence on wheat yields in the higher rainfall zones. In these areas where moisture is less frequently a limiting factor, wheat yields average 30 to 40 bushels an acre. Yields of 60 to 65 bushels are common on the better managed and well-fertilized fields.

Production of legume crops is limited oftener by moisture than by the fertility status, except on some of the forest-type soils that have nutrient deficiencies. Yields of dry peas are 1 thousand to 2 thousand pounds an acre. Alfalfa usually produces only one cutting a year unless rainfall is abnormally high in May and June.

THE CHIEF soil-management problems pertain to conservation of moisture, maintenance of fertility and organic matter, control of erosion and weeds, and balancing available nutrients with moisture.

Conservation of moisture is most important in the low-precipitation areas. Loss of moisture by evaporation is large. Water is also lost as runoff some years. The runoff losses are caused primarily by frozen soil and occur oftener in the northern areas (northern Palouse and Waterville areas) when the snow melts.

Deficiency of moisture in some soils, particularly in the southern part of the Columbia Plateau, is caused partly by shallowness to bedrock and the resultant lack of sufficient capacity for moisture storage.

Moisture conservation is a less acute problem in the zone of intermediate rainfall and is of concern only occasionally in the annual cropping area.

Keeping up soil fertility and organic matter, a problem over the entire region, becomes more important as the moisture supply increases. The loss of about one-third of the original soil organic matter has increased the deficiency of available nitrogen in most soils. The available nitrogen released by summer fallow is more likely to be sufficient for maximum yields in the low-precipitation zone. An application of nitrogen fertilizer may result in too much available nitrogen in years of low moisture supply and may cause shriveled kernels and reduced yields.

Balancing the available nitrogen with the moisture supply for the current crop is more difficult in the dry zone than in sections of higher precipitation. Moisture is more likely to be a limiting factor in the drier areas, and the estimate of the amount of precipitation that might be expected during the growing season is a more critical decision. Yields often are improved by the addition of nitrogen, but the risk is greater than in wetter areas.

Most of the deep soils in localities where annual precipitation exceeds 12 to 14 inches do not usually supply enough nitrogen for the maximum production possible with the moisture that is available. Nitrogen fertilizer has been used extensively in recent years to increase yields. Alfalfa and sweetclover are used in the annual cropping area in rotations to improve fertility and maintain organic matter.

Farmers generally recognize the need for balancing the rate of application of nitrogen with the supply of available moisture. Soil analyses that indicate the amount of available nitrogen and moisture supplies help them establish the proper rate of fertilization. Estimates of need for fertilizers are more satisfactorily made on summer-fallowed

Physical Characteristics of Pacific

Subarea	Precipitation (inches)	Land use	Topography	Parent material
Low precipitation area				
Mansfield-Timentwa Plateau	7–10	Wheat-summer fallow, grazing	Glacial till moraine	Gravelly till..
North Columbia Plateau.	8–12	....do.........	Nearly level, gently rolling	Loess, very fine sand to silt
Horse Heaven-Rattle-snake Hills	6–12	....do.........	Gently to moderately sloping	Very fine sand to silt loess
South Columbia Plateau.	8–12	....do.........	Gently sloping to rolling	....do.......
Intermediate precipitation area				
Waterville Plateau......	12–15	Wheat-summer fallow. Some livestock grazing	Undulating to gently rolling	Silty loess.....
Alicel-Enterprise area....	14–16	Wheat-summer fallow, livestock grazing	Gently to strongly rolling	Loess over alluvial matter
North-Palouse area......	13–17	Wheat-summer fallow, grazing	....do........	Loess over calcareous beds
Central Palouse area.....	14–18	Wheat-summer fallow, some livestock grazing	....do........	Deep, silty loess
Blue Mountain area.....	14–18	....do..........	Moderately to strongly rolling	....do.......
South Columbia Plateau.	13–17	Wheat-summer fallow, livestock grazing	....do........	Silty loess.....
Goldendale area........	12–17	Wheat-summer fallow, alfalfa, livestock grazing	Undulating to strongly sloping	Loess and alluvial materials
Tammany area.........	14–17	Wheat-summer fallow, grazing	Undulating to moderately sloping	Loess and alluvium
High precipitation area				
Moulson-Chesaw........	18–23	Wheat-summer fallow, alfalfa, livestock	Undulating to strongly sloping	Fine-textured glacial till
Eastern Palouse area.....	18–22	Annual cropping-wheat, peas, some livestock	Moderately to strongly rolling	Silty loess over older sediments
Blue Mountain area.....	18–25	....do..........	....do........	Silty loess and basalt residuum
Nez-Perce-Grangeville Plateau	18–25	Annual cropping-wheat, peas, alfalfa, livestock	Nearly level, undulating, to strongly rolling	Loess over older fine-textured sediments
Moscow Mountain foot-hills	22–28	Annual cropping-wheat, peas, beans, alfalfa, livestock	Gently to moderately rolling; steeply sloping	Loess over older sediments

Northwest Wheat Farming Region

Depth	Permeability	Internal drainage	Great soil groups	Supplemental information
Shallow over gravel	Rapid to excessive	Excessive....	Regosol to Brown	Numerous glacial erratics; islanded farming
Moderately deep to deep	Rapidly permeable	Well drained.	Brown......	Some caliche pavement as substratum
....do......	...do......	....do......	Sierozem to Brown	Limited regosolic sands, glacial lacustrine silts
....do......	...do......	....do......	....do......	Limited regosolic sands, some caliche
....do......	Moderately permeable	Moderately well drained	Chestnut, Chernozem, Prairie	Unusually advanced soil development for corresponding moisture area
....do......	....do......	....do......	Chestnut to Prairie	Some glacial outwash and fine-textured alluvial materials
....do......	Moderately rapid	....do......	Chestnut to Chernozem	Local outcropping quartz, to substratum caliche
Generally deep	Rapid to moderately rapid	Well to moderately well drained	....do......	Local shallow soils, calcareous substratum, solonetzic "slick" spots, eroded hilltops
....do......	....do......	....do......	....do......	Local shallow soils, calcareous substratum, solonetzic "slick" spots, eroded hilltops and pumice pockets
Moderately shallow to deep	Rapidly permeable	Well drained.	....do......	Frequent shallow soils, substratum variable, gravelly, basalt or older alluvial
Moderately deep to deep	Moderately rapid	Moderately well drained	....do......	Local shallow soils frequent "biscuit" islands of soil in basalt outcrop
....do......	Rapid.......	Well drained.	Chestnut....	Some solonetzic "slick" spots; some irrigation to orchards
Moderately shallow to deep	....do......	....do......	Chernozem..	Some limestone outcroppings; frequent calcareous soils
Generally deep	Moderately rapid	Moderately well drained	Chernozem to Prairie	Frequently eroded hilltops, steep topography, calcareous or dense clay substratum
Moderately shallow to deep	Moderately rapid to moderately slow	Moderately well to poorly drained	Prairie, Planosol, Chernozem	Frequent eroded hilltops, steep topography; small areas of soils residual from basalt
....do......	....do......	....do......	Prairie, Planosol, Brown Podzolic	Some clearing of forest land; some soils residual from basalt
....do......	....do......	....do......	Prairie, Brown Forest, Brown Podzolic	Local soils residual from granite; frequent heavy clay subsoil and substratum

land than on cropped land, because of the greater amounts of available nitrogen and moisture present in the fallowed land.

Fertilization with nitrogen or the use of green manure crops tends to raise the protein content of the wheat. The protein content of soft wheats usually does not exceed the desired optimum of a pastry-type flour when the fertilization rate is not in excess of that required for maximum yields. It is difficult to predict the rate of fertilization required for maximum yield for a particular year. An application of nitrogen that decreases the yield may cause soft wheat to have an excessive protein content. High-protein, soft white wheats are unsatisfactory as bread wheats, and they have little use except as feed.

Several other plant nutrients are deficient in some soils. The deficiencies are most pronounced for legume production on forest soils in the Moscow Mountain foothills and Nez Perce-Grangeville Plateau areas.

The problem also occurs, but to a lesser extent, for other crop and soil conditions in different sections of the region. Sulfur is the most generally deficient of these nutrients. The application of some of the trace elements, including boron and molybdenum, have improved the growth of legumes.

The difficulty encountered in establishing a vigorous legume crop seems to be associated with poor nodulation, but we do not know whether this problem is due to a nutrient deficiency.

The continuing decline in the content of organic matter will reduce the fertility level and impair the physical condition of the soil. The rate of decline in organic matter is greatest with the wheat-fallow cropping system. Organic matter is maintained or increased above the present level by the use of rotations that have a sod crop of sweetclover or alfalfa at least one-fourth of the time. Continuous cropping to wheat with a high rate of nitrogen fertilization also tends to maintain adequate organic matter.

Wind erosion is worst in the low-precipitation zone. Erosion by running water occurs in other sections. Both types of erosion are most severe on intensively tilled land that has inadequate vegetative cover—usually land that has been seeded or is being prepared for seeding to winter wheat.

Soil erosion by water occurs largely between November and April. It generally results from the longer, more intense rains and from snow melting on frozen ground. The high content of moisture in the soil during the winter reduces the rate of infiltration of water and leads to high runoff. Summerfallow land enters the months of high rainfall with considerable moisture, and therefore is subject to greater runoff losses than land on which a crop has withdrawn this excess water.

Intensive tillage of summer fallow is a common practice in the annual cropping zone to eradicate such weeds as Canada thistle, bindweed, and wild oats. Land in the summer-fallow zone is given extra tillage to control cheatgrass, gromwell, and tarweed. This tillage causes greater soil pulverization, loss of the mulch cover, and a wider use of summer fallow—factors that favor soil erosion.

Effective practices to control erosion include stubble mulch, cloddy tillage, crop rotations, contour stripcropping, and cover crops. Stubble mulch and cloddy tillage operations are the most effective for controlling both water and wind erosion on wheatland.

ADOPTION OF CONSERVATION practices has been inadequate in most sections of the region for effective control of erosion and maintenance of soil organic matter. Much of the land is farmed to the wheat-fallow or wheat-peas cropping systems and with tillage operations that pulverize the soil.

Stubble mulch has been used extensively in the sections that are subject to wind erosion. The practice is easier to adopt in this zone because of the low yields of straw. It has not been adopted widely in the areas of higher rainfall because of the problems encountered as the result of the greater quantities of straw produced and more difficult weed control. Stubble mulch reduces wheat yields more in areas of high precipitation.

Rotations that include a sod crop have been adopted (at least partly) by most farmers in the higher rainfall sections of the eastern Palouse and Blue Mountain areas and in the Moscow Mountain foothills and Nez Perce-Grangeville Plateau areas. Conservation rotations have been used very little in the rest of the region.

Utilization of crop residues by various methods has been extensively adopted; many farmers used to burn their straw. The large increase in the use of nitrogen fertilizer, plus the utilization of residues, has increased crop production and strengthened the program to maintain organic matter.

Stripcropping has been adopted to a limited extent, mostly in areas that have gentle slopes.

Scientific findings and experience of farmers have indicated that more effective conservation and efficient crop production can be achieved in the Pacific Northwest wheat region.

Erosion losses can be reduced substantially, where moisture conditions permit, by substituting rotation systems of cropping for summer fallow. Less tillage also would reduce runoff and erosion.

A wider adoption of stubble mulch tillage in areas of higher precipitation would reduce erosion losses sharply. Further improvements in tillage, fertilization, and weed control are necessary in order that the stubble mulching will be more widely accepted, however.

The cropping system should be adapted to the soil and climatic conditions of the particular locality. Fertilization should provide sufficient nutrients, in addition to those furnished by sod crops, to balance the supply of available moisture. With the return of crop residues to the soil, this soil-management system would be expected to maintain an adequate level of organic matter and sustained production.

The Grazing-Irrigated Region

Wynne Thorne

Mountains dominate the grazing-irrigated region of the West. The main spine of the Rockies divides the region somewhat east of center. The Sierra Nevada and the Coastal ranges on the west intercept moisture moving in from the Pacific; less rain falls east of them.

Precipitation is heavier near the western slope of the Rockies and reaches a maximum of 50 inches or more at the highest elevations. Rainfall again tapers off east of the Rockies, but not so much as in Nevada and western Utah.

Great variations sometimes occur within short distances. A small valley near the mountains may be covered with grass and trees, while less than 10 miles away the parched earth and scanty desert shrub vegetation give evidence of a drastically reduced rainfall. Many valleys in the mountains have occasional frosts in every month.

The mountains are less pronounced in Arizona and New Mexico. Desert conditions prevail generally. Rainfall is inadequate for crop production. Summer temperatures are high. Winters are mild. Some farming areas average 250 frost-free days a year.

A Great Plains type of climate prevails east of the Rocky Mountains. Temperatures often change quickly. Fluctuations in precipitation and temperature are greater than in the intermountain area.

The grazing-irrigated region is a land of extremes. People who are accustomed to the natural richness of the prairies and the humid forest lands may be appalled by the apparent aridity of much of this intermountain region when they see it the first time. They may agree with the report of Brigham Young's exploring parties that the only use of the land is to hold the rest of the earth together.

But close study of the agriculture of the region shows that there are essentially no wastelands. There are only different intensities of use. Productive irrigated pastures may graze a cow or more per acre—but in a desert shrub area 75 acres or more may be needed for one cow.

Irrigation is the key to an intensive agriculture in this area. Surplus moisture from the high elevations (principally above 7 thousand feet) is used on lands below. Ground waters are also pumped to supplement the water in streams and reservoirs.

The supply of irrigation water is adequate for only a small part of the land. Lands are chosen for irrigation according to suitability of topography for intensive agriculture, quality of the soil, and nearness to a water supply. Because less than 5 percent of the region is irrigated, the pattern of irrigated land appears on a map as only thin belts or isolated spots in the broad terrain of rangeland.

The intimate association of irrigated lands and rangelands favors livestock farming. The animals graze the range in appropriate seasons, and supplemental feed for them is grown under irrigation. Poultry and dairy industries are confined to irrigated regions and usually are concentrated near cities.

Income from livestock, other than from poultry and dairying, is more than 600 million dollars a year. The agricultural income from dairy products exceeds 100 million dollars and income from poultry is about 60 million dollars a year. Cash crops, another major source of income, bring more than 525 million dollars a year. Fruits, berries, and vegetable crops are major enterprises in some localities. Field crops, including sugar beets, potatoes, dry beans, small grains, corn, and sorghums, are grown extensively. Cotton is important in parts of Arizona, New Mexico, and Texas.

Noted for fruit production are the Yakima and Wenatchee areas of central Washington, parts of the Boise Valley of Idaho, the Flathead Lake region of Montana, the Wasatch Front region of Utah, the Virgin River Valleys of Utah and Nevada, the western slope of Colorado, and some of the irrigated valleys in eastern California.

General farming and cash crops are important in the Columbia Basin of Washington; the Lower Snake River area of Oregon and Idaho; the Upper Snake River Valleys of Idaho; Salt Lake, Utah, and Sevier Valleys of Utah; Yellowstone Valley, Big Horn Valley, and North Platte River areas of Wyoming; the eastern slope of Colorado, including the headwaters of the South Platte River; and the San Luis Valley at the headwaters of the Rio Grande. The lands along the Rio Grande and Pecos Rivers in New Mexico and Texas are irrigated and used for general farming, including cotton in the lower elevations.

Nonirrigated crops are important in scattered areas. Dry beans are grown in summer-rainfall areas of central New Mexico, southwestern Colorado, and southeastern Utah. Dryland wheat is important near the Palouse area, in south-central and southeastern Idaho, and in northern Utah. Alfalfa, barley, and wheatgrasses are also important. Native vegetation and soil charac-

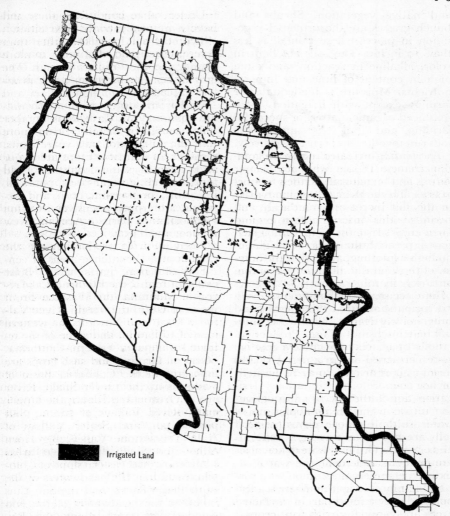

Irrigated Land

teristics are closely associated with climate. Short grasses are the dominant
native vegetation east of the Rocky
Mountains. Trees, grass, and shrubs
appear in the mountains according to
moisture, temperature, and soil conditions. Desert shrubs and the bunch
grasses are dominant west and south of
the Rockies. Sagebrush, rabbitbrush,
greasewood, creosote bush, shadscale,
and other shrub and browse plants predominate according to environmental
conditions. Native plants remain on
more than 90 percent of the land, and

their character and density are major
factors in determining the numbers of
livestock that can be grazed.

Almost every major great soil group
in the United States exists in this region. Soils typical of humid areas and
forests occur principally in the high
mountain areas and are not farmed,
except in northern Idaho and Washington. The principal cultivated soils
are those representative of arid zones.

Arid-region soils are generally low
in organic matter and nitrogen; the
amounts reflect somewhat the climate

and native vegetation. Shrubs and
bunch grasses are the principal vegetation in places where rainfall is less
than 10 inches. The soils are light in
color, alkaline in reaction, and often
high in content of lime and mineral
nutrients. Moisture is inadequate for
farming except with irrigation. Such
soils need organic matter for successful
farming, and until it is supplied the
soils run together and crust excessively.

As rainfall increases, native vegetation changes to sagebrush and larger
shrubs and bunch grasses, then to short
grasses. The content of organic matter
in the soil increases accordingly and
permits wider varieties of farming and
farm crops. In most of the unforested
parts, precipitation has been inadequate for leaching, and the soils therefore are generally alkaline in reaction
and rich in mineral nutrients. Zones
of lime accumulation are typical. They
are near the surface in the deserts and
progressively deeper in the higher rainfall belts.

Soils of all climatic and vegetative
zones are used for grazing. Dryland
farming is restricted to areas with 10
inches or more of precipitation. Irrigation agriculture occurs throughout
the region wherever combinations of
water, suitable topography, and good
soils are available. Nitrogen deficiencies are general. Phosphate deficiencies
are frequent. Iron deficiency, or lime-
induced chlorosis, is common with susceptible plants. Zinc, manganese, and
boron deficiencies occur in restricted
areas and especially with fruit crops.

Soil erosion is a problem in all arid
regions. Wind erosion occurs particularly in freshly cultivated Desert and
Brown soils. Water erosion increases
with rainfall. The limited rain in desert
sections may come in downpours.

SALINE AND ALKALI soils are widely
distributed throughout the region. Although the total acreage is large, these
salt-affected soils are so closely associated with other soils that only limited,
distinctive management practices are
used for them.

Under range conditions, these soils
have a naturally adapted vegetation.
Where the salt or alkali situation is
severe, usually no attempt is made to
change the vegetation, although overgrazing may drive out many desirable
forage plants.

Under irrigated conditions, the first
attempt is toward reclaiming these
soils, usually by installing drains and
leaching to remove salts. Alkali often
requires an additional treatment with
such amendments as gypsum or sulfur. Often reclamation is economically
infeasible, or poor-quality water per-
petuates the problem. Then salt- and
alkali-tolerant plants are selected, and
management practices to reduce salt
accumulation in the crop root zone
are adopted.

Soils that have developed under forests occur in the northern part of the
region and in scattered locations in the
mountains. The rainfall is generally
more than 20 inches where these soils
exist. Cultivation of these soils is confined principally to the northern zone.
Some of the soils are acid and need
lime treatment for alfalfa and other
acid-sensitive crops. Drainage is often
needed. Nutrient deficiencies commonly
encountered include nitrogen, phosphorus, potassium, boron, and sulfur.
A wide variety of crops is grown, and
although rainfall may reach 50 inches,
summer droughts are common. Supplemental irrigation is practiced close
to natural water sources.

It would seem that the grazing-irrigated region could be divided easily
into subregions with similar agricultural practices and products. But the
dominating influence of mountains
scatters areas of similar soil and climate. We can speak of types of farming
and cropping systems, but the areas involved may be distributed from Washington to New Mexico. For convenience, then, soil-management practices
are here discussed according to types of
farming that occur.

DRYLAND FARMING is crop production
without irrigation where annual pre-

cipitation is less than 20 inches. Areas of dryland farming occur in all States of the region, but notably in Washington, Oregon, Idaho, Montana, and Utah.

Winter wheat is the principal crop grown without irrigation where precipitation is less than 15 inches. Spring wheat is grown in limited areas in the region and in most areas in years of severe winter killing. Dry beans are grown in central New Mexico, southwestern Colorado, and southeastern Utah where there is a pattern of summer rainfall.

The yields of all dryland crops are broadly dependent on precipitation, but soil-management practices also influence available moisture, soil erosion, and nutrient supply.

The variety of possible crops increases as the moisture supply exceeds 15 inches a year. Alfalfa for seed is grown in the more favorable soils and moisture sites. Barley production has increased, primarily because of Federal limitations on wheat. Some grass seed is grown, particularly crested wheatgrass in the lower moisture areas, and intermediate, stiff hair, and tall wheatgrass as moisture exceeds 12 inches.

The fallow system of farming is recorded in the Bible. Modern power machinery has advanced it to almost an art. Each year the land in fallow in this region exceeds 2 million acres. The practice of alternating wheat and fallow assumes that by clean cultivation much of the moisture coming during the fallow period is stored for use during the crop year. Available soil nitrogen increases and weeds are controlled during fallow.

Fallow leaves the soil exposed and susceptible to erosion by wind and water. Many fallowed soils crust or develop compacted zones, which take in water so slowly that runoff and erosion are excessive.

New types and procedures of tillage aid in control of erosion and improve water intake. The moldboard and disk plows are being replaced with chisels, sweeps, and other implements, which open and loosen the soil while leaving most of the straw on the surface.

This stubble mulch or trashy fallow system works well in areas of limited rainfall where the amount of straw produced does not interfere with tillage. Tillage implements have been adapted to cover some of the straw when there is too much of it.

Tillage on the contour helps prevent runoff on the steeper slopes. Some broad-base terraces have been used in the region, but the practice is not popular. Steeper slopes and waterways are planted to permanent cover.

Tillage operations may cause compacted zones at a depth of 5 to 8 inches, or just below the usual plow depths. The zones can be controlled by growing alfalfa at moderate intervals. The most usual control measure, though, is fall tillage of stubble land with chisels or sweeps set to a depth just below the compacted zone. The effectiveness of this deeper tillage on compacted soils is evident in reduced runoff and deeper penetration of moisture.

Timing of operations is an important byproduct of power machinery. The soil can be broken in the fall or early spring before weeds or volunteer grain deplete moisture. Fallow operations with a rod weeder or other equipment can keep weeds under control, and planting can be timed in the short period in fall or spring when temperature and moisture are favorable.

Applications of nitrogen fertilizer have zoomed upward on dryland wheat since 1945. Recommended applications for wheat after fallow in Washington are 20 pounds of nitrogen in places that have less than 13 inches of rain, 30 pounds of nitrogen with 13–17 inches of rain, and 50 to 60 pounds of nitrogen for annual cropping in the higher rainfall belts. Recommendations are similar in Oregon and northern Idaho.

A standard treatment of 30 to 40 pounds of nitrogen is recommended in southern Idaho and northern Utah for areas of good soil that get 13 inches or more of precipitation. Sections that have an average annual precipitation of less than 12 inches do not respond consistently to nitrogen, and treatments are suggested only for years when the moisture outlook is favorable.

Fall and spring applications have given somewhat equal results if the spring treatments are made before very much growth occurs.

The Washington Agricultural Experiment Station recommends band placement under stubble mulch, but results in Idaho and Utah have not shown any consistent difference between banding and broadcast applications.

No consistent differences have been found among various nitrogen fertilizers when applied in the same manner and at equivalent rates of elemental nitrogen. When it is applied in the fall, nitrate nitrogen tends to leach deeper than ammonia. Somewhat better increases in yields have been obtained in Utah from broadcast spring applications of nitrate carriers than from ammonia carriers. This has been attributed to quicker movement of the nitrate into the soil under these conditions of limited rainfall. In places where leaching is a problem, ammonia-type fertilizers are recommended for fall treatments, and application is delayed until soil temperatures fall to about 50° F.

The various wheatgrasses and mixtures of wheatgrasses and alfalfa are planted on abandoned and retired dryland wheat areas and on steeper slopes for forage and for soil protection. A firm, clean seedbed is recommended. Planting the grasses in early fall or early spring in northern areas and late fall in southern areas is suggested. Alfalfa should be planted in early spring or during periods of heavy rainfall. Complete protection from grazing is usually needed for 2 years.

Alfalfa grown for seed on drylands should be planted in rows, usually 24 to 36 inches apart. Cultivation between the rows is practiced the first year to control weeds. Planting for seed production is not usually recommended when precipitation is less than 15 inches.

Alfalfa is grown for forage in some of the more favorable sites. Alfalfa improves the structure and the content of organic matter and nitrogen of the soils. A minimum of 5 years in alfalfa is required to impart maximum benefits to the soil.

Legumes in rotation tend to increase wheat yields in areas that have 16–18 inches or more of rain. At lower moisture levels, moisture depletion by the legumes offsets the benefits from nitrogen and organic matter residues. Peas and clover failed to benefit wheat yields when planted in alternate years on a deep loam soil from 1916 to 1952 at the Nephi Dryland Experiment Farm in central Utah, where the average rainfall is 12 inches. After the termination of the experiment and with wheat alternating with fallow, however, the residual benefit from the legumes was reflected in increases of 5 and 6 bushels of wheat the acre.

GENERAL IRRIGATED FARMS of the region include a variety of enterprises. Some livestock and cash crops usually are included, but the major source of income is not any single enterprise. These farms are widely scattered. There are many of them in the Columbia Basin of Washington and Oregon; along the Snake River; in the Great Basin; along the Rio Grande, Pecos, and Arkansas Rivers, and at the eastern front of the Rockies in Colorado and Wyoming.

The irrigation water comes primarily from rivers or mountain streams. Some water is pumped from underground supplies. Most of the water is of good quality. Low-quality water is encountered oftenest where drainage water and other return flows to stream beds are used a second or third time for irrigation.

General irrigated farms occur on a wide variety of soils and in a range of climates, but mostly they are below elevations of 5 thousand feet, where the growing season is long enough.

Many problems affecting soil management occur—small size of farms, poor rotations, salt and alkali in soils, poor drainage, irregular topography, inadequate supplies of irrigation water, weeds, low fertility, and erosion.

Several significant trends in improvement of general irrigated farms have taken place since 1945. Financial assistance from the Federal Government has helped improve land and distribution systems for irrigation water. The technical assistance for these programs is centered with the Soil Conservation Service, but it is also carried out by other Federal and State agencies. The technical assistance to farmers consists of making farm plans with changes in field layouts, irrigation systems, cropping systems, fertility practices, and general farm improvement and making the necessary surveys and plans.

Land leveling has become the most popular and extensive of these farm improvement programs. More than half the money paid for assistance to farmers by the Agricultural Stabilization and Conservation Committee in Utah in 1955 was for land leveling. With agronomic and engineering assistance, land is surveyed and the surface is reshaped to uniform slopes through the use of heavy power equipment, including carryalls and landplanes. The leveling reduces labor of irrigation and makes possible a more uniform distribution of water.

Leveled land must be handled with care. Poor plowing, failure to use a farm level, and erosion or deposition of soil by careless irrigation may destroy a leveling job in a few years.

Irrigation distribution systems have been improved. Often open ditches are replaced with underground pipe with risers at appropriate locations. Farm ditches are being stabilized to reduce erosion and increase the efficiency of irrigation.

Overnight storage reservoirs make possible a better job of irrigation, and are helpful also when the irrigation stream is too small for effective use. The reservoirs, which commonly hold 2 to 20 acre-feet of water, are at a high elevation near the cropland to permit use of the water on as much of a farm as possible.

Another important trend has been toward larger farm units. Modern machinery and farm practices have greatly increased the amount of land one man can operate, but only with increased employment opportunities since 1945 has there been a reduction in number of small farms. The large number of small farms is still a deterrent to many desirable practices, including crop rotations that improve soil and adequate measures to control weeds.

Crop rotations are less standardized on general irrigated farms than on most other farms. Because much of the income is from cash crops, there is a tendency to watch markets carefully and to plant crops that hold promise of largest income. Labor supply, the yearly outlook for water, and many less tangible factors also lead to major shifts in cropping.

Although there is an aspect of opportunism in crop selection, a basic element of crop rotation is usually followed. Alfalfa is the heart of the rotation on most general irrigated farms of the region. It serves the multiple purposes of being the major feed for livestock, aiding in weed control, building up organic matter and nitrogen in soil, improving the physical properties of soil, and aiding in controlling soil-borne insects and diseases.

Alfalfa is often planted with a nurse crop such as a small grain or peas, which are seeded at about half the usual rate. The successful use of nurse crops requires that irrigation practices favor the alfalfa rather than the nurse crop and that irrigation be continued after the nurse crop is harvested. Alfalfa is cut for hay 2 years or more, depending on the need for hay and prospects for cash crops.

Alfalfa is followed in rotations by a variety of crops, preferably crops that can take advantage of the nitrogen left by alfalfa and that can be managed without interference from alfalfa root residues. Potatoes and field corn or sweet corn are grown extensively following alfalfa. Other commonly used crops are beans, sorghums, cotton, and sugar beets.

Various crops are planted the second year following alfalfa—almost any of the vegetable crops, sugar beets, and the small grains. Land often is kept in row crops more than 2 years following alfalfa. In such long rotations, the row crops not immediately following a legume should be fertilized liberally. Usually a close-grown crop, such as peas or a small grain or clover, is alternated with row crops.

Fertilizer practices differ greatly. Phosphate usually is applied to land planted to alfalfa and such cash crops as sugar beets, cotton, potatoes, and vegetables. Corn and small grains seldom respond to phosphate treatments on well-managed irrigated farms.

Nitrogen fertilizers are commonly reserved for row crops planted the second year or later after alfalfa. Corn and sugar beets, however, usually need more nitrogen than is supplied through the rotation or farm manure.

Recommended fertilizer treatments include 80 to 120 pounds of available phosphate as superphosphate an acre at the time of planting alfalfa or clovers. Sugar beets should receive 40 to 120 pounds of nitrogen an acre (according to soil fertility), and phosphate and potash fertilizer as need is indicated by soil tests.

In Idaho, 80 pounds of nitrogen and 40 pounds of available phosphate are recommended for potatoes following a row crop, with 20 pounds less nitrogen following alfalfa.

Corn needs liberal treatments with nitrogen and irrigation water. Applications of 80 to 160 pounds of nitrogen an acre are recommended. Experiments in Arizona indicate that 100 pounds of nitrogen and 50 pounds of available phosphate are desirable for irrigated cotton.

Rotation pastures need highly fertile soils. A common fertility treatment is 80 to 120 pounds of available phosphate every third year and 10 to 15 tons of manure every second year. Irrigation is needed to meet the needs of drought-sensitive plants in the mix such as Ladino clover.

The moldboard plow is usually recommended for irrigation farms. Heavier textured soils should be fall plowed. Spring operations include a minimum of once over with a farm level and harrowing.

Alfalfa, small grains, and other close-planted crops are irrigated between borders by flooding from ditches. Row crops generally are irrigated by furrows. Subirrigation is practiced in limited areas where soil conditions permit. Sprinkler irrigation has been increasing rapidly, particularly in places where topography is unfavorable for surface applications.

All crops should be adequately supplied with water throughout the growing season. No advantage is gained from allowing crops to wilt or show distress from lack of water. Frequently such distress significantly reduces yields.

DAIRY FARMS numbered more than 17 thousand in this region in 1950. Almost half of them were in southern Idaho and central and northern Utah. Nearly all dairy farms are irrigated.

Their size varies, but in 1957 at least 20 cows were needed for a successful full-time operation. Assuming a minimum of 2.5 acres for each cow and her calves on the higher producing farms, a minimum size for a dairy-farm unit which produces most of its own feed would be about 50 acres. Usually dairy farms are much larger, and often more than 2.5 acres are required for a cow.

Each cow with calves might be expected to require about 0.4 acre for grain, 1.2 acres for hay, 1 acre for pasture, and 0.4 acre for silage. This might serve as a rough guide to rotations for a dairy farm. In most instances, however, a dairy farm produces some cash crops, and frequently part of the feed is purchased.

A dairy farm growing sugar beets

as a cash crop (which will also furnish beet tops and beet pulp for feed) would possibly be divided into 10 fields. A rotation of barley (nurse crop for alfalfa), alfalfa, alfalfa, alfalfa, alfalfa, corn (for silage), and sugar beets would occupy 7 fields. A rotation pasture would occupy three fields. Every 2 or 3 years a field would be plowed from pasture. The year preceding this, a field most recently used for sugar beets would be planted to pasture with a barley nurse crop. In order to make up for the overlapping, one year could be cut from alfalfa each year a pasture is planted.

This represents only one type of rotation adapted to a dairy farm in this area. Milo might be substituted for corn and cotton for sugar beets in the Southwest. Potatoes, tomatoes, beans, sweet corn, or some other crop could be used in place of sugar beets in other areas. The second row crop could be omitted on farms where dairying is the only interest, and the required number of fields could be reduced proportionately. The dairy enterprise does permit a standardized rotation with freedom for changes in the cash crop.

Dairy farms frequently have permanent pastures in poorly drained fields or on soils not suited to other crops. Such pastures are seldom adequate for high-producing cows but can be used for calves and dry stock.

In view of the need for a regular rotation of pastures and crops in sequence, a dairy farm should be carefully selected and planned. The soil should be deep and well drained. A finer textured soil can be used successfully here, though, than can be used on most general irrigated farms. The topography should be uniform and nearly flat to gently sloping. There should be an irrigation stream of two or more cubic feet per second so that pastures can be irrigated rapidly and uniformly. Many undesirable variations from this ideal occur, and allowance must be made for them in management practices.

A dairy enterprise usually creates a favorable soil fertility situation. Alfalfa and rotation pastures add organic matter and nitrogen to the soil. The manure from the animals furnishes added nutrients and is usually distributed on pastures and on land to be planted to row crops.

Phosphate is the principal commercial fertilizer used on dairy farms in most of this region. It is usually added to soil preceding the planting of alfalfa and pasture. If, as in the example, pasture is left in 6 years or more, supplemental phosphate is usually broadcast on the surface of the pastures every second or third year.

The phosphate added should provide 30 to 50 pounds of available phosphoric acid per acre per year, depending somewhat on the length of growing season and soil conditions. Farm manure treatments provide about 5 pounds of phosphate per ton and so may furnish an important part of the total needed throughout a rotation cycle.

Other plant nutrients may be needed under restricted conditions. Potash is usually needed in the northern cutover timberlands of Idaho, Washington, and Montana. Sulfur, boron, and lime often are needed in that area. Potassium may also be needed in spots throughout the entire region, but field tests by the various State agricultural experiment stations have shown only infrequently any response to potash fertilizers in other than forest soil areas. Some nitrogen fertilizers may be needed on row crops.

LIVESTOCK RANCHES involve the closest integration of the varied agricultural aspects of the region. Sheep or cattle graze the rangelands that lack water or are unsuited for crop production. Cropland is usually associated with these range operations to produce hay and other feeds to supplement the range feed. The amount of crops fed varies greatly with location and type of ranch.

Usually the sheep ranch has a summer and winter range, and supplemental feeding occurs principally during the lambing period and during exceptional winter weather when snow is too deep for range feeding.

The cattle ranch commonly involves more supplemental feeding than the sheep ranch. Often only a summer range is available for cattle in the northern half of the region. In practically the entire region the finishing of beef animals for the market must be done by dry-lot feeding, although many grass-fattened animals are sold for the market or for feeders.

High, short-season valleys in the mountain area are adapted principally to livestock production. The short season and occasional frosts almost every month during the summer limit the kinds of crops and the yields obtained. Agriculture is on an extensive, rather than an intensive, scale. Pasturelands usually are considered permanent pasture, and the cropland is planted to hay and grain. Often the principal hay crop is grass meadow, which is cut in August for hay and grazed during the fall. Alfalfa, when it is grown, is left in as long as possible. Small grains (usually barley) are grown only for a year or two while the land is being prepared to go back into alfalfa.

The alfalfa-small grain system presents no special soil-management problems not already discussed. In many instances, however, the climate, soil, and water would permit greater feed production if corn or sorghum followed the plowing out of alfalfa. Also, the alfalfa too often is inadequately fertilized or left in after the stands have become thin.

Many of the permanent pastures are on poorly drained land or land flooded for excessive periods. Such pastures in the higher altitudes are known as mountain meadows.

Mountain meadows occur in many mountain valleys where early spring runoff and streams of water are diverted over meadowland and allowed to run over the land almost continuously until the size of stream is inadequate to cover the area or until the meadow approaches the harvest stage.

Several million acres of such mountain meadowlands exist in the region.

The length and depth of continuous flooding determine the types of vegetation present. If flooding is for only 2 or 3 weeks during early spring runoff, many common grasses and legumes, such as bluegrass and whiteclover, are present. Areas flooded for long periods with shallow depths of water, usually less than 6 inches, develop mixtures of rushes, sedges, and grass. Many of these species are low in digestible nutrients and protein. When floods last long at depths greater than 6 inches, rushes and wiregrass tend to predominate, and the feed value is low.

Intermittent irrigation instead of continuous flooding does not increase the yield or quality of forage unless plant species are also changed.

Fertilizers applied to the mountain meadows increase yields, but often the increases are not profitable. The largest responses have been to nitrogen fertilizers. Phosphate fertilizers have not been beneficial except in places where clovers were present.

Extensive experiments in Colorado since 1950 have indicated that best results are had by a complete change in management, including plowing up the native sod, reseeding with improved mixtures, fertilizing, shifting to intermittent irrigation, and cutting at earlier stages of plant development. The rewards from these changes included higher yields and greater feed value of the hay produced.

In terms of pounds of beef produced per acre, continuously irrigated, unfertilized, late-cut hay near Gunnison, Colo., in 1951 produced 200 pounds. Fertilized, intermittently irrigated, early-cut, reseeded meadows produced about 800 pounds.

How to eradicate native sods is probably the biggest problem in reseeding old meadows. The sod is so tough that special equipment and a year or more are needed to break it down to a suitable seedbed.

Reseeding mixtures are varied according to soil, moisture, and climatic conditions. Grass species commonly used are mountain brome, smooth brome, orchard, tall fescue, and reed canary. Legumes include Ladino clover, whiteclover, alfalfa, alsike clover, and strawberry clover.

Much of the rangeland is federally owned and managed by Federal agencies, such as the Bureau of Land Management and the Forest Service. Privately owned range commonly represents better sites than does the public domain.

The most widely adopted practices for soil conservation and range improvement are grazing control, with a general trend to reduced numbers of livestock and better timing of grazing to protect desirable plants; developing sources of drinking water to promote more uniform grazing of the entire range; trucking sheep between ranges, rather than trailing them; and range reseeding.

Eradicating old brush stands, preparing a favorable seedbed, controlling depth of planting, timing planting operations, and protecting new seedlings until established are essential steps in range reseeding. Crested wheatgrass is the most extensively planted grass for reseeding ranges. It is also one of the most drought tolerant. Other grasses include intermediate, pubescent, and tall wheatgrasses, Russian wildrye, and Indian ricegrass. Common rye often is planted on favorable sites for temporary spring or fall grazing.

FRUIT is produced throughout the region, but commercial production is limited to a few somewhat isolated but important locations. Large volumes of apples, peaches, pears, apricots, and cherries are produced. Berries are grown extensively.

Essentially all fruit is produced under irrigation, which means water-holding capacity of the soil is less critical than in humid, nonirrigated regions. Orchard soils must be deep, permeable, well drained, and free of excess salt and alkali. Loam soils are most desirable, but orchard production is successful on sandy and gravelly soils and on many clay soils that are granulated and permeable.

Variations in rootstalks modify soil adaptations, but in general pears, plums, and apples seem adapted to soils of finer texture than peaches, cherries, or apricots. Grapes root deeply and have requirements similar to fruit trees. Berry crops are adapted to most areas where tree fruits grow.

Chlorosis is a problem in irrigated areas, and sites conducive to it should be avoided. No completely reliable criteria for identifying chlorotic areas are now available. In general, however, soils high in lime and particularly those which have a marly accumulation within 3 feet of the surface, combined with a fine texture and compact structure, should not be used for extensive fruit plantings unless preliminary trials indicate that chlorosis is not a problem.

Most fruit and berry crops are highly sensitive to salt and should not be planted on the saline or alkali soils. Peaches, apricots, and cherries seem especially sensitive to chlorides. After grapes have been established, they seem to tolerate moderate quantities of salt. Irrigation water should be low in salt and sodium.

The biggest limiting factor in commercial fruit production is climate. Air drainage is important. Good air drainage is favored by moderate, continuous slopes more than by short, steep ones. Air drainage inverts the usual altitude relations in which there is an average decrease of about 1° F. for every 300 feet of increase in altitude.

Other climatic factors, such as wind and hailstorms, may vary considerably between different sites in the same locality. Sites near the mouths of canyons may have sufficient wind to damage fruit. Windbreaks are helpful in those areas, but they should not be too close to the trees lest frost damage be increased on the leeward side.

The trend is toward planting fruit crops on land too steep for most other tilled crops. Orchards or vineyards to be planted on steep slopes and irrigated in furrows must be laid out with the rows on contour grades generally not exceeding 2 percent. This requires careful planning and often some preliminary smoothing of the soil surface to avoid extreme fluctuations in row width. Because of these difficulties and the problem of wetting any large proportion of the soil surface from furrows, sprinkler irrigation is being adopted for most areas of steep slopes.

Clean cultivation was formerly the common orchard practice. Recommendations now are for green manure crops or controlled weed growth to protect the soil and to build up the organic matter.

Tillage operations in orchards should be reduced to a minimum necessary to prepare land for irrigation and to plant and control cover crops and weeds at strategic intervals. Implements that penetrate the soil more than 4 or 5 inches may greatly injure tree roots.

Oil sprays to control interplanted vegetation in orchards have become common. They largely eliminate soil cultivation, especially in orchards irrigated by sprinkling. Oil sprays kill the vegetation and leave it as a mulch on the soil surface; the mulch aids soil granulation and encourages feeder roots near the soil surface. Reduced tillage may reduce soil compaction.

To wet the soil as uniformly as possible, irrigation furrows in orchards should be broad, shallow, and spaced at about 3-foot intervals between the tree rows. Border and basin systems often are used where the land is nearly level or has a uniform slope. Overhead sprinkling is used widely, and the practice is increasing. Special nozzles that throw the water out below the branches are used.

While trees draw water from soil depths of 5 feet or more, most feeder roots are in the upper 2 feet, and this zone should not be permitted to dry out between irrigations.

Organic matter is maintained in orchards through applications of farm manure and green manure. Rye, vetch, and sweetclover have been used extensively. Objections to sweetclover are its excessive growth and the fact that its demand for plant nutrients and soil moisture coincides with the peak demands of trees. Winter vetch and Austrian winter peas avoid competition with trees and give a good supply of organic matter by late spring or summer.

Alfalfa is used extensively for soil cover in apple and pear orchards. For peaches, apricots, and cherries grown on moderately coarse-textured soils, alfalfa furnishes undesirable competition for water and nutrients. Unless it is properly managed, alfalfa may encourage harmful insects, such as the tree leafhopper. Alfalfa is particularly helpful in orchards where chlorosis is a problem. Where alfalfa is grown, the top growth should be left in the orchard and worked into the soil, rather than harvested for hay.

Rye, mustard, and other nonlegumes need supplemental nitrogen for growth and decomposition. In central Washington, 200 pounds of ammonium sulfate an acre is recommended just before rye is planted.

For berries and grapes, it is usually not feasible to grow interplanted crops to maintain or build up organic supply. For these crops, soil organic matter should be built to a maximum before plantings are made. Supplemental additions can be made during the growth period as manure or mulches.

Irrigated fruit crops in the region have shown deficiencies of many elements. Nitrogen deficiencies are general. Phosphate deficiencies are not common, but some phosphate is widely used as an aid to cover and green manure crops between trees. Potassium is usually adequate although some growers believe potash improves quality.

Other elements frequently deficient are iron, zinc, manganese, and boron.

Nitrogen deficiencies are typified by light-green color in leaves and reduced growth and vigor of plants. There is no one rule to determine application rates of nitrogen fertilizers. A common plan is to add sufficient nitrogen to give the desired average length of annual terminal growth. A 12-inch growth is considered desirable for bearing peach trees in Washington. Optimum annual growths for many apple varieties have been suggested in some areas. A second plan is to add as much nitrogen as possible without seriously reducing fruit color or quality.

The preferred time for nitrogen applications varies with areas and types of fruit. Early spring or fall applications are generally favored for deciduous fruits. Late-summer treatments delay ripening and may increase frost damage by encouraging late growth. Actual annual treatments are 60 to 120 pounds of fertilizer nitrogen an acre. Most mixed fertilizers for established fruits contain about twice as much nitrogen as phosphate.

VEGETABLE CROPS are grown throughout the region, but extensive commercial production is limited to population centers and areas with moderate to long growing seasons. Vegetable crops generally are expensive to produce and market.

Deep, well-drained, sandy soils are preferred for winter and early planted vegetable crops. Medium-textured soils, mucks, and even light clays often are used for warm-season crops. Soils that are difficult to cultivate should be avoided because land planted to vegetable crops must be frequently worked.

A few vegetable crops, such as table beets, kale, and asparagus, produce well in rather saline soils. In general, though, saline soils are not adapted to large yields of high-quality produce.

Topography also is a major consideration. Many vegetables need careful control of soil moisture. Labor costs for irrigation often are high. The land should be nearly level or of a moderate, even grade to permit uniform wetting.

Many vegetables have small seeds and need a clean, firm, moist seedbed. Good, uniform stands must be obtained to maintain essential quality and yield. Crooked, uneven rows and rough land interfere with cultivation.

In areas with severe winters, clay loams and clay soils should be fall plowed if early vegetables are to be planted in the spring. The yield and quality of peas, lettuce, and other crops are greatly reduced when planted so late that growth must extend into hot weather.

Vegetable crops differ appreciably in rooting depth and irrigation requirements. Because different crops have different irrigation requirements, water should be available on demand.

Many vegetable crops remove large amounts of plant nutrients from the soil, so that liberal fertilization is necessary. Farm manure is customarily applied to vegetables if it is available. The most usual ratio of fertilizer for vegetables in this region is 1-1-0 or 2-1-0. Potassium is added more often to vegetable soils than for other crops. Tomatoes often crowd the growing season, and nitrogen is used conservatively to limit prolonged vegetative growth and delayed ripening of the fruit. The most usual fertilizer for tomatoes has a 1-2-0 ratio; if they are planted following alfalfa, no nitrogen is used.

SOIL-MANAGEMENT RESEARCH in the grazing-irrigated region since 1945 has emphasized the advantages of combining desirable practices. Improper tillage operations that cause soil compaction may nullify improved fertilizer and irrigation practices.

H. B. Peterson and J. C. Ballard reported studies with combinations of irrigation water and nitrogen fertilizer needed for maximum yields of sweet corn in northern Utah.

Without nitrogen fertilizer, there was little response to increased frequency of irrigation. With nitrogen fertilizer, but with no change in irrigation, yields increased only moderately. But when the nitrogen fertilizer treatment was increased to 200 pounds of elemental nitrogen to the acre and a continuous supply of moisture was maintained in the root zone, the yield increased nearly 300 percent.

The Northern Great Plains

E. B. Norum, B. A. Krantz, and H. J. Haas

The most compelling fact of agriculture in the cool, temperate Northern Great Plains is the irregular and generally deficient rainfall. The climate, topography, soil, and native vegetation together encourage an agriculture broadly devoted to the production of spring wheat and range livestock.

The climate of the easternmost part has been termed "dry-subhumid."

The drier central and western part may be characterized as semiarid.

The annual precipitation averages slightly more than 20 inches along the eastern border. It averages about 12 inches in north-central Montana, about 15 inches in southeastern Wyoming, and 15 to 22 inches in the Nebraska Sandhills. About three-fourths of the annual precipitation comes in the 6 months from April through September. Nearly half comes in May, June, and July.

In the more humid eastern section and in irrigated areas elsewhere, a greater diversity of crops is grown than in the less favored areas. Alfalfa, sugar beets, potatoes, flax, and corn are produced there. Moisture for crops becomes progressively more limiting to the westward, the variety of crops and the proportion of the land given to crop production are correspondingly less, and the proportion of land devoted to grassland for hay and grazing increases.

Broad zones of soils correspond to broad differences in climate and vegetation. The Chernozem, Chestnut, and Brown soil zones are alined in a generally north and south direction corresponding to climatic belts. The Chernozem soils, largely devoted to crops, occupy the most humid part. They have thick, black surface horizons and a large amount of organic matter. The Brown soils occur in the driest parts and are devoted primarily to grazing. They have thin, brown surface horizons and relatively little organic matter. The Chestnut soils, between the Chernozem and Brown soils and intermediate in these features, have thin, black or dark-brown surface horizons and moderate organic matter.

The topography generally permits cultivation. Steeply sloping land occurs in the Sandhills of Nebraska; the Black Hills in South Dakota; the deeply dissected, high, old terraces in Montana; and the river breaks in all parts.

Steep lands and sandy or thin soils usually are devoted to rangeland. Spring wheat is grown throughout the region if soil and topography are suitable over a large enough acreage. These factors and climate form a pattern that gives rise to the production of spring wheat in the northeast and range livestock in the western and southwestern parts.

In comparatively extensive areas, soil or topography, or both, assert themselves so as to warrant recognition of subregions. Thus the topography and the soils of the bed of glacial Lake Agassiz in eastern North Dakota and northwestern Minnesota—the Red River Valley—pose opportunities

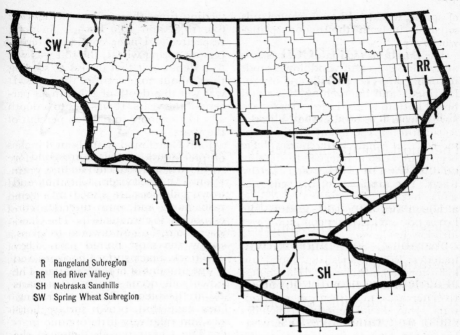

R   Rangeland Subregion
RR   Red River Valley
SH   Nebraska Sandhills
SW   Spring Wheat Subregion

and problems that set it apart from the extensive ground moraine to the west. The flatness of the terrain and the nearly stone-free soils developed on the clayey, silty, and sandy lake deposits lend themselves especially well to extensive production of spring wheat, barley, sugar beets, and potatoes. It is the most favored with moisture of any section of the region, and a high proportion of the rainfall soaks into the nearly level land. Much of the area is affected by poor drainage, however, which in some seasons results directly in considerable crop loss and handicaps the field operations, especially on the most clayey soils.

The spring-wheat subregion extends from the Red River Valley westward and southward to the range country of Montana and South Dakota. Its eastern part includes mainly loamy and sandy soils (of the Chernozem soil region), developed on varied glacial deposits. The gently undulating ground moraine is marked by low knolls, shallow swales, and closed depressions. There are occasional dry, small lake-

beds and deeper depressions, or potholes. Sandy soils, sometimes underlain by gravel, often occur on glacial lake terraces, on outwash plains, and along the larger watercourses and outflow channels of glacial melt water. The largest bodies of sandy soils are on materials deposited as deltas.

Soils within a field that consists mainly of gently undulating upland may include thin soils of knolls; thick, dark soils of lower slopes; and beds of extinct shallow glacial lakes. The closed depressions, or potholes, are a problem for crop production and make it harder to work the land with large machinery. The exposed knolls frequently are the point of inception of wind erosion.

The western part of the spring-wheat subregion includes soils of the Chestnut and Brown soil zones, which developed on loamy and sandy glacial deposits, weathered sandstones, and loamstones and ancient river deposits. An area of several counties in north-central Montana has soil and topography that are favorable to production of spring wheat, although rangelands separate it from the major spring-wheat area.

The Sandhills section of Nebraska is an extensive area of windblown sands in rounded or choppy hills and irregular ridges, and intervening draws and broad bottom lands. Large streams are few. Harold Rhoades, of the Nebraska Agricultural Experiment Station, observed that small watercourses have been obliterated at intervals by drifting sand, giving rise to lakes and marshy tracts. The sandiness of the soils presents hazards for cultivated crops, although they are good for range. The broad bottom lands are commonly wet meadow haylands.

The extensive rangeland to the west includes Brown soils developed on loamstones, sandstones, and clay shales; loess and old alluvium on high ancient river terraces; and, in northern Montana, some glacial deposits. It includes soils of the Chestnut soil zone in western South Dakota developed on clay shales and on saline and alkali loamstones, which generally are unsuited to cropping.

The soil-management problems of the Northern Great Plains would include most of those of other sections—management of fertility, conservation of moisture, control of erosion, maintenance of good soil structure, and drainage. Their relative importance and the range of treatment differ from those of the other sections, however.

EVEN IN THE YEARS when the total amount of precipitation for the growing season is adequate in the spring-wheat subregion, there may be long periods without rainfall. Crops in most years depend on available moisture stored in the soil at seeding time.

John Cole and Oscar Matthews, of the Department of Agriculture, reported results from 15 field stations in the Great Plains that showed the relationship between the yield of spring wheat and the depth to which the soil was wet at seeding time. When soil was wet to a depth of 1, 2, and 3 feet at seeding time, the average yields were 6.9, 12.6, and 19.9 bushels an acre, respectively. Under continuous cropping to spring wheat, the soil was wet to a depth of 1 foot or less at seeding time, about 30 percent of the years. It was wet to a depth of 2 feet in 44 percent of the years. It was wet to a depth of 3 feet or more in only 26 percent of the years.

John Cole found that about 8 inches of precipitation was required before spring wheat began to produce grain. Each additional inch of rain increased yields 2.2 bushels an acre. It was found in Saskatchewan that 5 or 6 inches of water—stored moisture plus crop-season rainfall—was needed to produce a minimum yield of 1 or 2 bushels of wheat an acre. At 10.5 inches of water, a yield of 14 bushels an acre was obtained. For higher levels of moisture, yields increased at a nearly constant rate of 6 bushels an acre for each additional inch of water.

This type of relationship led to adoption of the practice of summer fallowing, in which no crop is grown for one full season in order to effect storage of part of the moisture that comes during the period between removal of a grain crop and the seeding of the succeeding crop. The soil is tilled at intervals to control weeds.

Fallowing commonly increases by several inches the amount of water stored in the soil at seeding time. Cole and Matthews learned that soil after fallow was wet to a depth of 3 feet or more in 74 percent of the years and to 2 feet in 21 percent of the years. This improvement in moisture status of the soil is reflected in higher yields of wheat grown after fallow, especially in dry seasons. Yields after fallow in the better years may be only about 20 percent better than those of continuous wheat. Yields of wheat after fallow in the less favorable years are often double those of continuous wheat.

The additional water stored by fallowing represents a relatively small amount of the total precipitation during the fallow period. John Thysell, working at Mandan, N. Dak., showed that fallowing conserved 5 to 29 percent of the precipitation that fell in 19 fallow periods. The average was 20 percent.

Similar results were reported in Saskatchewan by W. J. Staple and J. J. Lehane.

The loss of 80 percent of the precipitation as runoff, evaporation, and transpiration by weeds during the fallow period emphasizes the need to reduce the losses. Little of the moisture is lost in most years by percolation except on sandy or gravelly soils.

Timeliness of the first tillage seems to be the most important variable in managing fallow. Initial tillage operations must be started by June 1 to prevent the loss of moisture through weeds. In a 36-year period at the Northern Great Plains Field Station at Mandan, the average yield of wheat was 4 bushels an acre higher on fallow plowed on June 1 than on fallow where tillage was delayed until July 1. Little difference in yield due to time of initial tillage may occur in years of above-average precipitation, but the difference is much greater than 4 bushels in dry years.

Attempts have been made to increase the amount of moisture stored in fallow by reducing runoff by leaving crop residues on the surface and by forming small basins or pits in the surface to catch and hold water. The type of tillage, however, has had little effect on the moisture content of the soil at seeding time and the yield of wheat.

The frequency of fallow for storing moisture depends mainly on the amount of precipitation. In the areas of lower rainfall, some farmers have used a system of alternate wheat and fallow. The practice has grown in favor. In the eastern part of the spring-wheat area where rainfall is higher, land often is fallowed only once in 3 or 4 years or almost not at all.

Fallowing also improves conditions for the next crop by controlling weeds and facilitating the accumulation of nitrogen in available form. Farmers in the eastern part of the spring-wheat

area and in the Red River Valley may fallow to control weeds or to accumulate available nitrogen in fields where the entire soil profile may be moist.

Many farmers in sections where corn can be grown with fair success prefer to substitute corn for fallow, although thereby they achieve only part of the benefits of fallow. The moisture status of soil usually is better following corn than after small grain, but is not so high as after fallow. Weeds may be controlled fairly well in corn, although not so well as by fallow. Yields of wheat after corn are lower than wheat after fallow, but are higher than when wheat is grown continuously.

The value of the corn, however, generally will more than offset the loss in wheat yields obtained when wheat follows corn instead of fallow. Consequently corn is substituted for fallow in much of the spring wheat area in southern North Dakota and central and northern South Dakota.

Some moisture conservation occurs from leaving stubble standing over winter to catch snow. On medium- and coarse-textured soils, spring plowing of stubble land generally is superior to fall plowing for seedbed preparation for grains except in the easternmost part of the area. Clay soils are not commonly plowed in the spring because it is hard to obtain desirable structure then.

Delayed seeding is common when soil moisture conditions are poor at the usual seeding time. That often requires a shift to a crop that will do well even if it is planted late. If plowing of land in alfalfa or grass is delayed until fall, planting may be delayed to permit accumulation of some moisture before seeding. Corn fits in well in those circumstances because its moisture demand usually is light until July and there is opportunity for considerable recharge of moisture and decay of residues to release nitrogen.

How GREAT are the losses of organic matter and other constituents from our soils? Have they had any effect on crop yields? What effects will they have in the future? What management practices should be used to maintain fertility? These questions are important to farmers and ranchers of the Northern Great Plains.

Losses of organic matter and nitrogen from soils of the spring-wheat subregion have been great in 30 or 40 years of cultivation.

Cropping for 34 years at five experiment stations in the Northern Great Plains resulted in a loss of 35 percent of the nitrogen and 41 percent of the organic matter that was present in the virgin sod. Results at 21 farms in North Dakota cropped on an average of 43 years were similar.

Experiments at Mandan and Sheridan, Wyo., indicate that alfalfa and grasses in the rotation reduce the rate of loss of organic matter. The average loss of nitrogen from the surface soil in 30 years at Mandan was 18 percent from the alfalfa rotation, 25 percent from the grass rotation, and 31 percent from a rotation without grass or alfalfa. The losses were 18, 13, and 27 percent, respectively, in 30 years at Sheridan. Thus grass or alfalfa in rotation with annual crops will reduce the loss of nitrogen but will not maintain it at its original level.

Barnyard manure applied in a rotation of corn, wheat, and oats at four experiment stations in the Northern Great Plains over a period of 29 to 40 years produced variable results. Yields of wheat and corn stover—but not corn grain—were higher in the manured rotation than in similar rotations without manure. Differences in yield, however, may become greater with continued cropping, since the nitrogen content of the soil in the nonmanured rotation declined faster than in the manured rotation. The nitrogen loss from the surface soil was 37 percent from the nonmanured rotations and 17 percent from the manured rotations.

Barnyard manure is relatively low in phosphorus, but one of its outstanding effects has been that of reducing the rate of decline of available phosphorus.

Manure should be used in the crop rotation when it is available. In a rotation of corn, wheat, and oats, the manure may be applied before plowing for corn. In a rotation that includes fallow, the manure may be applied to the land to be fallowed.

Generally it has not been profitable to plow under sweetclover, peas, or winter rye for green manure and fallow the rest of the season in the spring-wheat subregion, except in the years of above-average moisture. The gains achieved in years of more than average rainfall have been lost in the dry years. The draft of these crops on soil moisture apparently offsets other benefits from their use. The use of green manures has not appreciably retarded the loss of organic matter from surface soil, however.

THE USE OF COMMERCIAL fertilizers has expanded rapidly, especially in the eastern part of the spring-wheat subregion.

More than 80 percent of the soils in much of the spring-wheat area seem to be deficient in phosphorus to a degree that response may be expected from the use of phosphate fertilizers. In several hundred trials conducted by the North Dakota Agricultural Experiment Station between 1947 to 1956, applications of phosphate to spring wheat grown on fallow increased yields nearly 5 bushels an acre. Field response and soil tests in North Dakota indicate that soils west of the Missouri River are conspicuously deficient in phosphorus. Response to fertilization is much less consistent in the western part of the spring-wheat area, which is mainly in the Brown soil region and is in Montana and Wyoming.

Grains commonly mature 3 to 5 days earlier when they have adequate phosphorus, and the risk of injury by hot weather or storms is that much less. Research in Montana has shown that sawfly damage may be worse in wheat that has plenty of phosphate, however.

For small grains, drill attachment applications furnishing 25 to 35 pounds of available P_2O_5 an acre seem to be enough for most soils low in available phosphorus. Fifteen to 20 pounds of P_2O_5 is enough on soils moderately deficient in phosphorus. On fallowed soils that are cold or wet in the spring or release nitrogen at a relatively low rate, benefits may be expected when nitrogen is included with the phosphate for grain.

Nitrogen is usually deficient in the eastern part of the spring-wheat area, where grains are grown on land cropped the previous year. Little or no response is obtained from phosphate fertilizer unless nitrogen is also provided. Then 40 pounds of nitrogen an acre usually provides enough nitrogen for grains, but drill-row applications of that amount of nitrogen on small grains are not recommended, except when moisture conditions in the seedbed are very favorable. Twenty to 30 pounds of nitrogen an acre generally may be applied in the row with little danger to germination or early growth. If a farmer wants to apply more than that amount of nitrogen, he can get good results by broadcasting it the previous fall or in the spring before he prepares the seedbed. The needs for phosphate, however, are met most efficiently by drill application at seeding time.

Some farmers have been reluctant to use fertilizer for fear of "burning up" their crops. Joseph Zubriski conducted 18 trials at 6 branch experiment stations in North Dakota between 1952 and 1956. He demonstrated that the moisture in fertilized and unfertilized plots is usually about the same at the time of maturity, even though the more rapid growth of fertilized crops occasions somewhat earlier withdrawal of moisture. He made the tests over a wide range of conditions of seasonal moisture, and the relationship held true even when fertilizer promoted a large increase in yields. Further research is needed to determine the relationships between nutrient supply, plant growth, and use of soil moisture, but investigations so far have indicated that with adequate plant nutrition effi-

ciency of use of moisture by grains can be increased greatly even when moisture is limited, as it commonly is in the Northern Great Plains.

Leo Puhr and his associates at South Dakota State College found that nitrogen is the element most deficient for corn production in South Dakota.

The North Dakota Agricultural Experiment Station got good results from hill applications of 10 pounds of nitrogen and 40 pounds of P_2O_5 an acre. The response of corn to fertilizer depends largely on the moisture supply at silking time. Although corn shows marked response to fertilizer in the early stages of growth, often there is no response in yield of ear corn if the soil moisture is poor at silking time, even though the moisture conditions improve for the postsilking period.

Grasses grown in solid stand for seed and forage usually lack nitrogen. In trials near Dickinson, N. Dak., between 1951 and 1956,100 pounds of nitrogen an acre on crested wheatgrass increased seed production, yield, and protein content of the forage when the moisture was favorable.

Grasses grown for seed in cultivated rows generally are well supplied with nitrogen.

WIND EROSION continues to be a serious problem in some localities and is a threat on most cultivated soils. Sandy soils are especially subject to wind erosion because they often contain too little silt and clay to form large aggregates or clods resistant to wind action. Loams and clays more commonly have a fairly resistant structure in the autumn. Repeated freezing and thawing and wetting and drying often cause structure to deteriorate because of the formation of aggregates of a size susceptible to wind action. Soils high in clay are most subject to this type of deterioration.

Shelterbelts of trees, permanent or rotation seeding of grass, stripcropping, measures to preserve a protective cover of residue, timely tillage, and proper fertilization all have a place in a program to control wind erosion. Each in its own way reduces the velocity of the wind, cuts down the sweep of the wind, protects the surface, or maintains a soil structure that resists movement and abrasion by wind.

A few soils are so erodible that they can be stabilized only by permanent grass cover. In other soils, strips of grass or stubble, alternating with tilled land, may trap soil moved by wind. On medium-textured soils in the spring-wheat area, the strips should not be more than 20 rods wide and should be at right angles to the prevailing wind. Strips on soils susceptible to erosion must be narrower if they are to give protection against occasional strong winds. Alternate strips of grain and fallow should be used in localities where a wheat-fallow system is used.

Fallowing in large blocks creates a serious problem of wind erosion. Growing strips of corn at intervals in the fallow provides some protection and permits seeding the entire block to one crop the following year, but alternate stripping is a much surer measure.

Stubble-mulch tillage of fallow tends to leave crop residues on the surface and thus help to control wind erosion. Some implements, such as the sweep, straight blade, and the rod weeder, leave much of the crop residues on the surface. The one-way disk generally covers more of the crop residues, depending on the angle at which the disks are set, the rate of forward motion, and the depth of operation. The field cultivator with sweeps, a widely adopted implement for fallowing, gives excellent protection during early summer, but the residues tend to disappear with repeated tillage operations for weed control. The rod weeder, used in combination with sweep-type implements, controls weeds with fewer cultivations and helps to preserve residues on the surface. Excessive tillage tends to break down soil particles to a size susceptible to wind action.

Plowing in the spring instead of in the fall helps keep a protective cover on the land when wind erosion is worst.

Plowing and seeding in one operation by the use of the ponypress drill keeps structural disturbance of the plowed soil to a minimum. The press wheels tend to pack the soil and form parallel ridges, which are fairly effective in reducing erosion. Spring plowing is recommended because usually it gives higher yields of spring wheat than fall plowing.

Emergency control of wind erosion sometimes is necessary. The application of manure is practical and effective on small areas. The soil in larger fields may be tilled in strips consisting of single passes with a field cultivator or chisel to ridge the land and to turn up moist soil and clods. As the strips lose their effectiveness when they fill with soil or dry out, additional strips may be tilled and control may be achieved without tilling the entire field.

HEAVY SHOWERS and spring runoff cause water erosion on sloping land, especially land that is fallowed or on which corn is planted up and down hill. Stubble-mulch tillage leaves protective residues on the surface and keeps it favorable for water intake. Tillage that forms clods also tends to increase the intake of water by retarding the formation of crusts and so reduces the amount of soil moved in runoff. The use of contouring and contour stripping has increased the western areas, where the topography is suitable. Irregular topography precludes the practical application of the practices on most fields in the glaciated area.

Rotations including grass are recommended to reduce exposure and to develop a soil structure that resists erosion. Spring plowing of stubble land helps protect the soil during much of the year. The rapid establishment of a vegetative canopy may be encouraged by using appropriate fertilizers. Grassing of waterways is important to conserve soil and to forestall the development of gullies, which prevent the effective use of large equipment.

The structure of the soil is important for both crop performance and erosion control. Most tilled soils in the Northern Great Plains originally had good structure. Farming operations usually have brought about a reduction in the organic matter and a decline in the structure so that the soil is more apt to erode. Plowsoles, or tillage pans, and compacted zones also have been induced in some soils.

The formation of compacted zones in soils of otherwise good structure depends largely on moisture in the soil at the time of tillage. At the field station at Mandan, fine sandy loam soils that had been plowed every spring for more than 30 years showed evidence of the formation of a plowsole, but land that had been fall plowed was not thus affected. Land on which stubble has been permitted to stand over winter generally is moister in the spring than in the fall; we would expect it to be more subject to compaction in the spring from the action of the plow and the tractor wheel. Despite development of a plowsole in the spring-plowed plot, yields of wheat have continued to be higher than on fall-plowed fields.

Soil compaction very likely will become more severe and more widespread as heavier equipment—increasingly heavy tractors, trucks, and harvesting equipment—is used, unless the corrective measures are developed. Deep tillage, subsoiling, legumes, grasses, and other management practices may be corrective or preventive measures.

Soil-management problems in the Red River Valley are similar in kind to those of the spring-wheat region, but they differ in degree.

Moisture deficiency occurs less frequently and is seldom so severe in the Red River Valley. Fallowing is practiced mainly for weed control and for accumulating available nitrogen. Extended cultivation has changed soil fertility apparently in the same general way as in the spring-wheat region.

Ralph Young, of the North Dakota Agricultural Experiment Station, found that application of manure at a rate of 7 tons an acre every 4 years to Fargo clay over a period of 40 years helped maintain the available phosphorus and retarded the loss of soil organic matter. Applications of manure and phosphate markedly increased the yield of corn and wheat.

Sweetclover is grown widely for soil improvement, especially on the medium- and fine-textured soils. Soil on which sweetclover has been grown for green manure fallow usually is dry enough for seedbed preparation several days earlier than corresponding land fallowed without the sweetclover. Earlier seeding, reduction in water damage from spring rains, and improvement in nitrogen nutrition contribute in varying proportions to improve the following crop.

Theodore Stoa, of the experiment station at Fargo, demonstrated that sweetclover should be plowed early to prevent moisture deficiency and a reduction in yield of the following crop. Wheat following sweetclover plowed at bud stage gave an average yield of 31.5 bushels an acre between 1929 and 1956. Where the first crop was cut for hay and the second crop was plowed down for green manure, yields averaged 29 bushels an acre. On plots plowed in the fall after harvesting a crop of seed, the yields averaged 22.8 bushels an acre.

Phosphorus deficiency is widespread. A few farmers prefer to broadcast phosphate fertilizer in amounts to provide adequate levels for all crops, especially if they also grow alfalfa, potatoes, or sugar beets. Phosphate fertilizer generally increases yield and raises the protein content of alfalfa.

Nitrogen fertilization usually is needed for small grain, except when it is grown on land fallowed the previous season. The use of nitrogen-phosphorus fertilizer on grains on nonfallow land is more common here than in the area to the west. Some farmers apply 30 to 40 pounds of nitrogen to stubble land in the fall and plow it down, applying the phosphate and some nitrogen by drill attachment in the row with the seed in the spring.

Solid stands of grass are conspicuously deficient in nitrogen. In trials at the Fargo station from 1950 to 1956, J. F. Carter found that application of nitrogen increased severalfold the yields of bromegrass seed and forage. The nitrogen also increased the protein content of the forage. As a consequence of a better moisture supply, the response of grasses to nitrogen may be expected to be more consistent than in the drier sections.

General recommendations for fertilizer for sugar beets and potatoes include both potassium and phosphorus because the crops frequently have responded to them. Nitrogen consistently increased the yields of potatoes grown on cropped land.

Little research has been conducted to test the response to trace elements in the Red River Valley. Flax and soybeans grown on calcareous soils often show vegetative symptoms of iron deficiency. Zinc sprays on potatoes have increased yields in the valley.

Soils developed on sandy beach and delta deposits are subject to erosion. Control practices are established more easily than in the spring-wheat area, however, because rainfall generally is higher and snow cover is more continuous. Shelterbelts figure prominently in soil stabilization in these areas. Most of the fine- and medium-textured soils are plowed in the fall to facilitate early spring planting and to obtain benefits of the structure-improving effects of freezing and thawing and wetting and drying. Deterioration of soil structure by weather to a degree that erosion occurs is rather infrequent, but when it takes place in the winter, wind erosion may be serious. The erosion in spring is usually rather easily controlled by emergency tillage.

Maintenance of desirable structure of the fine-textured soils such as Fargo clay is of general concern to farmers. These soils often are hard to till. They are plastic when wet and often become hard when they are dry. The frequent use of grasses, preferably with alfalfa, makes it easier to work these soils. To maintain a desirable structure in them, attention has to be given to their moisture content before tillage or exposure to traffic.

Improvement of surface drainage would benefit much of the land in the Red River Valley. The land appears to be flat, but there is enough relief to permit concentration of runoff water in the shallow, closed depressions that are oriented in a northwesterly-southeasterly direction. Because natural surface drainage is weakly developed, extensive areas are poorly drained. In years of greater than average rainfall, field operations are often handicapped by wet soil, and considerable acreage may suffer from excess water. Moreover, widespread damage to soil structure results on fine-textured soil in the process of growing and harvesting crops in years of excess moisture. Many farmers spend several days each autumn developing and improving field drainage systems.

Saline soil conditions exist in several large and numerous small areas in the central Red River Valley of North Dakota. Surface drainage may help to improve some of these soils. A permanent solution requires improvement of internal drainage to flush the salts from the soil. Extensive research has been initiated to develop soil management and drainage practices that will alleviate the saline condition and improve crop production.

THE RANGE AREA is so vast and its sound use in livestock production so important that it is vital to determine best management practices under the climatic extremes of the Plains.

Soil-management problems on rangelands are similar to those of dry-farming, but the practices involved in solving them are somewhat different. Conservation of moisture is the main problem. All management efforts should be geared to the most effective use of the precipitation available.

George Rogler and Howard Haas, of the Northern Great Plains Field Station, studied range production as related to soil moisture and precipitation. They found a highly significant correlation (coefficient of 0.74) between the amount of fall soil moisture in the surface 6 feet and the native forage production the following season. This type of information is of value in forecasting range production. They also found a high correlation between the April–July precipitation and the yield the same season, but the highest correlation was found when the soil moisture plus the April–July rainfall was related to production.

Good grazing management can improve or maintain most native ranges. Because native range is a natural product of soil, climate, and vegetative factors, its management involves an understanding of those factors and an adjustment of grazing to fit them.

Conservation grazing is an effective method of restoring or maintaining the range. It allows the more important range forage plants to increase their density and vigor. The general recommendation is "take half and leave half."

Frank Rauzi, of the Department of Agriculture, made extensive studies of the ability of rangeland to absorb and store precipitation. He used a mobile rainfall applicator to compare water intake of good and poor range conditions on several hundred sites in the northern and central Great Plains. The rate of water intake was greatly influenced by soil characteristics, vegetal cover, and the intensity of past and present range use.

The rate of water intake was consistently higher on the good range sites with greater vegetal cover than that of the poor range sites. He learned, however, that the difference due to range condition was greater in soils of medium texture than in the very fine clays or the coarse sands. The water intake on the silt loams was 228 percent higher on the good range sites than on the poor sites. The greatest opportunity for improving water intake by good management therefore exists in the soils of medium texture. Greater

water infiltration is important for the increase of available moisture supply for forage production. Greater water intake also reduces runoff, erosion, flooding, and siltation.

Numerous attempts have been made to increase water intake and improve native range. These include range pitting, contour furrowing, contour plowing, and chiseling.

Oscar Barnes, working at Archer, Wyo., found that pitting of short-grass range increased water intake, increased grazing capacity by one-third, and resulted in an average yearly increase of 9 pounds of lamb an acre over a 10-year period. Even with the heavier stocking rate, the pitted pastures had 70 percent more carryover perennial grass than did the untreated pastures.

The pitting and thinning brought about an increase in western wheatgrass and other desirable species at the expense of the blue gramagrass. This change in plant composition persisted after 10 years of grazing.

The use of vegetative barriers of coarse, unpalatable plants to catch and hold snow appears to have potentialities in areas where blowing is a problem. These barriers, properly placed, can be used to distribute snow for added moisture on rangelands and in stock water dams.

Water spreading has been used to a limited degree on range and pasturelands in an effort to conserve water for increased production of forage. Water spreading is a simple form of flood irrigation accomplished by diverting runoff from normal channels and spreading the flow over adjacent flood plains or valley floors. It is used most effectively on relatively smooth, gently sloping plains with a grade of less than 1 percent. Many systems of dams, dikes, and ditches have been tried in water spreading, but the system usually is so constructed that the operation is automatic. It must be constructed so as to take care of storms of high intensity. Favorable sites available for water spreading are limited, but where it has been practiced, water spreading has

made it possible to increase the livestock numbers 5 to 10 times and has
reduced flood hazards and erosion
losses.

Drought, overstocking, overgrazing,
rodents, and other causes have depleted
the range in many places. Plowing and
overextension of cultivation have
harmed other range areas. Depleted
ranges and abandoned cultivated fields
often can be improved by reseeding.

Ralph Williams, at the Montana
Branch Station at Moccasin, reported
that wheat-stubble land seeded to
crested wheatgrass produced earlier
grazing, a longer grazing season, higher
carrying capacity, and 2.5 times more
feed an acre than the native range.
Good stands of crested wheatgrass remained after 15 years of grazing.

An efficient method of using seeded
pastures is to graze it in combination
with native range. Cool-season grasses,
such as crested wheat, can be grazed
2 to 3 weeks earlier than native range
and can be grazed at a high intensity
for 2 to 3 months during the spring.
Grazing on the native range can be
deferred consequently.

Correct grazing management is essential to the maintenance of seeded
range as well as the native range. Production in the moister areas is increased
by including a legume such as Ladak
alfalfa in the seeding mixtures with
grass. Applications of nitrogen have increased yields of crested wheatgrass at
the field stations at Mandan and
Newell, S. Dak. These practices have
not been used generally in the Northern
Great Plains, however.

Many attempts have been made to
seed high-producing legumes and
grasses in native rangeland, but the results mostly have not been satisfactory.

Clarence Becker, of the Wyoming
Agricultural Experiment Station, developed a range seeder that is especially adapted for seeding in native
range. It tills a strip 18 inches wide
and leaves 22 inches of undisturbed
native range between the tilled rows.
He made large field plantings of one-
half pound of Ladak alfalfa and 2.2

pounds of crested wheatgrass with 20
pounds of nitrogen an acre. The reno-
vating effect of the seeder eliminated
the competition for the seedlings and
stimulated the growth of western wheatgrass in the untilled strips. An excellent
stand of alfalfa and crested wheatgrass
was established at the end of the season.

Research by George Rogler at Mandan indicated that nitrogen fertilizer
can raise the production of a depleted
native range as well as that of a range
in good condition. Nitrogen fertilization of selected areas to get better distribution of livestock grazing of the
range has shown promise.

THE SANDHILLS have low-lying
sand dunes, which are erosive when
not covered with vegetation. All soil-
management practices here must be
geared to a grassland economy. The
precipitation—15 to 22 inches—is absorbed so fast by the sandy soil that
little runs off. In the numerous basins
and valleys among the hills the water
table often rises to the surface and
forms marshes and lakes. Ranchers in
the Sandhills have weathered severe
droughts better than ranchers elsewhere partly because of the relatively
stable water supply.

Many of the valleys and basins have
"wet meadows," which are used mainly
for hay. Their yields can be increased
by phosphorus and nitrogen fertilization. The quality of the hay can be increased by earlier harvesting, a practice many ranchers have adopted.

The greatest possibilities for improvement in soil management appear to
lie in increased production of the wet
meadows and the immediately surrounding areas, according to Harold
Rhoades, of the Nebraska Agricultural
Experiment Station. It is possible that
by pumping water from the lakes,
marshes, and wet meadows, some of
the upland areas could be irrigated.

FUTURE TRENDS in soil use and management in the Northern Great Plains
will involve local adjustments in the
type of agriculture to fit climatic ex-

tremes and improvements in management of water and conservation of soil moisture. In the drier parts of the Plains, that would necessitate a shift toward a grazing economy with larger units and, where possible, an integration of cropland farming and ranching.

Improved water management through irrigation projects, the development of many small watersheds and reservoirs, and improved water-spreading techniques on rangeland offer opportunities for improved and sustained agricultural production. To make the most effective use of this water, increased emphasis on soil and water conservation research will be essential.

The potentialities from improved moisture conservation and efficiency present a challenge. Many improvements have been made in methods of summer fallowing and residue management from the standpoint of erosion control and conservation. This and stripcropping, strip fallowing, and other practices have made great strides toward stabilizing the dry-farming economy. No great advance has been made in the moisture conservation aspect of fallowing since 1915, however. Only 15 to 25 percent of the rainfall during the fallow period is conserved and stored as soil moisture for subsequent crops. If the moisture storage could be increased even 10 to 20 percent, crop yields would be substantially increased and production would be stabilized greatly. Basic research is needed for a better understanding of soil moisture movement and evaporation.

Chemicals to control weeds are good possibilities for improving conservation of moisture under both crop and fallow conditions.

There are great potentialities for improvement of crops in the Northern Great Plains through improved plant nutrition. A large part of this improvement will depend on the wise use of commercial fertilizers.

The present use of fertilizer is but a small fraction of that which could be used with profit to farmers of the area.

The Winter Wheat and Grazing Region

J. A. Hobbs

The winter wheat and grazing region of the Great Plains includes the subhumid and eastern semiarid sections of the central and southern Great Plains. The rainfall is irregular. The soils mostly are fertile. Winter wheat is the main crop. Considerable land remains in native grass, which is grazed.

The average annual precipitation is more than 38 inches in the southeast and less than 14 inches along the western edge. That is enough moisture for satisfactory growth of adapted crops if one uses recommended practices.

Precipitation has been as low as 50 percent of average and higher than 200 percent of average in almost all parts of the region. Generally the number of years with below-average rainfall slightly exceeds the number with above-average precipitation. Seasonal as well as annual irregularities are common.

Considerable variation in temperature also occurs. The average growing season—the period without a killing frost—is closely related to the mean temperature for the different sections. The average growing season ranges from more than 210 days in the southeastern part to fewer than 140 days in the northwestern section.

The wide variations in climate would lead us to expect a wide variation in

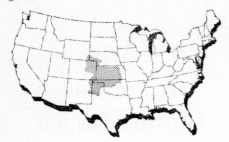

native vegetation. The variation does occur, but the native vegetation over the whole region is grass. Some small favored sites support trees. Bluestems, both big and little, and associated tall and mid grasses grow in the eastern parts. Farther west where it is drier, short grasses come into the native sward, until in the western section the short grasses, such as buffalograss and the gramagrasses, are the most common species on the uplands. Taller grasses tend to dominate on the sandier soils and on bottom lands.

A diversity of soils developed under this climate and native vegetation. The soils include the deep, dark Prairie and Reddish Prairie soils of the eastern sections; Chernozem soils in the central parts; and the shallower and lighter colored Chestnut, Reddish Chestnut, and Brown soils of the west.

Scattered through these zonal soils are some shallow soils on bedrock and some sandy soils and sand dunes. These soils and the fine-textured, tight, impermeable soils pose problems of management, but the areas are too small to designate and discuss here. The narrow belts of highly productive, alluvial soils along the many stream channels also are too small to delineate.

This winter wheat and grazing region can be divided into four subregions: The Flint Hills subregion, the Dakota Sandstone subregion, the subhumid wheat subregion, and the summer fallow subregion.

THE FLINT HILLS subregion is a rough, dissected section of shallow soils on shale and limestone bedrock. Mostly it is uncultivated and is used primarily for summer grazing. The bluestems and the associated grasses still prevail, and they and the climate and fertile soils have given to the Flint Hills a reputation of being one of the most productive native grass pasture areas in the United States.

Some breeding herds are maintained, but much of the land is leased to western or Texas cattlemen at a cash rent per animal for the season. The cattle are shipped in to pasture in April and May and are shipped east to market when they are in finished condition or when the pasture is no longer useful.

Areas of soils suited to cultivation are scattered over the relatively level ridgetops. They tend to be fine textured and have tight, impermeable subsoils. Colluvial and alluvial soils at the base of slopes and on the small bottom land areas also may be tillable. These level upland soils and the colluvial and alluvial soils are limited in extent, but they are highly important to farmers—winter feed and forage for stock come from them.

Good management of the soils of the Flint Hills is nearly synonymous with good management of pastures.

Management of grazing on range pastures usually involves the maximum utilization of grass, with efficient livestock production and maintenance of the range. The large numbers of transient cattle in the Flint Hills have meant that emphasis has been put on rapid gains during the early part of the pasturing season. That places a premium on the "early bite." To gain that end, annual burning of pastures has been practiced since the early 1880's, and the practice has been written into many leases.

That the range has been maintained under such conditions is due mainly to other features of the leasing agreements. Cattlemen have demanded adequate acreage allowances per animal to promote good gains. That and the fact that many animals attain market finish in midsummer permit the grasses to make a good growth in late summer.

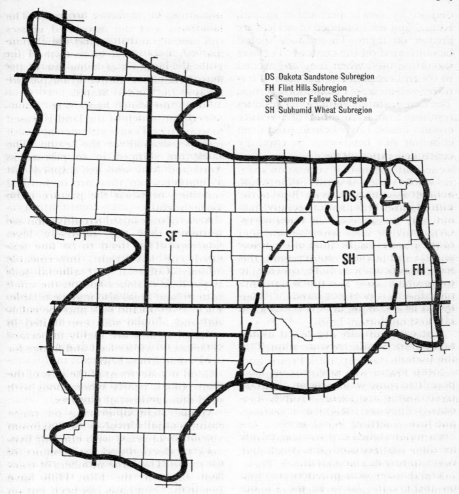

DS Dakota Sandstone Subregion
FH Flint Hills Subregion
SF Summer Fallow Subregion
SH Subhumid Wheat Subregion

Necessary reserves of carbohydrate thus are replenished in the grass roots and crowns.

Some deterioration has been noted, especially in pastures grazed the full season without reduction in stocking load and in smaller pastures, which almost always are overstocked.

The adjustment of acreage allowance to the productive capacity of the grass is highly important. Not all cattlemen realize that when range is "fully utilized" about half of the current year's growth should remain at the end of the pasture season.

Additional practices needed in these pasture areas include a reduction or complete prevention of burning and the provision of adequate and properly spaced watering and salting sites. Because wells are often inadequate in the long, dry seasons, ponds and other structures should be made to supplement the water supply. Places that have started to gully because of overgrazing should be fenced off and allowed to recover.

Danger of erosion is great on the sloping cultivated fields on the uplands. Many of the cultivated lands are underlain by slowly permeable subsoil. Runoff and the likelihood of soil loss are greater on them. These lands should be cultivated on the contour. Terraces should be used when they are needed to control erosion. Applications of fertilizer will increase production of crops. The denser stands and heavier residues resulting from fertilization help reduce erosion losses. Little benefit from deep chiseling has been seen in carefully controlled experiments.

THE DAKOTA SANDSTONE SUBREGION, another grazing area, is just west of the Flint Hills. Its soils are strongly acid and very low in available phosphorus. Originally the grass cover was like that of the Flint Hills. Because of the lower annual rainfall and poorer soils, this section succumbed more quickly to overgrazing. Now it is much more depleted, and it does not have the reputation as a grazing area that the Flint Hills region has.

The cattle usually are raised locally and retained until they are shipped to the market.

Steep slopes and overgrazing have permitted some water erosion. The cultivated soils are highly erosive. Frequently they are shallow over bedrock and are infertile. Wind erosion has been serious when dry weather or low fertility has reduced the vegetative cover to any sizable extent.

The management practices required on the grazing lands in the Dakota Sandstone subregion resemble those that should be used in the Flint Hills, but the use of the pastures should be more restricted because of lower productivity and lower rainfall. Larger acreages are required to carry the stock because the soils are less productive.

Some lands are cultivated on most farms to supplement the production of the range. Only soils that are reasonably level and relatively deep over bedrock should be cultivated.

Nitrogenous and phosphatic fertilizers generally are needed in the production of small grains and sorghum. Phosphatic fertilizers and frequent ap-

plications of limestone are needed for alfalfa.

Contour cultivation should be employed. Because of erosiveness of the soils, the lands steep enough to require terracing probably should not be cultivated. Terraces are not needed on native grass that is in good condition, regardless of slope.

THE SUBHUMID WHEAT SUBREGION comprises parts of the eastern half of Kansas and of Oklahoma east of the Panhandle.

Some pasture and rangelands are included, but the area consistently produces more wheat per acre of total farmland than any other subregion. Corn is raised in the northern and eastern parts. Sorghum is grown over the whole subregion. The availability of seed of adapted, high-yielding, hybrid sorghums undoubtedly will mean an increase in the acreage devoted to sorghum. Alfalfa also is an important crop on many soils in the north and east and on bottom lands elsewhere.

Many problem soils exist in this subregion, but the soils generally are productive and respond well to good management. The main problems are the irregularity of precipitation, the need for supplemental fertilization, and water erosion and wind erosion in some years.

Every effort should be made to reduce unnecessary losses of moisture from the soil—to lessen runoff to a practical minimum, control weeds, and cut evaporation losses.

Management practices that aid in reducing runoff losses are the ones that are also recommended for controlling water erosion. Contour cultivation, ridging on the contour, terrace construction, contour stripcropping, and reseeding steep areas to grass or trees will help to cut down moisture losses by runoff. On deep, permeable soils, the use of those practices may increase materially the moisture available for crop growth. On less permeable soils or on soils with limited moisture storage capacity, the gains in moisture may be smaller.

Stubble-mulch tillage is not adapted to medium- or fine-textured soils of this subregion in years of average or above-average precipitation. Some effort should be made nevertheless to keep some of the crop residues at or near the surface so as to increase or maintain soil permeability and reduce loss of soil by erosion. Stubble-mulch tillage should be used on sandy soils and may be used in drier than average seasons on the medium- and fine-textured soils.

Although 65 percent or more of the rain that falls on the land in this subregion is lost by evaporation, little progress has been made in developing methods for reducing the evaporation losses very much.

One practice that appears to hold promise in sorghum production, at least, is the use of the narrower rows. Evidence has been accumulating that on more favored sites yields of row-planted grain sorghums can be increased by spacing the rows at 20-inch intervals instead of 40 inches. Much of this increase appears to come from a reduction in evaporation from the soil surface. Even after small rains, the surface soils stay damp much longer in narrow rows than in wide rows.

Weeds are a major obstacle to putting this practice into use. Most sorghums in eastern Kansas and Oklahoma formerly were planted with row-crop machinery and cultivated 2 or 3 times after emergence. Cultivation of the growing crop is more difficult with 20-inch row spacing. The land should therefore be as free of weeds as possible at planting time in order to reduce the need for weed control. That will entail later planting of sorghums—not a serious matter, because much of the sorghum is planted too early anyway. Even with delayed planting and good weed-control measures before seeding, weeds may compete with the crop in years when conditions are not ideal for rapid, early growth of sorghum. The need for some cultivation of the narrow rows should therefore be anticipated.

Crops respond to fertilizer on most fields in this subhumid area. Usually combinations of nitrogen and phosphatic fertilizers give higher yields of small grains and sorghums. Corn requires mainly nitrogen applications, although phosphate may be beneficial on extremely early or extremely late plantings. Alfalfa requires applications of phosphate.

Because rates of application vary with the crop, soil, and cropping history, no general recommendations can be made. Nearly every county in this region has a soil-testing laboratory. Soil samples can be submitted for analysis to the laboratories, and the test results can be used as a basis for recommendation of fertilizer. Samples also can be submitted to the State soil-testing laboratories.

Many of the surface soils and some of the subsoils are acid in reaction. It would seem that these soils should be limed, especially for the production of legume crops, but in some localities where the surface soils are acid but the soils below the plow depth are neutral to alkaline, applications of lime have failed to increase yields of legumes. Consequently one should know the soil reaction not only in the surface soil but also in the subsoil before making a recommendation for lime.

A number of studies have been made to determine the best time and method of preparing a seedbed for wheat, corn, and sorghum. The studies have not shown any one implement to be markedly superior for preparing the seedbed. A particular implement may be successful in preparing a seedbed under certain conditions, but it might be unsatisfactory under different conditions of moisture and crop residue. In the western part of this section, the initial seedbed operation on a field can be done as well by a one-way disk plow as by a moldboard plow. Since the one-way is cheaper to operate, it may replace the moldboard plow for the initial tillage wherever the one-way will do a satisfactory job.

Studies on the time of tillage showed that altering the time of the first tillage operation in seedbed preparation affected yields greatly. At Manhattan, Kans., the effect of withholding plowing after July 15 until August 15 or September 15 reduced the subsequent wheat yields by about 1 bushel an acre for each week's delay after July 15. Similar results have been obtained in other areas.

Satisfactory seedbed preparation for corn and sorghums in this section also takes time. Spring plowing generally is to be recommended over fall plowing for corn and sorghums, but the plowing should be done early in the spring. There is no evidence in this section that cultivation of the land, whether in the growing crop or in preparation of the seedbed before planting, needs to be conducted oftener than necessary to control weeds and prepare a firm seedbed.

Experiments at Stillwater, Okla., and Manhattan have shown that acre yields of cereals may be increased by growing them after alfalfa or sweetclover.

Farther south and west, where moisture is more limiting, alfalfa and other legumes are rarely grown on the uplands because of the drought hazard in establishing the crop and because of the indifferent yields of legumes.

Various crops are grown in this subregion, but the acreage in wheat—when allotments were not in effect—was more than twice as great as the total acreage devoted to all other cultivated crops. When such a situation prevails and wheat is so much better adapted to the area than nearly any other crop, one can hardly expect farmers to be interested in crop rotations. In fact, it is not surprising that they restrict the acreage of other crops to the amounts that are needed to provide feed for their own livestock.

Sweetclover can be grown in the more humid areas of this section, but there seems to be little benefit from using sweetclover solely for green manuring purposes. About as good results in soil improvement can be obtained by pasturing it or using it as a

hay or seed crop, or by omitting the legume entirely (especially in the main wheat counties) and using large quantities of nitrogenous fertilizers.

THE SUMMER FALLOW SUBREGION is across the boundary between the western subhumid and eastern semiarid sections of the Great Plains. Its eastern boundary approximates the 25-inch rainfall line. Although this boundary marks the approximate eastern edge of summer fallowing in this region, the frequency of fallow varies within the subregion. Fallow is used on any particular field in the eastern part only about once in 4 or 5 years. Fields in the west usually are fallowed every other year.

The soils of this subregion usually are productive in years of average or above-average precipitation. On the breaks along the North Platte, South Platte, Republican, and Smoky Hill Rivers in Kansas and Nebraska, on the sand dune areas along the Arkansas River in eastern Colorado and western Kansas, and along the Cimarron and Canadian Rivers in Oklahoma and Texas, much of the land is not suited to cultivation.

A major problem in this subregion is the shortage of available moisture, which is evidenced by the great interest in (and response to) moisture-conservation practices and moisture storage. Another phase of this problem sometimes is overlooked: The importance of efficient utilization of stored moisture and current rainfall by crops. Even though wind erosion is more spectacular and causes severe crop losses, water erosion may cause even larger losses of soil from sloping fields in this section.

Crop responses to fertilization have been erratic and usually unprofitable on most soils. With continued grain production, the soils may become sufficiently depleted of fertility to respond regularly and profitably to fertilization.

Extensive tracts of grasslands could be found in all western counties in this region before the First World War.

Some of them were broken during and after the war. Still more land was broken from sod during and after the Second World War. The breakout continued until drought, beginning in 1952, and acreage allotments reduced the possibilities of quick profit from wheat production. The remaining grassland areas are covered mainly with the short grasses, but some mid grasses grow on the uplands in the west. Mid grasses and even tall grasses are found in addition to short grasses in the more humid areas on the uplands and on the sandy and bottom land soils.

Some rather large cattle enterprises flourish in localities where sodland occurs in large blocks. Elsewhere the size of the cattle venture is restricted by the acreage of grass. To maintain production on these grasslands, grazing pressure has to be reduced to that which will not destroy or damage the native species. That is not easy. Alternating periods of drought and adequate rainfall complicate the task of matching the stocking rate with the conditions of the range. Often the range is overgrazed.

Particularly on the sand dune areas great care should be taken in grazing. The soil is highly erosive. If even one knoll starts to erode in the wind, active erosion will spread to the surrounding dunelands or even to the sandy soils next to the dunes.

In places where overgrazing has depleted the cover to the point where wind erosion is active, it is hard to reestablish a cover. Perhaps the best way to reestablish native grass on these soils is to drill sorghums or Sudangrass on the land as protection for grass seedlings. To prevent later competition, the sorghum or Sudan stand should be mowed high if there is any danger of seed production. Adapted native or other grass species should then be drilled into the undisturbed cover. Species of tall and mid grasses are best adapted to reestablishment on sandy soils because their roots penetrate the soils quickly. This may be a critical factor in years of unfavorable moisture.

Drilling the grass seed one-half to three-fourths inch deep usually gives better results than broadcasting. Broadcasting pelleted grass seed from airplanes has not been entirely satisfactory in many places.

It will continue to be necessary to adjust stocking rates to range conditions in this subregion. To do so with a minimum of adjustment in the livestock enterprises, temporary pastures will have to be provided on cultivated parts of the farms. These pastures may have to be planted on fallow land. Reserve feed supplies will need to be stored in favorable years for use in periods of drought. Reserves for 2 to 4 years are not too much to have on hand.

Most of the land suited to cultivation (and some not suited) has been broken from sod and used for cultivated crops. Wheat is a still more predominant crop here than in the subhumid section. In this subregion, more than 75 percent of all land planted regularly to cereal and forage crops in the period before acreage allotments was seeded to wheat or was fallowed in preparation for wheat. Sorghums and a limited acreage of small grains, other than wheat, are raised here.

The problem of first importance on the cultivated lands, as in the range areas, is moisture conservation. All the known moisture conservation practices that can be applied practically to cultivated lands should be employed. These include contour cultivation and terracing on sloping lands. Weed control, including the control of volunteer grain, is important in the conservation of moisture. Weedy crops use as much soil moisture as weed-free crops, and the weeds may reduce yields as much as 50 percent.

Even when all possible moisture-conservation practices are used in the production of crops in this region, only 30 to 35 percent of the precipitation that falls during the growing period can be used by the crop. The rest is lost in a variety of ways. As the amount of rain during the growing season usually is insufficient for optimum yields, moisture from periods when no crop is growing must be stored in the soil for the use of subsequent crops. Methods of seedbed preparation thus are highly important.

The tillage implements used in the seedbed preparation for continuous wheat include plows, cultivators (both stiff and spring shanked), subsurface sweeps, disk-type equipment, and rodweeders. Experiments show that the moldboard plow can be replaced readily by other tillage tools. In fact, the use of the moldboard plow and other implements that incorporate crop residues with the soil should be discouraged because of their effects on susceptibility to wind erosion. The lister is rarely used for preparing a seedbed for wheat.

It is generally true that no one implement should be used to the exclusion of all others. For example, a one-way disk plow can be used profitably to incorporate some of the plant residues with the soil and thus reduce the difficulties that sometimes are encountered in drilling wheat through large amounts of stubble. If the one-way is used too frequently, however, all of the crop residues will be placed below the surface of the soil, and a serious wind erosion hazard will be produced. Other implements, such as the rodweeder and subsurface sweeps, should be used instead after an initial operation with the one-way.

Stubble-mulch tillage, which involves the use of undercutting equipment alone or with other tools, such as the one-way, probably is not so well adapted to continuous wheat production as it is to alternate fallow and wheat production. That does not mean that crop residues should not be left at or near the surface on continuous wheat land. Some residues should be left on the surface to maintain the infiltration capacity of the soil and to reduce the susceptibility of the soil to erosion. In the drier parts, where alternate fallow and wheat production is the common cropping system, and else-

where on fallow land, stubble-mulch tillage is one of the best methods of seedbed preparation. Yields will be as high or higher on this type of seedbed preparation as on more conventionally prepared land, and the danger of water and wind erosion will be reduced markedly.

There is little evidence that newer methods of seedbed preparation, such as chiseling and subsoiling, are more effective moisture conservers than those that employ more conventional tillage tools. Little difference in moisture storage in the soil has been brought about by the use of other implements. There is a good deal of evidence, however, that moisture conservation is greatly affected by timeliness of seedbed preparation.

Studies at the dryland stations in this section show that the moisture stored in the soil at seeding time may be increased 100 percent or more by starting the preparation of a wheat seedbed in early or mid-July instead of in late August or September. This extra moisture storage is accompanied by the release of larger supplies of nitrates. Both the moisture and the nitrates are needed for high crop yields.

Seedbed preparation in June or early July is possible in the southern part of this subregion. As seeding is done here quite late in the fall, a long time for moisture storage is permitted even under continuous wheat production. There is not much benefit here from the inclusion of a fallow period between wheat crops.

Farther north, however, where the time between wheat harvest and wheat seeding is shorter, yields of wheat even on seedbeds prepared as early as possible may not be satisfactory, and some other method of preparation may be necessary.

Over much of this dryland section, sufficient moisture cannot be stored in the soil from harvest to seeding time to supplement rainfall. There are only two practical ways by which greater supplies of moisture can be provided for crop use in this area—irrigation and summer fallow.

Irrigation is a practical solution to the moisture problem where water of good quality is available and the soils are suitable for irrigation. Although an expansion of irrigation in this region is assured, it can be used only on a limited number of farms.

Summer fallow therefore will have to be used to provide for the moisture needs of crops on most farms. Fallow is the practice of keeping the land free of live vegetation throughout a crop-growing period before the one in which a crop is normally produced.

The efficiency of moisture storage by fallow is relatively low. The efficiency of moisture storage during fallow for wheat averaged only about 16 percent at two places in Kansas. At Goodwell, Okla., the efficiency was estimated at 18 percent. Other studies show up to 20 percent efficiency. In other words, only 1 out of 5 or 6 inches of precipitation that fall during the fallow period is stored in the soil. It appears that fallow will store only about 3 to 5 more inches of water than early seedbed preparation will. That does not seem to be very much. Studies have shown, however, that each inch of water used by a wheat crop (water used equals stored water in soil plus precipitation from seeding to harvest) above a certain minimum produces an additional 2 bushels of wheat. Thus, these extra 3 to 5 inches of water stored during a fallow period may mean the production of 6 to 10 extra bushels of grain.

A good summer fallow must permit the storage of moisture and the release of nitrates and still must permit the control of erosion. To achieve these objectives, three main conditions must prevail: The surface soil should be cloddy and open; plant residues should be kept on the surface of the soil to facilitate water movement and prevent wind erosion; and weeds and volunteer grain must not be permitted to grow. The least cultivation that will control weeds and volunteer grain and prepare an adequate seedbed is the

cheapest and also the most effective.

Studies at all dryland experiment stations to determine the best method of fallowing for wheat and other crops show no large differences between yields resulting from different tillage treatments. At Hays, Kans., for instance, the use of a chisel to depths of 6 to 12 inches in August preceding the fallow year did not increase yields of the fallow crop over those on land where preparation was started in May by plowing. Many farmers nevertheless use the chisel for the first tillage operation in preparing the wheat seedbed. There seems to be little to recommend this practice, except for emergency erosion control.

Similarly, no large differences in yields have been obtained by preparing the fallow by sweep-type or disk-type equipment or by the moldboard plow. In spite of this, the use of implements that leave much of the crop residue on the surface is recommended because of the effect on erosiveness. No increase in crop yields could be demonstrated for the use of a lister or basin lister as a first tillage operation at Hays. Farther west, there appears to be some advantage to fall listing before fallowing.

Although there seems to be no marked superiority for any particular implement for seedbed preparation as measured by crop yields on experimental areas, studies have shown that the time of starting the fallowing operation may cause marked differences in yield. By and large, no advantage has been obtained by initiating tillage before May. In fact, there appears to be marked advantages to allowing the stubble to stand over winter to trap snow.

Large losses in yield result from delaying the first tillage operation into June. With the increase in fireweed (*Kochia* species) and Russian-thistle (*Salsola pestifer*) in summer fallow areas, there may be need to change the date for starting the fallowing operation. If these weeds grow up on the wheat stubble in profusion and threaten to remove all the moisture that might otherwise be stored, the land may need to be cultivated shortly after harvest to prevent this loss of moisture.

Even if every care is taken to insure the conservation and storage of all possible moisture, many occasions arise when moisture may not be sufficient. Thus every effort must be made to utilize the stored water efficiently.

The prospective yield of a wheat crop can be estimated with fair accuracy if the amount of moisture stored in the soil at seeding time is known. If a silt loam soil is moist to 3 feet, the prospect for high yields of wheat are good and chances of a failure are low. With smaller amounts of stored water, the chances for high yields become less and the possibilities of failures become increasingly great. Accordingly, if the amount of moisture available at wheat seeding time is determined, the chances of a good crop can be ascertained.

If it appears better not to seed wheat, the land can be held over for spring seeding of another crop in the hope that more water will be stored over winter, or the land can be fallowed to prevent dissipation of the stored water by an unprofitable crop.

Similarly, sometimes a wheat crop can be abandoned in early spring when the moisture condition in the soil is low enough to preclude the possibility of successful production. Land thus abandoned can store almost as much moisture during a fallow period as land not seeded to wheat subsequent to wheat harvest the year previously. Wheatland abandoned in April because of poor moisture reserves will produce more wheat after a fallow period than similar land allowed to remain in wheat and reseeded to wheat the same fall. Accordingly, abandonment in many instances may actually be a method of increasing crop production. It is advisable nevertheless to plant a spring-seeded crop on abandoned wheatland, fallowed the previous summer, because land should not be fallowed for two consecutive years.

A second serious problem in this section is erosion. Water erosion is most severe on bare, sloping lands. When adequate steps are taken to conserve all possible moisture for crop use, water erosion rarely should be a serious problem because the methods used to conserve moisture help control erosion.

The occurrence of wind erosion usually is associated with consecutive drought years, although other factors may influence the amount of soil drifting that will occur.

Nearly every farmer in the dryland section knows the principles of the control of wind erosion.

Several States in the region have laws that permit county commissioners to order emergency tillage conducted on farmland that is menacing neighboring lands by its erosiveness. The cost of this tillage is added to the taxes of the farm.

Conditions beyond a farmer's control sometimes may reduce vegetative cover enough that wind erosion may occur during the windy spring months. On the medium- to fine-textured soils, it may be possible to roughen the surface of the soil so that its erosiveness is greatly reduced. This is necessary in emergencies even in the growing crop. Sandier soils need plant material, either living or dead, to reduce their erosiveness to manageable proportions. That is one reason why sorghums, whose residues may be left undisturbed on the land until after the spring winds are past, are better adapted to sandier soils than small grains.

The stubble-mulch tillage has been highly recommended as a means of reducing water and wind erosion. This practice, particularly during the fallowing operation, has much to commend it. The residues are not completely destroyed by the tillage and remain mixed with the surface soil to help resist soil movement. Yet the residues are not sufficiently bulky after the fallow period to interfere with seeding even if the ordinary disk-type grain drill is used.

In the northern and central areas of this subregion, the prevailing direction of the winds that cause erosion is south-north. Planting crops in strips (east-west) across this prevailing direction will help to reduce erosion by cutting down the width of bare or fallowed fields. The alternate strips, to be effective, must provide protection against erosion in all seasons, but particularly in early spring. The destructive winds are not predominantly in any one direction in southern areas. Here stripcropping has much less to recommend it.

Areas of sandy soils are extensive in southwestern Kansas, the Panhandles of Oklahoma and Texas, southeastern Colorado, and northeastern New Mexico. Many have a low content of clay in the surface layers (2 to 5 percent) and are particularly erosive when they are cultivated. Deep plowing of certain of these soils will help control wind erosion. Where the erosive surface layers are underlain by subsoils with 12 to 25 percent of clay at depths that can be reached by large plows, deep plowing can be used successfully. If fine material cannot be brought to the surface by plowing, no improvement in wind erosion control is obtained.

Deep plowing is not a cure-all on sandy lands. Continued sifting by wind can cause deep-plowed land to lose its increased clay content and become as erosive as ever. The deep-plowed land can trap flying sand particles from neighboring farms. That will dilute the fine surface texture prepared by plowing. Deep-plowed land should be handled with a cropping system that will reduce to a minimum the loss of fine material from the soil. Deep plowing should be undertaken on a community basis.

Although low fertility is not usually considered a problem in most dryland areas, some crops on specific soils may respond to fertilization. In tests in most States in the region, only the sandy soils seemed to respond consistently enough to warrant the use of fertilizer. Since crop growth and fertilizer response in this section are tied so closely to situations of moisture and temperature, recommendations

as to fertilization have to take them into consideration. No areas in this subregion are known where response is obtained to applications of potash. Some areas are deficient in phosphorus, but most soils seem to have enough phosphate.

Nitrogen seems to be the element most likely to limit production. Sufficient nitrogen usually is present in dry years for the growth of the crop the moisture can produce. In fact, more than ample nitrogen supplies seem to be produced in dry seasons, because symptoms of nitrogen deficiency are rarely noticed in a wet year immediately following a dry year. Perhaps it takes several consecutive humid years to demonstrate nitrogen deficiency symptoms on noneroded dryland soils.

Crops on noneroded, productive, hard-land soils have not responded to applications of manure. Crops on sandy lands may respond to manure applications. Usually manure neither increases nor decreases crop growth. In several instances, however, lower yields have followed applications of manure. Applications of manure on poorly drained or eroded soils or on saline or alkali spots have improved soil properties and plant growth in many instances.

As wheat and sorghums and possibly corn in the northern areas are the cultivated crops best adapted to the dryland soils of this subregion, there appears to be little chance for crop rotations. In fact, many farmers who grow both wheat and sorghum on their farms as a regular practice tend to produce the wheat continuously, or alternately with fallow, on specific fields and to produce the sorghums on entirely different fields. A number of farmers alternate wheat and sorghums on individual fields, but the sorghums are planted only if the soils are too dry for wheat seeding in the fall or if the wheat crop fails to become established over winter. On the other hand, some farmers follow a sequence on their land of fallow, wheat, sorghum. Others use a cropping sequence of fallow, wheat, fallow, sorghum.

The Southern Plains

J. R. Johnston

Complex interrelationships among climate, geology, soils, vegetation, and man have produced the geography of the region that includes the Southern High Plains, the Rolling Red Plains, the West Crosstimbers, the Blackland Prairies, and the Edwards Plateau.

The climate is semiarid to humid. Winters are extremely cold in places and mild elsewhere. The summers usually are hot and dry. The growing season is 180 days in the northern part to 300 days in the southern part. The topography varies from nearly level to strongly rolling. Surface drainage is well developed, except in the part of the region that is on the Southern High Plains in Texas. The soils range from slightly acid to calcareous and from deep sands and clays to thin soils.

The cultivated crops are cotton, grain sorghums, peanuts, wheat, corn, oats, barley, grass, and legume forages. Cotton is the main cash crop, and growing it is a highly developed, mechanized enterprise in the Southern High Plains and Blackland Prairie of Texas.

Grain sorghum became a sizable cash and feed grain crop after combine and hybrid sorghums were developed. Wheat has been the leader in the Rolling Red Plains of Texas and Oklahoma.

Corn, oats, and barley are important in the Blackland Prairies. Forage sorghums are grown extensively for hay, silage, and bundle feed. Some alfalfa is grown in alluvial valleys and in places where water is plentiful for irrigation.

Much of the area is rangeland. The Edwards Plateau, the Rolling Red Plains, Crosstimbers, and Grand Prairie are predominantly rangeland. Buffalo, mesquite, gramas, bluestems, Indian, and tobosa grasses grow on them. Brush, mesquite, scrub oak, live oak, and post oak infest some rangeland.

THE SOILS in the High Plains are mainly the Amarillo, Brownfield, and Portales soils, which usually are red or reddish-brown and sandy in the surface. Some areas are loam and clay loam. The subsoils are red clay or sandy clay, blending at 2 to 5 feet into brown, buff, or yellow marl, which contains lime. These productive soils absorb moisture quickly, have good water-holding ability, and are easily worked. The sandier sections are subject to severe wind erosion if they are poorly managed.

Three large groups of soils occur in the Rolling Red Plains. The Miles-Vernon group ranges from sands to clays and are red, reddish-brown, or grayish-brown in the surface; red or reddish-brown subsoils have layers of lime accumulation. The St. Paul-Abilene group occurs only on relatively flat land and is generally of moderately fine texture in the surface and dark brown and fine textured in the subsoils. They are highly productive in seasons of good rainfall. The Zaneis-Renfrow group includes Reddish Prairie soils. In level areas they are deep; red or brown silt loam or very fine sandy loam surface mantles overlie red or brown clay or sandy clay subsoils. Large areas

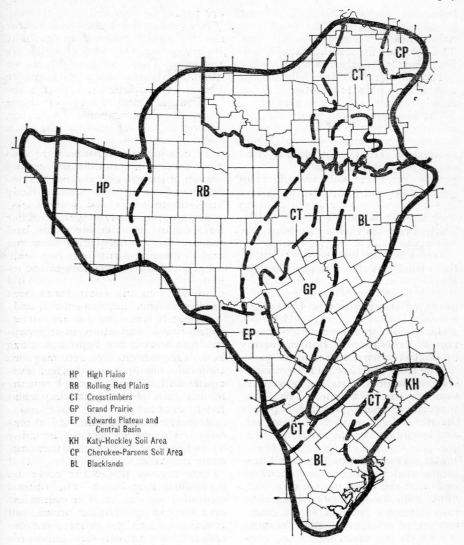

HP   High Plains
RB   Rolling Red Plains
CT   Crosstimbers
GP   Grand Prairie
EP   Edwards Plateau and
       Central Basin
KH   Katy-Hockley Soil Area
CP   Cherokee-Parsons Soil Area
BL   Blacklands

of these soils occupy sloping lands, where they are usually shallow.

The Crosstimbers area has predominantly Windthorst-Nimrod and associated soils. The Windthorst series is light colored in the surface and has red clay subsoils. The Nimrod series has sandy, light-colored surface soils over yellow, soft, pervious subsoils and is subject to severe wind erosion in the absence of plant cover.

The Valera-Ector association in the Edwards Plateau consists of shallow calcareous soils over limestone. They are light brown or dark, grayish brown in the surface and are associated with large areas of rough, stony land. This region, principally rangeland, is devoted to ranching with sheep, goats, and cattle.

The Grand Prairie has the San Saba-Denton group of soils, developed from

limestone. Large areas lack definite
profile development. The black San .
Saba series occurs mostly on flat land.
The Denton soils are brown and shallow. The Crawford series is red.

The Blackland Prairie soils are not
true Prairie soils but rather are like
Rendzina, with calcareous profiles.

The Houston-Austin group is dominant in the area. The Houston series
is dark, deep, calcareous, and highly
productive. The Austin series is thinner, sometimes lighter colored, and less
productive. These soils are subject to
severe sheet and gully erosion. Wilson
and Crockett soils occupy a strip on
the east side of the Blackland Prairie.
They are dark and noncalcareous over
substrata of calcareous clay.

The Victoria-Goliad soils occur in
the southern part of the region in the
Rio Grande Plain. The Victoria series
is dark brown or black and granular
in the surface over grayish-brown clay
subsoils. Goliad soils are black in the
surface, with red or reddish-brown,
crumbly, clay subsoils. Both are highly
productive when moisture is adequate.

The Katy-Hockley soils have light-
colored, more or less sandy surfaces
over gray-mottled, rather dense, fine-
textured subsoils. They are poorly
drained, acid, low in organic matter,
and low in natural productivity.

THE AVERAGE annual precipitation
in the region ranges from about 16
inches on the western edge to slightly
more than 40 inches on the eastern
side. Farmers and ranchmen know,
however, that these rainfall averages
can be quite misleading for any particular year. Farming and ranching
here must be based on a range of moisture conditions and must be flexible
enough to survive periodic dry years.

Extreme variations in seasonal and
yearly precipitation make production
uncertain year in and year out. Crops
may fail completely in years of extreme
droughts. Bumper crops may be harvested in years of above-normal rainfall. Variations in yearly and seasonal
precipitation occur oftener in the west-

ern part of the region than in the east.

Dry years and wet years do not occur
here in regular cycles. Any year may
be dry or wet. One-year droughts are
common. Two-year droughts occur
often. Droughts lasting 2 years or more
have occurred four times during the
agricultural history of the region. Long
droughts are ruinous for the farmer,
ranchman, and the businessman who is
unprepared for them.

Typical of the western part are winters of low precipitation and springs
and summers of fair amounts of rainfall. Much of the rain comes in May
and September.

The eastern part usually receives fair
amounts of precipitation in fall and
winter. The rainfall pattern in spring
and summer is like that in the west.

Crop yields for each area in the region in any given year under dryland
conditions depend more on the amount
of moisture than anything else.

At Big Spring, Tex., it was determined that precipitation between September 1 and the next September 1 can
be linked more closely to cotton yields
than calendar-year precipitation. Precipitation between October 1 and the
following October 1 is most important
for yields of kafir.

Research at Big Spring showed that
both preseasonal (September 1 to May
1) and seasonal (May 1 to September
1) precipitation were highly important
in determining the yield of cotton on
Amarillo fine sandy loam soil. Seasonal
rainfall, however, has a greater effect
on cotton yields than the preseasonal
moisture. The preseasonal precipitation period most important for kafir is
October 1 to June 1, and the most important seasonal period is June 1 to
September 1, although there is little
difference between that and the period
between May 1 to September 1. As
with cotton yields, seasonal precipitation affects kafir yields more than preseasonal precipitation does.

Extreme variations in temperature
sometimes do great damage to crops.
Early freezes on the High Plains of
Texas and the Rolling Red Plains of

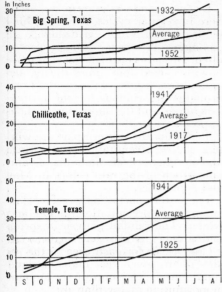

1. Precipitation by crop years (Sept. 1–Aug. 31) for wettest, average, and driest years at Big Spring, Tex. (1916–1953), Chillicothe, Tex. (1912–1953), and Temple, Tex. (1915–1953).

Oklahoma and Texas often have caused tremendous losses to growers of cotton and grain sorghum. Late spring freezes in the Crosstimbers and Blacklands often kill young corn, fruit, and vegetables. Very low winter temperatures often do great damage to winter grain and pasture in the southern and western parts of the region. High temperatures during tasseling time in the Blacklands are a major threat to corn yields. Since long periods of high temperatures usually occur simultaneously with drought, the combined effects of the two usually are very damaging.

The farmer can do little about the weather, but he can exercise considerable control over soil moisture by using conservation practices and adapted varieties of known maturity dates and by carefully observing proper planting dates. He can achieve more stability in crop production if he is well informed about climate and its vagaries.

Conservation and use of moisture is of utmost importance: The farmer's en-

tire soil-management program should be directed toward the absorption, storage, and most efficient use of as much precipitation as possible for a particular soil condition.

The storage of soil moisture during noncrop periods is a major aim. Data obtained at Riesel, Tex., show that soil moisture can be stored effectively for cotton, oats, and sweetclover production. The soil moisture year for fall-sown and for warm-season crops begins in September in the Blacklands, when storage of soil moisture can be started for the ensuing crop if the soil and farm-management program is a good one and if effective rainfall comes. The 3-foot Houston Black clay profile can store more than 7 inches of available moisture during the fall and early winter. Consumptive use of water by oats-sweetclover during the fall and winter is not greatly different from water lost from clean land that is being readied for cotton planting. During the low-rainfall months, available soil moisture in cotton soil drops considerably, possibly from direct evaporation, weed growth, seedbed preparation, or combinations of them.

The high consumptive use of water by oats-sweetclover in the spring creates storage space for moisture and thus reduces runoff and erosion in comparison to losses from land in row crop.

Terracing of sloping lands is essential in the Blacklands and other areas where excess runoff occurs so as to avoid washing and erosion. Blackland soils in row crops may be at or near their moisture-holding capacity in late April, May, and June. The heavy clay soils cannot absorb rapidly the rainfall that usually comes then in intense storms. To avoid severe gullying and erosion, the farmer needs a drainage terrace system for the orderly removal of the runoff.

Level, closed-end, broad-base terraces are used in the Rolling Red Plains and High Plains to control erosion and conserve moisture. The use of level terraces strictly for moisture conservation has been questioned in

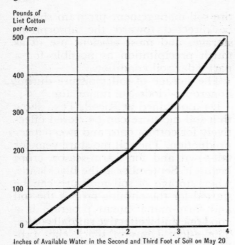

Inches of Available Water in the Second and Third Foot of Soil on May 20

2. *Relation between available soil moisture at planting time and yield of lint cotton at Texas Agricultural Experiment Station at Spur (1930–1952).*

3. *Rainfall and available soil moisture accumulation and evapotranspiration in 3-foot profile of Houston Black clay soil in oats-sweetclover and cotton at Riesel, Tex., hydrologic project for the 1954 crop year.*

recent years because crops growing in the channels are sometimes lost and water that percolates deeply in the terrace channel may be of no use to crops.

Contour furrowing and mulches are other practices the farmer can use to store and conserve soil moisture. Contour furrowing is a tried practice in western Oklahoma and western Texas. Grasses and legumes grown in rotation with soil-depleting crops in the Crosstimbers and Blacklands improve the physical condition of the soil and permit more rapid intake of water for storage. Management of crop residues on the surface protects the soil from the beating action of raindrops, prevents surface sealing, and encourages greater absorption of water.

In the early stages of land use for cultivated crops, plant nutrients in the soil probably were adequate and in line with available soil moisture.

In intensive cropping since then, however, various soils in the region have developed deficiencies of nitrogen and phosphorus. Nitrogen is the most generally limiting nutrient for the maximum use of available soil moisture by crops. In some soils and for some crops, lack of available soil phosphorus is a more limiting factor than nitrogen is.

The farmer in the more humid Crosstimbers and Blacklands has opportunity to grow the nitrogen requirements of his crops by good management of legumes. That is not the case in the less humid Rolling Red Plains and High Plains. There it usually is economically unwise to use available soil moisture for producing legume nitrogen; if nitrogen limits the most efficient use of available moisture, the nitrogen can be supplied as commercial fertilizer.

The farmer in the areas of higher rainfall must supply needed phosphorus for good growth of legumes. Phosphorus so applied usually satisfies the requirements of other crops in the rotation.

Research at the Blackland Agricultural Experiment Station at Temple, Tex., showed that phosphorus fertilization and the method of application are highly important in the growth of sweetclover and the production of nitrogen by legumes. Sixty pounds of phosphoric oxide an acre banded under Evergreen sweetclover brought about an assimilation of 172.6 pounds of nitrogen an acre in 4 months of growth in a moist spring.

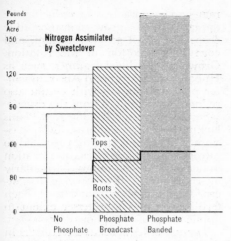

4. The effect of phosphate fertilization (300 pounds of 20 percent superphosphate per acre) on nitrogen assimilation by sweetclover growing on Houston Black clay, Temple, Tex.

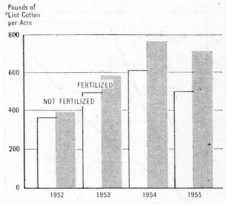

5. Effect of continued use of nitrogen and phosphorus fertilizer on cotton yields growing on Amarillo fine sandy loam, Texas Agricultural Experiment Station, Substation No. 8, Lubbock, Tex. (200 pounds 11–48–0 per acre in 1953, 275 pounds 13–39–0 per acre in 1954, and 200 pounds 16–20–0 per acre in 1955).

A good way to grow sweetclover is to interplant it with small grain in 14-inch rows and apply fertilizer in bands. H. J. Harper, of the Oklahoma Agricultural Experiment Station, developed the method, which was first used in the early 1930's and has been especially successful in drought periods.

A similar method of growing small grain and legumes was adopted at the Texas Agricultural Experiment Station at Beeville for winter, spring, and summer grazing. Sweetclover or alfalfa are interplanted with small grain in 36-inch rows.

Other cool-season crops, such as small grain, respond to phosphorus fertilization on many soils in the Blacklands. When soil tests show deficiencies of phosphorus, band fertilization of winter small grain is a good practice there.

Winter oats respond differently to nitrogen and phosphorus fertilization on various soils in the area. Maximum yields of small grain are not possible unless the soil contains enough available nitrogen and phosphorus. Yields of oats for 0, 30, and 60 pounds of nitrogen an acre without phosphate fertilization on Denton clay near Denton, Tex., were 20, 35, and 42 bushels

an acre, respectively. With 60 pounds of phosphoric oxide an acre and the same nitrogen treatments, the yields were 25, 63, and 71 bushels.

The cropping sequence used in the Blacklands and Grand Prairie areas is important from the standpoint of fertilizers required for various crops in the rotation. Research at the Texas Agricultural Experiment Station at McGregor disclosed that oats responded favorably to nitrogen and phosphorus fertilization when grown continuously, but did not respond when oats followed sweetclover (to which phosphate was applied) and cotton.

Crops growing in rotation with well-managed legumes on Blackland soils respond to the beneficial effects of the legume. Results from experiments conducted at Temple show that row crops following sweetclover (phosphate fertilized) do not respond to additional nitrogen and phosphorus fertilizers. Legumes in rotation improve the nutrient status in the soil, the soil structure, and soil moisture relationships for better crop growth.

Cotton root rot is a severe problem in cotton production in the Blacklands and Rolling Red Plains. The best soil-

Bushels per Acre

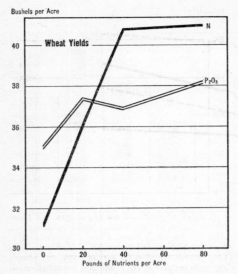

6. *Effect of nitrogen and phosphorus fertilization on yield of wheat at nine locations in western Oklahoma (1951–1952). Nitrogen applied as spring topdressing; all N plots received 40 pounds of P_2O_5 per acre in bands at seeding time. Phosphorus plots received 40 pounds of nitrogen per acre broadcast at planting time. Data reproduced from Oklahoma Agricultural Experiment Station Bulletin No. 432.*

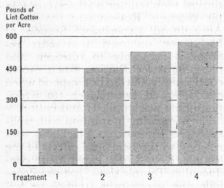

7. *Effect of irrigation on cotton production from Amarillo fine sandy loam soil at Lubbock, Tex. (1951–1954). Treatment No. 1—no irrigation; No. 2—preplanting irrigation of 8.2 inches; No. 3—preplanting application of 8.2 inches plus 4.3 inches in August; No. 4—preplanting application of 8.2 inches plus 3 inches in July and 4.3 inches in August. Average rainfall for the growing season during the 4 years—13.2 inches. Reproduced from Texas Agricultural Experiment Station Bulletin.*

management practice for reducing the damages is to grow nonsusceptible crops like small grain, sorghum, and corn before cotton in the rotation. Growing short-lived legumes, such as Hubam sweetclover and Austrian winter peas, in rotation with cotton also reduces the damages from the disease.

Some soils in the Rolling Red Plains lack nitrogen, phosphorus, and potassium. Cotton and sorghum respond to nitrogen and phosphorus fertilization under dryland conditions, particularly on sandy soils. Wheat growing in western Oklahoma also responds to nitrogen fertilization and to a lesser extent to applications of phosphorus.

The use of legumes and fertilizers in dryland farming in the High Plains has not been successful. Under irrigation, when both precipitation and irrigation water are precious items to be used with utmost care, fertilizers are useful for making better use of water.

A preplanting irrigation to fill the soil reservoir is an excellent practice to insure a good cotton crop each year. One or two irrigations in addition to the preplanting application can be profitable.

Nitrogen and phosphorus fertilizer is essential for continuous cotton under irrigation if maximum yields are to be obtained. Studies of the use of fertilizer at Lubbock showed that yield differences between fertilized and unfertilized continuous cotton become increasingly greater each year. Grain sorghum grown under irrigation in the High Plains requires more nitrogen fertilizer than does cotton.

Soil blowing and drifting can be serious on both cropland and rangeland. Ordinarily it is more serious on cropland, but overgrazed sandy rangelands can be damaged severely. Wind erosion on rangelands can be controlled by grazing management to maintain adequate cover, but that is difficult when you have limited feed reserves.

Prevention of wind erosion on cropland depends on effective surface roughness and vegetative cover. Surface roughness and stability of soil clods help combat wind erosion. Effective

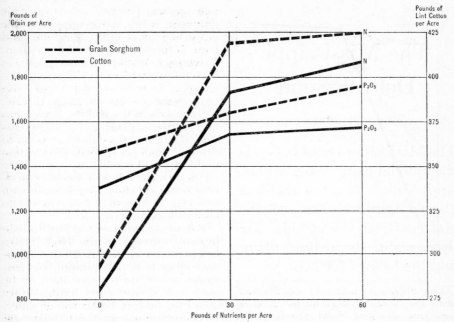

8. *Effect of nitrogen and phosphorus fertilizer on yield of grain sorghum and cotton on Miles fine sandy loam soil under dryland conditions at the Texas Agricultural Experiment Station, Chillicothe (1949–1953).*

surface roughness can be developed on heavy soils by emergency tillage, such as chiseling and listing.

Some sandy soils with heavy clay subsurface layers within 24 inches of the surface can be altered by bringing the clay to the surface by deep plowing. This practice has been carried on with varying success in the High Plains of Texas and the Rolling Red Plains.

An effective way to reduce wind erosion on cropland is the production and management of crop residues.

Cotton and peanuts, leading cash crops on sandy soils that are subject to wind erosion, produce little effective residues for protection against soil blowing. Sorghum, with fair growing conditions, produces residues that, properly managed, can be effective against soil blowing. Narrow spacing of rows of sorghum on soils subject to severe blowing and drifting is more effective than conventional 40-inch plantings. Tillage operations to keep the sorghum residues on the soil sur-

face help greatly in reducing blowing and drifting of soil.

Most cash-crop farmers have to rely on cotton and peanuts for a livelihood. They use various row combinations of high-residue producing crops (sorghum) and low-residue crops in order to insure some degree of protection against blowing. Growers of peanuts on sandy soils in the Crosstimbers plant two rows of grain sorghum and four to eight rows of peanuts in alternating strips.

Cotton growers in the High Plains use various row systems of cotton and sorghum and so achieve some protection against blowing. These various row systems are used for both wind erosion protection and more effective use of soil moisture. An approach to this two-sided problem is being made at the Department's field station at Big Spring, Tex., where a 2-year rotation of cotton and grain sorghum, in which 2 rows are cropped and 2 rows are fallow, is being studied.

The Mississippi
Delta Region

Perrin H. Grissom

The Mississippi Delta region is the alluvial plain of the Mississippi Valley. It stretches from Cape Girardeau, Mo., to the gulf coast, and it includes the flood plain, the deltaic plain, and the loessial terraces.

The elevation increases northward from sea level at the Gulf of Mexico to about 320 feet above sea level in Missouri. The loessial terraces rise 20 to 50 feet higher than the surrounding flood plain. The flood plain consists of low meander belts of ridges and intervening irregular flood basins.

Most of the surface features reflect the depositional activities of running water. The ridges and basins of the upper part of the deltaic plain are somewhat more uniform than the flood plain. The ridges stand higher above the general surface. The lowlands often are covered with water. The lowlands between the ridges give way to coastal marshes and bays, and the marsh areas are characterized by wave action. The loessial terraces are the portions of the alluvial fans of the tributary streams that stand above the general level of the flood plain and are blanketed with loesslike deposits.

The entire alluvial plain is slightly more than 650 miles long. It is 25 miles wide between Natchez, Miss., and Sicily Island, La., and 125 miles wide in the latitude of Helena, Ark. The average width is about 70 miles.

The land area in the Mississippi Valley comprises approximately 27 million acres. About 11.5 million acres of the total remain in forest.

The soil types reflect the action of floodwater. The soils vary from clay to sand and have poor to excessive internal drainage.

At least 30 States have contributed, through erosion, to the soils of the Mississippi Valley. The constant migration and shifting of the channels of the Mississippi and Ohio Rivers in earlier times and the overflows from many tributaries have largely determined the pattern of the surface soils. Alternation of silts, sands, and clays is characteristic of an alluvial profile.

The soil types along the old stream channels generally are fine sandy loams or loams. The broad, flat basins are mostly clay soils, and the intermediate areas, between the basins and the ridges, are silt loams and silty clay soils. As streams overflowed, the sand particles settled out along the stream. The silt and clay particles were held in suspension much longer and finally were deposited by relatively still water in broad, flat areas. The areas along the old stream channels occupied by the coarser textured soils generally rise 5 to 15 feet above the adjacent basins.

Just as water has been the chief factor in the formation of soils in the Mississippi alluvial plain, its management is a major factor in the management of soils.

The stream channels until recent years were inadequate to carry the waterload, and large areas were flooded frequently. Damage to crops and property was tremendous, but the alluvial deposits maintained and replenished an already fertile soil. The deposition usually was beneficial to the soils, but the floods and threat of floods made agriculture hazardous.

The construction of an elaborate levee system and the straightening of stream channels have reduced the possibilities of floods. It has become necessary to base the soil-management program on the soils on hand; further alteration by floodwaters should no longer be anticipated.

Probably in no area of the United States is the conflict between too much water and too little water as pronounced as in the Mississippi Delta region. Excess surface water seriously handicaps winter-growing crops in winter and spring, interferes with land preparation for spring-planted row crops, and often retards the growth of the young plants.

The total annual rainfall in the region is more than the amount required for optimum plant growth, but the distribution is such that water often is scarce in summer. Therefore drainage must be provided, and consideration must be given at the same time to the conservation of water.

Surface drainage, as such, is not necessarily a function of soil management, but the lack of it or the manner of achieving it may vitally influence soil management.

The need for drainage has long been recognized in this region. Lack of drainage has posed a constant threat to stability of yields and has been the chief cause of crop failure.

We can consider drainage as primary and secondary, or farm, drainage.

Primary drainage has reference to drainage in districts or local watersheds. It has been attempted generally through the organized efforts of landowners in a community or district. Such efforts have improved drainage immeasurably in some districts. A hodgepodge of districts has been organized, however, with little or no coordination among them. They have solved local problems, but new problems frequently have been created for other localities downstream.

Primary drainage must be achieved on a broad basis with more comprehensive planning. A successful primary drainage program will have its greatest impact on lands already in cultivation by removing excess water from them. It is doubtful whether the elimination of excess water will benefit land that is not already planted to cultivated crops.

Most of the soils remaining in forest were formed from slack-water sediments and have poor internal drainage. The removal of the excess surface water cannot be expected to affect

526

YEARBOOK OF AGRICULTURE 1957

greatly the natural soil characteristics, and these soils cannot be expected to become highly productive if farmers grow crops that require good aeration and good internal drainage.

Primary drainage is a prerequisite to field drainage, but field drainage is associated more closely with soil management.

Field drainage is necessary, yet the farm effort to provide field drainage in the Mississippi alluvial plain, especially in the loessial terrace areas, has been one major factor contributing to erosion, a poor physical condition of the soil, and a water shortage during periods of greatest need.

Surface drainage of fields may be achieved in two ways. One way is to provide enough structures to remove the water from each low place. The other is to arrange the rows to fit the land so that excess water may be removed—but slowly enough to minimize erosion. Grading and smoothing is necessary to provide the base for proper row alinement on much land.

Drainage by elevation also has been tried. Ridges and low places have been created artificially through the tillage methods. The result usually has been overdrainage of the high places and an extension of the poorly drained low places.

In the Mississippi alluvial valley as a whole, the philosophy in practice consists of moving a raindrop from its point of impact with the soil to the main drainage channels in the shortest time possible.

Water furrows, V-ditches, W-ditches, and rows laid out with the maximum attainable grade have been utilized. Those practices may be needed and may have merit, but their promiscuous use has been harmful. Of all these practices, the water furrow plowed by the mule probably has caused more erosion than any other single practice. The mule no longer is a major source of farm power, but the tractor-drawn road patrol and grader are used to make water furrows that may erode more soil than ever.

A desirable field drainage system for row crops should consist of field-size units, with rows laid out with a uniform slope down the row of 0.1 to 0.3 foot per 100 feet.

The drainage planning should embrace the idea of increasing the flow of water into the soil and reducing the flow from the soil. The number of ditches should be well planned and be kept to a minimum. The fields should be laid out so that turn alleys can also serve to meet the need for W-ditches. The V-ditches and flat-bottom ditches should have a permanent sod. When land grading is performed, it should meet the downslope specification and usually should not exceed a 0.5 foot per 100-foot cross slope. Drainage should be provided on a field basis, rather than a "pothole" basis.

AN ADEQUATE supply of moisture for growing crops also is important. The total annual rainfall of 45 to 60 inches exceeds the optimum requirements of 38 to 42 inches, but its distribution is such that a shortage often occurs in summer, when the average deficit in the northern part is 6 to 9 inches.

We can approach the solution in two ways. One is to increase the intake and storage of rain water. The other is supplemental irrigation.

The reduction of runoff by minimizing the slope down the row represents the first step in correcting moisture deficiencies. Water deficits also may be lessened by increasing moisture storage through improvement of the physical condition of the soil. The addition of organic matter and the elimination of restricting soil layers are two ways to improve the physical condition.

Practices that tend to conserve the natural moisture and to increase its efficiency will reduce the need for supplemental water, but tests at State agricultural experiment stations have shown irrigation to be profitable even though the best known water-conserving practices were utilized.

Some of the considerations involved in planning a supplemental irrigation program and factors associated with its application have definite implications for soil management. Some may apply only to this region. The alluvial soils generally have a relatively high water-holding ability, which permits an irrigation frequency ranging from 10 to 20 days for such crops as cotton and corn. Most of the fine sandy loam soils have enough silt to make it necessary to apply water more slowly than on other fine sandy loams. The clay soils crack when dry and, unlike most clay soils, permit a rapid infiltration of water—occasionally the rate of application is as high as an inch an hour.

A fundamental point in supplemental irrigation in this alluvial region is that lack of drainage has caused more crop losses than drought. Because rain is an ever-present possibility, it seems desirable to limit the irrigation of such crops as cotton, corn, and soybeans to the time when they are fruiting and maturing, except when irrigation is needed for germination. The young plants are more susceptible to excess water; rains are more likely in the period of early growth; and less moisture is evaporated and transpired then. Limiting the irrigation, as I suggested, means slightly less than the maximum yield potential within a given year, but it reduces the hazard in every year.

Irrigation here has utilized both sprinkler and surface methods. Planning is essential to the success of both. The surface methods require that pre-irrigation planning give more consideration to surface conditions than is required with sprinkler methods in order to insure a proper distribution of water. The requirements for surface irrigation will be met if the land is prepared so that drainage is provided and erosion is minimized.

THE PHYSICAL CONDITION of Delta soils frequently limits crop production. Poor physical condition has long been recognized on the clay soils, but the development of physical limitations on some of the lighter soils—or at least the awareness of them—did not occur until recent years. Among the factors that have had a deleterious effect on the physical properties are loss of organic matter, erosion, inadequate drainage, improper cultural practices, and traffic by equipment.

The relatively high temperatures and high moisture in the Delta are conducive to the rapid decomposition of organic material and its subsequent loss. Thus the soils quickly lost a major part of their original organic matter shortly after being brought into cultivation. The result was a lowered stability of structure, a reduced water intake, and more runoff. The conditions that are responsible for the depletion make it difficult to replenish or maintain adequate organic matter.

Although most of the land is gently rolling, erosion is serious. Most of the organic matter was in the top few inches and has been most affected by erosion. Furthermore, the ratio of sand, silt, and clay in the surface soil provided better physical condition than the deeper soil. The removal of the surface layer by sheet erosion leaves material with less desirable physical properties exposed or near the surface. Cultivation of soils when they were too wet has contributed to a breakdown of soil structure in many localities. Sometimes tillage has been excessive.

Hardpans and plowsoles have developed on many of the fine sandy loam and silt loam soils—the result of erosion, management systems that destroy the organic matter, and moving equipment over wet ground. The compacted zone resists water and root penetration. Plants then suffer from too much surface water in rainy weather and from lack of water when conditions are normal or dry.

Deep tillage, or subsoiling, eliminated temporarily the compacted zone in tests at the agricultural experiment stations of Mississippi and Louisiana. Where deep tillage was practiced on compacted soils, the water intake rate, water storage, and root development were increased and were reflected in higher yields. Deep tillage had no effect on clay soils, which crack, and on soils without hardpans. The practice is successful only when the soil is dry enough so that the compacted layer can be shattered.

Many Delta farmers, in attempts to improve the physical condition of soils by increasing the organic matter and reducing erosion, have grown winter legume crops, which they turn under before planting a summer crop. They have used vetch, Austrian winter peas, rough peas, and several clovers. About 300 thousand acres of winter legumes were planted annually in the Delta region of Mississippi, Arkansas, and Louisiana in 1945–1950, but since then the acreage seeded to winter legumes has been much less.

Evaluation of winter legumes at the Mississippi Agricultural Experiment Station revealed that they gave no improvement in physical condition that lasted beyond a few weeks; no increase in the organic matter in the soil; no increase in its water-holding ability; and no measurable benefit, except the nitrogen they furnished the subsequent crop.

Observations have indicated that winter legumes are not successful in controlling erosion with the current planting procedures. In fact, the preparation of land for planting the legumes probably contributed to erosion rather than retarded it.

A more promising variation has been in use on some farms. The winter legumes are allowed to reach maturity before they are turned under in June. The fields are fallowed during the summer months. A second legume crop is grown in the fall and winter and turned under green. This practice has not been evaluated experimentally.

Crop rotation has not been developed sufficiently in the Mississippi Delta for positive recommendations.

Agronomists, soil scientists, and farmers seem to agree that the only known way to improve the physical condition of the soil very much and to increase the organic matter by cropping is through the use of perennial sod crops. We are not sure how long the sod should be maintained, but a minimum of 3 to 5 years is indicated.

The use of a deep-rooted legume, such as sweetclover, for improving soil conditions has been studied at the experiment stations. Attempts to grow alfalfa on compacted soils have not been successful.

MECHANIZATION has changed crop production a great deal since 1945. The changeover from mulepower has given an opportunity for solving some problems, but it has brought some new ones. An example: The breakdown of structure because of cultivation while the soil was too wet has always plagued the farmer who used mules, but such cultivation was considered necessary to get the job done. Machines reduce the time required for a given operation so greatly that farmers no longer have to begin before the soil moisture is favorable. On the other hand, the speed that permits timeliness also encourages excessive treatment. The preplanting treatment should be sufficient to provide a good seedbed. Cultivation should be enough to control weeds and eliminate crusts. Tillage in excess of that can be harmful, especially on soils that are subject to compaction.

Because mechanization requires uniform fields, the preparation of land for drainage and irrigation fulfills the basic requirements for the operation of mechanical equipment. Conversely, equipment improperly designed or used incorrectly can spoil uniform surfaces. The use of one-way disk plows or one-way moldboard plows, for example, can destroy the uniformity of a field in one operation.

PROVIDING ENOUGH NUTRIENTS is a vital part of soil management.

Sufficient plant nutrients except nitrogen are contained in most Delta soils for maximum production. The general fertility level is relatively high. Deficiencies of phosphorus, potassium, and lime occur only on about 15 to 20 percent of the alluvial soils.

The highest level of plant nutrients

occurs nearest the Mississippi River in the areas of most recent overflows. The deficiencies are most pronounced in places where sediments from tributaries, originating in the nearby hill areas, exert the dominant influence on the soil conditions. No evidence of a lack of trace elements has been noted.

The fertility level of the loessial terrace soils is lower than that of the alluvial soils, and phosphate and potash are needed generally.

In supplementing the natural fertility with applications of fertilizer, the basic concept recommended and usually followed by farmers is that the crop, not the soil, be fertilized.

Nitrogen must be supplied for all nonlegume crops in the region. It may be furnished by legumes or by inorganic material. Cost is the determining factor. Generally it has been more economical to use commercial nitrogen for cultivated crops. In pasture production, the use of legumes in the sod mixture has proved to be the more economical source. In some pasture programs or periods when extremely high yields of forage are desired, however, the use of high rates of nitrogen to stimulate the grass may be required.

Just as price is the determining factor in the choice between commercial nitrogen and legume nitrogen, price and method of application should also be the chief consideration in choosing a source of commercial nitrogen.

Anhydrous ammonia, ammonium nitrate, ammonium sulfate, cyanamide, nitrate of soda, urea, and nitrolime are all used as sources of nitrogen in this region. Anhydrous ammonia supplied about 50 percent of the total in 1956. Ammonium nitrate furnished slightly more than 25 percent.

Anhydrous ammonia can be applied successfully on any soil that is in good tilth. It is difficult to apply ammonia on soils in poor tilth, particularly heavy clay soils, because ammonia must be sealed in the soil simultaneously with its injection. Other forms of nitrogen will usually prove more efficient on those soils and also, in most instances,

when close-growing crops are to be top-dressed. Again, sealing the ammonia in the soil is the limiting factor. If sealing can be done, ammonia will prove equal to other sources.

Most of the nitrogen is supplied by acid-forming sources. Because the pH ranged from 5.3 to 6.8 on most of the alluvial soils in 1956 and the loessial terraces were somewhat more acid, it seems certain that lime eventually will be required to neutralize the acidity. Few alluvial soils showed a response, however, except when some legumes are grown, and tests have not indicated that the acidity is increasing so fast as theoretical calculations imply. A much higher percentage of the loessial soils need lime.

In this area, where several of the nutrients exist in abundant amounts, the "balanced nutrient" idea has little or no practical application. It is important that each nutrient be supplied in adequate amounts, but no evidence exists to indicate that any given ratio must obtain between them under field conditions. Nitrogen is the only major nutrient that will be particularly harmful if it is used to excess. Even with nitrogen, the balancing must be with the plant and not with other plant nutrients.

CROP PRODUCTION is the ultimate objective of a soil-management program. For maximum yields and maximum efficiency in production, crops must be grown on soils to which they are adapted, or sufficient treatment must be applied to an unadapted soil to overcome the natural limitations.

The latter approach assumes that information is available to prescribe the necessary treatment. This was not the case in 1957 in the Delta region. It is desirable that the knowledge of soil management be increased sufficiently to make economics the factor that determines whether a crop should be grown on a given soil. In view of the present level of knowledge, however, practical considerations dictate that crops be grown on the soils where they are best adapted. The selection of the soil type must be followed up with other soil-management practices.

Cotton, soybeans, corn, oats, wheat, barley, alfalfa, sugarcane, rice, and pastures occupy more than 96 percent of the open land in the region.

Cotton is the leader. It is best adapted to the fine sandy loam, loam, and silt loam soils that have good internal drainage, but it can be grown profitably on most of the soils where surface drainage can be provided. Land preparation should be limited to the necessary tillage to provide a good seedbed—tillage should be deep when hardpans exist. Cultivation should be limited to the amount necessary to eliminate any crusting and to control weeds. Nitrogen must be supplied by legumes or by commercial fertilizers on all soils. The optimum rate ranges from 60 to 120 pounds of nitrogen an acre. Most soils may need the higher rate. Some soils need phosphorus and potash. The need to rotate cotton and high-residue crops or sod crops increases as the soil becomes finer.

On some of the better sandy loam soils, cotton can be grown continuously for an indefinite period if erosion is controlled, fertility is maintained at a high level, minimum tillage is practiced, and all tillage is done when soil moisture is favorable.

Soybeans rank second to cotton here. They grow equally well on fine sandy loam to clay soils. If satisfactory stands are obtained, the yields on clay soils are less variable and less affected by drought. Generally no fertilizer is needed except on loessial terrace soils, where potash is frequently deficient. We have no evidence that rotations are beneficial. In fact, some observations indicate that yields of soybeans tend to increase by successive cropping. Soybeans are especially susceptible to hardpan conditions.

Small grains are particularly well adapted to this region. Oats are better adapted to the lighter soils, although satisfactory yields can be produced on the clay soils. Wheat is adapted to most of the soils but is better suited to the clay soils than oats. Barley is adapted to the lighter soils but is limited by diseases in most of the southern part of the region. All three, especially barley, require good surface drainage. Nitrogen is the only plant nutrient generally required; 45 to 60 pounds of nitrogen an acre usually are best. The inability of the plants to resist lodging limits the rate of application. Nitrogen should be applied as a topdressing in late February or early March. Rotation with other crops may be necessary, particularly in the case of barley and wheat, to control disease.

The soil-management requirements for corn are essentially the same as those I listed for cotton, except that slightly higher rates of nitrogen (120 pounds an acre) are required. Lack of attention to production practices is the primary reason for low average corn yields in this region. Corn is well adapted, and average yields of more than 50 bushels an acre are attainable.

Alfalfa is planted on a larger acreage in the Delta region than any other hay crop. It is well adapted to silty clay and clay soils. Lack of surface drainage has been one of the chief causes of failure. In order to insure drainage where fields do not have uniform slopes, the soil should be formed into lands 50 to 130 feet wide and 8 to 14 inches high. A well-prepared, firm seedbed is necessary. Many of the soils require lime. Some need phosphorus and potassium. Most of the soils near the Mississippi River, however, are adequately supplied with all plant nutrients.

More sugarcane is grown in this region than in any other part of the United States. The acreage is concentrated largely in the lower part of Louisiana. Drainage is a major problem. Nitrogen is the one nutrient that must be generally applied.

Rice is adapted to clay and silty clay soils and to silt loams that have a compacted layer. The soil characteristics must be such that water movement through the profile is restricted. A rotation system is more necessary for rice than for any other crop grown in the Delta. Weed control is the primary purpose for the rotation, although improved structure and increased nitrogen are important secondary effects. The cropping sequence should provide for 1 to 2 years in rice and 1 to 3 years in lespedeza, soybeans, or pasture. One new and apparently promising rotation in some parts of Arkansas consists of 2 years in rice and 1 to 2 years of water fallow. A water level of 2 to 4 feet is maintained during the fallow period, and a crop of fish is produced. Nitrogen is the major nutrient that must be applied. Phosphorus may be needed on some soils. Lodging limits the rate of nitrogen application. The natural soil conditions and the present knowledge of management practices suggest a great potential rice production here if the market should demand it.

Pastures occupy 10 to 15 percent of the open land. The acreage has expanded rapidly since 1948. Most of the expansion has been on the silty clay and clay soils, except in places where a 3- to 5-year rotation with other crops is practiced. Establishment is a major problem, largely because of crusting and cracking of the soils. Land preparation in the fall and early spring seeding tend to minimize stand failures. Mixtures of grasses and legumes afford the most economical pastures, and ones which generally require little or no fertilization. Red clover and Johnsongrass for the lighter soils and tall fescue and Ladino clover for clay soils are two examples of adapted mixtures. Under intensive management systems where high forage production in late spring and summer is required, Coastal Bermuda-grass and Johnsongrass offer the best possibility. Each grass will require irrigation and the application of the equivalent of 1 pound of nitrogen a day during the growth period.

Soil management is seldom the limiting factor in pasture production. Rather, lack of knowledge of pasture crops and livestock management have usually limited the development of the pasture-livestock program.

The Coastal Prairies

R. K. Walker and R. J. Miears

The Coastal Prairie region in southwestern Louisiana and in southeastern Texas includes about 8 million acres. It almost parallels the coast of the Gulf of Mexico. A long, narrow band of coastal marshland lies between the prairie and the gulf.

The climate is subtropical. The average annual rainfall ranges from 58 inches in Louisiana to 34 inches in Texas. The average January temperature is 55° F. The average July temperature is 83° F. The average number of days between the last frost in spring and first frost in fall is 286. Extremely hot weather and severe cold weather seldom occur.

THE TOPOGRAPHY appears to be flat over wide areas, but the land slopes gradually to the gulf. The maximum elevation above sea level is slightly more than 100 feet, but most of the area is less than 50 feet above sea level. The prairie is bisected by many small streams and several large, well-defined streams with pronounced and fairly steep bordering slopes. Pimple mounds are conspicuous in several places.

The soils were formed from material carried by fresh water to the sea and deposited. These sediments were later uplifted and subjected to soil-forming processes under a grass cover.

The principal soils in Louisiana (and also in extensive sections in Texas) are deep, medium in texture, and slowly permeable. Crowley, Beaumont, and

Midland soils are the major series. The top 10 inches is a friable, light-brown silt loam, which becomes light gray when it dries thoroughly. The next 10 to 18 inches is a smooth, floury silt loam, which grades sharply into mottled yellow, red, and gray, heavy, plastic silty clay or clay. The thickness of the surface soil layer and the depth of subsoil vary considerably.

The large areas of deep, fine-textured, slowly permeable soils lie mainly in Texas. Lake Charles, Edna, and Beaumont are the major soil series. This group of soils is characterized by heavy, dense clay, with little difference between the topsoil and subsoil. The soils are sticky when wet but become slightly granular when dry. The surface soils are dark gray to black.

Extensive areas of deep, fine-textured, slowly permeable soils with dark-gray loam to clay surface soils also exist in the Coastal Prairie. They are sticky when wet but granular and crumbly when dry. Approximately 2.5 percent of the region is composed of bottom land.

About 90 percent of the Louisiana Coastal Prairie region is in cultivation. Only 25 percent of the Texas region is cultivated.

Rice production dominates the Louisiana and eastern Texas part of the Coastal Prairie.

In the extreme western part in Texas, the main crops are cotton, grain sorghums, and corn. Some rice is grown there also.

Cattle are raised in conjunction with the major crops. Approximately 75 percent of the Texas Coastal Prairie is in pasture. Vegetable crops and dairying are important in small areas near cities.

The general cropping system in the part where rice is the dominant crop is 1 year in rice and 2 years or more in native grass pasture. No definite cropping system is used over large areas in the western end of the region, but cotton generally is rotated with corn and grain sorghum, and winter legumes are grown in some localities in rotation with row crops.

The principal soil problems are poor drainage, both surface and internal; poor physical condition of soils; a low content of organic matter; and a relatively low fertility level. Lack of available nitrogen and phosphorus is the major deficiency.

SURFACE DRAINAGE of large portions of various watersheds was the dominant soil-management problem when the land was originally put into cultivation. Much emphasis has been placed on improvement of drainage of these areas by Federal, State, and local agencies. Some drainage projects have been completed. Others were in varying stages of completion in 1957, and much remained to be done to provide proper drainage of the entire area.

Individual farm drainage has been vastly improved by providing drainage ditches. Field drainage has been greatly improved by land-leveling practices. Conservation of irrigation water in flooding riceland is another result of land leveling, which has been done on an extensive scale and is a standard practice.

Poor internal drainage of the Coastal Prairie soils is an inherent characteristic that cannot be altered very much. This factor is favorable for keeping ricelands under a continuous flood during the growing season, but it prohibits the successful production of a large number of crops and makes the soil difficult to work for good seedbed preparation and cultivation.

A trend toward a rotation of improved pastures and rice has been evident in the Coastal Prairie rice area.

Results of longtime experimental work in Louisiana show that rotation

of improved pastures with rice will increase beef production from 46 to 271 pounds an acre annually and increase rice yields by 5 barrels an acre. The rotation also combats undesirable grasses, broad-leaved weeds, and "red rice," increases the fertility level of the soil, and improves its physical condition.

Improved pastures that may contain ryegrass, whiteclover, Dallisgrass, Bermuda-grass, and lespedeza, supplemented with oats or wheat for temporary winter grazing and with lespedeza or alyceclover for temporary summer grazing and hay production, provide high-quality grazing, hay, and grain in the area.

A NEED exists for supplementary irrigation of nearly all crops in the region, even though the annual rainfall is relatively high.

A large percentage of the total area has facilities for irrigating rice. The facilities can be used in supplementary irrigation on all adapted crops. Contour levees should be erected for all crops, except row crops, to permit intermittent flushing during dry periods. The vast supply of water, the existing pumping facilities, canals, and laterals, and the farmers' knowledge of flushing techniques make irrigation at low cost possible.

Soils that have been planted to rice for many years have a poor physical condition. Factors contributing to poor physical condition of the soils are: Low content of organic matter, poor internal drainage, working the land when it is wet, grazing under wet conditions, submergence over extended periods, and a high content of silt and clay.

A hard rain on a prepared seedbed, followed by rapid drying, results in a hard crust, which seals the soil surface. This condition prevents the emergence of young seedlings and retards the growth of young plants. A solution to this problem has been found for many crops following rice.

Winter and summer grasses, whiteclovers, lespedeza, oats, wheat, and flax have been grown successfully by seeding broadcast in rice stubble without any seedbed preparation. Forage and seed yields compare favorably with yields under prepared seedbed conditions. Adequate fertilization is necessary with either method of seeding.

A trend toward this method of seeding is expected because seedbed preparation involves no expense; seeding and fertilization by airplane can be made at any time that is convenient to the farmer, regardless of conditions of soil moisture; erosion can be controlled by a cover of stubble, straw, and undisturbed topsoil; and less bogging by livestock occurs when wet land has to be grazed.

Seedlings exhibit more vigor when they are established in a stubble and straw-covered surface than in a hard-crust surface, which sometimes follows preparation of the seedbed.

The production of large quantities of rice in excess of domestic consumption and export needs began in 1954. Severe acreage reductions were made under Government price-support and acreage-control program. Diversion of land once in rice to uses that will produce an economic return is necessary in the region.

RESEARCH STUDIES by the Texas and Louisiana Agricultural Experiment Stations show that few other crops are adapted to the poorly drained, highly impervious soils of the Coastal Prairie region. The major potential use for a large acreage of land normally planted to rice is improved pastures that will be used in rotation with rice.

Diversion of land use from rice to the production of livestock feed crops is also a possibility. Work at the Louisiana Rice Experiment Station, Crowley, La., has shown that oats, wheat, and grain sorghums can be grown in the area and that rice and its byproducts are an excellent source of feed.

Cottonseed products, molasses, and miscellaneous feeds are available and make possible the formulation of good feed for livestock at a low cost. A potential for a large increase in the use of feed exists because the beef cattle system in the area has largely been the maintenance of cows and marketing of calves at weaning age. Farmers could realize greater profits from their land and cattle by producing feed crops and marketing higher quality animals at heavier weights than under the present system.

THE USE OF COMMERCIAL fertilizers for the major crops in the region has increased greatly since 1945. Farmers tend to use the rates recommended on the basis of experiments in Texas and Louisiana. The major deficiencies are in available phosphorus and nitrogen.

All soils in the region need 40 to 80 pounds of nitrogen and 20 to 40 pounds of phosphoric oxide an acre for rice. An additional 20 pounds of potash is needed for light-textured soils. Maximum efficiency is obtained when the phosphorus and potash are applied during the period from seeding to 30 days after emergence of the rice plants. A part of the total nitrogen requirement can be applied with good results as late as eight weeks after emergence.

DURING THE FIRST YEAR of establishment, improved pastures need a minimum application of 40 pounds of nitrogen, 100 pounds of phosphoric oxide, and 60 pounds of potash an acre.

After the pastures are established, annual applications of 60 pounds of nitrogen, 40 pounds of phosphoric oxide, and 20 pounds of potash should be made.

The reaction of the more acid soils should be adjusted to pH 6.2 by the application of agricultural limestone. Wheat and oats for winter supple-mentary pasture and grain production have indicated a need for 80 pounds of nitrogen and 60 pounds of phosphoric oxide. Twenty pounds of potash an acre should be applied in potash-deficient areas. Applications of 40 pounds of nitrogen and 40 pounds of phosphoric oxide have produced maximum yields for grain production when grazing is not practiced.

Lespedeza and alyceclover for hay production have produced high yields with the addition of 20 pounds of nitrogen, 60 pounds of phosphoric oxide, and 20 pounds of potash.

COMPETITIVE BROAD-LEAVED weeds and grasses that thrive in water are one of the limiting factors in rice yields. The lands of the Coastal Prairie that have been planted to rice for a long time are highly infested with seed of plants that will grow in water. In rice growing, the land is submerged to an average depth of 4 to 5 inches when the rice is about 8 inches tall, and submergence is continuous throughout the growing season. Grass and weeds are controlled by submergence with water under ideal weather and soil conditions. Adverse conditions for quick germination of rice seed, rapid emergence, and the growth of plants are frequent, and permit the early growth of grass and broad-leaved plants.

If competitive plants attain a growth equal to the rice plants, they will persist in the water and cause a serious reduction in the yield and quality of the rice.

Broad-leaved plants can be controlled after they emerge by applying herbicides, such as 2,4-D and 2,4,5-T, but grasses are not sensitive to those chemicals. Research with applications of various chemicals before emergence, at emergence, and shortly after emergence has shown good possibilities that grasses can be controlled in rice by herbicides. Complete control of competitive vegetation will permit the rice plants to utilize fertilizers more efficiently and will also increase the yields and quality.

The Midland Feed Region

W. H. Pierre and F. F. Riecken

The Midland feed region, an area of about 220 million acres, extends from central Ohio to western Nebraska and from southwestern Missouri to central Minnesota.

It has 11.5 percent of the total land area of the United States and more than 34 percent of the total cropland. It produces more than two-thirds of our corn, oats, and soybeans and nearly one-half of our alfalfa. The value of the livestock in the region is about a third of the total of the entire country.

Most of the land in this productive region is level to gently rolling. The soils are generally medium to fine in texture. They have good structure and hold moisture well. They were formed chiefly from glacial and related soil material and are relatively young and productive. About 60 percent of the soil was formed under prairie vegetation. Being relatively high in organic matter and nitrogen, the soils have a high reservoir of fertility.

The rainfall in most of the Midland feed region is 30 to 40 inches annually. The west and northwest one-fourth receives about 22 to 30 inches, but this drier section gets about 75 percent of its total in April to September while crops are growing.

The growing season is long and warm and has about 180 frost-free days in the south and 140 frost-free days in the north. Only occasionally does corn fail to mature properly.

Corn, the crop of greatest overall economic advantage, is grown on more than 44 million acres. Oats, forages, soybeans, and wheat also are important.

The early systems of soil management in the region revolved largely around lime, legumes, and livestock. The idea was all right, but it was oversimplified and overgeneralized.

It had its greatest usefulness in the eastern part, where most soils are acid and relatively low in organic matter and nitrogen. Farmers in the western part recognized early that soil-management systems need to be directed more toward conservation and efficient utilization of moisture.

As soil-management systems have evolved in the region, however, the twin goals of the efficient and sustained production have been placed upon a broader base—that of providing plant nutrients in amounts and kinds needed; control of the water by drainage or by conservation measures; improving organic matter and soil tilth; control of soil erosion; and a fuller integration of all needed soil- and crop-management practices for each kind of soil.

Among the major soil-management practices in the Midland feed region are: Tillage methods to develop suitable seedbeds and to control weeds; the use of legumes in the crop rotation and of manures and crop residue as sources of nitrogen and organic matter; drainage of wet soils; liming of acid soils; the use of commercial fertilizers for improvement of soil fertility; special practices for erosion control, such as stripcropping, contour tillage, and terracing; and the use of moisture conservation practices and supplemental irrigation to some extent.

Even the best established practices

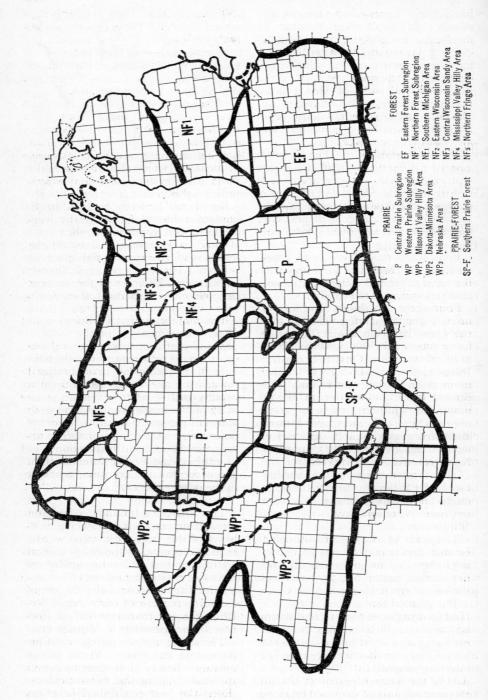

FOREST

EF　Eastern Forest Subregion
NF　Northern Forest Subregion
NF₁　Southern Michigan Area
NF₂　Eastern Wisconsin Area
NF₃　Central Wisconsin Sandy Area
NF₄　Mississippi Valley Hilly Area
NF₅　Northern Fringe Area

PRAIRIE

P　Central Prairie Subregion
WP　Western Prairie Subregion
WP₁　Missouri Valley Hilly Area
WP₂　Dakota-Minnesota Area
WP₃　Nebraska Area

PRAIRIE-FOREST

SP-F　Southern Prairie Forest

have been undergoing considerable changes in application because of mechanization and the changing agricultural pattern and because new facts have been discovered and a better understanding has been obtained of the suitability and value of various practices for different soils. Moreover, realization has grown that many practices must usually be combined into any soil-management system.

The proportion of the various crops varies in different parts of the region with climate, soil, or topography. That in turn affects the kind and amount of livestock, the type of farming, and the systems of soil management necessary for efficient and sustained production.

FIVE SUBREGIONS have been recognized in the Midland feed region on the basis of general differences in soils, climate, and type of farming.

Four of the subregions form approximately the area often referred to as the Corn Belt. They are the eastern forest subregion (EF), consisting mostly of northwestern Ohio and northern Indiana; the central prairie (P), mostly in northern Illinois, eastern and north-central Iowa, and south-central Minnesota; the southern prairie forest subregion (SP–F), in northern Missouri and parts of adjoining States; and the western prairie belt (WP), mostly in Nebraska and South Dakota.

The fifth subregion, the northern forest (NF), lies to the north and includes primarily southern Michigan, southern Wisconsin, and southeastern Minnesota.

The soils of the forest subregions, formed largely under forest vegetation, are lighter in color and generally lower in organic matter and in bases than the soils in the prairie subregions.

The general topography of the Midland feed region is level to undulating, but gently rolling or hilly lands are extensive in several of the subregions, particularly in the southern prairie-forest subregion (SP–F), the eastern part of the western prairie (WP), and the western part of the northern forest

(NF) subregions. They are subject to serious erosion. They require special management.

Extensive areas of level soils that require artificial drainage exist in the central prairie, the eastern forest, and the northern forest subregions.

Most soils of the region are deep and have a medium to fine texture. They therefore can store water well. Sandy soils, however, with low soil moisture-holding capacity, are fairly extensive in the northern forest subregion and in parts of the eastern forest and western prairie subregions.

Significant differences exist in the climate of the subregions. In the northern forest belt, for example, the climate is cooler and the length of the growing season is shorter than in the other subregions. Largely as a result of this, corn loses its dominance and forage crops become more important than in the other subregions.

The highest annual summer rainfall (April–September) is in the southern prairie-forest subregion in central Missouri, where it amounts to 26 inches. From there the rainfall drops gradually toward the north and east and rather rapidly to the west; it reaches a low of 17 inches in the western edge of the western prairie subregion. Moisture deficiency there is one of the serious limitations to corn production, and practices to conserve moisture and irrigation are much more important than in the other subregions.

THE CENTRAL PRAIRIE SUBREGION, approximately 40 million acres, is the heart of the Corn Belt and the Midland feed region. It consists of a nearly continuous area of level to gently rolling topography and extends from east-central Illinois to west-central Minnesota. It comprises nearly one-half of Illinois, more than one-half of Iowa, and about one-sixth of Minnesota.

The soils generally are the most productive in the region. Yields of corn averaged nearly 55 bushels an acre in the 1946–1955 period. More than one-third of the counties in the Illinois part of the area averaged slightly more than 60 bushels an acre.

Almost all the soils were developed under prairie vegetation and are dark in color and high in organic matter and total nitrogen. Having been formed predominantly from medium-textured parent material, either of glacial origin or of related windblown silts or loess material, the soils are generally permeable and quite favorable for tillage operations under a wide range of moisture conditions. A few, however, like the Rowe and Bryce soils of northeastern Illinois, were formed from fine-textured (heavy) glacial tills and are so impermeable that tile drainage does not work satisfactorily.

More than 25 percent of the soils of the central prairie subregion are of level to nearly level topography and usually require artificial drainage. The Webster and Clyde soils of Iowa and Minnesota and the Drummer-Sable soils of Illinois are typical examples of naturally poorly drained soils that have been extensively drained with tile.

The Muscatine silt loam soil, in eastern Iowa and central Illinois where the loess blankets the glacial till, is considered by some agronomists to be the best soil type in the region. In a sense it has become a benchmark soil, against which other soils are compared for productivity, yield, and suitability for crops. It has a thick, dark surface layer, occurs on nearly level slopes, and seldom requires artificial drainage.

Associated with the level soils in many places are soils of moderate slope and good natural drainage but apt to erode because of their topography when they are cropped intensively.

Because of the pronounced suitability of the soils of the central prairie subregion for corn and because of the marked economic advantage of corn over other feed crops, about 50 percent of the harvested cropland in the subregion is in corn, according to the 1950 Census, compared to about 38 percent in the whole region and to about 25 percent in the northern forest subregion.

The central prairie subregion also has the highest percentage of harvested cropland in soybeans, the other leading intertilled crop of the region. The total intertilled acreage, expressed as a percentage of the harvested cropland, is nearly 60 percent, compared to 28 percent in the northern forest subregion.

The most intensive grain production in the subregion is in east-central Illinois and parts of north-central Iowa, where the type of farming is cash grain (corn, oats, and soybeans). In all other parts, the feed usually is fed on the farms where it is grown, and raising hogs is a major enterprise. In northeastern Iowa and south-central Minnesota, where the acreages of hay and pasture are somewhat higher, dairying predominates. Livestock feeding and hogs are both important in east-central Iowa and west-central Illinois.

A system based on lime, legumes, and phosphates has been advocated and followed to some extent for several decades. Because of the intensive grain cropping, however, many soils have lost one-fourth to more than one-third of their original content of nitrogen and organic matter. With less than 10 percent of the harvested cropland in legume hay and approximately 50 percent in corn (1950 Census), the legumes cannot supply the nitrogen needs of the grain crops in the rotation.

Nitrogen fertilizers have come to have an important place. Experimental work has shown that the use of 80 to 100 pounds of fertilizer nitrogen on even the best of these prairie soils can sometimes double the yield of corn. If favorable relationships exist between the price of commercial nitrogen and the price of farm products, nitrogen fertilizers undoubtedly will become even more important in supplementing nitrogen from legumes and manure.

More phosphorus and potassium also are needed on these prairie soils, even though the total use of fertilizer tripled in the three States of the subregion between 1945 and 1956.

Another important problem is tillage, particularly as it relates to economy of operation and the maintaining of satisfactory tilth. Excessive tillage, especially for corn, has been partly responsible for a decline in soil organic matter, a deterioration of tilth, and (on sloping soils) an increase in soil erosion.

Experiments have proved that tillage operations can be cut considerably. Some farmers have adopted new methods, which are aimed at minimum tillage for corn in order to save time and money and to maintain better tilth, reduce soil compaction, and enhance water absorption. Among them are the substitution of chemicals for at least one cultivation in the control of weeds; the use of subsurface tillage instead of plowing, with residues left on the surface; and the so-called plow-plant method, in which the corn is planted in the wheel tracks immediately after plowing and the seedbed between the rows is kept loose with minimum tillage.

These new methods, combined with contour tillage, may become especially important on soils subject to erosion. Subsurface tillage with a mulch of crop residues can reduce erosion loss by at least one-half of the loss that comes with plowing and conventional tillage.

The central prairie subregion is also well adapted to alfalfa and other forages. These crops produce high yields and supply some nitrogen to the other crops in the rotation. Cheap nitrogen fertilizers and improved tillage methods, however, have made it possible to vary considerably the amount of legumes and grasses in the rotation without loss of productivity. In fact, it seems probable that on permeable, nonerosive soils high yields can be maintained with continuous corn under a system of heavy fertilization, green manuring, and proper management.

A wide range of choices in soil-management systems and in type of farming are therefore possible in the central prairie subregion. Likewise, because of its favorable soils and topography, this subregion is well adapted to mechanization and to other advances in technology.

THE EASTERN FOREST SUBREGION comprises an area of about 30 million acres in northwestern Ohio, northern Indiana, and southwestern Michigan. It gets 35 to 40 inches of well-distributed rainfall. It has a growing season of 160 to 180 days.

The soils, formed mostly under forest vegetation, generally are light in color and low in organic matter, although areas of dark-colored, poorly drained soils are extensive. Developed from various types of glacial material, they differ considerably in texture. Fine-textured soils, such as the Brookston and Paulding clays, are extensive in the lacustrine lake plain area of northwestern Ohio. Sands and sandy loam soils occur in northwestern Indiana. Most of the soils in other areas, however, have a friable loam to silt loam surface.

The land is mostly level to gently rolling, except on moraines and near the main streams, where the soils may be rolling to steep. Much of the land was originally poorly drained; most of it is now in drainage enterprises, but inadequate drainage still is a problem on many farms. Peat and muck soils are rather extensive in northwestern Indiana, and are drained by ditching and tiling.

The types of farming are many. Livestock farms predominate in the southern part; hog raising is the important enterprise, but there are also many cash-grain and dairy farms. Cash-grain production and dairying are relatively more important in the northern part. There are also many livestock and general farms.

The acreages in corn and soybeans are high, making up about 50 percent of the harvested crop, which is only about 10 percent less than in the central prairie subregion. Instead of oats, however, wheat is the most important small grain, especially in the southern part, where the acreage is about 50 percent greater than that of oats.

Small grain and hay are grown on 34 and 14 percent, respectively, of the harvested acreage. The amount of cropland pasture amounts to about 17 percent of the total cropland, which in 1949 was about 50 percent higher than in the central prairie subregion.

Because of the relatively small amounts of legumes in the rotations, nitrogen is a limiting element in crop production despite the large increase in the use of nitrogen fertilizer since 1945.

Sod crops (legumes and grasses) have been found to be especially beneficial to sugar beets and other crops in the rotation on the fine-textured soils of northwestern Ohio, partly because of their effect in improving soil structure. In experiments at the Ohio Agricultural Experiment Station, however, good results were had—even on these fine-textured soils—from the addition of large amounts of nitrogen with carbonaceous residues as a means of maintaining good tilth and yields.

Because, in general, the soils of this subregion have been farmed longer than those of any other subregion and because forest soils have a naturally lower fertility than prairie soils, fertilizers have been used for a longer time and in larger amounts than in other parts of the Midland feed region. Even greater amounts are needed, however, for most efficient production of pastures and harvested crops. Pastures on the more rolling, eroded soils are particularly in need of improvement through fertilization, liming, and legumes.

Liming has been practiced for many years, but most soils still are acid and in need of moderate amounts of lime—particularly for the good growth of alfalfa, which is exceeded in acreage by red clover, a less productive crop on most soils.

Some of the black sandy soils in northern Indiana and the fine-textured soils in northeastern Indiana have too little manganese for soybeans, oats, and wheat. Alfalfa in northern Indiana has responded to applications of boron.

The high acreage of intertilled crops and the usual type of tillage methods mean that the control of erosion has become an important problem on rolling lands. Contour tillage and stripcropping need to be used much more extensively in supplementing rotations. Minimum tillage methods also offer opportunities for reducing soil compaction, increasing water absorption, and reducing erosion. Mulch-residue tillage can be used effectively for erosion control on the coarser textured and the better aerated soils. Manure mulches also are effective.

Winter cover crops need to be used wherever feasible, especially because, of the relatively heavy precipitation in winter. On the sandy and muck soils in the northwestern part where wind erosion is a problem, cover crops of rye and other small grains are valuable. High amounts of fertilizers, especially potassium, are also necessary there.

Although the soils of the subregion are of lower natural fertility than the soils of the central prairie subregion, yields of corn are nearly as high—an average of 52 bushels in 1946–1955.

THE NORTHERN FOREST SUBREGION covers about 52 million acres in southern Wisconsin, southern Michigan, and east-central Minnesota.

Because the climate of most of the subregion is cooler and the growing season is shorter than in other parts of the Midland feed region, corn loses its dominance, and hay and pasture crops are more important. The total acreage of hay and cropland pasture is about double the acreage of corn (including corn for silage), whereas in the central prairie subregion it is about half. Dairy farming therefore predominates in most parts of the subregion, especially in eastern and southern Wisconsin. In southeastern Wisconsin and in the Mississippi Valley hill area, the corn yields compare favorably with those in the central prairie subregion, but in the other sections the yields averaged only about 40 to 45 bushels an acre in 1946–1955—no doubt because of the shorter growing season and the relatively poorer soils.

In most parts of the subregion are also many general livestock farms. In southern Michigan, some fruit and cash grain farming systems are followed; wheat is the principal small grain.

Nearly all the soils of this subregion were formed under forest vegetation and are light in color and low in organic matter, except in areas of poor natural drainage.

The largest area of productive soils is in the eastern Wisconsin area (NF2), where the topography generally is level or gently rolling. Most of the soils are loams to clay loams and of good permeability and water-holding capacity. Scattered areas of organic soils (peats and mucks) are in the poorly drained areas. Limited areas of sandy soils also occur.

The Mississippi Valley hilly area (NF4) is rolling or quite steep. The soils are mostly friable silt loams derived from glacial materials, primarily silty loess. Other soils, formed from limestone and sandstone, often are shallow, especially on the steeper slopes where rock outcroppings occur.

The soils in southern Michigan were formed from glacial material varying in texture from sand to clay. They are quite variable in texture, permeability, and management requirements. The topography mostly is nearly level to gently rolling, although glacial knolls and hills are common in some places.

The northern fringe area of Wisconsin and Minnesota (NF5) also is of glacial origin and variable in soil and topography. Sandy, relatively infertile soils are common, and some fine-textured soils with somewhat poor drainage occur in the Wisconsin part of the area. Peat and muck soils are common in the depressions in the morainic and rolling sections.

The least productive soils of the subregion are found in the central Wisconsin sandy area (NF3), which comprises all or parts of 10 counties. The soils are primarily droughty sands and loamy sands and poorly drained organic soils. The land is rolling in the east and nearly level in the west.

Because of differences in soil and climate, the soil-management systems in this subregion are quite variable. Commonly, however, the systems revolve around the fact that approximately 30 percent of the harvested cropland consists of legume-grass meadows. Alfalfa is grown extensively in the crop rotation in most places. Wisconsin alone grew more than 2 million acres of alfalfa in 1955, or nearly 10 percent of the total acreage in the United States. The acreage of alfalfa in Wisconsin is more than three-fourths that of corn, which is in considerable contrast to the part of Illinois in the central prairie subregion, which has only about 10 percent as much alfalfa as corn. The large acreage in legumes and the large amounts of manure produced mean that in general the nitrogen needs of the grain crops in the rotation are more nearly met without the use of nitrogen fertilizers than in most other parts of the region. Moreover, the high proportion of legume and grass meadows compared to corn in the crop rotation is particularly helpful in the control of erosion on sloping lands.

Since the soils of the northern forest subregion usually are quite acid, liming is a first essential, especially for alfalfa. Fertilization with phosphorus and potassium also is generally required for efficient crop production. Boron must be used in fertilizers for alfalfa on some soils.

Potassium generally is more deficient, especially on sandy soils, than in other subregions, partly because of the larger removal of potassium in crops. Alfalfa removes a great deal of potassium. So does corn when it is grown for silage or the stalks are removed.

Nitrogen fertilizers are also needed to supplement the nitrogen from legumes and manure, especially in places where the soil and the management system make high yields possible.

On the rolling lands of the subregion, especially in the Mississippi Valley hill area (NF4), where sheet and gully erosion is moderate to serious, special practices to control erosion are necessary. Stripcropping on the contour is practiced more extensively here than in any other area in the region, but it and terracing should be used even more. Research at La Crosse, Wis., showed that on permeable Fayette soils terraces are effective in controlling erosion, even on 12-percent slopes. Another important part of the soil-management system on the rougher lands is the improvement of the permanent pastureland by liming, fertilizing, and reseeding where necessary.

Drainage is important on many farms outside the Mississippi Valley hilly area, especially in southern Michigan, where more than 60 percent of the land is within drainage enterprises. Some soil areas on many farms are still in need of improvement by open-ditch and tile drainage.

A surface drainage system has been developed in Wisconsin for the gently sloping but slowly drained Spencer silt loam soils. It is based on the use of channel-type terraces with few or no ridges. It improves drainage and controls soil erosion.

Probably the greatest need for improved soil-management systems in this subregion is in the central Wisconsin sandy area (NF3) and on the extensive areas of sandy soils in Michigan (NF1) and Minnesota (NF5). Improvement of fertility is most important. Crops that usually do well on these sandy and droughty soils are alfalfa, winter grains, and corn for silage. Irrigation may increase the efficiency of production in places where enough water is available.

To control wind erosion on some of these soils, a greater use of cover crops and crop residues is wise. Stripcropping and windbreaks also may be necessary.

The muck and peat soils in southern Michigan, north-central Wisconsin, east-central Minnesota, and the northern part of the eastern forest subregion—some of which cover a few acres and some several thousand acres—have special requirements. They are potentially productive, but only a small percentage of the acreage has been developed. When they are drained they are utilized either for special crops like onions, celery, lettuce, mint, potatoes, and other vegetables, or for such general crops as corn, soybeans, sugar beets, hay, and pasture. In order to protect them from too rapid decomposition and subsidence once they are drained, the water table has to be kept at rather shallow depths, preferably at about 18 to 30 inches. The soils must also be protected from wind erosion. Cover crops, windbreaks, and sprinkler irrigation are effective in preventing wind blowing under intensive production. These soils also require specific fertilizer treatments, including various trace elements for certain crop and soil conditions.

Soil management on the fruit farms along the western shore of Lake Michigan and on the Door County Peninsula in Wisconsin is aimed at getting high yields of good fruit and controlling erosion. Clean cultivation may lead to serious erosion on sloping soils. On the other hand, the use of sod crops—instead of clean cultivation—may depress yields of fruits because of the competition with the trees for water and plant nutrients. The combination of sod cover, adequate fertilization (particularly nitrogen), and mulches of straw and other materials encourages good yields and control of erosion on sloping soils. Cover crops are also effective.

THE SOUTHERN PRAIRIE FOREST SUBREGION is in northern Missouri, south-central Iowa, west-central Illinois, and southeastern Kansas. The total area is about 36 million acres.

The area has many narrow to moderately broad tabular divides and strongly sloping flanks. Many of the steeper areas near the major streams were originally forested. The level and gently sloping areas were in tall-grass prairie, although trees also grew on many of the level places in the northeastern part.

Because of soil and topography, the subregion is naturally less favorable for the production of corn than the central prairie subregion. The soils of the southwestern part near the Missouri-Kansas border were formed from shales and sandstones and are low in productivity. They yielded about 25 bushels of corn an acre in 1946–1955.

In the rest of the area the soils on the gently sloping to level tabular divides were formed from silty loess. They have medium-textured surface layers. Those in the central part of the subregion have slowly permeable subsoils high in clay and are moderately productive. The more level sections have unfavorable subsoils for water and root penetration and are excessively wet in many spring seasons. Drainage is needed, but tiling is generally not practical. Drought may be a problem in summer. The average yield is about 40 bushels of corn an acre. In Illinois and in the northwestern part of the area, the loess-formed soils are somewhat more permeable and productive, averaging about 50 bushels of corn an acre.

The large amount of strongly sloping soils of relatively poor porosity is reflected in the acreages not in crops.

Only about one-half of the land consists of cropland, compared to about three-fourths in the central prairie subregion. Most of the uncropped land is in permanent pasture, chiefly bluegrass. Lespedeza is a leading pasture and hay crop in the southern part on soils of low fertility.

In the more rolling areas, where Lindley soils are dominant, trees of low-quality timber occur. Many of these areas could be used for permanent pasture, although costs of clearing and treatment may be high.

Intertilled crops are grown on about 45 percent of the cropland. Corn is the chief intertilled crop. Soybeans are grown in the northeastern part and some grain sorghums in the southwestern part. Much winter wheat is grown in the southern section, partly because the longer growing season permits earlier harvesting of soybeans and corn, which are then followed by fall plantings of wheat. In the Missouri-Kansas part of the subregion, lespedeza is grown with the winter wheat.

Yields of corn, soybeans, and oats generally are considerably lower than in the central prairie subregion. They can be increased by the greater use of lime and fertilizers. Moreover, the soil-management systems for the sloping soils need to provide for better control of erosion through improved rotations, contour cultivation, terracing, or a combination of them.

The livestock-pasture type of farming predominates. Dairy farms are common near the large cities. The types of farming reflect the adjustment of farming to soils and topography. With only about one-half of the land used for harvested crops, much of the land is used for grazing. Increased production from the improvement of permanent pastures offers much promise of increased returns. Though much of the pastureland is of low quality and many problems remain to be solved, production can be increased materially on more than 10 million acres of pastureland by liming, fertilization, and reseeding with the improved varieties, such as lespedeza, alfalfa, and birdsfoot trefoil.

THE WESTERN PRAIRIE SUBREGION covers about 60 million acres, primarily in eastern Nebraska and southeastern South Dakota but also in the neighboring parts of Minnesota, Iowa, Missouri, and Kansas. Because of climate and topography, moisture often limits crop yields.

Corn, the major crop, is grown on about 16 million acres—more than 40 percent of the total acreage of harvested crops. Yields of corn in 1946–1955 averaged about 45 bushels an acre in the eastern part and about 20 bushels without irrigation farther west.

The main type of farming is general farming. Considerable emphasis is put on livestock, primarily beef cattle and hogs. In the Nebraska area (WP3) winter wheat and grain sorghum are grown as cash crops. In the Dakota-

Minnesota area (WP2), oats, wheat, barley, and flax are sold.

Most of the soils were formed under prairie vegetation and are dark colored, high in organic matter and nitrogen, and generally fertile. In the Missouri-Kansas part of the area, however, some forest-formed soils occur. The soils of the South Dakota-Minnesota area were formed from Wisconsin glacial materials and are mostly of loam texture, but in the Missouri Valley hilly area (WP1) and the Nebraska area (WP3) the soils were dominantly formed from silty loess. The latter are well-drained, permeable silt loams except in south-central Nebraska and northwestern Kansas, where some soils are slowly permeable. In the northern part of the Nebraska area, there are several million acres of sandy soils.

Along the Missouri River, which more or less bisects the Nebraska-Iowa hilly area (WP1), the elevation is about a thousand feet above sea level. The adjacent hills are 50 to 100 feet higher. Deep, wide gullies form in the many small drainageways. Sheet erosion is a serious problem on the adjacent steep slopes. Research at the Soil Conservation Experimental Farm near Clarinda, Iowa, has shown the effectiveness of level terraces and contour listing, with legume-grass sod crops and crop residues, in controlling soil and water losses on the deep, permeable sloping soils of this hilly area. Although many farmers have applied these practices, conservation of soil and water remains one of the major problems.

The topography in the other parts of the subregion is mostly level to gently rolling. In the western part of the Nebraska area, which has an elevation of about 3 thousand feet, however, nearly level tabular divides are flanked by steep slopes, which are used for permanent pasture. The South Dakota-Minnesota area is mostly a level to gently rolling plain, although some glacial moraines and hills occur in the northern section.

Moisture conservation is an important matter in the whole subregion, especially in the western low-rainfall section. Stubble-mulch tillage for wheat, listing and minimum tillage methods for corn, and contour cultivation on slopes are used to conserve moisture and control erosion.

Because perennial legumes such as alfalfa lower the reserves of subsoil moisture, sweetclover seeded in the oats and plowed under as green manure has some advantages over alfalfa as a means of supplying nitrogen to the grain crops in the rotation, since it has much less effect on subsoil moisture.

Legumes and manure do not supply enough nitrogen for the grain crops in the rotation, and the use of nitrogen fertilizer has increased greatly since 1945. The need for phosphate fertilizer is considerably less than in the other subregions, but certain soils, such as the calcareous Ida soils of the Nebraska-Iowa hilly area, respond markedly to phosphate fertilizers. Potash fertilizers seldom are needed. Lime generally is not needed except for small amounts on some of the nearly level soils in the southeastern part.

As most of the soils are naturally well drained, artificial drainage is seldom a problem. On parts of the broad bottom lands of the Missouri River and on parts of the tributary streams, however, drainage is troublesome. Such fine-textured, slowly permeable soils as the Luton and Wabash have high water tables in wet seasons, but are difficult to drain.

In this western prairie subregion, where moisture is often limiting, interest has grown in supplemental irrigation. More than 1.5 million acres were irrigated in Nebraska in 1955. Much of it was along the bottom lands of the Platte and Republican Rivers and on the adjacent uplands, where the soils and topography are favorable for irrigation and where water supplies are good. An increasing acreage of alfalfa and corn has been irrigated. To obtain high yields of irrigated corn, the plant population must be high and large amounts of nitrogen fertilizer ordinarily must be used. In other parts of the subregion, topography, soils, and water supply are less favorable, and only a few farmers have tried to irrigate. Although the cropland is the main agricultural resource of this subregion, about one-third of the land is used partly or wholly for grazing. Because of less favorable climate, increased production from this land has fewer possibilities than from the permanent pastureland of the southern prairie forest subregion. Bluegrass is the common permanent pasture in the eastern part of the subregion, but native grasses are important in the western and northern parts, especially in the rolling glacial sections of South Dakota, where the lower lying wet areas furnish both pasture and hay.

ALTHOUGH THE DIFFERENT PARTS of the Midland feed region vary considerably in soils and climate, the subregions have a general similarity in soil use, primarily because on many farms the production pattern is dominated by corn and the use of legume-grass pastures as the main forage for livestock. Systems of soil management therefore cannot be identified closely with the different subregions but may vary considerably in any one subregion. In some subregions, however, the ratio of legume and grasses to corn, soybeans, and other intertilled crops in the rotation is much higher than in others.

To meet the twin goals of efficient and sustained production, it is important that the best combination of practices be used. However, the best combination may vary from farm to farm as well as from one area to another. Too, the value of one practice often is determined by the other practices.

For example, experiments in Iowa and other States showed that farmers on the better soils usually cannot expect to get much increase in corn yields from heavy fertilization with only 8 thousand to 9 thousand plants per acre, the plant population used commonly in 1945. In Iowa we found that the use of 80 pounds of nitrogen in fertilizers increased the yield of corn only

14 bushels an acre with a stand of 8 thousand plants to the acre but 28 bushels with 16 thousand plants an acre.

Another example of how several practices complement each other was had on the steep, calcareous Ida soils of the Missouri Valley hilly area. Terracing is an effective way to control erosion and conserve water, but without some meadow crops in the rotation the terraces need to be so close together on these steep soils as to be largely impractical. Moreover, in order to get satisfactory yields of legumes or corn on these phosphorus-deficient soils, large applications of phosphate fertilizers are necessary. Thus, in an experiment at the Western Iowa Experimental Farm at Castana, the average annual yields in a 4-year rotation of corn-oats-alfalfa-alfalfa was 0.6 ton an acre for alfalfa without phosphorus and 3.9 tons with applications of 240 pounds of phosphoric oxide as superphosphate for each rotation. Likewise, the yields of corn averaged 78 and 20 bushels with and without phosphate, respectively. On Ida soils, therefore, any one of the three practices (terracing, legume-grass rotation, and fertilization) without the other two is largely ineffective.

Soil-management systems are not inflexible, however: Under many soil conditions, there are alternative practices or systems of management that the farmer can select.

SOME SIGNIFICANT DEVELOPMENTS in agricultural technology have had an important influence on the soil-management systems of many Midland farms.

Increased mechanization has meant more timely tillage and other operations and greater efficiency of production. It has aided in the development of such improved tillage and erosion-control practices as mulch-residue tillage and terracing.

The use of chemicals to control weeds, insects, and diseases has helped to reduce hazards in crop production and may have an increasingly important effect on tillage practices, soil use, and crop yields. It was estimated that at least 4 million acres of land in corn in the Midwestern States were treated with insecticide or insecticide-fertilizer mixtures to control rootworm, wireworm, and other insects in 1956.

The greatly increased production and use of fertilizers have had a great impact. In Iowa, Minnesota, Nebraska, and Missouri, the use of fertilizers increased nearly 250 percent between 1945 and 1955, compared to about 50 percent in the entire United States.

The total use of fertilizers in the States of this region increased more than sixfold between 1939 and 1954. The use of nitrogen fertilizers increased more than twentyfold. About 20 percent of the farmers used fertilizer in 1939, and the average amount spent on a farm was about 55 dollars.

Fifteen years later, more than 60 percent of the farmers used fertilizer, and the amount spent averaged about 400 dollars.

The ready availability of large amounts of nitrogen fertilizers means that farmers are less dependent on nitrogen from legumes to supply the nitrogen needs of other crops in the rotation.

MARKED ADVANCES also have been made in the Midland feed region in evaluating the effects of alternative methods of controlling erosion under different conditions of soil and slope.

Values of permissible soil loss have been established for the major soil types, and the effectiveness of various erosion control practices and combination of practices in keeping the losses to these specified limits have been estimated on the basis of all research information available. Thus the estimated soil loss from a Tama silt loam soil on a 6-percent slope of 400 feet length when farmed in a corn-corn-oats-meadow rotation on the contour is estimated to be 8.8 tons an acre a year, which is considerably above the 4-ton maximum allowable limit established for this soil. Terraces reduced the estimated soil loss to 2.0 tons. A shifting to a corn-oats-meadow-

meadow rotation without terraces cut the estimated loss to 3.5 tons. Either method is satisfactory. Alternatively, the corn-corn-oats-meadow rotation could be retained if one of the new tillage methods such as residue-mulch tillage is adopted.

Farmers in the region have made great progress in applying the results of scientific research to soil management on their farms since 1945. The potentialities for improvement during the next decade are equally great.

This optimistic outlook is not surprising in view of the scientific findings of recent years from research laboratories and experimental fields.

Chemical soil tests for estimating the fertilizer needs of soil are now available and are being used in testing more than 1 million soil samples annually for farmers in the 12 North Central States. With increasing use of soil tests, even greater efficiency in fertilizer use can be obtained.

From the standpoint of sustained, longtime production, there is also great opportunity of utilizing more fully such specific erosion control practices as contour cultivation, stripcropping, and terracing. On dairy and livestock farms, where good use can be made of forages, there is an excellent opportunity of improving soil use by keeping more of the rolling soils in legumes and grasses. To do that may mean cropping the more level soils on the farm more intensively, a possibility now open to many farmers through improved fertilization and tillage practices.

Many soil-management problems, however, remain to be solved. There is need especially for basic studies to understand more fully the variations in properties and productive capacity of different soils. The Midland farmer needs to know more specifically how various individual practices can supplement or replace one another; what alternative combinations of practices are available for his particular soil and climatic conditions; and what these combinations mean in terms of immediate income and sustained production.

The Northern Lake States

R. J. Muckenhirn and K. C. Berger

The land of Hiawatha is a land of forests, clear streams, and thousands of lakes. It is a land of farms that produce dairy products, potatoes, and fruit; a land of industries that mine copper and iron ore and manufacture a host of products from wood; a land, too, for recreation, with lovely parks, summer homes, and winter resorts.

This northern portion of the Lake States, Minnesota, Wisconsin, and Michigan, extends about 600 miles from east to west and 250 miles from north to south. It includes more than 50 million acres in about 80 counties.

Most of its population of about 2 million persons live on farms or in towns. Farms generally are not large, being typically of 100 to 200 acres; many have forest land in addition. Dairy farming is the predominant enterprise. Potatoes and fruit are grown on specialized farms.

Most of the region has the uneven topography of a heavily glaciated country—gravelly hills and ridges, sandy plains, swamps, rock outcrops. The annual rainfall is 25 to 35 inches. About two-thirds of it falls in the warmer months. The climate is cool. The average annual temperature is about 40° F. Winters are cold. Snowfall totals 5 feet or more annually. The ground is covered with an inch or more of snow for 100 to 140 days of the year, a length of time that approximates or equals the frost-free period, or growing season, which is 80 to 140 days. The Great Lakes moderate the extremes of temperatures along their shores.

The soils are products of cool, moist forests and are light colored, acid, rather infertile, and low in organic matter. They vary greatly because of the diverse nature of the parent materials that the glaciers moved and mixed. Stones, sands, and gravels are common. Organic soils occupy millions of acres, but there are also smooth uplands, rocky ridges, outwash plains, and former lakebeds covered with deep silty or clayey soils. Poor soils are often intermixed with good soils—a fact that was partly responsible for failures by many settlers who were unfortunate in their choice of land.

Today a system of land zoning set up by the county and State governments helps to keep poorer lands in forest or recreational uses.

Forests rapidly are restoring the economic productivity of the lands. They offer part-time employment to many farmers and full-time employment for more than 100 thousand workers in logging and wood-using industries, especially pulp and paper mills. Forest fires, once a great hazard, are almost entirely controlled. Tree planting and forest management are enlarging and improving the stands. About 20 million acres are in publicly owned forests. An equal or greater acreage is in private ownership, sometimes in large tracts managed by timber or paper companies. Of the privately owned forest, about one-fourth is a part of farm holdings. The principal

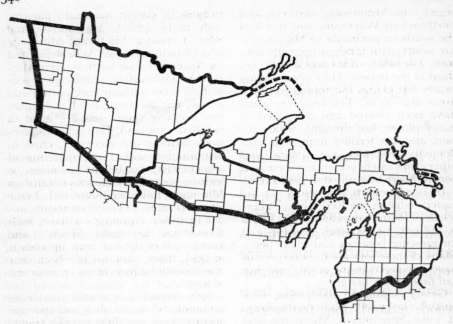

forest types are pine, spruce-fir, and hardwood.

Most farms are operated by owners and usually by one family. The proportion of tenant-operated farms is well under 20 percent. Many northern counties have as few as 5 percent of tenants on farms. Approximately one-fourth of the land area is in farms, and only one-tenth is cropped. Usually less than half the land of a county is in farms. In some counties as little as 5 percent is in farms. Land is still available for settlement, and prices are relatively low.

The cropland on a farm generally is only 40 acres. The limited crop acreage is one of the principal handicaps of northern farms. The average size of farms has been increasing, but it is still too small on thousands of farms to provide sufficient cropland and income. The pastured woodland on a farm often is larger than harvested cropland.

The farm population has been declining. The decline between 1940 and 1951 averaged 15 to 29 percent in northern Wisconsin counties; in a few counties the drop was more than 40 percent. The number of farms in the northern part of the Lake States declined about 20 percent during that period. The trend has continued since, although probably at a slower rate.

The family level of living index has risen. It was below the national average in 1950 for farm operator families, but it improved faster from 1945 to 1950 here than in the North Central States as a whole. Compared with the 12 North Central States, farm employment fell more rapidly, but manufacturing and other employment increased at nearly the same rate. The number of workers in manufacturing areas near Lake Superior increased at more than twice the rate for the 12 States.

The northern part of the Lake States, like the rest of the United States, has a declining rural but an increasing urban population. Its farms are becoming more mechanized and specialized, standards of living are rising, and its resources in forests, mines, and recreational facilities are being developed more fully and generally are better managed.

Soils in the southern part of this

region—in Minnesota, northern and northeastern Wisconsin, and much of the southern peninsula of Michigan— are sands, with sandy or gravelly subsoils. The sandy soils cover about one-third of the region. They often occupy nearly flat plains, but rolling to rough areas also occur. The smoother areas have been cleared and cultivated in many places, but drought, wind erosion, and low fertility limit their productivity. Potatoes, rye, alfalfa, and other crops can be grown, but these soils generally are best suited to pine forests.

In northwestern Minnesota, at the eastern edge of the Red River Valley, a belt of loamy sands and sandy loams is utilized for livestock farming and for growing potatoes and sugar beets. Many of these soils are dark colored or have clay layers in the profile and thus can hold water better.

Gently sloping to flat plains, with pinkish, clayey soils, occur on the shores of Lake Superior in Minnesota and Wisconsin and in Ontonagon and Chippewa Counties, Michigan. These plains were covered by Lake Superior in glacial times. Because the soils are relatively smooth, stone free, and usually rich in lime in the subsoil, they are used for hay, pasture, and small grains. The frost-free season along the lakeshore is somewhat longer, but slow drainage, clayey texture, and cool, moist summers limit farming possibilities. Much land, especially the more poorly drained, remains in forest. Lake-laid clays, mixed or covered with sand or silt, in northern Minnesota are used for pasture and forage crops, including alfalfa, and potatoes and root crops. A considerable amount of grass and legume seed is produced. Artificial drainage is often needed on cropland. The poorer and wetter uplands support second-growth hardwoods. The extensive peat bogs support spruce and tamarack.

Most of the rolling uplands has loamy soils, derived from glacial drift low in lime. These soils usually are poorly suited to farming, but the deeper and more fertile ones are intensively used. Some of these loamy soils have limy subsoils or parent materials, particularly in Houghton, Menominee, and Alger Counties, Michigan; Marinette and Oconto Counties, Wisconsin; and north-central and northwestern Minnesota. The surface soils often are as acid as those without limy parent materials, but the more level and stone-free areas of these soils are good to excellent cropland. Dairying and livestock farming are successful, often in combination with the production of strawberries, raspberries, potatoes, or legume seed. Deficiencies of sulfur in Minnesota have been observed. Trace elements may become deficient under intensive cropping on many soils throughout the region. Much of the loamy soils of the northern uplands is so acid, stony, shallow, or rough that it will continue in forest or be returned to forest.

Soils consisting of organic materials accumulated in marshes and swamps occupy about 5 million acres in Michigan, 8 million acres in Minnesota, and 3 million acres in Wisconsin. Much of this area is in the Northern Lake States region, where peat and muck cover 10 to 20 percent of the area, sometimes in large tracts of tens of thousands of acres, as in the vicinity of Red Lake, in Minnesota, but usually in areas of 1 acre to 1 thousand acres. The vegetation on the bogs consists of black spruce, tamarack, cedar, willows, or alder, often with mosses, especially sphagnum, and shrubs underneath. Many bog soils are very acid. Some areas in northern Minnesota are well supplied with lime and are called high-lime peats.

The peats of the Northern Lake States are seldom cultivated because of the cost of drainage, the need for fertilizers, and the shortness of the growing season. Frost occurs every month of the year in many bogs. Most of these northern peats and mucks are likely therefore to remain indefinitely in forest or other native vegetation.

Although rocky highlands, like the Porcupine Mountains of Michigan, occupy only a small part of the region, rock outcrops and shallow soils are common. One area in Minnesota extends over nearly 3 million acres, and smaller but important areas exist in all of the three States.

Most of the exposures consist of igneous and metamorphic rocks, covered with scattered deposits of glacial drift. These rocky lands very likely will remain in wilderness, entered only by those seeking recreation, furs, or mining prospects.

Most of the upland soils of the region are podzolized, low in fertility, and usually low in organic matter. The maintenance and improvement of fertility therefore is a major concern. Control of soil erosion, essential as it is on sloping lands, generally requires less attention than the management of fertility because of the high proportion of grasses and grains in the rotation and the relatively small size and gentle slopes of most fields.

With the exception of certain areas of lime-rich soils, as in western Minnesota, liming is essential for profitable farming. Limestone is seldom available locally and is relatively expensive. Soils usually are limed with marl or sludge from paper mills. The subsoil material of "red" clays near Lake Superior may have an equivalent of 35 to 40 percent of calcium carbonate and may be excavated and applied to correct soil acidity.

THE ROTATIONS on the dairy farms in the region usually consist of small grains, hay, and pasture. The hay consists mostly of red clover and timothy mixtures, although alfalfa is adapted to many areas. Alfalfa roots penetrate into the lime layer, and stands frequently last for many years because the abundant snow cover reduces winterkilling and frost heaving. Lime and high-potash fertilizers generally are necessary to maintain productive stands. The soils in this area are relatively low in available phosphorus and potassium and particularly low in nitrogen. Remarkable responses to topdressings of nitrogen and to nitro-

gen, phosphate, and potash mixtures have been obtained on the older grass sods. Yields of pasture often have been doubled and tripled with the application of 10-10-10 fertilizer or similar mixtures as a topdressing.

Small grains respond well to fertilization throughout the area. Usually a complete fertilizer with a nitrogen-phosphate-potash ratio of 1-4-4, at the rate of 200 to 300 pounds an acre, applied with the seed gives the best result. When alfalfa is seeded with the small grain, additional fertilizer is usually applied broadcast before planting or topdressed on the new seeding after the grain is harvested.

ON THE LOAMY SOILS of the rolling uplands in northwestern Minnesota, the soils formed from limy parent material are less acid and do not require liming for most farm crops. These soils generally are more level and are quite productive if they are free of stones. They are low in available phosphorus, potassium, and nitrogen and require fertilization for profitable crop yields.

Many of the soils formed from limy parent materials in Marinette and Oconto Counties in Wisconsin are also neutral or only slightly acid. Magnesium deficiency often occurs because of an unbalance between calcium and magnesium in the soil. Many of these soils are also low in available phosphorus and in potassium. Magnesium sulfate or sulfate of potash-magnesia is used for a fertilizer material to restore the proper magnesium balance to the soil. The use of sulfate of potash-magnesia also adds potassium needed for good crops of alfalfa and small grains in this area.

IN THE POTATO AREAS, the soils often are heavily fertilized to produce profitable yields. The available phosphorus content of the older potato soils has been built up through fertilization to levels of as much as 150 to 300 pounds an acre. It is still necessary to apply phosphorus fertilizer on them for high yields. The available potassium and nitrogen contents almost invariably are low, and it is necessary to apply 1 thousand to 2 thousand pounds an acre of fertilizer rich in nitrogen and potash. Small amounts of copper often are used in the fertilizer. The soils in many of the potato areas are very acid, with a pH of 4.4 to 5.4. When the soils become more acid than pH 5.0, the soluble manganese in the soil increases and may become toxic for potatoes. The excess of available manganese can be corrected by applying 300 to 500 pounds of finely ground dolomitic limestone, which reduces the availability of the manganese without raising the pH sufficiently so that scab will become a problem. The application also increases the content of available magnesium in the soil and thus corrects a deficiency that exists in many of the soils in the areas where potatoes are grown.

POTATOES usually are grown in a 3-year rotation of oats, red clover, and potatoes. Both the oats seed and the red clover seed are harvested. All the straw and hay are left on the field to provide organic matter. The application of 20 pounds an acre of borax or fertilizer borate as a topdressing to the clover seeding after the grain has been combined in the fall of the first year has increased the production of clover seed. Most of the potato soils in this region are deficient in available boron; legumes, such as red clover or alfalfa, also need boron.

Fruit, including strawberries and raspberries, is grown in many sections. Fruits require adequate fertilization with phosphate and potash and a topdressing of nitrogen in the spring. The berry crops are particularly adapted, because they grow best in acid soils with a high manganese content.

Some apples and cherries are produced in Wisconsin and northwestern Michigan. These fruits usually require nitrogen fertilization and quite often need potash.

The area is not well adapted to corn, but corn is grown along the southern margin of the region. Early maturing hybrids with adequate fertilization sometimes yield 70 to 100 bushels an acre. Most of the corn is used for silage. Fertilizer is particularly important to give the corn a good start in the spring. Often a plowed-down application of phosphate and potash and a sidedressing of nitrogen are needed.

Perhaps the most profitable crop to grow here for dairy farming is alfalfa, if the soils are adequately limed and fertilized. Stands can be maintained for years on the better soils if the soil is brought up to a proper level of lime and fertility and given relatively small, topdressed applications of fertilizer yearly.

DEFICIENCIES of boron, copper, magnesium, and sulfur may occur. Sulfur often is needed in north-central and northwestern Minnesota, particularly for legumes. Sulfur commonly is applied as gypsum, a hydrated calcium sulfate. Ordinary or 20-percent superphosphate contains about one-half gypsum as it is usually made, and will supply the necessary sulfur where it is used as a fertilizer.

Cobalt, a trace element not required by plants but essential for animals, is often deficient in the soils and crops in some parts of the area. Plants that grow on soils that have an adequate supply of available cobalt will take up enough cobalt so that livestock eating the feed and forage will be well supplied with it. The soils in Marinette and Oconto Counties in Wisconsin and a few other areas are low in cobalt, and cobalt deficiencies in sheep have been found. The deficiency is easily remedied by feeding salt fortified with cobalt.

The soils in some parts of the region are low in available phosphorus, and phosphorus deficiencies of livestock have been reported. The remedy is to feed calcium phosphate directly to the animal or to fertilize the crops with phosphate. The fertilization increases the phosphate contents of the crops and also increases yields.

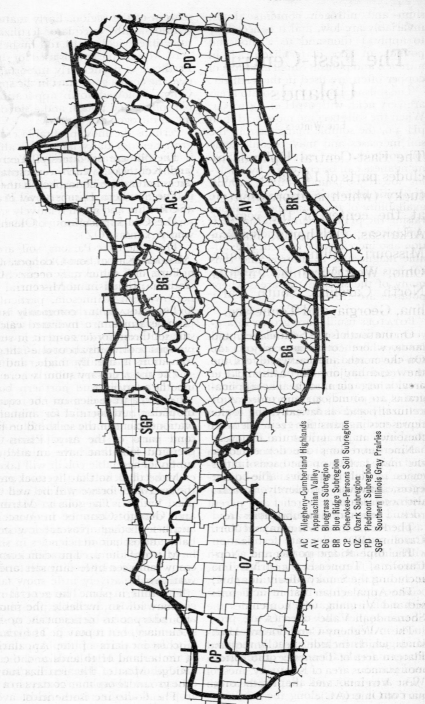

AC   Allegheny-Cumberland Highlands
AV   Appalachian Valley
BG   Bluegrass Subregion
BR   Blue Ridge Subregion
CP   Cherokee-Parsons Soil Subregion
OZ   Ozark Subregion
PD   Piedmont Subregion
SGP   Southern Illinois Gray Prairies

The East-Central Uplands

Eric Winters

The East-Central Uplands includes parts of 14 States—Kentucky (which is approximately at the center of the region), Arkansas, Oklahoma, Kansas, Missouri, Illinois, Indiana, Ohio, West Virginia, Virginia, North Carolina, South Carolina, Georgia, and Tennessee.

On the south is the Southeastern Uplands, where cotton is a major crop. On the north and eastward to Ohio, the region adjoins the Midland feed area, where corn, soybeans, and small grains are of major importance. Agriculturally and climatically, the region represents a transition zone between these two major agricultural regions.

Nine subregions are delineated on the map, largely on the basis of differences in soil properties. The differences, however, frequently correlate with such features as relief and parent rock. The important subregions are:

The Piedmont in Virginia and North Carolina (PD);

The Blue Ridge in Georgia, North Carolina, Tennessee, and Virginia, including the Smoky Mountains (BR);

The Appalachian Valley in Tennessee and Virginia, which includes the Shenandoah Valley area (AV);

The Allegheny-Cumberland Highlands, which include the Cumberland Plateau area of Tennessee, the eastern mountainous area of Kentucky, most of West Virginia, and the southeastern part of Ohio (AC);

The "bluegrass" areas of Tennessee and Kentucky, which represents soil areas naturally high in phosphate (BG);

The Southern Illinois Gray Prairies (SGP);

The Ozarks in Missouri, Oklahoma, and Arkansas (OZ);

The Cherokee-Parsons soil area of Missouri, Kansas, and Oklahoma (CP);

Parts of Kentucky, Tennessee, Ohio, Indiana, Illinois, and Missouri.

THE CLIMATE of the region is humid. Temperatures are medium warm on the southern borders and at lower elevations and medium cool at the high elevations and at the higher latitudes.

The total precipitation is 40 inches on the western and northern boundaries and 50 inches on the southern boundary. At some of the higher elevations, particularly in the Blue Ridge and parts of the Appalachian-Cumberland Highlands, the rainfall is 50 to 80 inches.

More than half of the total precipitation comes between April and October, but it is irregularly distributed, and droughts may be frequent. September through November generally is the driest period.

Much of the precipitation comes as snow at the higher latitudes and elevations. Relatively little snow falls in the southern part. The general range of snowfall is 5 inches at the southern boundary to 20 inches on the northern boundary, but it may be as high as 40 inches in parts of the Appalachian-Cumberland Highlands and the Blue Ridge. Most of the area has snow on the ground fewer than 20 days in a year. The 60-degree isotherm of average annual temperature nearly coincides with the southern boundary of the region. The 55-degree isotherm follows rather closely along the northern boundary from Kansas to Ohio. The 50-degree isotherm touches the boundary of the region in eastern Ohio and dips down into West Virginia and Virginia at the higher elevations.

The average January temperature for the southern part is 40° F. For the northern part it is 30°. The average July temperatures are 80° on the southern boundary, 75° on the northern boundary, and 70° at the higher elevations.

The date of the last killing frost in the spring ranges from March 30 to April 30, from south to north, and is as late as May 10 in some localities in the Appalachians. The first killing frost in the fall ranges from October 30 in the south to October 10 in the north and at higher elevations.

The growing season is 180 to 200 days in most of the region at lower elevations, 160 days for eastern Ohio, and 120 to 130 days for some areas of high elevation in the Appalachians.

The depth of frost penetration ranges from an average of 3 inches on the southern boundary to more than 15 inches at high latitudes and elevations.

Soils of the region have a number of properties in common, mostly because of the similarity in climate. The natural vegetation was mainly deciduous forest.

In such an environment, the well-drained upland soils usually have a surface layer (A horizon) that is acid, relatively light colored, low in organic matter, and medium in texture, due in part to eluviation of clay.

The subsoil (B horizon) of these soils is acid, very low in organic matter, brownish red to yellowish brown or even yellow or mottled in places where drainage is less rapid; it is finer in texture than the surface soil, partly because of clay accumulated from above. The permeability of the subsoil layer is only moderate because of its relatively high clay content.

The slow permeability of the subsoil and the low amount of organic matter, the medium texture, and weakly developed structure of the surface layer make these soils on sloping land susceptible to losses from erosion when they are not protected by vegetative cover, particularly when rainfall is intensive. If heavy rain comes when the surface soil is nearly saturated, the erosion hazard is especially great. Evidences of erosion, such as exposed subsoils and gullies on the sloping cultivated lands, are common.

Most of the soils originally were moderate to low in fertility, but many of them respond to good management.

The region represents a zone of transition from the Gray-Brown Podzolic to the Red-Yellow Podzolic soils. Members of both of these zonal great soil groups are present. Gray-Brown Podzolic soils generally occur at higher latitudes and at higher elevations and usually are developed from till and loess parent materials in Indiana and Illinois. Red-Yellow Podzolic soils are more common in areas of warmer temperatures. Intrazonal soil groups are represented chiefly by the Planosols, which generally are less permeable in the subsoil than the associated zonal soils. Slow permeability of subsoils may be associated with claypan development, as in southern Illinois, or with a fragipan development, as in western Kentucky.

The most important representative of the azonal soils is the alluvial soil group, which includes bottom lands adjacent to the major and minor streams and narrow bands of slope wash or colluvium at footslopes. Because these alluvial soils generally are higher in fertility and productivity than the associated soils of the area, they are important to the agriculture of the region, and the well-drained areas usually are farmed intensively. Large areas of other azonal soils, including Regosols and Lithosols, occur on steep slopes.

The transition in climate across the region from cool temperate to warm temperate is paralleled by a transition n agricultural practices. In the northern and cooler parts, for example, spring oats are grown, but winter oats are grown in the southern and warmer portions. Red clover and timothy are adapted in the cooler areas, but lespedeza and redtop are more widely used in the warmer portions. Winter annuals, such as crimson clover and ryegrass, are used widely in the southern part but not in the northern part. This wide range of adapted crops makes for great flexibility in rotations.

The total land area in the region is about 150 million acres, about 8 percent of the total area of the United States. About 102 million acres are in farms. The number of farms is approximately 1 million, which is 18 percent of the total number of farms in the United States. Many of the farms are classed as residential and part-time farms. Many are operated by their owners.

A little less than half of the total farmland is cropland. About a third is woodland. The average farm has about 50 acres of cropland and less than 20 acres of other land that may be used for pasture. The small average size of farms and the steep and irregular topography in many parts of the region militate against the adoption of large-scale field operations.

The leading field crop in total acreage is corn. Some 9 million acres were in corn here in 1950—11 percent of the country's total corn acreage. About half the country's total acreages of tobacco and lespedeza, 17 percent of the soybean acreage, 4 percent of the acreage each of wheat, barley, and oats, 13 percent of the clover, and 6 percent of the national acreage in alfalfa were grown in the region. Cotton and sorghum were of relatively minor importance.

The region had 15 percent of the total number of milk cows, 13 percent of the swine, 11 percent of cattle and calves, and 10 percent of the sheep in the United States in 1950. Livestock numbers are high in relation to the amount of feed grains produced, but the pasture season is long when moisture is adequate.

A regular rotation is not followed systematically on most farms, although most farmers generally alternate cultivated and close-growing crops.

The adjustment of the cropping pattern to the land has not always been the best. Row crops often have been grown on land that is so sloping that control of erosion and maintenance of productivity are difficult even with contour farming and terracing. Despite the small average size of farms, many areas of idle land occur throughout the region. Land well suited for intensive cultivation has not always been used for row crops, and some land has been cultivated more intensively than slope and other soil properties justify.

A common rotation sequence here is a cultivated crop; a small grain, seeded in the fall or the spring; and a close-growing crop or a meadow. Its length may be 4 years or more, depending on the time the meadow crop stays on the land. Modifications are common.

Two or more cultivated crops may be grown in sequence, with an intervening winter cover crop such as crimson clover or ryegrass. The cultivated crop commonly is corn, but it sometimes is soybeans, tobacco, or cotton. The meadow crop often is lespedeza (and grass), although in the cooler parts red clover (and grass) is used. The meadow crop may be alfalfa or alfalfa plus orchardgrass, which is seeded in the early fall after the small grain has been harvested and the land fallowed for a time to prepare a good seedbed and control weeds. The alfalfa and orchardgrass may stand then for several years, depending on how long vigorous production continues.

A 1-year rotation that is adapted to the warmer sections is small grain and lespedeza. The lespedeza is seeded in the spring in the small grain. This rotation works best with wheat because wheat can be planted later than oats and matures earlier in the summer.

Farm Characteristics of the United States and the East-Central Uplands (1950 Census)[1]

	The United States (000,000 omitted)	This Region (000,000 omitted)	Approximate percentage of U. S. total
Number of farms	5.38	1.02	18
Land area (acres)	1,904.	150.7	8
Land in farms (acres)	1,160.	102.	9
Total cropland (acres)	479.	49.3	10
Total woodland (acres)	220.	33.7	15
Corn (acres)	83.4	9.3	11
Tobacco (acres)	1.5	0.8	50
Lespedeza (acres)	6.9	3.6	52
Soybeans (acres)	11.4	2.0	17
Clover (acres)	18.6	2.5	13
Alfalfa (acres)	16.4	1.0	6
Wheat (acres)	71.2	3.2	4
Oats (acres)	37.2	1.6	4
Cattle and calves	77.5	8.5	11
Milk cows	21.4	3.2	15
Hogs and pigs	56.3	7.1	13
Sheep and lambs	31.4	3.0	10

[1] Data assembled from the special report, "Farms and Farm Characteristics by Economic Sub-Regions," which accompanied the 1950 Census. The Cherokee-Parsons soil area, of limited acreage, is not included in the special report or in this table.

The difficulty with barley is that disease builds up and yields are poor.

Another cropping system includes a cultivated crop every year with or without a winter cover crop. This rotation is restricted mostly to the nearly level lands along streams and the base of slopes. Continuous tobacco on the same ground is a common practice in the burley tobacco areas.

Soil fertility is less than it might be on the average farm. Manure is not available in large amounts on many farms because cattle are on pasture much of the year. Manure from the barnyard is used chiefly for tobacco, gardens, specialty crops, and corn.

Relatively small amounts of commercial fertilizer have been used to supplement the manure. The use of fertilizer has been increasing rapidly, but the amount applied on most farms in 1957 was still below amounts recommended by experiment stations.

Much of the cropland is more acid than desirable for most crops, although most farmers lime adequately for alfalfa, and many tobacco fields have been adequately limed.

Most of the fertilizer has been used for cash crops, including cotton, tobacco, small grains, and vegetables. Relatively little has been used for corn. The fertilizer has been applied mostly in bands or in the row. Most pastures and hay crops other than alfalfa have received inadequate amounts for best growth. Many pastures therefore contain a high proportion of broomsedge and other weedy growth.

The major tillage implements for seedbed preparation are the moldboard plow and the disk. Depth of plowing has been moderate on most farms. Relatively little subsoiling has been done. Some smaller farms have horses or mules for power.

Contour farming, stripcropping, and terracing are not widely practiced, largely because the irregular topography makes contour operations difficult. Most corn is drilled rather than checkrowed even where operations are not on the contour. Weed control within the row therefore depends on covering by the cultivator or on hand hoeing.

Supplemental irrigation has been used on fewer than 10 farms in a thousand. Nearly all irrigation is by some type of portable overhead sprinkler system. Irrigated crops include tobacco, truck crops, ornamental and nursery plants, pasture, alfalfa, and hay.

Average yields of most crops in the region have been only moderate. Average corn yields have been in the range of 25 to 35 bushels; wheat, 15 bushels; oats, 30; and soybeans, 15. Lespedeza hay has averaged about a ton to the acre; red clover and timothy, 1 to 2 tons; and alfalfa, a little more than 2 tons. Specialty crops, such as tobacco, which receive more intensive management, including higher fertilization, show yields nearer to the levels that accompany optimum conditions.

CERTAIN ADJUSTMENTS in soil management should result in more effective conservation of soil and more economic production of crops.

Cropping systems should be selected that make the best use of the soil resources on the farm. Corn, for example, is best adapted to the nearly level, permeable soils that permit rapid penetration of roots and hence give plants access to larger water supplies in dry periods and at the same time present little or no erosion problem. Deep, well-drained, alluvial soils along streams and the base of slopes are among those well adapted to corn and other summer row crops.

Alfalfa persists longer and produces higher yields on deep, well-drained, moderately sloping upland soils whose subsoils have medium fine to fine texture, such as the Decatur, Dunmore, Maury, Memphis, and Cecil series (which have red or brown subsoils) than it will on alluvial soils. Alfalfa roots penetrate deeply in well-drained soils, even though they are fine textured, and the crop can withstand longer periods of dry weather than most summer crops.

Soybeans are adapted to many soils and deserve consideration as the row crop in rotations on nearly level soils underlain with a fragipan layer, such as the Tilsit, Lawrence, and Grenada series. Periods of moisture stress common on these soils cause less reduction in yield of soybeans than in yields of corn. Usually it is easy to follow soybeans with a winter grain. Soybeans are harvested relatively early, compared to corn, unless it is cut and shocked. Thus the winter grain can be seeded in time to become well established before freezing weather.

Continuous pasture or hay crops might be grown on the strongly sloping land and land of moderate slope, which has some limitation for tillage, such as shallow depth to rock.

Compromises in land use are necessary on many farms in order to balance crop acreage with anticipated need for feed and cash sales. Adjustments in other management practices become important to help compensate for them.

Judicious use of lime to bring the reaction of the surface soil within the range of pH 6 to 7 for most crops is the first step in a sound fertility program. Research in North Carolina has indicated that a dollar spent for limestone will give a greater net return over a period of years than a dollar invested in any other soil amendment. All States have laboratories to which farmers may submit soil samples to be tested for acidity (and nutrient status). The response to fertilizers usually is greater on limed than on unlimed soils. The more widespread use of nitrogen materials, such as ammonium nitrate, urea, and anhydrous ammonia, which cause an increase in soil acidity, makes a sound liming program in the region more necessary.

More liberal use of fertilizer on most farms is the next suggestion.

Adequate fertilization for a rotation over a period of years allows much better development of roots of corn throughout a fine-textured subsoil (claypan) than when corn is not fertilized. The increased yields with fertilization may be due in part on some soils to the greater supply of water available to the plants because of more extensive root development.

Bigger supplies and lower prices of chemical nitrogen have helped change the thinking about corn in many places. Unless manure were available,

Approximate Percentages of Farms, Area, Acreage, and Livestock in the Subregions

Soil Management Subregion	PD	BR	AV	AC	BG	SGP	OZ	Remainder
Corresponding economic subregions...	19, 20, 25	33	18, 32	26, 29, 30, 31	45, 54	62	73, 82	44, 46, 51, 52, 53, 72
Number of farms.....	12	6	10	21	9	3	11	28
Land area..........	11	5	8	24	6	4	16	26
Land in farms......	11	4	7	21	8	4	15	30
Cropland...........	9	2	7	14	11	6	12	38
Woodland..........	18	6	7	23	4	2	21	24
Corn..............	9	2	6	12	7	7	6	51
Tobacco............	37	2	7	4	22	....	....	28
Lespedeza..........	14	1	10	6	10	3	23	32
Soybeans...........	2	1	1	4	1	25	2	62
Clover.............	8	3	12	39	7	2	7	23
Alfalfa.............	8	1	11	15	17	3	7	38
Wheat.............	9	1	7	12	4	7	7	52
Oats..............	7	2	8	12	4	7	26	34
Cattle.............	9	3	10	18	12	3	16	28
Dairy.............	9	4	10	15	13	3	16	28
Hogs.............	6	2	5	11	10	5	10	54
Sheep.............	3	1	9	28	38	2	6	19

most farmers used to feel that it was more profitable to grow corn in rotation with legumes to provide nitrogen rather than maintain high yields with commercial nitrogen fertilizers.

Studies in Missouri, Illinois, and other States suggest that continuous corn is entirely feasible on many nearly level soils where in the past corn was recommended only in rotation. With high degrees of fertility and large amounts of nitrogen as sidedressing, yields of continuous corn have been maintained at 100 bushels or more in a number of experiments. These high yields leave much stover to provide a mulch over winter to protect the soil against compaction and erosion and to be plowed back into the ground to maintain the levels of organic matter. Because of the difficulty of getting winter grains planted after corn and the poor yields obtained with spring oats in much of the region, continuous corn with high nitrogen fertilization promises to become a more general practice on soils suited to this sort of cropping system.

Permanent pasture and hayfields will be kept more productive if annual topdressings of fertilizer (including borax for alfalfa) are applied. Annual moderate applications of phosphate and potash are preferable to larger amounts every 2 or 3 years because of phosphate fixation with time and the luxury consumption of potash.

Small grain may compete severely with the overseeding of legume-grass if the rate of nitrogen topdressing is high. If maximum yields of small grains are desired, it may be best to prepare a seedbed after the small grain is harvested and plant the legume-grass in the late summer. The legume-grass seeding in small grain may be a failure in years of limited rainfall even though the nitrogen rate is kept at a moderate level.

Machinery passing over the land results in some soil compaction. The degree depends on the frequency of the operation, the weight of the equipment, and the properties of the soil, including its wetness. If the number of tillage operations can be reduced and tillage done when the soil is near the optimum content of moisture, a minimum of compaction should be expected. The use of chemical weedkillers would eliminate some of the tillage operations.

Many farmers may be using tillage equipment too much in the production of row crops, but many others are not using a mower enough in pastures to help control weeds. Adequate fertilization, moderate intensity of grazing, and more frequent use of a mower to clip stemy growth are still the best ways to control weeds in pastures.

Matching the crops to the soils of a farm, using the best adapted varieties, and maintaining adequate fertility levels for each crop produced should result in vigorous plant growth and higher yields. The protection given the soil surface by vigorous top growth and the binding together of soil particles by abundant root development may keep soil erosion at an acceptable minimum without such supporting practices as stripcropping and contour farming.

Supplemental irrigation is expensive. The response of crops to additional water does not occur every year and may prove disappointing in dry years if other soil-management practices have been neglected. The inadequate supply of water limits the use of irrigation on many farms.

Legislation is needed to clarify the water rights of farmers adjacent to streams. We need more information about ponds and reservoirs as sources of water for irrigation.

A sizable increase in average crop yields should result from the adjustment of soil-management programs by farmers in the region along the lines suggested. Corn might reasonably average 50 bushels to the acre; wheat, 25 bushels; oats, 40 bushels; soybeans, 20 to 25 bushels; lespedeza, 1 to 1.5 tons an acre; red clover and timothy, 2 tons; and alfalfa, 3 tons. Equally significant, particularly in terms of future soil productivity, would be the more effective conservation of the soil such adjustments would give.

The subregions of the East-Central Uplands differ from one another in many ways. We have outlined in broad terms some details of soil management in the region as a whole. Now let us consider each subregion separately.

THE PIEDMONT subregion includes all except the northern extremity of what is known as the Piedmont Physiographic Province in Virginia and the part of the province that is in the northern one-third of North Carolina. It extends from the coastal plain on the east to the foot of the Blue Ridge on the west. The range in elevation is about 400 feet to a thousand feet. The land is gently rolling, rolling, rough, and rough dissected. The gentler relief occurs mainly on the broader ridges between streams. Near the Blue Ridge there are steep hills, which are outliers of the mountains. More stream dissection occurs toward the fall line to the coastal plains. Drainage is to the Atlantic Ocean.

The climate is fairly uniform. The growing season is 190 to 210 days. The annual precipitation is 40 to 45 inches.

The underlying rock is mostly crystalline, although sedimentary formations occur. Crystalline rock, such as granite and gneiss, contains varying amounts of quartz, which persists in the weathered mantle largely as grains of sand.

Soils generally are acid and low in organic matter, nitrogen, and available phosphorus. Available potassium varies from medium to high, depending on the relative content of mica and feldspars in the parent material. The subsoil is usually much higher in potassium than the surface.

Cecil sandy loam is a representative soil and is classified in the Red-Yellow Podzolic group. It is developed on parent material resulting from the weathering of crystalline rocks. The surface is a light-brown, sandy loam. The subsoil is a red clay. Even on moderate slopes, the sandy surface erodes easily, and the fine-textured subsoil, which is harder to cultivate, is exposed.

Durham soils are lighter colored and somewhat sandier than Cecil because of the higher content of quartz in the parent material.

Davidson soils have darker surfaces and darker red subsoils than Cecil because of the more basic character of the rock from which parent materials were developed.

Soils over schist, sandstones, slates, and shales usually are shallow to rock and generally are poorly suited for cultivation. The most extensive soils in this subregion are those similar to the Cecil.

The average size of farms in the Piedmont approximates the average of farms in the whole region, but the amount of cropland per farm is only 75 percent and the amount of woodland is about 150 percent of that for the region.

The subregion has 9 percent of the total cropland and 37 percent of the tobacco acreage of the region. The greatest concentration of flue-cured tobacco production is in the southern part. Some dark-fired and air-cured, as well as flue-cured tobacco, are grown in the central part. Little or no tobacco is grown in the northern part, where farming is more diversified.

Lespedeza is a leading forage crop. The acreages of other forage crops, including alfalfa and clover, are about average for the region. Livestock numbers are about the same as elsewhere in the region, but there are fewer sheep and hogs. Some cotton is grown, mostly in the southern section, and some peanuts are grown in the eastern part.

The sandier soils, such as Durham and Appling, which are relatively low in organic matter, are preferred for flue-cured tobacco. Rotations are arranged to avoid turning legume residues ahead of tobacco, so that available nitrogen will be kept at a relatively low level consistent with high quality of leaf. Tobacco may be grown each year on nearly level areas, and a winter cover, such as ryegrass, is used. Tobacco may be grown every second or third year with corn or cotton intervening to help control diseases. Tobacco may be followed on sloping areas for 2 to 3 years by weedy fallow or by small grain overseeded with a grass, such as tall fescue.

Higher levels of nitrogen are acceptable for the other tobacco types, and soil-management adjustments are less critical on farms that do not grow flue-cured type. Nearly all producers have done an excellent job of raising tobacco, partly because of restrictions in acreage and partly because of the high cash returns. On many tobacco farms, less attention is given to management of soils used for crops other than tobacco, and the result is that their yields are lower than need be and the need for conservation is overlooked at times.

Adjustments in soil management that will result in higher yields, greater total feed production, and more effective soil conservation are possible on many farms. For example, a shift to more productive forage plants, such as alfalfa, involves selection of well-adapted soils and maintenance of adequate fertility levels, including correction of soil acidity by liming. A considerable increase in the total production of forage would result from replacing part of the lespedeza acreage with alfalfa, orchardgrass, Ladino clover, or tall meadow fescue.

Fencing out livestock from woodlands and removing cull trees deserve emphasis because of the large acreage of woodland on the average farm. Income can be increased from woodlands that are managed well.

Practices like contour farming and terracing should be given more consideration because of the relatively high erodibility of the many sandy soils.

Soil-management systems suggested for the Appalachian Valley subregion (page 562) are suitable also for the Piedmont subregion with some modifications to provide for more protection of the more erosive Piedmont soils.

THE BLUE RIDGE subregion lies mostly in western North Carolina, but parts of Virginia, Tennessee, Georgia, and South Carolina are within it.

Elevations are the highest of the whole region. Peaks in the Smoky Mountains reach 6,600 feet. The topography is steep and rugged. East of the Smokies the subregion has many of the characteristics of a rolling plateau, with elevations up to 4 thousand feet.

Drainage is largely into tributaries of the Tennessee River, which include the French Broad, Little Tennessee, and Hiawassee Rivers. The tributaries flow through deep gaps in the Smoky Mountains.

Parts of the subregion are popular as resort and recreational areas in the summer. The Great Smoky Mountain National Park, the Cherokee Indian Reservation, several reservoirs of the Tennessee Valley Authority, and other artificial lakes are in the area.

The climate is cooler than the average of the region. The range in average July temperatures, depending on elevation, is 68 to 74 degrees. The growing season is 150 to 190 days long, depending on latitude and elevation.

The range in average annual precipitation is 40 to 80 inches. The greatest precipitation occurs in the mountainous area where Georgia, North Carolina, and South Carolina meet. The least precipitation occurs in the vicinity of Asheville. The moist air coming up from the Gulf of Mexico loses much of its moisture as it passes over these peaks and is rather dry as it descends into the lower elevations to the north. The mountains along the Tennessee-North Carolina boundary represent another area of high rainfall because warm, moist air from the eastern Tennessee Valley loses its moisture as it flows up over the mountains.

Bedrock formations are some of the oldest in the United States, being mostly of Cambrian age or older. Metamorphic rocks predominate and include gneiss, schist, quartzite, and slate. Granites are also found and vary greatly in proportions of feldspar and quartz.

Soils, such as Ramsey, that are underlain by quartzite and slate are usually shallow (Lithosols) because of the resistance of such formations to weathering and because of the steep slopes on which they occur. These soils are best suited for forest and occur on much of the mountainous land along the Tennessee-North Carolina line.

Soils, such as the Fannin and Talladega, that developed over schist usually are shallow and high in potassium, but few are well suited to farming.

Upland soils most widely used for agriculture include the Ashe, Porters,

Halewood, and Hayesville. They are acid, low in available phosphorus, and low to high in potassium. These soils have been grouped with the Gray-Brown Podzolic soils. They have brownish-yellow to red subsoils, depending on the relative proportions of quartz to feldspars and mica in the parent material. The subsoils mostly are permeable and well drained. These soils, even where they occur on relatively steep slopes, are used on many farms for row crops in rotation largely because of the limited amount of cropland available. As a consequence, rather severe sheet erosion has occurred in many fields.

The most intensive cultivation is on alluvial soils, such as Tate and Tusquitee, developed on slope wash at the foot of slopes, and on Congaree of the first bottoms.

The average farm is about two-thirds the size of farms in the rest of the region, and its cropland is about one-third as much. Many farms are classified as residential. Many farmers work in towns to get extra income.

Temperature and moisture relations are favorable for the production of the high-quality vegetables. Mountain City, Tenn., is a major market for green beans. Cabbage is another important crop. Some lettuce is grown in the Georgia part of the subregion. Burley tobacco is grown on most farms. These intensive crops offer an opportunity for the utilization of family workers.

Clover is a leading forage crop. The most important class of livestock is dairy cattle.

Bottom lands and bases of slopes are used intensively for row crops. Well-drained fields usually are planted to a winter cover crop, such as crimson clover or ryegrass or small grain, or they may be used in short rotations. Cover crops may be omitted if the soils are subject to frequent flooding. Sloping land is in a rotation, such as corn, small grain, red clover, and grass. Strongly sloping fields are cultivated on the contour on most farms and sometimes are stripcropped. Contour stripcropping is a fairly general practice on the more extreme slopes used for row crops in rotation. Terraces are not widely used because so much of the land in rotations has slopes of more than 15 percent.

The use of lime has been limited by the relatively high transportation costs and the difficulty of spreading it on the steep slopes.

Fields are small on many farms because the farms themselves are small and land suitable for cropping is in rather narrow belts. Farms therefore cannot be reorganized in size and boundaries, but nevertheless the soil management could be improved.

More general use of sod crops and stripcropping on the steeper slopes would help reduce surface erosion. The more liberal use of lime and fertilizer would make it possible to grow such crops as orchardgrass, Ladino clover, red clover, and tall meadow fescue successfully, and yields of row crops could also be significantly increased. Excellent results have been obtained at the Georgia Mountain Experiment Station with a mixture of fescue and Ladino clover for dairy cows. More farmers might consider seeding such a pasture and hay mixture to increase the carrying capacity of their farms.

Because of the relatively large acreage of farmland in trees, improved management would increase the income derived from forest products and should facilitate the adoption of more effective soil-management programs on the pasture and cropland areas.

THE APPALACHIAN VALLEY subregion extends in a northeast-southwest direction across eastern Tennessee and western Virginia into Maryland. It separates the Appalachian-Cumberland Highlands subregion to the west from the Blue Ridge and Piedmont subregions to the east.

It consists of many long, parallel ridges and valleys, which often have a difference in elevation of more than 500 feet and have steep slopes. Elevations range from about 700 feet at

Chattanooga to more than 2 thousand feet in central Virginia. Roads and railroads tend to follow the valleys. The subregion attains maximum width in Tennessee, narrows greatly near Roanoke, Va., and becomes broader again to the north.

The Tennessee River drains the valley in southwestern Virginia and Tennessee. The New River provides drainage in central Virginia. The Roanoke, James, and Potomac Rivers drain the valley in northern Virginia.

From south to north, the average annual temperature ranges from 60° to 50° F., the average annual precipitation from 55 to 36 inches, and the average length of growing season from 210 to 170 days. Evapotranspiration is high in most of the subregion. Rainfall is erratic in summer, and the crops frequently suffer.

The rock underlying the subregion is nearly all sedimentary formations, which were tilted at all angles by the general faulting and folding in past ages. Limestones and dolomites are the most abundant rocks. Many dolomites are high in chert. Shales are next in abundance and are interbedded with limestone in many places. Sandstones cap some of the high ridges.

The mantle of parent material that resulted from the weathering of the underlying tilted rock averages considerably deeper than that overlying level-bedded rock in other subregions. The tilted rock layers apparently permit easier entrance of water and other weathering forces.

The soils generally are acid, low in nitrogen and available phosphorus, and low to medium in potassium.

Soils in the valleys are developed chiefly from limestones and shales. Over limestone bedrock, the soils (such as Dewey and Dunmore) are generally well drained, with medium-textured surface layers and fine-textured, red subsoils. Sink holes are frequent and add to the irregularity of the topography and the adequacy of drainage.

The surface soil and subsoil are medium in cation-exchange capacity.

Where shales form the bedrock, the soils are frequently less well drained, the subsoils tend to be yellowish rather than red, and the soils may be shallow to bedrock—in contrast to the moderate to great depth to bedrock in the limestone areas.

Surface erosion on many slopes that have been cultivated has been severe enough so that there is some mixing of subsoil with the remaining surface or even complete exposure of subsoil. The preparation of the seedbed is more difficult there. Upland soils in the small valleys belong to the Red-Yellow Podzolic great soil group.

Associated with these zonal soils are small areas of alluvial soils, which include bottom lands along streams and so-called colluvial slopewash at the base of slopes. These alluvial soils usually have a medium texture throughout the profile. They are well suited for intensive cultivation if they are well drained.

Soils on the ridges are developed chiefly from cherty dolomite and interbedded shales and limestones or shales and sandstones. Many of the soils are either high in chert or shallow to bedrock, which (in combination with the steep slopes) makes them poorly suited to tillage.

Many of the soils on slopes of steep ridges are classified as Lithosols, although some are grouped with the Red-Yellow Podzolic soils in the southern part and with the Gray-Brown Podzolic soils in the northern part.

The Appalachian Valley subregion contains about 10 percent of the farms but only 7 percent of the land in farms and of cropland of the region. Industry in the valley has developed rapidly near Roanoke and southward. Many farm owners thus have an opportunity for employment off the farm, which may account in large part for the small average size of farms. More than 80 percent of the farms are operated by their owners.

Forage crops, notably lespedeza, clover, and alfalfa, are relatively important here, and so is the number of live-

stock, particularly cattle and sheep, which represent 10 percent and 9 percent of the totals for the region.

A considerable acreage is in apple orchards in the northern part of the valley; Winchester, Va., is a center of apple growing and packing.

Burley tobacco is the important cash crop in the southern two-thirds of the valley, although the average allotment per farm is less than 1 acre.

A little cotton is grown in the extreme southern part, near Chattanooga.

Several distinct cropping systems often are used on the same farm. Steep, stony, or shallow soils are in trees or permanent pasture and meadow. Soils on moderate slopes are used for a rotation such as corn, small grain, and meadow. Smooth areas, including alluvial soils, are used intensively for corn or tobacco, with or without a cover crop.

Permanent pastures sometimes consist largely of broomsedge if little fertilization and mowing are done. Their carrying capacity is limited, but usually broomsedge provides surface protection against erosion. If lime and fertilizer have been used at least moderately and some mowing is done, bluegrass and whiteclover may constitute a high proportion of pasture cover, particularly at the somewhat higher elevations in northeastern Tennessee and Virginia. Tall meadow fescue is seeded on some farms, usually on wet soils and soils suitable for a rotation. Skillful management is needed to maintain whiteclover in the fescue.

Rotations on land of moderate slope usually have corn as the row crop. Seedbed preparation for corn is often started in the late fall or winter by plowing land that has been in lespedeza or some sod crop and leaving the soil surface rough. Some farmers subsoil behind the plow with a chisel to a depth of 12 to 15 inches. There is some evidence that less runoff may occur during winter on subsoiled fields.

Corn is drilled in rows and fertilized lightly. A survey in Tennessee in 1951 indicated that, on the average, corn received the equivalent of about 100 pounds an acre of 5–10–5 fertilizer. Many farmers cut and shock the corn so that small grain may be seeded early. Land preparation for small grain is usually done with a disk. A fertilizer high in phosphate is drilled with the small grain at a moderate rate (100–200 pounds an acre). Lespedeza commonly is overseeded on small grain in the spring without extra fertilization. Often the lespedeza is allowed to reseed for 1 or 2 years.

A few farmers grow alfalfa, orchardgrass, and whiteclover, or tall fescue and whiteclover, which commonly are seeded in the fall on a seedbed prepared after the small grain has been harvested. Lime and fertilizer are broadcast at a moderate rate at the time the seedbed is prepared. These crops are often allowed to stay on the land as long as a good stand persists, which may be 3 or 4 years or more, depending on management and weather.

Regular maintenance applications of fertilizer are not used by most farmers on either long- or short-term pastures.

Well-drained alluvial soils on slopes are preferred for tobacco (burley). The tobacco land is fertilized with about 10 tons of manure, if it is available, and a liberal amount of mixed fertilizer (500 to 1,000 pounds). Tobacco usually is grown on the same land year after year, and a cover crop, such as crimson clover and ryegrass, is planted after the tobacco is cut—a plan that increases the fertility level and productivity of tobacco fields.

Corn is grown continuously by some farmers on bottom lands where drainage in summer is adequate most years. Yields of corn on these alluvial soils are higher than on most other soils of the subregion, and good response to fertilization is expected because of favorable moisture relationships.

Supporting practices for erosion control are not widely used. Some row crops are planted on the contour, but little terracing or stripcropping is done, partly because of the low erodibility of many soils.

Average acre yields are approximately as follows: Corn, 25 to 35 bushels; wheat, 15 bushels; tobacco, 1,500 pounds; lespedeza, 1 ton; and alfalfa, 2 tons.

Most of the practices and combinations of practices that would result in greater average productivity and more effective conservation of soils are already in use on some farms in the subregion. Some adjustments in soil management involve considerable risk, because capital is required for buying fertilizers, seed, and livestock and for financing the operator until the final products are ready for sale. Other adjustments, such as shifting crops to areas of best adaptation, involve little risk, capital, or delay in receiving benefits.

Much of the well-drained, moderately sloping land, on which lespedeza is grown in rotation, is well adapted to alfalfa. Included are all of the well-drained soils with red to brown, fine-textured subsoils that are not shallow to bedrock and occur on slopes not too steep or cherty for mowers to be used.

Most farms in the Appalachian Valley subregion have considerable land on which alfalfa can be grown. Yields of alfalfa are about twice those of lespedeza because it has a longer growing season and its deeper root system is better able to get moisture during the frequent rainless periods.

To establish alfalfa on the average soil requires about 2 or 3 tons of lime, 1,000 pounds of fertilizer, and one-third of a bushel of seed. Sclerotinia (crown rot) offers a potential threat of partial loss of stand the first winter. After the first production year, maintenance applications of fertilizer are needed on most soils; the kind and amount are best determined by soil tests. Adequately fertilized and properly managed alfalfa stands have remained productive 5 to 10 years on such soils as Dewey and Dunmore, which developed from residual parent material. A stand usually does not last so long on soils from alluvial and colluvial parent materials. Orchardgrass in the alfalfa field increases surface protection and reduces erosion on the slopes.

Yields of corn and small grain are greater after alfalfa than after lespedeza, perhaps because of increased soil nitrogen, improved surface tilth and subsoil permeability, or other factors.

More intensive use of the alluvial soils that are adapted to tillage for corn and soybeans is an adjustment that involves little cost or risk. Some deep, medium-textured soils in bottoms and at the foot of slopes that are too wet for cultivation can be made suitable for summer crops by such practices as construction of diversion ditches and shallow field ditches. The initial cost is high if tile is needed.

Yields of 100 bushels or more of corn an acre are obtained on alluvial soils that receive high fertilization, along with other necessary practices such as using adapted varieties, proper spacing, and judicious cultivation.

More intensive use of alluvial soils for the row crops and higher yields through improved management relieves the pressure on sloping uplands for growing a row crop as frequently in a rotation. Less frequent use of row crops on sloping land also fits in well with the substitution of alfalfa for lespedeza (or red clover). The cost of seeding the alfalfa makes it desirable to maintain the stand as long as it is productive. Usually that means a longer rotation and the less frequent planting of a row crop than when lespedeza is the meadow crop.

Adjustments in management of long- and short-term pastures could improve productivity under average conditions. The restriction of grazing at critical periods is one important adjustment. Growth should be well started and the soil should be firm before cattle are allowed on the land in the spring. During dry periods in the summer, grazing should be stopped before the herbage is eaten so closely that the stand is injured.

Annual fertilization of pastures according to results of soil tests is another way to increase the production of forage. The use of any excess pasture herbage in the spring for grass silage provides a feed supply for use during drought periods.

Finally, a more general adoption of the practice of clipping pastures several times yearly to control weeds would be desirable.

Contour cultivation of sloping lands might often be the only supporting practice needed for effective erosion control if other suggestions for adjustments in land use were adopted generally. There would be places, however, where terraces would help meet special situations, and stripcropping might be desirable on extremely long slopes to supplement contouring.

Average yields that might reasonably be expected with the general adoption of the suggested adjustments would be: Corn, 50 to 60 bushels; wheat, 25 bushels; and alfalfa, 3 tons.

No spectacular increase in yields of lespedeza or alfalfa would be expected. In places where alfalfa is now grown, it is reasonably well fertilized at planting time. Because of the shallow root system of lespedeza, drought periods make its response to fertilization uncertain. An important consideration in respect to alfalfa would be the longer time that stands could be expected to remain productive.

THE APPALACHIAN-CUMBERLAND HIGHLANDS subregion represents one-fourth of the land area of the region. It includes nearly all of West Virginia, the southeastern part of Ohio, the eastern third of Kentucky, a narrow belt in Virginia adjacent to Kentucky and West Virginia, and the part of Tennessee that is designated as the Cumberland Plateau.

The highest elevations in the subregion are in the central part of West Virginia, where much of the land lies between 1.5 thousand and 3 thousand feet, and the maximum elevations exceed 4 thousand feet. The elevation of the Ohio River in northeastern Kentucky is below 500 feet.

Because of the great differences in elevation, dissection has been deep and intricate. Much of the land is rough, mountainous, and steeply sloping. Some smooth, undissected interstream areas do occur, such as those of the Cumberland Plateau in Tennessee.

The growing season lasts 140 to 150 days in Ohio, 130 to 180 days in West Virginia, and 180 to 190 days in Kentucky and Tennessee.

The total precipitation varies from 38 to 40 inches in Ohio and the northern sections of West Virginia to 50 or 55 inches in Tennessee and at the higher elevations in West Virginia. Fewer drought periods occur than in most other parts of the region.

The bedrock is mostly sandstones and shales. Limestone occurs occasionally. The rock usually is horizontally bedded, although some tilting of strata occurred near the Appalachian Valley border, particularly in Virginia. Coal deposits exist in many places, and mining is a major activity. There are some oil wells, as in West Virginia.

Soils mostly are relatively shallow, acid, and low in native fertility. Because the mantle of parent material over the sandstone and shale is shallow in most places, even moderate erosion in cultivated fields can be serious. The preferred use for much of the land is pasture, hay, or forest.

Muskingum, a Lithosol, is the dominant soil. Associated with it on the more moderate slopes are the Wellston and Zanesville soils in the Ohio area. They are classified as Gray-Brown Podzolic soils. They are deeper and more favorable for crop production than the Muskingum. Similar soils occur to a more limited extent on the smoother areas in West Virginia and Kentucky.

The dominant soil on the smooth areas of the Cumberland Plateau in Tennessee is Hartsells. Associated with it on the smooth land is the Tilsit, a Planosol with a fragipan layer.

At the West Virginia-Ohio border, there is an area of soils—Upshur and related series—which have a striking reddish color.

On the moderately rolling lands at the highest elevations in West Virginia are some areas of Podzol soils (Lee-

tonia), which are associated with Lithosols having some related properties (Dekalb). The amount of alluvial soils in the bottom lands along streams is small because rocks are hard and have resisted development of wide valleys or flood plains.

A small area of Red-Yellow Podzolic soils, similar to those of the Appalachian Valley subregion, occur in the Sequatchie Valley. It begins at about the middle of Tennessee in the Cumberland Plateau area and extends to Alabama.

Farms are about average in total size but have only about two-thirds as much cropland as the average farm in the region. Many are part-time and residential farms. The percentage of farms operated by owners is high.

Production of forage crops, particularly clover, is an important part of the farming program. Only 14 percent of the total cropland is included in this subregion, but 39 percent of the clover is produced. Forage crops are used primarily for livestock, including beef and dairy cattle, sheep, and hogs.

Lespedeza is relatively unimportant, except in the warmer parts of the subregion. Soybeans are a minor crop. A limited acreage is in tobacco and vegetables. Apples and peaches are grown in West Virginia near the Maryland border. Many apple trees grow in eastern Ohio.

Some farmers supplement their income from general farming by producing specialty crops and working off the farm, particularly in the coal mines.

Of great importance in soil-management programs is the maintenance of a high fertility level to promote an effective vegetative cover on the cultivated lands and the pastures and hayfields. Many of the soils have a high ability to fix phosphate; liberal amounts of it are needed.

In localities where calcitic limestone has been used generously, particularly on soils fertilized heavily with phosphate, a deficiency of zinc has been observed on corn in Tennessee and may develop in other places.

The response of crops to fertilization is excellent on soils to which the crops are well adapted because of the generally favorable distribution of moisture. Increased yields of cultivated crops through high fertilization would relieve some of the pressure to cultivate the more sloping lands.

All possible supplemental practices to control erosion should be used on sloping lands that are tilled—including contouring, stripcropping, and terracing.

Bluegrass grows well here. It probably is the most satisfactory base for permanent pastures. Rotational pastures, or short-term pastures, will be more productive if planted in orchardgrass, timothy, or bromegrass with a legume like Ladino clover. Considerable alfalfa is grown.

Yields of forage and hay crops on the Cumberland Plateau in Tennessee compare favorably with yields in other parts of the State where the growing season is longer but the moisture distribution is less favorable. High yields of other adapted crops are possible with better soil management, although the average amount of cropland per farm suited to intensive crops is smaller than in the region as a whole.

THE BLUEGRASS subregion consists of two separate areas, one in Kentucky and the other in Tennessee. Their outstanding feature is the high phosphate content of many of the soils, which largely accounts for the abundant growth of bluegrass and other pasture plants that are considered characteristic of this general subregion.

The Tennessee portion of the subregion, referred to as the Nashville Basin, is mostly level. The average elevation is about 600 feet. It is surrounded by the Highland Rim, which is several hundred feet higher in elevation. Outliers and ridges of the Highland Rim are numerous at the border of the Basin. Major drainage systems are the Cumberland River, which empties into the Ohio, and the Duck River, which empties into the Tennessee.

The Kentucky part of the subregion has elevations up to 1 thousand feet. A belt of rough land of higher elevation, called the Knobs, encircles the subregion in Kentucky, except in the north, where the Ohio River is the boundary. The major drainage systems are the Kentucky and Licking Rivers, which empty into the Ohio. Stream dissection is deep along the Ohio and Kentucky Rivers. Much upland adjacent to the streams, particularly in the northern section, is unsuited for cultivation. The land in the central portion (Inner Bluegrass) generally is smooth.

The growing season in Kentucky is about 180 days. The total precipitation is 40 to 45 inches. The growing season in Tennessee is 190 to 200 days, and the precipitation is about 50 inches. Summer rainfall is not well distributed. Evapotranspiration is high, and drought periods are frequent.

Limestones, many of which are more or less phosphatic, represent the dominant rock formations. Shales occur also, often interbedded with limestones. Sandstones are not extensive. All rocks are horizontally bedded. A thin deposit of glacial till (Illinoisan) occurs in the extreme northern portion in Kentucky. There is evidence of shallow loess in places near the Ohio.

Soils, such as Maury, which developed from highly phosphatic parent materials, have dark-brown, silt loam surface horizons and reddish-brown subsoils of medium-fine texture. Usually they are only moderately acid. They naturally are highly productive, particularly for small grains and legumes which have a high phosphate need.

Evidences of zinc deficiency, particularly on corn, occur where these soils have been limed to a pH of 6.5 or above.

Parent materials that are medium to low in phosphate often are high in clay. The soil series developed on them, such as Mimosa and Lowell, have fine-textured, slowly permeable, yellowish-brown subsoils. In the central part of the Nashville Basin are soil

series (such as Hagerstown and Tal-
bott), which are low in phosphate.
Similar soils are present in Kentucky
but have a more random distribution.
Many soil series, such as Eden, Fair-
mount, and Salvisa, are shallow to
bedrock and are best suited for pasture
or woodland.

Extensive areas of very shallow soils
in Tennessee, referred to as glades, are
covered chiefly with cedars.

The farms in this subregion are close
to the average size for the region as a
whole but have somewhat more cropland and considerably less woodland.
Burley tobacco is a leading crop, particularly in Kentucky. Corn acreage is
less than average for the region. Wheat
is the most important small grain in
Kentucky, and oats in Tennessee. A
relatively large acreage of alfalfa is
grown. Lespedeza is more important
relatively in Tennessee than in Kentucky. Some bluegrass seed is harvested
in Kentucky. Some cotton is produced
in the southern part of the subregion
in Tennessee.

Sheep are relatively the most important class of livestock. The relative
numbers of cattle and hogs are about
the same as for the region as a whole.

Many large residential farms, particularly near Lexington and Nashville,
are devoted primarily to grassland and
meadow for production of light horses
and other registered livestock. The high
phosphate content of the soils on most
of these farms encourages a vigorous
growth of bluegrass and whiteclover.
These are beautiful places of gracious
homes, fences of white board or stone,
and lovely green pastures and hayfields.

The commercial farmers in the Kentucky area build their crop production
programs mostly around burley tobacco. The individual farm acreage
allotments are large, compared to those
in the Appalachian Valley subregion,
for example, and much of the tobacco
is grown in a rotation.

A typical cropping sequence is tobacco, small grain, and meadow. Orchardgrass is often included in the seed
mixture for the meadow. Tobacco is
cut early enough so that it is convenient to plant small grain, usually wheat
or barley, in plenty of time for adequate fall growth. It is harder to get a
stand of small grain in the fall following corn than tobacco in a similar cropping sequence unless the corn is cut
and shocked.

The total tobacco acreage and the
allotment per farm are much smaller
in Tennessee. On many farms, therefore, tobacco is grown continuously in
the same field with a winter cover crop,
such as crimson clover and ryegrass,
in much the same way as tobacco is
produced in the Appalachian Valley.

Many of the more sloping and shallow soils throughout the subregion are
in bluegrass and whiteclover pasture.
Soils low in phosphorus also grow good
bluegrass and whiteclover when moderately limed and fertilized. Such pastures are productive in spring when
moisture is abundant and temperatures are cool. Production is again good
in the late fall after the cool, wet
weather begins. Grazing is limited during the summer, however.

Because feeds usually are short in summer, bluegrass pastures often are grazed
too closely in summer, and the stand is
hurt. Bitterweed and broomsedge are
common under such circumstances.
Bermuda-grass grows in many of the
pastures in Tennessee and provides excellent growth during the hot period
unless rainfall is extremely deficient.

The tendency has been to increase
the acreage of alfalfa and small grains
in the subregion. Most of the upland
soils suitable for cultivation are well
adapted to alfalfa. The continued adjustment to greater acreages of alfalfa
is an effective way to increase forage
production on many farms.

Small grains respond to high levels of
available phosphorus. They make
their major growth during the spring,
when moisture usually is adequate.
Small grains therefore are a dependable crop here. Small grain may be
grown for several years in sequence on
smoother lands; the land is left fallow
for a short time in summer in order to

prepare an adequate seedbed for the new crop. On more sloping lands and in other circumstances, small grain may be alternated with a meadow crop, and no row crop is used in the rotation. Nitrogen topdressings of 30 pounds or more in the late winter usually are necessary for best yields of small grain.

Restricting corn grown for grain to the alluvial soils at the foot of slopes and along small streams will help assure high average yields. Corn or corn and sorghum mixed for silage often is a more dependable feed source on upland soils than corn for grain. Even if moisture stress at tasseling time results in many barren stalks, a good yield of silage usually may be obtained. If lime is applied abundantly on soils high in phosphorus, corn may respond to zinc fertilization, particularly in cool, wet seasons.

Avoiding too close grazing of pastures in summer would help maintain the stand of desirable species and thus reduce the hazard of surface washing by summer showers. The frequent shortage of summer feed might be avoided by increased production of silage and alfalfa for supplemental use. Another alternative in Tennessee is the wider use of Bermuda-grass in pastures. Many farmers hesitate to plant Bermuda, although they utilize it effectively when it has volunteered.

The use of soil tests is especially important in the subregion to avoid application of phosphorus on soils that have a high native reserve. A number of soils in the subregion, however, do require some phosphate for best yields.

THE SOUTHERN ILLINOIS GRAY PRAIRIES subregion lies entirely within Illinois. Much of the area is nearly level. Streams that drain the area empty into the Wabash and Mississippi Rivers. Short, steep slopes border the streams.

Native vegetation was grass on the broad, nearly level areas and deciduous forest near the streams.

The average annual temperature is about 55° F., the average July temperature about 78°, and the average January temperature 31°. The average length of the growing season is 180 to 190 days.

The average annual precipitation is 40 to 42 inches. About half of the precipitation comes in the warm season, largely in local showers. The drought periods are common, and summer crops often are under moisture stress because of high evapotranspiration, the erratic distribution of rain, and the limitation—by claypan subsoils—of soil zone favorable to root extension.

Most of the area was covered with glacial till of Illinoisan age, which probably accounts in part for the smooth topography. After retreat of the glacier, perhaps 200 thousand years ago, there was a period of loess deposition. On smooth lands, the loess mantle is 30 to 45 inches deep. The soil parent materials have been leached thoroughly since they were deposited.

Most of the upland soils naturally are acid throughout, low in available nitrogen and phosphate, and medium to low in available potash. They have fine-textured clay subsoils, which are slowly permeable. The soils have low productivity for most crops unless the soil is skillfully managed. The A horizon is very silty because of the loess mantle, except on slopes where the finer textured subsoil has been exposed by erosion.

The surface of such soil series as the Cisne, developed under grass vegetation, is somewhat darker than that of the Wynoose, developed under forest, because of more organic matter.

Slick spots are common. They have enough exchangeable sodium in the subsoil to give them a high pH and to make them plastic and sticky when wet. In general, however, the surface layers of the slick spots are acid. The slick spots are lower in organic matter and have shallower surface layers over the claypan than do the associated soils. They are lower in productivity for most crops than adjacent soils and are less responsive to improved management.

Soils of the bottom lands, unless poorly drained, are more productive, particularly for summer crops, than the upland soils, but the total area of bottom lands here is not large.

Most soils of the subregion are intrazonal. They would be grouped as Argipan Planosols, except for the slick spots, which are classified as Solodized-Solonetz. The small areas of zonal soils are developed chiefly under forest vegetation on the moderate slopes near streams. These are classified as Gray-Brown Podzolic soils.

One of the major problems throughout the subregion is drainage because of the smooth topography and the impervious subsoils. Tile has not proved effective in the soils with claypans, and reliance has been placed primarily on surface drainage by shallow ditches and furrows. Erosion is not a problem on the smooth lands, but surface washing occurs on mild slopes because water penetrates the subsoil slowly, and runoff can be expected with rains heavy enough to saturate the surface.

Farms in the subregion are of about the same size as those in the whole region, but the amount of cropland per farm is about twice as large.

An outstanding feature is the large acreage of soybeans. Before the introduction of soybeans, the production of redtop seed was an important enterprise. Winter wheat is an important crop. Hogs and dairy cattle are the most important classes of livestock here.

Because of the effect of industrialization on farming programs, mention should be made of the coal mining in the southern part of the subregion and of the development of oil wells in the north-central part.

Information on the use and management of land is available from a survey of nearly 200 farms in Wayne County, Ill., which is fairly representative of the subregion. About one-half the tillable land was used for row crops (corn and soybeans), about one-third for grasses and legumes, and one-tenth for small grains, mostly wheat. About two-thirds of the tillable bottom land was used for corn and soybeans each year. Relatively few of the farmers followed a systematic crop sequence, but most of them shifted use of upland soils from row crops to sod crops periodically. Only 4 percent of the cropland was idle—less than the average for the subregion in most years.

A survey of the Crab Orchard Lake watershed in Williamson County, made at about the same time, showed 30 percent of idle land. Williamson County includes coal mines, and the average size of farms is small.

About one-third of the fields in row crops in Wayne County received no lime or fertilizer regularly. More than half the fields in grasses or legumes received no regular lime or fertilizer treatment. Rock phosphate is one of the widely used fertilizer materials in Illinois. Estimated yields without regular use of lime or fertilizer were: Corn, 33 bushels; soybeans, 14 bushels; and wheat, 10 bushels. With lime and fertilizer, the yields were: Corn, 51 bushels; soybeans, 20; wheat, 17.

A representative 4-year rotation for smooth uplands would be corn, soybeans, small grain, and meadow (redtop and lespedeza). A row crop each year, either corn or soybeans, is not uncommon on bottom lands. Occasionally a meadow is seeded after a considerable period in row crops. Row crops are grown less frequently on moderately sloping land, perhaps 1 year in 4 or 5; the rotation would be row crop, small grain, and meadow for 2 or 3 years.

Relatively little contour farming, stripcropping, or terracing is done on sloping land, largely because of the irregularity of the slopes and also because farmers depend on sod crops in the rotation to keep surface soil losses at a minimum. Little or no subsoiling is practiced because it has been found ineffective as a means of increasing the permeability of the claypan layer.

Results of research have indicated that the productive potential of soils in the Southern Illinois Gray Prairie subregion is much higher than had been estimated. Many farmers have adjusted their soil-management systems to conform more and more closely with the suggestions offered by the State agricultural experiment station, and their production levels offer a striking demonstration of the effectiveness of the soil-management systems.

Drainage is one of the first steps necessary in developing the soil-management system for the nearly level upland soils that have heavy subsoils. Shallow ditches and furrows are effective ways to remove excess surface water on those lands because of the slow permeability of subsoils, in which tile are not effective. Improvement of drainage lengthens the period in the spring when the soil is at moisture levels suitable for tillage.

Timeliness of seedbed preparation is assured by tractor equipment, which can work long hours to take advantage of the periods when soil moisture is best for tillage. Seedbeds are not difficult to prepare then—because of the silty nature of the surface soils—but the low organic content of the surface layers gives rise to a tendency to pack and crust after plowing or cultivation.

In developing the crop rotation, therefore, it is important to give attention to the maintenance of organic matter by using grass and legume sods regularly. Deep-rooting crops, such as sweetclover, seem to have a beneficial effect on soil productivity for a long time. A rotation that meets the prerequisites as outlined would be: Row crop, row crop, small grain, meadow (sod) crop. The meadow could be left down for the fifth year if desired.

A key practice in the rotation system is maintenance of adequate fertility levels through the use of recommended amounts of lime and fertilizer. Soils that have not been limed previously will need as much as 4 or 5 tons an acre to bring the pH between 6 and 7. Smaller amounts of lime, up to 2 tons an acre, may be needed as maintenance applications at intervals of 5 years or longer, as indicated by soil tests. When limestone is not used in excess, rock phosphate has proved satisfactory on these soils for meadow crops

if row crops in the rotation receive supplemental amounts of superphosphate—usually in a mixed fertilizer along with nitrogen and potash. Again, the rate should be adjusted according to information gained from soil tests. If livestock utilize the meadow, considerable farmyard manure may be available for use on corn.

It takes several years for yield levels to approach the maximum expected under the recommended soil-management system. Usually by the end of the second rotation cycle, however, the cumulative effects of the fertilization and crop-rotation practices have attained their maximum influence, including, apparently, whatever beneficial effect the deep-rooted legume may have on the subsoil.

On the more sloping upland areas in the subregion, the main features of the soil-management system are relatively the same. Surface drainage ceases to be an important problem, however, and control of erosion assumes great significance. Adjustments to meet the situation on sloping areas include a less intensive use of row crops, which may be accomplished by extending the meadow period or having only 1 year of a row crop in the rotation. On slopes exceeding 1.5 to 2 percent, supporting practices, particularly contour cultivation, may be desirable to help reduce erosion.

It is desirable that no row crops be used at all on slopes exceeding about 7 percent. Such areas may be used for long-term pasture, which may alternate with small grain occasionally. Another alternative is woodland. Particular attention needs to be given to gully control on these more sloping areas to avoid damaging the land.

The key to the management of bottom lands rests on drainage and the soil fertility. Because of overflow hazard, many bottom lands are not well adapted to small grains but can best be used for grasses, legumes, and cultivated crops, as corn and soybeans.

On fields of State agricultural experiment stations, yield levels of level claypan soils, such as Cisne silt loam, with recommended management have been 50 to 70 bushels of corn, about 20 bushels of soybeans, 20 to 30 bushels of wheat, and about 2 tons of hay. Higher yields of corn and soybeans could be expected on the tillable bottom lands.

THE OZARK subregion lies mainly in southern Missouri and northern Arkansas, west of the Mississippi bottom lands. It extends westward to include parts of three counties in northeastern Oklahoma.

Elevations of the uplands usually range between 1,000 and 1,500 feet. Elevations as high as 2,400 feet occur in Arkansas in the section known as the Boston Mountains. Much of the subregion has been intricately dissected by streams; this steep land is suitable chiefly for trees. Stream valleys tend to be narrow and have little bottom land. Relatively smooth to rolling areas occur on the interstream divides throughout the Ozark subregion but are most extensive in south-central Missouri.

The range in annual temperature is 55 to 60°; in annual precipitation, 42 to 50 inches; and in length of growing season, 170 to 210 days. The area in Arkansas with elevations above 1,500 feet has lower temperatures and shorter growing seasons than does the rest of the subregion in Arkansas.

Bedrock underlying most of the subregion are mostly cherty limestones and cherty dolomites. Limestones, sandstones, and shales occur less often. All rock is level bedded or nearly so. In Missouri, in the northeastern portion of the subregion, granitic rocks are exposed in some places. In this area of crystalline rock outcrop, known as the St. Francis Mountains, the topography is rough and rugged.

The soils were developed under deciduous forest vegetation on residual parent materials resulting from the weathering of the underlying rock. Soils over much of the subregion have a relatively high chert content, particularly those on steep slopes. Chert interferes with tillage and mowing and reduces the water-holding capacity of the soils so that crops may suffer sooner from lack of moisture. On the other hand, the cherty fragments on the surface protect the soils against the beating effect of raindrops and slow down the movement of water over the surface. Cherty soils therefore are much more resistant to erosion than if they were free of chert. Soils developed on the relatively smooth, interstream divides in the areas of cherty parent material have a relatively impervious fragipan about 22 inches below the surface. This fragipan interferes with the movement of water and limits root extension.

The very cherty soils on the steep slopes used to be classified as Clarksville. The somewhat less cherty soils, with red subsoils, on moderate to moderately steep slopes were grouped with the Baxter series. The soils with fragipans were grouped as Lebanon. These soils are similar to soils from cherty parent materials on the Highland Rim in Tennessee, which include the Bodine on the steep slopes, the Baxter on the moderate slopes, and the Dickson and Lawrence with fragipans on the smoother topography.

All the soils from cherty parent materials are strongly acid and low to very low in available nitrogen, phosphorus, and potassium. In some localities, particularly in the northwestern corner of Arkansas, soils exist that are relatively free of chert. They have a brown, rather than brown-gray, surface layer and a darker red subsoil. They are among the most productive upland soils of the subregion. Baxter is classified as Red-Yellow Podzolic soil, Clarksville as a Lithosol, and Lebanon as a Planosol.

Acreages of lespedeza and oats in relation to the total cropland per farm are about twice the regional average, but the acreages in corn, wheat, clover, and alfalfa are about half as large in relation to the amount of cropland per farm as those for the whole region. An important fruit and vegetable production area is in the extreme western part. Beef and dairy cattle are relatively important; hog numbers are average; and the number of sheep is much below the average for the region. A large broiler industry has developed in the western part.

Much of the land has been left in second-growth forest because of the limitations on crop production imposed by steep slopes and cherty soils. Some pasturing of the woodland is done at certain seasons. Land not in trees is used primarily for forage crops, particularly lespedeza or lespedeza and redtop. Yields of lespedeza are low, but it does make some growth under a wide range of fertility.

The use of fertilizer and lime is not great, partly because so many of the soils have physical properties that limit crop response to high levels of fertility.

Because of the large amount of sod and hay crops used in the cropping systems and the resistance to erosion of these cherty soils, supporting erosion control practices are not needed on many farms. Yields generally are low compared to those in the rest of the region. Data from Missouri indicate that average yields of corn are less than 25 bushels an acre. Other yields are correspondingly low.

It seems desirable to continue to emphasize forage production. Special consideration should be given to the liberal use of fertilizer and to the use of more productive forage species, such as orchardgrass and Ladino clover, on soils where adequate crop response to high fertility levels is to be expected.

Studies in Arkansas showed that beef gains of 300 pounds an acre can be obtained from liberally fertilized orchardgrass-legume and Bermuda-grass-legume mixtures. Tall fescue grew well under the same conditions and produced as much total forage, but beef gains were considerably lower. Beef gains on well-fertilized lespedeza pastures were erratic and averaged much lower, although in years with favorable moisture the total gains were comparable to those obtained from orchard-

grass. Production was good on Bermuda pastures even in years of drought when fertilization was adequate. Bermuda pastures produced less than 100 pounds of beef an acre without fertilizer. Bermuda was grazed fairly heavily and mowed occasionally to control weeds. Soils too cherty or shallow to assure good response of orchardgrass or Bermuda-grass to heavy fertilization might be left in native pasture or used for lespedeza or sericea, both of which will give some production with relatively little expense.

Land in orchardgrass pasture might be used occasionally for a row crop or small grain, since orchardgrass-legume mixtures do not form permanent sods but need reseeding occasionally. Bermuda-grass fields, however, would be considered permanent and ordinarily would not be used for other crops; forage production would be maintained at high levels by annual topdressings of fertilizer.

On soils that are not too cherty to prevent preparation of a good seedbed and are not so steep as to present a serious erosion hazard during cultivation, alfalfa with or without orchardgrass is well adapted after liming and liberal fertilization. Red clover is also adapted to such soils and fits well in short rotations such as corn, small grain, and meadow.

Research in Missouri indicates that high yields of corn can be obtained on some of the soils in the Ozark subregion if fertilization is liberal and other good practices, including close spacing, are used. Soils of the bottom lands with intermediate to good drainage could be used for continuous corn, and yields of 100 bushels an acre could be obtained. But it seems doubtful that high yields of corn could be expected on soils, such as Lebanon, that have a fragipan. Evidence indicates that plant roots, at least of annuals, do not penetrate the fragipan layer. Thus low yields of corn would be expected in seasons of limited rainfall because of lack of adequate moisture, even when fertilization is heavy. More consistent yields of soybeans and small grains would be expected on these soils, if they were not to be used for pasture or hay production.

THE CHEROKEE-PARSONS subregion, a small one, lies at the western extremity of the region. It adjoins the Ozark subregion on the east. Its western border touches the Flint Hills. It includes a few counties in Missouri, Kansas, and Oklahoma. Tulsa, Okla., is not far from the western boundary of the subregion.

Coal has been stripmined in the past, and old stripped areas form rough, nonagricultural lands. Elevations generally range between 500 and 1 thousand feet. The relief over much of the subregion is relatively smooth.

Total annual precipitation is about 44 inches at the edge of the Ozarks in Missouri and 38 inches near Tulsa. The length of growing season is 180 days in Missouri and more than 210 days in Oklahoma. Hot, dry winds frequently blow across this area in summer and aggravate the effect of rainless periods on summer crops by increasing the rate of evapotranspiration.

Bedrock includes shale, sandstone, and limestone, all of which lie nearly horizontally, with a slight dip to the west. The broad, smooth areas in general are underlain by shale and some limestone. Several eastward-facing escarpments are capped with sandstone; they are not very high, but they are the more broken areas. Evidence of some loess deposition is found in spots.

The native vegetation was dominantly prairiegrass, although some forested areas occurred naturally, chiefly in the bottom lands and on the hilly areas developed from somewhat sandy parent material. Soils developed under forest on the uplands from medium-textured parent materials are moderately acid, low in available nitrogen and phosphate, and medium to low in available potassium. Trees probably occurred on the medium-textured soils because of the amount of moisture available; medium-textured

soils have a much lower wilting point than fine-textured soils and are more permeable to roots.

Soils of the uplands developed under grass vegetation include the Parsons and Cherokee (Planosols), from fine-textured parent materials, and the Bates (Prairie soil), from medium-textured parent material.

Grassland surface soils are moderately to slightly acid, medium in nitrogen, low to medium in phosphate, and medium to high in potassium. Subsoils often are neutral to alkaline.

Soils developed from fine-textured parent material, such as the Parsons, have angular, blocky clay subsoils, which are slowly permeable to water and roots. Small amounts of gypsum often occur in the subsoils. Slick spots are frequent in the Planosol areas.

Farms in the Cherokee-Parsons subregion are larger than the average in the region. An area of diversified farming, it produces small grain, corn, sorghum, and hay. Some cotton is grown in the southern part and some soybeans in the northern part. Native pastures are common. Alfalfa will grow on some of the soils without lime or fertilizer, but the soils best adapted to alfalfa often need lime, phosphate, and potash for continuing satisfactory production.

Despite the relatively smooth topography, surface erosion is a problem on many farms. Much of the rainfall comes as intense showers in summer, when the soil under cultivation is most susceptible to erosion. The slow permeability of many subsoils restricts the rate of percolation and encourages runoff. Intensive grazing of pastures during dry periods also increases the susceptibility to erosion.

Corn yields are often disappointing because of extreme moisture stress during the summer. Hot, dry winds, particularly at the time of pollination and afterward, have a detrimental effect. Sorghum and cotton stand these periods of moisture stress better than corn and give more consistent yields.

Satisfactory yields depend on a combination of practices. The first is maintenance of adequate levels of fertility. Rates of liming and fertilization can best be adjusted on the basis of soil tests. Deep-rooted legumes, such as sweetclover, have an important place on the soils that are used in a rotation. On soils to which it is adapted, alfalfa would also help maintain organic matter and soil permeability.

It is doubtful if the good results obtained with corn in the Southern Illinois Gray Prairies could be duplicated in the Cherokee-Parsons area, because hot, dry winds are frequent here. Sorghums for grain and silage would yield in both wet and dry years.

Small grains and other crops, which make their major growth in spring when moisture stress occurs less frequently, deserve special attention in this subregion.

SEVERAL OTHER areas within the region that have similar soil problems are too small to justify separate delineation and treatment as subregions.

These areas occur in parts of six States as follows: The Highland Rim area of Tennessee; all of Kentucky west of the Appalachian-Cumberland Highlands and the Bluegrass subregions; the extreme southwestern part of Ohio; approximately the southern one-third of Indiana and Illinois, except the Southern Illinois Gray Prairie subregion; and the area in east-central Missouri along the Mississippi and Missouri Rivers.

Elevations of uplands are as high as 1,200 feet near the escarpment of the Appalachian-Cumberland Highlands in Tennessee and Kentucky and decline to the west to around 700 feet in Tennessee and 500 feet in Kentucky. Maximum elevations near the Ozarks in Missouri are about 900 feet. In Indiana, Illinois, and the rest of the area in Missouri, elevations range between 500 and 800 feet. The elevation of the Mississippi River at St. Louis is about 400 feet; at the junction with the Ohio, about 270 feet.

Uplands adjacent to these streams and their tributaries, which include the Tennessee and Cumberland Rivers, are extensively dissected and have many steep slopes.

The growing season averages about 180 days across the northern boundary of these areas in Ohio, Indiana, Illinois, and Missouri. It is as long as 210 days along the western boundary in Kentucky and Tennessee. Average annual precipitation is 40 to 45 inches in Missouri, Illinois, and Indiana, up to 50 inches in southern Kentucky, and 52 inches in Tennessee.

The acreage in corn and wheat and the number of hogs are nearly twice as great and the acreage of soybeans is more than twice as great per farm in these areas than in the whole region.

Corn, wheat, and soybeans are concentrated in the northern portion, where fertile bottom lands occur along the Mississippi, Missouri, Ohio, and Wabash Rivers.

Tobacco production is concentrated in the central portion. The largest acreage is in Kentucky. Production extends only a short distance northward from Kentucky along the river in Ohio and Indiana. Practically no tobacco is grown in Missouri and Illinois. The center of dark-fired tobacco production is along the Kentucky-Tennessee border near Clarksville and Springfield, Tenn., and Hopkinsville, Ky. Burley tobacco is grown throughout this area, although in smaller amounts; it is the major type grown throughout the portion of these areas in Tennessee south of the dark-fired tobacco area.

Less difference exists in the pattern of forage crop production, except that very little lespedeza is grown in southwest Ohio and the adjacent area in eastern Indiana. Little alfalfa is grown on the cherty soils of the Highland Rim in Kentucky and Tennessee. Commercial apple and peach orchards are in Illinois east of St. Louis. Another commercial peach area is in the southern part of Illinois.

Bedrock important in these areas includes sandstone, shales, limestone, and very cherty limestone. The land surface in areas underlain by limestone is characterized in many places by numerous sinkholes. There is limestone bedrock in the famous cave region of central Kentucky. Limestone rock continues north across the Ohio River into the unglaciated section of southern Indiana and southwest into the border counties of Tennessee near Clarksville. A narrow belt of relatively chert-free limestone extends across Tennessee adjacent to the Cumberland Plateau on the eastern Highland Rim. Another small area of limestone occurs near the Mississippi River in eastern Missouri.

Cherty limestones underlie most of the Highland Rim area of Tennessee and extend northeastward in Kentucky to the Appalachian-Cumberland Highland subregion. The weathered residues from them are stony, particularly on steeper slopes. Interbedded sandstone and shale rocks, underlain by coal deposits in most places, occur in Kentucky north and west of the limestone area and extend into Indiana. Interbedded limestone and shale occur on the eastern edge of Indiana and extend into southwestern Ohio. A small area of coastal plain materials is found in Kentucky between the Tennessee and Mississippi Rivers.

Old glacial drift overlies bedrock in parts of Missouri, Illinois, Indiana, and Ohio. Much of this glaciated area has a relatively smooth topography. Loess deposits of varying depth occur on most of the uplands with smooth relief near the Missouri, Mississippi, Ohio, and Wabash Rivers. The deposits are especially deep in western Illinois. Thin deposits of loess can be identified in Tennessee on the western Highland Rim, and loess covers all the coastal plains deposits in Kentucky where the topography is moderately smooth. Loess usually is not found on steep slopes, perhaps because it was removed by erosion as fast as it was deposited or has been eroded since.

Soils developed from relatively chert-free limestone residuum are productive, well adapted to a large number of crops, and moderately resistant to erosion. These soils have brown to light-brown surface layers and red subsoils. They include the Decatur and Cookeville on the Tennessee Eastern Highland Rim and in southern Kentucky; the Pembroke, which has a shallow layer of loess over limestone residuum and occurs chiefly northwest of Clarksville; and the Hagerstown in Missouri, Indiana, and the northern part of Kentucky.

Much of the land in the limestone areas is relatively smooth, although in places sinkholes have caused irregularities of slope that are inconvenient in cultivated fields. Soils of the bottom lands, such as the Huntington and Lindside, are fertile and productive of summer crops. The bottom lands along the smaller streams are fairly extensive and give opportunity for concentration of summer row crops to relieve somewhat the pressure for cultivated crops on the uplands.

Soils developed in the cherty limestone areas resemble those in the Ozark subregion, which also is a region largely of cherty to very cherty limestone bedrock. Some of these soils are not highly productive.

These cherty soils are among the most resistant to erosion, however. Bottom lands along small streams are relatively narrow because of the resistant nature of the bedrock and the alluvial soils therefore are of limited extent. Bodine, a Lithosol, occurs on steep slopes and is suited primarily for trees. Baxter, a Red-Yellow Podzolic soil, occurs on moderate slopes, is less cherty than Bodine, and has a brown-gray surface and yellowish-red subsoil. It is moderately well suited to cultivation; with fertilization, it is moderately productive. Dickson and Lawrence—Planosols—occur on relatively smooth topography and have little chert in the surface, but they have a fragipan at 20 to 24 inches. Mountview resembles Dickson but does not have a fragipan.

Dellrose, of minor extent, is an unusual soil that occurs below the Bodine and Baxter on steep slopes, where dissection from the Nashville Basin is cutting into the Highland Rim.

Because many of the cherty soils are adapted only for forests, management of woodland areas is important in obtaining maximum farm income.

Soils developed in the areas of interbedded sandstone and shale in Kentucky and Indiana resemble soils of the Appalachian-Cumberland Highland subregion.

Soil series include Muskingum, a Lithosol occurring most commonly on steep slopes; Wellston, on moderate slopes and with moderate depth over bedrock; and Tilsit, which has a fragipan and is on quite smooth areas.

The Muskingum is less extensive than in the Appalachian-Cumberland Highland subregion because the topography is less rugged and the soil mantle over bedrock is somewhat deeper. Present management practices and the recommended changes in the soil-management systems are similar to those described for the Appalachian-Cumberland Highland subregion, except as affected by the less favorable moisture conditions in summer.

Soils developed on moderately deep to deep loess include Memphis, Loring, and related soils. Where they occur on sloping lands, they are susceptible to erosion because of their silty nature.

Associated with them on smooth areas of western Kentucky is Grenada, which has a thick fragipan about 24 inches below the surface where no erosion has occurred. Where erosion has exposed the coastal plain materials on the slopes, Regosols of various kinds are found. Soils developed from loess are somewhat higher in available phosphate and potash than the average soil of the subregion. The use of fertilizer is important, nevertheless, in order to help maintain a vigorous plant cover.

More emphasis is desirable on the production of pasture and hay crops to keep the land surface covered a longer time. Sloping soils should not be in row crops for more than 1 year between sod crops.

Trees are recommended for critical

eroding areas. Controlled grazing of pastures will help maintain vigorous sod cover.

The glaciated areas in Indiana, Illinois, and Ohio with smooth relief have many soils with claypans similar to the soils of the Southern Illinois Gray Prairies that developed under forest vegetation. West of the Illinois Gray Prairie subregion are some claypan soils with moderately dark surface layers, which were developed under tall grass vegetation. Some slick spots occur in association with the Planosols developed under grass but are not so common as in the Southern Illinois Gray Prairie subregion. Because of the silty character of the surface layer of most of the soils in the glaciated areas, erosion is a serious problem in cultivated fields. Soil-management problems are like those of the Southern Illinois Gray Prairie subregion.

Soils developed over shale, and interbedded limestone and shale, in the unglaciated portions of southwest Ohio and adjacent areas of Indiana resemble those across the Ohio River in the outer portion of the Bluegrass subregion of Kentucky. Their suggested management would be similar.

Bottom land (alluvial) soils are extensive along the Wabash River, along the Ohio River from its junction with the Mississippi River to a point somewhat east of its junction with the Wabash River, and along the Mississippi from the north extremity of the region to a point about halfway to the Ohio junction. These bottom lands are fertile, but they often are flooded. Some levees have been constructed to protect the bottom lands from overflow. The control of weeds is a major problem in the bottom lands. Bottom lands along the Tennessee River have been largely flooded by the construction of Kentucky Dam near Paducah. Bottom land along the Cumberland River is fertile but relatively narrow. Except where it is too poorly drained, this land is well adapted for continuous production of summer crops, such as corn and soybeans.

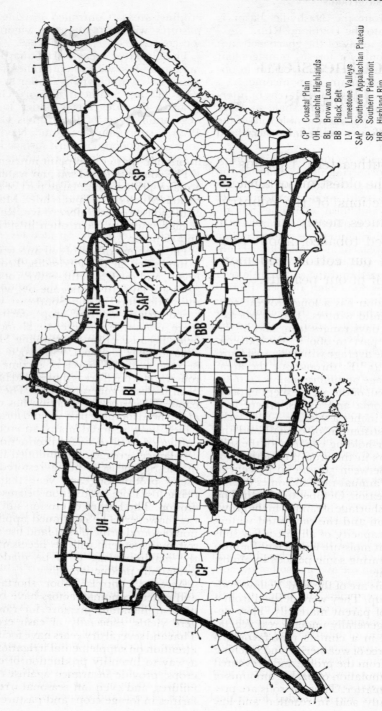

CP Coastal Plain
OH Ouachita Highlands
BL Brown Loam
BB Black Belt
LV Limestone Valleys
SAP Southern Appalachian Plateau
SP Southern Piedmont
HR Highland Rim

Southeastern Uplands

R. W. Pearson aud L. E. Ensminger

The Southeastern Uplands is one of the oldest major agricultural sections of the country. It produces nearly all of our flue-cured tobacco, about one-third of our cotton, and more than half of our peanuts.

The region has a long growing season and mild winters. The number of frost-free days ranges from 200 in the northern part to 260 in the extreme south. The average winter temperature is about 45° F. throughout the area. The average annual rainfall is 50 to 60 inches in all of the area, except in parts of Oklahoma and Texas, where it is about 35 inches a year.

The distribution of rainfall and the low water-holding capacity of the soils are factors in the crop production potential. Between 50 and 70 percent of the total annual rainfall comes during the cool season, October to March. The frequent shortage of rainfall in the growing season and the restricted water-holding capacity of all but a few soils mean that moisture is deficient for crop growth during some periods in almost every year.

The soils are of the Red-Yellow Podzolic group. They were derived from a variety of parent materials. They developed generally under forest vegetation and in a climate that favored a high degree of weathering and leaching of bases from the profile and prevented the accumulation of sizable amounts of organic matter. Thus the soils are predominantly acid in reaction and low in organic matter and plant nutrients.

The conservation of soil and water is a major problem in a large part of the region. Much of the land is hilly. Many of the soils are naturally erosive. Rains of high intensity occur often in spring and summer.

The problem of loss of soil and water is intensified in the Piedmont, Brown Loam, and the Clay Hill sections of the Coastal Plain. In years gone by, when the agriculture of the Southeast was based strictly on row crops, farmers there often were forced to abandon fields because of severe gullying. The situation has changed. Pulpwood has become a major source of income on rough and eroded areas that would have been useless a generation ago. The expanding livestock production has created a need for more pasture and forage, which have restored many an eroded cultivated field to useful production.

A larger acreage of abandoned land in the Southeast is being restored to useful production each year than is being lost from production because of erosion. The hazard of erosion still exists, however. The continued application of sound principles of land use and soil management will be necessary if the maximum use is to be made of potentially productive soils.

Acreage controls, labor shortages, and other economic factors have built up a tremendous pressure for raising acre yields, especially of cash crops. That and several dry years have focused attention on supplemental irrigation as a way to intensify production of cash crops, provide insurance against crop failures, and even out seasonal irregularities in forage crops and pastures.

Irrigation has a place in intensive crop and livestock production in the Southeast. In dairy farming, for example, great possibilities exist for marked increases in production of temporary grazing crops and for shifting the growing period right into the critically dry fall season.

Crops such as millet and Sudangrass are responsive to nitrogen and moisture. They grow fast and yield well. The use of supplemental irrigation to establish seedings early in the fall and to insure rapid growth can raise yields tremendously in autumn. At Thorsby, Ala., in 1955, for example, Starr millet and alfalfa drilled in alternate rows in late August, irrigated, and heavily fertilized, produced more than 4 tons of high-quality forage in September and October and went into the winter with a vigorous stand of alfalfa.

Supplemental irrigation will undoubtedly be an important factor in the production of such cash crops as cotton, vegetables, fruit, tobacco, and flower bulbs in some localities. It probably will not affect the average level of production of the major crops in the region as a whole in the immediate future, however, because such problems as water supply, cost of installation of irrigation systems, and the high level of management it requires for successful crop production will sharply limit its application.

But the best job of management with respect to fertilization, liming, control of insects, and other practices is essential before supplemental irrigation has a chance of becoming economically sound. Crop yields in the Southeast on the average have been limited by inadequate levels of available plant nutrients, and irrigation can only produce increased yields after these other limiting factors are removed. Irrigation without proper attention to other required practices could actually depress yields. For example, added water usually leads to more luxuriant foliage of cotton plants, and that favors the development of bollworms and weevils.

Another limiting factor is water supply for irrigation. The flow of the many streams in the region often is low during the dry season. The competition of several farmers for water for irrigation from such streams often dries them up.

Wells are not dependable as an economic source of irrigation water in much of the region. Farm ponds can help as an emergency supply, but ordinary ponds cannot provide enough water for full-scale irrigation of field crops. The importance of supplemental irrigation may continue to increase, but locally it will be determined largely by the availability of water.

Rates of fertilizer application on the better managed farms in the Southeast have increased since 1935. This increased rate, the relatively higher proportions of soluble constituents in fertilizers, and the low buffer capacity of many soils lead to another problem—that of the proper placement of fertilizer at planting to avoid seedling damage because of salt injury. Stand and yields, particularly of oilseed crops in much of the Southeast, are lowered when fertilizer is applied directly under the seed instead of at one side.

The question of the most effective placement of lime and starter fertilizer for permanent pasture has received considerable attention, but we do not have the complete answer. Bandseeding grass and legumes for pasture in combination with drilled fertilizer sometimes is superior to broadcast seeding and fertilizer placement, particularly when conditions are adverse to establishment of seedlings. The deep placement of lime and phosphate does not seem to be better than surface application for the maintenance of pasture sod. Of course, basic applications of lime and phosphate in preparation for establishing pasture should be incorporated in the plow layer. Further study of the problem will be necessary, however, before a dependable conclusion can be reached as to the value of building up the nutrient and base status of the deeper soil layers.

The soils of the Southeast and their management requirements differ considerably. Therefore the region has been subdivided into eight physiographic areas, within which the soils and their management problems are more nearly alike.

THE COASTAL PLAIN forms a belt of upland soils 100 to 300 miles wide along the Atlantic and gulf coasts. It includes about 115 million acres. It extends from south-central Texas to north-central North Carolina. It is the heart of the old Cotton Belt.

Considerable differences in rainfall within the geographic range of the Coastal Plain influence strongly the use and potentialities of the soils. Most of the region east of the Mississippi River gets 50 to 60 inches of rain, but precipitation drops off rapidly west of the river to only 31 inches in Guadalupe County in Texas.

The soils were developed from marine sands and clays and are predominantly sandy in their surface horizons. The topography is gently rolling to hilly. Both surface and internal drainage are generally good. Among the extensive series are the Norfolk, Ruston, Orangeburg, Red Bay, and Magnolia soils. The upland soils have light gray to red sandy surfaces, 5 to 10 inches deep, underlain by yellow-red, friable, sandy clay subsoils. The C horizon, beginning usually at 2 to 3 feet, is mottled gray to red, unconsolidated sands and clays.

Most farms in the Coastal Plain are relatively small. The numbers have tended to decline and the size has tended to increase as farm mechanization expands.

Since soils of the Coastal Plain have developed from parent materials that have been subjected to previous cycles of weathering, leaching, movement, and deposition, they are acid in reaction and their native fertility is low.

The relatively high temperatures, the large excess of rainfall over annual evapotranspiration, and the generally good internal drainage have caused rapid weathering and excessive leaching of the bases out of the soil profile.

The original pH values ranged generally around 5.0. The same conditions of texture and climate that favored development of highly leached soils have prevented the accumulation of significant amounts of organic matter and nitrogen. The total nitrogen content of soils of the Coastal Plain rarely exceeded 1 thousand pounds an acre even in the virgin state. Actually, soils of the Coastal Plain are exceptionally responsive to fertilization and good management.

There have been marked changes in the levels of the different nutrient elements of these soils since they were first put into cultivation. The phosphorus content has been raised sharply in some areas through the practice of applying several times as much phosphate fertilizer as is removed, especially for cotton, tobacco, and potatoes. There is evidence that improvement in the status of soil organic matter and nitrogen has occurred under good management. Content of potassium, on the other hand, has been decreased, since potassium generally has been applied in relatively low amounts, and it will leach out of the sandy soils.

There has been an improvement in the exchangeable base level of these soils since they were first cultivated. This gain is in danger of being lost because of another factor. Higher rates of nitrogen fertilizer are now used more than ever before, and the trend is toward still larger amounts on a number of crops. Most of these fertilizers are acid forming when applied to the soil. A 100-pound application of nitrogen as urea, ammonium nitrate, or anhydrous ammonia, for example, would require about 200 pounds of limestone to neutralize this residual acidity.

Texture creates serious problems in some places. Lack of sufficient fine material—so that the retention of moisture and nutrients is satisfactory—occurs in the Sandhill section of the Carolinas and Georgia, for example. At the other extreme are the areas of clays and sandy clays, which often do not permit ready infiltration. The available water-holding capacity of Coastal Plain soils as a whole is low. Several profiles of typical Orangeburg sandy loam in central Alabama have an average water-holding capacity of the surface 2-foot depth of only 2.11 inches. Because corn during its peak period of growth can remove up to 0.4 inch of water a day, that is a very limited supply for crops in an area where 2-week periods without rain are not uncommon in summer.

Another management problem in the Coastal Plain is the control of excessive soil loss by water erosion. Much of this area is rolling or hilly. About 20 percent of the soils have moderately severe to very severe erosion hazard.

In no extensive areas do genetic, or natural, pans or poor structure in the B horizon seriously impede root penetration or the movement of moisture. Induced pans, or compacted layers, are fairly common, however, particularly in the medium-textured soils. Sometimes these compacted layers restrict root development almost entirely to the plow layer. They occur immediately below the plow depth, usually between 5 and 10 inches, and they are easily accessible for mechanical disruption by deep plowing.

Cotton has long dominated the agriculture of the Coastal Plain as a cash crop. Tobacco is important in sections of Georgia and the Carolinas, peanuts in southwestern Georgia and southeastern Alabama, and potatoes in southwestern Alabama, but otherwise general farming based on cotton, corn, and forage crops is the rule.

Average yields of corn tend to be higher in the northeastern end of the region than in the southwest partly because of somewhat more favorable moisture conditions. The average yield in the Coastal Plain probably is no more than 20 bushels an acre—only 30 to 40 percent of potential yields.

Estimated applications of fertilizer in 1956 included 30 pounds each of nitrogen and phosphoric oxide and 20 pounds of potash—a rate of fertilization that would be nearly adequate for phosphorus and potassium on most of the soils long in cultivation; it would provide only about one-fourth of the needed nitrogen, however.

The average yield of cotton in the Coastal Plain is about 250 pounds of lint an acre. The lack of adequate nitrogen is a main limiting factor. It was estimated that 35 pounds of nitrogen, 45 pounds of phosphoric oxide, and 35 pounds of potash an acre were applied in 1954 in the Coastal Plain section of Alabama, which is reasonably typical of the region.

That would be adequate for phosphate (except in places that have not been fertilized for a long time), but it would be inadequate for potash, except maybe on the heavier soils. The amount of nitrogen was less than half as high as it should have been.

Tobacco has received higher rates of fertilization than any crop except potatoes in the Coastal Plain. Repeated, heavy fertilization has left large accumulations of phosphorus in soils of the tobacco areas, where usually more phosphorus than is needed is applied. About 80 percent of North Carolina tobacco soils were high in available phosphorus in 1951.

Peanuts are grown on about 720 thousand acres in southeastern Alabama and southwestern Georgia. Average yields are about 900 pounds an acre. Fertilizer applications have been estimated at 8 pounds of nitrogen, 32 pounds of phosphoric oxide, and 42 pounds of potash an acre. Experiments have shown that little response usually is to be had from phosphate and potassium above the average rates. Apparently one of the chief limiting factors in the production of peanuts is a lack of adequate levels of soil calcium and magnesium.

Production controls on cotton, tobacco, and peanuts, a growing recognition of the importance of grass and legumes in conservation, and favorable prices for livestock products in the postwar years gave impetus to a trend toward farm diversification through an expansion of livestock enterprises. Pasture and forage crops have assumed great importance. The Coastal Plain section of Alabama, which comprises roughly two-thirds of the total area of the State, for example, in 1955 had about 1 million acres each in corn and improved permanent pasture and hay crops and about 250 thousand acres each in cotton and peanuts.

Advances since 1940 or so in pasture and forage crop varieties and management have made possible high levels of beef and milk production through near year-long grazing throughout the Coastal Plain. Many cattlemen from other parts of the country, especially the Southwest, have become interested in this section and have shifted their operations to the Coastal Plain region of the Southeast.

A well-planned fertilization program is essential—especially lime, phosphate, and potash for legumes, and the general use of nitrogen with nonlegumes.

The average use of phosphate and potash on forage crops has been far below the recommended amounts. An average of less than 10 pounds of phosphoric oxide and 5 pounds of potash have been applied in the Southeast, but yield increases of at least 60 percent could be realized by the use of 40 pounds of each to the acre.

Improved permanent pasture is the foundation for any livestock system, but there are periods of low production, such as the coldest part of the winter and the normally dry late summer and fall. The gaps should be filled by supplemental grazing crops, such as small grain, winter legumes, lespedeza, millet, and Sudangrass. Improved varieties of millet and Sudangrass, properly fertilized, for example, can provide 2 to 4 tons of good forage within 8 to 10 weeks after planting when summer rainfall is normal.

Few definite rotations or systematic crop sequences have been used here. Fields well adapted to a given crop are planted more or less continuously to it. Accumulating evidence supports the view that high yields, at least of cotton and corn, can be had over relatively long periods when the crops are grown continuously, if adequate fertilization and other good management practices are observed. Cotton grown continuously since 1896 on Chesterfield sandy loam at Auburn, Ala., for example, averaged 1,200 pounds of seed cotton the last 16 years, compared to 812 pounds during the first 16. Corn grown continuously on a Norfolk sandy loam for 9 years in North Carolina at a high level of nitrogen fertilization produced an average of 85 bushels an acre the last 3 years, compared with 75 bushels at first.

The use of winter legumes as a cover crop has been considered a valuable practice to improve soil structure and add nitrogen to the soil. Fewer and fewer farmers have followed it, however. Perhaps no more than 15 percent of the acreage in row crops in the Coastal Plain was planted to winter cover crops in 1956—probably a reflection of the disease problems of some of the otherwise better adapted legumes and the increasing supplies of relatively cheap commercial nitrogen. Indeed, it is difficult to find evidence in research data that annual winter cover crops have any significant effect on soil properties and subsequent crop yields beyond that of the nitrogen supplied. Experiments have failed to show a buildup of organic matter in Coastal Plain soils beyond that realized through crop residues when reasonable fertilization was used.

The use of annual legumes as cover crops, as an emergency source of grazing during the late fall, winter, and early spring, and then as a green manure crop for the nitrogen gained appears to have considerable possibilities. Actually, the practice of grazing vetch and other such cover crops is fairly common. Its value in providing forage would be almost directly proportional to the earliness of seeding in the fall, since it would depend almost entirely on the growth made before the onset of winter.

The value of the legume cover crop from the standpoint of the nitrogen that it provides for the following crop has been shown to range all the way from practically nothing in unfavorable years to better than 100 pounds of nitrogen an acre in years of favorable temperature and moisture. Furthermore, in most years most of the growth made by the winter cover crop comes in the spring, when the row crops to follow should be planted. Thus there is competition between the need to delay turning the cover crop under as long as possible and the need to plant the row crop on time.

The low content of organic matter of soils of this area and the inability to build it up appreciably (because of the sandy texture of the soils and the high mean annual temperature and rainfall) mean that available native soil nitrogen is always sharply deficient for crop production.

In fact, recommendations as to nitrogen can be made almost without reference to the organic matter but with consideration only of the yields desired. Yields of corn on these soils without nitrogen, either commercial or legume nitrogen, generally do not exceed 25 bushels an acre. With adequate nitrogen and with other recommended practices, most of these soils will produce at least 80 bushels in years of normal rainfall. Even soils that have been cropped for decades without fertilization usually produce remarkably good yields when they are fertilized properly.

The diagram gives the average corn yields when different rates of nitrogen were applied in a large number of field tests in North Carolina in 1944–1952.

Similar responses to nitrogen have been reported throughout the Coastal Plain, although the average top yields tend to be somewhat lower in the central part and are definitely lower in the southwestern part because of less favorable distribution of rainfall.

The important thing, of course, is the fact that corn yields 3 to 5 times above the present average production can be achieved by observing improved management practices.

Some farmers believe that high rates of nitrogen will reduce corn yields in

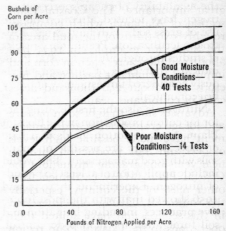

Response of corn to nitrogen fertilization in North Carolina under both good and poor moisture.

dry years. There is no increase in yield from the higher rates of fertilizer whenever deficiency of moisture limits the yield, but the results of field experiments throughout the Southeast fail to show that yields are reduced.

Observations of the carryover effect of nitrogen from one season to another have raised questions about the commonly held belief that nitrogen is quickly and completely leached out of the profile if it is not absorbed by plants soon after application. Larger amounts of applied nitrogen do remain in the soil for longer periods than people thought, but we cannot draw a definite conclusion because of doubt about the factors that affect conversion of ammoniacal nitrogen and the amount of water that percolates through the profile. We think it is safe to say that (except in years of low rainfall) measurable amounts of nitrogen applied before planting are removed from the root zone in sandy soils before the crop can absorb it.

Even if there were insignificant losses of nitrogen, split applications would still be advisable if high rates are used because of danger of salt damage.

The development of palatable grasses, such as Coastal Bermuda, which have an exceptionally high yield potential and a wide adaptability to climate, and the availability of cheap sources of nitrogen have focused attention on the use of grass sods with high rates of nitrogen fertilization. Preliminary results of studies throughout the Coastal Plain indicate that rates of nitrogen previously considered fantastic may actually be economical.

Nitrogen is also the first limiting factor for cotton production in the Coastal Plain. Average cotton yields of a bale or more an acre are possible on many soils with good management. This would include application of at least 80 pounds of nitrogen. Experiments in 1955 and 1956 showed that with the most intensive practices, including irrigation and soil fumigation for nematode control, there were strong yield responses to rates of nitrogen above 200 pounds an acre. In these experiments, a top yield of 3.8 bales was made with 240 pounds of nitrogen.

Typical of the response of improved grasses to nitrogen fertilization are the following results that F. L. Fisher and A. G. Caldwell obtained with Coastal Bermuda-grass on Lufkin fine sandy loam at College Station, Tex.:

Rate of Nitrogen	Hay yield	Protein yield
0	3.0	420
100	5.2	690
200	6.2	1,060
400	9.9	1,870
600	11.6	2,600
800	13.0	3,560

(The figures for nitrogen and protein content are pounds per acre. Hay is in tons per acre.)

The conversion of such data to yield of livestock or livestock products involves a number of assumptions, but we have a few figures that show direct evaluations in terms of beef. For example, E. H. DeVane found that the 4-year average beef yields from Coastal Bermuda-grass on a Tifton sandy loam in Georgia in the 6 months from April 1 to October 1 were (in pounds to the acre):

Rate of Nitrogen	Beef Gain
50	292
100	453
200	695

In this instance, each pound of nitrogen produced an average of 2.7 pounds of beef. Crimson clover growing with the Coastal Bermuda as the source of nitrogen produced 363 pounds of beef an acre—the equivalent of 74 pounds of nitrogen from commercial fertilizer.

As we indicated, phosphorus fertilization has been generally higher in reference to the requirements than the other elements, particularly in places where cotton, tobacco, and potatoes have been grown. This fact and the immobility of phosphate in the soil have resulted in a marked accumulation of phosphorus in the plow layer of cultivated soils of the Coastal Plain. Rates of application in 1956 therefore generally were nearly adequate for the cash crops but were critically low for pastures and forage legumes. We estimate that 30 to 50 percent of the acreage in "improved pastures" was not fertilized at all.

Because the levels of native soil potassium in the Coastal Plain are low and potassium does not accumulate very much in these light-textured soils, potassium generally is deficient for crop growth throughout the region. The use of potassium on corn, cotton, tobacco, and potatoes in 1956 probably was not far below their requirements, except in the Sandhills and areas where peanuts are grown in rotation. For pasture and forage crops, however, there was undoubtedly a large gap between rates used and needs. Usually 40 to 50 pounds of potash are required for maximum pasture yields in the Coastal Plain. Alfalfa requires four or five times as much.

Soils of the lower part of the Coastal Plain are sandier and contain considerably less mineral nutrients than those of the Clay Hill section to the north. Good forage species, such as white-clover and alfalfa, grow well with good management in the heavier soils, but they are not well adapted to the sandier areas. The annual lespedezas and sericea are more commonly used there, and they do not respond generally to applications of potash. Thus the question of forage quality and yield level is important in considering the potentials of the area with adequate potash fertilization. In order to establish and maintain stands of the better forage legumes, the use of relatively high rates of potash are necessary. In general, aside from the factor of quality, it appears likely that overall production of forage could be increased by at least 50 percent by the use of about 60 pounds of potash an acre.

In some areas in the Coastal Plain, the exceptionally low content of native potassium and base exchange capacity result in particularly severe deficiencies of potassium. The Sandhill belt of Georgia and the Carolinas is the largest such area. These soils are predominantly deep sands. Experiments extending over 19 years at the South Carolina Sandhill Experiment Station disclosed that yields of cotton improved with high rates of potassium fertilization, but failed to indicate any advantage for split application of the potassium fertilizer.

Boron is often recommended for alfalfa and clovers that are grown for seed. Boron is in short supply in many of the sandy soils of the Coastal Plain and is widely recommended for such crops as alfalfa and clovers.

H. T. Rogers conducted 70 experiments in central and southern Alabama and learned that alfalfa, vetch, whiteclover, red clover, crimson clover, and burclover almost invariably responded to applications of boron. Alfalfa produced an average of 58 percent more hay when boron was applied.

Cotton yields have improved in a number of instances with the addition of boron, manganese, and zinc in South Carolina.

Deficiencies of zinc exist in the Coastal Plain. Instances of marked increases in yields of corn after zinc was applied have been reported.

The soils that might have too little zinc for corn have been hard to identify in advance so that field experiments can be conducted on them. A deficiency of zinc seems to appear one year and fail to show up again in the same field. Zinc deficiency, or rosette, of pecans is much more definite. In a survey of 176 orchards in 20 counties in Alabama, T. B. Hagler found zinc deficiency, ranging from 14 percent within the highest producing group to 57 percent within the poorest producing orchards.

Serious deficiencies of calcium, magnesium, and sulfur also exist here.

An adequate liming program with dolomitic limestone would take care of the calcium and magnesium. Otherwise, or if calcitic limestone must be used, the need to apply magnesium in some other forms may arise. A survey by A. C. McClung in the Sandhills of North Carolina showed that 20 percent of the peach orchards were deficient in magnesium and an additional 20 percent were approaching a deficiency. A deficiency of magnesium also has been identified in cotton from time to time, usually in the sandier soils in places where liming had been neglected for a long time.

Some crops, including the grasses, need sulfur in relatively small amounts.

Others, such as clovers and cotton, require as much sulfur as phosphorus. Because sulfur exists in the soil in organic combination or as soluble inorganic salts, the amount of it in the strongly leached soils of low organic content is small. Serious deficiencies of sulfur undoubtedly would have occurred long ago except for the incidental amounts of calcium sulfate carried in ordinary superphosphate and the widespread use of ammonium sulfate as a source of nitrogen in mixed fertilizers. Concentrated superphosphate, which contains little or no sulfur, has been used more and more in mixed fertilizers. The use of higher degrees of ammoniation and of urea to supply the nitrogen of mixed fertilizers has largely replaced ammonium sulfate. Sulfur therefore has renewed importance. It is significant that in a number of instances crops have responded to sulfur additions 1 to 3 years after farmers started to use fertilizers that contained no sulfur.

The use of lime on soils of the Coastal Plain is far below the needed level. The need of legumes for lime was recognized and stressed in the past, but little thought was given to the requirements of the row crops. The expanding use of high rates of acid-forming nitrogen fertilizers has put an added strain on the base status of these already acid soils. As a result, the need for lime on many cropped fields has been increasing rapidly.

Furthermore, the use of heavy rates of soluble nitrogenous fertilizers on very sandy soils may markedly acidify the deeper soil layers, where correction by the addition of limestone is impractical. This is another reason why excess acidity should be corrected before extensive changes in soil reaction occur.

Experiments on Norfolk soil in North Carolina showed a net return of 25 dollars an acre from the application of a ton of limestone to peanuts when the soil was only moderately acid. Spanish and runner peanuts in southern Alabama responded to applications of lime when the exchangeable calcium level of the soil was below about 700 pounds calcium carbonate equivalent an acre. Increases in yield ranged up to 1,200 pounds of nuts an acre. Yield increases of cotton from lime applications have been relatively lower than those of forage crops and peanuts, but sizable increases have occurred frequently even on moderately acid soils.

THE SOUTHERN APPALACHIAN PLATEAU comprises a series of relatively flat-topped ridges in northeastern Alabama and northwestern Georgia. The mean annual temperature is about 60°. There are about 200 frost-free days a year. Rainfall is fairly well distributed.

Small, family-operated general farms are the rule. The tilled land is intensively farmed. Rates of fertilization and average yields are high.

The soils, developed from interbedded sandstones and shales, are mostly fine sandy loams and silt loams. They are low in organic matter and mineral plant nutrients and acid in reaction. The soils developed from shale tend to be finer and shallower and present more of a problem regarding water infiltration and erosion hazards than those derived from sandstone.

The most important soil series, the Hartsells, has a grayish-brown, very fine, sandy-loam A horizon. It is underlain at 6 to 9 inches by a yellowish-brown, friable, sandy clay B horizon. The weathered sandstone usually occurs at about 2.5 to 3.5 feet.

Of the soils derived from shale, the Enders is probably the most important series. It usually has a loam texture in the surface and is underlain by a clay loam B horizon. It occurs in gently rolling to steeply rolling places and is particularly susceptible to erosion.

The soils from sandstone and shale, because of their high content of silt, form oriented particle crusts following rains and drying winds, often to the extent of preventing emergence of seedlings and reducing penetration of water. The soils, especially the Hartsells, are responsive to management.

Cotton has long been the major cash crop. Acreage was reduced about 25 percent between 1935 and 1956, but increased acre yields more than offset the reduction.

The rates of nitrogen, phosphoric oxide, potash, trace elements, and lime required for maximum yield of the different crops are nearly identical to those of the normal upland Coastal Plain soils, such as the Norfolk.

The production potential for some crops, such as cotton and corn, may be slightly higher than for soils of the Coastal Plain, chiefly because of better distribution of rainfall and fewer insect problems.

THE OUACHITA HIGHLANDS occupy some 11 million acres in north-central and western Arkansas and about 4.5 million acres in east-central Oklahoma. The topography is rugged. The elevation is about 500 feet to more than 2 thousand feet above sea level. The mean annual rainfall is 40 to 50 inches.

More than one-half of the area is in forest. About one-fifth is in pasture.

The soils were developed from sandstones and shales. Areas of shallow, stony soils are extensive, but about 30 percent of the area has deep, medium-textured soils of good productivity.

Hanceville and Conway soils, typical of the agricultural soils, are relatively deep and light-gray to grayish-brown, sandy-textured, surface soils, underlain by friable sandy clay to clay subsoils.

The soils developed from shale are somewhat finer in texture than the ones from sandstone. Most of these soils have good internal drainage.

The upland soils have a low inherent fertility, but they are fairly responsive to management. Poor distribution of rainfall and deficiency of plant nutrients limit crop production.

The alluvial soils of the area are not very extensive but are highly productive. Farming is mostly in the relatively level valleys, which make up only about one-third of the area of the region. More than one-half of the total area is in timber. About 20 percent is in pasture. Farms generally are small and are devoted to general agriculture.

The pattern of farming, the susceptibility to erosion, and the problems of soil management are much like those in the Coastal Plain.

Cotton, corn, and pasture and meadow crops are grown on most of the farms. Cotton is the major source of income. Fruit and truck crops are grown in some localities.

The soils are reasonably responsive to treatment and have good production potentials if they are managed well. The major problem is to control erosion and maintain adequate levels of plant nutrients.

THE SOUTHERN PIEDMONT extends from North Carolina southwestward through South Carolina and Georgia into Alabama.

Its soils were developed from igneous rocks and range in texture from sandy loams to clay loams. Cecil is the most extensive series. Other important soil series are Madison, Lloyd, Davidson, and Appling.

Most of the Piedmont is hilly. Because of the steep slopes and the erosive nature of the soils, erosion has been severe.

Most of what is now mapped as Cecil clay loam was developed from crystalline rocks that contained large amounts of quartz. Erosion has removed the sandy surface from a large part of the area, however, and the exposed subsoil is now designated as Cecil clay loam instead of an eroded phase of Cecil sandy loam.

The inherent mineral nutrient level of the Piedmont soils is fairly high. The total potash in the surface 6 inches ranges from about 5 thousand to 15 thousand pounds an acre. Soil tests of 11 thousand samples in North Carolina revealed that available potassium was higher in Piedmont soils than in those of the other areas of the State.

The soils were generally deficient in phosphorus when they were brought into cultivation, but considerable phosphorus has accumulated as a result of past fertilization. Even though these soils have a high ability to fix phosphorus, experiments at the Alabama Agricultural Experiment Station showed that the accumulated phosphorus has an important residual value.

The nitrogen status of the Piedmont soils is like that of other soils in the Southeast in that satisfactory yields of nonlegumes cannot be produced without commercial or legume nitrogen.

These soils have an adequate supply of most trace elements, although boron is generally recommended for alfalfa throughout the area. Zinc deficiency has been observed on corn grown on the coarse soils.

Because erosion has removed the surface soil in many places, subsoils are now frequently farmed. Because the subsoils usually are high in clay, problems of workability and water infiltration occur.

Places where the surface soil has been removed are called galled spots. Because of their poor physical condition, they usually are unproductive. A study of the relative productivity of A, B, and C horizons of a Cecil sandy loam, when exposed by erosion, showed that the A horizon was more than 3 times as productive as the B horizon and 11 times more productive than the C horizon.

Drainage usually is not a problem here except in numerous small bottoms. Galled spots become hard and compacted if they are not stirred frequently. The ground does not crack appreciably upon drying. Infiltration is slow when the spots become hard, and the soil may be wet to only a couple of inches by the intense, frequent thundershowers. It is hard to get a satisfactory stand or yield of most crops in such places. The low yields are probably due to the droughty condition brought about by slow intake of water.

The galled spots respond to lime and fertilizer. The addition of manure or crop residues along with lime and fertilizer is more effective. Mulching the eroded areas with crop residues helps increase stands and reduce runoff.

Cotton, corn, forage crops, and oats are leading crops in the Piedmont. The acreage of cotton in the Piedmont area of Alabama has been reduced by about 73 percent since 1935, and the acreage devoted to improved pasture and forage and woodland has increased.

This change to forest and livestock is desirable from the standpoint of the erosion hazard and the best long-term use of the more susceptible areas.

The soils are moderately acid. Twenty-one samples of Cecil sandy loam and clay loam from Alabama had a pH range of 4.68 to 6.25. The average was about 5.5. Lime requirements for the same soils ranged from 1 thousand to 6 thousand pounds an acre.

Cotton in the Piedmont area of Alabama receives an average of about 40 pounds of nitrogen an acre, 44 pounds of phosphoric oxide, and 30 pounds of potash. That is somewhat less than the amounts generally recommended for cotton. Other crops are not fertilized so well as cotton.

Yields are relatively low. In the Piedmont of Alabama, the average yield of cotton is about 300 pounds of lint; corn yields are 15 to 20 bushels.

Satisfactory yields of most adapted row crops can be made on the Piedmont soils that are suited to cultivation despite their critical management requirements and poor moisture relationships. Corn yields at the Piedmont substation, at Camp Hill, Ala., ranged from 30 to 80 bushels in 1949–1955. Moisture was a limiting factor in most of those years. Oats yielded 60 to 100 bushels an acre and grass-clover mixtures about 4 tons of hay.

Potential cotton yields in the Piedmont are also somewhat lower than for most other areas of the Southeast where cotton is grown, and again moisture is probably the main limiting factor. The average yield in experiments in 1949–1953 in the Piedmont section of Alabama, Georgia, and South Carolina was 1,402 pounds of seed cotton. Adequate fertilization and other good management practices were used in the tests. In the same years and at the same locations, the average yield with irrigation was 1,947 pounds.

At Auburn, Ala., corn was a total failure in 1952 and 1954 without irrigation, but produced 54 and 65 bushels, respectively, with irrigation. Tests at Athens, Ga., showed that irrigated corn averaged 84.9 bushels in 1946–1954, compared to 59.4 bushels for unirrigated corn. As a practical matter, however, only a restricted acreage could be irrigated in the Piedmont because of the limited water supply.

Many fields that were not well adapted to the production of row crops have been put into improved pasture and forage crops, such as lespedeza sericea. An average yield of 3 tons of lespedeza hay in 1948–1953 was reported at the Piedmont substation, and alfalfa averaged better than 4 tons an acre in 1953–1954.

Field experiments in Georgia in 1955 proved that Cecil soil has a high yield potential for coastal and common Bermuda-grass and crimson clover when liberally fertilized and properly managed. In the second year after establishment, 17 thousand pounds of clover-grass hay an acre was produced with the application of 400 pounds of nitrogen and 200 pounds each of phosphoric oxide and potash an acre.

Pine for pulpwood is being produced on thousands of acres in the Piedmont that are too steep or stony for other use —another important step in the direction of diversification and application of the principles of good use of land.

THE LIMESTONE VALLEYS contain soils of limestone origin and are mainly in the Tennessee and Coosa River Valleys in Alabama. Small areas are in northwestern Georgia. The soils, predominantly red, have a texture from clay loams to silt loams. The Decatur, Dewey, and Cumberland represent the better soils of the valleys. Their inherent fertility is high.

The topography is level to undulating. Gully erosion is not widespread. Surface drainage is a problem on the more level areas. Water ponds in spots after a hard rain. Most of the area is open land and is well suited to the use of machinery.

Even though these soils were developed from limestone, they have become moderately acid as a result of cropping and intensive weathering. Twenty-two samples of Decatur soils from Alabama had an average pH of 5.48 and a range of 4.95 to 6.30. Their lime requirements averaged 1,635 pounds, with a range of 225 pounds to 3 thousand pounds an acre.

Cotton has been the major cash crop, but (as elsewhere in the Southeast) it is declining in terms of acreage and income. Beef cattle and dairying have become important enterprises.

These valleys are among the best cotton-producing areas in the Southeast. The average yield of lint cotton in 1945–1954 was more than 325 pounds an acre although the cotton received an average of only 25 pounds of nitrogen, 40 pounds of phosphoric oxide, and 20 pounds of potash an acre. That is less than present recommenda-

tions, which call for 36 pounds of nitrogen, 48 pounds of phosphoric oxide, and 24 pounds an acre of potash for the more fertile red soils of the valleys. For the less fertile soils, the recommendation is for the same amount of phosphorus, but the nitrogen and potash are each increased to 48 pounds.

The average yield of corn in 1945–1954 was about 25 bushels. That is lower than the land can produce with good management. It has been estimated that the average fertilization for corn amounts to 45 pounds of nitrogen, 30 pounds of phosphoric oxide, and 25 pounds of potash an acre. The use of phosphorus and potash is about in line with recommendations, but the use of nitrogen is only one-half as great as is recommended.

Small grains are extensively grown for grazing and grain. Oats receive an estimated average of 35 pounds of nitrogen, 48 pounds of phosphoric oxide, and 25 pounds of potash an acre. The amount of phosphate is as high as is recommended, but the amount of potash is 15 to 25 pounds less than recommended applications. The amount of nitrogen is less than the 90 to 100 pounds recommended for oats used for grazing and grain.

Alfalfa is well adapted to the limestone valley soils. It is grown primarily for hay and to some extent for alfalfa meal. The soils contain fair amounts of potash, but alfalfa should receive about 200 pounds of potash at establishment and annually thereafter. Severe potash deficiency of cotton has been observed on these soils following alfalfa—an indication that the alfalfa had too little potash. When this condition occurs, exceptionally heavy applications of potash on cotton are needed.

Soils of this area have no peculiar management problems. Good yields can be obtained by proper fertilization and good cultural practices. Yields of cotton and corn without fertilization are higher on these soils than most any other in the Southeast, but yields from fertilized plots are often not so high as yields from other areas. Apparently moisture is often a limiting factor.

Lack of available nitrogen probably is a limiting factor for nonlegumes oftener than other nutrients are. Data from the Tennessee Valley substation at Bella Mina, Ala., showed that 36 pounds of nitrogen increased cotton yields 466 pounds of seed cotton. Phosphorus and potash also are needed, but the response to them usually is lower. Even with good fertilization, cotton yields usually do not go much above a bale an acre.

Average yields of corn on well-fertilized plots have not been high at the Tennessee Valley substation. In 1955, however, corn yielded up to 126 bushels an acre. Moisture was probably the limiting factor in most other years. Average corn production on these valley soils could be increased tremendously by better management practices.

Proof of that was furnished by a study conducted by the Georgia Agricultural Experiment Station. The production practices and yields of farmers in the 100-bushel corn club were compared with usual practices and yields for farmers in the limestone valleys of northwest Georgia. Farmers who followed usual production methods averaged 18 bushels an acre, whereas the farmers using improved practices averaged 119 bushels an acre. They used better seed, much more fertilizer, and an average of 4 tons of manure an acre.

Yields of 100 bushels or more of oats on well-fertilized plots have been obtained frequently. Oats mature at a season when moisture usually is not limiting.

The soils usually require some lime for the best growth of legumes and certain nonlegumes. Two tons of lime an acre is usually adequate for alfalfa. When properly limed and fertilized, alfalfa has produced 4 tons or more of hay an acre. Whiteclover and crimson clover and vetch on the more acid soils should receive 2 tons of lime an acre.

Cotton can be expected to respond to lime on soils more acid than pH 5.5. A condition of cotton known as crinkle leaf has been observed in the Tennessee Valley. It may occur on soils having a pH of less than 5.0. It is probably due to manganese toxicity. The condition can be corrected by liming.

Very likely marked increases in yield of field and forage crops are possible with irrigation. Since there are larger and better distributed supplies of surface and ground water in the valleys than in some other areas of the Southeast, the future of supplemental irrigation here seems promising.

THE BROWN LOAM AREA forms a belt east of the Mississippi River flood plain. It extends from northwestern Tennessee south across Mississippi to the lowlands of the gulf coast.

The area is covered with a mantle of wind-deposited silt over Coastal Plain material. This loess is rather deep (up to 200 feet) along the Mississippi River bluffs, but thins out to the east and finally disappears some 30 to 50 miles from its western edge. The topography ranges from level to hilly.

The principal upland soils are Memphis, Loring, Grenada, Callaway, and Henry—listed in the order of decreasing degree of internal drainage from good to poor. These soils are predominantly silt loams and have well-developed profiles. The surface soil has been lost by erosion from much of the area, and the exposed B horizon has a heavier texture (usually silty clay loam) than the original A horizon.

The area has been intensively farmed for more than 100 years. General farming is based on cotton and corn. The farms generally are small; 83 percent of them had fewer than 100 acres in 1950.

Soils on slopes of 4 or 5 percent or more are subject to severe erosion. Row cropping in the past has resulted in excessive erosion over the entire area. The land surface in some localities is covered with a network of deep gullies.

The soils have been subjected to intense weathering, erosion, and leaching and consequently are low in mineral nutrients and organic matter. They are acid in reaction.

Definite hardpans exist in many of the

upland soils, particularly the Henry, Callaway, and Grenada, in which they usually occur within the surface 18 inches. The pans restrict the movement of moisture and plant roots and intensify the effects of long wet or dry periods. The soils usually have a satisfactory water-holding capacity, but their high content of silt and low level of organic matter sometimes cause low infiltration rates.

The erosion hazard, acreage controls, and difficult problems of soil management have caused a decline in the acreage planted to row crops. A gradual shift has started toward less dependence on row crops and more on livestock.

Rates of fertilization generally have been below satisfactory levels. Corn in the Tennessee Brown Loam area has had only about 8 pounds of nitrogen an acre; the average yield has been about 20 bushels. Cotton has received about 8 pounds of nitrogen and 16 pounds each of phosphoric oxide and potash; the average yield is estimated at about 325 pounds of lint.

Bermuda-grass, annual lespedeza, lespedeza sericea, and crimson clover are commonly grown, but generally low yields reflect the low average rates of fertilization. On the better upland soils of the Tennessee Brown Loam area, for example, it was found that yields of lespedeza averaged only about 1 ton of hay an acre. Yields of permanent pastures also have been low.

The soils, when put to the use for which they are best suited, have good potentials for crop production, however. The first consideration is to fit the cropping system to the soil with respect to its drainage, workability, susceptibility to erosion, and moisture relations.

The hilly phase of the upland soils might well be in forest, the sloping phase in pasture or forest, the gently sloping phase in pasture, the undulating phase in close-growing crops, and the gently undulating to level phase in row crops.

A carefully planned fertilization and liming program is necessary. Studies at the Brown Loam Branch Experiment Station at Raymond, Miss., in 1949 and 1950 showed that 296 pounds of beef an acre were produced between November and May when 100 pounds of nitrogen and 60 pounds of phosphoric oxide were applied on fall-planted oats that were grazed compared to 198 pounds on the check plots. The addition of potash did not improve yields. Later studies with other winter-grazing crops indicated that such combinations as oats and crimson clover or ryegrass and crimson clover produce up to 400 pounds of beef an acre during the cool season.

A number of experiments in Mississippi in 1948–1951 showed yield responses from 36 to 145 percent by permanent pasture on typical Brown Loam soils to phosphate applications; yields were about 6 thousand pounds of dry matter. Coastal Bermuda-grass can be grown well on these soils, although there has been a lag in its use in the area. Its very high potential production makes it one of the most desirable sod grasses here.

Cotton grown on adapted land can produce excellent yields with proper fertilization, insect control, and other required practices. The average potential yield in Tennessee under commercial farming conditions has been estimated to be a bale, or slightly more, an acre; the estimate should also apply to similar soils and management levels farther south. In experiments at four locations in Mississippi in 1954, a very dry year, the average for the highest yielding treatment was a bale an acre.

In these tests, in which the recommended practices were followed, there was no response to potash and little response to phosphate, but the addition of nitrogen brought a large increase in yields.

Corn yield on the upland soils often is limited by inadequate moisture. Yields at the Mississippi Brown Loam Branch Experiment Station were limited by moisture in 1952, 1953, and 1954, when no response was found to more than 60 pounds of nitrogen an acre, although in years of good rainfall as much as 150 pounds is required for maximum yield. Good yields, estimated to average 75 bushels an acre, can be made in most years on the less droughty bottom-land soils, compared to about 45 bushels on the upland soils.

The recommended practices to control runoff are cultivation on the contour, use of sodded waterways, the judicious use of tillage to improve the infiltration rate, and the addition of organic matter to the soil.

When hardpans occur within the upper foot of the soil profile, they can be broken by ordinary subsoiling equipment. Tests in Mississippi indicated that mechanical destruction of the hardpan would be beneficial in the years when moisture is limited but not to the extent of complete crop failure. It would also improve internal drainage and aeration in years of excessive rainfall. The decision whether to subsoil in a specific instance, however, would depend on the depth of the pan at that location, the cost, and the crops to be grown.

THE BLACK PRAIRIE AREA—or Black Belt—is a relatively narrow band of heavy clay soils, about 20 miles wide, that extends from the eastern part of Alabama to the northeastern corner of Mississippi. The land is gently rolling and is well suited to the use of large machinery. The soils are sticky when wet, and large cracks form when the soils are dry.

The area, which comprises about 10 percent of the arable land in Alabama and Mississippi, is different from most of the Coastal Plain in that the soils were formed from chalk and very heavy marine clay deposits. About one-third of the area has calcareous soils, chiefly Sumter and Houston. The rest is made up of gray to red acid clay soils, the more important of which are Vaiden, Eutaw, and Oktibbeha.

Grass was the primary native vegetation, and the area was known as the Black Prairie or canebrakes. A soil survey in 1902 of Perry County, Ala.,

showed that the Black Prairie soil there was Houston clay. Today most of it would be mapped as Sumter clay, which is generally considered to be an eroded phase of Houston, in which the weathered chalk appears at or near the surface.

Most of the soils were fairly well supplied with native potassium, but deficiencies of potassium have become widespread after long cropping. The virgin soils had too little phosphorus.

The Black Belt for many years was one of the leading cotton-producing sections in the Southeast. The arrival of the boll weevil about 1914 was a serious blow, however, and cotton production declined rapidly afterward. The boll weevil was more serious here than in some other areas because the heavy, poorly drained soils made it almost impossible to plant cotton early enough to reduce damage from weevils to tolerable levels.

The fact that the natural vegetation of the area was grass and clover influenced research workers, when declining incomes and abandonment of land followed the elimination of cotton as a major source of income, to consider means of stimulating the growth of pasture and forage plants and to develop a livestock program to utilize the forage.

Early studies in Alabama and elsewhere have shown that most of the soils responded well to superphosphate but poorly to potash.

The acid soils need lime for most legumes. The chalk that occurs in outcrops and on eroded hillsides may be used as a cheap source of lime. Because it may have a calcium carbonate equivalent of 50 or 60 percent, it should be used at double the rate recommended for good agricultural lime. As a rule, it may be spread at less cost than an equivalent amount of agricultural lime can be spread.

Permanent pastures are an important part of the forage program. Dallisgrass-whiteclover is the main mixture in them. Johnsongrass is used extensively as a hay and pasture crop and often is grown with vetch or Caley peas. The legumes extend the length of the grazing season and furnish nitrogen for the Johnsongrass.

Nevertheless, less than one-half of the open permanent pastureland is considered improved, and only about 25 percent of the improved pastures are fertilized regularly. The acreage of pasture that is fertilized receives an estimated average of 10 pounds of nitrogen, 70 pounds of phosphoric oxide, and 25 pounds of potash an acre annually. That means that when the total acreage of improved pasture is considered, the average application is only about 2 to 3 pounds of nitrogen, 18 pounds of phosphoric oxide, and 6 pounds of potash an acre.

Sizable acreages of small grain are grown for grazing and grain, but cotton and corn are not grown to any great extent in the Black Belt of Alabama. A considerably larger proportion of the Black Belt soils in Mississippi are in row crops than in Alabama.

Most forage and pasture crops can be grown successfully with proper fertilization, and the production of forage for conversion to meat and milk could be increased greatly. The improved pastures receive only about 25 percent of the recommended amounts of phosphate and potash. If all the open land were improved and well fertilized, the income from livestock products could be more than doubled.

Some forage plants cannot be grown on the calcareous soils here, although the climate suits them. Crimson clover and annual lespedeza become chlorotic because available iron is insufficient. Sericea has not done well in some places. Alfalfa has yielded well on the calcareous soils, but it is not recommended for the heavy acid soils. Well-fertilized alfalfa grown on limed soil at the Black Belt substation at Marion Junction, Ala., produced nearly 5 tons of hay as an average in 1948–1954.

Liberal applications of superphosphate are necessary for the establishment and maintenance of good clover-grass pastures. As in other areas long

in cultivation in the Southeast, considerable phosphorus has accumulated in the older, well-fertilized pastures, and less phosphorus is now required annually for good production. Workers at the Alabama Agricultural Experiment Station discovered that 400 pounds of superphosphate annually increased the yield of beef 119 pounds an acre as an average. Average beef gains in a 3-year period were 366 pounds with superphosphate alone and 435 pounds with superphosphate plus 150 pounds of potash every 3 years.

The lime requirement of the acid soils of the Black Belt is much the same as those of other acid soils of the Southeast despite their high exchange capacity and low pH value. These montmorillonitic soils have a much higher content of exchangeable calcium and a higher percentage of base saturation for a given pH level than the kaolinitic soils of the region. Thus, although some of the soils have a pH as low as 5.0, only moderate amounts of lime are needed for most crops. Even on the more acid soils, an application of 2 tons of lime an acre is usually enough for Dallisgrass-whiteclover pastures.

Some row crops are grown in the area. Branch Experiment Station at Brooksville, Miss., has shown that with power equipment and improved insecticides excellent yields of cotton and corn can be made. Yields of corn in 1949–1955 ranged from 20 bushels an acre in a year of severe drought to slightly more than 100 bushels in years of good rain.

For high yields of corn and cotton, liberal applications of the three major nutrient elements are needed. In years of normal rainfall, corn has responded well to 150 pounds of nitrogen and 60 pounds of phosphoric oxide an acre.

THE HIGHLAND RIM has soils that are derived from cherty limestone and are frequently underlain by fragipans on the more level sites.

They are acid and have low inherent fertility but are responsive to good management. They are well suited to general farming.

Florida and Flatwoods

J. R. Henderson and F. B. Smith

The Florida Peninsula and adjacent Flatwoods include all or part of 10 counties in eastern South Carolina, 20 counties in eastern Georgia, and 64 of the 67 counties in Florida.

It is a low coastal plain, which has more than 5 thousand miles of indented coastline. No point is more than 100 miles inland from the Gulf of Mexico or the Atlantic Ocean. Inward from the coast a series of seven old shorelines mark the boundaries of marine terraces whose maximum elevations are 25, 42, 70, 100, 170, 215, and 270 feet above sea level. The highest points are in Pasco and Polk Counties in Florida.

The drainage systems are variable. Several large streams enter from the north and west and receive drainage from tributaries that rise within the region. Streams are rare in the central ridge of the Florida Peninsula. Most of the surplus water seeps rapidly into numerous lakes that dot the terrain or into underground cavities caused by the dissolving of the underlying limestone. The lower lying flat terraces do not have well-defined drainage systems. Runoff moves slowly through broad sloughs into the shallow lakes or sluggish streams and finally into the gulf or ocean.

Relief and parent materials, with their accompanying effects on drainage and related conditions, have been dominant factors in forming the characteristics of the soils. Except for alluvial deposits along the larger streams and organic deposits in wet areas, the formations upon which the soils have developed consist of limestones, marls, and noncalcareous marine deposits of mixtures of sands, silt, and clay.

Limestones underlie the entire region but are exposed in only a few places, mainly in central Florida, where they have weathered to form the parent materials of an important group of phosphatic soils.

The thickness of the unconsolidated mantle varies. It is quite thick in some places. It is so thin in other places that the calcium status and other characteristics of the soil are influenced by the underlying limestones.

Soil characteristics are major factors that affect the practices used in the production of crops, but climate, especially seasonal temperature, is more important in determining the kinds of crops and the seasons they are grown.

The average January temperatures range from 48.7° F. at Horry, S. C., to 69.9° at Key West, Fla. Summer temperatures have a narrower range; the averages for July range from about 80° to slightly above 83°.

Temperatures in summer are lower and winter temperatures are higher near the coasts than they are inland. The heat of summer is tempered by sea breezes, and winter temperatures are moderated by the warm waters of the gulf and ocean. Lakes, which are numerous in the central part of the Florida Peninsula, also have a moderating effect on temperatures locally.

The average number of days without killing frost is approximately 250 in inland points of the northern part to 365 at Key West, off the southern tip of Florida.

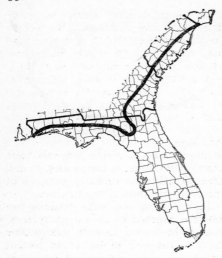

No part of the mainland is frost free, but sometimes several winters in succession may have no frost in sections of central and southern Florida. Cold waves occasionally do considerable damage to crops, especially citrus fruit and winter vegetables.

The average annual rainfall at stations on the mainland is 46 to 64 inches. The annual rainfall generally is highest at the southern and western extremities of Florida and lowest along the northern part of the Atlantic coast and in areas inland from the middle part of the gulf coast. Rainfall varies considerably from year to year. Longtime records indicate that the totals for the wettest years may double those of driest years at any given place.

Seasonal distribution of rainfall is characterized by a rainy season—June, July, August, and September—when more than half of the annual precipitation occurs. Otherwise the monthly distribution of rainfall usually is good, but in some months crops suffer from lack of water. April and November are the driest months, but dry periods may occur in any month. Occasional heavy downpours, sometimes accompanied by winds of high velocity, damage growing crops considerably.

The favorable climate permits successful production of a variety of crops,

even though many of the soils are inherently of low productivity. This fact tends to lessen the significance of soil differences and increase the importance of good soil management.

The major problems of soil management include selecting soils within climatically favorable areas that are (or can be made) suitable for the crops to be grown, establishing favorable conditions of soil moisture, controlling erosion and leaching, and liming and fertilizing to overcome nutrient deficiencies and meet crop requirements.

Citrus, avocados, gladiolus, mangoes, and winter vegetables are grown in the warmer areas in central and southern Florida. Most field crops, tung, and pecans are grown in the northern parts. Citrus fruit, other fruit, nuts, watermelons, and most field crops are grown on well-drained soils. Sugarcane for syrup is grown mainly on well-drained soils in the northern section. Sugarcane for sugar is grown mainly on organic soils in southern Florida. Most vegetables are grown on soils whose water table is not far below the surface.

Permanent pastures exist in all parts of the region and on a wide variety of soils. Selection of varieties is based partly on conditions of climate or soil moisture. For example, pangola, Para, and carib grasses are grown only in central and southern Florida, and whiteclover is grown only on moist soils that are not subject to flooding for extended periods.

The establishment of favorable soil moisture conditions through drainage or irrigation is an important consideration, especially in the production of crops of high value.

Natural drainage of the soils varies from excessive to very poor. Removal of excess water from the poorly drained soils is necessary. The somewhat poorly drained soils are easily drained with shallow ditches at frequent intervals.

More elaborate systems, including dikes, main canals, and numerous lateral ditches, are required in areas of poorly drained soils.

Winter vegetables, the principal crops

grown under irrigation, are irrigated even on soils that must be drained.

The well to moderately well-drained soils of central Florida are droughty, especially during dry periods in spring.

Runoff and erosion are of minor importance in the region. Some erosion may occur on the sloping areas that have shallow, sandy clay loam and sandy clay subsoils. Contour cultivation is recommended on steeper slopes.

Severe wind erosion in some areas of the well-drained sands occurs during the winter and spring, when the soils are bare. Moving sand does considerable damage to young crops, but one can reduce its force by leaving strips of winter cover crops, such as lupine and small grains, across the field at frequent intervals at right angles to the direction of the prevailing wind.

Leaching losses may be serious on the well-drained and moderately well-drained soils, which are used for citrus, watermelons, and such general field crops as corn, peanuts, flue-cured tobacco, and pasture grasses. Liming to pH 5.5 or above and growing winter cover crops are recommended to reduce such losses.

Most of the mineral soils respond to additions of nitrogen, phosphorus, and potash. The organic soils require little or no nitrogen fertilization but need relatively large amounts of phosphorus and potassium. Mineral and organic soils, particularly those that are strongly acid or are poorly supplied with calcium or magnesium, respond to additions of lime.

Because of the low buffer capacity of most of the mineral soils, lime is applied with caution so as to avoid injury, which has been associated with heavy applications of lime on some well-drained sands. Consequently the tendency has been to avoid using lime, and some soils have become strongly acid. The liming of acid soils nevertheless has increased markedly.

Certain long-continued practices to control insects and diseases may produce unfavorable conditions. For example, the use of sulfur sprays and dusts on citrus trees permits accumulations of sulfur in the soil; it is readily oxidized and leached to produce subsoil acidity, which is not easily controlled by surface applications of lime. The treatment of the soil with sulfur to control scab of potatoes and the use of acid-forming fertilizers often bring about conditions unfavorable to the growth of the nitrifying organisms. Maintaining the soil reaction at pH 5.4 gives good control of scab and permits fairly rapid nitrification. Extremely acid to strongly acid sands have low phosphorus-fixing power; applied phosphate is lost readily by leaching until they are limed.

Deficiencies of the secondary elements appear to be less general than those of the elements required in larger amounts, but they demand equally as much attention in some circumstances.

Magnesium deficiency is most pronounced in the sands, especially those in well-drained areas, where it is responsible for bronzing of citrus.

Copper deficiencies have been noted on raw organic soils in the Everglades and elsewhere and in many areas of mineral soils. Applications of copper in those places help control dieback and ammoniation of citrus and promote normal growth of pangolagrass, oats, peanuts, and other field crops.

Marl frenching of citrus trees and the occurrence of similar leaf patterns in the foliage of various other plants growing on marl or other high-lime soils and on some of the well-drained sands indicate a deficiency of manganese.

Zinc deficiencies, which show up as frenching of citrus, bronzing of tung, rosette of pecans, and white bud of corn, are rather general. The addition of small amounts of boron is an aid in the production of celery and clovers on Leon and similar soils in the Flatwoods of central and southern Florida.

Response to applications of the trace elements has not been determined for all the various soils and crop combinations in the region. It is possible that deficiencies of them are more widespread than we have realized. Until more specific information is obtained, the use of trace elements for all crops on all soils is not recommended because of the additional expense and the possibility of building up toxic concentrations. Preliminary results of research indicate that large amounts of copper have accumulated in citrus groves as a result of applying too much copper in fertilizers and sprays.

More than a million tons and 851 grades of mixed fertilizer were used in Florida in 1955. Of the total tonnage, 199 grades accounted for 96 percent, 34 accounted for 73 percent, and 11 accounted for 51 percent.

The tendency to operate fertilizer mixing plants on a prescription basis has grown, but certain ratios and grades are used generally for fertilization of the various classes of crops on mineral and organic soils.

Grades with ratios of 0–1–3, 0–1–2, 0–1–1, or 0–2–1 are used for almost all crops on organic soils. The amount of potash is less as the length of period in cultivation increases. Sugarcane on organic soils gets potash only.

Ratios of grades used for production of various crops on mineral soils are approximately as follows: Corn, cotton, small grains, pearlmillet—1–2–2 or 1–3–3, with nitrogen sidedressing; leguminous field crops—0–1–1, 0–1–2, 0–1–3, or 1–4–4; flue-cured tobacco—1–3–3 or 1–3–4; grass pastures—1–2–1 for establishment and 1–1–1 alternated with nitrogen only for maintenance; vegetables—1–1–1 or 1–2–2, with nitrogen or 1–0–1 sidedressing; citrus—1–1–1, 2–1–2, or 1–0–1, with magnesium.

The ratio of the grades of mixed fertilizers used on most bearing citrus groves has changed gradually since the early 1930's from 1–2–1, to 1–1–1, to 2–1–2, and finally to 1–0–1. This change followed the discovery that phosphorus accumulates in sandy soils that are maintained at the proper pH level. It seems desirable to make this type of change in the fertilization of other crops on soils on which large amounts of phosphorus have been used.

The Northeast

N. C. Brady, R. A. Struchtemeyer, and R. B. Musgrave

The cool, humid Northeast is dairy country. Climate favors pastures, the hay crops, and the animals themselves. Dairying enables the northeastern farmer to maintain his position in the increasingly competitive business of farming.

Because of his northerly location, the growing season for his crops is much shorter than that of farmers farther south. The relatively rough topography makes it necessary to farm small fields. The average size of a farm, 111 acres, is approximately half the national average. Consequently the northeasterner cannot compete with the midwestern and western farmers in the production of cash grain crops, which require large acreages and are handled with machines.

There are more than 3 million milk cows in this region—about 15 percent of the total in the United States. The value of dairy products makes up an even higher proportion of the Nation's total, 26 percent.

Hay and pasture crops, so necessary for milk production, are relatively more important in the Northeast than in the Nation as a whole. Corn and wheat, on the other hand, are not so widely grown as in other parts of the country.

The Northeast includes between 5 and 6 percent of the land area of the United States. Included in the region are the New England States, New York, all but three counties in Penn-

sylvania, parts or all of 17 counties in northeastern Ohio, 9 counties in the northern Piedmont section of Maryland, the northwestern one-third of New Jersey, parts or all of 7 counties in Virginia, and Preston County in West Virginia.

The average annual temperature varies from somewhat less than 40° F. in northern Maine and the mountainous sections of Vermont, New Hampshire, and New York, to about 55° in southern Maryland and northern Virginia. Average January temperatures are as low as 10° in northern Maine and 16° in the Adirondacks of New York and as high as 30° in southern Maryland and northern Virginia.

In the northern part, as well as in the areas of higher altitude, the summers are cool. The average daily July temperature in Aroostook County in Maine, for example, is 65°. The average maximum July temperature in northern Maryland and southeastern Pennsylvania is about 76°.

The average annual frost-free growing season in the Adirondack section of New York and the upland areas in northern New England is 90 to 120 days. It exceeds 200 days in southeastern Pennsylvania and along such large bodies of water as Lake Erie and the Atlantic Ocean. In the upland areas of New York, Pennsylvania, Maryland, and West Virginia, the growing season is 140 to 160 days. Farther south it often is 200 days or longer.

Rainfall in the Northeast generally is 25 to 45 inches a year. Average annual rainfall in excess of 56 inches occurs in Middlesex County in Connecticut. As little as 28 inches falls in western New York.

The seasonal distribution of the rainfall is especially good for growing crops. Slightly more than half of the total precipitation generally falls in spring and summer. The rainfall in the growing season (April to October) varies from 18 inches in west-central New York to more than 30 inches in Coos County, N. H.

The average annual snowfall in Franklin County, in northern New York, is more than 150 inches. It is more than 100 inches in northern Maine and less than 20 inches in the northern Piedmont areas of Maryland and Virginia.

The sunshine is ample for grassland agriculture. Full sunshine occurs during 55 to 65 percent of the daylight hours in the summer months—an average of 8 to 9 hours of sunshine daily in June, July, and August.

The Northeastern region topographically has four major divisions—mountainous, upland plateau, lowland plain, and ridge and valley.

Much of the mountainous areas—the Adirondacks of northern New York, the Green Mountains of Vermont and Massachusetts, and part of the White Mountains of New Hampshire and Maine—are largely nonagricultural. A considerable part of three other mountainous areas—the Catskills in southeastern New York, the Allegheny Mountains in Pennsylvania, and the Taconic Mountains bordering Vermont, Massachusetts, and New York—have valleys and gentler slopes that are cultivated as small farms. The steeper slopes are woodlands.

The upland plateau includes most of the inland, nonmountainous areas of New England and the northern Piedmont area of northwestern New Jersey, southeastern Pennsylvania, central Maryland, and northern Virginia. Also included is the Allegheny Plateau, which makes up most of southern and central New York, northern and southwestern Pennsylvania, and northeastern Ohio. The northern part of this plateau was disturbed by glaciation.

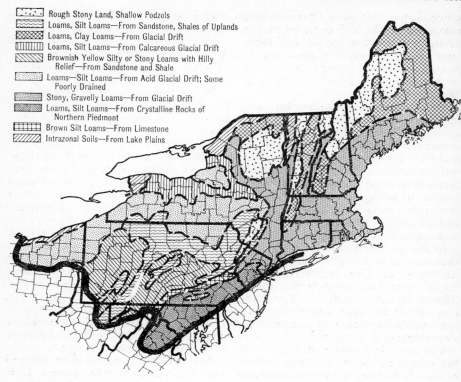

Rough Stony Land, Shallow Podzols
Loams, Silt Loams—From Sandstone, Shales of Uplands
Loams, Clay Loams—From Glacial Drift
Loams, Silt Loams—From Calcareous Glacial Drift
Brownish Yellow Silty or Stony Loams with Hilly Relief—From Sandstone and Shale
Loams—Silt Loams—From Acid Glacial Drift; Some Poorly Drained
Stony, Gravelly Loams—From Glacial Drift
Loams, Silt Loams—From Crystalline Rocks of Northern Piedmont
Brown Silt Loams—From Limestone
Intrazonal Soils—From Lake Plains

The three major lowland areas are the seaboard lowland in the New England States, the Mohawk River Valley in New York, and the so-called lake plain area of western New York, northwestern Pennsylvania, and northern Ohio.

The ridge and valley division is small but important. It is made up of a series of parallel ridges separated by narrow, fertile valleys. It runs from south-central Pennsylvania northeastward to the Hudson River and includes the Hudson River Valley in New York.

THE SOILS came from parent material that varied from hard, crystalline rocks to lake-plain sands and clays. Most of the region was visited by glaciers from the north. They mixed older soils with various kinds of rocks, such as sandstone, shales, limestones, and clays. The southern part, including Maryland, Virginia, and southern Pennsylvania, have not been glaci-

ated, and the soils are older and more weathered.

The soils of the Northeast are in five major groups: Podzols; Brown Podzolics and Weak Podzols; Gray-Brown Podzolics; Red-Yellow Podzolics; and Hydromorphic soils. The first four occur on well-drained areas. Soils in the the last group have poor or impeded drainage.

The Podzols are in northern Maine, New Hampshire, and Vermont and in the higher mountainous sections, especially in New York and Massachusetts. They are highly acid. On their surface in the natural state, organic matter accumulates. It occurs over a gray-white, infertile, sandy layer, which is characteristic of the soils. Podzols, properly fertilized and limed, are good vegetable soils, although their sandy texture makes them somewhat droughty.

The Brown Podzolic soils lie to the

south of the Podzols in New England and occur along with weak Podzols in the plateau areas of New York. They also are quite acid. They are generally somewhat heavier in texture than the Podzols, silt loams, and loams dominating the area. The Brown Podzolic soils are somewhat more fertile than the Podzols, but they are quite deficient in lime and phosphorus. The surface horizons are fairly high in organic matter, but because of their acidity the nutrients held in the organic form are released slowly for plant growth.

The largest areas of Gray-Brown Podzolic soils are in Pennsylvania and northeastern Ohio.

Another small but agriculturally important area is that of the so-called limestone soils south of Lake Ontario in New York. These soils generally are more productive than the Podzols or Brown Podzolics, which are somewhat acid. Because of the higher lime content in their surface, the organic matter does not generally occur as a separate layer on the surface. The action of earthworms has incorporated it into the upper part of the mineral soils; therefore they have less tendency toward acid leaching and their nutrient content and productivity are somewhat higher than that of soils in the Podzol and Brown Podzolic groups.

The Gray-Brown Podzolic soils are the most important agricultural group in this region. A wide range of crops grow on them.

Associated with the Gray-Brown Podzolic soils in southern Pennsylvania, Maryland, and Virginia are soils belonging to the Red-Yellow Podzolic group. They are red and yellow (particularly their subsoils), as contrasted with the more subdued gray and brown colors of the soils to the north. The Red-Yellow Podzolics, which generally are less productive than the Gray-Brown Podzolic soils, respond to good management. Because of their somewhat higher content of iron oxides, their capacity to render phosphorus unavailable often is quite high. Since they are formed in a somewhat warmer climate than the Gray-Brown Podzolic soils, their contents of organic matter are lower. Additions of fertilizer therefore must be higher to attain the same yields as those on the Gray-Brown Podzolic soils.

Hydromorphic soils exist in all parts of the region. Because they have impeded or poor drainage, crop production on them is generally somewhat less than that on the neighboring well-drained soils.

Poor drainage is serious in southern New York, northern Pennsylvania, and northeastern Ohio, where the soils have been developed from sandstone and shale, most of which was reworked by the advancing glaciers. This parent material and the soil-forming processes have left an impervious pan in the subsoil, which water penetrates slowly. Although the land is rolling and hilly, many of the uplands have impeded drainage.

Drainage is an important factor in the management of soils of other areas. For example, in the glaciated portion—as in the St. Lawrence River Valley in northern New York and south of Lake Ontario—are relatively large areas of silt and clay deposits laid down in old glacial lake bottoms. Because of the relatively flat topography and the heavy texture of these soils, removing excess water, especially in spring, becomes a major problem.

THE NORTHEAST has seven generalized types of farming areas.

Dairying is the main enterprise in four of the regions. Other important supporting enterprises are carried on in the other three. The four dairy regions are: Specialized dairying; dairying and cash crops; dairy, poultry, and mixed farming; and dairy and general farming.

One of the remaining regions is an area of special crops and general farming, centered in Aroostook County, Maine. Another, an area of fruit, truck, and mixed farming, is along the southern shores of Lake Ontario and Lake Erie. The seventh area is largely non-agricultural and includes a large part of

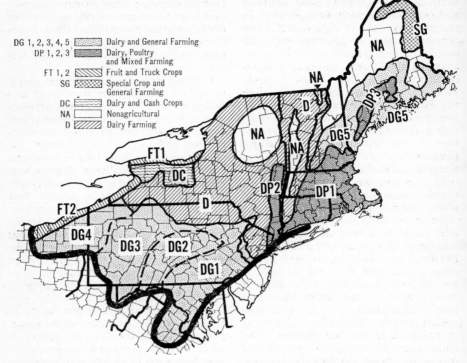

DG 1, 2, 3, 4, 5 ▦ Dairy and General Farming
DP 1, 2, 3 ▨ Dairy, Poultry
and Mixed Farming
FT 1, 2 ▧ Fruit and Truck Crops
SG ▩ Special Crop and
General Farming
DC ≋ Dairy and Cash Crops
NA ☐ Nonagricultural
D ▨ Dairy Farming

northern and western Maine and the
mountainous areas of northern New
Hampshire, northern New York, and
southeastern Vermont.

THE SPECIALIZED DAIRY AREA (D on
the map) comprises about one-fourth
of the total agricultural land in the
Northeast. It includes most of New
York and Vermont, the northern tier
of Pennsylvania counties, and the Piedmont area of New Jersey. The western
counties of Massachusetts and Connecticut also are included.

The area is gently rolling (as in certain parts of the St. Lawrence Valley)
to relatively steep (as in the Catskills of
southeastern New York and northeastern Pennsylvania). Much of the southern part is a dissected plateau of hills
and valleys. The valleys, generally
flat to gently rolling, are intensively
cropped. The upland ridges may be
quite steep and generally forested. Their
gentle slopes are covered with pastures

and cropland. The tops of some of
the ridges are relatively flat and also
are used for intensive cropping.

The elevation varies from 200 to 300
feet in the St. Lawrence Valley in
northern New York to more than 2
thousand feet in the Catskills. The relatively high elevation in the Catskills
and the Allegheny Plateau in southern
New York and northern Pennsylvania
influences the climate and makes the
areas rather inaccessible in winter.

Crops support the dairy enterprise.
A typical rotation is corn, small grain,
and several years of hay (generally
clover and timothy the first year and
largely timothy thereafter). Because of
the need for large acreages of hay and
pasture, the average size of farms is
larger here than in any other area in
the Northeast. The harvested cropland
is about the same as in the other
regions, however.

Corn is grown in the valleys or on
the more gently sloping uplands. Corn

accounted for nearly 11 percent of the harvested cropland in 1950. About 80 percent of it was cut for silage. Most of the grain corn for feed is imported from the Midwest.

The total acreage in small grain is slightly greater than that of corn. About 10 percent of the harvested cropland is in oats and 2.5 percent in wheat. Barley and rye are minor crops.

Oats generally give a low return per acre, but are quite popular as a companion crop in establishing new hay seedings. Since oats are spring sown, they can be conveniently grown in rotation with corn in the higher altitudes where the growing season is too short to grow a good crop of corn and then to establish a winter small grain.

Winter wheat is also used as a companion crop and is an important cash crop. Labor income from the production of wheat has been higher in recent years than from any other crop commonly grown here.

Corn and small grain are important in supplying the feed for dairying, but in acreage the hay and pastures are more important—about 70 percent of the harvested cropland in 1950 was in pasture and hay crops. Pastures occupy part of the cropland and some woodlands and areas set aside for permanent grazing. About 28 percent of the total land was in pastures in 1950.

Most of the forage crops are cut for hay or used for pasture. About 1.5 percent was cut green and used for grass silage in 1950.

About 70 percent of the hayland area was in clover and timothy in 1950. Slightly more than 6 percent of the total hay acreage was devoted to alfalfa. Some 24 percent of the hayland produced miscellaneous hay mixtures.

Irish potatoes are grown on some of the better drained soils on the broad ridges in Steuben and adjoining counties in southern New York. Vegetables are grown in several muck areas.

The yields of most crops are lower in the specialized dairy area than in areas of general farming and cash-crop farming—one reason why farms are larger in the specialized dairying area.

Hay and pasture crops protect much of the sloping lands. Cropping them more intensively would mean serious erosion. The steeper farmlands are being returned to forests.

Contour farming and stripcropping have been used less extensively than they should be. Some dairymen and potato farmers in southern New York and northern Pennsylvania use alternate strips of potatoes and legume sod crops. Legumes help hold the soils in place and supply organic matter and nitrogen to the soil.

Most of the row crops are grown in the valleys or on the gentler slopes. Farmers who have limited fields of valley land put them in corn for several years in succession and apply enough manure and fertilizers to prevent a reduction in soil productivity.

Because of its relatively high yield, corn is generally more adequately fertilized than any other crop in the rotation. Corn receives most of the available barnyard manure; rates of 8 to 12 tons an acre are common. Approximately 400 pounds of a commercial fertilizer (such as 5–10–5) are applied at planting time. A sidedressing of nitrogen sometimes is made when the corn is about knee high.

A few hundred pounds of 5–10–5 may be drilled with the seed of small grain at planting time. Nitrogen also may be topdressed in the spring.

Seldom are the hay crops adequately fertilized. The more progressive farmers topdress legume-grass mixtures with phosphate and potash. Mostly, however, pastures and hay meadows receive little fertilizer and only an occasional topdressing with manure.

The soils of the region are acid. Soil tests from several counties in southern New York showed that more than 35 percent of the soils had pH values below 5.5. The pH of more than 70 percent of the soils was less than 6.2. Red clover requires soils with pH values above 6.0 and alfalfa above 6.5. Lack of lime therefore inhibits growth of legumes here.

Approximate Proportion of Cropland in Different Crops and Crop Yields

	Percentage of harvested cropland in—		Approximate average yields per acre in—	
Crop	Northeast	United States	Northeast	United States
Corn.....................	16	25	43 bushels	36 bushels
Wheat....................	10	19	23 bushels	17 bushels
Oats.....................	10	11	33 bushels	33 bushels
Barley...................	1.5	3	32 bushels	25 bushels
Potatoes.................	2	0.6	266 bushels	202 bushels
All hay..................	50	22	1.48 tons	1.37 tons.

Increases in Yields From Recommended Fertilizer and Manure Treatments in West-Central New York

	Yields from—	
Crop	No treatment	Recommended fertilizers and manure
Corn (bushels)..	63	102
Oats (bushels)...	55	88
Wheat (bushels).	33	47
Alfalfa (2d year).	1.60	3.67
Clover........	1.27	3.01

A Comparison of Farm and Dairy Enterprises in the Northeast With Those in the Whole Country in 1949

	The Northeast	The United States
Total land area (millions of acres)................	109	1,904
Percentage of land in farms.	45	61
Average farm size (acres)..	111	215
Value of farmland per acre.	$106	$65
Thousands of milk cows...	3,111	21,223
Value of dairy products (millions)............	$813	$3,079

Approximate Average Yields in Several Dairy Subregions in the Northeast

Dairy Area	Corn (bushels)	Wheat (bushels)	Oats (bushels)	Alfalfa (tons)	Clover-Timothy (tons)
Specialized (D)....................	39.1	23.4	25.3	1.88	1.33
With General Farming (DG–1)......	52.1	23.9	30.8	2.12	1.52
With General Farming (DG–2)......	46.7	22.1	30.1	1.82	1.21
With General Farming (DG–3)......	45.4	22.4	30.2	1.63	1.21
With General Farming (DG–4)......	51.9	26.9	33.2	1.96	1.47
With Cash Crops (DC).............	45.0	27.3	31.2	1.90	1.35

Increases From Using Limestone and Superphosphate in a Dairy Farm Rotation in the Specialized Dairy Region in Southern New York

	Yield increases from adding 2 tons limestone per 6-year rotation	
Crop	Alone	With superphosphate
Corn (silage).........................	1.0 tons........	2.4 tons.
Oats................................	5.8 bushels........	15.1 bushels.
Wheat...............................	7.8 bushels........	15.2 bushels.
Hay (total 3 years)...................	1.76 tons.........	2.51 tons.

Average Yields of Grain and Hay Crops in Lancaster and York Counties and in Pennsylvania. (1950 Census Data)

	Average yields per acre in—		
Crop	Lancaster County	York County	Pennsylvania (State area)
Corn (bushels)...............................	58	53	49
Wheat (bushels)..............................	26	23	23
Oats (bushels)...............................	34	33	31
Alfalfa hay (tons)............................	2.25	2.11	1.93
Timothy-clover (tons)........................	1.76	1.40	1.36

Tillage practices are seldom responsible for serious problems in this area. The soils are generally plowed only twice during a rotation—once for corn and once for the small grain. Fall plowing for oats, however, often leaves the soil unprotected during the late fall, winter, and early spring, and some damage from erosion occurs.

Poor drainage is troublesome in northern Pennsylvania and southern New York. Because the condition often occurs on the less productive upland soils, tile drainage seldom is economically practical. Diversion terraces, while seldom used, sometimes help keep the surface water from wet areas.

Most farm operations are delayed in the spring until the wet spots have dried enough to allow the passage of implements over the land. Late planting shortens even more a growing season that at best is none too long.

Yields of crops in this region are limited most by inadequate lime and fertilizer and by insufficient control of soil water. The response of the crops to fertilizer (and even more to limestone) often has been demonstrated in the area. Examples of increases to be expected from limestone are given in a table, which summarizes results of an experiment in which all plots received 18 tons of manure in each 6-year rotation. Profitable increases in yield were obtained, especially of the small grains and hay crops. Higher yields were had when both limestone and superphosphate were applied.

Limestone, phosphate, and potash are needed to keep vigorous, highly productive stands of such long-lived legumes as alfalfa and birdsfoot trefoil. Applications of fertilizers high in nitrogen have been profitable on fields where timothy remains as the hay crop. In fact, grass yields in the Northeast can be more than doubled by economic applications of nitrogen fertilizer.

The proper choice of crop to fit different soil conditions also is important. Where limestone has been added to well-drained soils, alfalfa should be used more extensively. Yields of 4 to 5 tons an acre have been obtained with improved varieties and proper management. Although the acreage in alfalfa has increased, the potential acreage is far above what has been used for it.

Birdsfoot trefoil has shown promise in localities where drainage is a problem. It is slow to establish, but it grows under a wide range of conditions and can be used for pasture and hay. It yields better than nonlegumes and its quality is superior. Birdsfoot responds well to fertilizer and lime. On soils too wet for alfalfa, it helps protect the soil and returns organic matter to the soil.

The proper choice of crop is also important in pastures and hayfields that contain only grasses. For example, orchardgrass responds better to applications of nitrogen than timothy does, especially when an aftermath growth follows irrigation.

Early planting of a crop such as oats is essential for maximum production. In New York, yields are reduced by 1 bushel for every day the planting date is delayed beyond April 15.

A number of conservation practices will be helpful here. Contour stripcropping in one place in New York gave potato yields of 18 bushels an acre more than yields obtained with up-and-down-hill farming and reduced losses of soil and water substantially. The control of the runoff from the uplands helps to prevent the accumulation of water in flat areas.

Dairy farmers in this area are steadily improving their soil-management practices. Increased crop yields and higher milk production on fewer cultivated acres are evidence of this fact. The productive potential of the soils is considerably in excess of what is realized, however.

THE SOUTHEASTERN DAIRY AND GENERAL FARMING areas are in the southern part of the region in Pennsylvania, Ohio, Maryland, and Virginia and in southern Maine and New Hampshire. Farming is somewhat more diversified than in the specialized dairy area. Dairying is combined with other livestock enterprises, such as poultry and the production of feed grains and wheat, fruit, truck, or canning crops.

On the basis of land use and location, there are five dairy and general farming areas in the Northeast. Area DG–1 is the most intensively cropped and the most important agriculturally. It includes the northern Piedmont area of Maryland, Virginia, and southeast Pennsylvania and part of the Appalachian Valley section inland from the Piedmont. More than 70 percent of the total land in this region is in farms, and more than half of it is in cropland. The soils are among the most productive in the Northeast. Included are the Manor, Penn, and Chester Upland soils of southeastern Pennsylvania and Maryland and the Cecil, Davidson, and Bucks series in the Virginia and Maryland portion of the area. These well-drained, gray-brown to reddish-brown soils are especially responsive to good management and proper fertilization.

Some highly productive soils of the limestone valleys also are included. The great valley, 1 to 20 miles wide, extends from eastern Pennsylvania southeastward into Maryland and Virginia. Another important and highly productive area of limestone soils is on the Lancaster Plain, which makes up about half of Lancaster County, Pa.

The Hagerstown, Frankstown, and Duffield soils are developed from limestone and are famous for their productive capacity. The long growing season and mild winters, generally favorable topography, low elevation, and productive soils make this area a highly favored agricultural section.

Besides dairy products and poultry, the area produces cash crops, which make for a well-balanced agriculture. A rotation of corn, oats, wheat, and hay is followed on some dairy farms, but row and cash crops not necessary for dairying are grown on most farms. Nearly 30 percent of the cropland was in corn in 1950; about 85 percent of it was harvested for grain. Wheat, grown mostly for sale, occupied about 20 percent of the cropland. In some counties,

such as Lancaster and Franklin in Pennsylvania, the wheat acreage nearly equaled that of corn for grain, while in Carroll County, Md., more wheat than corn was grown. Oats, which are not commonly used as a companion crop for new seedings, were planted on only 6 percent of the cropland in 1950. Winter barley, which grows better in this area than anywhere else in the Northeast, occupied about 5 percent of the cropland.

The yields of grain have been considerably higher than in the region of specialized dairying. Average county corn grain yields, for example, were about 45 to 60 bushels an acre. Yields of wheat and hay were a little higher than those of adjoining regions.

The average yield of alfalfa hay in Lancaster County in 1950 was about 2.25 tons an acre; some farmers got more than 4 tons an acre. About 27 percent of the cropland was in hay crops in 1950. About one-fifth of this was alfalfa; the remainder was clover-timothy and mixed hay or (in southern Maryland and Virginia) lespedeza hay. Long lays of hay are not common in this area. Except for the alfalfa and lespedeza fields, hayland is commonly plowed after 1 or 2 years.

About 2.1, 3.6, and 3.0 percent of the harvest cropland is devoted to potatoes, vegetables, and fruit crops, respectively. Many farmers grow potatoes for home use. Potatoes are grown commercially in Lehigh, Lancaster, Northampton, and York Counties in Pennsylvania. Vegetables are grown for market in Bucks County, Pa., and near heavily populated areas. Apples are grown extensively in Adams, Berks, and Franklin Counties, Pa., and Washington County, Md. Tobacco is grown on the limestone soils of Lancaster County, but is relatively unimportant elsewhere. Poultry is also a major source of income in this area.

The soils in the area (DG–1) are not naturally high in fertility. Because they developed under a relatively mild climate that favored microbial activity, the content of native organic matter is lower than in soils to the north. Also, the more extensive use of cash crops results in a lower return of organic matter to the soils.

Most of the soils (including those developed on limestone) are somewhat acid and need lime for best production. As the soils are well weathered, their native nutrient-supplying power is not high, and they have a tendency to change applied phosphates to insoluble compounds.

The soils respond well to good care, however. Generally they are friable loams and clay loams and are easy to work. Moisture infiltrates readily, and the proportion of well-drained soils is favorable. Because farmers can apply enough lime and fertilizer to make up for natural deficiencies of nutrients, yields usually are not limited by poor soil conditions.

Erosion has not become widespread, because of the generally good physical condition of the soils, the gentle slopes, and the use of contour farming.

In some localities—notably the more sloping uplands in the Piedmont area and of the hillsides in the inland valleys and ridges, however, serious sheet erosion has occurred. Much of this land, which at one time was under cultivation, has been allowed to return to forest. Also, with an increase in dairying in the Maryland and Virginia sections of the region, a higher proportion of the tillable land is kept in sod crops.

Soil-management practices generally are good. Most row and cash crops receive moderate applications of fertilizer and barnyard manure. Limestone also is applied periodically to replace the lime lost by leaching and crop removal and to make possible the growth of high-yielding legumes.

The farms are considerably smaller than the average for the Northeast, and they are probably more carefully managed than any in the region. Such care is rewarded with high production and the maintenance of soil productivity.

A comparison of average yields with those obtained by better farmers shows that yields can be increased by improved soil management. Yields of corn in Carroll County, Md., and in Lancaster County, Pa., in 1950 averaged 54 and 58 bushels an acre, respectively. Both figures are higher than the State averages of Maryland and Pennsylvania, but they are lower than the 75 to 100 bushels that more progressive farmers get regularly.

The yield of hay crops also is below the potential. County averages of alfalfa seldom are more than 2 tons an acre. Averages of timothy-red clover are generally 1.5 tons or less. Such yields are about half of those obtained when adequate lime and fertilizer are applied and adapted varieties are used.

The increase in the acreage of alfalfa in this area has contributed toward better soil management. The nitrogen and organic matter supplied by growing alfalfa, and the tendency to keep alfalfa stands longer than those of clover and timothy have meant greater protection against erosion and maintenance of greater fertility.

The general adoption of the lime, fertilizer, cropping, and cultural practices already in use by some farmers is needed to realize the productive potential of this area. Somewhat greater attention should be paid to liming and fertilizing for forage crops.

THE DAIRY AND GENERAL FARMING AREA of central Pennsylvania (DG–2 on the map) is in a ridge and valley section, in which narrow, even-topped, parallel mountain ridges run northeast to southwest. Most of the farmland is in valleys between the ridges.

The ridges generally are composed of sandstones and conglomerates that resist weathering, and the soils on them are quite stony and infertile. The sides of the ridges are quite steep. Some of the ridges are nearly 2 thousand feet above sea level.

Valley soils, which generally are developed on limestone and shale, are more productive than the upland soils and have fewer stones, but in most counties they make up less than 10 percent of the land area. Most of the

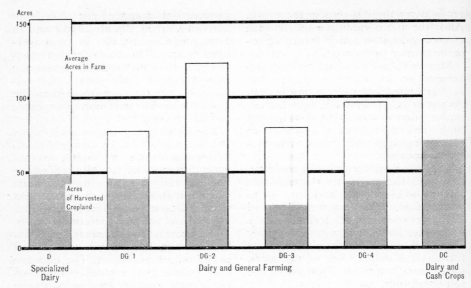

1. *Average size of farms in the various dairying regions. Except for Areas DG–3 and DC, the acres of harvested cropland per farm are about the same.*

valleys are narrow, but in Center, Huntingdon, and Blair Counties they are relatively broad. Near University Park, in Center County, the Nittany Valley is several miles wide.

Some of the valley soils developed from shales have imperfect or poor drainage. In Montour and Northumberland Counties, for example, about one-third of them are thus affected. The average growing season is about 20 days shorter than in area DG–1.

About one-half the total land in area DG–2 was in farms in 1950. Slightly more than one-fourth was in cropland. The proportion of land in woods on and off farms was somewhat higher than in area DG–1. Although the average size of farm was larger than that of area DG–1, the acreage of cropland per farm was about the same.

Crops grown in this area are the same as those in southeastern Pennsylvania. Dominant rotations are those involving corn, small grains, and hay. The proportion of cropland in corn, barley, potatoes, and vegetables, however, is slightly less than that for area DG–1. About one-sixth of the harvest-

ed cropland is devoted to oats each year. Hay and pasture occupy about one-third of the total cropland.

Much steep, sloping land, formerly cropped or pastured, has reverted to forests. Other abandoned areas have not been reforested. Also some formerly cropped fields are now used for pasture only. They need improvement, but these pastures offer some protection against erosion.

The soil-management practices in the valleys of central Pennsylvania are about the same as those in southeastern Pennsylvania. The well-drained soils from limestone and shale are easy to work, and their stable structure allows the absorption of most of the rain.

The plow layers of the soils developed from impure limestones are acid. Applications of agricultural limestone are necessary for good growth of such crops as alfalfa and clover. The limestone in the lower horizons makes it possible to keep a good stand of legumes once they are established. Shale soils of the valleys and the upland pasturelands are especially low in lime.

Even the better valley soils are naturally deficient in the major plant foods, notably in phosphorus and nitrogen. Phosphorus is especially important in the legume hay meadows. Nitrogen is added for corn, small grains, and vegetables.

The dairy and general farming operations help to maintain the soil organic matter. The dairy animals supply manure, and the legumes needed for dairying furnish nitrogen and organic matter. Where adequate limestone and fertilizer have not been applied, the organic matter returned to the soil is insufficient. Such soils— especially on sharply rolling land—are subject to erosion.

Soil management on the upland ridges is quite different from that in the valleys. Most of the steep upland soils, especially the more stony and shallow ones, are not suited for cultivation. They are acid and low in organic matter and fertility. Even grasses grow poorly without added nutrients. Consequently these areas are mostly in forest, although some abandoned fields have not been reforested. Pines and hemlocks seem to do best on these soils.

The soils in the reforested lands are fairly well protected from erosion. The practice of allowing livestock to graze farm woodlots, however, has led to serious erosion damage in some places. The animals kill much of the undergrowth, trample the soil, and leave it compacted and unprotected.

The more progressive farmers have approached the productive potential of the valley soils. Their yields of corn are far above the 47-bushel average of the region. Their alfalfa yields are generally double the 1.8-ton average.

To do that, they have chosen their crops wisely. Their well-drained soils are planted to a rotation such as corn (or vegetables), oats (or wheat), and 2 years (or more) of alfalfa. They apply lime to encourage the growth of alfalfa, which has consistently outyielded clover-timothy on well-drained soils.

Barnyard manure, at the rate of 8 to 10 tons an acre, is applied before the corn. About 300 pounds of starter fertilizer, such as 5–10–10 or 10–10–10, are added for corn. Results of soil tests determine the choice of analysis of the fertilizer and the need for sidedressings of nitrogen. Corn yields average 75 to 90 bushels an acre.

Oats are planted early and fertilized at planting time with about 300 pounds of 5–10–10 or 0–20–20. On soils low in organic matter, a topdressing with 20 to 30 pounds of nitrogen frequently pays. These practices give yields of oats much higher than the 30-bushel average for the area and allow good seedings of alfalfa.

For alfalfa, enough lime should be applied before planting and about 200 pounds of a fertilizer such as 0–20–20 topdressed after both the first and the second cuttings each year.

On soils not well enough drained for alfalfa, a rotation such as corn, oats, wheat, and clover-timothy might be used. The corn and small grains are well fertilized and the lime level is kept adequate for the hay.

The progressive farmer recognizes the advantages of contour farming, particularly on rolling land. The valley lands, especially those along the valley walls, are planted in contour strips. Diversion terraces are necessary in some instances to control runoff and reduce erosion. On the more strongly sloping land, the rotations are lengthened to allow for more hay and pasture. This keeps a higher proportion of the land under cover.

The more steeply sloping upland pastures should be improved or reforested. Adequate lime and fertilizer are needed to increase the productivity of pastures. Areas too steep and shallow or infertile for pastures are best suited for woodlands.

The productive potential of this area can best be reached by more intensive fertilization and liming of the best farm land, more attention to the fertility and soil requirements of the hay crops, water management through contour farming, improvement of upland pastures, and the reforestation of abandoned upland areas.

THE GENERAL FARMING AND DAIRY REGION of the southwestern and mountain sections of Pennsylvania (DG–3) is mostly in the Allegheny Plateau section. Also included on the east and northeastern sides is part of the Allegheny Mountain section of Center, Clinton, Lycoming, and Sullivan Counties.

The land is rolling to hilly in the Plateau section and mountainous in the east. The land is more level in the southern part. Elevations are up to 2 thousand feet in the east and 1,500 feet in the southwestern parts.

The growing season is 140–170 days. The soils, which generally are quite acid, developed mostly from sandstone and shales. In some sections, especially in the southern two-thirds of the area, limestone and coal beds exist with the sandstone and shale. The limestone has resulted in the more productive soils.

Coal mining, the oil and gas industry, and other industries have offered some employment for farmers and have encouraged much part-time farming. In some sections there are few commercial farms, but most of the farming is on a part-time or subsistence basis.

About 30 percent of the total land area was in farms in 1950. Only 4.4 percent of the total land in Cameron County was in farms. In Elk and Pike Counties about 10 percent was in farms. Washington and Armstrong Counties had 69.6 and 33.8 percent, respectively, of the total land in farms.

About one-sixth of the total land area was used as cropland. Approximately two-thirds of this was harvested. Again there was considerable variation from county to county. About 28 percent of the total land was in cropland in Armstrong and Washington Counties and less than 3 percent in Pike and Elk Counties.

The average size of farms in the area is about 80 acres. The acreage of harvested cropland per farm is the smallest in the northeast—only about 26 acres is 1949—a reflection of part-time farming and, in some sections, the few commercial farms.

The proportion of cropland planted to corn and wheat is much lower than in central and southeastern Pennsylvania. Less than 20 percent of the harvested cropland was planted to corn in 1949 and about 13 percent to wheat. Some 40 percent of the harvested cropland was in hay crops. Most of the hay is clover and timothy; about 10 percent is alfalfa. Buckwheat—on 2 percent of the harvested cropland—is more widely grown in this region than elsewhere in the Northeast. There is a considerable amount of home gardening.

Dairying is the leading enterprise in areas where the topography and soils allow a large enough farming operation, notably in the southern part. In most of the remainder of the region, the hilly topography, elevation, and generally infertile soils are not conducive to the operation of large dairy farms. Throughout the southwestern two-thirds of the region, poultry is an important enterprise.

Farming is largely of the self-sufficient type in much of the northern and northeastern area. Because of the relatively steep slopes and infertile and thin upland soils, most of the farming is done on alluvial soils along the streams. The land values are determined in places primarily by the coal and oil deposits and frequently have forced shifts away from farming. Employment opportunities in the industries have made farmers less dependent on farming for a living and less willing to follow the best land-use practices.

Adequate applications of lime, fertilizer, and manure are made infrequently. Crop yields, especially of hay crops, therefore are lower than elsewhere in Pennsylvania. Serious erosion has occurred in hilly areas where adequate forest cover is lacking.

Farming is much more advanced and better organized in the southern and southwestern part of the region. The soils are derived from sandstone, shale, and some limestone. Consequently they are less acid than those to the north. The topography is generally less steep, and there is greater opportunity for commercial farming. A more adequate lime and fertility program is needed on these fields, however, to make them most effective in producing crops and cover. Barnyard manure from the dairy farms is valuable in maintaining fertility and organic matter. Although manure, lime, and fertilizer are not used so effectively in this area as in southeastern Pennsylvania, they have helped the dairy farmer to stay in business.

The need for hay and pasture for the dairy enterprise has helped curtail soil erosion and runoff. Most of the pasture and hayland is in the uplands, which need protection. The increased acreage of alfalfa has been made possible only by an adequate liming program.

There is little opportunity to improve land and soil management in northern and northeastern counties of this area.

The land in forests should probably be increased in some cases to give better soil protection and better returns to the owners. Some steep, stony lands not already in State or national forests should probably be reforested as part of the public domain.

The alluvial soils near streams and some more level upland areas offer some opportunity for increasing production. Their yields of corn, wheat, oats and hay can be increased by the use of fertilizer and limestone. The generally high elevation and shorter growing season probably limit the yields of corn and hay.

The hillier land, even in the south and southwest, should remain in adapted forest trees. When pastures are essential on this kind of land, increased production and cover can be obtained by liming and fertilizing. The seeding of improved grasses and legumes for hay and pasture would make these areas more productive. Good yields of Ladino-orchardgrass have been obtained in Westmoreland County when fertilization with potash and phosphate was adequate. This forage mixture gave about 3.5 tons of hay an acre a year on moderately well-drained soil. Other legume-grass mixtures gave yields far better than the average yield.

Orchardgrass, tall fescue, and tall oatgrass responded well to nitrogen.

The adoption of more conservation practices would be wise in this area. Although adequate lime, fertilizer, and manure are the first requisites in obtaining good ground cover, contour farming and stripcropping would also be effective in reducing erosion. In places where contour stripcropping is not feasible, it is advisable to use some of the more gently sloping fields somewhat more intensively and to keep the steeper areas in hay and pasture.

THE DAIRY AND GENERAL FARMING REGION of northwestern Pennsylvania and northeastern Ohio (DG–4) includes all or part of five counties in northwestern Pennsylvania and all or part of 18 counties in northeastern Ohio. The topography is somewhat smoother than that to the east and south. Drainage is poor in much of northwestern Pennsylvania because of the compact nature of the glacial till. Drainage is somewhat better in northeastern Ohio, and the farmland is considerably more valuable.

Altitudes exceed 1,900 feet on the mountain ridges in the eastern part of the region. The growing season is about 130 to 170 days. Annual precipitation averages 36 to 42 inches. Summer rainfall is usually adequate for most crops. Spring rains frequently delay the planting of crops.

The soils have developed from glacial deposits made up mostly of sandstones and shales, with relatively little limestone. They therefore are acid in the surface. Soils in their native state are only medium in productivity. The well and moderately well-drained soils, such as the Wooster, Canfield, Rittman, and Ellsworth, however, respond well to good management. Pasture and hay crops dominate on the soils with restricted drainage, and response to good management is not so marked. Even so, crop yields are good in the region as a whole.

About 70 percent of the land was in farms in 1949. Except for urban counties, such as Cuyahoga, the proportion of land in farms was higher in Ohio than in Pennsylvania. More than 90 percent of the total land was in farms in Wayne County.

More than half the land in farms was in cropland. Permanent and improved pasture made up nearly 23 percent of the total land. About one-fourth of the harvested cropland was in corn, about one-fifth in wheat, and slightly less in oats. Hay occupied about 30 percent of the harvested cropland. Alfalfa accounted for only about 10 percent of the hay acreage. Crops for the dairy enterprise were supplemented with a sizable acreage of grain crops.

Corn yields in 1949 averaged about 52 bushels an acre. The average wheat yield was about 27 bushels, the highest of any general farming dairy region in the Northeast. Hay yields were high.

Soil- and crop-management practices are more advanced than those in area DG–3. The soils are generally somewhat more productive, especially those having good drainage. The native fertility of the soils is not high, but crops respond well to applications of commercial fertilizer. Barnyard manure, which is commonly applied on the sod ahead of corn, helps maintain soil fertility and good structure.

Applications of limestone must be made to acid soils to assure the best growth of plants, even nonlegumes. Applications of lime are essential on the better drained soils for alfalfa.

Erosion damage is less extensive in this area than in the hillier areas. Both the topography and the system of farming, which keeps a good cover on much of the cropped land, help to control excessive erosion damage. Because of the generally high value of land in the region, however, erosion is serious where it has occurred. Where row crops are used, some damage has occurred, especially in areas where a short rotation is followed. Under these conditions, much of the land is unprotected, especially during the early spring and summer. Also, where drainage of the soil is slow, runoff from the surface must take place and erosion

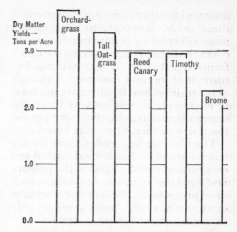

2. *In Westmoreland County, Pa., grasses differed in their ability to make use of added nitrogen. One hundred pounds per year were added in each case, along with phosphate and potash.*

results. Contour farming is common.

Drainage is a serious problem in the eastern and northern part. In Crawford County, Pa., for example, more than 50 percent of the soils have poor or imperfect drainage.

Tile drainage has been installed on some of the more level areas, but the cost of installing tile often is greater than the value of the land. Also, the topography is not always well suited for effective drainage patterns. Soils such as the Mahoning and Trumbull have heavy subsoils, and lateral movement of water to the tile lines is slow.

The advantages of alfalfa as a forage legume have been recognized by many farmers. Yields of alfalfa in some counties in northeastern Ohio increased six-fold between 1949 and 1954. More than 10 percent of the cropland in Wayne, Stark, and Medina Counties was in alfalfa in 1954.

Corn and small grain, as well as the hay and pasture crops, respond well to fertilizer. On the better drained soils, such as Wooster, yields of more than 80 bushels of corn an acre are common. The application of complete fertilizer and the growing of improved hybrids make these yields possible.

Wheat yields on a well-managed

Wooster silt loam soil have been approximately double those on poorly managed soils. Yields of red clover under the best management are triple those obtained with no treatment, and alfalfa is even more responsive.

In the soil areas where drainage is a problem, response to lime and fertilizer depends largely on the improvement of drainage. There are fields and parts of fields, however, where local seepage spots can be tile drained. The installation of diversion terraces on the more sloping fields would help prevent the concentration of water in the lower places.

Contour stripcropping has advantages in addition to drainage improvement. For example, H. L. Borst, of the Ohio Agricultural Experiment Station, reported yields of corn 11 bushels an acre higher on contoured plots than on up-and-down-hill plots.

THE DAIRY AND CASH CROP AREA—DC on the map—is in western and west-central New York and includes the northern Allegheny Plateau.

There is some steeply sloping land, but the terrain often is undulating or gently rolling. The elevation is 600 to 1,200 feet above sea level. The growing season is 145 to 175 days.

Rainfall is less than in most of the Northeast. About 20 percent of the area has less than 30 inches of precipitation a year. Summer rainfall frequently is critical, especially in the section south of Rochester, Monroe County. Irrigation has been profitable on some sandy soils on which vegetables are grown.

The soils here are among the more productive in the Northeast. They have developed mostly from lime-containing materials mixed by the glaciers. Silts and clays laid down in old glacial lake bottoms in some localities have developed into reasonably productive soils. Associated with them are sandy and gravelly soils developed from old beach and outwash deposits. These are good vegetable soils but may be droughty.

Dairy farming is dominant. Truck crops, grains, fruit, and dry beans also are important.

More than 75 percent of the total land area was in farms in 1949—a higher proportion than in any other dairy farming area in the Northeast. About one-half the land in farms was in cropland. The remainder was in permanent pasture or woodland.

The average size of farm, about 135 acres, is larger than in any other dairy and general-farming area in the Northeast. The harvested acreage per farm is also higher. The land values are higher than in the specialized dairy area to the east and south, but they are considerably lower than those in areas DG–1 and DG–4.

The crops grown here are the same as in other Northeastern dairy areas, but the proportion of wheat and cash crops is higher. More than 20 percent of the harvested cropland was in wheat in 1949—the highest percentage in the Northeast. The average wheat yield (27.3 bushels an acre) is higher than elsewhere in the Northeast.

Eleven percent of the harvested cropland was in corn; about half of it was used for silage and half for grain.

Hay crops occupy a high proportion of the land—more than 27 percent in 1949. Nearly one-third of this acreage was alfalfa. An abundance of deep, well-drained soils with a high content of lime has encouraged the growing of alfalfa. Yields of hay are generally high.

Potatoes and other vegetables are grown on about 7 percent of the cropland and fruits on about 3 percent. Most of the dry beans grown in New York are raised in this region. Vegetables for canning are important. Snap beans, peas, and sweet corn are major cash crops.

The chief fruit crops are apples, pears, peaches, cherries, and grapes. Apples are grown throughout the area. The others, especially grapes and cherries, tend to be concentrated along the shores of the Finger Lakes in New York.

The use of fertilizer and lime to supplement native soil fertility is common and essential in this area. Applications of fertilizer for cash crops are generally adequate. Vegetables frequently receive as much as 1 thousand pounds of 5–10–10 or 5–10–5 fertilizer. Although the fertilizers are not always the ones recommended by the experiment stations, lack of fertilizer is seldom the limiting factor in growing vegetables on the better farms.

Fertilization of hay and feed crops is considerably better than in the dairy region to the east and south, but nevertheless applications of fertilizer frequently are insufficient to maintain a productive soil, particularly on hayland. The nutrients removed by large hay crops are not always replenished by topdressings. Although the soils have a fairly high availability of potassium, continued removal of potassium and other elements may eventually deplete them.

The grain crops almost always receive some fertilizer. Fertilizers of a 5–10–5 analysis are applied at planting at rates of 200 to 400 pounds an acre. For wheat, a topdressing of additional nitrogen is sometimes applied the next spring. Some farmers also sidedress corn with 20 to 40 pounds of nitrogen.

Lime is applied regularly by some farmers. Applications of limestone generally are profitable and are essential for crops (such as alfalfa and cabbage) with high requirement of lime. Despite the demonstrated advantage of applying lime, however, much of the soil is still too acid for best crop growth.

The maintenance of organic matter has become a problem on farms where cash crops occupy much of the land. Essentially no crop residues are returned to the soil when such crops as canning peas and beets and dry beans are grown. A serious consequence of too little organic matter is the packing and crusting of the soil, which hinder the emergence of seedlings.

Erosion has done serious damage in many fields in western New York, although it has been less obvious than in other areas because the deep, friable soils are reasonably productive even in places where erosion has occurred.

The acreage of land farmed on the contour is small.

The terrain in some sections discourages contour farming because stripcropping would result in small, irregular fields. In many localities, however, stripcropping and other practices could well be adopted.

Tile drainage systems are common on the better soils, where vegetable and other cash crops are grown. Soils, such as Kendaia and Lyons, which are developed from lime-containing glacial deposits, are poorly drained. Where effective tile drainage systems have been installed, these soils are productive, especially for vegetable crops.

Progressive farmers adequately fertilize their vegetable and cash crops. They use soil tests and cropping history to determine the kind and amount of high-analysis fertilizers to apply. They use a good balance between the row crops and grain and hay crops.

Lime is especially critical for legumes. Large acreages of acid soils could be made suitable for alfalfa with proper liming. Applications of phosphate and potash would help prolong the life of the legume hay crops. In fields where only grass hay remains, applications of 50 to 75 pounds of nitrogen to the acre have been profitable.

We have ample evidence that adoption of improved fertilizer and liming practices would pay off with higher yields and more productive soils. Corn yields double the average in this area (45 bushels an acre) are common. With adequate lime and fertilizer, the more productive alfalfa varieties have produced more than double the average regional yield (1.9 tons an acre).

Where contour farming and stripcropping are impractical because of the irregular topography, other means of minimizing erosion are being used. The more strongly sloping fields are kept in sod or grain crops. Tillage is kept to a minimum, so that the soil is left loose and absorptive. The soil is kept in a highly productive state—even row crops protect the soil better if the plants are giving maximum production. To that end, irrigation is effective and economical in some places.

Tile drainage has improved productivity in some areas and would probably pay off in others. Drainage, besides creating better soil conditions for plant growth, produces higher yields by permitting earlier land tillage.

FRUIT, TRUCK AND DAIRY FARMING AREAS—FT–1 and FT–2 on the map—extend along the southern shores of Lake Ontario and Lake Erie in the so-called Lake Plain province. The region averages 3 to 5 miles in width along Lake Erie. South of Lake Ontario it generally is 10 to 25 miles wide. The tempering effect of the lakes has favored the production of fruit and truck crops. The elevation is 200 to 300 feet above the level of the lakes. Maximum elevation is about 750 feet above sea level in Ohio and about 500 feet along Lake Ontario in New York. The growing season is 160 to 190 days.

The land is generally level to gently rolling, but on old beach ridges the slopes are somewhat steeper. The soils are developed on lake-laid materials and vary in texture from sands to silty clay loams. The heavier soils are in the more level areas; the sandy and gravelly soils are on old beach ridges.

Dairying is prominent in these areas; more than half the cropland is devoted to dairying. Farm income depends largely on the truck, fruit, and other cash crops, however.

Nearly 75 percent of the total land in area FT–1 (New York) and about 60 percent of the land in area FT–2 (Ohio and Pennsylvania) was in farms in 1949. In both areas (especially in FT–2), an increasing proportion of the land is used for industrial and municipal expansion. Industrial cities, such as Cleveland, Erie, Rochester, and Buffalo, have taken over more and more farmland each year. Only 20 percent of the total land in the area south of Lake Erie was harvested cropland in 1949. Much of the remainder was used for homesites and factories.

The proportion of the cropland in corn, grain, and hay crops in area FT–1 is slightly less than that of the dairying and general farming area to the south. The acreage of orchards and vegetable crops, on the other hand, is higher. The 1950 Census of Agriculture showed approximately 25 percent of the harvested cropland in fruits and vegetables.

In the four counties bordering Lake Ontario are about 70 percent of New York's plum and peach trees, 80 percent of the cherries, 50 percent of the pears, 40 percent of the apples, and 10 percent of the grapes. Along the south shore of Lake Erie these fruits are also important. Chautauqua County, N. Y., produces more than half the State's grapes. Erie County, Pa., produces more than 90 percent of the grapes produced in that State. Ashtabula and Lake Counties in Ohio also produce many grapes, apples, and peaches.

About 70 percent of the tomatoes produced in New York are grown near the two lakes. Special crops, such as snap beans, green peas, cucumbers, cabbage, and table beets, are other high-value crops grown here.

The management of the soils on dairy farms is essentially the same as that for the areas to the south. Applications of fertilizer for the fruit and vegetable crops generally are adequate. The cost of fertilizer is small compared to the value of the crops produced. Applications of nutrients, especially phosphorus, are frequently much larger than the amounts removed by crops.

Little attention has been paid to liming, because most of the cash crops here are not sensitive to acid conditions. Where legumes such as alfalfa are grown in rotation with truck crops, however, limestone must be applied. Sulfur-containing sprays have caused extreme acid conditions to develop under some fruit trees.

Erosion often is a problem in orchards and vineyards. For some crops, such as grapes and peaches, the soil is generally kept clean-cultivated most of the year, and much of the area thus is exposed to erosion. Except where sod crops are included in the cropping system, the maintenance of organic matter is a problem where fruit and truck crops are grown.

Irrigation of truck crops has increased since 1945. Because of the frequency of droughts, additional water often can be applied profitably to the more valuable crops. The main limiting factor in the future development of irrigation in this region is the lack of sources of irrigation water.

Fertility problems on dairy farms can be handled in much the same manner as in the dairy area to the south. For fruit and vegetables the most significant contributions can be made by soil and tissue testing to assure proper balance of lime and other nutrients.

The maintenance of organic matter and the control of erosion should receive high priority. The use of cover crops—such as bromegrass or rye—would be effective in peach and cherry orchards.

A continuous grass sod has been found helpful in apple orchards. The sod must receive small applications of nitrogen and sometimes phosphorus and potash. Applications of a magnesium-containing limestone are recommended when spray materials have created acid conditions under the trees.

Tile drainage is beneficial on some of the heavier orchard soils. Because of the deep roots of fruit trees, adequate aeration must be provided for optimum fruit production—a fact that should be borne in mind in selecting a site.

THE DAIRY, POULTRY, AND MIXED FARMING AREA—DP–2 on the map—is almost entirely in the Hudson River Valley in New York. Dairying is less important than in the surrounding specialized dairy region. Poultry, fruit, and cash and truck crops supplement dairying.

The growing season is 15 to 30 days longer than in the uplands to the east.

Although many of the soils have developed on lake-deposited materials, the areas of upland soils are extensive. The soils vary in texture from silty clays to sands and gravelly loams. The heavier soils are used for forage crops. The better drained loams and silt loams make good orchard sites. The coarser soils, primarily of the northern part, are used for vegetables.

Limestone is present in the parent materials of the soils in much of this area, but in most places the lime has been leached from the surface soils, leaving them acid. Many of the upland soils are developed from acid materials and are even more acid.

Hay, pasture, and feed crops, which are needed for the dairy enterprise, occupy about two-thirds of the cropland.

Much of the poultry feed—and the feed for the dairy animals—is purchased from outside the area. Eggs and other poultry products have a ready market in New York City.

Apples are the most extensively grown orchard crop. Cherries, grapes, peaches, and pears are also important.

Because of nearness to market and the possibility for early production, sweet corn, tomatoes, and other vegetables are major cash crops. The acreage in nursery crops is not great, but the income from flowers and shrubbery is considerable.

The management of dairy farms here is not greatly different from that in the surrounding specialized dairy area, but the agriculture is somewhat better balanced because it is more diversified.

Less fertilizer and lime are used on forage crops than is desirable. A higher proportion of the land is in legumes than in the specialized dairy area, but much of the pasture and hay land is in grass because the fertility level is too low for long-lived legumes.

The fertilization of the vegetable and fruit crops is more nearly adequate. Corn, tomatoes, and other vegetables have responded well to fertilization. Lime is applied less often than it should be, especially in sections where dairying and general farming are joined.

The maintenance of the organic matter in the soil has become a problem, especially in the more intensively cropped places. Row cropping and clean cultivation for fruit production leaves the soil unprotected and subject to erosion. Erosion has become serious in some upland areas.

Methods of improving soil management in this area are much the same as those recommended in nearby sections. They include: For the forage and field crops—liming and fertilizing the better drained soils and establishing alfalfa wherever possible; applying phosphorus and potash as a topdressing for hay and pastures; using complete fertilizers for the grass meadows; fertilizing corn and small grains adequately. For the vegetable and cash crops— maintaining adequate fertilization, using soil tests as a guide; growing them in rotation with sod crops, especially such legumes as alfalfa; using cover crops wherever feasible to keep the soil covered in the late fall and early spring. For the fruit crops—maintaining an adequate fertilizer program; using sod and winter cover crops when orchard culture will allow; using barnyard manure where available to help keep the cover; using dolomitic limestone under trees where high acidity has resulted from sulfur spray applications.

Much of the upland is irregularly rolling and not well suited for contour farming, but some sections can be so managed. The drainage of the heavier, relatively flat soils can be improved.

THE NEW ENGLAND STATES, which include Connecticut, Maine, Massachusetts, New Hampshire, Rhode Island, and Vermont, embrace an area of 67,384 square miles.

Much of New England is a country of ancient, worn-down mountains, a land of extremely complex rock structure. It also has been modified by the invasions and retreats of the continental ice sheets of the Wisconsin Age.

The modified land area has been divided (in order of age) into four physiographic type areas—the residuals of the ancient mountains, the dissected uplands, the interior lowlands, and the coastal lowlands.

The rainfall is generally enough for almost any adapted farm crop. It is about 50 inches in some parts of Connecticut and less than 32 inches in the extreme north. Severe, widespread droughts are uncommon, and extremely dry years are few.

The prevailing temperatures average about 67° F. in summer and 20° to 30° in winter. The growing season varies from 100 to 125 days in the northern parts to nearly 200 days in the southern section. The variations in the length of the growing season, which are due to topography and exposure, determine to a marked degree the crops that are grown.

The soils vary greatly because of the many different kinds of parent materials in the region. Most of the soils are classified as Podzols or Brown-Podzolics. They are highly acid as a result of years of leaching under forest vegetation. They are quite infertile.

The acidity has favored accumulations of organic matter on the surface of uncultivated soils. It is also responsible for the slow decomposition of organic matter when the land is tilled, especially if the soils have not been limed. The soils are generally shallow in the steeply sloping regions, and the land is in forests.

The local differences in soils, due to factors such as drainage and type of parent material, determine the management and production patterns. Differences in soil texture and the presence or absence of limestone in the parent materials determine the suitability for cash and forage crops.

Loss of soil from erosion is not a major problem in New England because 70 percent of the area is forested; some 85 percent of the agricultural land is frozen or covered with snow several months of the year; and precipitation usually is gentle.

Agriculture in New England has undergone many changes. Wheat, wool, and beef were produced extensively until about 1830. The production of those commodities shifted westward in the latter part of the 19th century as new agricultural lands were opened up. At the same time the New England States expanded their production of more intensively grown crops, such as potatoes, cranberries, blueberries, tobacco, and apples. This shift has continued to the present. The poultry business also has expanded in parts of the region.

The maximum extension of New England agriculture occurred about 1880, when about 207 thousand farms occupied 22 million acres, 5 million of which were in crops. By 1950, the number of farms had dropped to 103 thousand and the acres in farms to 12.5 million acres, of which only 1.8 million acres were in crops.

Dairying has remained important in New England agriculture. Pasture and hay have helped maintain soil productivity in many sections.

About 70 percent of New England is in forest. Trees are the natural vegetation, and abandoned farmland quickly becomes reforested. Spruce and balsam fir are important commercial types in the north. White pine dominates the central areas. Northern hardwoods are important in the southern portion. There are great woodlands in northern Maine, smaller forested areas in the mountains of New Hampshire and Vermont, and small, scattered tracts elsewhere.

Agriculturally, important differences exist between the Northern States (Maine, New Hampshire, and Vermont) and those in the south (Connecticut, Massachusetts, and Rhode Island). About 35 percent of the land area of southern New England was in farms in 1949. Farming is much more intensive in the southern part.

New England is classified generally as a dairying area, but it has several subclassifications—specialized dairy; dairy, poultry, and mixed farming; dairy and general farming; specialized crops; and nonagricultural land.

Most of the nonagricultural land is in forests. Some tracts, particularly in northern New England, have never been in farmland, and much of the land is owned by large concerns.

Better silvicultural practices will increase the yield from the timbered areas and provide maximum cover for the soils. A good portion of the woodland areas of parts of New England is not well suited to crops because of poor drainage, shallow soils, and presence of stones and boulders.

Of the many local areas of intense land use in New England, the largest is in Aroostook County, Maine, where potato production is the major farm enterprise. Good management practices have resulted in average yields of nearly 500 bushels an acre—more than double the national average.

Another area of specialization is the tobacco area of Hartford County, Conn.

Lack of plant nutrients is seldom a problem in the intensively cropped areas. Although the soils are naturally infertile, fertilization at rates of 2 thousand to 3 thousand pounds an acre are common, especially in Aroostook County. Sometimes those rates may be excessive and wasteful, but growers regard them as a form of insurance on crops of high value.

Because of the intensive cultivation in those areas, soil erosion becomes a problem. Little organic matter can be returned to the soils. More serious, however, is the lack of adequate ground cover early in the summer. In some of the old maps of soil erosion, Aroostook County was listed as the only problem area in New England. The problem might be more intense there than elsewhere in New England, but other areas with a maximum of cultivated crops and few cover crops have suffered damage from erosion.

One of the two dairy and poultry farming regions of New England is in southern New England and includes most of Connecticut, Massachusetts, and Rhode Island and part of New Hampshire. The other (DP–2) is in central Maine.

The 1950 Census figures for the dairy, poultry, and mixed farming area of central Maine show that hay is the most extensive crop grown. The poultry industry expanded rapidly from 1940 to 1950, and in 1957 accounted for a major share of the farmers' income. Poultry competes with potatoes as the leading source of income for Maine farmers. The acreage in feed grains has not expanded. The poultry area in central Maine has been one of the few feed-deficit areas in this country. It could produce most of its own feed if some of the area devoted to hay or wildgrass were diverted to feed crops and properly managed.

The poultry business of southern New England is more intensive than in central Maine. Southern New England produces relatively little feed. Feed is purchased from the Midwest and fed to the animals.

The dairy and general farming area (DG–5) is mainly in the southern parts of Maine and New Hampshire. Land use in the northern New England dairy and general farming area is much less intensive than in the dairy and poultry area of that State.

In the dairy and poultry area of central Maine (DP–3), an average of about 45.5 percent of the area was in farms in 1949, and the counties averaged 63,628 acres of harvested crops.

In the dairy and general farming area (DG–5) only about 29.4 percent of the land area was in farms, and the counties selected as representative of this area averaged only about 25,818 acres of cropland per county.

Land use is less intensive in area DG–5. Farmers in general receive a part of their livelihood from some place other than the farm. If the family does depend on the farm for sole support, the standard of living is lower than in the more intensive farming areas.

The most important trends in the use of land resources of New England are these: A decided decline in the acreage of agricultural land; some reduction in acreage of rural lands because of industrial expansion, wide highways, and the like; rapid expansion in the use of land for recreation; and continued exploitation of forests.

The return of land to forests offers the obvious advantage of better soil protection. It also offers a source of income, which sometimes is better than the income realized from cropping marginal lands. The reforestation of some of the more sloping uplands consequently should be encouraged, especially in sections where the soils are thin and infertile.

About 19 percent of the land in farms designated as cropland in 1957 cannot be cropped in the regular rotation because of erosion hazards or physical limitations. One percent of the area should be reforested, 3 percent should be in permanent grass cover, and the remaining 15 percent should be used for permanent meadows.

Participation in conservation programs has been good in some sections, but to achieve the objectives of conservation in a reasonable time, the rate must be speeded up.

The use of fertilizers has been high in this area for many years. There is little need for increased fertilization on the intensively grown crops, but greater fertilization of forage crops should be encouraged. Phosphorus and potash are especially beneficial for the forage legumes. Many of the coarser soils are low in available potash, and their phosphorus levels are inadequate for such crops as alfalfa and red clover. Heavy fertilization of meadows with a complete fertilizer high in nitrogen has produced good yields of forage.

Agricultural limestone needs to be used in greater amounts in all of the New England States. The amounts applied in 1954 in each of the six States might well be doubled.

Proper management could double the production of the forested lands.

Drainage, renovation of hay pastures, and fertilization could raise forage yields about 30 percent.

Increases in yields of nonforage crops can be expected from improvements in fertility, changes in land use, and conservation of water for crop use. The increases in yields of small grains would be sizable, while those of vegetables, potatoes, and tobacco would be slight.

Middle Atlantic Coastal Plain

William J. Hanna and S. S. Obenshain

The Middle Atlantic Coastal Plain embraces parts of New York, New Jersey, Delaware, Maryland, Virginia, and North Carolina. It begins as a narrow strip at Long Island and gradually widens to nearly 200 miles in North Carolina.

Some of the land has been farmed for more than 200 years. Almost all of the present county boundary lines were established before 1750.

The region has 6 million inhabitants, and in large cities near it are another 14 million persons.

Agriculture is secondary to industry in the northern part. A more serious reduction in agricultural areas was made by residential construction than by industry during the early 1950's.

Because of the high population density and location along the Atlantic coast, much of the land is utilized as recreational areas, which mostly are along the sandy coastal beaches and have little agricultural value, although some farmland is being converted to parks and golf courses.

The average January temperature varies between 48° F. in southern North Carolina and 30° on Long Island in New York. The average July temperature has a somewhat narrower range—from 80° in North Carolina to 72° in New York.

The average number of days without killing frost is about 180 on Long Island and in central New Jersey. There are 290 frost-free days on the outer banks of North Carolina at Cape Hatteras. The average date of the first killing frost is October 20 in parts of New Jersey, northern Delaware, and Maryland, and November 30 along the southeastern coast of North Carolina. The average dates of the last killing frost in spring are March 5 in North Carolina, and April 25 in central New Jersey and on Long Island.

The highest annual precipitation in the region is about 56 inches in the vicinity of Beaufort, N. C. The lowest is about 36 inches in Calvert and St. Mary's Counties in southern Maryland. April to September precipitation ranges from 20 inches in southern New Jersey and southeastern Maryland to 34 inches near Beaufort. Much of the summer rain comes in afternoon thunderstorms.

The region lies in the path of occasional hurricanes, which move up the coast from the Caribbean area in the autumn. The hurricanes usually are accompanied by heavy rain and strong winds, which may be destructive.

Because of the proximity to the ocean and numerous bays, the relative humidity is high in many coastal sections.

The topography is level to hilly. The hills are mostly in the inner Coastal Plain near the streams. The elevation ranges from sea level along the many tidal streams and bays to a little more than 300 feet in southern Maryland.

The higher elevations along the inland boundary have well-developed drainageways. North of the James River and the mouth of the Chesapeake Bay, the region is a series of relatively narrow peninsulas lying between rather deeply cut stream beds. Drainage has been established to both sides of the peninsulas.

Where the Coastal Plain is wider in New Jersey, southern Virginia, and North Carolina, the seaward portions on the lower terraces and the upland flats on the intermediate terraces do not have well-defined drainageways and therefore have extensive swampy areas, notably the Dismal Swamp along the Virginia-North Carolina border and the Mattamuskeet area in North

Carolina. Scattered swampy upland flats, or "pocosins," also exist in Virginia, the Carolina Bays in North Carolina, and swamps in the New Jersey "Pine Barrens." Large areas of tidal marsh and coastal beach occur along the coastline of the bays and the sea, particularly in New Jersey, Virginia, and North Carolina.

Nearness to cities and soil type were among the factors that determined farming systems. Modern transportation and competition from distant areas reduced the importance of nearness to large cities, but much of the dairying and vegetable farming are still located around them.

Other factors that influence the farming systems and crops are labor costs, particularly near the larger cities, and Government controls, including price supports and acreage control. For example, a large acreage formerly used for tobacco, cotton, and peanuts in North Carolina and Virginia was shifted in the early 1950's to corn and soybeans.

The most common crops are corn and small grains, but many vegetables and potatoes also are grown in much of the region. In the North Carolina Coastal Plain, cash grain, tobacco, peanuts, and cotton are the characteristic types of farms. The leading crops in the Coastal Plain of Virginia are cash grain, peanuts, cotton, and vegetables. Poultry, dairy, and vegetable farms are the characteristic types in the northern part.

Vegetables to be marketed fresh have long been grown on the sandy soils of the Coastal Plain near New York, Philadelphia, Wilmington, Baltimore, and Washington. Much of the market garden areas have been lost since 1940 to urban and industrial encroachment, especially in Nassau County, N. Y.; Camden County, N. J.; Baltimore County, Md.; and Norfolk County, Va.

Production of vegetables for processing is an important enterprise in most of the northern part. A large part of the acreage of well-drained soils is devoted to vegetable production, and somewhat more than half of the produce goes to processing plants. The remainder is sold on the fresh market. Vegetable crops, including potatoes, are given first priority on best soils in New Jersey, Delaware, Maryland, and parts of Virginia.

Poultry is the main farm enterprise in the area north of Chesapeake Bay. Chickens are grown on almost all farms of the region, but large-scale production is concentrated in two general areas—Monmouth, Ocean, Atlantic, and Cumberland Counties in New Jersey, and the central part of Delaware and the Eastern Shore of Maryland and Virginia. Egg production is foremost in New Jersey.

Poultry farms are mostly on the very sandy soils. Only a small fraction of the feed is produced on the farm. Cultivated land, if any, is used for poultry ranges or for vegetable crops. In the Delaware-Maryland-Virginia peninsula, where broiler production is the chief poultry enterprise, a much larger proportion of the feed is grown in the vicinity, but even there more than half of the grains fed to poultry come from outside those States.

A smaller area is devoted to the duckling industry of Suffolk County, N. Y. Almost all the feed is shipped in.

Dairying is second only to poultry production as a farm enterprise in the Atlantic Coastal Plain north of Chesapeake Bay. Much of the dairying is concentrated on the soils that are less well drained. Such areas include Burlington and Salem Counties in New Jersey, northern Delaware, and the northern part of the Eastern Shore of Maryland.

Two major crops are white potatoes and sweetpotatoes. The value of both

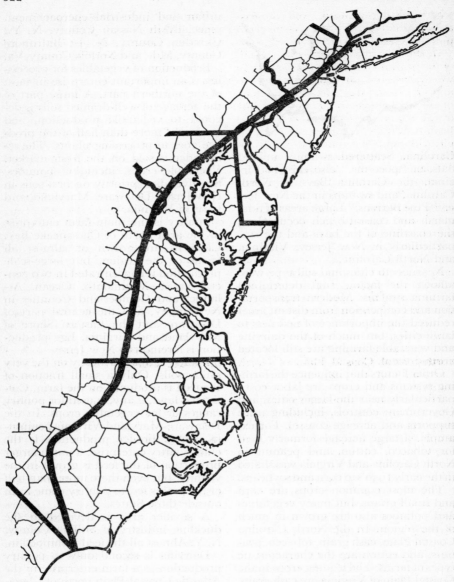

crops in 1949 was about the same as for all vegetables. White potatoes are grown throughout the region. Sweet-potatoes are grown on the sandier soils and in areas that have a growing season of 190 to 200 days.

Corn is grown on more acres in the region than any other crop. In the part north of Virginia, corn and small

grains are grown in support of live-stock. Corn and soybeans grown for cash sale of grain occupy a large acre-age of less well-drained soils in North Carolina and Virginia. In the flat-woods area of northeastern North Carolina and southeastern Virginia these are the major crops in value as well as in acreage. Even in the areas where cotton, peanuts, and tobacco are of greater cash value, corn occupies more acres than any other crops.

In the Virginia Coastal Plain north of the peanut area, small grains, mostly wheat, are grown in rotation with corn and soybeans. Hogs, the only livestock of any importance in the southern part of the region, are concentrated in the peanut belt, where they are used to glean the nuts not removed in normal harvesting operations.

Tobacco is the principal crop in southern Maryland and the central Coastal Plain of North Carolina. Because of its high acre value, tobacco is given first priority for well-drained soils best suited for its production.

Cotton is grown only in the southern sections and is of major importance only in North Carolina, where it occupies about 15 percent of the cropland of the central and upper Coastal Plain. Peanuts are grown in the southern part of this area. This crop is more limited in distribution than either cotton or tobacco and is important only in the north-central Coastal Plain of North Carolina and the adjoining area in southern Virginia.

Fruit crops of importance are apples, peaches, and strawberries. Blueberries flourish in small areas of muck or near-muck soils in New Jersey and North Carolina. Cranberries are grown in a small area of soils with a high-water table in and around Burlington County, N. J. Most of the apples and peaches are grown north of Chesapeake Bay. Strawberries are grown throughout the region, usually on the less well-drained soils of vegetable farms. Watermelons and cantaloups are major crops south of the Chesapeake and in a small area of southern Delaware and the Eastern Shore.

Forest products, especially pulpwood, should be listed as a crop in the southern part of the region, where much of the poorly drained soils are suited to woodland.

Specialty crops include nursery stock, muskrats, and wildlife for hunting and fishing.

THE COASTAL PLAIN slopes gently seaward, mostly in a series of more or less parallel terraces. The terraces extend inland along the bays and streams. At least seven terrace levels have been distinguished along the Coastal Plain; they are more easily recognized in the southern part of the region.

The highly variable material of the Coastal Plain was transported from the higher elevation of the Atlantic slope and deposited in layers or unconsolidated beds, which vary in texture from fine-grained silts and clays to coarse sands and gravel. The deposits are thought to be a mixture of marine, alluvial, and glaciofluvial materials. Some disturbance of the surface layers has been caused by local wind action in the northern portion.

The zonal soils include Gray-Brown Podzolic and Red-Yellow Podzolic soils. They are well drained and on the higher elevations, but they occupy less than one-fourth of the area. The Gray-Brown Podzolic soils of the north and the Red-Yellow Podzolic soils of the south merge in this region with much overlapping. There are limited areas of Podzols in the northern part of the region on well-drained sections of the outer Coastal Plain.

The intrazonal soils are Ground-water Podzols, Humic Gley, and Low Humic Gley soils. The Ground-water Podzols are in the poorly drained and very poorly drained areas of the outer Coastal Plain from New Jersey to North Carolina. The Gley soils were developed under conditions of impeded drainage. These two groups of soils cover more than one-third of the area of the region and include more than one-half of the farmland.

Sandy soils with little profile development are a characteristic of the outer Coastal Plain in the region. Where surface drainage is good, these soils are droughty because of excessive internal drainage. They are almost entirely in forests.

Miscellaneous soils include the swamps, tidal marshes, and coastal dunes—about one-third of the area.

The effect of parent material on variation in soil development in the Coastal Plain has been due largely to textural differences. The beds of sands, clays, and gravels of which the Coastal Plain is formed are generally thin along their western edge and become deeper toward the coast.

The soils of the Coastal Plain-Piedmont Province boundary may have subsoil or substrata of material from the province other than the one from which the surface originated. That occurs where the Coastal Plain surface is thin and where fluvial Piedmont material has been deposited over Coastal Plain material on stream terraces.

More slope to seaward occurs in the more elevated western part of the region, where drainageways have been established, than in the seaward portion, which is nearly level. The textural composition of the deposits varies from coarse gravels to fine clays. The surface texture varies from sands to silty clay loam. The subsoils are sands to plastic, sticky clays. The sands generally are unsuitable for crops other than those of very high market value and are mostly devoted to forests. Soils with fine texture throughout the profile are usually wet, but in places where surface drainage is provided they are used for corn, soybeans, and other crops that are tolerant of somewhat reduced soil aeration.

The soils of intermediate texture, with good surface drainage, have a wide adaptation but are used generally for crops of highest value.

Because of the effects of climate and parent materials, the soils are all acid under natural conditions. The pH of undisturbed soils ranges from somewhat less than 4.0 in some of the swamps and bogs to about 5.0 in the upland sands.

The content of organic matter ranges from less than 1 percent in the well-drained sands to 90 percent or more in the organic soils. The cation-exchange capacity of the soils of this region is low compared to soils of most of the other regions.

Vermiculite, kaolinite, and illite clays predominate in the clay fraction of the soils. Many acres of sandy soils with little organic matter have cation-exchange capacities of only 2 to 3 milliequivalents per 100 grams. The fact that 50 percent or more of the low cation-exchange capacities of these soils resides in the soil organic matter emphasizes the importance of soil-management problems associated with organic matter in many Coastal Plain soils.

MANY OF THE SOIL-MANAGEMENT problems arise from attempts to grow crops on soils that are not suitable.

The soil property that limits adaptation of many crops is the lack of adequate drainage and aeration, which also makes it difficult to prepare the land at the proper time and may prevent adequate cultivation of the crop.

The fact that bright tobacco, which is one of the highest acre-value crops in the region, is grown in a limited area and only on selected soils, is a good illustration of soil adaptation. The same is true of alfalfa, which also has a high requirement of air and water. Only minor adjustments can be made in fitting the soil for a particular crop, even by expensive operations, such as artificial drainage. Crops that are less sensitive to excess water and lack of oxygen can be grown on a wider variety of soils and fewer adjustments are necessary in adapting unsuitable soils to their use.

The liming materials are an inexpensive source of calcium and magnesium. Calcium deficiency by itself is not a problem in the region, except for peanuts. Calcium has been added to the soils in phosphatic fertilizers in considerable amounts—probably enough to meet the nutritional requirements of most crops. As the use of more concentrated phosphatic fertilizers containing smaller amounts of calcium increases, lime will become more important as a source of calcium.

The need of magnesium is widespread throughout the region, particularly in the sandier areas. The need for magnesium in most of these soils is easily net by including a source of magnesium in the fertilizer to be used or by the use of dolomitic limestone. If soil tests indicate a need for lime and magnesium, the most economical source of magnesium is dolomitic limestone.

The overuse of lime is to be avoided as much as the underuse. Vegetable crops on sandy soils are more sensitive in this respect than most other crops and soils. Soils derived from glauconitic (greensand) material in New Jersey have a low content of available manganese. Their optimum pH levels are only slightly above 6.0 for peaches, spinach, and a number of other crops. Other Coastal Plain soils are inherently low in manganese, and those with low buffer capacity are particularly susceptible to manganese deficiency due to overliming.

The soils of the region respond to additions of nitrogen, phosphorus, and potassium.

Nitrogen is probably the nutrient element most often in short supply here. The climate and the sandy soils mean that soils have a low storage capacity for nitrogen. Nitrogen added to the soils in organic or inorganic form is converted quickly to the soluble nitrate form, which is not retained by the soil and thus is fairly rapidly lost in the percolating rain water.

On very sandy soils of good drainage, frequent small applications of nitrogen fertilizer should be made for some crops. The number and frequency of the applications will increase with the sand content and the nitrogen requirement of the crop. Control of nitrogen supply can be obtained to some degree by the use of less soluble fertilizer materials or by making use of the temporary nitrogen storage capacity of residues and green manure crops.

One must make sure that the carbon-nitrogen ratio of the organic material is low enough so that nitrogen will be applied to the crop during decomposition rather than to micro-organisms that compete with the crop for the available nitrogen supply. It may be necessary to add some nitrogen to organic residues, such as small grain straw and stubble. Manures or legumes may serve as the source of nitrogen. A winter cover crop of crimson clover is equivalent to 50 pounds or more of fertilizer nitrogen.

Continued use of phosphatic fertilizer over the past century has resulted in building up a phosphorus supply in the Coastal Plain soils. Surveys of results of soil tests indicate that in some areas more than three-fourths of the soils have a relatively high level of available phosphorus. They originally were low in available phosphorus. This buildup in phosphorus has resulted from continued use of large amounts of fertilizers containing phosphorus, the low phosphorus-fixing capacity of most Coastal Plain soils, and the low solubility and leachability of most soil phosphorus compounds.

Soil tests should be used to determine the phosphorus needs of a soil and crop. If phosphorus is badly needed, not more than 10 to 20 percent of the phosphorus added in fertilizers can be expected to be available to the current crop.

Maximum availability of phosphorus occurs at about pH 6.5. In soils of a moderate to low phosphorus level, a more efficient use of applied phosphorus is obtained by placing the fertilizer in concentrated bands or zones close to the plants rather than mixing uniformly with the soil. If the crop requirements for phosphorus are high, as for sweet corn and spinach, the whole soil must be maintained at a high phosphorus level to get the most profitable yields.

Potassium fertilization is necessary for almost all soils and crops of the Middle Atlantic Coast. Despite heavy applications over many years, there is relatively little buildup of potassium in these soils, as is the case with phosphorus. Summaries of soil tests indicate only a slight residual effect—and that on soils of loam and finer texture that have relatively high cation-exchange capacities.

As a general rule, a mixed fertilizer

626

YEARBOOK OF AGRICULTURE 1957

containing nitrogen, phosphorus, and potassium should be the basic application for this region for all crops other than legumes. Phosphorus and potassium should be used individually only in special cases, as indicated by soil tests, to correct unbalanced conditions. Nitrogen should be added as a supplement to the mixed fertilizer as required by the crop, soil, and weather conditions.

The use of trace elements is of secondary importance here. Deficiencies of boron, iron, molybdenum, manganese, and zinc have been found. We do not recommend that they be added to fertilizers unless a need for a particular element has been demonstrated for the soil and crop in question.

THE SELECTION OF ROTATIONS is one of the most discussed and least understood of all soil-management practices. Rotations should be made to fit soil conditions and the farming enterprise. The number of satisfactory rotations in this region is quite large because of the wide variety of crops.

One of the objectives of rotations is to increase soil productivity by reducing the incidence of diseases and insect pests, which often build up in a soil under continuous single cropping. The rotation of tobacco with other crops to control soil diseases, particularly black shank, is becoming an indispensable practice in North Carolina. Serious infestation of soils by nematodes in nonrotated fields of sweet corn, tomatoes, and other crops is forcing rotation and often expensive soil treatment for effective control.

An equally important objective of rotation is to maintain a supply of decomposing organic material in the soil. This is a source of plant nutrients and of various organic compounds which aid in the stabilization of soil aggregates. The importance and economic value of the use of winter green manure crops in this region has been demonstrated many times for a number of vegetable crops. Winter cover crops protect the soil against erosion, discourage growth of weeds, and absorb excess nutrients

from previous fertilization that might otherwise be lost by leaching.

Most rotations will include corn. In the northern part, the following rotations are most satisfactory: Corn, small grain, clover—2 to 4 years; corn, small grain, clover, corn, soybeans—5 years; corn, grass-legume—2 to 4 years.

A 2-year rotation of corn and soybeans for grain probably is as good as any for the less well-drained soils on level topography. A 1-year rotation of small grain and soybeans is widely used in Virginia. Rotations that include sod should be extended on soils that are susceptible to erosion or if forage and hay requirements for livestock are high.

Tomatoes fit very well into a rotation of small grain and sod as an alternate crop for corn. Other vegetables, such as sweet corn, can be added to such a rotation of 3 to 4 years with 1 year of sod.

Experiments in New Jersey and other States have shown that the total yield of crops for 3 years following a year of sod exceeds that for 4 years of continuous cultivation.

Winter cover crops of crimson clover, small grain, or ryegrass should follow all summer vegetables that are not to be followed by sod.

Potatoes do not fit into rotations with most other crops because soils for potatoes must be held at approximately pH 5.0 to control scab. Potatoes alternated with soybeans in a 2-year rotation with winter cover crop following the potatoes or a rotation of potatoes and small grain over 2 or 3 years are probably the best rotations for potatoes.

In some vegetable soils, the main objective of certain rotations is to reduce the amount of tillage. Soil compaction from traffic is a major problem in some areas of extensive vegetable farming. The best way to overcome it is to rest the land with sod and reduce the cultivation by using chemical weedkillers. The number of cultivations might be cut from four or five to two. One or two cultivations seem to be essential to achieve adequate infiltration of water and aeration of the soil.

We have little evidence to indicate that the moldboard plow should be replaced as the basic tillage instrument here. The plow gives the only satisfactory seedbed preparation for most crops of the region. For certain vegetable crops, where the crop residue is small, however, disk harrowing gives sufficient land preparation.

A different type of seedbed preparation is sometimes used for corn and soybeans in the wet soils of North Carolina and southern Virginia. Instead of flat plowing with a moldboard plow, the land is broken with listers ("middle busters") so that the rows are planted on top of ridges. That does not improve the overall drainage, but it does enable one to work the soil earlier in the spring. Many farmers on these wet soils plow and cultivate in narrow strips (150 to 200 feet wide) between lateral drains in such a way as to make the high point of the land midway between the laterals. The land slopes gently toward each lateral. Cross furrows made diagonally across rows after planting and each cultivation aid in removing surface water.

Deep tillage, with or without deep placement of lime and fertilizer, is but little used and is of doubtful value in this region.

Erosion from water and wind is light to moderate here. Wind erosion is more prevalent on the cultivated very sandy soils and coastal beaches. Very steep land near streams in the inner Coastal Plain is almost all under permanent tree cover. Sloping land used for cultivation can usually be protected by contour planting with strip-cropping to break the very long slopes.

Although the Middle Atlantic Coastal Plain has an average of about 40 inches of rain a year, supplemental irrigation is proving to be a profitable practice on many farms. Periods of 2 weeks with less than 0.2 inch of rain occur about once a year. Periods of 2 to 3 weeks with that amount of rain occur about once every 2 years. Such dry spells during a critical growth period may severely reduce yields.

Yields of vegetables and potatoes grown in a 3-year rotation with 1 year of sod without irrigation equaled the yields from continuous cultivation of these crops with irrigation in dry years. Irrigation increased the yield of the continuously cultivated crops by nearly 100 percent. Any practice that will reduce runoff and erosion and increase the rate of water infiltration into the soil will increase the supply of available water for the crop. It appears, then, that only the crops of higher value can be profitably irrigated. These include vegetables, potatoes, and tobacco.

The agricultural potential of the region is at least three times the 1950 production. The total area of the region is approximately 26 million acres. Of this, 55 percent was in farms and only about 50 percent of the farmland was in cropland and pasture in 1954. Thus, only 27 percent—7,150,000 acres—was used for crops and pasture.

Another 25 percent of the acreage of the region could be cleared and drained for agricultural purposes. The expense of bringing those acres into production was not economically justified in 1957 at a time of agricultural surpluses of many crops in this country.

Agriculture will meet serious competition for irrigation water in this region from industrial and urban interests before the end of this century. Efficient soil management, including rotations with sod and cover crops, can reduce the drought damage to crops by improving the permeability and the available moisture-holding capacity of soils and increasing the rooting depth of crops.

One of the more urgent needs is zoning to preserve the agricultural potential of the region. We think rural zoning control should be extended. Many thousands of acres of productive farmlands have been lost to highways, airports, industrial sites, and residential areas because people have not considered the future of soil, farming, and living.

Soil Management
for Pastures

R. R. Robinson, R. E. Blaser, and
H. B. Peterson

Pastures are grown on very good and on very poor soils. Their fertilization, plant species, and grazing management vary accordingly.

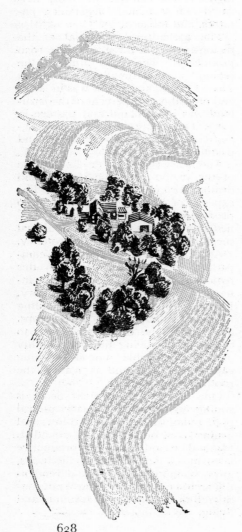

A large acreage of pasture is on land too rough, steep, poorly drained, or otherwise unsuited for tilled crops, but such pastures occasionally may be renovated to introduce higher yielding species. Good management is particularly important because productive pastures should be kept as long as possible before renovation again becomes necessary.

Soils that are rough, steep, stony, or wet may be utilized for truly permanent pastures. The pasture species on them will be those in equilibrium with soil conditions, climate, and grazing management.

Irrigated pastures in the West often are seeded on some of the best soil. Much of the acreage, however, is on soils that are hard to cultivate. They are poorly drained and contain salt and alkali.

Some forage plants are well adapted to these adverse conditions and can be productive with proper management.

Tall wheatgrass or tall fescue, for example, tolerate saline and alkali conditions. Planted in the bottom of furrows or with a deep-furrow drill, they usually will become established and produce considerable forage of fair quality. They also improve the physical condition of the soil and facilitate leaching of the salts if drainage can be established. After such growth, it is possible to introduce more desirable species.

SOIL MANAGEMENT for pasture establishment varies widely, depending on the soil conditions and on the pasture species or mixtures to be sown.

Pastures in a regular crop rotation are seeded on land that is already plowed and fitted for a good seedbed. Seedings may be with or without a companion crop of a small grain. A companion crop is desirable on soils that crust easily and on those where wind damage is a hazard. Experiments by G. H. Stringfield and L. E. Thatcher in Ohio and by investigators in other Midwestern States have shown that successful seedings can be made directly in corn if the corn rows are spaced 5 to 7 feet apart.

Experiments conducted by J. L. Haynes and Dr. Thatcher in Ohio and substantiated by experiments in Michigan, Pennsylvania, and other places showed that better stands and more vigorous seedlings can be obtained by drilling phosphate fertilizer in narrow bands at a depth of about 1.5 inches and seeding directly above it. Band seeding was done in the early experiments with a grain drill, in which the tubes from the grass seedbox were extended so that the seed was dropped directly over the band of phosphate. Placing the phosphate directly below the seed seems to be particularly desirable on soils low in fertility and when the weather is apt to be unfavorable. In seedings made late in the season on poor soils, the increased growth resulting from placing the fertilizer near the young seedling may mean the difference between failure and success.

On highly fertile soils, band placements appear to have little if any advantage over conventional methods of fertilizer application.

Certain precautions must be observed in banding fertilizer for grasses and legumes. Because the young roots grow straight down with little branching during the first few weeks, the fertilizer must be directly below the seed—but the roots will be burned if the salt concentration in the band is too high. There is no danger of burning from phosphate fertilizers, but potassium and nitrogen should be used sparingly in the band, particularly if the seeding is likely to be followed by dry weather. Additional potash, if needed, should be mixed with the soil.

RUNDOWN PASTURES on land too rough or too steep to plow have been improved by renovation. The old sod is broken up, lime and fertilizer are added, and adapted grasses and legumes are seeded. Pasture renovation is used on poor sods and on dense grass sods from which legumes have disappeared. In either case, but particularly on the good sods, the roots must be cut so that the grass will die; otherwise the new seeding may be crowded out by the rapid regrowth of the old sod.

An annual may be planted for a season on land that is not too rough. That allows for further tillage and better eradication of the old sod before establishing a permanent pasture mixture.

A heavy cutaway disk, often called a bush and bog harrow, is particularly effective for pasture renovation. A heavy field cultivator also may be used, although on heavy sods it may roll up the sod if the shovels are not widely spaced.

Grasses are hard to kill by tillage in the late fall or early spring because the old sod recovers rapidly if it has enough moisture. During hot, dry weather, on the other hand, the soil is so hard that tillage is ineffective. The ideal time to disk is immediately after a heavy rain early in the summer. Even then one will have to disk again after 2 or 3 weeks.

Experiments at several stations show that some of the new herbicides (such as Dalapon) are effective in killing the old sod. Most of the experiments indicate that a combination of herbicides and tillage may be more satisfactory than either alone. The herbicide, even if it does not kill the grass, will make tillage easier and more effective.

Probably the choice of a herbicide will be determined by the species of grasses or weeds in the pasture, weather conditions, and the cost of the material.

Fertilization and seeding practices are similar to those on tilled land except that the rate of phosphate fertilization should be greatly increased on most pastures not previously renovated or fertilized. Erosion usually is not a problem because the old sod is an effective mulch.

Kentucky bluegrass is one of the few pasture species in which establishment is not a problem. In the Northern and Eastern States, fields that are limed, fertilized, and managed as pastures ultimately will become Kentucky bluegrass pastures, with varying amounts of whiteclover. In fact, for years the standard practice for improving old povertygrass and broomsedge pastures was to topdress with lime and fertilizer. Within 2 or 3 years after fertilization, a vigorous volunteer stand of Kentucky bluegrass and whiteclover crowds out those poor-land grasses.

THE IDEAL PASTURE consists of nearly equal stands of grasses and legumes. Lime and fertilizer are essential for soils of the Eastern States in attaining this ideal mixture.

Fertilization is complicated, however, by the fact that the species, grown in close association, vary in fertilizer requirements, habit of growth, and response to grazing management. That may seem confusing at first, but in practice it is a matter of maintaining the legumes by fertilization and grazing management. On soils where legumes are not well adapted, however, it is more practical to grow grasses alone than to attempt to maintain legumes.

Fertilization for grasses is quite different than for grass-legume mixtures. Most of the State experiment stations have bulletins giving details that should be followed for local conditions. Besides more common fertilizer elements, the application of some boron is recommended for alfalfa in the Eastern States. Deficiencies of sulfur occur in some

parts of the West and the South. Deficiencies of other trace elements in pastures have been reported.

LIME applied to pastures penetrates the soil very slowly. On acid soils it is therefore particularly desirable to work lime into the soil before seeding. The maintenance requirements of the pasture for lime can be met by topdressing, based on soil tests. The amount will depend on weather conditions, the soil, and the productivity of the pasture. Generally it is less than on tilled land.

THE IMPORTANCE of phosphate fertilization for legumes is well known. It has taken some time for its value for grasses to be generally recognized, however, partly because we did not realize the interrelations of nitrogen and phosphate fertilization.

Pure grass sods are low in available nitrogen. Phosphate fertilization of an old grass pasture, even though the soil is low in available phosphate, gives little increase in yields because of the low level of available nitrogen. If nitrogen is applied, however, the response to phosphate is remarkable.

Phosphate fertilizers on pastures are not lost through leaching, and the losses in crop removal are relatively small. The rates of application depend largely on the amounts of available phosphate in the soil and the productive potential of the land. The frequency of application of phosphate is not important on most soils. For example, 120 pounds of phosphoric oxide— P_2O_5—an acre every third year or 40 pounds of P_2O_5 an acre every year, are nearly equally effective. If phosphate is the only fertilizer applied, therefore, it is cheaper to apply heavier rates at longer intervals and so save the costs of spreading it.

POTASSIUM behaves quite differently from phosphorus both in the soil and in the plant, and fertilizer practices differ accordingly.

A high-producing pasture requires 100 to 150 pounds of potash an acre annually. It can absorb as much as 400 pounds. This extremely high absorption—luxury consumption—of potash is a waste of potassium, as it serves no useful purpose to the plant or the grazing animal. Potash fertilization is necessary for good pastures, but the rate should not be excessive.

Over a period of years, pastures—as compared to meadows—need considerably less potash because all of the potash in the hay is removed, whereas the grazing animal removes only 20 to 25 percent.

An illustration is provided in experiments by B. A. Brown in Connecticut. On a field that had been grazed over a period of years, potash gave no increase in yield. On an adjoining field cut for hay, the level of available potash in the soil was so low that legumes could not be grown without liberal applications of potash.

Luxury consumption of potash is much greater in grasses than in legumes. R. E. Blaser and N. C. Brady, in experiments at Cornell University, found that Ladino clover on a soil low in available potash contained 0.96 percent potash, compared to 1.96 percent for grasses growing in association with the clover. Liberal fertilization increased the potash content to 2.47 percent for Ladino clover and 3.18 percent for the grass.

In experiments at the Regional Pasture Research Laboratory in Pennsylvania on plots that received 400 pounds of muriate of potash an acre annually, alfalfa averaged 2.36 percent potassium, compared to 3.89 percent for orchardgrass growing in the same plots. That means that in grass-legume mixtures the legume is the first to suffer if the soil is low in potash.

In grass-legume mixtures, potash must be applied to meet the needs of the legume even though there may be some luxury consumption by grass.

Potash should be applied twice a year on many soils. On sandy soils, particularly those where the growing season is long and yields are high, more applications may be needed.

Legumes show easily recognizable symptoms of potash deficiency—white spots along the margin of the leaves, followed by yellowing of the leaf margins and eventually the entire leaf. Potash deficiencies often can be detected and additional fertilizer applied in time to save the legume.

The emphasis on potash for legumes has sometimes led to the wrong conclusion that grasses do not require potash fertilization. Because grasses remove more potash from the soil than legumes, they deplete the soil faster.

In experiments at the Regional Pasture Research Laboratory, pure stands of alfalfa and of orchardgrass were grown with and without potash fertilization. All plots received lime and phosphate. The grass received nitrogen fertilizer. The increase in yield from potash fertilization was higher the first harvest year for alfalfa than for orchardgrass. By the third year, however, the increases in yield from potash fertilization were higher for the orchardgrass than for alfalfa.

The application of potash is not common on irrigated pastures west of the Missouri River. The soils generally are well supplied, or the water contains considerable potash. Fertilizer should be applied if soil or plant tests indicate a need for it on a particular farm.

NITROGEN fertilization of pastures can be expected to become more and more profitable. The greatest returns will be from pure grasses on soils not suited to maintenance of legumes and on good soils where it may be desirable to maintain pure grasses for a time following loss of legumes.

The amount of nitrogen used depends on the need for pasture on the particular farm and on soil and climate. Under favorable rainfall and a long growing season, nitrogen may well be applied several times a year at rates exceeding 200 pounds an acre a year.

Nitrogen fertilizer is used on good grass-legume mixtures only in special cases—for example, to provide for early spring grazing. Because most grasses grow earlier in the spring than legumes do, nitrogen fertilization can be used to stimulate earlier growth. Only a small field usually is fertilized for this purpose, and the grass is grazed early to avoid crowding out the legume.

Many grass-legume mixtures have only fair stands of legumes, and nitrogen fixation is not adequate for high production. It is desirable then to use nitrogen fertilizer to supplement the nitrogen fixed by the legume plants. Then grazing must be carefully controlled and on most soils in the East additional potash must be applied to prevent the grass from crowding out the legume.

SUPPLEMENTAL IRRIGATION is one possible solution to the problem of providing abundant high-quality pasture during midsummer.

Increases in pasture production from irrigation were reviewed by John R. Carreker and James H. Lillard in *Water*, the 1955 Yearbook of Agriculture. Under irrigation, adapted forage crop species adequately fertilized can be expected to produce about 50 pounds of dry forage an acre a day during midsummer. Without irrigation, yields may drop off to zero for short periods. The increase from irrigation, therefore, may range from 0 to 50 pounds of dry matter an acre a day.

Rotation grazing of irrigated pastures is an integral part of soil management. Irrigation water should be applied after the animals are removed from the pasture. The movement of the animals over the wet lands is harmful to the plants and tends to puddle the soil. Moreover, the plants recover more rapidly following grazing if water is adequate.

On many farms the available water supply is not adequate for irrigation. On others, the anticipated returns may not justify the cost. But it is possible to increase midsummer grazing through the use of adapted species and suitable grazing management.

Alfalfa is particularly well adapted to hot, dry weather. In most years it makes excellent growth during midsummer. With proper management, it may be grazed without injury to the stand.

The growth of adapted grasses can be increased greatly during midsummer by proper fertilization. If the soil is well fertilized, growth will start immediately following a rain and will continue until moisture is depleted.

At low levels of soil fertility, water will be transpired at almost the same rate, but growth will be poor even when moisture is adequate.

In an experiment conducted in Pennsylvania during 2 successive years of subnormal rainfall, R. R. Robinson and V. G. Sprague obtained an average of only 415 pounds of dry matter an acre during July and August from an orchardgrass sod on a good soil. Liberal amounts of nitrogen fertilizer increased the average yields to 1,575 pounds. Fertilization and irrigation raised the yields to 2,750 pounds. Even though rainfall was below normal and yields were limited by dry weather, it was possible to increase midsummer production by adequate fertilization.

CONTROLLED GRAZING is essential for high production of forage crops. All forage crops after clipping or grazing draw upon stored carbohydrate reserves in starting new growth. The reserves are replenished as the plants recover. Various grasses and legumes differ in the extent of depletion of reserves after clipping and in the rate of recovery. Alfalfa is particularly susceptible to continued depletion of root reserves and must not be grazed or clipped too frequently.

The responses of Ladino clover, however, are quite different from those of alfalfa. The stem of Ladino clover grows along the surface of the ground and a leaf develops at each node. When growing with a tall, vigorous grass, each new leaf of clover arises in rather dense shade; under such conditions, new growth draws heavily on the plant reserves. This weakens the plants and may lead to complete loss of the clover.

Highly significant, however, is the fact that Ladino clover stores carbohydrate reserves in the prostrate stems, but the grasses store a large part of the reserves in the lower part of the stem. Thus close grazing actually will remove part of the reserves of the grass but not of Ladino clover. Frequent grazing to hold the grass in check is essential to maintain Ladino clover in a mixed sod. That is particularly important if the grass has been stimulated by nitrogen fertilization.

Soil Management on Ranges

C. H. Wasser, Lincoln Ellison, and R. E. Wagner

Three-fourths of the area west of the 100th meridian—about 40 percent of the total land area of the United States—is spoken of as "range" in reference to its use by livestock.

On this vast area there are estimated to be about 9 million range cattle, 9.5 million sheep, and (in the 11 Western States) some 4 million big-game animals—deer, elk, antelope, bighorn sheep, and mountain goats.

Nearly 200 million acres of forested range in the Southeastern States are grazed by livestock. Here some 7 million cattle forage for at least part of the year, in addition to some sheep, innumerable hogs, and large numbers of game animals.

The value of this range-forage resource certainly amounts to many millions of dollars annually. Such sums result from the vastness of the range, not from high values per acre. An index to the low economic value of rangeland in general is the fact of public ownership. Some 54 percent of the 11 States is federally owned.

The grazing resource cannot be evaluated by itself. Western grazing lands occupy a considerable part of the drainage basins of major western rivers. The grazing management that is employed on them has much to do with the maintenance of stable streamflow and freedom from silt.

Inasmuch as practically all forested lands are grazed by livestock or wildlife, intimate relationships exist among grazing and forest management, wildlife habitat, and recreational uses. The value of these associated uses may be such that grazing can have an economic impact far beyond the value of the livestock products themselves.

RANGELANDS ARE of many kinds and uses. They vary from extensive grasslands of the plains to high alpine slopes and meadows, from the deserts of the Great Basin and Southwest to the open forests of western mountains and piney woods of the South.

Some ranges are used for yearlong grazing, like the desert grasslands of the Southwest. Some, like the subalpine herblands of the West, are grazed only in midsummer after the snow melts. Others, like certain desert-shrub types, are grazed primarily in winter when livestock water is available. Ranges at intermediate elevations, dominated by sagebrush, pinyon-juniper, or mountain brush, are grazed by livestock in spring and fall, and by big-game animals in winter.

CONSIDERABLE OVERLAP exists between soil management for range and soil management for pasture—partly because the effects of cropping vegetation and compacting soil by grazing animals are likely to be similar on ranges and on pastures, but even more because no sharp line separates grazing lands that are classified as pasture from those that are classified as range. Pasture management strives to increase production through such measures as periodic seeding, fertilization, and irrigation. The approach of the pasture manager is agronomic—whenever the productivity of his pasture drops, he plows it up and plants it over, or he applies fertilizer or water. His pastures are usually composed of tame plants, seldom of species native to the site. Utilization is relatively heavy. The maintenance of the vegetation indefinitely is not the pasture manager's criterion of success: High production is his primary criterion.

Range management, on the other hand, strives to improve the forage resource mainly by manipulating the grazing animal and by the infrequent use of such natural agencies as fire. The approach of the range manager is ecological, and he tries to achieve relatively long-time objectives. His ranges are mostly dominated by forage plants native to the site. His chief criteria of success are the maintenance of an adequate cover of living plants and litter to protect the soil and the perpetuation and increase of desirable forage species. Range utilization, as compared with pasture utilization, is light.

One other distinction might be drawn. The pasture manager avoids erosion, of course, but because of more luxuriant plant cover or gentler terrain, erosion is less commonly a serious problem on pastures than on ranges. Ordinarily he is more concerned with improving soil fertility. In contrast, the range manager may have as a primary objective protection of the soil against accelerated erosion in order to keep the normal productivity of the site.

THE SITE is the fundamental ecological unit of range management.

The site—or range complex, or ecosystem—is made up of many different but closely interrelated parts that involve elements of topography, climate, vegetation, animals, and soil.

Animals may change the composition of vegetation by selective grazing and by trampling. By disseminating seed, they may introduce new species—

sometimes desirable, sometimes undesirable. The effects of grazing are not necessarily damaging, either to vegetation or soil. Grazing has a stimulating effect on growth under certain conditions and, as a general rule, if the grazed plants are given an opportunity to make regrowth, foliage removal is not injurious.

Animals may accelerate erosion by removing the plant cover, by compacting the soil, or by actual displacement of very loose or very wet soil. On certain big-game ranges in early spring as the snow is leaving, for example, the soil may be so churned by the hoofs of animals that far more damage is done than by the amount of forage the animals eat. Contribution to soil fertility through animal waste is probably not of too great importance on rangelands; it is offset by the loss in plant nutrients through removal of the animals.

Vegetation is intimately involved in the management of soil. Living plants and the litter they produce alter the climate near the soil surface by casting shade and obstructing wind. The lowered light intensity, more equable temperature, higher atmospheric humidity, and reduced evaporational loss from the soil (as compared with open spaces free of vegetation) favor a more luxuriant population of animals and plants than could endure if the protecting vegetation were not there. Not only is vegetation an essential agent in the building of soil; it provides a protective cover of living crowns and dead parts—litter or mulch—essential to soil preservation. Because vegetation depends on soil for its existence and because of the formation and protection of soil by vegetation, the two are closely and obviously interdependent.

Soil provides a place for plants to grow and supplies them with water and nutrients. Soil nutrients on western ranges are usually sufficient, although there are some exceptions. In southeastern ranges, as on eastern pasturelands, nutrient deficiencies are more common. Most western range soils have an important role as a storage reservoir for water, making possible development of all higher vegetation and prolonging the discharge of water into streams. Soil moisture is the critical element on most western ranges: It has been said that the most important fertilizer in the West is the oxide of hydrogen.

A significant characteristic of most rangelands with a normal plant cover is that the surface of the soil is highly permeable to water. Because of this fact, large volumes of snowmelt and sudden, dashing rains are readily absorbed. When the cover becomes greatly reduced or when the soil is compacted by trampling, the surface becomes relatively impermeable, and water from torrential rains runs over it, eating away the soil and, in extreme cases, causing destructive floods.

Emphasis on site is significant from the standpoint of soil management. Experience has shown that emphasis on plants alone—particularly upon a single species—can be disastrous. Much damage has been done to the soil by basing standards of range use solely on plant indicators, so that certain sites have deteriorated beyond repair.

SINCE ON ANY RANGE SITE these components are normally in adjustment to one another, any very great pressure on one is bound to affect the rest, and in time the character of the whole complex undergoes change.

If mixed herbaceous vegetation is grazed heavily for many years by cattle, for example, the grasses diminish and the broad-leaved plants increase because cattle tend to graze the grasses more severely. If the same range were heavily grazed by sheep year after year, an opposite trend toward loss of broad-leaved plants and dominance by grasses may occur. Still more severe grazing may eliminate all perennials, so that the site can support only those opportunists of the plant world, annual weeds. If grazing pressure is lightened, the disturbed area is recolonized by successive invasions of perennials. Over the years, if no further disturbance oc-

curs, one community succeeds another until the original native cover returns.

Such trends are referred to as secondary succession or disturbance succession, in contradistinction to the changes involved in the slow development of soil and vegetation over the ages, or primary succession.

While these changes in the vegetation are going on, changes are also taking place in the soil. The most marked are the building up of the mulch and increase in soil structure and in amount of pore space. With those changes, more effective absorption of water and more luxuriant plant growth occur. An increased organic content and improved structure encourage more activity on the part of soil micro-organisms, so that the normal process of soil development goes forward.

An important distinction needs to be made between successional trend and trends involving accelerated soil erosion. The latter are referred to as destructive change. The former may alter the soil—the latter destroys it. The former is orderly and is reversible—the latter is chaotic and irreversible.

Restoration of the original cover in the course of secondary succession on the range usually can be reckoned in terms of decades. When any material amount of soil is lost from the site, however, to all intents and purposes it is gone for good. It cannot be replaced in our lifetime—or in many lifetimes to come. Repair of destructive change therefore is a much more serious matter than range improvement through secondary succession.

THE RANGE MANAGER's first concern is with the adequacy of the vegetation—living plants and organic mulch—to protect the soil. If soil is being lost at an accelerated rate, he modifies his grazing management to encourage a more vigorous growth of herbaceous plants and allow a greater accumulation of organic materials for a protective mulch on the soil surface. He lessens trampling or utilization, or both, in order to accomplish this.

If he is assured that soil is not being lost at an accelerated rate, the stage is set for improvement of both soil and vegetation by constructive successional trends. Through manner, time, and intensity of grazing, he strives to set in motion trends that will result in a desired species composition, all the while maintaining the integrity of the site with plant cover adequate in amount and dispersion to protect the soil.

Plant residues are essential for this protection because they break the impact of rain and prevent puddling. They minimize raindrop splash and dislodgement of soil particles and minimize erosion by wind.

Research on the Great Plains has indicated that 1 thousand to 3 thousand pounds of air-dry plant materials per acre are required to protect the soil against wind erosion, and from 1,500 to 5 thousand pounds per acre to protect it against water erosion, depending on the kind of soil.

Studies on the loose granitic soils in southwestern Idaho have indicated a minimum requirement of 70 percent cover of vegetation and litter on the better sites to protect the surface. The studies also showed that the dispersion of vegetation was important: 4 inches across bare spaces in the wheatgrass type and 2 inches in the cheatgrass type were considered the biggest openings that could be tolerated on range in good condition.

Similar conclusions were reached on subalpine range on clay soil in central Utah. The normal plant and litter cover on well-developed soils was found to be well dispersed—that is, with only small openings—upon two-thirds to three-fourths of the soil surface.

But plant residues do more than just protect the soil. Even though range management is directed primarily toward that objective, there are important auxiliary benefits. Together with organic matter from decaying roots, plant residues on the surface improve soil structure through increasing the aggregation of soil particles and increasing pore space. This effect increases the ability of the soil to absorb water quickly, so that much of the rainfall that runs off a bared, eroding surface is stored in the soil of good tilth and may subsequently be utilized in plant growth.

Studies in western Oregon show that a surface mulch promotes formation of large water-stable aggregates particularly and it conserves a significant amount of soil water. Similarly, in southern Arizona, infiltration of water was shown to be much greater on mulched than on unmulched plots. In this instance, a 20-percent increase in conserved moisture resulted in doubling forage production.

THE BASIC OBJECTIVE of range management—a dense and well-dispersed cover of vegetation and mulch that provides adequate protection and imparts desirable characteristics to the soil—is economically attainable on most ranges by managing the grazing.

Soil management is accomplished on perhaps as much as 90 percent of the range area almost solely by manipulating grazing animals in accordance with four rules of good range usage:

Grazing the kind or kinds of animals that will economically utilize and perpetuate the desirable forage plants growing naturally on each range;

Distributing livestock evenly to insure uniform use of forage on usable portions of each range unit;

Adjusting the grazing use of each unit seasonally to meet the growth requirements of the desired forage plants;

Adjusting the numbers of grazing animals to attain an intensity of forage use that will maintain normal forage and soil productivity.

These considerations are basic to economical livestock production and to the maintenance of forage and soil productivity on all ranges. We call them the cardinal principles of range management.

The kind or kinds of animals to graze on a particular range depend on the major forage plants or mixtures, range developments, poisonous plants and pests present, and on other factors.

Some ranges, the coarser grasslands of the Great Plains, for example, naturally support one predominant class of forage and are efficiently grazed by one kind of stock.

Many ranges support mixtures of grasses and broad-leaved herbs or woody plants. The proportions of forage classes in such mixtures tend to shift when sheep or cattle graze them year after year. Many such ranges may be utilized more efficiently and the desired forage balance may be maintained by stocking with both cattle and sheep and sometimes with goats as well, if other conditions are favorable. Care must be taken to replace a single kind of stock with the proper proportion of other kinds to avoid double use of the forage, but some mixed forage types may support more total animal units of grazing under dual use.

Grazing animals tend to concentrate on certain parts of ranges and to avoid others. The tendency varies with the kind of animal and is influenced by topography, the location and abundance of water, and other factors. Excessive concentration results in undesirable changes in cover, trampling damage, and erosion from "sore spots," while leaving areas of forage unused.

Well-spaced water developments, proper location and movement of salt and supplemental feeds, fencing, riding, and herding aid in obtaining more uniform grazing use on usable parts.

Grazing the plants before they have made much growth in early season may damage ranges. Physiological injury to the plants results from repeated grazing before they have an opportunity to make regrowth and manufacture plant foods. This period also coincides with a wet-soil condition on many mountain ranges. In attempting to obtain their food requirements from short, succulent forage under such conditions, animals uproot plants and puddle the soil. Reduced infiltration and excessive erosion commonly result. Early-season grazing on ranges having firm and moderately dry soil surfaces rarely causes appreciable damage if livestock are moved to other units while the forage is recovering.

In places where continuous use of the range must be made during the spring or summer, it is necessary ordinarily to delay grazing until after adequate forage has been produced and the soils are drier. Close grazing during the heading and flowering stages generally is most injurious to forage plants. Grazing should be slackened during this period, or the stock should be rotated to other parts of the range in such a way that each range unit is rested until after seed maturity one year in every three or four, to maintain the forage cover in a thrifty condition.

INTENSITY of grazing use markedly affects cover and soil.

Forage plants tolerate only a certain degree of foliage removal without physiological injury. Most of the important forage plants withstand removal of about 50 percent of the weight of their annual herbage production under rather ideal conditions. The popular rule of management— "graze half and leave half"—is a general guide.

But the rule has many exceptions. Ranges grazed after the forage plants have matured frequently tolerate closer use without injury. The more desirable shrubs on desert winter ranges in Utah withstand the removal of as much as 75 percent of the forage. Lighter summer use, on the order of 35 percent, or even less, of the better forage species generally is necessary to maintain soil stability and high production on mountain rangelands having steep slopes and erosive soils.

Tests of grazing intensity at the Manitou Experimental Forest in Colorado illustrate the comparative effects of moderate and heavy stocking upon the plants, range cover, and site. The study areas are situated in the ponderosa-pine zone and have predominantly granitic soils. Annual precipitation averages about 16 inches and is concentrated mostly during the summer months, a considerable proportion of it coming as sudden thundershowers. The perennial bunch-grasses, mainly Arizona fescue and mountain muhly, dominate the forage cover. Moderate grazing removed 30 to 40 percent of the grass herbage. Heavy grazing removed 50 percent or more of the grass herbage but with different effects after 9 years of use.

Heavy grazing reduced the growth of roots and aboveground parts of the major forage grasses, and some forage species produced fewer seedstalks. Other indications that the vigor of the major forage species is impaired by heavy grazing were a greater proportion of the plants with dead centers and a tendency for the clumps to break up into smaller units.

Range cover was composed predominantly of bunchgrasses on moderately grazed areas after 9 years of such treatment. Short grasses, especially blue grama, and weedy herbs had replaced much of the bunchgrass on heavily grazed range. Forage production also declined, and only about two-thirds as much litter remained on the heavily grazed areas as on the moderately grazed ranges.

Tests of water absorption revealed that the infiltration rate on the moderately grazed units was nearly twice (2.28 inches an hour) that of the heavily grazed ranges (1.18 inches an hour). Similarly, the amount of soil erosion occurring with each inch of surface runoff was nearly twice as much from heavily grazed ranges (263 pounds an acre) as from moderately grazed areas (121 pounds an acre).

The moderately grazed ranges produced 16 pounds of beef per acre and an average income of 864 dollars per section (640 acres). Heavily grazed areas produced 14.8 pounds of beef per acre and an average income of 473 dollars per section. Better forage conditions meant more finish on cattle grazing the moderately utilized ranges.

Many ranges have deteriorated and are in need of restoration. The choice of remedial measures on them depends on the degree of forage and site deple-

tion and the expenditures that can be justified by potential productivity and other benefits, as erosion control.

If a reasonable proportion of the desirable forage plants remains, improved grazing practices may accomplish the improvement economically. Lighter stocking may be all that is needed on many ranges.

DEFERRED GRAZING—withholding grazing until after seed matures—on a part of the range to permit natural revegetation and establishment of seedlings may hasten recovery. Other parts of the range may be similarly deferred later on. This deferred and rotation grazing is especially effective on bunchgrass ranges, which need seed production for natural revegetation.

Deferred grazing is practicable if the range is fenced into units so that the stock can be controlled. On large, unfenced ranges, fencing the watering facilities and withholding salt on areas in need of improvement is somewhat effective in obtaining deferred grazing. Herders can control the movements of sheep to avoid grazing specified units until after seed matures.

A once-over system of sheep grazing is employed on mountain rangelands that have high watershed values to avoid repeated use of forage and to reduce trailing. This practice has brought increased gains in lamb weights and improved conditions.

Measures to conserve soil and moisture plus proper grazing may hasten the recovery on some sites. Contour furrowing, pitting, and water spreading have improved some ranges.

CONTOUR FURROWING of rangelands helps to retain and store runoff water to stimulate greater growth of forage, especially on rundown ranges. On Great Plains ranges that have deteriorated to a short-grass sod, the taller, more productive grasses are increased. Small furrows, 4 to 6 inches in cross section and not more than 5 feet apart, are more effective than larger or wider spaced furrows in stimulating the vegetation. The retained moisture encourages the rapid spread of forage plants that have rootstalks and runners, and bunchgrasses may be stimulated to produce seed.

Contour furrows protect adjacent, lower lying lands from the effects of runoff and siltation. At the Central Great Plains Experimental Watershed in Nebraska, runoff was reduced 84 to 94 percent after native grasslands were contoured.

More elaborate contour trenches are built to restore deteriorated parts of mountain ranges. The Davis County watershed in the Wasatch Mountains of Utah is an example. During the 1920's and early 1930's, destructive mud-rock floods originated there on spots that had been heavily grazed, trampled, and bedded upon by sheep for many years. Contour trenches were built in the mid-1930's. The denuded areas were seeded to perennial grasses. The trenches held the water from torrential storms and hastened reestablishment of the plant cover. The vegetation restored the infiltration capacity of the soil. Surface runoff was controlled. Flooding stopped.

RANGE PITTING has been used increasingly on semiarid lands. An eccentric disk, with disks set 2 inches off center, is used to construct pits. Adjacent disks are set off center in different directions, and the machine gouges out pits that are separated by undisturbed sod. The small depressions hold a considerable volume of water, which stimulates forage growth and aids range recovery, especially in places where scant or uneven precipitation is largely lost by evaporation or runoff.

Pitting is particularly effective on short-grass ranges. At the Archer Field Station in Wyoming, pitting increased sheep-days of grazing by 22 percent and lamb gains by 19 percent, and left 25 percent more ungrazed grass at the end of the grazing season.

WATER SPREADING is a practical way to control erosion and the movement of silt and to convert runoff to useful purposes. Runoff is diverted from water courses—normal channels, arroyos, gullies—and spread over adjacent flood plains or valley floors. This method of flood irrigation may be controlled by a system of dams, dikes, and ditches. The commonest type of water-spreading system consists of a dam placed in the watercourse, with gradient ditches or terraces leading the water out to gentle slopes, where it is released through a system of dikes. Spreader systems are constructed so that operation is usually automatic whenever adequate runoff occurs; hence, sites suitable for water-spreading systems must be selected with care.

The construction of an effective water-spreading system usually is costly. Systems that are properly designed and constructed on suitable sites, however, may yield good returns on the investment through increased production of forage and livestock.

The Alzada water-spreading area in Montana increased over threefold in grazing values after treatment and showed an annual net return of 13 percent on the original investment.

After a water-spreading system was built on 800 acres of a 23,000-acre range in Montana, the treated area supported more livestock than the rest of the range. The increased forage production permitted the rancher to rest—and improve—the surrounding range.

Many millions of acres of rangeland support sparse or otherwise undesirable cover, which cannot be restored by grazing-management practices in our generation. A sizable proportion of it is abandoned cropland. Several decades will elapse before a productive cover of desirable forage plants and soil stability are restored on such sites by natural processes. Properly planned and conducted reseeding programs may restore much of this land to productive use in much less time, often within 2 or 3 years.

Ranges are seeded artificially to achieve several goals. Ranchers are seeding increasing acreages to accom-

640 YEARBOOK OF AGRICULTURE 1957

modate existing herds and make their enterprises more efficient and economical.

Research and experience in several regions have shown that grazing capacity may be increased severalfold by seeding. Seasonal balance of forage supplies is a problem on many ranges. Seeding to adapted cool-season grasses—crested wheatgrass and smooth bromegrass, for example—provides earlier forage and extends the productive pasturing season on many ranges. Such seeded pastures have made it possible to defer or lighten the use of native ranges. Consideration is being given to the feasibility of restoring browse on depleted big-game ranges by seeding and planting.

An increasing use is made of seeding to restore desirable soil and site conditions on disturbed areas—burned watersheds; skid trails, roads, and landings on cutover, forested ranges; and blowouts and dunes on sandy rangelands. Such conservation structures as gully plugs, check dams, dikes, and water diversion outlets are stabilized and maintained cheaply by establishing a suitable plant cover.

Soil restoration also is an important objective in the revegetation of abandoned croplands and depleted ranges. Studies in Kansas and Oklahoma indicated that only about 3 years was required for seeded native grass to refill cultivated land with grass roots to a depth of 4 feet and leave the soil in a condition comparable with that of a virgin sod. The grasses greatly improved the general physical condition of the soil and its ability to absorb water, retain moisture, and resist erosion. Soil fertility, however, was not improved when grasses were seeded without a legume. That points up a problem of considerable importance.

Experience and research indicate that the productivity of seeded grasses, particularly those that are not native to the site, tends to run out or the stand becomes sodbound unless fertilized or renovated frequently. These high-yielding stands eventually exhaust the nutrient reserves accumulated during periods when the site was occupied by sparse, low-producing vegetation. Adapted legumes seeded in mixtures with such grasses tend to maintain the production at a higher level, but perennial or self-seeding legumes adapted to the adverse conditions on most ranges are as yet generally lacking.

CONTROL OF UNDESIRABLE plants is one of the principal objectives of managed grazing. If undesirable species have gained the upper hand and dominate the site, however, mere manipulation of the grazing animals may take too long, and more direct action may be desired.

There are so many kinds of undesirable plants—for example, mesquite in the Southwest, rabbitbrush in the Intermountain area, and goatweed in the Northwest and California—and the techniques for their control are so varied that it will not be possible to list them all here. We mention a few general principles.

BURNING is used a great deal to control undesirable, nonsprouting shrubs, such as big sagebrush. It is inexpensive and effective for range improvement in certain circumstances. A serious drawback is that burning exposes the soil to erosion. It is especially serious when a highly inflammable cover type like cheatgrass develops after repeated burning. Another drawback is the encouragement burning gives to sprouting shrubs, which are even less desirable than the species destroyed.

Mechanical methods include grubbing by hand, plowing, disking, railing, harrowing, and beating with a flailing device. Junipers in the Southwest may be pushed over with a bulldozer or by chains dragged between tractors. Mechanical methods leave plant residues that protect the soil and sometimes prepare the soil for seeding. They may even be utilized as part of the seeding operation.

Chemicals have been used particularly against sagebrush. Because the plant cover is little disturbed, spraying is not likely to cause accelerated erosion. The chemicals commonly used include 2,4-D and 2,4,5-T. Like fire, these herbicides seem less effective in controlling species that sprout readily from the roots or stem crowns.

Insects have been used to control undesirable plants. Chrysomelid beetles have been used successfully in California and parts of the Northwest against goatweed in places where mechanical methods, fire, and spraying are useless.

A basic principle is that the destruction of the undesirable plants is not enough. They must be replaced with something better, or something worse may take their place.

Is there enough of an understory of desirable forage plants to take over the site? If not, seeding of adapted species should be made part of the plan. Are there undesirable species in the understory that would also be encouraged when the dominant species is destroyed? If so, it may be better to let well enough alone.

The control treatment must be adapted to the life cycle of the plant that is being removed. For example, it is best to plow or burn sagebrush in spring or early summer. To do so in late summer or fall while seed is being produced is almost certain to result in a heavy seedling stand and more sagebrush eventually than was present before the treatment.

Always after improvement efforts have been made, careful grazing management is essential, particularly when the plant cover has been greatly disturbed, there is danger of soil erosion, and the plant community has been opened up to invasion by undesirable species. Grazing freshly burned range, for example, may weaken the desirable forage species one is trying to invigorate and encourage the reestablishment of the undesirable species.

FERTILIZATION is an important part of the grassland economy where rain is plentiful, but its place on the range in drier regions is by no means established. We have little research or experience to indicate where, when, and how fertilizers can be used profitably on ranches.

Studies at scattered places in the West suggest some possibilities of improving the range by the wise use of fertilizers.

At Sunol, Calif., for example, unfertilized annual range produced an average of 1,284 pounds of forage an acre annually for 5 years, compared to 4,166 pounds on a similar area fertilized with 200 pounds an acre of ammonium phosphate-sulfate (16–20–0) annually. The grazing date in the spring was advanced by 6 weeks, and the length of the green-feed period was doubled. Fewer fluctuations in production occurred from year to year when fertilizer was used.

At the San Joaquin Experimental Range in California, application of sulfur-bearing fertilizers stimulated native clovers and improved the forage on soils of granitic origin where sulfur is deficient. Fertilization at a rate equivalent to 60 pounds of sulfur an acre applied every 3 years gave an average annual increase of air-dry forage of about 900 pounds an acre at a cost of about 4 dollars an acre for the fertilizer and spreading.

Some species use fertilizers more efficiently than others—a particularly significant point to bear in mind. For example, no amount of additional phosphorus would improve burclover growth on Placentia and San Joaquin soils in California even though the soils are deficient in phosphate. When rose, crimson, and subterranean clovers were seeded on phosphated plots, however, yields of forage increased from less than 1 thousand pounds an acre to more than 4 thousand pounds, and protein was increased more than sixfold.

Certain grasses use nitrogen more efficiently than others. In northern California, some reseeded perennial grasses, such as intermediate wheatgrass, have given outstanding responses to nitrogen. Native Idaho fescue has given little or no response, but sometimes has actually produced less with nitrogen than without.

Near Havre, Mont., yields of hay as high as 1 thousand pounds an acre annually for 6 years were obtained when barnyard manure was applied on native range. About 80 pounds an acre was obtained from untreated range. Near Mandan, N. Dak., nitrogen has increased the production of the native range and reseeded introduced species, such as crested wheatgrass, smooth bromegrass, and Russian wildrye.

From native grass on cleared virgin brushland at the Red Plains Conservation Experiment Station, Guthrie, Okla., 133 pounds of beef an acre were produced when phosphate and nitrogen fertilizers were applied. Only 84 pounds an acre were produced without fertilizer. This represents nearly a 60-percent increase in animal gain from fertilization at an annual rate equivalent to 100 pounds of superphosphate and 33 pounds of nitrogen to the acre.

Range grasses in some parts of southern Texas do not contain enough phosphorus to provide adequate nutrition for grazing livestock. Range fertilization is employed there to increase the yield of forage and to improve its phosphorus content. An experiment was conducted on the King Ranch near Falfurrias to determine the most practical methods of supplying phosphorus to range cattle and to determine the effect of phosphate on the yield and chemical composition of forage. Phosphate applied to such rangelands prevented phosphorus deficiency in cattle. The application of about 200 pounds of 48-percent triple superphosphate to the acre increased the yield and phosphorus content of forage for a period of 4 to 5 years.

A new band-seeding method of establishing pastures has shown promise in range seeding trials. The seed is drilled over bands of fertilizer placed 1 to 2 inches below the seed. Available fertilizer is thus made accessible to seedling plants.

Grasses

E. A. Hollowell

The most important grasses of which seed or vegetative propagating material is available in quantity are listed here.

The characterization of grass species and varieties as related to soils is not specific, because the interaction with climatic factors may greatly vary the growth responses of the plants to any set of soil conditions. Unfavorable factors such as acidity, alkalinity, salinity, and texture, which affect the adaptation of species, within limits may be compensated for by optimum conditions of other factors, such as moisture.

BEACHGRASSES (*Ammophila* species) are perennials. They grow in moderately acid to neutral soils and tolerate high salinity. They need shallow to deep, fine sand to loamy sands and moist to very moist conditions. They are benefited by applications of nitrogen. They are adapted to cool conditions and are winter hardy. They are used to control dunes and blowing soil.

American beachgrass (*A. breviligulata*)—see Beachgrasses.

European beachgrass (*A. arenaria*)—see Beachgrasses.

BERMUDA-GRASS (*Cynodon dactylon*) grows in shallow to deep, highly acid to neutral soils and is tolerant of high salinity. It likes gravelly loam to well-drained clay. It tolerates drought periods but prefers heavy moisture. Applications of nitrogen are beneficial. It is adapted to the Southern and Southwestern States.

The starred names differ from those in USDA Service and Regulatory Announcements No. 156, reprinted August 1956.

Coastal and Suwannee are better adapted to deep sands. Midland is hardier. Greenfield grows better at low nutrient levels.

BLUEGRASSES (*Poa*) comprise many perennial species, which are adapted to a wide range of soil and climatic conditions and are widely distributed throughout the United States.

Big bluegrass (*P. ampla*) grows in slightly acid to slightly alkaline soils. It is not tolerant of salinity. Soils should be of average depth or deep, gravelly loam to well-drained clay. It prefers moist conditions, although it tolerates drought. Applications of nitrogen are beneficial. A perennial, it is adapted to the Northwestern States.

Bulbous bluegrass (*P. bulbosa*) grows in moderately acid to slightly alkaline soils. It is not tolerant of salinity. Deep or moderately deep silt loam to poorly drained clay are suitable. It needs moist to very moist conditions. Applications of nitrogen are helpful. It is adapted to cool-summer temperatures. It is a perennial and is grown mostly in the coastal section of the West.

Canada bluegrass (*P. compreśsa*) grows in highly acid to neutral, shallow or moderately deep, loamy sand or poorly drained clay. It tolerates moist to very moist conditions but is not tolerant of salinity. Applications of nitrogen benefit it. This perennial is adapted mostly to the humid Northeastern States and grows at relatively low nutrient levels.

Kentucky bluegrass (*P. pratensis*), a perennial, grows in slightly acid to slightly alkaline soils of average depth, deep silt loam, and well-drained clay. It needs moist to very moist conditions. Available phosphorus and calcium stimulate growth. It is adapted to the Northern States and upper South, particularly in places where available phosphate is abundant. It is adversely affected by high summer temperatures.

The rough bluegrass (*P. trivialis*) is a perennial that grows in moderately acid to neutral soils of shallow to average depth. Sandy loams to poorly drained clays are preferred. It is adapt-ed to cool conditions of the Northern States. It is somewhat tolerant of shade.

BLUESTEM GRASSES, of many species, differ widely in adaptation to soil conditions. They grow in slightly acid to moderately alkaline soils. They are benefited slightly by application of nitrogen. They are adapted to a wide range of climatic conditions and are grown mainly in the Great Plains.

The following are the more important perennial bluestems.

Angleton grass (*Andropogon nodosus*) grows in moderately acid to neutral soils of average depth to deep, fine sand, and poorly drained clays. It is tolerant of high salinity. It requires moist to heavy-moisture conditions, but may survive periods of drought. It is adapted to the gulf coast region. The application of nitrogen is helpful.

Australian bluestem (*A. intermedius*) grows in fine sand to sandy loam of average depth or deeper. It is drought resistant. It is adapted to the southern Great Plains. It is not hardy.

Big bluestem (*A. gerardi**) grows in slightly acid to slightly alkaline soils and in sandy loam to poorly drained clay of average depth. It tolerates dry to moist conditions. It is adapted to the central Great Plains.

Caucasian bluestem (*A. caucasicus*) is benefited by applications of nitrogen.

Little bluestem (*A. scoparius*) is more winter hardy and is better adapted to the northern Great Plains and to sandy soils on the southern high plains and to clay and sandy soils with good moisture.

Sand bluestem (*A. hallii*) grows in deep, fine sand to silt loams. It is adapted to conditions in the central and southern Great Plains.

Yellow bluestem (*A. ischaemum*) is tolerant of moderate salinity, is drought resistant, and is particularly adapted for use on eroded soils.

BROMEGRASSES (*Bromus*) include many species of perennials and annuals, which grow under widely different conditions and are benefited by the application of nitrogen. The perennials are adapted to the Northern States. The winter annuals grow in the South and the western coastal sections.

Field bromegrass (*B. arvensis*) grows in moderately acid to neutral soils and is not tolerant of salinity. Shallow to deep, sandy loam to poorly drained clay and moist to heavy-moisture conditions are preferred. It is a winter annual in Eastern and Pacific States.

Harlan bromegrass (*B. stamineus*) is a winter annual in California. (See Mountain bromegrass.)

Meadow bromegrass (*B. erectus*), a perennial, is widely distributed in the Northern States. (See Mountain bromegrass.)

Mountain bromegrass (*B. carinatus**) grows in slightly acid to slightly alkaline soil and is not tolerant of salinity. It grows in shallow to deep, fine sand to clay and requires moist conditions. This perennial is adapted to the Rocky Mountain and Pacific coastal regions.

Rescuegrass (*B. catharticus*) is adapted to the coastal section of the Western States and the lower South. It is a winter annual or a short-lived perennial.

Smooth bromegrass (*B. inermis*) grows in moderately acid to moderately alkaline soils and is not tolerant of salinity. It does best on deep sandy loam and well-drained clays that are moist. A perennial, it is widely adapted in the Central and Northern States.

BUFFALOGRASS (*Buchloë dactyloides*) grows in slightly acid to moderately alkaline soils. It tolerates slight salinity. It needs shallow to moderately deep loam or well-drained clays and dry to moist conditions. It is drought resistant and is benefited slightly by applications of nitrogen. A warm-season perennial, it is particularly adapted to the heavy soils of the Great Plains.

BULBOUS BARLEY (*Hordeum bulbosum*) grows in neutral to moderately alkaline soil and is tolerant of slight salinity. It grows in sandy loam to clay loam of shallow or average depth. It needs moist to very moist conditions but will tolerate drought periods. It is moderately benefited by applications of nitrogen. It grows in winter, is adapted to the central part of the coastal region of the West, and is useful for eroded soils.

CANARYGRASSES include many perennial and annual species of *Phalaris*. They grow under a wide range of soil and climatic conditions.

Hardinggrass (*P. tuberosa* var. *stenoptera*) grows in slightly acid to highly alkaline soils and tolerates moderate salinity. It thrives in moist or very moist silt loam or poorly drained clay of average or greater depth. The application of nitrogen is helpful. It grows in winter and spring; in summer it remains dormant in the tuber stage. It grows in heavy soils in Oregon and California and to a limited extent in the gulf coast section of Texas.

Reed canarygrass (*P. arundinacea*), a perennial, grows in slightly acid to neutral, shallow to deep, silt loam to muck in moist or swampy conditions. It is not tolerant of salinity. It is widely grown in the Northern States. It will stand flooding for short periods. Nitrogen is beneficial.

CARPETGRASS (*Axonopus affinis*) grows in highly acid to slightly acid soils of shallow to average depth and of fine sand to clay loam. It requires a great deal of moisture and tolerates swampy conditions. It is benefited slightly by application of nitrogen. It is widely grown in the gulf coast section of the South. It is a perennial, warm-season grass, particularly adapted to low-lying sands. It does not tolerate salinity.

Centipedegrass (*Eremochloa ophiuroides*) grows in highly acid to neutral soils and is not tolerant of salinity. It needs shallow to deep, gravelly loam to loam and moist to very moist conditions. It is used mainly as a lawn grass and is best adapted to the sandy soils of the Southern States. It grows at low nutrient levels and is shade tolerant.

Desert saltgrass (*Distichlis stricta*) grows

in slightly acid to highly alkaline soils and will tolerate high salinity. It grows in loam or poorly drained clay of shallow to average depth and moist to swampy conditions. It will tolerate drought, however. A perennial, it is adapted to the low salty soils of the intermountain and west coast States.

DROPSEEDS include many species of *Sporobolus*, which grow in a wide range of soil and climatic conditions. They are adapted to the southern Great Plains and the Southwestern States. They are benefited slightly by the application of nitrogen.

Alkali sacaton (S. airoides) grows in neutral to highly alkaline soil and is tolerant of high salinity. It grows in fine sand to clay loam and is a perennial. It stands dry conditions.

Sacatongrass (S. wrightii) is less tolerant of alkaline and saline conditions and requires more moisture than alkali sacaton.

Sand dropseed (S. cryptandrus), a perennial, grows in neutral to moderately alkaline soil. It is tolerant of slight salinity and dry conditions.

FESCUE (*Festuca* species) is adapted to a wide range of soil and climatic conditions in the Northern States and in the South at higher altitudes.

Arizona fescue (F. arizonica) grows in slightly acid to neutral soil of shallow to average depth—silt loam to clay loam and dry to moist conditions. It is benefited slightly by applications of nitrogen. It grows in open pineland and is adapted to high altitudes of the Southwestern States.

Hard fescue (F. ovina var. *duriuscula)* will tolerate drier sites and lower nutrient levels than sheep fescue.

Idaho fescue (F. idahoensis) grows in slightly acid to slightly alkaline soil of average depth—loamy sand to well-drained clay and dry to moist conditions. It is slightly benefited by applications of nitrogen. It is adapted to cool to cold temperatures in the Central and Northern Intermountain States. It does not tolerate salinity.

Meadow fescue (F. elatior) grows in highly acid to neutral soil of shallow to average depth—silt loam to poorly drained clay and moist conditions. It is adapted to humid parts of the Central States and the Pacific Northwest coastal region. It is not fully hardy.

Red fescue (F. rubra) grows in moderately acid to neutral soils. It does not tolerate salinity. It grows in deep, sandy loam to well-drained clay. It needs moist to very moist conditions and is benefited by applications of nitrogen. It is adapted to the Northern States. It tolerates shade and is used widely in lawns.

Sheep fescue (F. ovina) grows in highly acid to neutral soils and is not tolerant of salinity. It prefers gravelly loam and well-drained clay. It is used mainly as a lawn grass and is adapted to shady sites in the Northern States.

Tall fescue (F. arundinacea) grows in highly acid to moderately alkaline soils. It needs shallow to deep, gravelly loam to poorly drained clay and moist to very moist conditions. It is widely adapted in the North, upper South, and Southwest. It will tolerate short periods of drought.

FOXTAIL MILLET (*Setaria italica*) grows in moderately acid to slightly alkaline soils. It is not tolerant of salinity. Deep, sandy loam to well-drained clay, moist to very moist are preferred. Applications of nitrogen are beneficial. It is a summer annual and is widely adapted throughout the Northern States and the Great Plains. It will tolerate short periods of drought.

GRAMAGRASSES include many species of *Bouteloua*. The most important are perennials. They grow in neutral to moderately alkaline soil and are not tolerant of salinity. They require soil of average depth—silt loam to well-drained clay—and dry to moist conditions. They are adapted to the Great Plains and intermountain regions. They are drought resistant and are benefited slightly by the application of nitrogen.

Black grama (B. eriopoda) tolerates

slight salinity and is more drought resistant than other gramagrasses.

Blue grama (B. gracilis) is widely adapted from relatively moist to dry conditions and to sandy and hard lands.

Hairy grama (B. hirsuta) is particularly adapted to sandy, rocky, caliche soils.

Side-oats grama (B. curtipendula) requires more moisture than blue grama.

INDIANGRASS, YELLOW *(Sorghastrum nutans)* requires fairly deep soils and reasonable moisture.

JAPANESE LAWNGRASS *(Zoysia japonica)* grows in acid to neutral soils. It is not tolerant of salinity. Shallow to deep, gravelly loam to poorly drained clay and moist to very moist conditions are preferred. It is tolerant of short droughts. It is benefited by applications of nitrogen, although it grows at relatively low nutrient level. It is a summer-growing perennial and is used for lawns. It is adapted to the humid Eastern States that have high summer temperatures.

JAPANESE MILLET *(Echinochloa crusgalli* var. *frumentacea)* grows in moderately acid to neutral soils and is not tolerant of salinity. Soils should be of shallow to average depth and sandy loam to well-drained clay. It needs heavy moisture and is benefited by applications of nitrogen. A summer annual, it is adapted to the Northeastern States.

JOHNSONGRASS *(Sorghum halepense)* grows in slightly acid to slightly alkaline soils. It is not tolerant of salinity. Soils should be of average to deep silt loam to poorly drained clay, moist to very moist. Applications of nitrogen are beneficial. It is adapted to the Southern States. A perennial, it grows well in fertile soils.

LOVEGRASS *(Eragrostis)* has many annual and perennial species, few of which have agricultural value. Some species are adapted to sands to clay loams and dry or moist conditions.

Boer lovegrass (E. chloromelas), a per-

ennial, grows in slightly acid to moderately alkaline soils and is not tolerant of salinity. It likes gravelly loam to clay soils. It is adapted to the Southwestern States. It is drought resistant but not cold tolerant.

Lehmann lovegrass (E. lehmanniana) (see Boer lovegrass).

Sand lovegrass (E. trichodes) is particularly adapted to sandy soils and to the central and southern Great Plains.

Weeping lovegrass (E. curvula) is most widely adapted, especially on dry, sandy soils and is used in the dry regions in the South and Southwest.

MANILA LAWNGRASS* *(Zoysia matrella)* is adapted to conditions of the Southeastern States. (See Japanese lawngrass.)

MEADOW FOXTAIL *(Alopecurus pratensis)* grows in moderately acid to neutral soils. It will tolerate slight salinity. It needs soil of average depth to deep, silt loam and clay loam and moist to very moist conditions. It tolerates flooding and is benefited by applications of nitrogen. It is a perennial, cool-season grass, particularly adapted to the Pacific Northwest.

MESQUITEGRASSES *(Hilaria)* include several species that grow in neutral to moderately alkaline soils and are tolerant of moderate salinity. They grow in shallow to deep sandy loam to clay loam in very dry or dry conditions. They are perennials and are adapted to dry conditions of the Southwest.

Curly-mesquite (H. belangeri) is more abundant in low desertlike sites.

Galleta (H. jamesii) will tolerate drier sites.

Tobosa (H. mutica) (see Galleta.)

NEEDLEGRASS *(Stipa)* has many species that are adapted to a wide range of soil and climatic conditions. They are generally adapted to the northern Great Plains and the intermountain and Pacific coast regions.

Green needlegrass (S. viridula) is a perennial, adapted to the northern Great

Plains. It is benefited by applications of nitrogen.

Needle-and-thread grass (*S. comata*) grows in neutral soils to moderately alkaline soils and are not tolerant of salinity. Soils should be shallow to moderately deep, sandy loam to well-drained clay. They stand dry to moist conditions and are benefited slightly by applications of nitrogen. They are adapted to the northern Great Plains and intermountain regions.

Purple needlegrass (*S. pulchra*) is adapted to coastal ranges of the West.

ORCHARDGRASS (*Dactylis glomerata*) grows in moderately acid to neutral soils. It is not tolerant of salinity and likes shallow to deep gravelly loam to poorly drained clay and moist to very moist conditions. It is benefited by applications of nitrogen. It is a perennial and is widely adapted in the Northern States and the upper South.

PANGOLAGRASS (*Digitaria decumbens*) grows in highly acid to neutral soils and is not tolerant of salinity. It needs moist to very moist conditions but will tolerate periods of drought. It is adapted to the sandy soils of Florida but requires added fertility. It is a perennial. It is not winter hardy.

PANICUM GRASSES (*Panicum*) include many annual and perennial species, which are adapted to a wide range of soil and climatic conditions. They are widely distributed, mainly in the warmer climates.

Blue panicgrass (*P. antidotale*) grows in moderately acid to slightly alkaline soils. It is not tolerant of salinity. Sandy loam to well-drained, fertile clay of average depth or deep are preferred. It is adapted to southern parts of the Great Plains and the Southwest. It is drought resistant but not winter hardy.

Guineagrass (*P. maximum*) grows in highly acid to slightly acid soils and is not tolerant of salinity. A perennial, it is adapted to subtropical and tropical conditions and requires applications of nitrogen.

Paragrass (*P. purpurascens*) grows in highly acid to neutral soils and is not tolerant of salinity. It requires moist to very moist conditions and tolerates some flooding. It is benefited by applications of nitrogen. It is subtropical to tropical in adaptation. It is a perennial and is propagated vegetatively.

Proso millet (*P. miliaceum*) grows in moderately acid or neutral and shallow or deep, sandy loam in dry to moist conditions. It is benefited by an application of nitrogen. A summer annual, it is cultivated for seed in the central and northern Great Plains.

Switchgrass (*P. virgatum*), a perennial, is adapted mainly to the central and southern parts of the Great Plains. It prefers sandy loams that are reasonably well supplied with moisture.

Vine mesquitegrass (*P. obtusum*) grows in neutral to moderately alkaline soils. It tolerates slight salinity. Soils should be of shallow to average depth and sandy loam to well-drained clay. It prefers dry conditions. A perennial, it grows in the Southwestern States and is drought resistant.

PASPALUM GRASSES (*Paspalum*) include many perennial species, which grow in highly acid to neutral soils—shallow to deep, gravelly loam to poorly drained clay and moist to swampy conditions. They are adapted principally to the Gulf Coast States and California. They are not hardy. Some species grow when nutrient levels are relatively low.

Bahiagrass (*P. notatum*) is adapted to drier sites and low nutrient levels.

Dallisgrass (*P. dilatatum*) requires higher nutrient levels than other species and is less adapted to fine sand and loam sand.

PENNISETUM GRASSES (*Pennisetum*) include many annual and perennial species, which grow in a wide range of soil and moisture conditions. They are adapted to climates in the South.

Buffelgrass (*P. ciliare*), a perennial, grows in slightly acid to slightly alkaline soils and is tolerant of slight salinity. Soils should be of average depth—

fine sand to well-drained clay. It stands dry to moist conditions and is moderately drought resistant. It grows in southern Texas and is particularly adapted to sandy soils. It requires applications of nitrogen. It is not hardy. Blue buffel is better on heavy soils.

Kikuyugrass (*P. clandestinum*) is a perennial that grows in neutral to moderately alkaline soils. It is tolerant of moderate salinity. Shallow to deep, fine sand to well-drained clay are preferred. It is adapted to subtropical and tropical conditions. It grows in California.

Napiergrass (*P. purpureum*) grows in highly acid to neutral soils. It does not tolerate salinity. Its preferred soils are of average depth or deep, fine sand or clay loam. This perennial requires moist or very moist conditions. It is benefited by an application of nitrogen. It is adapted to subtropical or tropical conditions. It grows in Florida.

Pearl millet (*P. glaucum*) grows in highly acid to neutral soils and is not tolerant of salinity. Deep, fine sand or loam are best. It requires a great deal of moisture and is benefited by nitrogen. It is a summer annual adapted to the South.

PERENNIAL VELDTGRASS * (*Ehrharta calycina*) grows in neutral to moderately alkaline soil. It is tolerant of slight salinity and likes shallow to deep loam and well-drained clay and dry to moist conditions. It is benefited slightly by an application of nitrogen. It is adapted to central and coastal areas of California. It is a drought-resistant perennial.

REDTOP AND BENTGRASSES (*Agrostis*) include many species that grow in highly acid to neutral soils and are not tolerant of salinity. Shallow, moist, gravelly loam to muck are preferred. They tolerate swampy conditions and benefit from the application of nitrogen. They grow when nutrient levels are relatively low. They are cool-season grasses and are suited to humid sections of the Northern States.

Colonial bentgrass (*A. tenuis*), *creeping bentgrass* (*A. palustris*), and *redtop* (*A. alba*) are important perennials.

RHODESGRASS (*Chloris gayana*) grows in moderately acid to highly alkaline soils. It tolerates moderate salinity. Soils of average depth to deep, loam and well-drained clay are preferred. It tolerates dry conditions. Applications of nitrogen are beneficial in the Southwestern States. It is a perennial but is not hardy.

RICEGRASSES (*Oryzopsis*) comprise many species, which grow in slightly acid to moderately alkaline soils and are tolerant of slight salinity. They thrive in sandy loam to clay loam that is of average depth or deeper. They stand very dry to dry conditions and are tolerant of wide ranges of temperature. They are mainly adapted to the western intermountain region. They are benefited slightly by application of nitrogen.

Indian ricegrass (*O. hymenoides*) is drought resistant. It is a perennial.

Smilo (*O. miliacea*) tolerates dry or moist conditions. It is grown in California in places that have wet winters and dry summers.

RYEGRASSES are annual and short-lived perennial species of *Lolium*. They grow in highly acid to neutral soils and are not tolerant of salinity. Shallow to deep, fine sand to poorly drained clay are suitable, as are moist to very moist conditions. They are benefited by the application of nitrogen. Some species are widely adapted in most States.

Italian ryegrass (*L. multiflorum*) is adapted as a winter annual in the South and as a summer annual in the North.

Perennial ryegrass (*L. perenne*) is a short-lived perennial. It is adapted to conditions of the Pacific Northwest and limited areas of the Northeast.

ST. AUGUSTINEGRASS (*Stenotaphrum secundatum*) grows in highly acid to slightly alkaline soils. It is not tolerant of salinity. It grows in shallow to deep, gravelly loam to muck in wet or swampy conditions. It is benefited by applications of nitrogen. It is adapted to the gulf coast region. It is used mostly for shady lawns. It is a perennial.

SUDANGRASS (*Sorghum sudanense**) grows in moderately acid to neutral soils of average depth or deep, loamy sand to well-drained clay. It requires moist conditions although it tolerates drought periods after it is established. It is benefited by the application of nitrogen under moist conditions. It is a summer annual adapted to localities of high summer temperatures.

TALL OATGRASS (*Arrhenatherum elatius*) is a short-lived perennial that grows in moderately acid to neutral soils and is moderately tolerant of salinity. Soils should be of shallow to average depth and loam to poorly drained clay. It requires moist to very moist conditions but thrives in rich, well-drained soils. It is adapted to the Northern States.

TIMOTHY (*Phleum pratense*) grows in highly acid to neutral soils. It is not tolerant of salinity. It is benefited by applications of nitrogen. It is widely adapted in the Northern States in sandy loam or poorly drained clay.

VELVETGRASS (*Holcus lanatus*) grows in highly acid to slightly acid soils. It is not tolerant of salinity. Soils should be of shallow to average depth and fine sand to poorly drained clay. It requires heavy moisture. It is benefited by applications of nitrogen, although it grows at a low nutrient level. It is adapted to the Northern States and the upper South. It will tolerate swampy sites. It is mostly a weed.

WHEATGRASSES (*Agropyron*) include many native and introduced species. They grow under a wide range of soil conditions but are not adapted to acid soils. Some species tolerate salinity and are adapted to the drier sites. They are benefited by applications of nitrogenous fertilizers when the shortage of moisture is not acute. They are widely distributed in the Western States.

Beardless wheatgrass (*A. inerme*) is slightly more tolerant of drought in the Pacific Northwest, where it is best adapted, than crested wheatgrass.

Bluebunch wheatgrass (*A. spicatum*) requires semihumid conditions and a higher nutrient level.

Crested wheatgrass (*A. desertorum*) grows in neutral to slightly alkaline soils. It is tolerant of moderate salinity, gravelly loam or well-drained clay of average depth, and dry to moist conditions.

Fairway wheatgrass (*A. cristatum*) is better adapted to extreme northern conditions than crested wheatgrass.

Intermediate wheatgrass (*A. intermedium*) is less drought tolerant and requires a higher nutrient level. It is adapted to well-drained, sandy loam to clay loam. It is less hardy.

Pubescent wheatgrass (*A. trichophorum*) tolerates a lower nutrient level than intermediate wheatgrass.

Quackgrass (*A. repens*) grows in highly acid to neutral soils. It is not tolerant of salinity. Soils should be of average depth to deep, fine sand to clay loam. It demands moist to very moist conditions. It is benefited by applications of nitrogen. It is adapted to the humid Northern States. It is weedy.

Siberian wheatgrass (*A. sibericum*) is better adapted to sandy soils having hardpans than crested wheatgrass.

Slender wheatgrass (*A. trachycaulum*) requires more moisture than crested wheatgrass.

Streambank wheatgrass (*A. riparium*) is tolerant of heavy moisture. It forms dense sod for waterways.

Tall wheatgrass (*A. elongatum*) tolerates poor drainage and high salinity.

Thickspike wheatgrass (*A. dasystachyum*) (see Crested wheatgrass).

Western wheatgrass (*A. smithii*) is better adapted to moist swales and has a wider range of climatic adaptation.

WILDRYE includes many perennial species of *Elymus*. They grow in a wide range of soil and climatic conditions. Some are benefited by the application of nitrogen. At least one species is found in nearly every State.

Blue wildrye (*E. glaucus*) grows on drier sites than Siberian wildrye.

Canada wildrye (*E. canadensis*) grows in highly acid to moderately alkaline soils and tolerates moderate salinity. It requires shallow to deep, gravelly loam to clay and moist to very moist conditions. It is benefited by the application of nitrogen. It is a widely adapted species.

Giant wildrye (*E. condensatus*) grows in neutral to moderately alkaline soils. It is tolerant to moderate salinity. A perennial, it needs shallow to deep, stony loam to well-drained clay and very dry to moist conditions. It is benefited slightly by the application of nitrogen. It is moderately drought resistant and is widely distributed throughout the dry areas of the West.

Russian wildrye (*E. junceus*) grows in neutral to moderately alkaline soils. It tolerates high salinity. It requires soil of average depth to deep, sandy loam to clay loam and dry to moist conditions. It requires a high nutrient level and is benefited by applications of nitrogen. It is particularly adapted to the northern parts of the Great Plains and farther west.

Siberian wildrye (*E. giganteus*) grows in slightly acid to moderately alkaline soil. It is not tolerant of salinity. It tolerates dry to moist conditions and is benefited slightly by applications of nitrogen. It is particularly useful for the stabilization of inland sand dunes but is not adapted to coastal conditions.

Legumes

E. A. Hollowell

The legumes listed here are those of which seed is available and which are of greatest importance in agriculture.

All of those I list here are benefited by applications of calcium, phospho-

rus, or potassium when the supply in the soil is exhausted or unavailable.

Trace elements may have to be supplied to the plants for high yield of forage and seed and for persistence. Such needs are mostly of local occurrence and are related to soils of specific texture and origin.

Legumes vary in their ability to make growth at different levels of soil acidity and alkalinity, but slightly acid to neutral soils are generally best.

Nitrogen is an essential nutrient for all legumes. Inoculated legumes can get the nitrogen they require from the air through the interaction of compatible symbiotic nitrogen-fixing bacteria, which infect the roots and cause nodules to form on them.

Soil texture is an important factor among the water and temperature relationships that different species require for maximum growth. High yields of forage and seed and the persistence of plants reflect the interaction of favorable climatic and soil factors. Within limits, if the other factors are favorable, plants can tolerate one or more unfavorable conditions, which, however, cause variations in the range of responses.

ALFALFA (*Medicago sativa*) grows in slightly alkaline soils of average depth to deep, sandy loam to well-drained clay. It tolerates slight salinity, but it will not tolerate wet, poorly drained soil. Moist conditions are needed for seedling establishment.

Alfalfa tolerates periods of drought if moisture is available to the roots. It is benefited by applications of mineral nutrients when needed. Its requirements of available minerals are high. It is widely adapted to different climates if proper varieties are used.

ALYCECLOVER (*Alysicarpus vaginalis*) grows in highly acid to neutral soils. It is not tolerant of salinity. The soils may be of shallow to average depth

---

The starred names differ from those in USDA Service and Regulatory Announcements No. 156, reprinted August 1956.

and fine sand to silt loams. It requires moist or heavy-moisture conditions. Applications of mineral nutrients when needed are beneficial. It is a summer annual and is particularly adapted to sandy soils of the Gulf Coast States. It requires high temperatures and a long growing season.

CLOVERS (TRUE) (*Trifolium* species) grow under a wide range of soil and climatic conditions. One species tolerates moderate salinity. It requires available mineral nutrients of phosphorus, calcium, and potassium, which must be applied if the soil lacks them. The many species of true clovers thrive in cool, humid climates and under irrigation. They are perennials and winter annuals. They have restricted use as summer annuals.

Alsike clover (*Trifolium hybridum*) grows in moderately acid to neutral soil. It is not tolerant of salinity. It needs shallow to deep, silt loam, or muck soils and moist to heavy-moisture conditions. It tolerates swampy conditions for short periods. A perennial, it behaves as a biennial in the Northern States. It is particularly valuable for poorly drained soils. It is grown as a winter annual in Southern States.

Ball clover (*Trifolium nigrescens*) grows in moderately acid to neutral soils of shallow to average depth, and of fine sand to clay. It is not tolerant of salinity. It makes growth at a relatively low nutrient level. A winter annual, it is adapted to the Southern States.

Berseem clover (*Trifolium alexandrinum*) grows in slightly acid to slightly alkaline soil. It tolerates slight salinity in soils of average depth to deep, silt loams to poorly drained clays. It needs moist conditions. A winter annual, it is the least winter hardy of all clovers. It is grown successfully in southern California, Arizona, New Mexico, and parts of southern Texas.

Cluster clover (*Trifolium glomeratum*) grows in moderately acid to neutral soils. It is not tolerant of salinity. Soils should be shallow or of average depth and fine sand to silt loam. It needs moist to heavy-moisture conditions and is best adapted to conditions of southern Mississippi. It is a winter annual and is restricted in adaptation.

Crimson clover (*Trifolium incarnatum*) thrives in soils that are moderately acid to neutral and shallow to deep, fine sand to well-drained clay. It needs moist to heavy-moisture conditions, but does not thrive in waterlogged soils. It is not tolerant of salinity. It is widely adapted as a winter annual in the southern and Pacific regions and as a summer annual in northern Maine.

Lappa clover (*Trifolium lappaceum*) grows in neutral to slightly alkaline soils and loam to poorly drained clays of shallow or average depth. Ample moisture is needed. It does not tolerate salinity. It is a winter annual, specifically adapted to wet, heavy soils in the lower Southern States.

Large hop clover (*Trifolium campestre**) grows in moderately acid to neutral soils. It is not tolerant of salinity. Soils should be shallow to deep, ranging from gravelly loam to clay. Moist to very moist conditions are required, but nutrient levels can be relatively low. A winter annual, it is adapted to the Southern States and coastal sections in the West.

Small hop clover (*Trifolium dubium*) is more tolerant of unfavorable climate and low nutrient levels than large hop clover, but otherwise requires similar conditions.

Persian clover (*Trifolium resupinatum*) grows in slightly acid to slightly alkaline soils of average depth, deep silt loam, or poorly drained clay that are moist to very moist. It is a winter annual, especially adapted to low, heavy, wet soils of the Southern States and coastal sections of the West. It is not tolerant of salinity.

Red clover (*Trifolium pratense*) will grow in moderately acid to neutral soils, deep, sandy loam, and well-drained clay soils. It does not stand salinity. It is a perennial but behaves mostly as a biennial in the Northern States or a winter annual in the South. It has wide adaptation throughout most of the United States. It needs plenty of moisture.

Rose clover (*Trifolium hirtum*) grows in slightly acid soils to slightly alkaline soils of shallow to average depth, silt loams, and well-drained clay. It needs moist to heavy-moisture conditions. A winter annual, it is adapted to hill sites of California rangelands.

Strawberry clover (*Trifolium fragiferum*) grows in neutral to slightly alkaline soil. It tolerates moderate salinity. It grows in shallow to deep, sandy loam to poorly drained clay. It needs moist to heavy-moisture conditions. It tolerates flooding. It is a perennial and is adapted to the poorly drained, salty soils of the Western States.

Striata clover (*Trifolium striatum*) grows in slightly acid to slightly alkaline soils of average depth to deep, loam to poorly drained clay. It is not tolerant of salinity. It requires moist to heavy-moisture conditions. It is a winter annual adapted to heavy, limy soils in the South.

Sub clover (*Trifolium subterraneum*) grows in moderate acid to neutral soils. It is not tolerant of salinity or waterlogged soils. It prefers shallow or deep, gravelly loam or well-drained clay. It is adapted to the coastal section of the west coast and parts of the South. It is a winter annual. Varieties appear to differ in adaptation to different soil conditions.

Whiteclover (*Trifolium repens*) grows in moderately acid to slightly alkaline soils. It is not tolerant of salinity. It needs shallow to deep, fine sand or poorly drained clays and moist to heavy-moisture conditions. It is widely adapted throughout most of the United States. A perennial, it behaves mostly as a winter annual in the South and as a biennial and perennial in the Northern States. Varieties differ in nutrient requirements for high production. Ladino has a high requirement of nutrients.

COWPEA (*Vigna sinensis*) grows in highly acid to neutral soil. It is not tolerant of salinity. It needs soils of shallow to average depth, fine sand to well-drained clay, and moist to heavy-moisture conditions. It is benefited by the application of mineral nutrients when needed, but it will grow at relatively low levels of nutrients. It is a summer annual and has many varieties. It is adapted to the South.

CROWN VETCH (*Coronilla varia*) grows in highly acid to neutral soils. It is not tolerant of salinity and requires shallow to deep, gravelly loam to well-drained clay soils and moist to heavy-moisture conditions. Applications of mineral nutrients, when needed, are beneficial. It is a perennial and is unpalatable to livestock. It is adapted to a wide range of conditions in the Northern States.

FIELDPEA (*Pisum sativum*) is one species, of several types, which grow in moderately acid to neutral soils of average depth or in deep, fine sand or clay loam. It prefers moist to heavy-moisture conditions. It is benefited by the application of mineral nutrients, when needed. It requires cool temperatures. It is a summer annual in the Northern States and a winter annual in the Southern States. The Austrian winter fieldpea is more winter hardy than the other types.

GUAR (*Cyamopsis tetragonoloba*) grows in moderately acid to moderately alkaline soils. It is tolerant of moderate salinity. Soils of average depth to deep, fine sand to well-drained clay loam are all right for it. Guar requires moist soil for stand establishment; thereafter it will tolerate dry conditions. It is benefited by an application of mineral nutrients when needed. A summer annual, it is adapted to the hot climate and long, dry growing season of the Southwestern States.

INDIGO (*Indigofera*) includes two species that grow in highly acid to neutral soils. They are not tolerant of salinity. Soils may be of shallow to average depth and fine sand to clay loam,

Moist to high-moisture conditions are needed. They are subtropical and tropical plants—summer annuals and perennials that require high temperatures and a long growing season. Some species are toxic to livestock.

Creeping indigo (*I. endecaphylla*), a perennial, is toxic to livestock. It is grown mostly in Puerto Rico.

Hairy indigo (*I. hirsuta*) is an annual. It has limited adaptation to sandy soils in Florida.

KUDZU (*Pueraria lobata**) grows in highly acid to neutral soils. It is not tolerant of salinity. Shallow to deep, gravelly loam and well-drained clay and moist to heavy-moist conditions are suitable. It is benefited by the application of mineral nutrients when they are needed, although the plants can utilize nutrients from relatively unavailable sources. It is a perennial with a viny type of growth. It is adapted to the Southern States. It is not hardy.

LESPEDEZA (*Lespedeza* species) has several annual and perennial species that grow in highly acid to slightly acid soils but do not tolerate salinity. Shallow soils and soils of average depth and gravelly loam to clay loam soils are suitable. Moist to heavy-moisture conditions are needed. Mineral nutrients may be needed. It is grown mostly in the Southern States. It is tolerant of high summer temperatures and relatively low nutrient levels and requires a relatively long growing season.

Bicolor lespedeza (*L. bicolor*) is a perennial, woody species, used mostly for erosion control and bird feed. It is adapted best to loam and clay soils.

Korean lespedeza (*L. stipulacea*) is an annual.

Sericea lespedeza (*L. cuneata*) is a perennial that is less palatable than the annual species.

Striate lespedeza (*L. striata*) is an annual that requires a longer growing season than Korean lespedeza.

LUPINES comprise many annual and perennial species, which grow in high-

ly acid to neutral soils and are not tolerant of salinity. Soils are shallow to deep, gravelly loam to loam. Moist to heavy-moisture conditions are needed. Applications of mineral nutrients may be beneficial, but the lupines grow at low nutrient levels.

Species of agricultural value are grown as winter annuals. They generally are adapted to the Gulf States. Some species are toxic to livestock.

Blue lupine (*Lupinus angustifolius*) is of two types—bitter blue, which is toxic to livestock, and sweet blue, which is palatable.

Yellow lupine (*L. luteus*) is the least hardy of the listed species.

White lupine (*L. albus*) is grown as a winter annual in the Southern States. It is hardier than blue lupine and yellow lupine.

MEDICKS OR BURCLOVERS comprise several species of *Medicago*. They grow in slightly acid to moderately alkaline soils and will tolerate salinity. They like shallow to deep, sandy loam to well-drained clay and moist conditions. They are benefited by applications of mineral nutrients when needed. They require available calcium for best growth.

Most species behave as winter annuals. They are adapted to the limestone and neutral soils of the Southern States and coastal section of California.

Black medick (*M. lupulina*) is the most winter hardy of the listed species. It is a winter annual in the South and a summer annual in the North. It is less exacting in its calcium requirement than the other species.

Buttonclover (*M. orbicularis*), *California burclover* (*M. hispida*), *Spotted medick* (*M. arabica*)—see Medicks.

MUNG BEAN (*Phaseolus aureus*) will tolerate droughty conditions. A summer annual, it is grown mostly in Oklahoma. (See Cowpea.)

PEAVINE comprises several species of *Lathyrus*, which grow in slightly acid to slightly alkaline soils but are not tolerant to salinity. Soils are shallow to deep, silt loam to poorly drained clays. It needs heavy moisture. Applications of mineral nutrients may be helpful. They are best adapted to heavy, wet soils of the southern and coastal section of the Western States.

Roughpea (*L. hirsutus*) is a winter annual, grown mostly in the heavy, dark-colored soils of the Southern States.

Tangier pea (*L. tingitanus*), a winter annual, has a wide range of soil adaptation. It is used in the western coastal sections and Southern States.

RATTLEBOX—many species of *Crotalaria*—grow in highly acid to neutral soil. They are not tolerant of salinity and require moist to heavy-moisture conditions. The plants will grow at relatively low nutrient levels, but fertilizers may be beneficial. They are summer annuals and are particularly adapted to the sandy soils of the Southern States.

Some species, toxic to livestock, are used mostly for green manure.

Lance crotalaria (*C. lanceolata*)—see Rattlebox.

Showy crotalaria (*C. spectabilis*) is poisonous.

Slenderleaf crotalaria (*C. intermedia*), *Striped crotalaria* (*C. mucronata* (*striata*))—see Rattlebox.

SESBANIA (*Sesbania exalsata*) grows in highly acid to neutral soils.

It is tolerant of slight salinity. The soils can be of shallow to average depth and gravelly loam or well-drained clays. Moist conditions are required for seedling establishment; thereafter plants tolerate periods of drought. Applications of needed mineral nutrients are beneficial, although plants grow at a relatively low nutrient level. It is a summer annual. It is adapted to the Southern and Southwestern States.

SOYBEANS (*Glycine max*) grow in highly acid to slightly alkaline soils—shallow to deep, fine sand to muck. They need moist to heavy-moisture conditions and do not tolerate salinity. They are benefited by the application of mineral nutrients when needed. Soybeans are adapted to most States, except dryland regions and localities where cool daily temperatures prevail.

SWEETCLOVER (*Melilotus*) includes two species that are widely grown. Slightly acid to moderately alkaline soils are needed. They will tolerate slight to moderate salinity and grow on shallow to deep, gravelly loam to poorly drained clay. Moisture is needed for stand establishment; after that they will tolerate dry conditions. Fertilization may be beneficial. The plants particularly require readily available calcium.

The two important species are widely grown throughout the United States wherever the soil is neutral or sufficient lime is applied to correct acidity.

Sourclover (*Melilotus indica*) is a winter annual only adapted to the Gulf and Southwestern States.

White sweetclover (*Melilotus alba*) has biennial and annual forms. The annual forms are used as winter annuals in the South and as summer annuals in the Northern States.

Yellow sweetclover (*Melilotus officinalis*), a biennial, will grow under slightly more adverse climatic conditions than white sweetclover.

TREFOIL includes several perennial and annual species of *Lotus*. Trefoil grows in moderately acid to neutral soil. It is tolerant to salinity and grows in soils of shallow or average depth—sandy loam to poorly drained clay. Moist to very moist conditions are needed. It is adapted to the Northern States and tolerates short dry periods.

Big trefoil (*L. uliginosus*) is less winter hardy than birdsfoot but is better adapted to swampy conditions. It is a perennial.

Birdsfoot trefoil (*L. corniculatus*) is more winter hardy than big trefoil. It is a perennial.

Narrowleaf birdsfoot trefoil (*L. tenuis*) is a perennial and is more tolerant of high salinity.

VELVETBEAN (*Stizolobium deeringianum*) includes several varieties that differ in maturity. They are grown as summer annuals with corn in Southern States. (See Cowpea.)

VETCHES include many species of *Vicia*, which grow in highly acid to slightly alkaline soils. They are tolerant of slight salinity. Shallow to deep, fine sand to poorly drained clays and moist to heavy-moisture conditions are preferred. Some species are adapted to a wide range of climatic conditions.

Common vetch (*V. sativa*) is a winter annual in West Coast and Southern States.

Hairy vetch (*V. villosa*) is a winter or summer annual. It is the most winter hardy of all vetches.

Hungarian vetch (*V. pannonica*), a winter annual, is grown mostly in the milder sections of the west coast.

Purple vetch (*V. bengalensis*) is a winter annual. It is the least hardy. It is adapted to California and Southwestern States.

Woollypod vetch (*V. dasycarpa*) is grown in the Gulf States and the coastal section of the Pacific States. It is a winter annual.

Tobacco

W. E. Colwell

Tobacco is unusually sensitive to soil conditions. Practices known to be effective for other crops often must be modified because of its sensitivity to the nitrogen supply, soilborne diseases, excess water, and physical properties of the soil.

Flue-cured or bright tobacco generally is grown on light-colored, sandy loams and fine sandy loams in the Piedmont and Coastal Plain of the South

Atlantic States. Fields best suited for this type of tobacco have relatively low levels of organic matter and calcium and a friable, sandy clay subsoil.

The heavier soils used for bright tobacco are usually in the Piedmont. The subsoil has a vital bearing on the suitability of the land for high-quality tobacco. It should be heavy enough to retain moisture yet permit root penetration and air exchange.

The nitrogen supply has to be controlled within narrow limits. Legumes cannot be used in the rotation except on the very sandy soils. Even then they should not immediately precede tobacco, because normal ripening requires a declining nitrogen supply. Otherwise, the leaves are green, coarse, and, when cured, dark and without a desirable flavor or aroma. They may also contain unusually high levels of protein nitrogen or nicotine.

To avoid those troubles, nonleguminous crops are used in rotation with tobacco, and the nitrogen supply is regulated with commercial fertilizer. It is common to apply 35 to 50 pounds of nitrogen an acre—or more or less, depending on the kind of soil.

About 65 pounds of phosphoric oxide (P_2O_5) an acre are required to maintain the high level of soil phosphate that characterizes most tobacco soils that have been heavily fertilized for many years. Potash is applied in amounts ranging between 90 and 130 pounds of K_2O.

The choice of cropping practice is dictated largely by the soilborne diseases and the need for protection against loss of soil and water.

Varieties resistant to three common diseases—bacterial wilt, black shank, and fusarium wilt—are available, but the widespread occurrence of nematodes has created a serious problem. None of the commercial varieties available in 1957 carried resistance to nematodes, and the grower has had to depend on soil fumigation and crop rotation.

Three groups of nematodes attack tobacco—root knot, meadow, and stunt. Among them are species and strains that differ in their preference for crops. For example, corn rotated with tobacco generally gives good control of root knot, but it is ineffective against some strains of root knot nematode. Corn is a favored host of the meadow and the stunt nematodes, and therefore has little or no value in this control. Oats followed by weeds generally may give good control of all kinds of nematodes.

Careful study of the disease problem, proper selection of varieties, and proper methods of soil fumigation against nematodes are needed to assure the production of tobacco of good quality.

Often the combination of practices required for control of disease brings new problems of soil management.

For example, the use of soil fumigation may require adjustment in the nitrogen composition of the fertilizer because of reduced nitrification rates. The addition of chlorides through the fumigant or irrigation water may call for a reduction of fertilizer chlorine. The grower who irrigates is tempted to use the fields nearest the source of water more intensively in shorter rotations.

Tobacco is highly sensitive to a waterlogged soil. Flooding injury may be apparent within an hour after a heavy rain on a hot day. If drainage is impeded so that the root zone remains saturated for several days, permanent injury or death usually results.

Layout of rows, especially on slightly rolling fields, is important from the standpoint of proper drainage and conservation of topsoil.

In experiments near Raleigh, N. C., control of row grade was an effective management practice to cope with rains of heavy intensity during the critical summer period. A contour row system was set up between terraces so that each row had a slight but continuous grade and carried its own water, as a miniature terrace. Flat middles between rows ridged in the conventional way gave better control of water than did the V-shaped middles. This method provides a broad water channel. Undecomposed residue left on the surface helped to reduce loss of soil and water during the summer. Winter cover crops and other residues incorporated in the soil decayed too quickly to be of benefit during the summer.

BURLEY TOBACCO, like the fire-cured and dark air-cured types, requires highly fertile soils, quite different from bright tobacco. Entirely different systems of management therefore must be followed.

Burley tobacco is grown mainly on

Relative Suitability of Certain Crops for Controlling Nematodes

Crop	Root knot	Meadow	Stunt
Corn	Excellent	Poor	Poor.
Cotton	Excellent	Poor	Fair.
Crabgrass	Excellent	Poor	(?).
Crotalaria	Excellent	(?)	Excellent.
Fescue	Excellent	Good	Fair.
Lespedeza (Kobe, Korean, Sericea)	Poor	Good	Fair.
Lespedeza (Rowan)[1]	Excellent	Good	Fair.
Millet	Excellent	(?)	Fair.
Milo	Excellent	Poor	Poor.
Peanuts [1]	Excellent	Good	Excellent.
Redtop	Excellent	(?)	(?).
Small grain cover crop	Excellent	Poor	Poor.
Oats for grain followed by crabgrass	Good	Poor	(?).
Oats for grain followed by weeds	Good	Good	Good.
Sudangrass	Excellent	(?)	Poor.
Sweetpotatoes	Poor	Excellent	Poor.
Weeds	Good	Excellent	Excellent.

[1] Rowan lespedeza and peanuts are susceptible to *Meloidogyne hapla* species of the root knot nematode, which is commonest in peanut-growing areas.

silt loams of limestone origin in the bluegrass region of Kentucky and the Central Valley of Tennessee. Farm manure and the use of grasses and legumes of various types in rotations are beneficial. Two years or more of sod well fertilized with phosphate and potash make a desirable cropping practice ahead of burley tobacco.

Under those conditions and with manure, it is common to supply directly to the tobacco crop 20 to 40 pounds of nitrogen an acre, bringing the total to a level between 90 and 120 pounds. Flue-cured types have a total requirement of about one-third to one-half that amount, which is applied directly to the tobacco crop.

It makes but little difference which grasses or legumes are used in the rotation just so they occupy the land during most of the rotation.

Bluegrass, orchardgrass, fescue, timothy, redtop, and smooth bromegrass sods have been used successfully. Red clover, sweetclover, Korean lespedeza, and alfalfa have been used in rotations alone and in combination with grass. Combinations of these grasses and legumes over a period of years have produced tobacco of good quality.

Good production has been obtained consistently at the Kentucky Agricultural Experiment Station from sod rotations, but erratic results have been had from continuous tobacco.

Black root rot, once a major consideration in developing a program of soil management, is controlled by using varieties resistant to it. Nematodes have been less troublesome than with flue-cured tobacco.

Soil management for fire-cured and dark air-cured tobacco is essentially the same as for burley. The soils are somewhat less fertile than those used for burley, and higher nitrogen rates do not have the same undesirable effect on quality.

MARYLAND TOBACCO, a light, air-cured type, is produced on loams, sandy loams, and loamy sands of medium fertility.

Two-year and three-year rotations predominate. The latter include a grass-legume mixture. Rotations have largely replaced the continuous culture methods, which involved long rest periods after a series of years of tobacco after tobacco.

The fertilization practices are quite similar to those for flue-cured leaf. Barnyard manure in large amounts prevents normal ripening of the leaf.

CIGAR TOBACCO is grown on many soil types because requirements differ for wrapper, binder, and filler classes of leaf. In the Connecticut Valley, sandy to very fine, well-drained sandy loams predominate. Near Quincy, Fla., the soils used for cigar wrapper are like those used for flue-cured types. The soils of Wisconsin used for cigar binder are dark brown, of silt loam texture, and fairly high in organic matter.

Near Lancaster, Pa., the soils used to produce cigar filler are highly fertile, yellow to brown loams or silt loams. The soils for cigar filler in southwestern Ohio are silt loams and silty clay loams of dull brown to gray color.

Rotations of 3 to 5 years are generally practiced following legume-grass sod or corn.

Continuous tobacco is the rule for the cigar-wrapper tobacco of the Connecticut Valley. Artificial shade is required. Rotation of crops is considered impractical. It is said that tobacco has been grown continuously on the same fields for more than 50 years without deterioration in yield or quality. That has been possible because of the heavy manuring and fertilization and because no highly destructive soilborne diseases have developed.

Continuous culture of tobacco is not without its problems, however. It is common to rest shade-tobacco land after 4 or 5 years, when yields and quality begin to decline. Some fields remain in high production only 2 or 3 years. Corn or potatoes may be planted. Sometimes the tobacco fields are left in fallow.

The best management practices in

the Florida-Georgia area include a 2-year rotation, with cockleburs or Texas millet planted in summer and oats in winter. Fumigation of the soil to control nematodes as a fall treatment is essential in this rotation.

It is common to apply to the tobacco crop 200 pounds of nitrogen an acre— 120 pounds of P_2O_5 and 200 pounds of K_2O. A cover crop of oats or rye is commonly used. One of its major values is to conserve plant nutrients against leaching. In a lysimeter experiment at Windsor, Conn., a cover crop of oats took up 56 pounds of nitrogen, 44 pounds of calcium, 24 pounds of potassium, and 8 pounds of magnesium to the acre in a year, and so kept the nutrients from leaching away.

Managing Soils for Rice

M. B. Sturgis

Most of the rice planted in the United States is grown in fields that are flooded to a depth of 3 to 9 inches through most of the growing period. The rice does not naturally need it, but flooding insures that the moisture requirement is met and controls weeds.

The practical benefits of flooding are associated with the development of such chemical conditions as poor aeration, low oxygen tension, and the loss or accumulation of reduced products. The management of soils planted to rice and crops rotated with rice therefore demands special consideration.

Rice is grown mostly in silt loam, clay loam, silty clay, and clay soils that

are nearly level or flat. The runoff is slow. The soils are slowly permeable after they have been saturated.

They have been derived from Recent alluvial deposits or from Pleistocene sediments on terraces adjoining the newer alluvial deposits. The most widely used soils are of the Crowley, Lake Charles, Beaumont, Sharkey, Mhoon, Portland, Miller, Stockton, Sacramento, Yolo, Willows, and Capay series.

The Crowley, Lake Charles, and Beaumont soils are Planosols developed on the Pleistocene Prairie terrace. They differ from the others in being older or in having more pronounced differences between the surface and subsoil layers. They are low in available phosphorus and total phosphorus.

The rice areas have an abundance of good irrigation water.

Most of the water used on rice in Arkansas comes from wells owned by individual farmers. It is pumped from water levels 25 to 60 feet or more below the surface.

Most of the rice in Louisiana and Texas is irrigated by water pumped from rivers and bayous that pass through or are adjacent to the fields. The water is pumped in short lifts from the streams and distributed in surface canals by privately owned canal companies to the farms. Some farmers pump or siphon water from the larger streams.

About 35 percent of the rice grown in Louisiana and 20 percent of the rice in Texas is irrigated from wells on the farms. Ten percent of the rice acreage in California and a large part of the acreage in Mississippi are irrigated from wells.

The amount of water required to produce a rice crop in Arkansas is about 30 acre-inches, including the rain during the growing season. The crop in Louisiana and Texas requires about 48 acre-inches, of which usually 20 inches comes from rainfall during the growing season.

In California, which has the highest water requirement, 48 acre-inches or more are used. Ten feet may be used on some types of soil, but the selection of other crops for those soils should be considered. The value of irrigation water as a regulator for maintaining uniform temperature for better crop growth also is a factor in California.

The quality of the irrigation water generally is good and contains less than 600 parts per million (p.p.m.) of soluble salts. Water that contains more than that amount of sodium chloride should not be used to irrigate dry soils and cannot be used throughout the growing season and year after year without injury to both crop and soil.

In years of less than normal rainfall, brackish water intrudes from the Gulf of Mexico into the streams and waterways that supply irrigation water for the Gulf Coastal Prairie soils of Louisiana and Texas. In those areas, wells are often drilled into water-bearing strata that touch nearby salt domes. They may become salty in periods of heavy drawdown. When the concentration of the water reaches 1,200 p.p.m. of sodium chloride, two or more floodings seriously damage the crop and in a few years may produce harmful conditions in the soil. Sometimes the electrical conductivity values of saturation extracts of the soils have risen above 4.0 millimhos per centimeter at 25 C., the pH above 7.5, the contents of soluble salts above 1,000 p.p.m., and the sodium saturations to nearly 15 percent.

The effects of the continued use of salt water include increases in compactness or bulk density of the soil and loss of permeability of the soil to air and water.

Rice is more tolerant of water containing a mixture of soluble salts that contain relatively little sodium and chlorides. When the dissolved salts in the irrigation water is lower in concentration than the soluble salts in the soil, rice has been grown during the time that the saline and saline-alkali soils are being reclaimed. If the damage to soil from the use of salt water is not of long standing, it can be corrected by flushing and increasing the surface drainage.

In the Gulf Coastal region, where damage frequently occurs from the intrusion of sea water or from salt water let loose in drilling oil wells, the salts can be removed from the soil by smoothing the surface of the field with land leveling equipment and by opening surface ditches, so that the rain water will flush the surface of the soil and move to the drainage canals as quickly as possible. By leaving the land fallow after smoothing and establishing surface drainage, the high rainfall will remove the excess salts in 2 years or more.

FIVE MAJOR PROBLEMS are involved in managing soils planted to rice: The maintenance of soil organic matter and nitrogen and the aggregation necessary for desirable structure; the development of drainage that permits the rotation of rice with other crops; the development of more efficient methods for the application of fertilizers to rice and to crops rotated with rice; crop rotations; and the control of weeds.

Planting a field to rice year after year or in 2-year rotations with fallow or other crops brings rapid losses of nitrogen and organic matter. The losses commonly are associated with declines in the aggregation of the soil particles and the development of poor physical conditions, such as crusting and compaction.

The content of soil nitrogen in a field of Crowley silt loam in Louisiana, which had been planted to rice 40 years, dropped from 0.20 to 0.08 percent. The soil organic matter also declined to 1.6 percent, which was approximately 40 percent of the amount present in the virgin soil or at the time the soil was first planted to rice. The water-stable aggregates of sizes between 0.1 and 2.0 millimeters in diameter in the virgin soil was 68 percent. The soil that had been planted to rice 40 years had 11 percent. This particular area of deflocculated soil is an example of one that breaks up to large clods when it is plowed, and it crusts badly when rained on after the seedbed is prepared.

The rice growers recognize the importance of increasing and maintaining nitrogen and organic matter in the soils. To do that, the land must be kept out of rice for longer periods. It also has to be better drained to allow for the development of pasture sods and the growth of other grains and deeper rooted crops. The lower demand for rice in the mid-1950's encouraged the use of pastures and longer rotations with rice.

In Arkansas, 4-year rotations have produced larger yields of rice. In a rotation of soybeans (cultivated in rows), fall oats, soybeans (turned under for soil improvement), and 2 years of rice, the increase in yields of rice was 21 bushels an acre for the first crop and 10 bushels for the second crop. Weeds were controlled while the arable crops grew.

In Gulf Coastal prairie areas, the rotation of 3 years of improved clover-grass-lespedeza pastures with 2 years in rice has become an established practice. The increase in yield of the first crop of rice, due to turning under the pasture sod, has been more than 30 bushels an acre. The increase in yield of the second crop of rice may be only 5 bushels.

Estimates in Louisiana indicate that turning the pasture sods from 3 years of improved pastures increased the soil organic matter by about 5 thousand pounds an acre and gained about 180 pounds of soil nitrogen. The problem of the small effects of the sod residue on increasing the yield of the second crop of rice may be related to the loss of nitrogen by biochemical reduction of nitrates or to the loss of soluble forms of nitrogen by surface washing. The rotation of rice with pastures also combats the weed infestations and improves structure.

The questions of how stable is the improvement in soil structure and how deep and what methods to use in turning pasture sods and other crop residues before seeding rice need more practical answers than can be given now.

The tendency has been to plow shallow, but earlier research in Arkansas showed that plowing to a depth of 9 inches was more effective than either the 6-inch or 3-inch depths.

The soil drainage in most of the rice areas is over the surface. Many of the terrace areas originally had low hummocks or mounds. The continued culture of rice has tended to reduce the small variations in relief, but only with the newer land planes could the small elevations and depressions in ricefields be smoothed practically.

Rather wide variations exist, however, in the productivity of some fields, which are due to the original natural relief. The smoothing and the better drainage prevent the development of alkaline conditions on the mounds or in depressions. The smoothing or leveling is a particular requirement before seeding in water. In topdressing with fertilizers when the floodwater is removed or allowed to evaporate before fertilizers are applied, the water should be removed uniformly from the surface so that most of the feeder roots, which are in the immediate surface of the soil, can absorb the nutrients quickly.

If nitrogen fertilizers are thrown into alkaline water, some nitrates will be lost by reduction to gaseous nitrogen and some ammonia will be lost by volatilization. Good drainage is necessary for the development of pastures and their utilization. Drainage is important if other fall-sown grains and row crops are to be rotated with rice.

THE FERTILIZER recommendations vary for the different areas. Nearly all of the soils are deficient in nitrogen. The prairie or terrace areas are low in available phosphorus and available potassium. Rice on the clays and clay loams of this group does not generally respond to applications of potassium. Relatively few areas of the alluvial soils are deficient in either phosphorus or potassium. Phosphorus, however, is more likely to be deficient than potassium. Nitrogen is commonly the only nutrient element applied to rice on the Recent alluvial soils.

The amount of nitrogen applied in fertilizers is 30 to 90 pounds an acre. If phosphoric oxide is applied, the amount is 20 to 50 pounds an acre. If potash is added, the amount is 15 to 50 pounds an acre.

The applied fertilizers have increased yields generally from 9 bushels to more than 35 bushels an acre.

Rice does not require a very high level of soil fertility for profitable production. Now that it is harvested largely by the combine and only the grain—the rough rice—has to be removed from the fields, not much of the plant food is removed. A harvest of 50 bushels of rough rice an acre—which is approximately an average yield—removes 29 pounds of nitrogen, 16 pounds of phosphoric oxide, and 9 pounds of potash.

When large amounts of straw are produced, there is a tendency to burn it to make it easier to prepare the seedbed. The straw should be spread and returned to the soil to conserve organic matter and plant nutrients. The removal or burning of straw increases markedly the loss of potassium.

Experiments in rice-growing States indicate a low efficiency in use of fertilizers on rice—particularly nitrogen. Some of it is due to the reduction of part of the nitrates to gaseous nitrogen, a relatively smaller amount to the loss of ammonia by volatilization, and some to the competition from weeds.

Normal, well-aerated soils have an oxidation-reduction potential above 0.5 volt at pH 5. Reducing conditions in waterlogged or flooded soils occur below an oxidation-reduction potential of 0.3 volt. At pH 7, these values would be 0.4 volt and 0.2 volt, respectively. Oxidation-reduction potentials below 0.2 volt commonly occur in soils planted to rice within 4 to 10 days after flooding. At oxidation-reduction potentials below 0.2 volt in the soil, nitrates will be reduced to nitrogen gas or ammonia and sulfates will be reduced to sulfides. The nitrates that

have accumulated in the soil from nitrification or directly from the application of fertilizer to be fully effective must be absorbed before flooding or within a few days after the rice is flooded.

Ammonia or the ammonium forms of nitrogen are more desirable for the fertilization of rice.

The grower, when he places the fertilizer, should take into account the benefits derived from keeping the nitrogen in the ammonium form until it can be absorbed by the roots. Within 10 days or less after flooding, a reducing zone develops immediately below the surface of the soil. The free oxygen in the zone is used faster than it can diffuse from the soil-water interface. The process of nitrification is stopped. The ammonium form of nitrogen remains unchanged and is held by the colloidal complexes, from which it is available to the roots. Nitrates that occur in the reducing zone may be reduced to gaseous nitrogen and lost.

If nitrogen fertilizers are broadcast on the surface before flooding or broadcast into the floodwater, the oxidative changes of ammonia to gaseous nitrogen may also occur to some extent.

Some evidence is at hand that the availability of soil phosphorus is increased by flooding with nonalkaline water. The availability of soil potassium is increased by flooding particularly as the water temperatures increase. Benefits from potassium applied to rice is greatest in the early stages of growth.

Complete and mixed fertilizers can be applied best by drilling or disking them into the soil at seeding or just before.

Ammonia or the ammonium forms of nitrogen drilled into the soil to a depth of 3 to 4 inches at seeding or just before will be held by the soil in the more available ammonium state within easy contact by the rice roots and more removed from the weeds sprouting on the surface.

The application of topdressing by broadcasting the fertilizer into floodwater is not so effective as applying the fertilizer after the fields have been drained so that the roots at the immediate surface of the soil can quickly absorb the nutrients. Some ammonia may be lost by volatilization if the floodwater is alkaline and hot.

A rather common practice in the terrace areas is to apply 300 to 400 pounds an acre of 5–10–5 or 3–12–12 fertilizers or their equivalents in higher grades by drilling or disking at or just before seeding and then topdressing not later than 8 weeks after emergence with 30 to 50 pounds of nitrogen as ammonium sulfate, urea, or ammonium nitrate.

The application of anhydrous ammonia to a depth of 3 to 4 inches and drilling mixtures of phosphorus and potassium at or just before planting the rice has been tried. Some growers inject complete liquid fertilizers to depths of 2 inches or more before planting. If only nitrogen fertilizers are used, all or part of the nitrogen as ammonia may be applied before seeding, or all or part of it may be applied in the solid forms.

If split applications as topdressing are used, nitrogen in the solid forms are broadcast on the rice by airplane from just after emergence to not later than 8 weeks after emergence.

RICE GROWS BEST in slightly acid or neutral soils.

The development of improved grass-clover pastures and their rotation with rice is particularly important in the cattle-rice type of farming that has been prevalent in Louisiana and Texas and has been increasing in Arkansas and Mississippi. Many of the soils of the cattle-rice areas are acid and need to be limed. The soil should be limed to pH 6.5 before seeding clovers.

If liming is necessary, liberal applications of phosphorus and potassium usually are necessary for the establishment of pastures that contain legumes. Small amounts of nitrogen also are applied before seeding the grass-legume pastures. After the establishment of the clover-grass pastures, topdressing with nitrogen fertilizer may be desirable to stimulate grass growth, and annual applications of small amounts of nitrogen and lesser amounts of phosphorus and potassium are used than was applied before seeding.

The need for nitrogen varies inversely with the legume growth. The demand for potassium declines after establishment. The other grain crops grown in rotation with rice have about the same nitrogen requirements as rice, but have much higher phosphorus requirements. The annual legumes, such as soybeans, vetch, and lespedeza, need more phosphorus and potassium than rice.

The rapid deterioration of soil organic matter and desirable soil structure that are associated more or less with continuous cropping to rice are experiences in all rice-growing localities. Intermittent flooding and draining increases the hydrolytic decomposition processes in the soil and the removal of the decomposition products over the surface.

Leaving a badly deteriorated land to idle fallow is the simplest—if not the most effective—way to stop deterioration and improve soil productivity.

All rotations have proved to be better than continuous rice, but the longer rotations, which allow the land to remain out of rice for at least 2 years in succession, are more desirable.

Some 2-year rotations, in which a legume is turned under, however, are effective in supplying nitrogen and maintaining or increasing soil organic matter. The most effective rotations for soil improvement are those that include 2 years or more in grass-clover pastures; the sods are turned under before rice or a row crop.

The most inclusive rotations have been developed in Arkansas. They include: A rotation of soybeans, followed by a winter legume with rice; a rotation of rice, followed by lespedeza with the first crop of lespedeza seeded in the rice stubble and followed by a second crop of lespedeza; a 4-year rotation of cotton and a winter legume, soybeans, winter oats, and lespedeza, followed by rice; and a 5-year rotation of soybeans, winter oats, lespedeza, and 2 years in rice.

A 6-year, rice-pasture-row crop rotation has been used in the rice-livestock areas. It consists of 2 years of rice with a permanent pasture mixture of whiteclover, alsike clover, redtop, and ryegrass, which is seeded in the second rice crop by plane after the water is removed for harvesting. Lespedeza is overseeded in the spring. The pasture is grazed 3 years, and then is followed by a row crop, which could be corn, grain sorghum, or soybeans.

Two-year rotations in the Gulf Coastal areas include rice and lespedeza; rice and cotton with or without winter legume; rice and winter oats or wheat; rice and oats followed by lespedeza; rice and sorghum.

The rotation of 2 or 3 years of clover-grass-lespedeza pastures with 2 years of rice has gained in importance in the Gulf Coastal areas. A relatively large acreage is left in idle fallow for 1 year or more after each rice crop, however. The fallow land is grazed and produces about 50 pounds of beef an acre.

In California, rice is rotated with wheat, barley, beans, milo, and Ladino clover. One rotation includes rice, beans, wheat, and beans. Green-manuring crops, such as purple vetch, have become more popular. The vetch or other legume is sown in the standing rice a few days before the water is drained off before harvesting. The gains in nitrogen and the physical improvements in the soil from turning under the legume are effective.

THE CONTROL OF WEEDS in rice fields is an unsolved problem. Crop rotations that involve cultivated row crops and the use of pasture rotations where the land remains out of rice for 2 years or more tend to reduce weed infestations greatly. The use of clean seed is important.

Field Crops

John H. Martin

Climate, rather than soil, is the chief factor in determining where most field crops are adapted. Crop plants with fine, fibrous roots, including wheat, oats, and barley, are best suited to medium or heavy soils.

Plants with thicker roots, such as corn, alfalfa, and sugar beets, succeed well on sandy loam soils but also are well adapted to heavy soils.

Crops like grain sorghum often produce high yields on heavy soils in wet seasons in the drier regions but may fail on heavy soils in a dry year, when fair crops are obtained on sandy soils.

Soils that are high in nitrogen are unsuitable for small grains because excessive nitrogen encourages lodging and the development of rust and delays maturity. Those adverse effects, which seldom occur in other crops, such as sorghum and corn, can be avoided to some extent in small grains by applying phosphorus and potash.

The soil type has only a minor role in determining the adaptation of different varieties of a given crop, except as it affects the abundance of soil moisture or nitrogen. Differences in soil moisture, as influenced by local topography, however, may determine the best variety to be grown. Quick-maturing varieties having small plants thus may be best suited to rolling uplands, and larger and later varieties are best for rich bottom lands.

CEREAL OR GRAIN CROPS include barley, buckwheat, corn, grain sorghum, oats, rice, rye, and wheat.

Barley (*Hordeum vulgare*) requires a

well-drained sandy loam to clay, which has a reaction of pH 6 to 8.5 and is 2.5 to 8 feet deep. It is very tolerant to salinity. It is more tolerant to sandy soil texture but less tolerant to acidity than are wheat and oats.

Buckwheat (Fagopyrum esculentum) needs a sandy loam to clay or drained marshland (pH 4.5 to 7.5) 2 to 4 feet deep. It is suited to infertile soils, especially those low in available phosphorus, and is very tolerant of acidity.

Corn (Zea mays) grows in well-drained, sandy to clay loam of a pH of 5.5 to 8 and 2 to 8 feet deep. Good fertility is essential for high yields, especially when corn is grown in thick stands. Corn responds well to abundant nitrogen. Calcareous soils are likely to be deficient in available potash and phosphorus.

Grain sorghum (Sorghum vulgare) requires well-drained sandy to clay soils 3 to 8 feet deep and having a pH of 5 to 8.5. It tolerates salinity. In semiarid regions it succeeds best on silt loam or clay loam soils in the wetter years and on sandy soils in dry years. Lighter soils provide better water infiltration and reduced vegetative growth, which lessens injury from drought.

Oats (Avena sativa and A. byzantina) grow in well-drained, fine sandy loam to clay, which has a pH of 5 to 8.5 and is 2.5 to 8 feet deep. Excessive soil nitrates favor lodging, and sometimes enough are absorbed by the plants to make oats hay poisonous to livestock. Manganese deficiency sometimes is evident in oats grown on peat soils.

Rice (Oryza sativa) grows in loam to heavy clay (adobe) that has a retentive subsoil and a reaction of pH 4.5 to 7.5 and is 2 to 3 feet deep. The soil must be wet or flooded. It is sensitive to salinity in excess of 500 grains per gallon of water. The potash requirement is low, but abundant ammonium nitrogen is essential to high yields.

Rye (Secale cereale) is more tolerant of sandy soils than is wheat, oats, and barley. Rye grows in sand to clay soil of pH 4.5 to 8.5 and 3 to 8 feet deep.

Wheat (Triticum species) prefers well-drained silt loam or clay loam but will grow in fine sandy loam to clay—pH 5 to 8.5; depth 2.5 to 8 feet. It requires balanced fertility and ample available nitrates to produce grain of high protein content.

FIBER CROPS include cotton, hemp, ramie, broomcorn, and flax.

Cotton (Gossypium hirsutum and G. barbadense) grows in soils that are sand to heavy clay, deep and well drained, reasonably high in organic matter, and pH 5.2 to 8 in reaction. Its indeterminate fruiting habit permits it to mature the number of bolls that can be supported by the extent of vegetative growth. Limited nitrogen reduces both total growth and yield. Deficiencies of potash cause extreme earliness and premature defoliation. Phosphorus is necessary for adequate maturity.

Hemp (Cannabis sativa) requires well-drained loam, silt loam, or clay loam; pH 5 to 7; 3 to 6 feet deep.

Ramie (Boehmeria nivea) grows in loam or muck, pH 5 to 7 in reaction, and 2 to 4 feet deep. Abundant fertility is necessary for successive heavy crops through the season.

Broomcorn (Sorghum vulgare): See Grain sorghum.

SUGAR CROPS include sugar beet, sugarcane, and sorgo.

Sugar beet (Beta vulgaris) grows in deep clay to silt loam, or sometimes fine sandy loam or muck, alkaline to slightly acid, well drained, and free from hardpan. It is very tolerant of salinity. It requires ample available phosphorus and responds to abundant nitrogen. It is sensitive to boron deficiency and to manganese deficiency on slightly alkaline soils in the Great Lakes region.

Sugarcane (Saccharum officinarum) needs loam, clay loam, or muck, including calcareous soils and soils derived from volcanic ash. Sandy loams require more moisture and fertilizers. The pH should be 5 to 8. Depth should be 1.5 to 5 feet, but the shallower soils are suitable only if moisture and fertility are abundant. Muck soils require applications of mineral fertilizers, except nitrogen, and usually such trace elements as iron, manganese, and copper.

Sorgo (*sweet sorghum*) (*Sorghum vulgare*) grows in well-drained sand to clay loam—pH 5 to 8.5, and depth 3 to 8 feet. Excessive nitrogen results in sorgo sirup of low quality.

AMONG THE OIL CROPS are castorbean, flax, mustard, mint, safflower, and sesame.

Castorbean (*Ricinus communis*) grows in sandy loam to loam, 3 to 5 feet deep and pH 5 to 8 in reaction. It is not tolerant of drought during flowering.

Flax (*Linum usitatissimum*) grows in well-drained loam to clay loam—pH 5 to 8 for seedflax and pH 5 to 7 for fiber flax. Alkaline soils are assumed to be unfavorable for the production of good linen fibers.

Yellow mustard (*Brassica alba*) requires fine sandy loam to clay. Brown mustard (*B. juncea*) grows in sandy loam. The reaction is pH 6 to 8. A soil depth of 3 to 5 feet is needed.

Mint (*Mentha piperita* and *M. spicata*) grows in sandy loam, loam, or muck of pH 6 to 7.5. It needs a constant supply of soil moisture.

Safflower (*Carthamus tinctorius*) grows in well-drained sandy loam to clay of pH 5 to 8 and a depth of 3 to 5 feet. It tolerates salinity.

Sesame (*Sesamum indicum*) needs well-drained sandy loam to clay loam, 3 to 5 feet in depth and pH 6 to 8.5 in reaction. It stands medium drought.

MISCELLANEOUS CROPS include hops and guayule.

Hops (*Humulus lupulus*) grow on deep, sandy, well-drained loam to loam soil, 6 to 8 in pH. Soil moisture must be adequate. Soils of high salinity are unsuitable.

Guayule (*Parthenium argentatum*), a rubber crop, needs deep sand to sandy loam, 5 to 8.5 in pH. It does not tolerate salinity. It is highly tolerant to drought after the plants are established because the roots may penetrate to a depth of 25 to 30 feet.

Home Gardens and Lawns

Charles E. Kellogg

The management of our garden soils follows the same principles as the management of field soils, but we use different practices. In our gardens we aim for variety, and we have a wide range of plants—grasses, annuals, perennials, shrubs, vines, and trees.

We try to have flowers and fruits through the seasons and ornamentals for sun and shade. Yet the total number of plants is small, and we can treat them individually. Even with simple handtools, we have a chance to apply the principles of soil management over a wide range of combinations more precisely than the farmer can do for a few crops in big fields.

We have little choice in selecting our garden soils. Rarely can we choose level, stone-free, sunny, "rich loam" soils, which are recommended so blithely in the garden books and on the backs of seed packets. Once the location of the house is fixed, we must take the soils we find and make the best of them. Oftener than not, the soils around the house are not well suited, as they are, to the plants we want to grow, especially if builders have destroyed the natural surface soil and left thin topsoil over fills of trash and raw earth.

Thus many new home gardeners may begin with soils that are too hilly, too sandy, too clayey, too dry, too wet, or too infertile for good gardens. But good garden soils can be made from them.

By "garden," I refer to all the cared-for soils and plants around the home—the kitchen garden, flowerbeds, lawns, and plantings of trees and shrubs. Included is a variety of plants that have unlike soil requirements. Some need shade. Others want full sun. Some prefer a slightly acid or neutral soil. Others do best in strongly acid ones. Some should have high soil fertility, others do well in poor soil.

The central problem of soil management in gardens is to develop and maintain a proper relationship between each plant and the immediate soil in which it grows.

Aside from pure luck, the gardener's success depends upon knowing two sets of factors: The requirements of the different plants he can grow and the characteristics of the soils in his garden.

Some plant can be found for almost any kind of soil as it is. And almost any kind of soil can be modified by management to grow any climatically adapted plant if one is willing to go to the trouble. Most successful gardeners try to find satisfying combinations of plants that require a minimum of soil change for good growth. Yet others go to a lot of trouble to change their soils to make them suitable for particular plants they want to have in their gardens. Some may even make drastic changes in a soil already about ideal for azaleas to have one suitable for roses, or the other way around.

One could hardly overemphasize the critical relationship between a plant and the soil in which it grows. Admiration of a plant in the catalog, at the flower show, or in a friend's garden is not enough of a basis for deciding to put it in our own garden, unless we know that its requirements can be satisfied by our garden soil as it is or as we can change it.

Gardening is an art, and many home gardens are outdoor living rooms. No one can say what is practical for home gardeners in general. Some are satisfied with almost any kind of green and growing things as long as the soil is neatly covered and the plants look healthy—a sensible goal for persons with only a mild interest in gardening.

A large money budget is not necessary for a good garden, even on poor soil. Far more important is the work budget—the care and attention the garden will be given throughout the season, not simply during a short spring bustle that is followed by neglect in summer and autumn.

THE PLACE for the garden is normally near the house. Even the kitchen garden is best there unless the soil in some distant place is a great deal better for vegetables and fruits. Near the house there is time to do the little things, before a pest, a drought, or a nutrient deficiency becomes serious. The watchful eye of the gardener is the best fertilizer for his garden.

To begin a garden, we need to know several things about our own place: The basic soil conditions; the air drainage and frostiness; the water supply we can count on, both natural and artificial; the light that falls on the plants during the seasons; and the protection required against hazards of wind, tree roots, and animals.

TO LEARN ABOUT THE SOILS we must dig—not simply into the surface, but down to about 3 feet or even more, if deep hardpans or other barriers to roots and water are suspected. The lower layers of soil control the supplies of nutrients, air, and water for deep roots. The movement of water out of the surface soil itself depends upon permeable layers beneath.

Most soils consist of a series of definite layers, or horizons, one above the other, with different colors and other properties. The horizons have been produced by the longtime effects of the climate and vegetation acting on the mineral matter. The horizons collectively are called the soil profile. Very young soils may not have horizons. Examples include those in the flood plains along streams, recent sand dunes, or new soil made by earthfills. If the gardener digs into an ordinary upland soil and finds no regular horizons, he can be reasonably certain that the soil has been moved about and mixed up not long before.

The main things to look for are depth, texture, structure, color, drainage, the slope and exposure, acidity, nutrients, and contamination.

Depth. Three kinds of soil depth are important. The dark-colored surface soil is normally the most mellow and most fertile. This is deepest in the black soils developed under grass, like those in Iowa and the Dakotas. It is normally very thin in the desert and only moderately thick under the forest of humid regions. On steep slopes it is commonly very thin. Builders often destroy this dark-colored surface soil completely or may cover it with raw, earthy material from excavations.

Then we need to know the depth of the whole soil, both surface and subsoil (or A and B horizons), over the raw substratum of weathered rock or other earthy material that has not been changed to true soil.

Finally, we should know how deep the whole soil and other loose, earthy material is over solid rock. The material under many soils is loose and porous to great depths. Other soils are thin over hard rocks with only a small space for roots and water storage. Such soils generally can support only drought-resistant plants that normally have shallow roots.

Texture. The relative proportion of sand, silt, and clay, or soil texture, of each horizon is important because it affects many other properties and because many recommendations are keyed to it. The texture in most soils changes from horizon to horizon. Commonly the subsoil, or B horizon, contains more clay than the surface soil above it or the substratum beneath it.

Classes of soil texture start with sand, which has only a little silt and clay. Then with increasing amounts of clay, the principal classes are loamy sand, sandy loam, loam, silt loam, clay loam, and clay.

With a little practice, you can easily distinguish them by squeezing a moist sample of the soil between your fingers. The sands are harsh and gritty, and the particles scarcely hold together at all. Loamy sands are gritty, too, but the particles cling together when moist. At the other extreme, clay can be squeezed into a smooth smear. The silt loam makes a rough and broken smear. Clay loams are intermediate. Loams give only a very rough smear; sandy loams give scarcely any.

Garden soils of intermediate texture—the sandy loams, loams, and silt loams—are easiest to handle. Sands and loamy sands are permeable, but they hold rather small quantities of water and are said to be droughty soils. Clays tend to become hard and massive unless they are handled carefully.

Structure. The individual soil particles in the ideal garden soil are grouped into stable granules or crumbs. Next best are blocky, nutlike aggregates, between which roots and water can move. Worst of all are the structureless soils.

At the one extreme are sands, in which each grain is by itself. Such soils hold little water between rains and are easily blown about by the wind.

At the other extreme are massive soils with no regular structural forms. Commonly clayey soils deficient in organic matter become massive if plowed, stirred, or walked on when they are wet. But massive hardpans can form from loams and even from sands with some cementing material to hold the particles together. Wherever they occur within the depth of normal rooting for garden plants, such massive soil must be reworked to make it granular or blocky. It is not enough simply to break up massive clods of clay. Organic matter must be added, or the fragments flow back together into masses when they are wet again.

Color. Soil color by itself is not important, but it suggests other conditions that are. Color, along with other evidence, can tell the gardener a great deal about drainage, the amount of organic matter in the soil, and the general level of productivity.

Brownish-black and dark-brown colors generally suggest a good supply of organic matter. In wooded areas where the normal upland soils are brown, black colors in the surface of soils in low ground suggest muck and poor drainage. Well-drained soils developed under tall grasses, like many in the Middle West, have black or nearly black surface soils. But a few black soils are poor in organic matter and easily lose their structure and become massive.

Solid red or yellow colors generally (but not always) suggest fairly good to free drainage. Yellow suggests leaching and a low supply of plant nutrients. So do the grays or whites in upland areas of good drainage. But in low ground, especially if the surface soil is nearly black, gray horizons (called gley) indicate poor drainage—too poor for ordinary garden plants. White colors in dry regions suggest soils too salty or too limy for most plants.

Some horizons beneath the surface are mottled. Imperfectly weathered rock just above the solid rock may look like this. But the commonest cause of mottling in soils is imperfect drainage, now or in the recent past: The soil is saturated with water, or waterlogged, part of the time and pervious to air, or aerated, part of the time.

Drainage. Imperfectly drained soils that are well drained during the summer and wet only in winter and early spring can support annual garden plants, but the roots of perennials cannot live over the winter in them. Even annuals do poorly if periods of waterlogging occur during their growing seasons. Often there is little evidence in the surface soil alone of poor drainage beneath. Thus it is important that you identify such conditions in advance so you can take appropriate steps for drainage or for plant selection.

If you have any doubt about drainage, you can dig some holes to the depth that roots normally grow—say to 2 or 3 feet, depending on the plants—and fill them with water. For all garden plants that require well-drained soils, the water should disappear within 30 minutes or an hour. If it does not disappear within 24 hours, only shallow-rooted plants could be expected to survive.

Slope and exposure. The slope of the surface soil has a lot to do with drainage, runoff, and erosion. Highly permeable soils that admit water rapidly can be used for cultivated plants on fairly steep slopes. On soils of slow to moderate permeability, small terraces are needed to slow down the runoff water, partly to give it more time to soak into the soil and partly to prevent washing.

You need to look at the whole slope, since it may begin above your garden and carry water from higher ground over your garden. If so, you should plan a diversion terrace on the upper side of the garden to intercept the excess runoff water and to guide it harmlessly to a prepared outlet.

Water tends to accumulate on nearly flat soils that are only slowly permeable unless ditches or special drains are made.

The direction of the slope is often critical. South-facing slopes in warm areas may be too hot for plants that do well on north-facing slopes. Many gardeners in warm areas find it easier to maintain good bluegrass lawns on north-facing slopes than on south-facing ones. The south-facing slopes in cool sections may be much better than north-facing ones for vegetables and flowers that require a warm surface soil.

Acidity and nutrients cannot be seen, of course. They can be guessed at from the vigor of growing plants. The soil in which blueberries and the like grow wild is strongly acid. If roses and bluegrass are doing well, it probably is not.

Acidity and nutrients can be measured accurately only on samples in the laboratory. I suggest that field tests be made for acidity only, but if you have some flair for chemistry you can try the tests for nutrients.

Most upland soils in humid forested regions are likely to be too acid for vegetables, a bit too acid for most flowers, and too low in plant nutrients for best growth. A generous application of fertilizers rich in phosphorus and potassium usually should be given at the start. But many shrubs and flowers and a few fruits demand an acid soil. Most of the flowers need medium rather than high fertility, and some of the herbs want even low fertility.

Until you get a representative sample of each kind of your soil tested for acidity and plant nutrients, you are working a great deal in the dark. Samples should be taken carefully to represent an even slice or core of the surface soil that is normally spaded, down to 5 to 8 inches, say, and of the soil beneath to about 20 inches. If the layers above 20 inches are strongly contrasting, it is better to have a separate sample of each. Samples of unlike soils, or of unlike horizons from the same soil, should not be mixed. Generally it is best to write to a laboratory before you collect the samples to meet any special requirements of the laboratory.

Contamination. In areas of disturbed soil, you need to be on the lookout for buried trash. Fragments of tar paper, concrete, and other rubbish should be removed. Any buried pieces of plaster or concrete are bad for acid-loving plants like azaleas and may cause chlorosis, or yellowing, of the leaves.

Commonly the worst places for buried materials are near the house, where shrubs and flowerbeds are needed. The excavations for basements usually are made somewhat larger than necessary so that after the walls are finished a V-shaped space is left just outside the wall. Careless builders allow rubbish to accumulate in this space and at the end simply cover it with a layer of topsoil. It should have been filled with soil and packed to protect the basement wall from accumulations of water. For plantings near the house it often is necessary therefore to remove a large amount of miscellaneous rubbish.

Other bad spots that your examination may uncover include old buried roadways or sidewalks and spots of oil-soaked soil. They must be dug up and removed.

THE AIR DRAINAGE of the garden affects its frostiness. If the garden is relatively high on a slope, the cold air moves or drains away from it into the low ground, so that plants escape the late-spring and early-autumn frosts that kill plants in the low ground. The gardener in low ground thus cannot count on so long a growing season as his neighbors on high ground with good air drainage. Plants growing on muck soils on low ground are even more subject to frost damage than plants growing on mineral soils on low ground. When you estimate the frost-free days from the reports of the nearby weather station, you should take these local ground conditions into account.

WATER should be available for all of the garden except the parts that have only naturalized wild plants entirely adapted to the natural soil. A dependable source of irrigation water is essential in dry regions. Even in humid regions, short periods of drought cause damage that nullifies much of the benefit from other good practices.

You can conserve soil water so that you need only a little if you prepare the soil properly, build terraces where they are helpful, and use mulches to protect the surface. But this little is often critical for carrying through fine plants in the kitchen garden and among the ornamentals.

Evergreens need watering during severe winter droughts as well as summer droughts.

In cities where the use of water for gardens may be regulated during dry spells, the resourceful home gardener may find a way to store some of the rainwater in a pond or cistern.

THE LIGHT REQUIREMENTS of plants vary greatly. You need to study your place to determine the hours of sunshine for the various parts of it, remembering that under deciduous trees there is little shade in winter and early spring and heavy shade in summer.

Nearly all vegetables and fruits do best in full sun, although the salad crops need shade in warm sections. Tomatoes, one of the most important vegetables in a small garden, grow fairly well in half the normal sunshine. The moving shade of a tree is less harmful to sun-loving plants than the dead shade of a building.

Other plants prefer shade. A few fine ornamentals flourish in the continuous shade on the north side of a building. Several of the ornamentals do well with winter and spring sun and summer shade, as under an oak tree.

Some lawn grasses prefer full sun and others partial shade. Ivy or other ground cover is more satisfactory than grass in heavy shade.

Many ornamental plants that seem to wither in full sun are really injured by high soil temperatures. If good mulches keep their roots cool, they do all right in full sun. Ordinarily clematis is one of these. Azaleas prefer partial shade, but they may do well in the sun if kept well mulched with something like sawdust.

Some of the trouble with plants growing near trees and big shrubs that is commonly put down to shade is due to root competition.

PLANTS NEED PROTECTION from competing roots, wind, and animals.

Roots from a competing tree may be pruned by digging a trench along one side—or even more if the tree is growing normally. A steel barrier may be placed in the trench to whatever depth the roots penetrate, say 2 to 4 feet, as a permanent protection for flowerbeds, vegetables, and shrubs.

Plants vary in their reaction to the roots of other plants. Azaleas, for example, grow well among oak trees, but roses do not. Yet azaleas grow poorly in competition with elm or maple roots. In fact, lawns, flowerbeds, and fine shrubs do badly near elms, maples, cottonwoods, poplars, and willows, which are not for small gardens.

In very large gardens near a woods, some gardeners dig deep, open trenches as a protection against roots, but they are unsightly and dangerous.

Many failures due to competing roots are incorrectly laid to the soil or its shade. Even small plants can rob the others. Forsythia roots, for example, are very bad robbers, and so are those of American bittersweet. Some iris are bad. Unless the roots of strong growers are kept pruned, they take over in a mixed garden. Flowerbeds may be protected from grass roots with 4-inch steel barriers and from most shrub roots with 12-inch barriers.

Wind is a serious hazard in many parts of the country—hot winds in summer, cold winds in winter, or both. Usually windbreaks of ornamental trees, especially evergreens, can be planted if the soil is suitable and if water is available. Winds may be very destructive in a few places around the garden during the winter. Those spots can be identified by their barrenness of snow when the rest of the garden is covered with it. Mature shrubs often thrive in such places if moved into them, but little shrubs of the same kind perish.

Animals are not useful in the garden. Kitchen gardens can be destroyed by rabbits. Dogs are probably the most commonly destructive in most home gardens. It is not worth while trying to grow fine flowering shrubs in some communities without fences.

TILLAGE is commonly the first step in preparing the garden soil. Organic matter, fertilizers, and other soil amendments are commonly mixed into the soil at the same time.

Large gardens can be plowed with machines, but small plots and small areas for flowerbeds and individual shrubs or trees should be spaded. Deep, fertile, granular soil, receptive of roots and water, may not have to be plowed or spaded very much, but usually some tillage is necessary.

The objectives of tillage are to produce and to maintain as deep a rooting zone of fertile granular soil as possible, control weeds, and keep the soil receptive of water.

The development and maintenance of good structure is the main reason for

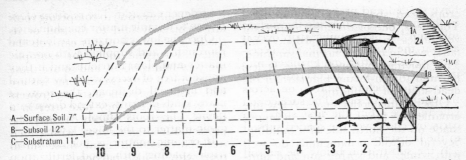

A—Surface Soil 7"
B—Subsoil 12"
C—Substratum 11"

Triple spading: 1A and 2A strips of surface soil are removed, and later moved to cover the last two strips at 9A and 10A; 1B strip of subsoil is removed, and added finally to 10B; 1C strip of substratum is spaded; 2B subsoil is spaded, mixed, and placed above 1C; 3A surface soil is put above moved subsoil in place of the original 1A.

plowing and spading. Considering the soil most gardeners have, this means working a great deal of organic matter into the soil—not just once, but often.

Much has been said about the use of synthetic soil conditioners—polyacrolytes. They do not bring about good structure when they are simply added to massive soil, but they help greatly to stabilize the granular structure of soil after such a structure has already been obtained by proper treatment, including tillage at the right moisture content.

For spading or stirring, a sample of the soil should just crumble in the hand after it has been formed into a ball and squeezed. Tillage of wet and sticky soils causes them to lose their granular structure and become massive, especially if they contain much clay and little organic matter. Once a clayey soil is badly puddled, it often takes years of careful handling to produce good structure.

It often is convenient to apply fertilizers and lime, besides organic matter, to the lower layers when spading. Most plant nutrients in time are carried down into the soil by rain and irrigation water if applied to the surface, but the movement is slow in clayey soils. Phosphorus especially moves down very slowly, although deeply rooted plants move it from their surface roots into their deep roots, where it becomes available to new plants after the old roots decompose.

Deep spading of the surface soil is rarely good practice in the garden except in the few soils that have little or no contrast between the horizons. The surface soil should be spaded to a depth of about 5 inches in dry sites and 7 or 8 inches in normally moist ones, without mixing in more than a very little of any lighter colored subsoil at any one time.

Subsoil spading usually is necessary in most garden soils for good, deep rooting. That is, very many garden soils should be spaded to a considerable depth, but each major layer should be spaded separately and not mixed with the others. That is called double or triple spading if two or three layers are spaded separately.

Let us take as a common example a soil that has a dark-colored surface horizon of intermediate texture about 7 inches thick overlying a clayey subsoil that goes to 20 inches with a fairly pervious substratum below that.

Double spading is called for. You start spading at one end of the garden or flowerbed by removing entirely a 2- or 3-foot strip of surface soil to 7 inches and piling it to one side. Then you spade the subsoil for 13 inches—making a total depth from the surface of 20 inches—and mix in the necessary sawdust, compost, or manure (as organic matter to improve structure), any needed lime (to correct acidity), and the basic fertilizers. When you have spaded and prepared the subsoil in this first strip, you spade the surface soil from the next similar strip over it and at the same time mix the necessary organic matter and fertilizers into it. Then the newly uncovered subsoil is spaded as before—and so on across the entire bed or plot. The surface soil you remove from the first strip you carry over to cover the spaded subsoil in the last strip.

If the substratum below the subsoil is also massive and needs improvement for proper rooting and for proper movement of water, you carry out three layers of spading. You put the surface soil from the first two strips at the end of the plot and the subsoil from the first strip to one side.

Then the substratum is spaded and treated. The subsoil from the second strip is treated with organic matter and other materials, and you spade it over the freshly spaded substratum of the first strip. The surface soil from the third strip you place over the freshly spaded subsoil of the first strip. This triple spading is carried across the whole plot. The subsoil from the first strip is used in the last one and the surface soil from the first two strips cover the last two.

If the soil is massive, mere spading does little good: When it is wet again, the soil particles settle back together— the deeper layers are heavily pressed by the weight of the ones above them.

Besides spading, you need to add abundant organic matter and the basic fertilizers for good structure and adequate nutrition of deep roots.

The organic matter has a direct effect in bringing about lines of weakness and preventing the settling of the soil particles into solid masses. But more important, in well-drained soils the organisms decompose the organic matter and produce compounds that lead to natural soil granulation.

These organisms need nutrients, especially nitrogen and phosphorus, which are deficient in sawdust, peat, and most organic materials (except high-quality compost and manure) that

a gardener can add. The relation of nitrogen to organic matter I explain later.

Once the lower horizons are loosened thoroughly and supplied with organic matter and plant nutrients and if they are kept free of excess water by natural and artificial drainage, the roots of many kinds of plants extend down into them. The roots supply further organic matter to the lower layers.

If organic matter is not available, triple spading with good fertilization can be successful if the soil is planted immediately to a deep-rooted legume like sweetclover or kudzu. After a year or two of vigorous growth, these plants produce a large amount of organic matter above and below the surface. The aboveground part can be cut and spaded into the surface soil or mixed with other materials for the compost. Such treatments may delay the garden for a year or so, but they are often worthwhile.

The soil for small beds and little places for individual shrubs and trees can be improved in the same way. Each soil layer is removed and piled to one side separately. It is replaced after organic matter and fertilizers are added to it. If the soil has hardpans or very heavy claypans, it is best to discard those layers and replace them with good garden soil, with surface soil from a fertile field, or (for acid-loving plants) with soil from a woods.

In a small place, a trench about 18 inches wide can be prepared in this same way for tomatoes or for dahlias and other flowers.

Cultivation after the soil is spaded and during the growing season follows the same general rule about soil moisture. If the clayey soils are stirred or tramped when wet, they lose their granulation. If the garden must be walked on, broad boards should be laid down. Yet garden soils should be kept free of weeds and porous to water. Since so many of our rains in the United States come as sharp showers, a hard crust on the surface allows much of the water to run off and be lost before the soil becomes permeable. Then, too, after plants have fair size, surface tillage needs to be shallow and gentle so as not to harm surface roots. A good mulch can go a long way in substituting for tillage—it helps prevent crusting, promotes the entry of water, and suppresses weeds.

ORGANIC MATTER is a vital material of which most gardeners rarely have enough.

Organic matter has several functions in the garden soils—as food for microorganisms and tiny animals within the soil, as a source of plant nutrients, and as a mulch. It also improves soil structure.

Its promotion of granular structure aids root growth and the entrance of water and air into the soil, reduces crusting and losses of surface soil by blowing or washing, and increases the ability of the soil to hold both water and nutrients for use by plants. Mulches help to control temperature, to reduce evaporation losses, and to suppress weeds. (Mulches of coarse sand and small stones have some of the same effects, too.) Organic matter, especially manure or compost derived from a wide range of normally growing plants, furnishes the growing plants a balanced supply of slowly available nutrients, including the trace elements.

The living roots, micro-organisms, and small creatures, such as earthworms, are a part of the total organic matter in the soil. Besides them, the garden soil contains three general classes of organic matter—the fresh remains of plants, partly decomposed materials, and the more or less stable, dark-colored humus, which is slowly decomposed to water, carbon dioxide, and ash. During the decomposition of fresh materials, a vast number of intermediate organic compounds appear before the formation of humus. Some of them are toxic in large amounts, but in normally well-drained soils they are transitory, and are themselves decomposed so soon that large amounts are never present. This decomposition is carried out by the tiny animals and the micro-organisms. The organic matter

furnishes them food for growth and the nutrients in it are thereby released for use by plants.

The fresh materials vary widely in their rates of decomposition and in the amounts of plant nutrients they release, especially the amounts of nitrogen.

Cottonseed meal and meat scraps, for example, decompose rapidly and furnish so much nitrogen that they are regarded primarily as fertilizers. Next come freshly cut clover and grass. Wheat straw decomposes moderately fast but is low in protein and so furnishes little nitrogen. Oak leaves and pine needles are even more resistant. Finally, sawdust and wood chips decompose very slowly and furnish negligible amounts of plant nutrients to the soil. Because they decompose slowly they are good mulches, especially in warm, moist regions. As we shall see in a moment, dry straw, tree leaves, and sawdust actually reduce the nitrogen available to plants when first added to the soil.

Among the partly decomposed materials, animal manure is important. Nearly pure manure is also a kind of fertilizer; often it is dried and sold in bags. It decomposes rapidly and gives the soil a balanced supply of plant nutrients. Manure that has much dry straw and wood chips with it decomposes more slowly.

Leaf mold, the partially decomposed leaves just above the mineral soil in the woods, is an excellent material, especially for mulching acid-loving plants. It decomposes slowly and furnishes some nutrients. Most peats decompose slowly and furnish minor supplies of nutrients.

COMPOST is a major source of organic matter to the gardener who has trees. It can be used as a slowly available source of nutrients and as a mulch and to improve the structure of soils.

The chief aim in composting is to produce an organic matter approximately like that in a fertile soil, in which the organic matter has about 10 parts of carbon for each part of nitrogen, or, as we say, a C/N ratio of 10.

The plant materials most commonly available to the gardener—autumn leaves and straw or other plant stems— are dry, coarse, and much higher in carbon, with a C/N ratio of 30 or higher. If they are added directly, it is hard to mix them evenly with the soil, considerable moisture is needed to moisten them in advance of decomposition, and the excess carbon as carbohydrate furnishes the bacteria a great deal of energy food. With this food, which acts like sugar, they increase enormously in numbers, taking out of the soil phosphorus and nitrogen, which otherwise would be available to plants.

For a field or a very large garden, it is most practical to add these materials directly to the surface soil, together with enough nitrogen and phosphorus to balance the carbohydrate, and plow all of it into the soil. But for small gardens and flower beds it is best to arrange for partial decomposition in advance in a compost pile. The product can be added as needed in preparing beds or as a mulch.

You should have a rick or open bin in which to make the compost. You can use ordinary wire fence or boards attached to solid posts, or open brickwork, to make such a rick some 3 to 8 feet high and 3 to 5 feet wide and of any convenient length. One end should be made with removable sides for convenience in building up the compost and for taking out the material.

Material like autumn leaves can be laid down in layers some 6 to 12 inches thick. To each layer is added some nitrogen and phosphorus (and magnesium sulfate—or epsom salt—in the humid East, or dolomitic limestone, if none of the compost is to be used for acid-loving plants) and a half-inch layer of soil.

The leaves should be moistened as they are added. The pile is built up in this way, layer after layer, and finally topped with a 1- to 2-inch layer of garden soil.

As it is built up, the material should

Material To Add in Making Compost

Material	Rate in cups per tightly packed bushel
FOR GENERAL PURPOSES, INCLUDING ACID-LOVING SHRUBS:	
Combination A:	
Ammonium sulfate............	1
Superphosphate (20 percent)....	1/2
Epsom salt.................	1/16
Combination B:	
Mixed fertilizer 10–6–4........	1 1/2
or	
Mixed fertilizer 5–10–5.........	2 1/2
FOR KITCHEN GARDEN OR FLOWERS NOT REQUIRING ACID SOIL:	
Combination C:	
Ammonium sulfate............	1
Superphosphate (20 percent)....	1/2
Ground dolomitic limestone or wood ashes................	2/3
Combination D:	
Like B, above, plus ground dolomitic limestone or wood ashes.	2/3

be packed with the feet around the margins but only lightly in the middle— so that the center will settle more than the margins and water added to the surface will gradually moisten the whole.

Some gardeners use pits, but it is better to build from the surface of level ground. The material needs to be moist but not soggy. Decomposition without air leads to loss of nitrogen.

If lime is needed in compost intended for the kitchen garden, wood ashes can be used instead. If nitrogen and phosphorus are not available separately, a mixed fertilizer can be used. If considerable manure or fresh clover hay is used, the amounts of nitrogen and phosphorus can be reduced proportionately.

The table suggests some alternative mixtures in making compost with leaves or straw as the main material.

After 2 or 3 months of moderate to warm weather, the pile should be turned for best results, although that is not entirely necessary. In turning into another rick, you can cut down vertical sections in the old one and put them horizontally in the new one, being careful to keep any dry materials to the inside.

In regions having cool, frosty winters, compost made from autumn leaves in November and December may be turned the following May or June.

A pile that is made too large may overheat, with a loss of nitrogen.

If the pile is kept reasonably moist and has a cap of garden soil (besides the soil between the layers), it should have no odor.

Applications of good compost or stable manure to the garden are about 4 to 40 bushels to 1,000 square feet.

OTHER ORGANIC MATERIALS may be used as mulches. Straw free of weed seeds is good, especially for small fruits, although it is a fire hazard and does not look neat in a garden.

Sawdust and wood chips are useful to mix into clayey soils to improve their structure and as mulches. Since they contain some slowly soluble carbohydrates, nitrogen must be added with them over and above that recommended for the soil otherwise. About 1 or 2 cupfuls of ammonium sulfate is used for each bushel. Perhaps well-rotted sawdust is somewhat better, but fresh sawdust is used successfully. When moistened, it gives nearly ideal acidity for azaleas and other acid-loving plants. For the kitchen garden and the rose garden it is well to use about one-fourth to one-half cupful of finely ground dolomitic limestone with each bushel.

A 3- to 5-inch mulch of sawdust is recommended around shrubs and other tall plants. Gardeners particular about the appearance of their intimate gardens can put a light covering of well-rotted compost over the sawdust or wood chips.

Cover crops are helpful on garden soils used for annual plants, both flowers and vegetables. Winter wheat, rye, ryegrass, or other winter-hardy crops may be planted in autumn. They protect the soil and absorb nutrients that would otherwise be lost. In the spring you have a supply of succulent, nutrient-rich organic matter to spade into the surface. This is very fresh organic matter and makes little contribution to the basic supply of humus.

THE CONTROL OF WATER is essential for the garden except in spots naturalized to wild plants that can endure wet, dry, or alternately wet and dry conditions.

Most soils lose a part of the water that falls on them through runoff from the surface, percolation through the soil, evaporation from the surface, and transpiration through plants.

Much of a gardener's success depends upon keeping these losses to a minimum, except the transpiration from his wanted plant, and on being sure that excess water does not accumulate in the pore spaces of the soil at the expense of air. Actually, it is not the excess water that injures plants in poorly drained soils, but the lack of air.

The ideal garden soil admits nearly all the water that falls on it, holds a large quantity within the fine capillaries between rains, allows any excess to drain away, is protected by surface mulches from excessive evaporation, and has no weeds. It should be added that a sandy garden soil subject to heavy leaching during the cool, rainy periods should have a cover of growing plants that take in nutrients that would otherwise be leached away. These are returned to the surface soil again when the plants are spaded under in the spring or the material can be taken to the compost pile.

Terraces are needed on sloping soils. To make full use of the water that falls during sharp showers, we need to have the soil granular. But in addition, on sloping soils, little, winding terraces, usually at a slight angle to the contour, to slow down the water are necessary. You can make several individual level terraces out of small stones the size of quart cans or gallon jugs with low walls on the downslope side of each large plant or small group of plants. These stones guide the water into the soil. With terraces, most of the plants can thus be planted or set out on level ground.

Drainage of wet soils can be accomplished in several ways. The simplest method is to throw up beds of soil above the original ground level, with places between for the excess water to collect and to flow away.

Irrigation is needed to some degree in most gardens. In fact, the more we do to improve our soils and to protect our plants, the more important it becomes to provide water for the critical periods so that we do not lose the benefit from all our other work.

A soil in good tilth, properly fertilized and well mulched, requires much less irrigation than a poorly managed one. Yet critical periods are fairly common when even the best garden soil needs water for fine plants.

Most of us irrigate when we see that our plants have started to wilt. That is too late for best results. When plants wilt, at least some damage has already been done. For a few dollars you can buy an instrument (called a tensiometer) to keep in your garden soil during the summer. Such an instrument indicates the moisture content and tells you when to irrigate before plants begin to wilt.

Depending on convenience, you may irrigate in small ditches, with a porous hose, or by sprays. The important thing is to irrigate well when it is done.

Excess salts can do a lot of harm. They are commonly associated with poor drainage in arid and semiarid regions, or with the use of salty irrigation water, or both. Readers having this kind of problem in their gardens are referred to the special chapter on the reclamation and management of saline and alkaline soils.

CONTROLLING THE REACTION of the garden soil is one of the important adjustments the gardener can make for his plants. Many plants can grow quite well over a wide range of soil reaction (acid-neutral-alkaline), especially when other growing conditions are good, but most plants do best within a rather narrow range.

The garden vegetables, most of the common annual flowers, most lawn grasses, and many herbaceous perennials and shrubs do best in slightly to

very slightly acid soil—about pH 6.1 to 6.9. The term "pH" is a quantitative measure of the degree of acidity:

	pH
Extremely acid	Below 4.5.
Very strongly acid	4.5–5.0.
Strongly acid	5.1–5.5.
Medium acid	5.6–6.0.
Slightly acid	6.1–6.5.
Neutral	6.6–7.3.
Mildly alkaline	7.4–7.8.
Moderately alkaline	7.9–8.4.
Strongly alkaline	8.5–9.0.
Very strongly alkaline	9.1 and higher.

A more acid soil than pH 6.5 is better for many plants, especially those that grow naturally under a forest with acid leaf litter. A few examples are given in the table and more are listed in my book, *Our Garden Soils.*

Any plants like these having an ideal soil pH range so far on the acid side usually do better in soil that has no free lime within the rooting zone. Such free lime occurs naturally in some soils, especially in subhumid and semiarid regions. It may have been added accidentally as ashes or in rubbish. Or it may have been added when garden soils were treated to make them best for vegetables, lawns, or other plants intolerant of strong acidity.

Other things being equal, such as structure, moisture, and organic matter, the micro-organisms that decompose organic matter, that transform organic nitrogen into forms most suitable to plant roots, and that fix nitrogen from the air grow best at about pH 6.5. Near this same soil pH, 6.5, conditions are best for the availability to plants, without toxic amounts, of most plant nutrients.

Among the trace elements, iron, manganese, copper, and zinc become less available as the pH rises. Iron chlorosis, a yellowing disease of plant leaves due to iron deficiency, is a common symptom of acid-loving plants growing on soils containing free lime.

On the other hand, availability of nearly all important plant nutrients except iron diminishes with increasing acidity, phosphorus especially.

Most upland soils developed under

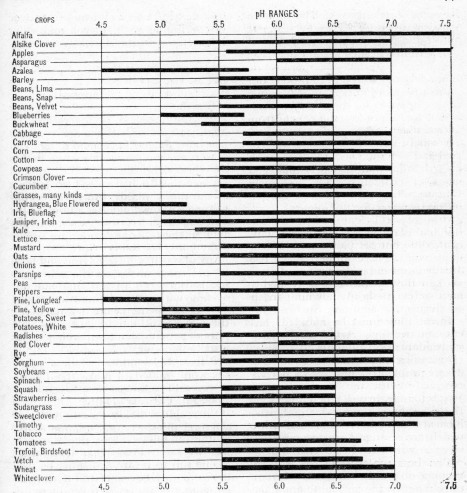

Suitable pH Ranges for Various Crops and Ornamental Plants

forests in the humid sections are too acid for the best growth of lawns, vegetables, and many other plants. They require liming. Most soils developed under grass and shrubs in the subhumid or dry sections do not need lime.

Since pH measures only the intensity of soil acidity, and not the total amount, applications of lime for soils of the same pH increase with increasing total amounts of clay, with increasing activity of the clay, and with increasing amounts of organic matter.

The table overleaf gives some general guidelines for the application of finely ground limestone, all of which passes a 10-mesh screen and at least one-half passes through a 100-mesh screen. Only one-half as much burned lime should be used. If the organic matter in the soil is very high, the amounts should be increased about one-fourth over those given in the table. If the organic matter is very low, the amounts of lime should be reduced by about one-fourth.

You should bear in mind that the in-

Suggested Applications of Finely Ground Limestone To Raise the pH of a 7-Inch Layer of Several Textural Classes of Acid Soils, in Pounds per 1,000 Square Feet

| | pH 4.5 to 5.5 | | pH 5.5 to 6.5 | |
Textural class	Northern and Central States	Southern Coastal States	Northern and Central States	Southern Coastal States
Sands and loamy sands..	25	15	30	20
Sandy loams...	45	25	55	35
Loams........	60	40	85	50
Silt loams......	80	60	105	75
Clay loams.....	100	80	120	100
Muck........	200	175	225	200

dividual horizons of your soil may have quite different pH values and lime requirements. For example, many soils are medium acid in the surface, strongly acid in the subsoil, and only slightly acid or even slightly alkaline in the substratum.

Overliming must be avoided. It is easy to overlime very fertile soils in which only small amounts are required to make a big change. Overliming causes problems of nutrient deficiency, especially with the trace elements. Partly for this reason it is better to use finely ground limestone than either burned lime or hydrated lime, both of which are strong. Any unevenness in spreading may lead to overliming.

The best material of all is finely ground dolomitic limestone. It contains magnesium carbonate and calcium carbonate. Most soils needing lime are likely to be deficient to some degree in both magnesium and calcium as plant nutrients. Furthermore, because dolomitic limestone becomes nearly in-

soluble at pH 7 or higher, the danger of overliming with uneven spreading is greatly reduced. Finally, if a very strongly acid soil is to be used for vegetables or lawns, it is better to raise the pH in two applications a year or so apart than in one big application.

For the acid-loving plants, you may have the problem of increasing the acidity of the soil. If the soil contains free lime, the most practical thing to do is to remove it, say to about 20 inches for rhododendrons and azaleas, and replace it with naturally acid surface soil from the woods. But for soils containing little or no free lime, sulfur can be added according to the amount shown in the table below.

Amounts for sandy loams are intermediate between those for sand and loam. It is not commonly practical to use soils more clayey than loam for acid-loving plants. The gardener can grow acid-loving plants by removing the clayey soil and replacing all or a part of it with sandy soil mixed with acid organic matter.

Although aluminum sulfate often is recommended to gardeners for increasing the acidity of the soil, it has a toxic salt effect on plants if it is used in large amounts. Small amounts are not very effective. About 7 pounds of aluminum sulfate is required to accomplish the same effect as 1 pound of sulfur.

The soil to be treated must be well drained. A mixture of sulfur and organic matter in wet soils produces hydrogen sulfide, an ill-smelling substance that is toxic to plants.

Whenever possible, it is best to prepare the soil at the proper pH for acid-loving plants in advance. The soil can

Suggested Application of Ordinary Powdered Sulfur To Reduce the pH of an 8-Inch Layer of Soil, as Indicated in Pints per 100 Square feet

| | Pints of sulfur for 100 square feet to reach pH of— | | | | | | | | | |
| | 4.5 | | 5.0 | | 5.5 | | 6.0 | | 6.5 | |
Original pH of soil	Sand	Loam	Sand	Loam	Sand	Loam	Sand	Loam	Sand	Loam
5.0.............	2/3	2								
5.5.............	1 1/3	4	2/3	2						
6.0.............	2	5 1/2	1 1/3	4	2/3	2				
6.5.............	2 1/2	8	2	5 1/2	1 1/3	4	2/3	2		
7.0.............	3	10	2 1/2	8	2	5 1/2	1 1/3	4	2/3	2

be kept moist while the reactions take place, followed by a thorough moistening to leach out any soluble materials before planting. If the plants are already established before you discover that the soil is not acid enough, you can mix one-half to 1 tablespoonful of sulfur into the surface soil just above the roots for an area of about 1 square foot.

Besides sulfur, the use of acid mulches (such as pine needles, sawdust, and acid peat) and the continued use of ammonium sulfate as a nitrogen fertilizer tend to increase soil acidity.

A BALANCE OF PLANT NUTRIENTS in the soil is essential for good growth. Most gardeners realize this and may tend to oversimplify the problem of soil productivity by getting a big bag of fertilizer from the store, spreading it on the soil, and then feel they have done the job. That can be helpful, but the plant nutrients are no more important than proper structure, adequate supplies of water, and the control of soil temperature with mulches.

Besides the carbon, oxygen, and hydrogen from air and water, plants take at least 12 essential elements from the soil. Deficiencies in nitrogen, phosphorus, and potassium are most widespread; those elements are most commonly contained in mixed fertilizers. Calcium and magnesium ordinarily are included in liming materials, and at least small amounts are in most mixed fertilizers. Sulfur is abundant in most arid soils; it is contained in some fertilizers; and enough falls in the rain near cities. Six trace elements are needed by plants in tiny amounts: Iron, boron, manganese, copper, zinc, and molybdenum. Each of the 12 elements is important as a fertilizer somewhere in the world.

Vanadium and chlorine also are essential to plants, but we would not expect them to limit plant growth in garden soils. Occasionally, however, a soil may be found that contains toxic amounts of some of these trace elements or of others.

Each of the 12 elements is contained in manure and in compost made from normally growing plants, although usually not in the best proportions to make a good garden soil from a naturally infertile one. It would take a long time to build up the phosphorus content of a highly phosphorus-deficient soil with compost and manure alone. It is more practical to use chemical fertilizer in addition to organic matter.

With the general scarcity of good manure and good compost and the general use of mixed fertilizers rich in nitrogen, phosphorus, and potassium, gardeners must pay increasing attention to the trace elements in order to have a proper balance among the nutrients at a high level of fertility.

The balance among the nutrients—not only the total amounts of them—is important. In many of the naturally infertile, leached soils of the eastern part of the country, for example, a lack of boron may be the factor that limits plant growth. Unless it is added, the gardener does not get the advantage of other fertilizers and good practices. Boron is especially important for tomatoes and other plants in the kitchen garden. Zinc also is rather commonly deficient; white streaks on the leaves of sweet corn indicate its lack.

The common basic elements, especially calcium, magnesium, and potassium, must be in proper relationship to one another for good nutrition. Thus the use of a large amount of a pure calcium liming material can bring on magnesium deficiency, often exhibited by a chlorosis, or yellowing, of the older leaves, which spreads to the younger leaves. An excess of either magnesium or potassium can depress the intake of the other by plants.

Phosphorus, potassium, and nitrogen need to be in reasonable balance. An excess of nitrogen causes spindly, flabby plants susceptible to disease. Where gardeners use a lot of manure or compost and fertilizers rich in nitrogen, they are inclined to have big plants with lots of leaves and relatively few flowers and fruits. The addition of potassium to such a soil strengthens the plant. The addition of phosphorus encourages more fruiting, earliness, and root growth.

An excess of both phosphorus and nitrogen together, and especially where potassium is low, may stimulate iron deficiency, which causes chlorosis. This, of course, is especially bad for acid-loving plants if the soil pH is too high anyway.

Chlorosis can also be caused by manganese deficiency and by zinc deficiency, but it is most commonly due to either iron deficiency or magnesium deficiency. In the latter, the old leaves turn yellow early, and the yellowing spreads to the new leaves. With iron deficiency, the yellowing starts with the young leaves and progresses to the old ones. A nitrogen deficiency also can cause grayish or yellowish leaves, which tend to mature abnormally early.

The serious gardener finds it well worth his time to become familiar with the functions of the individual nutrients in plants and their common reactions in the soil, as explained in other chapters.

Estimating the amounts of fertilizer to apply depends upon three separate sets of more basic estimates: The nutrients already in the soil, plus those normally added in any compost or manure; the general requirements of the specific plants to be grown; and the amounts of the nutrients contained in the various fertilizer materials available for use.

None of the fertilizers consists 100 percent of plant nutrients. The actual plant nutrients are parts of other compounds, and some other materials may have been added to keep the fertilizer in good physical condition. Thus, if you use ordinary superphosphate as a source of phosphorus and 20 pounds of phosphoric oxide are called for, you would apply 100 pounds of the material, because ordinary superphosphate has only 20 percent of phosphoric oxide.

Our calculations are further complicated by the old trade practice of expressing the amounts of phosphorus in terms of phosphoric oxide (P_2O_5) rather than as elemental phosphorus (P). Similarly, the plant nutrient content of a potassium fertilizer is expressed as potash (K_2O), rather than as potassium (K). I hope that these practices will be changed, so that all nutrients are shown as the elements. That is now done with nitrogen (N).

A laboratory soil test is the best means for estimating the existing supplies of available plant nutrients, along with the appearance and abundance of previous plant growth. But these results cannot be followed blindly since the same test result indicates somewhat different fertilizer recommendations for different soils in the various parts of the country. A qualified soil-testing laboratory takes these factors into account in the interpretation of their tests. Thus when you send samples to the laboratory for testing, the more precise the information about previous plant growth and about the soil that you furnish the laboratory, the better the recommendations you receive from the laboratory.

Suggestions about the needs of specific kinds of plants for normal growth are given elsewhere in this book.

The following suggestions about groups of garden plants are given as rough general guides. Readers should be aware that individual plants within these groups vary considerably. After each group of plants, I indicate roughly their fertility requirements for nitrogen, phosphorus, and potassium as high, low, or medium.

Vegetables. . . . . High.
Herbs. . . . . Medium to low.
Lawn grasses. . . . . Medium to high.
Fruits. . . . . Medium.
Annual flowers. . . . . Medium.
Perennial flowers. . . . . Medium to low.
Shrubs, deciduous. . . . . . . Medium to low.
Shrubs, evergreen. . . . . . . Low.
Shade trees, deciduous. . . Medium to low.
Shade trees, evergreen. . . Low.

The table on the next page is designed as a rough guide to the amounts of nitrogen, phosphorus, and potassium to use on garden soils of various textures and of low or high fertility, as indicated by present plant growth or soil tests. The figures I give are not for the fertilizers themselves; they refer to the net plant nutrients in fertilizers as nitrogen, phosphoric oxide, and potash. The high part of the range is for plants responding to high levels of fertility for the element, and the low range is for plants needing only low amounts of the element.

Suppose that our garden soil is a loam of low fertility and we want to prepare it for vegetables. As a general guide, we should need about 2 pounds of nitrogen, 3 of phosphoric oxide, and 2 of potash. That would amount to 20 pounds per 1,000 square feet of a 10–15–10 mixed fertilizer, containing 10 percent of nitrogen, 15 percent of phosphoric oxide, and 10 percent of potash. Instead of a 10–15–10, we could use 40 pounds of the more common 5–10–5, which would give us just what we need of nitrogen and potassium with a little extra phosphorus.

When preparing a garden soil for vegetables, flowers, and lawns, the necessary limestone and basic fertilizer, as suggested above, can be spread on the surface and spaded in along with about 10 to 20 bushels of manure or good compost for each 1,000 square feet. If the lower layers also need improvement, they may be given similar treatments with variations in the lime according to the degree of acidity.

Many gardens also need one or more of the trace elements, especially where little manure or compost is used.

Magnesium can be had with dolomitic limestone where it is used. Most mixed fertilizers contain some. If limestone is not used, as for acid-loving plants, ordinary epsom salt can be used at a rate of one-half cupful per 100 square feet for sandy soils and twice that for clayey soils.

For iron, gardeners have usually depended upon sprays having around 1 to 2 percent of iron as ferrous sulfate. One wants to be sure to use high-quality materials containing no residual acids. With woody plants, such spraying may need to be done every year to prevent chlorosis if the soil pH is too high or if it contains free lime. More effective iron fertilizers have appeared on the market under various trade names. They are some kind of iron chelates. Commonly they are added to the soil in water solutions, in accordance with the suggestions for the specific materials, although some spray them on the plants. But such spraying is not necessary except for curing an immediate situation. I have seen rather serious cases of iron chlorosis in azaleas cured within 10 days after treatment of the soil directly under the plant with an iron chelate dissolved in water.

Ordinary borax may be used to supply boron, which often is important in the kitchen garden on soils that were originally acid. You must be careful to spread it evenly at low rates of about 5 ounces, or 1 tablespoonful, to 100 square feet for sandy soils, or up to 3 times that amount for clayey soils. Such small amounts can be spread more easily if they are mixed with the bulkier fertilizers or with sand. For safety, a whole garden and lawn can be

Suggested Amounts of Nitrogen, Phosphoric Oxide, and Potash To Use as Fertilizer for Soils of Various Textures With Low and High Fertility, in Pounds Per 1,000 Square Feet

General soil class		Nutrients		
Texture	Fertility level	Nitrogen (N)	Phosphoric oxide (P_2O_5)	Potash (K_2O)
Sandy soils................	Low	1 to 4	2 to 5	1 to 4
	High	0 to 2	0 to 3	1/2 to 3
Loamy soils..............	Low	1 to 4	2 to 5	1 to 4
	High	0 to 2	0 to 3	0 to 2
Clayey soils.............	Low	1 to 4	3 to 6	2 to 5
	High	0 to 2	0 to 3	0 to 3
Muck soils...............	Low	1/2 to 3	3 to 6	1 to 7
	High	0 to 2	1 to 4	0 to 3

given a light application every 2 or 3 years. Although celery, cauliflower, apples, beets, and tomatoes are especially sensitive to a deficiency of boron, beans are easily harmed by a slight excess of boron.

To treat soils deficient in manganese you may use about a tablespoonful of manganese sulfate per 100 square feet. If plants are already suffering chlorosis from manganese deficiency, a 1- or 2-percent solution of manganese sulfate may be sprayed on the plants, as with iron.

Zinc deficiency is rather uncommon except with citrus, pecans, and sweet corn. All plants need at least a little. Where deficiencies are suspected, zinc sulfate may be sprayed or applied to the soil in the same amounts as recommended for manganese sulfate.

Copper deficiencies are most likely in newly developed peat soils or in old, highly leached sandy soils. Applications of copper sulfate should not exceed 1.5 teaspoonfuls on sandy soil or more than 4 tablespoonfuls on peat soil for 100 square feet.

Very old, leached soils may have too little molybdenum for growing clover in the lawn mixture. If you suspect such a deficiency you may use approximately one-half teaspoonful of sodium molybdate for each 100 square feet. Excessive amounts are toxic.

Sulfur is a limiting factor in parts of the Pacific Northwest, the northern Lake States, and some of the highlands of the Middle Atlantic States far from cities or industrial establishments. If ordinary superphosphate is used, either directly or in low-analysis mixed fertilizers, sufficient sulfur is obtained that way. If a deficiency is known or suspected, it may be overcome by the use of ordinary powdered sulfur at the rate of about 1 cupful for 100 square feet. Certainly it is not needed on many gardens.

The trade offers to gardeners a few special mixed fertilizers to supply the minor nutrients. Those from dependable companies are good to use if you are sure that none of the nutrients is already present in excessive amounts.

The amounts of fertilizer materials I have discussed so far are based upon broadcast applications over an area. Once the soil for the kitchen garden is well built up in fertility—especially in calcium, magnesium, phosphorus, potassium, and the trace elements—it is usual to place the fertilizer in bands about 1.5 inches beneath and to one side of the seeds. You may dig a V-shaped trench on each side of the guide line for the row and add the fertilizer. These little trenches may be filled, and a shallow one made for the seeds themselves directly on the line for the row. Similar local placement can be made in bands around individual tomato plants, cabbages, and others. For such local placement, the recommended amounts of fertilizers are reduced by about half.

With high applications of compost or manure, the broadcast treatments may also be reduced by about half.

With sweet corn, tomatoes, and long-season salad crops, especially in gardens below the 42d parallel, it is helpful to give the plants additional nitrogen after they are well started. With tomatoes, this is after the first set of fruit. The application on sweet corn should be made when the plants are about 24 inches high. Nitrogen fertilizer is added in a small band by the side of the plants within the surface inch or so of soil. One may use about three-fourths cupful of ammonium sulfate, or its equivalent in some other nitrogen fertilizer, for each 100 feet of row, with the rows about 2 feet apart. Slightly lower amounts are used for plants in narrower rows and slightly higher if they are in wider rows. For an individual tomato plant about 2 teaspoonfuls of ammonium sulfate can be mixed into the surface inch of soil in a circular band beginning 4 inches from the plant and extending to about 12 inches from it.

These recommendations are very generalized, but they may still seem a bit complicated to a few readers. Those in a hurry can treat the "average" kitchen garden or flowerbed (if there is an "average") with 1,000 pounds of manure and 20 pounds of a 10–10–10 fertilizer per 1,000 square feet and hope for fair success. This will not fit all plants.

Recommendations as to fertilizers in bulletins and those based on the results of soil tests from a reliable laboratory are usually given in terms of pounds per acre or pounds per 1,000 square feet. Since most gardeners do not have proper scales for weighing these materials, tables are given (next pages) to show how such recommendations may be converted into ordinary household measures—pints, cups, tablespoons, and teaspoons. The values are not precise but are near enough for applications in the ordinary garden. One pint is equivalent to 2 cups, or 32 tablespoons, or 96 teaspoons. Figures in the tables refer to level-full measures, except those marked s, which are slightly less than full, and those marked with h, which are slightly heaped.

A pint of water weighs 1.0427 pounds. So for materials having that same weight, one may convert directly from pounds to pints, although most of them are lighter than water. The common materials have been grouped according to their weight, and calculations were made on the assumption that materials are dry and loose and are scooped up without packing.

One table gives the equivalents for various groups of materials in volume measure for 100 square feet from recommendations given in pounds per acre or pounds per 1,000 square feet. The next table translates these volume measures per 100 square feet into volume measures required for rows or individual plants at different spacings.

Suppose, for example, the recommendations for 1,000 square feet of garden soil are 80 pounds of finely ground limestone, 28 pounds of ordinary superphosphate, 2 pounds of ammonium sulfate, and 6 ounces of borax. By finding the proper group in the first table, we find that these same recommendations become respectively 6 pints, 3

pints, 8 tablespoonfuls, and 1 tablespoonful for 100 square feet. In the other table, we find that for tomato plants spaced 2.25 by 2.25 feet the rates for individual plants are, respectively, ½ cupful, 5 tablespoonfuls, 1 teaspoonful, and ⅛ teaspoonful. Thus we see that the materials are used at very different rates and how easily it would be to get an excess of nitrogen and borax.

LAWNS are a special problem to many gardeners. The basic principles of good soil structure, drainage, irrigation, acidity, and plant nutrients apply to the garden soils used for lawns about as they do to those used for vegetables and flowers. The same may be said for light and root competition.

Somehow, gardeners have the notion that any space not used for flowers, shrubs, and trees around the home should be seeded to lawn grass. This does not hold. Grasses cannot be expected to do well in heavy shade amid competing tree roots. In areas of relatively mild winters, several other ground covers, such as periwinkle or English ivy, do better, both in the shade and on steep banks, provided that the growing ends are tipped into the soil to give a solid root mat. Where shade and much walking are both handicaps to grass, flagstones can well be laid.

Establishing a proper grade is the first step in developing a lawn. When building a house, it is best to scoop up any good surface soil and lay it aside. The materials excavated from a basement space should be carted away, except for those needed in the lower part of deep fills, say in holes or depressions. Even for such fills, heavy raw clays should be avoided because drainage is slow through them.

Following completion of the excavation, grade lines should be planned in even gentle slopes away from the house. The grade lines should allow for an addition of good surface soil or "topsoil" of 3 to 10 inches, depending on the character of the subsoil. If the subgrade material is soil of medium texture and can be worked into good

Weights of Various Fertilizing Materials per Acre, per 1,000 Square Feet, and per 100 Square Feet and the Approximate Equivalent-volume Measures for 100 Square Feet, Grouped According to Weight in Comparison with that of Water

Materials	Weights specified per—			Volume Measure for 100 Sq. Ft.
	Acre	1,000 Sq. Ft.	100 Sq. Ft.	
	Pounds	*Pounds*	*Pounds*	*Pints*
Weight about the same as that of water..... Examples: Cal-Nitro (or A–N–L), manure salts.	1,300	30	3	3
	870	20	2	2
	435	10	1	1
				Cups
	220	5	1/2	1
	110	2 1/2	1/4	1/2
				Pints
Weight about 1 3/10 that of water........... Examples: Ground limestone, ground dolomitic limestone, granular sodium nitrate, potassium sulfate.	5,660	130	13	10
	3,485	80	8	6
	870	20	2	1 1/2
			Ounces	
	565	13	21	1
				Cup
	280	6 1/2	11	1
	Pounds			*Pints*
Weight about 9/10 that of water........... Examples: Ammonium phosphate, triple superphosphate, superphosphate, mixed fertilizers (5–10–5, 4–8–4, etc.), potassium chloride.	1,960	45	4 1/2	5
	1,650	38	3 3/4	4
	1,220	28	2 3/4	3
	1,000	23	2 1/4	2 1/2
			Ounces	
	785	18	30	2
	610	14	21	1 1/2
	390	9	15	1
				Cups
	300	7	11	1 1/2
	200	4 3/4	7 1/2	1
	100	2 1/4	3 1/2	1/2
	Ounces			*Tbs.*
	50	18	2	4
	11	5	1/2	1
	Pounds	*Pounds*	*Pounds*	*Pints*
Weight about 8/10 that of water............ Examples: Epsom salt, bonemeal.	1,740	40	4	5
	650	15	1 1/2	2
			Ounces	*Cups*
	175	4	6 1/2	1
				Tbs.
	44	1	1 1/2	4
	Pounds			*Pints*
Weight about 7/10 that of water............ Examples: Activated sewage sludge, urea, ammonium sulfate, granular ammonium nitrate, aluminum sulfate, granular borax.	1,740	40	4	6
	1,525	35	3 1/2	5
	650	15	1 1/2	2
			Ounces	
	300	7	11	1
				Cup
	150	3 1/2	5 1/2	1
				Tbs.
	44	1	1 1/2	4
	Ounces			
	11	5	1/2	1
	Pounds	*Pounds*	*Pounds*	*Pints*
Weight about 6/10 that of water............ Examples: Cottonseed meal, sulfur, fish scrap.	1,300	30	3	5
	545	12 1/2	1 1/4	2
			Ounces	
	260	6	10	1
				Cup
	130	3	5	1

Weights of Various Fertilizing Materials—Continued

Materials	Acre	1,000 Sq. Ft.	100 Sq. Ft.	Volume Measure for 100 Sq. Ft.
	Pounds	*Pounds*	*Pounds*	*Pints*
	1,100	25	2½	5
	435	10	1	2
			Ounces	
Weight about 5/10 that of water. Example: Hydrated lime.	220	5	8	1 *Cup*
	110	2½	4	1
	Tons		*Pounds*	*Bushels*
Manure (moist):				
Loose	13	600	60	2
Packed	13	600	60	1
Dry straw or leaves packed tightly with hands.	5	250	25	2

Approximate Equivalent-volume Measures of Fertilizer Materials to use in the Row and per Plant at Various Rates per 100 Square Feet

Rates per 100 square feet	Rates per 10 feet, rows spaced— 3 ft.	2 ft.	1 ft.	Rates per plant, spaced— 5×5 ft.	2¼×2¼ ft.	2×1½ ft.
Pints	*Pints*	*Pints*	*Pints*	*Pints*	*Cups*	*Cups*
10	3	2	1	2½	1	½
	Cups	*Cups*	*Cups*	*Cups*		
6	3½	2½	1¼	3	h ½	h ¼
5	3	2	1	2¼	½	¼
					Tbs.	*Tbs.*
4	2½	1½	¾	2	6½	h 3
3	1¾	1¼	h ½	1½	5	2½
2½	1½	1	½	1¼	4	2
			Tbs.			
2	1¼	¾	6½	1	3¼	1½
1½	h ¾	h ½	5	¾	2½	h 1
		Tbs.				*Tsp.*
1	½	6	3¼	½	1½	2½
Cups				*Tbs.*		
1½	½	5	2½	6	1	1½
	Tbs.				*Tsp.*	
1	5	3¼	1½	4	2½	¾
½	2½	1½	¾	2	1¼	½
Tbs.		*Tsp.*	*Tsp.*			
4	1¼	2½	1¼	1	½	¼
Tsp.						
1	1	h ½	⅓	¼	⅙	1/12
Bushels	*Bushels*	*Pecks*	*Quarts*	*Bushel*	*Quarts*	*Quarts*
2	h ½	1½	6	½	3	1½
	Peck			*Peck*		
1	h 1	e 1	3	1	1½	¾

h = Slightly heaped.   e = A trifle less than full.

structure rather easily, a thin topsoil of 3 to 4 inches is adequate, but if the subgrade material is nearly structure-less, either single-grained sand or massive clay, a thick topsoil is called for.

Steeply sloping soils cannot be expected to support good lawns. Any steep slope should be broken up by stone walls or terraces so that the actual lawn has even, gentle slopes.

If the garden area slopes upward at the back of the house, considerable excavation may be needed and combinations of walls and drainage outlets may have to be built so that all the water from the slope is intercepted and flows slowly away from the house without danger of flooding the house or of eroding the soil during heavy storms.

Many steep soils, especially in the relatively dry Western States, are not stable; during periods of prolonged rain, masses of soil tend to slide. Heavy stone retaining walls, well anchored back into the hill and with deep foundations, are necessary for safety. Such construction calls for the services of a skilled engineer familiar with soil stabilization and drainage.

In building a new home and garden in any wooded area, arrangements should be made to protect selected trees. Builders should not be permitted to destroy the nice oaks and other slow-growing trees that can be saved. It takes too long to replace them from small ones. Most of the rapidly growing trees are a nuisance in a small garden because their relatively shallow roots compete directly with the grass and with other garden plants.

Trees selected for saving should be protected against machines used during excavation and grading by heavy planks about 6 feet long placed vertically around the tree and bound to it with heavy wire around the planks. If the final grade line is much below the original one, the trees cannot be saved, of course. If the soil was originally poorly or imperfectly drained and the new cuttings for roadways suddenly change the soil to a well-drained one, the older trees will probably die be-

cause their surface roots will not be able to supply enough water. Younger trees may be saved by watering until new roots have grown more deeply.

Trees can endure significant additions of soil where the grade line is above the original ground line only if wells are built around them. More than a 6-inch layer is hazardous without such a well. Wells are built of brick or stone from the original soil surface to the top of the new grade. The upper rim of the well is made level and is flush with the new grade only on the upper side of the slope. Wells are about 6 feet in diameter for mature trees. If the new grade line is no more than about 16 inches above the original, the well alone is enough to aerate the roots while they are being reestablished. If the added soil is deeper than that, a layer of coarse rock fragments, covered with fine stones and topped with some gravel and sand, should be laid outside the well on the ground out to the tips of the branches before the new soil or soil material is added. With tile laid through the well into this coarse layer, the roots can get air during the several years needed for the trees to establish roots in the new situation.

Having prepared the subgrade in even, gentle slopes, it should be firmed so that fills will not settle after the lawn is established. If the material is acid, ground limestone should be added. It can be fertilized on the basis of a soil test, but usually 30 pounds of ordinary superphosphate and 10 pounds of potassium sulfate to 1,000 square feet will not be far wrong. Manure, compost, or other organic materials should be worked into the subgrade material if it is clayey or if the soil tends to become massive.

After the subgrade is well prepared, the topsoil, already saved or brought in from a fertile meadow, should be added and graded for the final surface. This soil should be limed if it is acid and fertilized according to need. Generally a rough fertilizer recommendation that applies to many lawns is 25 pounds of a 10-10-10 mixed fertilizer or 50 pounds of 5-10-5 to start; fertilizers having a higher amount of nitrogen may be applied after the grass is established, say 25 pounds of a 10-6-4 to 1,000 square feet. If one is sure that phosphorus and potassium already exist in the soil in adequate supply, a nitrogen fertilizer that becomes available slowly without "burning" the grass is best.

The soil needs to be firm and free of big air pockets, but not hard. Rolling the surface of clayey soils should be avoided because it promotes the formation of hard crusts.

Lawn grasses may be established by sodding the soil surface, by sprigging individual plants or plugs, or by seeding. General recommendations for kinds of grasses to use are given in Department of Agriculture Home and Garden Bulletin No. 51, *Better Lawns*. Recommendations also can easily be had from your State agricultural experiment station.

Good weed-free sod is both expensive and hard to come by. Weeds in the lawn make a serious problem to many gardeners. It is far easier to keep them out and prevent them from going to seed than it is to eradicate them once they are established in the turf. So the careful gardener prefers sprigs and clean seed over weedy sod.

It is easier to use sod than seed on fairly steep slopes that are to be grassed. When sod is placed on such slopes, many flattish wooden stakes, about 1 to 2 inches wide and 6 inches long, should be driven through it until the tops are just flush with the surface of the sod. These hold the sod from slipping down the slope during wet periods before the grasses become rooted in the soil beneath.

In warm areas, grasses like Bermudagrass, St. Augustinegrass, and *Zoysia* can be set as plugs or sprigs or as small sods. Even in the Central States *Zoysia* is becoming more popular because of its vigorous growth and resistance to drought, heat, and disease, despite the fact that it remains brown during the winter. Plugs of this grass are commonly set out in late spring or midsummer at 1-foot intervals in new lawns. It is well fertilized, watered and weeded while it is getting started. Once the whole soil is well covered, weeds have difficulty establishing themselves.

Lawns in cool areas can be seeded during the spring; but in warm areas early autumn is best so that roots become well established before periods of high heat. Grass seeds are sown most evenly with a machine, but good results can be had with hand broadcasting on a windless day if half is sown in strips laid out one way and the other half in strips laid out across the first ones.

The seed is lightly covered with hand raking and watered lightly with a gentle, fine spray. Only new grass seedings are watered frequently and lightly. Mature lawns should be watered deeply if they are watered at all.

On sloping soils where there is danger of heavy rains before the grass is established, coarsely woven cloth or erosion netting can be staked down over the newly seeded surface to protect it from washing. It is held by small wooden stakes driven down flush with the surface; both stakes and netting will rot away.

After establishing the lawn, if the gardener finds small depressions from soil settling, shallow ones may be filled gradually over a period of years by sifting one-half inch of good garden soil onto the established grass from time to time.

The established lawn needs continual care on most soils. Occasional applications of finely ground limestone may be needed to keep the reaction at about pH 6.5. More than this should not be used. If the soil has been fertilized well with phosphorus and potassium and if any other deficiencies have been corrected at the start, an annual application of a mixed fertilizer high in nitrogen is commonly used.

Most recommendations suggest an application of something like 20 or 25 pounds per 1,000 square feet of a

10–6–4 fertilizer in the spring. Unless it is applied carefully when the grass is dry and unless the application is followed by rain or thorough sprinkling, "burning" of the grass is likely. It is much better to split the applications into two or three lighter ones over an interval of some weeks. You can buy a slowly available but high-analysis nitrogen fertilizer that does not burn the grass but gives a slow, continuous supply to the plants throughout the growing season.

In warm, humid areas, however, spring applications of nitrogen often stimulate fungus diseases, especially on clayey soils. Bluegrass, for example, responds readily to nitrogen fertilizer. The plants are luscious and tender. Then during hot, humid days in late May or June, damping-off and brown patch may nearly destroy these susceptible plants. Under such conditions, the main application of fertilizer can be made in early autumn, after the danger of these diseases is past. The grass plants go into the winter with good root reserves and should be given only very light applications of nitrogen during the remainder of the year, except in the shade under the trees, where they should have light to medium applications in spring and summer.

CLOSE CLIPPING with the mower is a common cause of poor lawns, especially in warm places where the hot rays of the sun fall directly on the crowns of the plants. With the mower set high, the clipped plants can stand more heat. A mixture of clover helps to shade the crowns of bluegrass. In cool regions, the grass may be clipped down to 1 inch, but in warm areas 1.5 or 2 inches is better.

Frequently it is wise to leave the clippings on the lawn, because the clippings help to maintain organic matter and nutrients in the surface soil. Heavy clippings from infrequent mowings, however, should be removed to the compost pile and not left as a smothering mat over the grass.

Ornamental Plants

S. L. Emsweller, N. W. Stuart, and Curtis May

The adaptation of ornamental trees, shrubs, bulbs, and flowering plants to a region is determined more by climatic conditions than by soil. Many varieties of such plants as camellias and azaleas can be grown only where the winters are mild.

Some herbaceous perennials, such as delphiniums, are satisfactory only in sections where cool summer temperatures prevail. Late-flowering varieties of such plants as chrysanthemums cannot be grown without protection in places where frosts come early.

One type of soil may be preferable to another for the growth of certain species of ornamentals, but there are no data regarding the best soil type for most ornamental plants. Recommendations are based almost entirely on observations of good growth in a particular type of soil, but plants of the same species often grow well in different types of soil.

ORNAMENTAL PLANTS often are planted in localities where the soil type is far from ideal. It is possible in most instances to replace or modify the physical characteristics and fertility of the soil for ornamentals. A deep, friable, well-drained, sandy loam that contains ample organic matter usually is considered suitable for most ornamentals, but some will thrive on soils less favorable.

Since some ornamental plants are

known to grow well in the same general soil type, we discuss such groups together in the paragraphs that follow. Information is usually available at State agricultural experiment stations as to what kinds of plants are best adapted in your climatic zone.

SHRUBS are widely grown throughout the United States for use in landscaping homes, gardens, streets, and parks. Their selection is usually governed by the color of flower, fruit, and foliage; time of blooming; ultimate size; and general availability. Environmental factors, such as temperature, light, water, and soil, however, determine the adaptability and amount of growth in a particular place.

THE NATURALLY occurring soil may limit growth because of poor structure and drainage, lack of essential nutrients, or unfavorable soil reaction. Many shrubs will tolerate or even thrive on a wide range of soils, but others are more exacting, particularly as to soil reaction.

Shrubs that require acid soil:
Rhododendron, Azalea (*Rhododendron* species)
Serviceberry (*Amelanchier* species)
Strawberry-tree (*Arbutus unedo*)
Heather (*Calluna* species)
Summersweet (*Clethra* species)
Broom (*Cytisus* species)
Heath (*Erica* species)
Wintergreen (*Gaultheria procumbens*)
Hollies (*Ilex* species)
Common Juniper (*Juniperus communis* and varieties)
Laurel (*Kalmia* species)
Box Sandmyrtle (*Leiophyllum buxifolium*)
Leucothoe (*Leucothoe* species)
Bayberry (*Myrica* species)
Blueberry (*Vaccinium* species)
Hobblebush (*Viburnum alnifolium*)

Azaleas, as typical of this group of plants, grow best at pH 4.5 to 5.5 in well-drained sandy loam that contains a plentiful quantity of organic matter, including partly rotted oak leaves,

twigs, bog peat, and old sawdust. Soil structure is most important and must permit ample aeration in the root area and high water-holding capacity. (Some shrubs, such as juniper and bayberry, require an acid soil but tolerate dry sites.) A mulch of peat moss or oak leaves maintained throughout the year at a depth of 2 to 3 inches tends to control soil reaction, provide some nutrients, and maintain iron availability. The main nutrient required is nitrogen, which can be supplied in organic form from cottonseed and soybean meal or as ammonium sulfate.

CHLOROSIS—a yellowing—of azalea leaves, which results from iron deficiency caused by root injury, lack of acidity, use of excessive amounts of lime and phosphorus, poor drainage, and certain nutrient deficiencies, can be corrected temporarily by spraying the plants with ferrous sulfate or by applying chelated iron to the soil. These treatments cannot substitute for good soil and growing conditions, however.

Certain shrubs, such as the barberry, daphne, and lilac, grow well under neutral or slightly alkaline conditions sometimes found in the humid regions. They and many other species will grow in slightly acid soils, however. Their growth is generally influenced more by light, fertility level, and water than by soil reaction.

SHADE AND ORNAMENTAL TREES, within their climatic limitations, in most instances grow best on a fertile, well-drained loam, but they will tolerate a wide variety of soil conditions.

A poor internal soil drainage, with resulting poor aeration, is detrimental to the growth of most species of trees, but some kinds will grow on wet sites.

Poor soils unsuited for satisfactory growth of shade trees usually may be modified by the addition of sand, peat, or decayed leaves or by installing drains, so that good growth can be obtained.

Before selecting shade trees, you will do well to consult your State agricultural experiment station, or other local authorities, about the kinds best suited for your locality.

In the following list we give examples of kinds of trees that require special types of soil for good growth or that will grow in certain types of soils:

Trees that need an acid soil:
Pin Oak (*Quercus palustris*); becomes chlorotic on neutral or alkaline soil.
Strawberry-tree (*Arbutus unedo*)

Trees that will grow on relatively dry soils:
Velvet Ash (*Fraxinus velutina*)
Acacia (most species)
Tree-of-Heaven (*Ailanthus altissima*)
Boxelder (*Acer negundo*)
Chinaberry (*Melia azedarach*)
Smooth Arizona Cypress (*Cupressus arizonica bonita*)
Carob (*Ceratona siliqua*)
Giant Evergreen Chinquapin (*Castanopsis chrysophylla*)
California Peppertree (*Schinus molle*)
Eucalyptus (most species)
Green Ash (*Fraxinus pennsylvanica lanceolata*)
Hop Hornbeam (*Ostrya virginiana*)
Pignut Hickory (*Carya glabra*)
American Hornbeam (*Carpinus caroliniana*)
Eastern Redcedar (*Juniperus virginiana*)
Jujube (*Zizyphus jujube*)
Pacific Madrone (*Arbutus menziesi*)
Mimosa (*Albizzia julibrissin*)
Chestnut Oak (*Quercus montana*)
Oregon White Oak (*Quercus garryana*)
White Poplar (*Populus alba*)
Fremont Cottonwood (*Populus fremonti*)
Jerusalem-thorn (*Parkinsonia aculeata*)
Blue Paloverde (*Cercidium floridum*)
Ponderosa Pine (*Pinus ponderosa*)
Brazil Peppertree, Christmas-berry Tree (*Schinus terebinthifolius*)
Torrey Pine (*Pinus torreyana*)
Virginia Pine, Scrub Pine (*Pinus virginiana*)
Pitch Pine (*Pinus rigida*)

Russian Olive (*Elaeagnus angustifolia*)
Sassafras (*Sassafras albidum officinale*)

Trees that will grow on wet soils:
Alders (several species)
Baldcypress (*Taxodium distichum*)
Cajeput Tree (*Melaleuca leucadendron*)
Dahoon (*Ilex cassine*)
Eastern Larch, or Tamarack (*Larix laricina*)
Poplars (*Populus*)—most species will grow on wet soils.
Whitecedar Falsecypress (*Chamaecyparis thyoides*)
Red Maple (*Acer rubrum*)
Pin Oak (*Quercus palustris*)
Water-elm (*Planera aquatica*)
Sweetbay Magnolia (*Magnolia virginiana*)
American Sweetgum (*Liquidambar styraciflua*)
Willow (*Salix*) (most species)

Trees that will grow on gravelly soils:
Tree-of-Heaven (*Ailanthus altissima*)
Dahurian Birch (*Betula davurica*)
Common Honeylocust (*Gleditsia triacanthos*)
Nordmann Fir (*Abies nordmanniana*)—will grow on gravelly hardpan.
Mimosa (*Albizzia julibrissin*)
Oregon White Oak (*Quercus garryana*)
Mugho Pine, or Swiss Mountain Pine (*Pinus mugo*)
Common Paper-mulberry (*Broussonetia papyrifera*)
Common Sassafras (*Sassafras albidum* (*officinale*))

Trees that will grow on dry, alkaline soil in the West:
Fremont Cottonwood (*Populus fremonti*)
Jujube (*Zizyphus jujube*)
Velvet Ash (*Fraxinus velutina*)

Trees that grow well on alkaline soils in the East:
Eastern Redcedar (*Juniperus virginiana*)

Franklinia (*Franklinia alatamaha*)—
prefers slightly alkaline, moist,
but well-drained soil.
Beech (*Fagus*)

Trees that will grow on very sandy soil:
Australian Tea-tree (*Leptospermum
laevigatum*)
Ailanthus (*Ailanthus altissima*)
Smooth Arizona Cypress (*Cupressus
arizonica bonita*)
Pfitzer Juniper (*Juniperus chinensis
pfitzeriana*)
Savin Juniper (*Juniperus sabina*)
Creeping Juniper (*Juniperus hori-
zontalis*)
Shore Juniper (*Juniperus compacta*)—
on sandy shores.
Jerusalem-thorn (*Parkinsonia acu-
leata*)
Mimosa (*Albizzia julibrissin*)
Silk-oak Grevillea (*Grevillea robusta*)
Pitch Pine (*Pinus rigida*)
Scotch Pine (*Pinus sylvestris*)

FLOWERING BULBS prefer a friable,
fertile, and well-drained soil.

They perform very well on sandy
loams, loams, and even clay loams if
drainage is good. The prevailing soil
and air temperatures are greater limiting factors than soil type, because the
type of soil may be amended, but we
can do little about the weather.

High soil fertility is important with
all flowering bulbs. Even in sandy soils,
good results may be had if the soil is
fertile. There is considerable evidence,
however, that high levels of nitrogen
(especially from organic sources such
as animal manures) increase the activity of some soil fungi that attack and
destroy flowering bulbs.

The problem of drainage is important with some bulbs. Many of the lilies (such as testaceum, candidum, and
auratum) will not tolerate poor drainage. Others (such as pardalinum, par-
ryi, and canadense) perform very well
in wet soils if the soil moisture is not
stagnant. Such conditions are provided
at the edge of running streams or on
slopes fed by springs.

There is very little evidence as to the
acidity or alkalinity preferences of flowering bulbs. In general it appears that
most bulbs perform well when the soil
is slightly acid. Some lilies, such as
speciosum, auratum, and philadelphi-
cum, prefer soils more acid than candidum or longiflorum.

Until more acceptable evidence is
available, it is impossible to make
any definite recommendations regarding either optimum fertilizer or pH
requirements of flowering bulbs.

HERBACEOUS PERENNIALS grow very
well on a wide variety of soil types, if
the soil is well drained. Sandy loams,
loams, and silt loams usually meet the
requirements of good drainage. Sands
and loamy sands also are satisfactory,
but they may require frequent applications of water.

Since the perennials will occupy the
space for several years, it is important
to put the soil in a good state of fertility before the plants are set out.

Unfortunately, little scientific data
are available as to the preferable soil
types or fertilizer requirements for the
numerous kinds of perennial ornamental plants available to gardeners.

More information is available as to
the effect of acid or alkaline soils on
growth of some perennials. Even here,
however, there is very little in the way
of experimental data comparing plant
response when grown under a wide
range of acid or alkaline soils. Most
perennials appear to perform best when
the soil is slightly acid.

GOOD ANNUAL FLOWERS may be grown
on a wide range of soil types. Because
many of these plants are shallow rooted,
good drainage is less essential for them
than for bulbs and perennials. Light,
friable soils, such as sandy loams and
loams, will produce good annuals.

The length of the growing season
and the air temperatures are of prime
importance in growing many annuals.
The range of such annuals as stocks
(*Matthiola incana*) and sweetpeas (*Lathyrus odoratus*), depends on cool air
temperatures rather than soil type.

Vegetables

Victor R. Boswell

All vegetable crops listed here (except watercress and taro) require soils that are well drained and are either naturally very fertile or well fertilized, regardless of the other soil characteristics that may be required or tolerated.

The soils also must have high moisture-holding capacity unless irrigation is available or rains are frequent and adequate.

These two requirements will not be repeated in the paragraphs that follow, but the requirements must be kept in mind.

It is not practicable here to list specific recommendations for applying manures and other organic matter, commercial fertilizer, and soil amendments for the several crops as grown on numerous different soils. Those subjects are treated in other chapters. Local sources of information also should be consulted.

Most vegetable crops on most mineral soils respond well to additions of organic matter and commercial fertilizers containing nitrogen, phosphorus, and potassium in the ratio of approximately 1–1.5–1 to 1–2–1, with judicious topdressings of readily available nitrogen during the early and middle stages of growth.

Leafy crops and corn typically use a high proportion of nitrogen. Fruit-, seed-, root-, and tuber-vegetables use a moderate proportion of nitrogen.

All crops on muck soils require less nitrogen and more potassium than on most mineral soils.

Only a few exceptions to these general requirements will be noted in the paragraphs that deal with individual vegetable crops.

If a soil is more acid than the optimum pH range given for individual crops in the following paragraphs, the soil should be limed to bring its acidity within the range indicated. Crops generally will tolerate a somewhat higher pH on the soils of the West that have naturally high pH values than they will on soils in the East with naturally low pH values that have been raised to high values by liming.

Artichoke, globe (*Cynara scolymus*), a deep-rooted perennial, does well on almost any deep, well-drained soil except one that is very sandy, droughty, or highly calcareous. A high content of organic matter in the soil and relatively cool temperatures are favorable. The plant is well adapted to a cool, moist climate, but the top is injured by freezing.

Artichoke, Jerusalem (*Helianthus tuberosus*) has an optimum pH of 6.5 to 7.5. Only well-drained soils of medium texture (sandy loams and loams) are recommended for this plant. Yields are low on sandy soils, plants blow over badly on sandy and muck soils, and tubers are unreasonably difficult to harvest thoroughly from fine-textured soils that tend to become hard.

Asparagus (*Asparagus officinalis*) is a perennial, cool-weather plant that tolerates high salt and boron content of soil. Asparagus requires an annual rest period preferably imposed by cold, and is unproductive in the southern third of the United States. Deep (3 or 4 feet or more), friable soil is necessary for extensive root penetration. Sandy loam, muck, or silty muck soils are best. Loams and silt loams are productive and widely used but tend to warm up later than sandy loams. Heavy clay loams and clays are unsatisfactory because they are cold in the spring, are hard to manage, and are conducive to the production of crooked spears. Sandy soils and subsoils tend to be droughty and sandy surface soils are

693

subject to blowing, thereby damaging the young spears. The optimum pH is 6.0 to 7.0 on soils in the East and up to 8.0 on soils in the West.

Beans, blackeye: See peas, southern.

Beans, common (Phaseolus vulgaris): The optimum pH is about 5.8 to 6.5 on soils in the East; on western soils it is 6.0 to 7.5. Both garden and field types of common beans are very sensitive to high salt and boron content of the soil. The bean plant is a relatively shallow-rooted, warm-weather annual. The soil need not be more than 1 to 2 feet deep if an adequate water and nutrient supply can be assured. Crops of high value, such as snap beans for early market, are profitably grown on light sandy loams and even on sandy soils when they are well fertilized. Rich loams, silt loams, and clay loams are best for main-crop snap beans for market or processing and for field beans to be harvested dry. Friability, good tilth, and freedom from baking and crusting are important in obtaining good stands in the field. Inoculation with nitrogen-fixing bacteria is rarely profitable. Applications of nitrogen should be moderate.

Beans, lima (Phaseolus lunatus): Optimum soil conditions are generally similar to those required by common beans. Lima beans are moderately tolerant of salts and relatively high boron in the soil; they are less sensitive than common beans. Good drainage, warmth of soil, good tilth, and freedom from compaction or crusting are especially important in obtaining normal seedling emergence.

Beets, garden or table (Beta vulgaris): The optimum pH is 6.0 to 7.5 in eastern soils and up to 8.5 in western soils. The beet, a cool-weather plant, is the most tolerant of garden vegetables to high salt and boron content of the soil. It has a high boron requirement; often it needs added boron to prevent internal black spot of the edible roots. It is highly intolerant of high soil acidity. The soil should be very deep (4 feet or more) and well drained. Sandy loams, friable loams, and mucks are pre-ferred. Soils that become crusted or hard interfere with seedling emergence and often cause the edible roots to become misshapen.

Broccoli, sprouting (Brassica oleracea var. botrytis): (See cabbage.) Sprouting broccoli is somewhat more sensitive to heat than is cabbage.

Brussels sprouts (Brassica oleracea var. gemmifera): (See cabbage.) This vegetable is very sensitive to high temperature. The most and firmest "heads" develop in a cool coastal climate. It is generally grown for autumn harvest.

Cabbage (Brassica oleracea var. capitata): The optimum pH is 6.0 to 7.0 in the East and up to 7.5 in the West. High pH helps control club root, a serious soilborne disease in many districts. Cabbage is moderately tolerant to high salt content and tolerant to high boron content of the soil. This cool-weather plant grows well in almost any well-drained soil of moderate (2 feet) depth or more, provided ample water is available. Sandy soils require heavy applications of organic matter and fertilizer. Timely transplanting and cultivating may be difficult on heavy silt loam, clay loam, or the clay soils. Once established and properly fertilized, however, cabbage grows well on such soils. Sandy loams are best for early crops; loams and heavier soils are satisfactory for midseason and late crops of cabbage. Muck soils of high lime content are very satisfactory.

Cantaloups: See muskmelons.

Carrots (Daucus carota): The optimum pH is 5.5 to 7.0. Carrots have little tolerance to high salt content, but are moderately tolerant to high boron in the soil. They require a very deep, well-drained soil, preferably a sandy loam or muck. Carrots are grown extensively on loams and silt loams, but it is usually difficult to establish good stands of plants on such fine-textured soils, which tend to form a crust, unless crust formation can be avoided. Careful control of soil moisture by furrow irrigation permits use of heavier soils than is feasible in districts of heavy rainfall. Clay soils and rocky soils impair root shape and harvest from clay soils is difficult. Coarse, undecomposed organic matter in the surface soil also tends to impair root shape.

Celeriac (Apium graveolens var. *rapaceum)*: Optimum requirements for this "root crop" are similar to those of celery but are less exacting. It can be grown with fair success in any good garden soil.

Celery (Apium graveolens): The optimum pH is 5.8 to 7.0. Celery is intolerant of high salt content of the soil. So-called high lime mucks (pH 6.0 to 7.0) are ideal for this cool-weather crop. Very acid mucks (below pH 5.5) and alkaline mucks (above pH 7.0) are not desirable unless pH can be economically corrected.

Celery is shallow rooted and may thrive on soils only 1.5 to 2 feet deep above the water table or above hardpan. The plant has a heavy demand for water and nutrients and tolerates neither drought nor poor drainage of the surface 1.5 to 2 feet. Although mucks are ideal, celery is grown extensively on loamy sands, sandy loams and loams, and to some extent even on silt loams and clay loams provided the latter are friable and well supplied with moisture. Establishment of transplants is more difficult in coarse and fine-textured soils than in muck and medium-textured soils. Fine-textured soils are to be avoided unless soil moisture can be effectively controlled by irrigation.

Chayote (Sechium edule): (See cucurbits.) This long-season, hot-weather vine crop produces single-seeded, pear-shaped or round fruits that weigh one-half pound or more. Fruit quality is similar to that of squash.

Chinese cabbage (Brassica pekinensis and B. chinensis): (See cabbage.) Chinese cabbage is more sensitive to high temperature than is cabbage. It forms poor heads and tends to bolt in hot weather. In most parts of the country it is best grown for autumn harvest or for winter harvest in winter-vegetable districts.

Collards (Brassica oleracea var. *viridis)*: (See cabbage.) The optimum pH is 6.0 to 7.5. Collards are hardy. Generally they are grown for autumn harvest or, in the milder parts, for winter and early spring harvest.

Corn, sweet (Zea mays): (See corn, page 664.)

Cucumbers (Cucumis sativus): (See cucurbits.)

Cucurbits: (Cucumbers, muskmelons, watermelons, squash, pumpkins, gourds, and chayote.) Soil requirements of all are similar, but those of muskmelons and watermelons are somewhat more exacting than those of the others. (See muskmelon and watermelon.)

A generally satisfactory pH is 5.5 to 7.0 on soils in the East and up to 7.5 on soils in the West. This group of plants is generally sensitive to high salt content of the soil and moderately sensitive to high boron content. Typically shallow-rooted, the cucurbits require as little as 1.5 to 2 feet of good soil above rock, hardpan, or other poor substrate if ample water can be provided, but deeper soils are better.

Cucurbits are grown most extensively on loamy sands, sandy loams, and loams, but cucumbers, squashes, and pumpkins for midseason or late crops are productive on friable silt loams and clay loams. Crops for early market are grown on the lighter soils, which warm up and can be worked earlier than heavy soils. Additions of organic matter to mineral soils are beneficial. Muck soils are not suitable because they tend to produce excessive vine growth at the expense of fruit and tend to be too cool.

Dasheen (Colocasia esculenta): (See taro.)

Eggplant (Solanum melongena): The optimum pH is 5.5 to 6.5. Eggplant needs a deep soil (4 feet or more) to accommodate its extensive and deeply penetrating roots. Most commonly grown on fine sands, loamy sands, and sandy loams, eggplant will thrive on deep loams, silt loams, and clay loams. Muck soils are not recommended.

Endive, Escarolle (Cichorium endivia): (See lettuce.)

Fennel, Florence (Foeniculum vulgare): The optimum pH range is 5.0 to 6.0. Other soil requirements are similar to those of celery but are less exacting.

Garlic (Allium sativum): The optimum pH range is 5.5 to 8.0. Other soil requirements are similar to those of onions, except that fine-textured soils that become hard are even less desirable for garlic than for onions.

Horseradish (Armoracia rusticana): The optimum pH is 6.0 to 7.0. Horseradish is grown commercially as an annual, but in home gardens is often grown as a perennial. For commercial production, deep (3 to 4 feet or more), sandy loams and friable loams are needed. If side roots and surplus shoots are to be removed from planted root cuttings as in commercial practice, a loose, friable soil is essential. For home use, any good garden soil will suffice.

Kale (Brassica oleracea var. viridis): Kale is highly tolerant to high salt content of the soil. Other soil requirements are similar to those of cabbage.

Kohlrabi (Brassica oleracea var. gongylodes): (See cabbage.) Kohlrabi is usually sown in place instead of being transplanted, as are plants of cabbage. Fine-textured soils that bake or crust tend to interfere with seedling emergence and cultivation. Once plants are well established, they grow well in fertile, fine-textured soils and in sandy loams and loams.

Leeks (Allium porrum): The optimum pH is 6.0 to 8.0. Other soil requirements are like those of onions.

Lettuce (Lactuca sativa): The optimum pH is 5.8 to 6.6 on soils in the East and up to 7.5 in the West. This cool-weather annual plant is moderately tolerant to high salt content and to boron content in the soil. Without irrigation, the soil depth should be 2 to 3 feet or more. Lettuce is grown commercially on soils ranging from loamy sands through sandy loams, loams, and clay loams to clays. Loams and mucks (high lime) are best. Sands and clays can be used effectively only where soil moisture is under good control. Skill in irrigation and cultural opera-

tions is especially important in obtaining good stands of lettuce on the very heavy soils. Sandy soils generally are not recommended.

Muskmelons, including cantaloups *(Cucumis melo):* The optimum pH is 6.0 to 7.0 on eastern soils and up to 7.5 on western soils. Muskmelons are not tolerant to high salt or boron content of the soil. A soil depth of 2 feet or more should be available. Early muskmelons are grown on sandy and sandy loam soils. Loams, silt loams, and even silty clay loams are used successfully for later crops. Sandy loams and loams are best. Muck soils and clays are unsuited.

Mustard (Brassica juncea and others): (See cabbage.) Seed of mustard is very small and produces relatively weak seedlings. Good stands of plants are difficult to obtain on sandy soils and on the fine-textured soils, which tend to pack or crust, unless soil moisture is under control.

Okra (Hibiscus esculentus): The optimum pH is 6.0 to 7.0 on eastern soils and up to 7.5 on western soils. The extensive root system of this large, warm-weather plant requires a soil 3 to 4 feet deep. It grows well on any rich garden or truck-crop soil.

Onions (Allium cepa): The optimum pH is 5.8 to 7.0 in the East and up to 7.5 in the West. Onions are moderately tolerant to a high salt content and tolerant to a high boron content of the soil. Relatively shallow rooted, they require a soil depth of 1.5 to 2 feet. The water supply should therefore be relatively frequent, or the water-holding capacity of the soil must be high, as in mucks, loams, and silt loams, all of which are good soils for onions. Sandy loams are good if the water supply is ample. Sands, clay loams, and clays are undesirable.

Oyster plant: (See salsify.)

Parsley (Petroselinum crispum): The optimum pH is 5.0 to 7.0. This cool-season plant will grow well on any good garden or truck-crop soil, once the plants are established. The seedlings, like those of carrots, start slowly, are weak, and cannot push through compact or crusted soil. Mucks, sandy loams, and friable loams are best, but sands, silts, and clay loams can be used if the water is under control.

Parsley, turnip rooted (Petroselinum crispum): The optimum pH is 5.0 to 7.0. Other soil requirements are the same as for carrots.

Parsnips (Pastinaca sativa): (See carrots.)

Peas, garden or English (Pisum sativum): The optimum pH is 6.0 to 7.5. This cool-season plant has a low to medium tolerance to high salt content, medium tolerance to high boron content, and low tolerance to high acidity of the soil. The calcium need is high.

Good soil drainage is especially important, because root rots are destructive in wet soils. A soil depth of at least 1.5 to 2 feet is desirable. Peas are well adapted to sandy loams for early-season production but are more extensively grown on loams, silt loams, and silty clay loams. Clay loams are suitable where water supply is under control, but are likely to be troublesome in regions of heavy rainfall. Sands and clays are not desirable.

Peas respond well to inoculation with nitrogen-fixing bacteria if the calcium supply is adequate. Despite the nitrogen-fixing relationship, peas respond to a moderately high ratio of nitrogen, especially during early growth.

Peas, southern or edible cowpea (Vigna sinensis): The optimum pH is 5.0 to 6.5 on eastern soils and up to 7.0 on western soils. These peas tolerate acid soils.

The cowpea, a hot-weather plant, is adapted to a wide range of soils. For growing as dry blackeye beans in the West, the sandy loams and friable loams with a relatively low salt content are superior to the finer textured alluvial, the Red Desert, and the clay soils. Most agricultural soils in the East and South, except sands, are satisfactory, although loams and silt loams are best.

Inoculation with nitrogen-fixing bacteria is advantageous. A high nitrogen supply tends to produce excessive vegetation in proportion to pods.

Peppers (Capsicum frutescens): The optimum pH is 5.5 to 7.0. The garden pepper, a warm-weather plant, is moderately tolerant to a high salt content and only slightly tolerant to high boron in the soil. It is grown successfully on many kinds of soil, ranging from fine sands through sandy loams, loams, silt loams, and clay loams. The coarser textured soils are preferred for early crops. The finer textured soils are preferred for later crops. Peppers can be grown on muck, but other crops are usually more profitable.

Pimentos: (See peppers.)

Potatoes (Solanum tuberosum): The potato grows well over a pH range from 4.5 to 7.0, but the soilborne disease called scab often becomes serious above pH 5.5. From the standpoints of both high yield and scab control, the optimum pH for potatoes is 5.0 to 5.5, but large acreages of potatoes are grown on western soils at pH about 7.0.

The potato, a cool-weather crop, is moderately tolerant to a high salt content and a high boron content of the soil. It is grown successfully on muck soils and on mineral soils 2 to 3 feet deep or more—fine sands, gravelly soils, sandy loams, loams, silt loams, and clay loams. Sandy loams are best for early crops. Loams, silt loams, and mucks are best for late crops.

Good drainage and a sustained, moderately high soil moisture are important. Clay loams and clays make harvesting difficult and leave the harvested potatoes unattractively dirty.

Pumpkins (Cucurbita pepo and C. moschata): (See cucurbits.)

Radishes (Raphanus sativus): The optimum pH is 5.0 to 7.0. Radish is highly intolerant to a high salt content of the soil and is moderately tolerant to a high boron content. Only the small, quick-growing type is popular in the United States. A cool-weather crop, the radish should be grown rapidly.

The root system of the small, globe-shaped type is shallow and requires good soil only about 1 foot deep. The small, long forms of radish, however, require soil 2 to 3 feet deep.

Radishes grow well on any fertile soil, except the fine-textured soils that become very hard; in them, the edible roots may become misshapen. Sandy loams, friable loams, and mucks are best for commercial production.

Rhubarb (Rheum rhaponticum): The optimum pH is 5.5 to 6.5. This cool-weather, hardy perennial thrives best in regions where the soil freezes at least a few inches deep each winter. For good production it needs a very deep (6 to 8 feet), rich, well-drained soil. The sandy loams, which warm up early, are best for early harvest. Heavier production, however, may be expected on rich loams and silt loams. Rhubarb is grown on clay loams and on mucks, but they are not preferred. The plant is a gross feeder and is benefited by heavy applications of manure and fertilizer. The excessive use of nitrate of soda may develop undesirably high content of nitrates in the edible petioles.

Rutabaga (Brassica napus var. *napobrassica)*: The optimum pH is 5.5 to 7.0 on eastern soils and up to 7.5 on western soils. Rutabaga has a relatively high need for boron. This medium long-season, cool-weather plant produces a surprisingly large and deep root system. For best plant development, the soil should be at least 4 to 5 feet deep. Loams and silt loams are preferred. Sandy loams are generally a little less productive. Clays tend to cause the marketable roots to be misshapen and to make harvest difficult.

Salsify (Tragopogon porrifolius): The optimum pH is 6.0 to 7.5. Other soil requirements are the same as for carrots. It is less difficult to get good stands of salsify than of carrots.

Shallots (Allium ascalonicum): The optimum pH is 5.5 to 7.0. This minor cool-weather plant, similar to the "bunching" type of onion, is seldom grown commercially except in southern Louisiana. The plant is relatively shallow rooted and is grown best on loam soils, although sandy loams and silt loams are also good. Sandy soils and clays are undesirable.

Sorrel (Rumex acetosa): It tolerates a pH of 4.0 to 7.0. This minor greens "vegetable" is a perennial kin to dock (a common perennial weed) and is sometimes called "sour grass." It will grow in soils too acid for other vegetables, ranging from sandy soil to clay and muck. Like most plants, it grows better in rich soils than in poor ones.

Spinach (Spinacia oleracea): The optimum pH is 6.0 to 7.0. It is rather highly tolerant to high salt content and boron content in the soil and is very sensitive to high acidity. Additions of manganese may be needed to correct chlorosis on strongly alkaline soils. The root system is shallow; the soil need not be more than 1.5 to 2 feet deep, but it must be well drained and highly fertile for good yields. Sandy loams are satisfactory for early market crops, but the more fertile, deep loams, silt loams, clay loams, and mucks are preferred where earliness is not important. Clay soils can be used where moisture in the soil is under control.

Squash (Cucurbita pepo, C. moschata, and *C. maxima)*: (See cucurbits.)

Sweet corn (Zea mays): (See also corn, page 664. Optimum pH is 5.5 to 7.0. Sweet corn is moderately tolerant to high salt and to high boron content of the soil. It grows well on any well-drained soil that produces good yields of other crops. Deep, naturally rich soils that are easy to work are preferred but are not essential. Sweet corn requires relatively heavy manuring and fertilizing of soils that are not naturally highly fertile. Fine sandy loams and sandy loams are best for crops for early market; loams, silt loams, clay loams and clays can be used for later crops.

Sweetpotato (Ipomoea batatas): The optimum pH is 5.5 to 6.5; good yields are possible in a pH range of 5.2 to 7.0. Sweetpotato is best adapted to slightly acid soils and has little tolerance to either high salt or high boron content of the soil. Loamy fine sand, loamy sand, and sandy loam surface soils are suitable for sweetpotatoes when they are well fertilized and underlaid by firm, well-drained subsoils of finer texture at approximately 1 foot depth. Sandy or gravelly subsoils tend to be infertile and droughty and to cause too deep penetration of the enlarged roots; the results are poor shape of the roots and difficulty of harvest. Friable, moderately deep loams and silt loams, such as Lintonia silt loam, are very desirable. Clay loams and clays are conducive to poor root shape and difficult harvest; they are not recommended. Muck soils cause poor root shape, although large tonnages can be produced on them in the South. Sweetpotato requires high potash, medium phosphorus, and medium to low nitrogen supplies.

Swiss chard (Beta vulgaris var. cicla): The optimum pH is 6.0 to 7.5. This leafy form of beet is highly tolerant to high salt and high boron content of the soil. It can be grown successfully on any good garden or truck-crop soil from loamy sands and sandy loams to clay loams and muck, if the soil is not strongly acid.

Taro (Colocasia esculenta): This tropical tuber-bearing plant is a form of elephant's ear and is suited only to the warmest parts of this country. It requires 7 months of warm weather to make a crop. Best results are obtained with a very moist, preferably well-drained soil, although taro will tolerate longer periods of flooding and wet soil than most garden crops. Deep, rich, sandy loams and loams are best, but mucks can be used. Prolonged excessive wetness of soil impairs the eating quality of the tubers. High organic matter and high fertility of the soil are essential for good results.

Tomato (Lycopersicon esculentum): The optimum pH is 5.5 to 7.0 in the East and up to 7.5 in the West. The tomato has medium high tolerance to both high salt and high boron content of the soil. It is one of the most widely adaptable of vegetables. Most varieties produce a large root system that will fill the soil to a depth of 4 feet if the soil is suitable. It is grown commercially on soils ranging from fine sands

to marls and clays. It is rarely grown on mucks. Manganese additions are necessary on marls. On the sands and sandy loams, heavy to very heavy fertilization is necessary.

The tomato has a high requirement for phosphorus and potassium. Nitrogenous fertilizers and manures must be used judiciously because excess nitrogen often causes excessive plant growth, dropping of blossoms, and consequent low yields. Tomato is very sensitive to fluctuations in water or in nutrients, which commonly cause blossom end rot of fruit and dropping of blossoms. The best yields are obtained on deep (4 feet or more), rich loams, silt loams, and clay loams that are well supplied with moisture.

Turnips (Brassica rapa): The optimum pH is 5.5 to 6.8. Turnips tolerate a high boron content in the soil. Roots for early market and greens for market and processing are commonly grown on sandy loams. Roots for storage and forage are better grown on the more fertile loams and silt loams. Rich clays can produce heavy yields if the soil moisture is under control.

Watercress (Radicula nasturtium-aquaticum): The optimum pH is 6.0 to 8.0. Watercress is grown commercially in running spring water, chiefly in limestone regions where the water is high in calcium and carries adequate amounts of other nutrients, including nitrates. The plants are set in 2 to 4 inches of compost on carefully graded bottoms of flooded beds. Other than preparation of compost, no fertilization is commonly given.

Watermelons (Citrullus vulgaris): The optimum pH is 5.5 to 6.5. (See also cucurbits, page 694.)

Watermelon, a warm-weather plant, is grown chiefly on loamy sands, sandy loams, and well-drained loams. The plant is a gross feeder and responds well to heavy applications of manure and other organic matter and to fertilizer, but it is not adapted to mucks. Certain friable silt loams are satisfactory, but clay loams and clays are not recommended.

Soil Management for Orchards

Damon Boynton and John R. Magness

Orchard trees grow and produce in one place for 15 to 50 years or more. By the time they are in bearing, they have extensive root systems that extend outward from the trunk and downward several feet if the soil has an open texture and is well drained.

The roots can take up nutrients throughout a long season—probably all year in mild climates. The nutrients may be stored in the roots and trunks until they are used in new growth of leaves, stems, and fruits.

The ideal soil for orchard trees is deep, well drained, free of impervious layers that restrict development of the roots, good in water-holding ability, and slightly acid—pH 5.5 to 6.5.

The danger of injury by low temperatures exists in nearly all deciduous orchard regions of the United States, especially in spring during the early growth period. Sites selected for orchards therefore are protected from spring frost as much as possible. They may be to the south and east of large bodies of water or in elevated locations, where air drainage is good. Low areas, in which cold air tends to settle, are avoided.

Often the elevated and sloping sites that are most nearly frost free do not have the deepest and best soil. The problem of preventing soil erosion on them is serious, particularly if the orchard has to be cultivated during the season when heavy rains are likely. Planting the trees on the contour may be a solution.

Good soil-management practices in orchards require that soil fertility is maintained; that water from rain or irrigation penetrates the soil readily and is not lost by runoff; that soil structure is not unduly injured, despite the hauling of heavy equipment through the orchard; and that conditions favor the growth and fruitfulness of the trees from decade to decade.

Practices that give such results vary with the kind of orchard and the part of the country.

THE APPLE is a deep-rooted, long-lived, slow-growing deciduous tree of the Temperate Zone.

The production of its leaf surface, most of its vegetative growth, its flowering, the early development of the crop, and the initiation of buds for the bloom of the following year all take place in about 9 weeks of the spring and early summer.

In the summer and early fall until harvest, the fruit grows, and the leaves continue to make foods, which may be used at once or stored for the spring growth of the next year. The tree increases its resistance to winter cold in the late autumn after harvest.

These facts have a bearing on the systems of soil management in apple orchards.

The main climatic problems in the regions where apples are an important crop are the hazards of frost during the early growing season, the possibility of freezing in winter, and too little rain or too much rain during the growing season.

The location of the orchard determines the degree of frost hazard. The two natural protections against frost hazard are bodies of water large enough to reduce daily variations in temperature and hillsides or valley slopes that permit the coldest air to move to lower elevations. Most apple orchards are on sloping lands.

The hardiest varieties of apples can

stand temperatures down to 30° F. below zero in midwinter without injury. The least hardy may show injuries at 20° below zero.

All varieties are more susceptible to winter injury if they bore a heavy crop the preceding season, if their leaf surface was poor, and if late vegetative growth caused the trees to go into winter lacking hardiness.

The prevailing climate in a region determines the hazard of killing winter temperatures. The location of the site offers only a slight degree of protection, except when it is near a large body of water that does not freeze over.

Soil management that fosters a healthy leaf surface and permits hardening of the trees for winter helps to reduce losses from winter injury.

The average rainfall, its distribution during the year, the ability of the soil to hold water, and the intensity of evaporation of water from leaf and soil surfaces determine the probabilities of water deficiency in apple orchards.

In sites where soils are shallow or in areas where the annual rainfall is below 30 inches and where less than 15 inches of rain falls during the growing season and transpiration is relatively rapid, the moisture may be deficient often enough to justify supplementary irrigation. Irrigation is necessary if the yearly rainfall is less than 20 inches, less than 10 inches falls during the growing season, and transpiration is high. Practices to conserve moisture are valuable in places where rainfall is marginal. They may involve special modifications of soil management.

In areas where spring rainfall may be excessive, control of fungus diseases becomes a matter of primary importance at the same time that accumulation of excess water in the soil may make it difficult to move heavy spray equipment through the orchard.

APPLE ORCHARDS grow on many different kinds of soils, which vary in texture from heavy clay to light, sandy loam and in nutrient content from low to high fertility.

The soil-management practices that are best for a particular soil situation depend on the depth of rooting of the trees and the fertility in the zone of rooting.

If the soil in a humid climate is well aerated and of medium texture and permits rooting to a depth of 4 feet or more, it has a large enough reservoir for available moisture so that special practices to conserve moisture are unnecessary. They would be needed, however, if rooting is restricted to a zone less than 3 feet deep.

Soil-management practices that promote fertility and supplementary applications of fertilizer likewise are most significant on soils of low fertility. They may give little benefit in places where the initial soil fertility was high.

Anyone who plans to plant an apple orchard should give special attention first to contouring, tile drainage, and orchard roads.

Contour planting may be desirable even though erosion is to be controlled by permanent sod management on hillside locations. It is often the best way to provide orchard roads for sprayers and other equipment.

As there may be a good deal of traffic in apple orchards during the spraying season, the roadways need special protection against gullying.

Although a tile drainage will not change a poor orchard soil into a first-rate one, the use of tile lines to drain out the wet spots often pays big dividends by reducing the difficulties of spraying and other practices during wet weather or in the early spring after a winter of water accumulation.

Special problems of fertility and management arise because apple trees remain in the same positions many years.

Acidifying fungicides and fertilizers that enter the soil mainly under the trees may cause the leaching of replaceable calcium, magnesium, and potassium at a much faster rate and to a greater depth under the trees than between them—a reason for magnesium deficiency in apple orchards planted on soils that initially were acid. The resulting loss of fertility has been a major cause of the disappearance of grass cover under the trees in mature apple orchards. Fungicide or insecticide spray materials may accumulate in the soil and harm plants under the trees.

THE SOIL-MANAGEMENT systems that are available for use in apple orchards include systems based on annual tillage or cultivation and systems based on permanent sod. Supplementary practices that may be combined with either or both systems include irrigation, mulching with organic residues or plant materials, fertilization with nitrogen and other inorganic nutrients, liming, and the use of cover crops.

Many variations of the basic systems and their combination with supplementary practices have been used successfully in apple orchards.

During the early life of an apple orchard, cultivation at least in the tree rows during the first half of the growing season is an almost universal practice. In the first 3 to 5 years, when the trees are small, intense competition for nutrients and water can develop between the small tree and the grass and weeds around it.

Cultivation reduces the competition easily and economically. The branches are short enough in the early years to make possible the use of harrows and other tillage tools to eliminate the plants close to the trunks. Since the terminal growth of the young tree is completed by the end of July, cultivation is needed particularly from April until August.

Thereafter it is customary to allow annual grass and weeds to form a cover during the fall and winter. The cover crop reduces or prevents erosion and permits the trees to harden their tissues against the coldest winter temperatures. If the volunteer cover growth is sparse, cover crops may be seeded in late summer on a rough seedbed in the orchard.

Many grasses and legumes have been used as cover crops in apple orchards. Because of the shade and low fertility in many orchards, strong-growing winter annual grains or grasses usually have been found to be superior to legumes for this purpose.

Among those that have been used are rye and domestic ryegrass. They are seeded on a rough seedbed in August or September and disked down the following spring.

Of the leguminous plants that can furnish satisfactory annual cover, sweetclover has been successful. Both ryegrass and sweetclover are sometimes carried over from one year to the next by permitting some of the plants to survive in the spring as a source of natural seeding in midsummer.

Several implements may be used for cultivation. The disk and spring-tooth harrows are commonly used. Newer tools that cut and shred the cover crop and stir the soil to a shallow depth have been tried in orchards.

Many orchardists no longer cultivate mature orchards annually except to prepare furrows for irrigation in arid regions or to conserve moisture. Even in irrigated regions, the tendency has been away from cultivation as sprinklers have supplanted the use of furrows for distributing water.

If annual cultivation is used in mature apple orchards, tillage usually is limited to the period before mid-June. Terminal growth on bearing trees is finished by then, and the growth of the fruit can continue satisfactorily until harvest if the leaf surface and moisture supply are adequate. Some restriction in the supply of nitrogen caused by the development of volunteer cover on the orchard floor at this time may encourage the development of color in the fruit and tend to improve its storage life.

In cultivated apple orchards, supplementary mulching with undecomposed straw and materials like it can be used only in limited spots under the trees as they foul the equipment.

Lime and phosphate fertilizers are more rapidly available when applied to cultivated orchards than to those in a permanent sod because they are promptly mixed with the surface soil.

Most nitrogen fertilizers and some others are so soluble that stirring them into the soil does not increase the efficiency of use.

Sod culture, the most common soil-management system in apple orchards, lends itself to the relatively modest requirements for growth of mature apple trees. It helps control erosion. Because of the competition of the sod for nitrogen, relatively little nitrogen is available under it except for a short period after the fertilizer is applied. It is possible therefore to control the nitrogen level of trees growing under sod culture—making them high in nitrogen by nitrogen fertilization in the early spring before the bloom and growth periods, and low in nitrogen in late summer and early fall, when the fruit is maturing and the trees are hardening their wood for the winter.

Sod culture combines well with supplementary nitrogen fertilization and with supplementary mulching programs. Hay and straw are satisfactory sources of supplementary nutrient elements and help conserve water in orchards where the soil is shallow and water may become a limiting factor after short periods of drought. Under sod culture, on the other hand, the availability of slowly soluble materials like lime and phosphorus applied to the soil surface is slower than it is in cultivated soils.

Sod management of a mature orchard often brings with it an increase in the need for supplementary nitrogen fertilization over the requirements under a cultivation program. If the surface cover is mainly nonleguminous and mulching is not a part of the program, nitrogen fertilization is required almost always. It can be carried out in various ways, but the nitrogen treatment, to be effective, must raise the nitrogen level of the trees in the early growing season to a level that permits satisfactory set of fruit, vegetative growth, and initiation of flower buds for the crops of the following year. One-half pound to 2 pounds of actual

nitrogen in an inorganic fertilizer may be used annually in order to obtain these effects.

The effects of sod management on the availability of nutrients other than nitrogen vary under different conditions of soil and climate. Potassium availability sometimes may be increased in soils where potassium deficiency symptoms appear under cultivation. This seems to be related partly to the contribution of the permanent cover in bringing potassium continually to the surface in available form and partly to the fact that the development of apple tree roots in the surface 3 inches, permitted under sod culture, gives opportunity for exploration of this region of the horizon. In dry years, however, the presence of sod cover may have the opposite effect on the availability of potassium.

Mulching orchards that are under sod with hay or straw is a supplementary practice that has been useful in a number of places. The effects of the mulch blanket vary in relation to the materials used and the climatic and soil conditions of the orchard.

The effects may include conservation of soil moisture, which may raise the levels of soil moisture under the trees during dry periods; an increase in the amount of available soil nitrogen, which may improve growth and yield responses comparable to those caused by fertilization with commercial nitrogenous materials; and an increase in the amount of available soil potassium, phosphorus, and other nutrients.

Mulching generally has been a satisfactory way to overcome a deficiency of potassium—but not necessarily other nutrients. Benefits from mulching at times appear to be greater than those to be expected from nitrogen and potassium.

The main problems that accompany the large-scale use of mulching are the costs and mechanical difficulties of application and the special hazards of fire and damage by mice.

Because the cost of applying mulch usually is much more than the outlays for buying and applying commercial fertilizer of equivalent nutrient content, special benefits beyond the effects of ordinary fertilizers usually are required to justify mulching. The benefits come oftenest in localities where the soil is shallow and water conservation and fertility are special problems.

A permanent sod culture implies the maintenance of a cover of vegetation throughout the year. In such a system of culture, the growth must be mowed or knocked down at least once in the growing season. It has been customary to use a tractor-drawn, cutter-bar mower for the work under and around the branches of the tree. Increasing use has been made of horizontal rotary shredders, which can cut directly behind the tractor more efficiently than a cutter-bar mower.

The disk harrow and machine shredders that have vertical beaters or knives may partly cultivate the permanent sod without eliminating it.

Among the legumes that are sometimes used for permanent sod in apple orchards are alfalfa, crimson clover, Ladino clover, and birdsfoot trefoil. Among the grasses that have been recommended are orchardgrass, Kentucky bluegrass, and bromegrass. The success of pure stands or seeding mixtures containing these and other species depends on the prevailing climate, the physical and chemical conditions of the soil, the amount of sunlight that reaches the orchard floor, and details of management.

Two conditions limit the success of seeding mixtures in the orchards.

Legumes usually do not survive for long under the branches of apple trees, probably because of the effects of low light and unfavorable soil conditions. The practical usefulness of legumes in young orchards therefore is limited— as the trees expand in perimeter, an increasing proportion of the orchard floor is occupied by grasses that are adapted to those particular conditions of light and soil.

The second condition is fertility. Orchardists often must broadcast complete fertilizers over the entire orchard floor and may need also to counteract extreme acidity under the trees by liming in order to insure a permanent sod.

Because the different species of legumes and grass on an orchard floor adjust themselves to the general situation and the differences of light and fertility, the use of a mixture containing several adapted legumes and grasses is a sounder practice than the use of only one species to establish a sod.

Before seeding and at intervals after establishment of the sod, a light broadcast application of complete fertilizer (plus liming when the soil reaction goes below pH 5.5) will insure a satisfactory permanent cover. The proportions of grasses and legumes in time may change completely from what was originally seeded, but the result will be good.

Perennial woody vines and saplings may establish themselves and multiply in an apple orchard that has a permanent sod. Among them are poison-ivy and brambles. They may be eliminated by sprays of weedkillers, but it is hard to kill them if they have taken over a large part of the orchard floor. Then there is hazard of injury to the trees. Spot spraying of the invading weeds before they have become a serious problem therefore is much better. An annual inspection and spot treatment of this sort should be a regular part of the soil-management program in many apple orchards. At the same time there is almost always need for treatment of the hedgerow shrubs, trees, and vines with low-pressure sprays of herbicides.

THE PEAR, like the apple, is a long-lived, slow-growing deciduous tree of the Temperate Zone. Its growth and flowering habits are like those of the apple.

Pears are grown commercially in a narrower climatic range than apples. Pears generally are grown mostly in the milder, drier, and warmer parts of the apple region because the main commercial varieties bloom somewhat earlier and have less cold resistance than hardy varieties of apple.

Pear growing is more important in the irrigated valleys of the West than in the humid East, where pear blight (*Erwinia amylovorus*) is harder to control. Because of the blight, pears are grown but little commercially south of Pennsylvania on the east coast. Blight-resistant kinds, which generally are inferior in quality, must be used there.

Pears grow on many types of soil in the commercial pear regions of the United States. Because the tree is somewhat more tolerant of poorly aerated soil than some other species are, pears have been planted on some heavy soils, notably in parts of Oregon.

Soil-management systems used in pear orchards are the same as for apples.

Sod culture is almost universal in the Northeastern States.

Because vigorously growing pear trees are more susceptible to blight than less vegetative ones, trees in the East seldom are allowed to be very vegetative, and sod culture is used to hold growth to a minimum. Light fertilization or mulch may be used occasionally to bring the trees to the level of vigor required for moderate productivity. Even newly planted pear trees may be started in the East under sod culture with mulch or manure.

In the West, where irrigation is required and blight is controlled more easily, cultivation is usually practiced during the growing season, and weeds and grass cover the land in winter.

Supplementary fertilization with nitrogen and other nutrients, if they are lacking, is a common practice. The fertilizers usually are applied in bands under the spread of the branches.

The cover crops that are successful in apple orchards are satisfactory in pear orchards.

Two CHERRY SPECIES are important commercially in the United States— *Prunus cerasus*, the sour cherry, and *P. avium*, the sweet cherry.

The sour cherry is a small, spreading, rather vegetative tree of the Temperate Zone. It is about as hardy as the least hardy varieties of pear. Because it blooms early in the spring, it must be planted in situations protected from spring frost by large bodies of water or by air drainage. Most of our sour cherries are produced in the Northeastern and North Central States, especially near the Great Lakes.

The sweet cherry is a large, upright tree. It is less hardy than the sour cherry and blooms a little earlier. Thus it grows in the more protected situations. Because the fruit tends to crack if rain comes when it approaches maturity, about three-quarters of our sweet cherries are produced in the Pacific and Intermountain States, where summers generally are dry.

The sweet and sour cherries must be kept reasonably vegetative to produce well. As they are somewhat lacking in winter hardiness and the cultural conditions that favor vegetation may delay hardening of the tissues for winter, some special problems of soil management arise.

Because both sweet and sour cherries are sensitive to the effects of imperfect aeration in the subsoil, they are grown mostly on deep soils of light texture.

Cultivation, cover cropping, and supplemental fertilization are commonly practiced throughout the life of the orchard to promote the necessary vegetative growth. The period of cultivation often lasts until early July, so that the growth of cover crop or volunteer grasses and weeds does not interfere with harvest operations.

On soils of only moderate fertility, supplementary spring applications of nitrogen fertilizer are made annually. The combination of cultivation and application of nitrogen usually encourages vegetative growth enough.

Often a deficiency of potassium occurs in cherry orchards in the East. Zinc often is deficient in the West. A deficiency of potassium is controlled by applying muriate or sulfate of potash every 2 or 3 years. Zinc deficiency is corrected by spraying the trees with zinc sulfate solution before the buds break in spring. Enough is absorbed through leaf scars, growth cracks, and other breaks in the bark largely to correct the deficiency.

The development of a good cover crop near the end of the summer is important to reduce erosion and to check vegetative growth and permit the trees to harden their tissues before winter. The success of volunteer or seeded cover crops in the late summer depends on fertility and moisture conditions. A light application of complete fertilizer of low nitrogen content broadcast over the entire orchard floor greatly improves the stand of the cover in many cherry orchards.

Winter annuals, grains or grasses, or perennials that can be treated as winter annuals are useful for cover crops.

Rye, domestic ryegrass, and field bromegrass (*Bromus arvensis*) are examples of the kind of plants that germinate and establish themselves on a rough seedbed in late August and September and can be worked down the next spring. Ryegrass and brome respond to trashy cultivation—a system whereby the cover crop is torn up but not eliminated in the spring and early summer and enough plants may produce seed to regenerate the cover without reseeding. This procedure has been used for several years in some orchards before a new seeding is needed.

Sod culture combined with mulching has been successful in places where erosion is serious or the soil is shallow. In the Door County section of Wisconsin, for instance, bedrock high in lime is apt to be close to the surface, and sour cherry trees commonly show symptoms of potassium deficiency. Mulching the trees is the most effective means of restoring them to productivity.

In places where the soil is deep and erosion is not a major problem, however, many growers of sour cherries prefer to practice cultivation and cover cropping. A permanent sod and sod-mulching culture are commoner with sweet cherries than sour cherries for two reasons: The sweet cherry tree is more subject to winter injury of the trunk and crotches as a result of too

much vegetative growth than is the sour cherry, and the sweet cherry may be quite productive at lower levels of vegetative growth and therefore responds less readily to cultivation, as compared to sod culture.

A LITTLE MORE than half of our peach crop is produced west of the Rocky Mountains. Rainfall there generally is low, and little of it comes in the growing season.

Irrigation by flooding, furrows, or sprinklers supplies the needed moisture. Orchards on level ground and soils of moderate texture, common in the valleys of California, are flood irrigated. Furrow or sprinkler irrigation is used on light soils and sloping sites.

Most of the soils are nearly neutral in reaction. Nitrogen is the main nutrient that must be supplied. Zinc may be needed in many orchards. Chlorosis, caused by too little iron in available form, is present in some areas.

The States east of the Great Plains produce a little less than half of our peach crop. Most orchards are not irrigated. The soil must be managed to conserve moisture, avoid soil erosion, and maintain good fertility. Nitrogen is applied to practically all orchards. Potassium is generally needed in the Coastal Plain of the Gulf and Atlantic States and in localities in other sections. Magnesium may be needed in the Atlantic and Gulf Coastal Plains.

Peach trees have shallower roots than most other tree fruits and do not tolerate competition with grass or other vegetation so well as apples and pears. For that reason, few peach orchards are maintained in sod. Nearly all receive some cultivation.

Because the peach blooms early and is subject to damage by spring frost, orchards in many sections are planted on elevated sites and often on sloping land. Soil erosion therefore is a serious problem, particularly where rainfall may be heavy in summer.

The peach crop is produced entirely on "new" wood—the growth of the preceding season. Trees, to remain productive, therefore must make strong growth each year. The growth of terminal shoots should be 12 to 15 inches and well distributed each season. Relatively heavy pruning and adequate fertilization and soil-management programs achieve that.

The orchards in nearly all peach areas are cultivated in the spring and are given shallow cultivation two or three times more up to harvest to keep the orchard relatively free of grass and weeds. A cover crop may be seeded after harvest. More commonly, weed growth is allowed to develop to provide winter cover and organic matter for incorporating into the soil the following spring.

The peach fruits grow most rapidly during a period of about a month before harvest. If water is insufficient then, the final size and quality of the fruits will be poor. It is important therefore to keep other vegetation from competing for water during and before that critical period, especially if irrigation is not available.

One-half to three-fourths pound of actual nitrogen a tree generally is applied to full-bearing orchards. Larger amounts of nitrogen may reduce the coloring of the fruit on varieties that generally do not have a very high color. That amount of nitrogen is needed to maintain satisfactory growth and fruitfulness. Nitrogen generally is applied in early spring, preferably 2 or 3 weeks before growth starts. Applications in the fall are satisfactory if winter rainfall is not excessive.

On sites where erosion is a problem, a fast-growing cover crop should be seeded immediately after harvest in order to obtain maximum cover for winter. Rye and vetch are commonly used in the Eastern States. This cover is allowed to grow until spring.

The time of disking down the cover in spring is an important and sometimes difficult decision for the grower. There has been little difference in effect on the trees from early (before bloom) disking as compared with late (after bloom) disking. The later disking adds more organic matter to the soil and more crop debris to reduce erosion. There is some evidence, however, that a growing cover crop results in slightly lower temperatures in the orchards on frosty nights than occur above cultivated soil. Some growers in areas where the frost hazard is high therefore cut in the cover crop or volunteer growth before the trees bloom. If erosion is likely to be serious, however, the additional erosion control from later disking of a heavier cover is to be preferred even at the slightly greater risk of frost damage.

When erosion is an important factor, the cover crop should be allowed to develop heavy spring growth. Rye may be left until the heading stage, which generally occurs 3 to 4 weeks after the peaches bloom. It is then cut down, generally by disking. The disk blades, if they are set nearly straight, will cut down the cover crop but leave much of it on the surface, where it does the most good in preventing erosion. Two or three similar diskings may be needed later to prevent new weed growth up to harvest.

In areas where erosion is not a problem and a heavy growth of weeds develops after cultivation has stopped, weeds provide satisfactory cover in winter. Cultivation in the spring then usually precedes bloom in order to reduce the frost hazard.

Difficulty has been experienced in many peach-producing areas in attempting to establish young orchards on land from which old trees have recently been removed. A number of factors may be responsible. The soil may be made acid by sulfur sprays and acid-forming fertilizers. Nematodes, which attack peach roots, and possibly insects that feed on the roots may have accumulated in the soil in places.

Moderate applications of lime mixed with the soil before planting young trees have been helpful in acid soils. Soil fumigation has been beneficial on some soils. Combinations of liming and fumigation have been better than either alone in some instances.

MOST OF OUR COMMERCIAL plum and prune production is in the irrigated valleys of the Western States. Soil-management practices are similar to those we outlined for peaches.

Orchards generally are cultivated in the spring and maintained in cultivation through the summer. Most of the prunes for drying are allowed to drop to the ground. The soil in such orchards is cultivated at intervals to harvest and then is thoroughly prepared and smoothed down in order to have a good surface from which the fruits may be picked up easily. After harvest, weed growth is allowed to develop or a cover crop is planted.

APRICOTS are the earliest of the tree fruits to bloom. They are grown commercially almost entirely in the Pacific coast valleys, which are relatively free from spring frosts. Elevated sites with good air drainage are more essential for apricots than for other fruits.

The areas of apricot production receive little summer rainfall. Erosion is not serious in most apricot orchards.

Soil-management practices are essentially the same as for peaches. Orchards are cultivated in late winter or early spring and maintained under cultivation until after the fruit harvest, which is in July in most districts. Weed growth is allowed to develop after harvest for cover and organic matter.

THE PECAN is the largest orchard tree grown in the United States. Trees on suitable soil may attain a height of 60 feet and a branch spread of 80 feet or more. To allow for such development, mature pecan trees on deep, fertile soils should be at least 75 feet apart. The trees in orchards are initially set 40 to 50 feet apart, and alternate trees are removed when they begin to crowd at 20 to 25 years of age.

At such distance of planting, intercrops are often grown during the early years of the orchard. Cultivated and fertilized intercrops, such as cotton, have been satisfactory. The conditions that promote the growth of cotton are generally favorable for the growth of the trees.

When the trees have attained bearing age, a management program involving pasturing of cattle among the trees generally has been satisfactory.

Winter legumes or mixtures of legumes and grains may be seeded in the fall. They should be well fertilized with potassium and phosphorus and with some nitrogen if a grain is used in the mixture. Five hundred pounds an acre of 0–10–10 fertilizer for legumes or of 4–10–10 fertilizer for a mixture of legumes and grain should be applied when the winter cover crop is seeded. Such fertilization makes for a heavy growth of cover crop and a large production of feed for grazing in most parts of the pecan area, which is almost the same area as the Cotton Belt.

Some legume cover crops will reseed themselves if they are left in the orchard and allowed to seed in the spring.

The orchard may be given a relatively shallow disking in the spring. Disking may be repeated at intervals in summer to hold growth in check.

Bermuda-grass is present in many orchards and may be pastured in summer. If it is not pastured, shallow cultivation at approximately monthly intervals is wise to hold the growth.

Pecans are harvested in October and November. The nuts are shaken from the tree and picked up from the ground. It is important not to have vegetation in the orchard then. Orchards therefore are usually cultivated or mowed just before harvest.

If Bermuda-grass is allowed to grow and is pastured during the summer, additional nitrogen to maintain growth of the grass and trees may be necessary. It should be broadcast in the spring.

The pecan needs more zinc than some other crop plants do. Zinc deficiency, which causes rosette, may be serious in many orchards. The zinc may be applied to the surface of acid soils and will penetrate to the roots. On neutral or alkaline soils, however, zinc applied to the soils generally is not effective. The deficiency then can be corrected by applying a zinc sulfate solution as a spray to the foliage. Two pounds of zinc sulfate in 100 gallons of water is generally used.

THE PERSIAN (ENGLISH) WALNUT is grown commercially in the United States in California and Oregon. The trees attain large size. The distance between mature trees on fertile soil should be at least 50 feet.

Most of the orchards in California and a few of those in Oregon are irrigated. Nearly all orchards are handled with summer cultivation and winter cover crops.

As with pecans, nut harvest is in late fall, and it is desirable to have the soil smooth and relatively free of vegetative growth at that time. Often the cover crop is seeded just in advance of harvest, so little growth will have been made to interfere with harvesting. These cover crops grow through the winter and are turned into the soil in the spring. Occasional shallow summer cultivation is given to control weeds.

In the walnut-producing localities, nitrogen is the chief fertilizer element needed. Most orchards are given about 100 pounds of elemental nitrogen an acre. Boron is needed to promote maximum production in some areas, particularly in Oregon.

THE FOLLOWING PARAGRAPHS give some details about other fruit and nut crops.

The almond (Prunus amygdalus) blossoms so early that commercial culture is limited largely to California. Spring frosts destroy the crop in most other sections. Well-drained, light-textured soils (pH 5 to 8) are ideal. The almond will tolerate well-drained clays but not waterlogged soil. The tree is drought tolerant and often is planted where the moisture supply is limited, but it needs ample moisture for good production. It has some tolerance to salt and alkali.

Avocado (Persea americana), a tropical fruit, is subject to injury when temperatures go below 28° F. It is unusually sensitive to poorly drained soil.

It grows successfully on marl soils of southern Florida. Rather open, well-drained soils (pH 5 to 7.5) are ideal. It will not tolerate salt in soil or irrigation water.

Blackberry (Rubus) varieties are available that are adapted to all sections of the United States, except the coldest parts and the southern half of Florida. Because they bloom late, spring frosts are not a hazard, but the canes are subject to injury by low winter temperatures. Blackberries thrive best on medium-textured, sandy loams to clay loams (pH 5 to 7.5). They do poorly on coarse sands or poorly drained clays. The plants are easily killed by waterlogged conditions but need ample moisture for good production.

Various species of blueberry (Vaccinium) grow in nearly all areas of the United States where soils are acid. They cannot be grown satisfactorily in soils above pH 6 in reaction. They thrive best in moist but well-drained soils from sandy loams to well-drained clays. They do best under permanent mulches, particularly sawdust. The plants seem unable to obtain necessary iron under neutral or alkaline soil conditions. The best pH range is 4.5 to 5.5.

The Chinese chestnut (Castanea mollissima) is the only chestnut that can be recommended for planting in the United States. It is resistant to chestnut blight, the disease that has destroyed the native chestnut. It is suited to the areas where peaches can be grown. It is subject to winter injury in areas where temperatures may drop to —20° F. It does not tolerate poorly drained soil but succeeds on well-drained, fine sands and loams (pH 5 to 7). It is not tolerant to salt or alkali.

The cranberry (Vaccinium macrocarpon) is the most exacting in soil requirements of our fruits. The plant is native to swampy areas in the Northeastern States and as far south as North Carolina. The vine is not hardy to very low temperature. It survives when it is covered with snow or ice and water in the North. It requires porous, acid soil (pH 4 to 5). Peat bogs are largely used for cranberries. They are leveled. The surface soil usually is removed. Then the bogs are coated with about 2 inches of sand before planting. They are diked so they can be flooded during the winter to protect the vines. During the growing season, the water table is maintained about 2 feet below the surface; in dry weather, it is raised periodically to wet the soil. Culture of cranberries in mineral soil generally is not satisfactory.

The date palm (*Phoenix dactylifera*) requires extremely hot, arid conditions and abundant soil moisture, supplied by surface irrigation or subirrigation. Culture in the United States is limited to desert areas of southern California and Arizona. Rainfall during the ripening season will cause the crop to ferment and to sour on the tree. Soil should be deep and open and well drained (pH 5.5 to 8.5). Loamy sands to sandy loams are preferred, but the date palm will thrive on well-drained clays. It is one of the most salt tolerant of fruit plants.

The fig (*Ficus carica*) will withstand temperatures to 15° F. when fully dormant. Lower temperatures frequently injure or kill the tops. Commercial culture is largely in California, but plantings for home and local market exist throughout the Southern States and along the Atlantic seaboard to New Jersey. They are not exacting as to soils. They thrive in well-drained soils from fine sands to clays (pH 5 to 8). They are sensitive to nematodes. The soil should be fumigated before planting if many nematodes are present. Fig trees are moderately tolerant to salt.

Filbert (*Corylus avellana*) is grown commercially in the United States, mostly in western Oregon and Washington. Varieties suited to median latitudes of the Eastern States are available. The trees are rather shallow rooted and are not tolerant to a high water table or poorly drained soil. They thrive best on sandy loams to clay loams (pH 5 to 7.5), but will grow on well-drained clays. They are rather intolerant to salt and alkali.

Grapes (*Vitis* species) can be grown in all sections of the United States. The vines require winter covering in the coldest localities. Grapes thrive best on well-aerated soils—medium sands to loams (pH 5 to 8) are ideal, but grapes will tolerate well-drained clays. The plants root deeply and are more drought resistant than most fruits. They are medium in salt tolerance.

Grapefruit (*Citrus paradisii*) are subtropical evergreen trees that are subject to injury if temperatures go below about 27° F. They are adapted to a wide range of soils, but different rootstocks are used on fine-textured soils (pH 5 to 8). A medium-textured soil is ideal, but the trees can be grown on moderately well-drained clays or clay loams. They are rather tolerant to salt and alkalinity.

Lemon (*Citrus limon*) is a little tenderer than oranges or grapefruit, is more subject to disease in humid climates, and is more sensitive to unfavorable soil conditions and to salt and alkalinity. It thrives best on medium to light-textured, well-drained soil (pH 5 to 7.5) but it can be grown on well-drained clay loam.

Olive (*Olea europaea*) is a rather small, evergreen tree. It will endure temperatures as low as 15° F. It is highly drought resistant. It has been widely planted in areas of limited water supply, but it requires good soil moisture for maximum production. Commercial production has not been successful in areas with humid summers, such as the Gulf States, although trees there will bear some fruits. Trees do not tolerate waterlogged soil. Open, well-drained sandy loams to clay loams (pH 5 to 8) are ideal. It is moderately tolerant to salt and alkaline soil.

Orange (*Citrus sinensis*) will tolerate temperatures as low as about 27° F. without serious injury. It can be grown on a wide range of soils, but it thrives best on medium- to open-textured, well-drained soils (pH 5 to 8). On soils of finer texture, special stocks must be used. For maximum production, ample moisture must be available throughout the year, although the tree will tolerate temporary conditions of water shortage. Roots die in water-logged soil rather quickly. It is moderately tolerant of salt.

Raspberry (*Rubus*) thrives in the northern half of the United States, except in the coldest sections. They do not grow and fruit satisfactorily in the South. They require ample moisture, but they are sensitive to waterlogged soil. They thrive best on sandy loams to clay loams (pH 5 to 7.5) but will grow in well-drained clay. They are relatively shallow rooted and grow best, especially in the warmer locations, if they are kept mulched with organic material.

Strawberry (*Fragaria*) may be grown in all parts of the United States. They require a winter cover of mulch in cold areas. Because plants root to 2 feet, the water table should be lower than that. They thrive on loamy sands (pH 5 to 7.5). They can be grown on well-drained clays, but soils of light to medium texture are preferred. They are not tolerant of salt or alkali.

Tung (*Aleurites fordii*) is a nonedible nut crop that is grown for oil for industrial use. It is adapted to areas where temperatures rarely go below 15° F., but where a moderate winter cold occurs. They are grown mainly within 150 miles of the Gulf of Mexico in northern Florida and southern Georgia and west to Texas. They are subject to spring-frost damage and fall or winter cold. Their roots are relatively shallow. The trees do not thrive and produce satisfactorily on coarse sands or fine-textured clay. Deep, well-drained, fine sands to loams (pH 5 to 7) are ideal. Somewhat heavy fertilization with nitrogen, potassium, zinc, and copper is required in some places. The trees do not stand salt or alkali in soil.

The black walnut (*Juglans nigra*) is a native tree in the middle latitudes from Iowa and Kansas to the Atlantic. Its soil requirement is similar to that of the Persian walnut. Sandy loams to well-drained clay loams (pH 5.5 to 8) are ideal. It does not tolerate a high water table or poorly drained subsoils.

Soil Management for Forest Trees

Frank W. Woods, Otis L. Copeland, Jr., and Carl E. Ostrom

A rising demand for wood is forcing the Nation to increase the productivity of its existing forest land, develop areas previously considered too poor for commercial timber, and rehabilitate eroded lands.

Forest managers, in their efforts to increase the supply of wood, are striving to regulate soil moisture, check soilborne diseases, improve soil fertility and structure, and prevent erosion.

It is not yet practical to manage forest soils as intensively as land planted with field crops. Less is known about the subject, and the value of the timber crop does not always justify large per-acre investments. The forest manager still has relatively few direct controls over his land; he must rely on manipulation of the plant cover to accomplish many things that the farmer does with harrow, fertilizer, and irrigation.

Nevertheless, advances in technology and the pressures on land are bringing a change.

ENOUGH WATER at the right time—that is the tree growers' main problem:

Some lowlands and hardpan sites have drainage troubles, but such areas are local and occupy a relatively small total acreage. The total annual precipitation is ample for tree growth in forested regions, but much of the water comes when trees cannot use it.

A deficiency of soil moisture usually

is the most important limitation to the survival of tree seedlings in the field. An effective and practical means for increasing soil moisture for seedlings is to minimize the amount transpired by weed plants. The method of doing so varies with the species of tree that is being grown and with the nature and size of the competing weeds.

Scalping—removing surface vegetation for a radius of 10 to 20 inches from the planting spot—is used commonly on poor sites and on good sites where competition is severe. It sets back the weeds long enough for the young seedling to become established. A planting lane, prepared by plowing or harrowing strips, gives greater freedom from competition for a longer time.

On the deep sands of the southern Coastal Plain, all competing vegetation (mainly scrub oak and wiregrass) must be removed before pines can be planted successfully. Two trips over the site with heavy root rakes, harrows, or double drum choppers usually will do the job. (Oaks should be allowed to resprout before the second trip.) Pine survival is good on these bare sites, and a part of the cost of site preparation is offset by the greater ease of planting.

When most of the vegetation is removed or turned under, the hazard of fire is small, at least for a few years. So far there is no indication that erosion, whether by wind or water, is a problem on these deep, coarse sands. On fine-textured and shallow soils, however, the removal of all vegetation can cause large evaporation losses and damage the site through erosion or in other ways.

A good stand of natural seedlings often is obtained by harrowing or otherwise scarifying the soil immediately before seedfall. Properly timed logging operations can serve the same purpose at practically no extra cost. Scarifying is not recommended in forest types where root damage results in a high incidence of root rot.

After tree stands are established, soil moisture can still be conserved most readily by removing competing vegetation. The individual weed trees are usually chopped down, girdled, or treated with chemicals, such as 2,4-D and 2,4,5-T. If brush or shrubs are abundant, chemical foliage sprays may be necessary. In the Lake States and elsewhere, airplanes have been effective in applying chemicals over large areas to release conifers suppressed by undesirable broad-leaved trees.

Controlled fire is used often to reduce the competition from understory shrubs temporarily. Woody shrubs nearly always resprout after burning, however, and the number of stems per acre may be increased instead of reduced. The fact that burning often kills desirable trees also limits its use.

Irrigation cannot be recommended as a general forestry practice, but open ditches sometimes are used to supply water to special forest lands, such as those set aside for seed orchards. Such high-value land may justify large investments to insure good seed crops in drought years.

TOO MUCH SOIL MOISTURE is a problem in thousands of acres of forests in the Eastern States. These wetland forests are of spruce, fir, and tamarack in the Lake States. They are cypress, swamp hardwoods, and pond pine (*Pinus serotina*) in the South.

Excessive wetness of the soil or a high water table limits the kinds of trees that will live on an area and usually retards their growth. Sometimes the remedy is simply drainage of the excess water. Near Brunswick, Ga., for example, the removal of excess surface water by ditching has permitted the invasion of fast-growing slash pine into slower growing open stands of cypress.

But more often the best remedy is water control, which implies keeping the water table at the desired level through drainage carefully controlled by gates in the ditches. In the subtropical climate of southern Florida, where the summers are extremely wet and the winters extremely dry, a commercial tree nursery is alternately

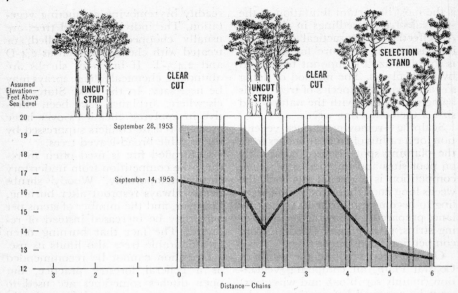

Typical water table profiles from a series of temporary wells extending from a clearcut area into a selectively cut stand of loblolly pine in eastern North Carolina.

drained in summer and irrigated in winter.

The problem of too much water in some seasons and too little in others is accentuated on hardpan soils in times of abundant rainfall. The pan impedes percolation of water down through the soil and results in a perched water table very close to the surface. Then in dry seasons the water in the shallow upper layers soon is exhausted, and the pan prevents the roots from growing into moister depths. A grassy savannah develops on such sites. Tests have been started in Florida to see if planted pines will succeed on the mounds thrown up by subsoil plows that break through the hardpan. The trees have responded favorably, but results have not been conclusive.

Tree species vary in their tolerance of a high water table. On reservoir areas of the Tennessee Valley Authority, all woody species were killed when the root crowns were periodically flooded for more than half the time during a number of successive growing seasons.

Extensive upland swamp areas, called pocosins, occur in eastern North Carolina. They support stands of pond pine, which grow rather slowly and are hard to protect, manage, and harvest because of the high water level. Studies have shown that these lands, if given proper water control, can be converted to a crop of more valuable loblolly pine (*Pinus taeda*) with a considerably higher rate of volume growth per acre.

Trees themselves can exert a decided effect on the water table by "pumping" water off into the air through transpiration, particularly in low-lying flatwoods areas.

The drawing illustrates the difference in water table level on cutover land compared with that under a stand of loblolly pine on the Bigwoods Experimental Forest on the Coastal Plain of eastern North Carolina.

The water table level is an important consideration in the culture and harvesting of cypress in the Deep South. A lumber company at Harvey, La., creates levees around cypress areas and pumps in 30 inches of water to permit rafting out the logs with the aid of motorboats. The trees are girdled several months before harvest so that they will dry out and float well. Cypress seedlings will stand only about 3 days of complete submergence when in leaf. It is possible with careful nursery culture to produce 3-foot cypress seedlings in a season for planting on flooded areas.

FOREST DISEASES are often related to soil conditions.

In the northern Rockies, for example, pole blight of western white pine is most severe on shallow, rocky soils or on soils whose dense hardpan restricts root development. It is seldom serious on deep, well-developed soils that store water readily.

The dieback of sweetgum may be connected with soil conditions.

Several dry years may be the cause of a canker of yellow-poplar in Mississippi. It has been suggested that the fungus associated with the canker is always present, but is inactive until drought lowers the vigor of the trees.

Impeded drainage also causes diseases. Loblolly pine plantations in the Southeast are affected by spot die-out on heavy soils that have poor drainage and aeration. Cultural methods to correct these diseases need much more investigation. The best recommendation we can give is to recognize and avoid hazardous sites for these species.

A research team at Cornell University has developed a drainage-hazard scale for grouping soils according to their suitability for planting to red pine:

Subsoil drainage	Suitability for red pine
Excessive to well	Suitable
Moderate	Uncertain
Imperfect, poor, or very poor ..	Hazardous
Alkaline soils, all drainage levels.	Hazardous

As the scale implies, good drainage usually means good growth, but red pine in Wisconsin suffers from needle droop disease in sands or sandy loams that have low water-holding ability. It is hard to find a rule that will apply generally to all sites and all strains of a species.

Littleleaf disease of shortleaf pine has been associated with poor aeration and imperfect drainage. A littleleaf hazard rating has been developed based on four observable soil characteristics—degree of erosion, subsoil consistence, depth to zone of greatly reduced permeability, and subsoil mottling. This soil-rating system predicts which soils will support disease-free stands.

Soil management that minimizes soil disturbance, soil drying, and mortality of rootlets may reduce the birch dieback in the Northeastern States and in eastern Canada.

In a study carried out in New Brunswick, raising the average summer soil temperature 2° C. above normal, by the use of soil heating cables, caused rootlet mortality to rise from 6 percent to 60 percent the same year. The trees were healthy when the study began, but they soon showed typical dieback symptoms. The effects of excessive temperatures are worse on light, shallow soils.

In the West and North, especially in the Lake States, high temperatures of surface soil kill or injure newly planted seedlings, and mulch or other protection often is needed. Heat injury is much less frequent in the South, probably because the southern pines form bark very early—and bark is an efficient insulator.

THE FERTILITY REQUIREMENTS of trees are not well understood, but they seem to vary greatly, especially among the pines. It is possible that mineral deficiencies are partly responsible for some loss of growth that is ascribed to fungi, drought, or excess water.

The most practical step in maintaining good fertility in forest soils is to build up and maintain a mull type of humus. The humus is like a sponge in absorbing water and helps hold mineral elements in the upper soil layers. It is the seat of the greatest microbiological activity and acts as a nutrient reservoir. Humus may be deficient in warm and hot climates because decomposition of organic matter proceeds rapidly and continues throughout the year. In cold climates with short growing seasons, slow decomposition may permit accumulation of litter and humus to such an extent that water, percolating through, becomes highly acid and leaches out minerals in the upper horizons.

Nitrogen fertilizers have often increased tree growth but are too expensive for general use in forests. Experiments in Washington have shown that carefully controlled applications of nitrogen can improve the quality of Douglas-fir grown for Christmas trees.

When fertilization becomes generally feasible, it may well be done by foliage application rather than through the soil. This will allow rapid applications to extensive areas and efficient use of the fertilizer. Broadcast applications of fertilizer can be detrimental. Weeds and grasses may respond vigorously to fertilizer and smother pine seedlings or rob them of soil moisture.

Some of the most extensive soil amendment and fertilizer tests conducted in the United States were made in connection with the littleleaf disease of shortleaf pine. Fertilization with 200 pounds of available nitrogen to the acre, from sodium nitrate or ammonium sulfate, prevented the onset of disease symptoms in healthy trees and improved diseased trees. Still better results were obtained when potassium and phosphorus were included.

The micronutrients—the trace elements—may increase tree growth even when applied in small amounts.

Many plantations of Monterey pine in Australia were growing very poorly—except the trees next to fence rows. Investigation revealed that the soil was deficient in zinc but that the rainwater dissolved minute quantities of zinc from the galvanized fence wire. Growth in the entire stand was stimulated by adding tiny amounts of zinc to the soil.

Some elements are absolutely necessary in trace quantities but are toxic in slightly higher concentrations. In some agricultural soils in Florida, toxicity symptoms appeared when molybde-num was added every year for 5 years instead of once every 5 years.

Levels of forest soil fertility can be raised temporarily by burning the litter and ground cover. Burning releases nonvolatile minerals, but the loss of potential humus may eventually cancel the immediate gain. Studies in California and Oregon indicated that only a small percentage of the land area of a burn actually receives a severe burn. Both pH and soil fertility are increased for a few years; if the soil erosion hazard is not increased, the survival and growth of planted tree seedlings may be excellent.

Fertility problems in the Lake States sometimes have been corrected by breaking a hardpan to release mineral elements. Plowing has proved to be highly satisfactory but cannot be done if the pan is too deep to be reached with a subsoil plow.

COMPACTION OF THE SOIL, so that roots cannot penetrate, sometimes is a problem. Some cultivated land in Mississippi has been abandoned because of compaction of soil and formation of plowsole. Cottonwoods are often planted in those areas. If the plowsoles are ripped with a chisel before trees are set out, the roots develop faster, and the available water is increased.

Repeated trampling by grazing cattle, especially when the soil is wet, can injure a site through destruction of organic matter, increased compaction, reduced storage of moisture, increased light intensity, lower humidity, and higher soil temperatures.

Heavy logging machinery should not be used on soils or in seasons when compaction is likely.

Synthetic soil conditioners may have use in restoring compacted soils in intensively used areas like parks, logging ramps, and campgrounds, but they have not yet proved practical for general forestry purposes.

SOIL STABILIZATION is usually no problem in undisturbed forests, but once the forest cover is removed, erosion and loss of storage capacity may take place. Stabilization difficulties are greatest in the mountainous areas, but they can be serious in flatlands, particularly in soils high in organic matter.

Logging sometimes improves the forest seedbed. On most sites, however, the danger of erosion requires that logging be carried out with minimum disturbance of the ground cover. Depending on the erosive character of the soils, logging in mountainous national forests is done under restrictions: Downslope logging usually is not permitted, grades are carefully planned, diversion ditches are essential, and the logging roads must be "put to bed" after they are abandoned.

Soil stabilization is especially important in the chaparral watersheds of southern California. The year after a fire, erosion may be 30 times greater than before. Sowing black mustard from airplanes is an economical and effective way to get some plant cover to hold the soil in place until the chaparral reoccupies the site.

MANAGEMENT of soils in forest nurseries is advanced further than management of forest soils.

Nurseries have a high per-acre value and can be treated intensively. Their soils are important because the success of plantings depends to a large extent on the use of thrifty, disease-free planting stock. Among the more troublesome nursery diseases are root rots, damping-off, nutritional deficiencies, frost-heaving, winterkill, drought, and heat injuries.

Proper drainage of wet nursery sites and care in the selection of water to be used for irrigation will decrease root rot and damping-off. Tile drains or open-ditch drains are effective, especially when the seedbeds also are elevated. The use of highly saline water for irrigation is unwise, as it may lower soil acidity and favor certain seedling diseases.

Nutrient deficiencies and chlorosis commonly occur in nursery beds depleted by intensive use. Sawdust generally improves soil tilth and the vigor and size of seedlings. Amendments such as nitrogen, phosphorus, and potassium, however, must also be added. Complete fertilizers are more beneficial than applications of single elements unless the latter are special-purpose applications. If any chlorosis and stunting are evident, foliage sprays or soil applications of potassium, phosphorus, magnesium, manganese, and iron may give a favorable response.

Shelterbelts and Windbreaks

Ernest J. George, Ralph A. Read, E. W. Johnson, and A. E. Ferber

Shelterbelts and windbreaks are plantings of trees and shrubs that are high and dense enough to reduce wind velocity and prevent the drifting of snow.

They have many values and purposes: To protect the farm home and buildings; to shelter livestock, stack areas, and feed lots; to protect orchards, gardens, and cultivated fields and crops against winds that might erode the soil, injure seedlings, or damage the maturing crops; to hold snow on the land to increase soil moisture; to prevent highways from becoming blocked by drifted snow; to provide habitat for birds; to provide, sometimes, posts, poles, and fuelwood; and to please the eye.

Shelterbelts and windbreaks are planted most extensively in the Prairies and Plains, between the forested regions of the Mississippi River States and the Rocky Mountains. It is primarily a grassland area, sparse in natural tree growth. It has diverse soils, high rates of evaporation and transpiration, extremes in temperature, and droughts.

Only hardy species of trees grow in the Plains, and their growth depends largely on the relationship between water and soil. Soil moisture and soil air greatly influence the vigor, growth, and longevity of trees.

The amount of yearly precipitation and the amount that enters the soil largely determine the degree of success obtained with trees and shrubs in the Great Plains.

The average rainfall in the northern Great Plains is 24 inches a year in the eastern part and about 12 inches in the west. In the southern Great Plains it is 30 inches along the eastern boundary and about 12 inches farther west.

About 76 percent of the average annual precipitation falls during the growing season—April to September in the northern section. Another 18 percent falls as snow, which can be of great benefit when it is retained by trees or other vegetation.

Sixty-five percent of the annual precipitation falls during the growing season in the southern Great Plains.

The best soils for shelterbelts and windbreaks in the dryland sections usually are sandy or silty loams. Clay soils usually are considered to be submarginal for tree growth in the drier regions. Extremely sandy soils easily take in water, but they store little moisture. The moisture in sandy loam soils is more evenly distributed to greater depths than in fine-textured soils, and the trees there develop deeper and more extensive root systems. Less rain is required on the porous sandy loam soil than on the fine-textured soils in which water penetrates slowly. A higher percentage of the water held by the soil is available in the coarser textured ones.

We estimate that not more than 25 percent of the annual precipitation becomes available for plants as effective soil moisture, although that varies with the nature of the soil. Part of the precipitation that falls may be lost by runoff, part is lost by interception in the wooded overstory, and part of what does enter the soil is lost by evaporation.

Fine-textured soils, such as clays, have a slow water-infiltration rate, and the runoff may be higher during high-intensity storms. They can hold more water, but a higher percentage of the water is not available for plant use.

Their slower infiltration rate and greater water-holding ability prevent a given amount of moisture from penetrating as deeply as it would on the coarser soils. The soil-held water that is not available for plant use may vary from 10 to 15 percent in clays to 2 to 4 percent in sandy soils.

J. S. Cole and O. R. Mathews, of the Department of Agriculture, reported that the available water for wheat averages nearly 1 inch for every foot in depth of soil (to 6 feet) for sandy soils, almost 1.25 inches for very fine sandy loam, and 1.44 for silty clay loam.

The amounts of available moisture in the area occupied by roots are too small to maintain a vigorous tree growth. Trees in a relatively young planting sometimes have the advantage of drawing on moisture stored in the soil before planting.

Studies at the Northern Great Plains Field Station, Mandan, N. Dak., disclosed that tree roots do not penetrate a dry layer of soil, even though there might be a supply of moisture just below it.

Only in localities where snowdrifts are deep is the exhausted soil moisture replenished beyond the first 2 feet during the dormant period. Trees and shrubs have to live on current moisture after they have exhausted the stored moisture in the root zone. Only in small, isolated places is the water table near enough to the surface to benefit trees and other crops, even in years of highly favorable moisture.

Moisture is not a factor if irrigation water is available, drainage is good, and annual precipitation exceeds 25 inches in the Northern States and 35 inches in the Southern States.

WHEN MOISTURE is as limited as it is in the Great Plains, soil texture largely determines the depth of rooting of trees and shrubs. Rooting is ordinarily shallower in the fine-textured soils (which have a slower water intake rate) than in the coarse-textured ones. Precipitation of a given amount does not penetrate so deeply. Species that normally develop a taproot in their natural environment seldom develop such a root system in the Plains.

A. F. Yeager, of the North Dakota Agricultural Experiment Station, studied the depth of rooting of 31 species of trees and shrubs growing in Fargo clay, most of which are commonly planted for shelterbelt purposes. They were 10 to 43 years old. They had been growing under a mean annual rainfall of 22.34 inches. He discovered that 97.3 percent of the roots of all species were growing in the upper 4 feet of soil. The deepest penetration of roots (by a 16-year-old apple tree) was 10 feet, 3 inches and the shallowest penetration (by a 10-year-old butternut tree) was 2 feet, 8 inches. Only three species had roots in the sixth foot of soil. Roots of cottonwood extended out a distance of 75 feet; those of American elm extended 63 feet; and those of other species spread out 8 to 54 feet.

Dr. Yeager made further studies to compare the rooting habits of trees and shrubs when each was grown on sandy and clay soils that had normal rainfall and in low areas that received runoff from heavy rains and melting snow. Rooting was deeper on both types of soil when they received supplemental water. Roots of golden willow grew 6 feet 8 inches deep on clay soils on the site where rainfall was normal and 14 feet on the wet site.

Observations of the rooting habits of cottonwood trees on river sandbars that were partly eroded away by water action revealed that the roots went straight down for at least 15 feet. Cottonwood is shallow rooted when it grows on dryland sites.

Studies made at the Mandan station in the 1930's of trees that had died as a result of drought showed that the trees and shrubs that grew on a fine sandy loam had a high percentage of the roots in the first 3 feet of soil. A plentiful supply of available moisture was present below the roots in the 7th through the 10th foot.

Later investigations in blocks of trees and shrubs that were planted in soil wet to field capacity in the first 10 feet at the time of planting showed that the roots had completely exhausted all available moisture to a depth of 10 feet, and perhaps beyond, by the 12th growing season. Sampling to determine the moisture content by foot intervals in the first 10 feet was done at the beginning and the end of each growing season. Plantings of trees and shrubs at spacings of 5 by 10, 10 by 10, 10 by 15, and 15 by 15 feet all had exhausted the available moisture at about the same time to depths of 10 feet.

SOME SOILS in the Great Plains contain a high concentration of salts, which usually prevent tree growth. Some species are more tolerant of salts than others, but those that do survive usually are stunted and deformed and have a much shorter life span than those growing on less salty soils. Adequate drainage often helps in this situation.

Studies conducted by the Mandan station in farm shelterbelts disclosed that the roots of trees planted in the salt-affected soils did not penetrate to a greater depth than the depth of planting. Roots of trees planted in these soils spread out horizontally or formed a corkscrew type of growth in the hole.

Observations made by the Southern Great Plains Field Station in November 1940, at Tucumcari, N. Mex., indicated that 60 percent of all the roots of Chinese elm were in the top 3 feet when the planting was made in fine sandy soil. About one-third of the feeder roots were in the 0- to 1-foot zone.

Plantings of windbreaks in the southern part of the Great Plains in soils that had a definite hardpan at a depth of 36 inches survived from 1931 to 1936, when all available moisture became exhausted. Species included Chinese elm, thornless honeylocust, Scotch pine, and Austrian pine. Similar results were noted during the drought of the early and mid-1950's.

Many planting sites on the High Plains are underlain by caliche at various elevations. Tree roots will not penetrate a caliche of a hard, compact form, but they can penetrate a caliche that has considerable gravel content and utilize stored moisture.

ANYTHING ONE CAN DO to improve soil moisture within the windbreaks and on nearby cropland is helpful. In the northern and central parts of the Great Plains, the most feasible methods for increasing and retaining soil moisture when irrigation water is not available are by trapping drifting snow and practicing good tillage to prevent loss of soil moisture by competitive growth and evaporation.

When shelterbelts and windbreaks are planted for purely protective purposes that do not involve the growing of crops, the plantings should be so designed that they will hold the drifting snow within the trees, preferably through the entire width of the belt. Packed snowdrifts that are in trees in early March yield about 1 inch of water for each 3 to 4 inches of snow. Snowdrifts 4 to 6 feet deep are not uncommon in farmstead shelterbelts at that time of year. Their water potential often is greater than the normal annual precipitation of the area.

The additional soil moisture furnished trees and shrubs by melting snowdrifts among the trees explains at least in part why trees in the northern and central Plains will survive in good condition for longer periods than those of the southern Plains, where effective precipitation is about the same.

Trees and shrubs planted for the protection of fields and crops require fewer rows and less density than those planted for the protection of farmsteads. It is well to let some snow filter through and spread over the fields.

Field shelterbelts, as a rule, do not build up the moisture supply among the trees or on the adjacent field as do the drifts that are held within the farmstead shelterbelt, but they hold this potential moisture on the land, rather than permit it to be blown off fields and into ravines and coulees.

If field windbreaks are to control damage to soils and crops by reducing wind velocity, they must be adequate in design, length, and numbers. A series of belts may be needed.

They should be placed to give protection against all prevailing winds.

Long belts of trees across fields can be expected to reduce wind velocity to an extent that less snow will be blown off. Evaporation and transpiration from the soil and crops will be less. Less abrasion of newly emerged seedlings and less erosion will occur.

Trees sometimes compete with the crop for moisture in the zone next to the windbreak. Sometimes they are of benefit in that zone because of the additional moisture that is made available by the trapped snow.

W. J. Staple and J. J. Lehane, of the Soil Research Laboratory, Swift Current, Saskatchewan, studied the soil moisture used by a wheat crop on either side of single-row field hedges for distances of 15, 30, 75, 120, and 165 feet in both directions and at the center point between hedges. Sampling was done at seeding and harvest times to depths of 48 inches. Moisture used by the wheat crop dropped from a mean of 5.6 and 4.9 inches at the 15-foot distance on the west and east sides of the hedges, respectively, to 3.2 inches at the center mark between hedges.

Wheat yields at the 15-foot distance from the hedges declined on the west and east sides from 26.8 and 26.5 bushels, respectively, to 19.8 bushels in the center. An exception was the 30-foot distance on the west side, where the mean yield was 27.5 bushels. The areas of increased use of soil moisture corresponded to those occupied by snowdrifts during the winter.

A. E. Ferber, A. L. Ford, and S. A. McCrory reported in 1955 the result of a survey made in South Dakota, in which 331 farmers were asked to give estimated crop yields grown on fields protected by windbreaks for the years 1952, 1953, and 1954. Increased yield estimates for 1 year or more of the 3 years were given by 83 percent of the farmers. No differences in yield were noted by 11.8 percent, and 5.4 percent noted increased yields but could not estimate the amounts. They observed that the moisture from snowdrifts and the reduction in wind velocity made the difference in yields.

In places where sapping of the crop by trees is pronounced, periodic cutting or pruning of roots by the use of a subsoiling plow or blade about 15 feet from the trees—when they are dormant—will reduce the competition for moisture by the trees.

Many farmers take advantage of better moisture conditions created by snowdrifts adjacent to shelterbelts by planting tame hay and alfalfa crops that can best use the additional moisture early in the season. Tree roots may sap the land so much within 50 feet of the trees that a late-maturing crop is not worth harvesting.

A WELL-DESIGNED SYSTEM of field shelterbelts will protect fields and crops from prevailing winds. A typical system consists of a belt of 3 to 5 rows of trees on the west side; it extends north-south the full length of the field. A series of belts, 1 to 5 rows deep, is located in an east-west direction at right angles to the belt on the west.

The first of the east-west belts in the northern and central regions should be set in about 200 feet from the north and south sides of the field to prevent drifting of snow on the section-line highways. The other series of east-west belts would follow at intervals of 600 to 800 feet.

In the southern region, single rows of trees or tall shrubs planted on the south sides of fields help protect crops against hot winds.

Farmstead windbreaks and shelterbelts in the northern and central Great Plains should ordinarily be located to the north and west sides of the farm buildings for protection against strong, cold winter winds and drifting snow.

Some of the localities that have winter winds from the southwest require plantings on the south also. The belts should be long enough to give protection to all buildings and feed lot areas used during the winter. The inside row of trees should be located approximately 100 feet from the farm building and feed lot sites.

Often it is possible to lay out the shelterbelt on the contour to conserve moisture and to lead in supplemental water from adjacent fields or ditches. If a limited area of the shelterbelt plot contains soil in which trees do not grow well, it might be removed and replaced with better soil. That helps to prevent growth gaps in the shelterbelt.

It is generally not advisable to plant more than 8 rows of trees because that is usually the maximum width over which beneficial supplemental water may be expected from snowdrifts on the northern and central Plains. Each additional row of trees unnecessary for protective purposes adds to the competition for moisture experienced by the trees necessary for protection.

Fruit and vegetable crops need protection—particularly on the south and west—from dry and hot winds. It is also desirable to provide a narrow shelterbelt on the north for trapping snow on the crop area.

The shelterbelt trees should be planted no closer than 50 feet to the orchard or garden area. Three rows of trees on the south and west and one or two rows on the north will provide the necessary protection. Species having wide-spreading root systems, such as poplar, cottonwood, American elm, and Siberian elm should be avoided. Poplar and cottonwood roots will extend out for distances of 75 to 100 feet away from the parent trees.

Trees planted along highways as a living snowfence should be far enough from the right-of-way to keep snow from drifting on the highway. Narrow windbreaks placed 100 feet back from the right-of-way generally will serve that purpose and may also protect fields and crops.

THE EXTREMES OF CLIMATE in the Great Plains dictate the species of trees and shrubs that can be grown successfully.

Many species not native to the Plains cannot be planted there because they tolerate neither cold nor drought. Some species are not cold tolerant under drought conditions but are hardy when soil moisture conditions are favorable. Others tend to mature late in the fall and frequently are badly injured by frosts in early fall. Frosts in late spring after growth has started may injure the trees and shrubs.

It is wise to use species with low water requirements on upland soils. Those best suited to the site should be planted on land prepared by clean fallow the year before planting. In places where soils vary within a planting, it is advisable to use species that are recommended for each type of soil.

Conifers are best if they can be established and grown successfully because they provide year-round protection and usually are more drought tolerant.

Cottonwoods and willows do well on irrigated sites and in places where the water table is high.

THE DISTANCE that trees should be spaced apart in the row and the distance between rows depend somewhat on the number of rows to be used in the shelterbelt. For 1-row plantings, trees should be spaced about 6 feet apart in the row and shrubs should be spaced about 4 feet apart. When two or more rows are used, the shrubs in the outside rows should be spaced 3 to 4 feet apart.

Redcedar, if it is used in the outside row, should be spaced 4 to 5 feet apart. Spruce can be spaced 6 feet apart.

All trees in interior rows should be spaced 6 to 8 feet apart in the northern region, 8 to 12 feet apart in the central Plains, and 12 to 15 feet apart in the southern Plains.

Rows should be spaced 12 to 15 feet apart in the northern and central Plains and 16 to 20 feet apart in the southern Plains. Species should be spaced relatively close in the rows to provide compactness and density.

Allowances for root space can best be adjusted by altering the distances between rows.

NURSERY-GROWN PLANTING STOCK is best for dryland shelterbelts. One- or 2-year seedlings one-fourth to three-eighths inch in diameter just above the swelling of the root collar and 16 to 30 inches tall are the best planting stock.

Conifers may be planted as bare-rooted transplants, but the use of potted stock may assure a higher rate of survival. Farmers who want to pot their own trees can buy seedlings from a nursery and put the trees in cans 5 to 6 inches high and 2 to 3 inches in diameter. Pots may be made of light asphalt paper if cans are not available. The small trees should be kept in the pots for a year.

Tree planting in the northern and central Great Plains is best done in April and May. January to March are the best months farther south.

If the trees are received from the nursery in the fall or early spring, they should be heeled in until planting time. If storage is for over winter, a deep trench should be dug that will take all of the roots and part of the tops. The roots and lower parts of the stems are then covered with soil, which is thoroughly packed and watered. Spring heeling in does not require quite so thorough a job, but it should be done so that the roots do not dry out.

Most tree planting in the Plains is done by machines. If machines are not available or it is not practical to use them, one should dig holes large and deep enough to spread out the roots.

The slit method, or planting behind a shovel, may be used when the soil is wet and the trees have few branched roots. Potted evergreens may be planted with a machine if the containers are less than 3 inches in diameter. Larger containers may be planted with post-hole diggers or shovels.

Care should be taken to prevent drying out of roots by wind and sun during the planting operation. The trees should be carried in a pail of water or wrapped in a wet sack.

All trees that fail to grow the first year should be replaced the following spring. Each year's delay makes it more difficult to establish young trees in an older planting because of the increased growth of the older trees and their competition for soil moisture.

Success with shelterbelts depends on the care one gives them. Clean cultivation should be practiced both between rows and between trees in the row as long as it is possible to do so or until the tree shades the soil to an extent that weed growth is negligible. Competitive weed and grass growth must be controlled if trees are to be successful on dryland sites.

Duckfoot, sweep-type, and spring tooth cultivators, which can be attached to a tractor, are suitable for the center area between rows. They leave the soil in good condition to absorb precipitation and to prevent soil blowing. Single disks should not be used because they ridge the soil against the trees and leave the centers low, thus causing heavy runoff on sloping land. Heavy mulches of hay and straw should not be used as a substitute for cultivation. Their use, when necessary, should be confined to control of erosion.

Livestock can damage or ruin windbreaks and shelterbelts. Cattle and sheep particularly pack the soil and make it less receptive to the intake of water. All types of stock browse and damage the limbs of trees and shrubs. They should be excluded from the shelterbelt. A fence, if it is necessary, should be built when the planting is made.

A clean-cultivated strip should be maintained on all sides of every shelterbelt to prevent entrance of fire from the outside. The cultivated strip will also help to prevent the entrance of weeds and sod. It should be maintained for the life span of the shelterbelt.

The use of cover crops should be confined to light, sandy soils that are subject to wind erosion. A few rows of vegetables, corn, or a narrow band of grain planted between the rows of trees will help to control soil blowing. When the tree rows become dense enough to reduce wind velocities, the practice of planting cover crops should be discontinued.

If irrigation of shelterbelts is possible—usually it is not—tree rows can be planted closer together than the distances recommended for dry sites. The shelterbelt should not be watered for about a month before the first killing frost, when the trees should be hardening off for winter. Irrigation after growth ceases or before the final freeze-up is advisable when the soil is dry.

ADDITIONAL INFORMATION on the planting and care of windbreaks and shelterbelts in the Great Plains may be obtained from the Extension Service of the respective Plains States; the local Soil Conservation District office; the Northern Great Plains Field Station, Mandan, N. Dak.; the Cheyenne Horticultural Field Station, Cheyenne, Wyo.; and the Southern Great Plains Field Station, Woodward, Okla.

Soil and the Growth of Forests

Earl L. Stone, Jr., and Paul E. Lemmon

In the soil, trees get nutrients essential for growth, the great quantities of water their leaves evaporate, and anchorage for their roots. The kind of soil strongly influences the character and growth of forests.

Trees may be said to blend with the soil, rather than grow on it. Their great permanent root systems extend widely in and over the mineral soil, and usually as deeply as aeration or obstructions will allow. Fallen leaves and twigs are incorporated into the mineral soil or accumulate above it as a distinctive organic layer. The chemical makeup of these additions brings about effects that are characteristic of the tree species and affect productivity in time.

The environment, or site, in which a forest grows includes all of the permanent or recurring factors of soil, physiography, climate, and biota. Without careful study it is often impossible to know the particular factors responsible for present forest conditions or how far management may be able to change matters. A simple example is found in the jack pine forests, some of which occur on soils too sandy and dry for better trees. But jack pine also dominates more fertile soils temporarily after other species have been displaced by fire. These two kinds of jack pine forests require quite different management. The better we understand such relationships the more effectively we can utilize our soil resources for wood production, water yield, watershed protection, grazing, and wildlife. Ordinarily, extensive forest management can only adjust land use to soil limitations and capabilities. Intensive management includes the possibility of modifying soil characteristics, for example, by drainage or fertilization, in the interest of economic production.

Adequate seed production is the first step in regenerating, or producing, a new forest. Tree seeds also are a major food source for many kinds of wildlife. Many important tree species tend to produce heavy seed crops only at irregular intervals, however, with lesser amounts or none in intervening years. This periodicity creates difficulties in restocking cut over areas before weeds or unwanted species predominate, and it obviously affects wildlife numbers.

The factors controlling seed formation are imperfectly known, but trees low in vigor are poor producers. Flowering and fruiting often make heavy demands on nutrient stores within the tree, and it seems plain that soil factors, particularly fertility, affect fruitfulness. Confirmation is provided by R. F. Chandler's observations of sugar maple and beech on a soil low in available nitrogen in southern New York. On plots heavily fertilized with nitrogen, a calculated seed production index of the larger trees was 0.85 to 1.00, whereas that for adjacent untreated check plots varied between 0.03 and 0.37. Similarly, G. H. Schubert, of the California Forest and Range Experiment Station, found that large sugar pines fertilized with ammonium phosphate bore three times as many cones as the unfertilized controls.

Other soil characteristics affect seed production. Studies by H. H. Chapman with longleaf pine in Louisiana demonstrated that trees on a dry site more favorable for growth produced more than twice the number of seed than comparable trees on the nearby poorly drained soil.

THE GERMINATION of seeds and the establishment of seedlings in a competitive environment are critical stages in the perpetuation of most forests. Germination requires suitable conditions of oxygen, temperature, moisture, and sometimes light. The specific needs differ somewhat according to species. These requirements continue as the new seedlings establish themselves and make increasing demands for soil nutrients and light.

A single soil provides unequal opportunities to the different species of the locality because of their differences in season of seedfall, requirements for germination, and susceptibility to hazards of the environment. Longleaf pine, for example, germinates in late fall and the mild winter months when soil moisture usually is ample. Loblolly pine, however, germinates in spring and is exposed to greater hazards when dry weather occurs in the germination period or soon thereafter.

Destructive fires reduce the selective influence of soils on forest composition and result in establishment of hardy species having seedling or sprouting habits adapted to such catastrophes.

In most American forests the variety of trees is so great that soil features alone seldom prevent perpetuation of some sort of forest after cutting or fire. The number and kind of desirable species in the new forest, however, are often fixed by the combination of soil, seedbed, and weather following seed fall. Successful regeneration of economically valuable trees is the outcome of seed production, germination, and establishment, and in the managed forest is usually considered a tribute to the forester's skill or good fortune.

SOIL TEMPERATURE affects the germination of seeds, establishment of seedlings, and growth of trees. Most tree seeds seem to germinate best between 68° and 75° F. W. R. Adams, at the University of Vermont, observed a tenfold increase in the germination of seeds of white pine when he increased the soil temperature from 57° to 76°. G. A. Pearson's early studies in Arizona disclosed that ponderosa pine germinated slowly until soil temperatures measured in late afternoon exceeded 65°. Douglas-fir, bristle-cone pine, and Engelmann spruce, species that normally grow at higher altitudes, germinated completely at soil temperatures of 5° to 7° lower.

Mr. Pearson also noted that roots of blue spruce grew vigorously when soil temperatures reached 49° or 50° in the afternoon. Douglas-fir roots began growth at 50° to 52°. Ponderosa pine roots, however, began growth only after 4 days with soil temperatures of 52° to 54°. From these and other studies, he concluded that low soil temperatures set the upper limits of elevations at which regeneration of ponderosa pine occurs.

Other investigators learned that the rate or extent of root growth increases with temperature up to some maximum. W. W. Barney, at Duke University, for example, observed that the daily root elongation of 2-week-old loblolly pine seedlings was greater by 1 millimeter for each increase of 7° to 9° in temperature up to 68° to 77°. A rise in temperature beyond that point caused a reduction in the rate of elongation. Heavily shaded soils, cool northerly slopes, and "cold" soils that warm slowly because of excessive moisture therefore may sometimes retard both germination and development. Such delay may affect the composition of a stand by reducing the number of less cold-tolerant species.

High surface temperatures cause serious mortality to germinating seeds and seedlings on bare soil in the open. As long as soil remains moist, its high conductivity and heat capacity prevent an excessive rise in temperature. Dry surface soils in full sunlight, however, often reach 120° to 125°, which is the critical range for seedling injury, and may exceed 150°.

Studies in Idaho demonstrated that burned-over mineral surfaces reached slightly higher temperatures than unburned soil, but that the maximum value of 161° occurred on dry organic layers or duff. In those circumstances, only hardy species or protected individuals survive the first summer. In places where such injury is common, protected slopes, surface moisture, and even sparse vegetative cover become significant in survival of seedlings and the ultimate composition of forests.

Germination is inhibited on excessively acid or alkaline soils and by high concentrations of soluble salts. Such conditions are infrequent in most forest regions, however. Extreme acidity from oxidation of iron pyrite occasionally prevents both natural and artificial reforestation of spoil banks of strip mines.

Similarly, temporary alkalinity and high salt concentrations near heavy ash deposits hinder seedling development. Salt injury occasionally occurs in nurseries and plantations following high or irregular rates of application of commercial fertilizer. Saline soils along seacoasts and at the arid margins of the forest sometimes create special problems for tree growth.

The soil reaction and other chemical properties usually affect the development, rather than germination, of seedlings. For instance, many conifers will germinate over the wide range of pH 2.0 to pH 11.0. Seedlings in general develop best between pH 4.5 and 6.0, although species differ widely in their adaptability to soil reaction. Trees sometimes occur naturally on soils that have a reaction higher or lower than the range considered favorable to them in nursery production.

These chemical factors exert major influences on seedling development and growth by making nutrients less or more available, by upsetting the nutrient balance within the plant, and by influencing the growth of disease-causing organisms. Factors, as yet unexplained, prevent the growth of some conifers and sensitive hardwoods on calcareous soils, but other species flourish under the same conditions. Several species are adversely affected even at reactions near pH 7.0. Perhaps too much attention has been given to soil reaction itself and too little to its associations with nutrient supply and microbial activity.

SOIL FERTILITY usually is thought to become important only after the initial establishment period. Small-seeded species, however, have little reserves and depend almost immediately on photosynthesis and on the inorganic nutrients they take up from the soil.

Differences in fertility among soils probably are important but are noticed only when the supply of one or more nutrients becomes critically low. Like light and temperature, fertility differences can affect establishment through their influence on the rapidity of development early in the season.

Pathogens and beneficial mycorhizal fungi are affected by soil moisture, temperature, reaction, fertility, and management.

Damping-off fungi kill many seedlings under natural conditions and can be catastrophic in forest nurseries. L. F. Roth and A. J. Riker studied the life history of two common damping-off fungi in sandy nursery soils in Wisconsin. They found that variation in soil reaction between pH 5.5 and 7.0 had little influence on the total damping-off of red pine, although Pythium was the more common above pH 6.0. In another study, Rhizoctonia was found to cause its greatest injury at pH 4.5. Temperature usually was important in determining severity of injury, but soil moisture determined which of the two fungal species predominated.

The use of acid soils and surface acidification have been the principal means of combating losses due to damping-off in nurseries. These methods are still useful although their limitations are now better understood. Information about associations between soil types and severity of seedling diseases is often useful in planning direct seeding and locating and managing forest-tree nurseries.

Normal nutrition and growth of coniferous seedlings (and perhaps of some hardwoods) do not occur in some soils unless the roots are infected with mycorhizal fungi. Such fungi almost invariably are present in soils where their tree hosts occur naturally. Lack of mycorhizae has been a problem mainly in nursery production on prairie soils and in drained bogs and with conifers planted outside their natural range. Evidence is lacking on the desirability of particular fungal species or their adaptability to soil conditions. There are indications, however, that small differences in soil temperature may affect mycorhizal relationships in yellow birch seedlings.

LACK OF OXYGEN, whether seasonal or continuous, restricts the depth of root growth and activity on poorly drained soils. Older trees on such sites depend on widely spreading root systems, but feebly rooted seedlings are severely handicapped, especially when the soil moisture changes rapidly. In poorly drained soils and swamps, seedlings and larger trees alike often are confined to the small elevations of treefall mounds and old stumps, which form islets above the general level of soil saturation.

R. F. Tarrant, of the Pacific Northwest Forest and Range Experiment Station, has pointed out the relationship between soil drainage and the natural distribution of lodgepole and ponderosa pines. Lodgepole pine appears more commonly on the poorly drained sites, but ponderosa pine is partial to well-drained sites. A very slight difference in elevation is enough to allow one or the other species to become the dominant vegetation. Similar response to soil aeration can be found in most forest regions.

The limiting effects of soil saturation on the establishment of seedlings are sometimes made clear by the results of drainage. Ditching of a North Carolina coastal plain swamp, which supported only baldcypress, thus was soon followed by dense reproduction of slash pine from nearby trees.

SOIL MOISTURE, through its direct and indirect influences, perhaps is oftenest the critical factor in germination, early survival, and growth. Differences in the physical properties of soils, physiographic position, vegetation, and climate affect available soil moisture.

Because seed germination and early survival involve mainly the surface soil, one has to recognize surface conditions and existing vegetation as major influences during that period.

Friable, moist mineral soil is considered the preferred seedbed for most tree species. Its ability to hold moisture strongly affects germination. For instance, the volcanic cinder soils of the Southwest drain so rapidly that ponderosa pine seed cannot germinate unless rains occur almost daily. Nearby clay loams retain moisture needed for germination, but seedlings have difficulty because of soil compaction, a con-

dition accentuated by trampling by livestock and logging in wet weather. In consequence, regeneration is usually best on sandy and gravelly loams.

Similar observations have been made in studying regeneration in the Douglas-fir region in the West and in many places in the ponderosa pine and other types. Regeneration often is found abundantly on the lighter textured soils, even though these sites may be inferior for later growth and production.

The mineral soil in many forest regions normally is covered with leaf litter, duff, or raw humus. When these layers remain moist, as on poorly drained sites, in areas of heavy and frequent rainfall, on northerly sheltered aspects, or under protection of an overstory of trees, they offer favorable seedbeds for adapted species. More commonly such layers fluctuate in moisture content, drying rapidly in rainless periods. Hence seeds either do not germinate, or are killed soon after. The success of seedlings that do develop often depends on rapid growth of their roots into mineral soil where moisture conditions are more stable.

Soil preparation to improve seedbeds and planting sites is routine in European forests and sometimes is practiced in the United States. Prescribed fire before seedfall removes interfering litter, or duff, and reduces competition. It may be timed to allow some regrowth to protect the soil or seedlings. Broadcast burning of logging slash leaves a seedbed free of competing vegetation, well adapted to certain species. Disking, harrowing, and distribution of logging operations also break up the surface organic layer and help seedlings become established.

Soil moisture and frequently soil fertility indirectly affect seed germination and seedlings by determining the kind and amount of vegetation present on an area.

H. H. Chapman emphasized the influence of soil type on the establishment of longleaf pine in central Louisiana. On a Myatt soil, 2 percent of the seedfall in 1921 and 1922 became established as 1- and 2-year seedlings, but on a dryer Montrose soil nearby the percentage was 5. The difference was due to the greater number of hardwoods on the moist Myatt soil, which created a greater area of hardwood leaf litter unfavorable for germination of pine.

Seedbed conditions may differ greatly within distances of a few feet, and successful regeneration of an area often depends on many favorable "micro sites" rather than on average conditions. Examples are treefall hummocks or masses of upturned mineral soil left by the great windthrows. Coniferous stumps and wood persist in cool regions in various stages of decay up to a century or more, and masses of rotten wood are common in the forest floor. The sustained moisture content of these materials under a forest canopy, with other advantages such as temperature and elevation, is exceptionally favorable for some species. Seedlings in dense spruce stands may occur chiefly on such sites. The low amount of nutrients in rotten wood probably accounts for the slow growth of seedlings in wood alone. More demanding species, such as sugar maple, soon yellow and die. Masses of rotten wood exposed to full sunlight after heavy cutting sometimes dry thoroughly, killing seedlings rooted entirely within it.

As TREE GROWTH proceeds beyond the first stages, the habitat is enlarged to include the space above and below the surface of the soil. There is an intense, continuous struggle between plants for water, nutrients, light, and space, which we call competition.

Competition tends to be greatest among plants that make similar demands on the same supply of resources. Its outcome is dominance by some plants, subordination for others, and death to those that do not adjust themselves.

Foresters are concerned with two classes of competition during this stage of growth: Among trees of desirable species, and between desirable trees and other vegetation such as grass, brush, and less desirable trees.

In the first class, competition is regulated readily by thinnings and cuttings, which remove surplus or mature individuals. Properly done, this diverts resources above and within the soil to the use of the remaining trees, usually without loss of total growth. Many economic and biological considerations determine thinning procedure, but soil has a large influence.

The maximum density of forests on very dry, infertile, or otherwise adverse sites often is determined by competition within the soil alone, rather than among the individual crowns. In closed forests, both tops and roots quickly occupy the growing space released by thinning. The number of years between such thinnings and the amount of growing stock to be left depend directly upon the growth rate, which is primarily a function of the site. The degree of competition a species can endure and its responsiveness to thinning may differ according to soil, and the same is true of seedling establishment in the openings created by thinning. Thinning procedures therefore must take into account the habitat requirements and stand conditions. Frequently this has not been done because too little was known about the exact relationships between soil and the regulation of competition. It is probable that thinning always will be something of an empirical art, however, because of the numerous variables and judgments involved.

The second class of competition relates especially to stand improvement. In each climatic area, the kinds and amount of competing vegetation encountered at various stages of stand development are influenced decidedly by the history and use of the land. Within such patterns, however, soil factors often determine the intensity and kind of competition and the efforts needed to control competition.

Studies by T. S. Coile, of Duke University, illustrate the effect soil has on the development of hardwood understories beneath pine stands in the southeastern Piedmont region. He related the density of the most important understory species, flowering dogwood, redgum, and redcedar, to the texture and depth of the surface soil and the plasticity of the subsoil. Dogwood occupied a greater area on fine-textured soil than on medium and coarse soils, but with redgum this condition was reversed. Hence the competition to be faced in regenerating the pine is associated with mappable soil characteristics.

Other relationships between soil and such competition are known generally. The common observation is that brush, grass, and other herbaceous vegetation increase in kind and density with soil fertility and favorable moisture supplies. Less valuable tree species may increase also and, unlike lesser vegetation, continue to compete in older stands unless they are removed. Seedlings and saplings of desired species therefore often face greater competition on soils of inherently greater productive capacity. For this reason many species are most readily managed on soils of the lower site qualities. This is especially true of certain conifers that tolerate relatively low moisture or fertility levels better than their hardwood competitors do. Examples are found in old-field white pine in New England and in natural softwood stands of the Adirondack region.

Silviculturists find, however, that tolerance—the amount of shade a species seemingly can endure—sometimes is greater on the more fertile sites. This may compensate in part for the disadvantages small trees often suffer from shading by other plants on the better sites and promote their regeneration. Again, on favorable soils, vigorous species that respond to high fertility and moisture, such as white ash, can outstrip heavy competition.

The number of pounds or bushels of produce per acre furnishes an accurate yardstick for rating productiveness of farm crops and soils. Productiveness of forest lands and the growth rate of tree species are less conveniently measured, for the crop is not harvested for many years and then often gradually. Nevertheless, well-founded estimates of productivity are as essential in forest management as in agriculture.

The total volume of wood produced per acre theoretically is the best index of productivity. Several complications make accurate values of potential volume difficult to obtain and hence they are used chiefly in the form of yield tables applicable to large areas. Fortunately, height of trees is often closely related to volume. Accordingly, in even-aged stands height growth is the most widely used measure of relative productivity. Usually this measure is expressed as the height attained at a standard age, termed site index.

The best sites commonly produce 2.5 to 4 times more total volume than the poorest. Differences in merchantable wood and value are even greater. Differences in height between extremes of site quality classes are seldom more than 1.5 to 2.5 times. Thus the effect on productivity of a change of 10 or 20 feet in site index is greater than the relative heights alone suggest.

The use of site index ordinarily is restricted to even-aged stands older than 20 to 30 years. Even then the idealized curves of height over age cannot be expected to describe the full variety of growth patterns created by diverse soils and site conditions. Early, rapid growth is sometimes followed by slower development. Again, sites showing mediocre or poor early growth may in later years exceed other sites, whose quality was originally thought to be the same. One reason for this is differing susceptibility to infrequent injuries, as from drought or changes in water table. Growth during an advanced period, such as the last 10 or 20 years, therefore is sometimes considered a more sensitive index to site quality than total height.

The increased attention to productivity of forest lands in recent years has brought numerous studies of correlations between site index and specific habitat factors. Usually site differences within a given climatic zone have been found to be associated with measurable or mappable features of soil and physiography. The precise nature of these associations often is unknown or complex, but their general action can be understood in terms of moisture demand, moisture supply, nutrient supplies, and other conditions that affect the development of roots, including anchorage and aeration. We discuss each in turn.

MOISTURE DEMAND of forests, or potential evapotranspiration, is imposed by the heat energy absorbed from solar radiation and warm air. Forests apparently tend to transpire in proportion to the energy received, as long as moisture is abundant. Direction of the slope (or aspect), steepness, and position greatly affect transpiration in our latitudes. There ordinarily are large differences in moisture demand between steep, north-facing slopes and south-facing slopes. Ravines, coves, valley bottoms, and lower slopes that are in shadow part of the day receive less heat energy and consequently may show lower moisture demand. Upper slopes often are less favorable than lower or midslope positions. This effect usually is attributed to exposure, but it includes associated influences of soil depth, subsurface moisture flow, and the shadowing of lower slopes.

As soil moisture becomes less freely available, transpiration diminishes somewhat, although the effect on growth is not well known. When soil moisture drops below a certain range, however, the capacity of the root system to absorb falls far below evaporative demand. Then transpiration and all growth activities drop rapidly to very low levels.

Many species of trees withstand conditions near or at the wilting point for some time without serious mortality, but their growth is arrested until soil moisture is restored. Such secondary effects of drought as disease and insect hazards, however, can be serious.

Northerly aspects, or other protection, reduce the rate at which soil moisture is withdrawn and presumably mitigate the results of moisture stresses when they occur. In contrast, the likelihood of drought injury and its severity are greater on southerly and southwesterly slopes, in most parts of the country. Forest type and growth rate often are determined therefore by slope and aspect in conjunction with slope position.

Inherent differences in rooting depth and season of growth among tree species affect the uptake of moisture, but otherwise differences among species may be smaller than we generally believe. Studies by Robert Zahner in southern Arkansas, for example, demonstrated that comparable stands of oak and pine withdrew soil moisture at almost identical rates, each averaging about 0.25 acre-inch a day for 6 weeks.

THE AVERAGE TOTAL precipitation may be relatively uniform over large areas, but in mountainous terrain or with changes in elevation, large local differences occur within short distances, and then rainfall must be taken into account, even in localized studies of soil influences.

Our investigations of Douglas-fir in the Willamette Valley of Oregon revealed a 16-foot increase in site index, independent of other soil factors, as annual precipitation increased from 30 to 110 inches. A similar effect was observed for the same species in southwestern Washington, where a 30-foot change in site index reflected an increase in precipitation from 40 to 120 inches. The gains in growth rate are modest compared to the large differences in rainfall. The influence of annual precipitation here, however, is not through the total amount, most of which falls in winter, but because of the availability of moisture during the dry summer. Seasonal rainfall would be a better measure if accurate data concerning it were available.

Storage of soil moisture is of major importance relative to the amount and distribution of rainfall, moisture demand of forests, and the season of growth. Exceptions occur in places where trees reach permanent ground water tables or temporary subsurface flow occurs. Such sites often are highly productive. Most forests, however, depend entirely on stored soil moisture to sustain activity during the intervals between heavy rains.

Trees withdraw a tremendous amount of moisture from soil when conditions are right. A young plantation of loblolly pine in South Carolina, for example, reduced the moisture content of a Cecil clay loam to wilting point over a depth greater than 5.5 feet during one dry season. In so doing, the trees had withdrawn more than 9 acre-inches of stored moisture. Similarly, an aspen stand in Utah, with roots extending at least 6 feet deep, removed 11 inches of stored moisture. Such relatively large stored moisture values frequently equal or exceed the growing season rainfall of dryer forest climates. Shallow soils with storage capacities of less than a few inches often cannot supply moisture long enough to maintain growth through droughts. By affecting the rate of water withdrawal, soil slope and aspect reduce or prolong the length of time that stored moisture will suffice. Aspect therefore is more significant for growth of trees on shallow soils than for those with an ample moisture reservoir.

Soils differ in their ability to store moisture. Gravel and coarse stone reduce the volume available for storage. Coarse-textured soils store relatively less moisture than those with finer textures. Moisture is readily available, however, in coarse-textured soils, and considerable amounts are accessible to trees with roots extending 10 or 20 feet deep. These soils are "dry sites" only for shallow-rooted vegetation.

The depth of effective moisture absorption varies with pattern of root behavior. Some deep soils offer little hindrance to downward extension and roots will penetrate them to depths characteristic of the species. In contrast are soils in which impenetrable layers within a few feet of the surface stop the penetration of roots. Bedrock, compact horizons, claypans, gley horizons (zones of very poor aeration), and packed sands create such barriers.

Tree growth often is closely related to the thickness of friable soil above such layers. Soil aeration, as well as moisture retention, is affected by the position and kind of the limiting layer. Shallow soil above a gley horizon, or compact zone, retains more moisture than the same thickness over permeable rock, but it is less well aerated. Because individual species respond in different ways to these two limitations, the response of tree growth to depth varies with other soil characteristics.

In still other soils, roots develop freely in a surface layer that may be a few inches or a few feet thick. At some depth, however, changes in soil texture, consistence, structure, or aeration reduce but do not wholly prevent the development and activity of roots. Depth of rooting in these soils is indeterminate and does not accurately reflect the soil volume that trees can use effectively. Poor aeration of deeper layers, for example, can delay root activity until late in the season when the soil above has dried. Roots are confined in dense subsoils to established channels and cleavage planes, and may reach only a part of the resources in such layers. A moderate degree of restriction may be favorable, however, particularly in coarse-textured soils because of increased moisture retention.

THE SUPPLIES of nutrients and moisture that affect tree growth are closely associated with effective soil volume and its physical makeup.

The depth to a limiting layer or substratum has a broad general importance. It has been correlated with the site index of oaks in Iowa and West Virginia, loblolly and shortleaf pines in the southeastern Piedmont, introduced larches in New York, old-growth conifers in California, and second-growth Douglas-fir in Oregon and Washington.

Growth rate frequently has been related to the texture, consistence, and mottling of the subsoil. Many specific measurements—such as the moisture equivalent, texture, silt-plus-clay, imbitional water (an empirical measure of moisture retention, related to the amount and kind of clay) of the subsoil, and gravel content—correlate closely with tree growth in some localities. The usefulness of the measurements depends on particular associations with moisture storage, nutrient supply, and opportunity for root development. Such associations ordinarily hold true only over a limited area and may have little value elsewhere.

Correlations such as those mentioned above lead some writers to assume that moisture relationships alone are responsible for most site differences. In actuality, such correlations generally fail to separate the relative influences of moisture and nutrient supply because these often vary together. Thus with soils of similar composition, moisture-holding ability and the rate at which mineral nutrients are supplied are both related to soil texture. Measures of one tend to include the other. Likewise, the greater the available volume of soil, the greater the opportunity for absorption of both nutrients and water.

Deeper soil layers sometimes are richer in mineral nutrients than the surface layers, and the sustained soil moisture of deep soils allows a longer period for active nutrient absorption. The same considerations suggest why the nutrient supplies available to deep-rooted forest trees often cannot be determined by analysis of the surface soil.

The importance of sufficient nutrients is emphasized by examples of acute deficiencies in some North American forests, both natural and planted. Fertilization with potassium, phosphorus, magnesium, and nitrogen, or the presence of a legume, has markedly increased growth in some areas.

For example, S. O. Heiberg and D. P. White, of the New York State College of Forestry, found that a deficient red pine stand treated once with 200 pounds of potassium fertilizer an acre approximately doubled in height growth for several years thereafter.

In Washington, S. P. Gessel and R. B. Walker observed a similar increase following yearly applications of 100 pounds of nitrogen per acre to young Douglas-fir on heavily burned soils. Deficiency and response could be detected in both instances by content of the element in the foliage. The circumstances of deficiency and response generally are much the same as with other crop plants.

It is difficult to measure the capacity of different soils to supply available nutrients. The amounts of nutrients plants can use are influenced by soil mineralogy and weathering, organic matter, microbial activity, and physical variables. Forests on adjacent areas of contrasting rocks, such as sandstone and limestone, often reveal how strongly inherent chemical and weathering differences affect the species present and their growth.

Statistical correlations of site index with the soil and physiographic properties that influence the supply of moisture and nutrients often account for much of the natural variability in site quality. Equations based on selected variables commonly allow us to predict the site index with an average error of estimate of about 10 percent. These high correlations between growth rate and physical characteristics were all obtained, however, with species such as oaks, pines, larches, and Douglas-fir, which are less sensitive to variations in fertility than many hardwoods.

The response of hardwood species to soil nitrogen is known from the work of H. L. Mitchell and R. F. Chandler in New York. They used leaf analysis to characterize available nitrogen in second-growth stands of the Northeast. "Nitrogen tolerant" species, such as red oak, aspen, and red maple, grew relatively well with low supplies, although growth improved up to a point as more nitrogen became available. "Nitrogen demanding" species, like white ash, tulip poplar, and basswood, grew poorly at the lower levels, but growth rate increased continuously up to the maximum nitrogen levels that they found. Thus nitrogen supplies strongly affect the competitive abilities of different species. Accordingly, factors that control the availability of soil nitrogen tend to influence forest composition as well as growth.

THE QUANTITIES OF NUTRIENTS taken up by forest crops are relatively large. A compilation of European data by P. J. Rennie in the journal, *Plant and Soil*, 1956, indicates that the aboveground woody parts of 100-year-old coniferous stands contain approximately 800 pounds an acre of calcium, 400 pounds of potassium, and 65 pounds of phosphorus. These values are averages from nine stands of larch, spruce, and fir. They are exclusive of foliage but include the amounts in intermediate thinnings.

About two-thirds of the calcium and one-half of the phosphorus in these amounts would be removed from the forest in stemwood and bark. Nutrients contained in the roots, foliage, and recently fallen organic matter add to the totals absorbed from the soil. Quantities taken up by hardwood species are even greater, particularly of calcium, but those by Scotch pine are much less.

The quantity of an element absorbed does not necessarily indicate the actual requirement for vigorous growth. Nevertheless, as Mr. Rennie emphasized, soils of very low inherent productivity—like some weathered, highly silicious sands—cannot supply the nutrients needed for sustained forest production. In other nutrient-poor soils, slow availability of nutrients and restrictions on root development limit the uptake and growth. Artificial fertilization may be the only feasible means of increasing productivity on such sites.

The texture and mineralogy of most forest soils in the United States suggest that normal release of mineral nutrients can meet requirements such as we cited, so that removal in the usual forest products is not likely to cause depletion. But attention must be directed to the condition of soils already depleted or naturally infertile and to means of maintaining fertility reserves if they are critical.

ROOT DEVELOPMENT, anchorage, and aeration, beyond what we have already said, have a profound bearing on the growth of forests as they relate to soil. The ultimate influences of soil are not fully expressed by early growth rate. Rooting habit and development sometimes differ greatly on sites identical in growth rate and so affect the characteristics of a stand in later years.

Trees with root systems limited by compact horizons or gley layers are susceptible to windthrow damage. This possibility is increased by certain soil textures or saturated conditions that loosen the holding effectiveness of roots. Bedrock close to the surface acts similarly, unless large fissures allow a firm anchorage. Roots resting on coarse-grained rock are sometimes worn away as trees sway in violent winds, leaving large openings for entrance of decay.

Occasional periods of very poor subsoil aeration, perhaps occurring at long intervals, can prune off the deeper root system and thus affect growth.

NATURAL SOIL BODY features that can be mapped or recognized readily are especially useful in managing large forest properties. Hence there now is great interest in correlating site index, or other elements of productivity, with them. This is a somewhat different approach from the one that relates a single or few habitat factors to forest growth.

Soil properties—texture, depth, drainage, mineralogy, slope, and presence of certain horizons—occur together. By their combinations they characterize the various soil classification units that soil scientists recognize. Natural units such as soil series and types are based on distinctive origin and morphology. The soil units therefore include the individual factors already mentioned as associated with growth, as well as additional properties and combinations that cannot be treated separately in correlation studies. Moreover, these soil units are recurring features of the landscape and can be mapped in a practicable manner.

Many earlier attempts to relate soil type to forest type and growth rate were not fully successful, for several reasons. Tree growth does not necessarily respond to the changes in properties that separate adjacent soil units, and all species do not respond alike.

The deeply penetrating root systems sometimes encounter conditions not reflected in the surface soil. Many valuable relationships appear, nevertheless, when soil units are accurately conceived and delineated on maps.

The basis for these relationships may be the classificational units themselves or broader divisions formed by combining units of similar capabilities, as in regard to moisture retention and nutrient supply. These broader divisions may be subdivided as necessary into phases according to different depths or slope directions. Several examples demonstrate that grouped soil types or other units, skillfully used, can indicate site quality. Aside from being useful to the manager of land now in timber, soil surveys with this kind of interpretative information are useful in forecasting the growth potential of open land before purchase or planting. They can be applied also to young stands or to cutover areas where direct measurements of site index cannot be made.

Moreover, the results of many soil-site correlation studies based on specific factors can be interpreted into soil survey mapping units. For instance, site index of loblolly and shortleaf pines in the southeastern Piedmont region has been correlated with subsoil plasticity and depth of friable soil above, other factors being held essentially constant. Plasticity, however, was found to be characteristic of soil type. Accordingly, with this information, depth phases of soil types can serve as indexes of productivity.

The site type gives the forester a clue as to how well the species present in disturbed stands are adapted to the site and what trends he can expect.

Further, each mapping unit can be rated, qualitatively or quantitatively, for attributes important in forest management. Susceptibility to windthrow, trafficability, erosion hazard, and likelihood of soil damage by wet weather logging, are closely related to soil physical characteristics. Other attributes are ease of regeneration, encroachment of undesirable species, and soil-influenced diseases or insects.

Forest Practices and Productivity

V. L. Harper, Bernard Frank, and W. E. McQuilkin

Four forest practices are related closely to the productivity of soils: Prescribed and controlled burning; monoculture (growing a single species in pure stands); grazing by livestock; and harvesting commercial timber.

Three of them—burning, grazing, and harvesting—if not done properly, may destroy or alter the organic material, compact the soil, and cause erosion.

FIRE has been a major force in shaping the development and character of timberlands. The regeneration and perpetuation of many species and forest types in the past have depended largely on fire. Examples are the long-leaf pine in the South, pitch pine in the East, lodgepole pine and Douglas-fir in the West, aspen, white birch, and various types of scrub oak.

Some of our best species are among those that regenerate after fires, but most wildfires are highly destructive to whatever forest growth is present at the time and to the soils that support the forest.

The fact that some valuable species regenerate most abundantly after fire, however, has contributed to an increasing interest in prescribed, controlled burning as a tool in the management of forests.

Prescribed burning is the burning of a specified area at a specified intensity for a definite purpose. It calls for the selection of the proper year and season and a day and time of day when moisture in the fuel, wind, and related factors are such that the fire will have the specified intensity. So controlled, these fires are unlike wildfires, which we make every effort to prevent.

Controlled burning usually is prescribed for one or more purposes: To reduce the volume of fuel and thereby facilitate the prevention of wildfires and the suppression of any that may occur; to kill or weaken undesirable hardwoods or reduce grass and shrub competition in pine stands; to facilitate the establishment of pine reproduction by removing competing plants and thick litter; to control disease, notably the brown spot disease on longleaf pine; to improve habitat for upland game birds and other wildlife; to remove brush, debris, or other impediments to livestock grazing and otherwise to improve forage production on forest ranges.

Fire affects soils biologically, chemically, and physically.

Some of the forms of plant and animal life—bacteria, fungi, insects, millipedes, earthworms—which are beneficial in breaking down litter and incorporating organic material into the soil, are consumed in burned litter. Others in layers immediately beneath

may be killed by heat. Changes also occur in the populations and species of organisms, as evidenced by the increase in nitrification, a product of the activities of certain kinds of bacteria. Altogether, controlled fires ordinarily are not hot enough or so deep-burning as to destroy all of these plant and animal populations, and the temporary reductions in numbers probably are of little consequence.

Fire releases the mineral nutrients that are bound up in the litter and humus. Some may be utilized by plants and some may be lost by washing or leaching. In any event, the quick release by fire means fewer nutrients for gradual release later under the normal processes of litter decomposition. Furthermore, nitrogen is volatilized and is lost entirely.

Soil acidity is temporarily reduced by the release of calcium, potassium, and other elements that form an alkaline ash. The reduced acidity, in the case of strongly acid soils, may temporarily increase the availability of such mineral nutrients as phosphorus. The ash minerals and the accelerated decomposition of organic matter combine to stimulate a quick flush of vegetative growth.

A fire hot enough to oxidize humus from the upper layers of mineral soil alters the texture of those layers. Fires of that intensity seldom occur with prescribed burning, however, except possibly in slash piles, but even in them, temperatures in the mineral soil at a depth of 1 inch have rarely been found to exceed 175° to 200° F.

The reduction in organic matter on the surface touches off dire secondary, or indirect, effects. The effects may be minor if a generally unbroken mat of partly decomposed litter (or of organic matter incorporated in the uppermost layer of soil) remains after the burn.

But if the insulating blanket of organic matter is removed entirely, the upper layers of soil undergo greater and more frequent fluctuations in temperature, which probably (depending on season and latitude) are unfavorable to tree growth. They also undergo more frequent and more severe drying, which definitely harms growth. The feeding roots of forest trees typically are concentrated near the soil surface, where the mineral nutrients released from decomposing litter are most abundant. The nutrients can be absorbed only when the soil contains available water. Destruction of the surface litter therefore destroys this reservoir of nutrients. It also curtails the availability of the remaining nutrients by exposing the soil to excessive drying.

The lack of moisture is aggravated by the action of rainfall on bare soil. Puddling may occur at the surface and seal the pores, slow infiltration, and lead to greater runoff. The water that enters the soil carries fine particles, which reduce pore spaces, slow down infiltration and percolation even more, and inhibit aeration.

Without surface litter, the activities of soil-burrowing insects, worms, and similar animal forms are reduced. Soil compaction results. The increased runoff means less storage of water in the soil and smaller supplies of water for the forest vegetation and for the maintenance of streamflow. Impermeable concrete frost forms to a greater degree in exposed soil than under litter in the cooler regions. That means still more runoff and less infiltration and storage of water.

Those effects generally develop most markedly in soils of finer texture and least in sands, loamy sands, and coarse sands. Therefore burning is prescribed most widely in areas of coarse sandy soils. If burning is done on fine-textured soils, it should be done at a low intensity and infrequently, so as to preserve part of the organic matter.

To the extent that the vegetative cover is killed or set back and the soil is exposed to the elements, the soil surface and the site as a whole will be made drier by the action of more sunlight, higher temperatures, more wind movement, and lower humidity. Organic matter remaining after the burn is subject to accelerated oxidation and

dissipation. Drastic opening of the vegetative cover thus compounds the detrimental effects of burning the organic mantle, unless grass or herbaceous growth come in soon afterward and provide new sources of organic matter. At worst, soil washing or blowing may occur and gullies develop on sloping land. Such effects are to be avoided in prescribed burning. The burner must understand these tendencies, however, so that he may keep the intensity of the fire below the point that causes such damage.

Changes in the plant cover will be reflected in the type and amount of litter deposited after the burn. If the cover has been greatly reduced, as might be done where the objective is to establish pine reproduction after harvest cutting, the annual litter fall for some years may not be enough to form a continuous mulch over the soil. Much of the beneficial effects of a continuous litter mulch in maintaining soil porosity, equalizing temperature, reducing evaporation, and releasing nutrients would be sacrificed until a tree cover develops again.

A less drastic treatment—for instance, a burn to kill back sapling and sprout hardwoods in an established pine stand—might not reduce seriously the amount of litter deposited annually but would alter its composition. If the hardwood elements in the stand are set back or killed, the subsequent litter fall would be essentially pure pine. Straight pine litter tends to decompose more slowly than mixed pine-hardwood litter, and there is less release of nutrients and less incorporation of humus into the soil. Rapid leaching of the bases from the upper soil layer frequently occurs in northern climates. Particularly under dense stands of the coarse-needled southern pines, the slower decomposition may cause thick accumulations of duff. These processes do not necessarily mean reduced soil productivity, but the stimulating effects of most hardwood litter on bacterial activity (and hence on decomposition of humus) generally favor the inclusion of most types of broad-leaved vegetation in the overstory or understory of established pine stands.

Burning also directly or indirectly affects plant roots, especially when it brings about marked changes in species composition. The vegetation that remains or becomes established on the site after fire will have less competition for soil moisture and nutrients, since the other plants will have been killed.

The changes may be limited to certain depths or may extend throughout the depth of root penetration. For instance, the destruction of shallow-rooted plants affects moisture and nutrient relations in the upper soil levels, but the effects of killing or retarding deep-rooted tree species—oaks, yellow-poplars, hickories, elm, and the like—may extend to considerable depths.

The decay of roots following the death of plants has numerous beneficial effects. Nutrients are released, and the physical and biological reactions deep within the soil favor improved soil structure, internal drainage, and aeration. We must note some exceptions, however. Sometimes, especially on steep slopes, the death of roots may cause soil instability and prescribed fire there is of questionable value.

Fire is used mainly in the Douglas-fir region, to dispose of logging slash after clear-cutting operations. The purposes are to reduce the hazard of wildfire and to improve seedbed conditions for the new crop of timber.

Studies of the effects of this practice upon the soil emphasize the importance of burning only when weather conditions assure low intensity—that is, shortly after a heavy rain when only the uppermost layers of litter have dried. Heavier burns have resulted in losses of up to 75 percent of the organic matter. In some instances, nutrients were so depleted that coniferous reproduction was unable to compete successfully against weed and brush growth that would not have been an important problem on an unburned site.

In properly controlled slash burning,

only about half the area is touched by fire at all, and only 1 to 4 percent of the area—the spots of heavy slash accumulation—burns so hotly as to have notably adverse effects on the soil.

Prescribed burning in the ponderosa pine types of the West and Southwest is somewhat experimental, although some thousands of acres have been so burned. The main purpose has been reduction of fuel—grass, litter, brush, and snags—to reduce the wildfire hazard.

Other possible objectives are being investigated. Among them are seedbed preparation, improvement of wildlife habitat, and thinning of too dense pine thickets. Burning for these purposes is not now generally recommended, but further research may point the way to at least limited use of fire in that way.

Prescribed burning as a tool in forest management probably is more firmly established in the southern and middle Atlantic Coastal Plain than anywhere else. The lower Coastal Plains of sandy soils are less subject to adverse effects from fire than the heavier soils of the upper Coastal Plains, Piedmont, and mountains. Fire is used in the Coastal Plain pine lands to reduce fuels, to keep hardwoods in check and favor pine, to prepare seedbeds for establishment of pine production, and (in the longleaf pine region) to control the brown spot disease of that species.

Monoculture—the establishment of forest plantations of single species of trees—has been a common practice because it is simpler and less expensive than to put in a planned mixture and because the later thinnings and other management activities also are simpler and less expensive to carry out.

Nature also sometimes creates practically pure stands of single species, especially after fire or the abandonment of cleared land. Mixed stands can be converted to single-species stands by cutting, poisoning, or prescribed burning.

The practice of monoculture in this country is limited mainly to coniferous species—chiefly the pines, except in the Northwest, where Douglas-fir is dominant. Spruces, firs, and larches are also involved to a lesser extent. Hardwoods also may be grown in pure stands, but the acreage is relatively small and—except for beech—hardwoods rarely are suspected of causing adverse effects upon soil; generally they are regarded as soil builders.

We use the terms "monoculture" and "pure stands" to refer only to the forest overstory. Many other plant species—herbs, shrubs, and sometimes tree reproduction—commonly are present in the understory.

A notion that monoculture harms the soil arose in Europe in the early 1900's, particularly with reference to spruce but also in connection with Scotch pine, fir, and larch. The trees did not thrive, developed poor form, sometimes lacked wind-firmness, and were unusually susceptible to insects and disease. The soils under such stands typically showed signs of low productivity, such as little organic matter and mineral nutrients and low rates of litter decomposition. Hardpan layers, poor internal drainage, and poor aeration also existed. Usually a raw humus layer and podsolization (formation of a leached, ashlike soil layer) or incipient podsolization were present. Both also were taken to indicate low productivity.

As forest planting expanded in America, similar soil conditions were observed here. Even natural stands sometimes showed the same tendencies, particularly those that had seeded in on abandoned farmlands.

The association of monoculture with poor soil conditions—and hence poor growth of timber—was interpreted by many European foresters as a cause-and-effect relationship. The idea was widely accepted by American foresters.

In support of this interpretation, much importance has been attached to the fact that most conifers do not withdraw as much lime from the soil and redeposit it in their litter as do most hardwoods. Coniferous litter (except

that of the cedars and of firs and larch sometimes) therefore tends to alter into a strongly acid humus that, in the cooler, humid climates of northern Europe and our Northern States, favors podsolization. Podsolization has been interpreted as a sign of soil deterioration, and it has been postulated that the low nutrient content, hardpan, and other "symptoms" of low productivity also result from decomposition of the pure, single-species litter laid down under monoculture.

Podsolization and mor types of humus, long regarded as signs of soil deterioration and low productivity, are now recognized as normal developments under certain combinations of climate, vegetation, and parent soil material. Podsols covered with mor humus do, in fact, support excellent spruce, hemlock, and other forest growth of mixed or pure composition.

Where monoculture has been unsuccessful, it was not because this practice itself degraded the soil, but because the soil was already degraded from past abuse before the present forest was established; the species or particular race of the species used was not adapted to the site; or the pure stands were highly susceptible to insect or disease epidemics.

The first situation—previously degraded soil—is likely to be encountered where plantations are established on "wornout" agricultural land, but may also occur on nonagricultural land that has been repeatedly burned, too heavily grazed, or clear-cut and destructively logged.

In extreme cases of land abuse, perhaps no species or mixture of species would thrive during the first forest rotation. In less extreme cases, success might depend on the choice of a species better adapted to the deteriorated site.

In any event, establishment of forest on such land has commonly been by monoculture; tree growth is most likely to be unthrifty on such land; unthrifty growth, in turn, stimulated search for causes and the repeated observance of unhealthy soil conditions. Monoculture was indicted, despite the fact that pure stands that happened to have been established on better soils grew well. The latter observations were often rationalized by the speculation that they also would eventually decline under continued monoculture.

The failures of poorly adapted species relate closely to the deficiencies of previously degraded soils, but the inherent characteristics of even healthy soils also must be considered. In eastern Canada, for example, red spruce and black spruce thrive on imperfectly drained heavy soils, whereas white spruce needs richer and better aerated soils for good growth.

Nearly all climatically adapted species thrive on good forest soils. The number of species that will thrive on other soils declines sharply with the degree of soil impairment. In Europe, Scotch pine might have succeeded where Norway spruce failed, and vice versa. In our Eastern States, jack pine or red pine might succeed where spruce or white pine would fail. Furthermore, certain races within a species may be better adapted to a given climate and soil condition than other races. Such races exist in many species. Scotch pine, European larch, and Douglas-fir are examples. Some of the poor results attributed to monoculture very likely were due to the use of a poorly adapted species or race.

Hardwoods on sites to which they are not suited often fail even more decidedly than conifers, whether in monoculture or in mixtures. Monoculture of hardwoods (beech excepted), however, has seldom been charged with causing soil deterioration, although some foresters may consider it undesirable for other reasons. The fact that soils under hardwood litter are less inclined to form Podsols than under conifer litter doubtless is one reason that hardwoods have not been incriminated. They simply did not conform to the now outmoded theory that podsolization and low soil productivity go hand in hand.

In short, the idea that monoculture is a cause of soil deterioration is questioned. Coniferous monoculture in general is less effective for building up soil than some other types of forest culture, but it does conserve soil values and improves them in many instances through litter decomposition, root growth, and other biological activities. The merits of monoculture may be debatable on other grounds—economics and insect and disease risks—and should be decided on the basis of those factors. The paramount consideration with respect to soil is to choose species and races that are well adapted to prevailing conditions.

Whether with monoculture or mixed species, soils of low productivity often can be improved for tree growth by application of soil amendments or by certain cultural practices. Cost is the limiting factor in most instances. Amendments may be organic matter, phosphorus or other mineral nutrients, or lime. They may be applied before a stand is established or afterward. Organic matter often is the most crucial need, along with mineral nutrients and nitrogen, notably on badly eroded areas, spoil banks, sand dunes, and the like. In such sites, the application of an organic mulch may spell the difference between success and failure.

Before planting an area of barren soil, conditions may be greatly improved by liming, fertilizing, and growing a crop or two of some plant, like cereal rye, that will produce a large bulk of organic matter. Inclusion of legumes in such a soil-improving cover crop theoretically would be desirable, but there is little experience in American forest practice on which to base a recommendation regarding planted legumes, other than the use of black locust, which markedly increases the availability of nitrogen in hardwood plantations and thus stimulates their growth.

Sandy, windswept areas may need wind barriers or the liberal use of brush and mulch to arrest movement of soil and to supply organic matter. Certain small trees or shrubs that have low moisture and nutrient requirements may be used in some exposed sites as nurse species.

Alder has been used for this purpose in Europe, and a few attempts to use gray birch and black locust have been made in this country.

Growth in dense, established stands can be improved by thinnings to open the stand to greater air movement, light, and warmth. It reduces the competition for moisture and nutrients, promotes faster decomposition of humus, and favors development of desirable understory vegetation.

The establishment and maintenance of a hardwood understory probably is the most generally practicable way to upgrade soil productivity in coniferous monoculture. The hardwoods might have to be underplanted in an occasional critical situation, but usually they invade naturally or can be encouraged to invade by moderate opening of the coniferous stand.

The admixture of hardwood litter with that of the conifer promotes faster decomposition of the organic matter, reduces acidity, and stimulates nitrification.

Some hardwoods are better in this respect than others. Studies in South Carolina and Mississippi indicate that redbud, dogwood, yellow-poplar, and hickory are among the more beneficial species. Basswood, ash, birch, and elm also are good soil builders. The oaks and beech are of less value, as their litter carries a lower content of basic elements and is more resistant to decomposition.

The beneficial effects of hardwood litter derive primarily from its higher content of calcium and other nutrient elements. A study in the South Carolina Piedmont showed 3 to 5 times as much calcium in mixed hardwood litter as in litter of shortleaf pine.

A study in New England showed that hardwood litter attracts a different population of soil organisms than does the litter of white pine and thereby brings about more incorporation of humus into the mineral soil.

The practice of maintaining an understory of hardwoods under coniferous monoculture and the use of fire to reduce hardwoods in pine stands may seem to imply working at cross purposes. True, an element of contradiction is involved; similarly, planting and thinning also are contradictory, but only superficially so. The mark of the forester's skill is to be found in using or fostering each process at the time and in the degree that best accomplish a desired end.

WHETHER TO GRAZE forest land and when and how much are questions that have puzzled farmers and other owners who want to grow timber. The extent to which grazing affects the productivity of the soil for forest growth depends largely on the intensity of grazing, the season of use, the type and condition of the soil, the climate and topography, and the character of the tree and ground cover.

Our discussion pertains only to forest grazing. Land held and managed solely for range or pasture poses different problems that need other treatment.

Grazing that ignores the capabilities of an area can be detrimental to the soil. Damage by livestock is caused by trampling of the soil; disintegration and dissipation of litter—largely caused by trampling; and reduction or destruction of the undergrowth vegetation. All lead directly or indirectly to soil compaction; reduced porosity and hence lower infiltration rates; less water storage in the soil; and higher surface runoff, perhaps with increased erosion. They are the same array of adverse effects as are brought about by too intense or too frequent fires, plus the added element of trampling.

The physical effects of trampling are important. Cattle treads are reported to average 24 pounds static pressure to the square inch, and sheep 9 pounds to the square inch. Higher pressures undoubtedly are exerted by animals in motion.

Because of the trampling, soil compaction tends to be worse under grazing than after a fire. When grazed woods are also burned to improve forage conditions, the adverse effects tend to be compounded—as indicated in studies of pine woodlands in the Georgia Coastal Plain, which reveal that the compaction resulting from grazing not only is increased by burning, but that the increase also is proportional to the frequency of the burning. The increase in grazing compaction after fire is due to the destruction of organic material that would have persisted under grazing alone.

Soil texture, moisture content, and organic content considerably affect the impact of grazing on productivity. Soils of fine texture (silts and clays) and low organic content generally are most susceptible to compaction. Trampling is most damaging when soils are wet. Frost action also may have a part. It works both ways, tending to loosen soils by its expansion and heaving action but favoring compaction to the extent that soil aggregates are broken down into finer particles.

Properly timed and controlled grazing in pine stands can yield benefits besides the value of the forage. It may be used for some of the same purposes as prescribed burning—to reduce the volume of flash fuels (grass and other herbs), to reduce the density of ground cover and favor establishment of tree reproduction, and to curtail the growth of hardwoods. For some special purposes, hogs or goats may do the job better than cattle. Except for reducing the volume of fuels, however, grazing for these purposes becomes in a large part a silvicultural tool; it must be skillfully timed and controlled, and sometimes the animals must be removed from the area when the purpose has been accomplished.

Grazing of forest lands to utilize forage values is practiced in various regions. It commonly occurs in the West in the extensive ponderosa pine type. It may occur in open stands of some other coniferous types. Spruce, fir, and hemlock types, however, mostly grow too densely to produce much undergrowth forage. Grazing in

the East is a practicable use of the forest mainly in the pine types of the South, although it is practiced rather widely also in hardwood stands throughout the East.

The situation is somewhat precarious in the ponderosa pine lands of the West, because of the prevalence of the heavier soils and sloping topography and the frequency of drought and torrential thunderstorms. These factors predispose to soil damage wherever the normal volume and vigor of the ground-cover vegetation have been substantially reduced. Grazing in this region is a well-established and economically sound practice, but proper control of its intensity here is especially important. Removal by grazing of no more than 30 to 40 percent of the forage growth is usually recommended.

Considerable grazing is practiced in the longleaf-slash pine forests of the South. The soils often are sandy and are not subject to serious damage from compaction, and the yields of forage often are very good.

In a longleaf pine forest in east Texas, which averaged about 50 percent full stocking of timber, a forage yield of 1,200 pounds an acre has been reported, but yields of about a fourth or a third as much forage have been reported in pure hardwood and mixed pine-hardwood stands.

Moderate grazing appears to be practicable and justifiable in open-crowned pine forest on sandy soils.

Hardwood types in the Eastern and Central States are grazed extensively, but most investigators agree that the practice damages the soil—partly because hardwoods commonly occupy the heavier, finer textured soils that are most sensitive to compaction and partly because not enough tough grass roots exist to provide resistance to compaction. These soils when compacted have much less ability to absorb water; because of the reduction in the protective influence of vegetative and litter cover, they are subject to wider changes in temperature and moisture.

Investigators also agree on the low quality of the forage usually produced under hardwoods. Forage volumes are very low, except in open stands, as in the Ozark Mountains of Missouri, and even there they seldom exceed 500 pounds an acre. Cattle thus reap little benefit, except shade and exercise, from grazing a hardwood forest—and the farmer ends up with a poorer woodlot for timber production and watershed protection.

In forest types where grazing is practicable—mainly in the pine forests of the West and South—the adverse effects of the practice upon soil productivity may vary with its intensity. Grazing that leaves enough vegetation and litter on the ground to protect the soil and that leaves the forage species in good vigor will not reduce soil productivity seriously.

METHODS OF HARVESTING TIMBER may have far-reaching effects on the future productivity of the forest soil.

Two aspects of the harvesting operation, each of which may set in motion a distinct chain of effects, are to be recognized. One is the intensity of the cut, which may vary from light thinning to clear-cutting. The other is the time, methods, and equipment used in the logging operation.

Intensity of cut bears upon soil productivity in much the same manner as fire, except that organic matter on the ground is not consumed. That is, the greater the opening of the stand or the greater the changes in species composition, the more profound are the effects on the soil.

In the extreme instance of clear-cutting, the site thus exposed is subject to greater variations or extremes of light, temperature, humidity, and wind. The existing litter undergoes accelerated breakdown, with little annual replacement. Unless a new cover develops soon, the soil may be bared and exposed to the full drying force of the weather and the full force of rain. This, as after fire, can lead to compaction of soil, reduced rates of infiltra-

tion, less water storage, more surface runoff, and possible erosion.

The degree to which this chain of events develops depends on soil texture and structure, slope, the character of the precipitation, and the amount of low vegetation that survives the logging or appears immediately afterward. Again, light soils are least subject to adverse effects. Heavier soils, especially those on steep slopes, are most likely to suffer damage. Prompt development of sprout, shrub, and herbaceous cover will greatly ameliorate the effects of exposure. In this connection, sprouting hardwoods can be beneficial in preserving soil values, regardless of their worth as timber species.

Rarely will a site be, or long remain, completely bare after clear-cutting. Natural revegetation soon starts, or sometimes the area may be replanted. The point of concern is that, after clear-cutting, the site and soil will be exposed to some degree—perhaps to a large degree for a time—and to that extent are subject to some adverse effects.

The forest manager who understands soil values tries to keep the degree and duration of exposure to a minimum consonant with silvicultural and economic objectives. He will clear-cut only when it seems definitely dictated by technically sound considerations and he will manage his cuttings as to obtain prompt reestablishment of an adequate protective cover on the soil.

Partial cuttings have proportionately less impact than clear-cuttings. If enough stand is reserved to maintain a good mantle of litter, the detrimental effects are not likely to be serious. In dense coniferous stands, as we noted earlier, moderate thinnings may be beneficial in terms of soil values by promoting the activity of soil organisms and the decomposition of litter and by facilitating the establishment of understory vegetation.

Changes in stand composition by cutting practices mean changes in future litter composition. They are not likely to be of much significance unless the cutting left a pure coniferous stand, such as cutting all hardwoods from a pine-hardwood stand. In that event, we have established monoculture or (if more than one coniferous species is represented) a situation similar to monoculture. Our earlier comments on litter decomposition under monoculture apply here. Pure coniferous litter tends to be somewhat less effective than mixed litter for building up a soil, but the differences in litter values need not deter one from growing pure stands of adapted species if such monoculture is desirable for any reason.

The logging operation may seriously damage soil values. A substantial proportion of the area—up to 40 percent—may be compacted by haul roads, skid trails, and yarding activities. Roads and skid trails, improperly located and improperly built, provide channels for surface runoff and, in steep terrain, erosion. Skidding often causes the greatest damage. The widespread practice of downhill skidding on steep slopes by horse or tractor leads almost always to gullying and movement of soil and debris on to lower flats or into streams.

Techniques have been developed for minimizing logging damage, and studies indicate that use of such techniques does not necessarily involve added expense—they usually reduce costs.

One of the essential requirements for low-damage logging is proper layout of roads and trails: Lay them out across (not up and down) slopes, do not exceed specified grades, and be sure to avoid undercutting unstable soil or rock masses. Provide adequate drainage to handle heavy storm waters or melting snow. Avoid stream channels as far as possible. Build with a minimum of earth movement. Maintain roads while in use. Provide further stabilization at the end of the job by installing water bars, mulching, and seeding grasses and herbs.

The amount of soil compaction resulting from logging varies with the kind and weight of equipment employed, the frequency with which it traverses the same ground (for example, on and between skid trails), and the weather while the equipment is operating. Among various types of power vehicles, track-laying tractors generally apply the least pressure on the surface—between 3 and 9 pounds to the square inch, depending on their weight, length, and width of track. The compaction may extend to a depth of 12 inches directly beneath the tracks or wheels and to a width of 12 to 18 inches on each side of them. The husky horses often used to skid logs generally apply more pressure per unit area than do most tractors of the wheeled type. The logs themselves as they are dragged over the ground and heavy ground-skidding cables also cause some compacting.

Tractor logging, on a previously undisturbed area of silty clay and clay loam soils, increased the density of the upper soil layers 2.4 percent, reduced macropore space 10 percent, and reduced permeability 35 percent over the area as a whole. On the skid roads, volume weight of the soil increased 15 percent, macropore space dropped 53 percent, and permeability declined 93 percent from the values prevailing in undisturbed soil.

Research Services

H. C. Knoblauch

State agricultural experiment stations for a long time have been leaders in research in soil science. The objective has been to develop methods of soil management that make production more efficient and maintain soil fertility.

Antedating them were various State Geological and Agricultural Survey

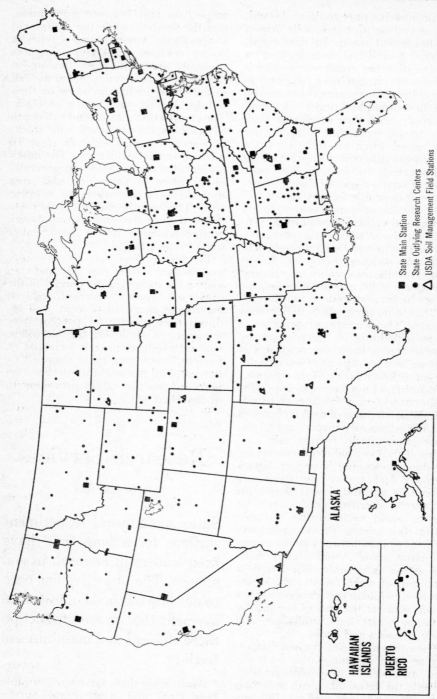

Locations of agricultural research centers maintained by State agricultural experiment stations and the USDA.

■ State Main Station
● State Outlying Research Centers
△ USDA Soil Management Field Stations

ALASKA

HAWAIIAN ISLANDS

PUERTO RICO

Reports on the chemical nature of soils and plants and the effect of fertilizers on plant growth. The first of the reports was published in 1821 by the New York Board of Agriculture. About 30 States had geological surveys, and the reports were the background for the intensive work of the experiment stations.

THE CONNECTICUT LEGISLATURE in 1875 passed a resolution establishing an agricultural experiment station. Its early work had to do with the analysis of fertilizers. Farmers and fertilizer manufacturers met in 1876 in Connecticut and recommended that all fertilizers sold in the State carry a guarantee as to composition, which was to be determined by analysis at the experiment station. Out of that project grew the concept of combining intensive laboratory study with systematic and continued field trials to help farmers solve their problems.

The United States Department of Agriculture began work on the chemical analysis of soils and plants at about the time it was established in 1865.

The Pennsylvania, Illinois, and New Jersey Agricultural Experiment Stations started some of the earliest comprehensive field investigations of soil-management problems in this country.

Experiments that started in Pennsylvania in 1882 indicate the scope of the early studies. They evaluated a number of soil treatments, such as fertilizer materials, lime, gypsum, crop rotations, and farm manure.

Many State agricultural experiment stations were established in the East and Midwest in the next three decades. They undertook systematic investigations of soil-management problems. Investigations on soils in relation to climate were carried on in the Weather Bureau in 1893. Soils research in the Department of Agriculture was organized in the Division of Agricultural Soils in 1894.

The Department of Agriculture established 18 field stations in 9 States by 1913. Many of them dealt with soil and water problems related to plant production in a region.

Field studies of soil management (except soil fertility) received minor consideration by the Department of Agriculture before 1940, but in 1942 the Department embarked on an expanded program of soil-management research. Most of the program is being carried out in cooperation with the State agricultural experiment stations.

The early investigations attempted to determine what could be added to the soil to maintain and increase crop production. Progress in the chemical industry made it possible to obtain the various chemicals that could be applied to the soil, and their effect on crop growth, yield, and soil conditions was measured.

CURRENT RESEARCH programs of the State stations and the Department of Agriculture place increasing emphasis on the physical and related biological and chemical properties of soils that limit production of crops and lead to recommendations to maintain or restore a desirable soil physical condition.

The recommendations on soil-management practices are based on results of many studies in laboratories, fields, and greenhouses of the chemical and physical reactions in the soil. Differences in climate, soil, and plants mean that the research must be conducted in many locations. The current program, even though it is extensive, does not provide information for all areas. For localities in which no research results are available, recommendations are based on results obtained in related conditions.

Support for the program is obtained from Federal and State sources and from contributions by industry for work on specific problems. Much of the work is carried on cooperatively by the Federal Government and the States. Because a large part of the research in soil management involves adaptation of findings to local conditions, it is carried on entirely by the States, Alaska, Hawaii, and Puerto Rico.

The Department of Agriculture and the State agricultural experiment stations established soil and fertilizer research committees in 1947. Four regional committees and one national committee were organized to review existing programs of soil research, determine whether additional research was needed, and organize projects of regional value and to coordinate the programs of research that are being conducted at several hundred locations.

RESULTS OF THE RESEARCH usually are presented on the basis of a particular soil type. Because the soils have not been surveyed and classified in some localities, no soil-type name is available. The important characteristics of most of the soils in the major agricultural areas are known, however. Publications of the experiment stations and the Department give assistance in determining how results under one set of conditions will apply to areas where detailed information is not available.

The map shows the locations of the State agricultural experiment stations, State substations, and the field stations of the Department of Agriculture. The Federal stations indicated on the map include only those where soil-management research was conducted in 1957.

I give the names and addresses of the State agricultural experiment stations and the stations of the United States Department of Agriculture where soil-management research information may be obtained:

STATE AGRICULTURAL EXPERIMENT STATIONS: Alabama, Auburn; Alaska, Palmer; Arizona, Tucson; Arkansas, Fayetteville; California, Berkeley, Davis, Los Angeles, Riverside; Colorado, Fort Collins; Connecticut, New Haven, Storrs; Delaware, Newark; Florida, Gainesville; Georgia, Athens, Experiment, Tifton; Hawaii, Honolulu; Idaho, Moscow; Illinois, Urbana; Indiana, Lafayette; Iowa, Ames; Kansas, Manhattan; Kentucky, Lexington; Louisiana, Baton Rouge; Maine, Orono; Maryland, College Park; Massa-

chusetts, Amherst; Michigan, East Lansing; Minnesota, St. Paul; Mississippi, State College; Missouri, Columbia; Montana, Bozeman; Nebraska, Lincoln; Nevada, Reno; New Hampshire, Durham; New Jersey, New Brunswick; New Mexico, State College; New York, Geneva, Ithaca; North Carolina, Raleigh; North Dakota, Fargo; Ohio, Columbus, Wooster; Oklahoma, Stillwater; Oregon, Corvallis; Pennsylvania, University Park; Puerto Rico, Rio Piedras; Rhode Island, Kingston; South Carolina, Clemson; South Dakota, College Station; Tennessee, Knoxville; Texas, College Station; Utah, Logan; Vermont, Burlington; Virginia, Blacksburg; Washington, Pullman; West Virginia, Morgantown; Wisconsin, Madison; Wyoming, Laramie.

FEDERAL FIELD STATIONS WHERE SOIL MANAGEMENT WORK IS UNDERWAY (Soil and Water Conservation Research Branch, Agricultural Research Service).

EASTERN SECTION

I. Federal Field Stations:

1. Southeastern Tidewater Conservation Experiment Station: Fleming, Ga. Address inquiries to Superintendent, Southeastern Tidewater Experiment Station, Fleming, Ga.

2. Southern Piedmont Conservation Experiment Station: Watkinsville, Ga. Address inquiries to Superintendent, Southern Piedmont Conservation Experiment Station, Watkinsville, Ga.

3. Soil Conservation Experiment Farm: Marcellus, N. Y. Address inquiries to Eastern Soil and Water Management Section, Bailey Hall, Cornell University, Ithaca, N. Y.

4. U. S. Soil, Plant, and Nutrition Laboratory: Cornell University, Ithaca, N. Y.

5. Beltsville, Md. Address inquiries to Soil and Water Conservation Research Branch, Beltsville, Md.

II. State Field Stations where Eastern Section Staff are stationed include McCredie, Mo.; Elsberry, Mo.; La

Crosse, Wis.; Tifton, Ga.; Clarinda, Iowa; Beaconsfield, Iowa; Joliet, Ill.; Norfolk, Va.; and Thorsby, Ala.

III. Eastern Section personnel are also stationed at the State experiment stations in Pennsylvania, New Jersey, New York, Ohio, Indiana, Illinois, Iowa, Wisconsin, Missouri, Mississippi, Louisiana, Alabama, Georgia, South Carolina, North Carolina, Virginia, and Puerto Rico.

WESTERN SECTION

I. Federal Field Stations:

1. Southwestern Irrigation Field Station, Brawley, Calif. Address inquiries to Superintendent.
2. U. S. Salinity Laboratory, Riverside, Calif. Address inquiries to Superintendent.
3. U. S. Akron Field Station, Akron, Colo. Address inquiries to Superintendent.
4. U. S. Northern Great Plains Field Station, Mandan, N. Dak. Address inquiries to Superintendent.
5. U. S. Southern Great Plains Field Station, Woodward, Okla. Address inquiries to Superintendent.
6. Newell Irrigation and Dryland Field Station, Newell, S. Dak. Address inquiries to Superintendent.
7. Amarillo Experiment Station, Bushland, Tex. Address inquiries to Superintendent.
8. U. S. Big Spring Field Station, Big Spring, Tex. Address inquiries to Superintendent.
9. Blackland Conservation Experiment Station, Temple, Tex. Address inquiries to Superintendent.
10. Beltsville, Md. Address inquiries to Soil and Water Conservation Research Branch.

II. State-owned stations where Western Section staff are headquartered include: Citrus Experiment Station, Riverside, Calif.; Tetonia Branch Station, St. Anthony, Idaho; Garden City Branch Station, Garden City, Kans.; Fort Hays Branch Station, Hays, Kans.; Northern Montana Branch Station, Havre, Mont.; Huntley Branch

Station, Huntley, Mont.; Eastern Montana Branch Station, Sidney, Mont.; Scottsbluff Experiment Station, Mitchell, Nebr.; North Platte Substation, North Platte, Nebr.; Northeastern New Mexico Substation, Tucumcari, N. Mex.; Panhandle Experiment Station, Goodwell, Okla.; Red Plains Conservation Experiment Station, Guthrie, Okla.; Umatilla Branch Experiment Station, Hermiston, Oreg.; Pendleton Branch Experiment Station, Pendleton, Oreg.; Sherman Branch Experiment Station, Moro, Oreg.; Weslaco Substation, Weslaco, Tex.; Irrigation Experiment Station, Prosser, Wash.; Sheridan Substation, Sheridan, Wyo.

III. Western Section staff are stationed at the following State agricultural experiment stations: Washington, Oregon, Utah, Nevada, New Mexico, Colorado, Wyoming, Montana, South Dakota, Nebraska, Kansas, Oklahoma, and Texas.

IV. Western Section staff are stationed also at the following additional locations: Phoenix, Ariz.; Yuma, Ariz.; Bakersfield, Calif.; Berkeley, Calif.; Los Angeles, Calif.; Pomona, Calif.; Merced, Calif.; Grand Junction, Colo.; Gunnison, Colo.; Boise, Idaho; Billings, Mont.; Shadehill, S. Dak.

LETTERS OF INQUIRY to the State agricultural experiment stations for information about soil-management research should be addressed to the Director, Agricultural Experiment Station, at the address given. Inquiries to the Federal field stations should be addressed to the Director at the address given.

TO THE LIST OF SOURCES of information should be added the county agricultural agents, whose offices usually are in the county seats. They can give advice on methods of soil management, such as the preparation and management of soils for the production of crops, grass, and trees. They are familiar with the practices that are best for local conditions. They have copies or lists of available publications.

Contributors

Firman E. Bear Editor of *Soil Science*, Rutgers University. Author, *Soils and Fertilizers;* editor, *Chemistry of the Soil.*

Kenneth C. Beeson Director, United States Plant, Soil, and Nutrition Laboratory, Ithaca, N. Y.

K. C. Berger Professor of soils, University of Wisconsin, Madison.

B. D. Blakely Head agronomist, Soil Conservation Service, Washington, D. C.

R. E. Blaser Professor of agronomy, Virginia Polytechnic Institute, Blacksburg.

Victor R. Boswell Head, Vegetable Crops Branch, Crops Research Division, Agricultural Research Service, Beltsville, Md.

C. A. Bower Soil scientist, United States Salinity Laboratory, Riverside, Calif.

Damon Boynton Professor of pomology, Cornell University. Editor and business manager, American Society for Horticultural Science. Formerly director of research and education and head of the Plant Industry Department, Inter-American Institute of Agricultural Science, Turrialba, Costa Rica.

N. C. Brady Professor, soil science and head, Department of Agronomy, Cornell University, Ithaca, N. Y.

F. E. Broadbent Associate professor of soil microbiology and associate soil microbiologist, Experiment Station, University of California, Davis. Previously associated with the California Citrus Experiment Station and with Cornell University.

J. C. Brown Soil scientist, Soil and Water Conservation Research Branch, Agricultural Research Service, Beltsville, Md.

Robert L. Brown Deputy State Conservationist, Soil Conservation Service, Portland, Oreg.

Charles P. Butler Agricultural economist, Southern Field Research Section, Production Economics Research Branch, Agricultural Research Service, Clemson, S. C.

H. B. Cheney Head, Department of Soils, Oregon State College, Corvallis. Formerly extension agronomist, Iowa State College.

W. S. Chepil Soil scientist, Western Section, Soil and Water Conservation Research Branch, Kansas State College, Manhattan.

Francis E. Clark Principal microbiologist, Soil and Water Conservation Research Branch, Agricultural Research Service, Beltsville, Md.

Andrew R. Aandahl Principal soil correlator, Great Plains States, Soil Conservation Service, University of Nebraska, Lincoln.

J. Richard Adams In charge of studies of fertilizer supplies and consumption trends, Soil and Water Conservation Research Branch, Agricultural Research Service, Beltsville, Md.

D. G. Aldrich Chairman, Department of Soils and Plant Nutrition, professor of soil science, and chemist in the Experiment Station, University of California, Davis-Berkeley.

Lyle T. Alexander In charge, Soil Survey Laboratories, Soil Conservation Service, Washington, D. C.

W. H. Allaway Head, Soils and Plant Relationships Section, Soil and Water Conservation Research Branch, Agricultural Research Service, Beltsville, Md.

Franklin E. Allison Principal soil scientist, Soil and Water Conservation Research Branch, Agricultural Research Service, Beltsville, Md.

Myron S. Anderson Senior chemist, Soil and Water Conservation Research Branch, Agricultural Research Service, Beltsville, Md.

J. H. Atkinson Assistant professor, Department of Agricultural Economics, Purdue University, Lafayette, Ind. Formerly agricultural economist, Farm Credit Administration.

Carleton P. Barnes Research coordinator, Agricultural Research Service. Executive secretary, Soils, Water, and Fertilizer Research Advisory Committee, Department of Agriculture. Washington, D. C.

W. V. Bartholomew Professor of soils, North Carolina State College, Raleigh, N. C. Previously professor in charge of soil microbiology, Iowa State College.

N. T. Coleman Professor of soils, North Carolina State College, Raleigh.

W. E. Colwell Assistant director, North Carolina Agricultural Experiment Station, Raleigh. Formerly professor of agronomy and head, Agronomy Department, North Carolina State College.

R. L. Cook Head, Soil Science Department, Michigan State University, East Lansing.

Otis L. Copeland, Jr. Forest pathologist, Intermountain Forest Experiment Station, United States Forest Service, Spokane, Wash.

J. J. Coyle Agricultural engineering specialist, Engineering Division, Soil Conservation Service, Washington, D. C.

C. W. Crickman Assistant head, Northern Field Research Section, Production Economics Research Branch, Agricultural Research Service, Washington, D. C.

Wayne D. Criddle Irrigation engineer, Western Soil and Water Management Section, Soil and Water Conservation Research Branch, Agricultural Research Service, and professor of irrigation and drainage, Utah State University, Logan.

L. A. Dean Soil science adviser, International Cooperation Administration, New Delhi, India. Formerly soil scientist, Soil and Water Conservation Research Branch, Agricultural Research Service, Beltsville, Md.

T. W. Edminster Agricultural engineer, Eastern Soil and Water Management Section, Soil and Water Conservation Research Branch, Agricultural Research Service.

Lincoln Ellison Plant ecologist, Intermountain Forest and Range Experiment Station, United States Forest Service, Ogden, Utah.

S. L. Emsweller Principal horticulturist, Horticultural Crops Research Branch, Agricultural Research Service, Beltsville, Md.

L. E. Ensminger Soil chemist and professor of soils, Alabama Polytechnic Institute, Auburn.

Chester E. Evans Assistant head, Western Soil and Water Management Section, Soil and Water Conservation Research Branch, Agricultural Research Service, Beltsville, Md. Formerly associate agronomist, Ohio Agricultural Experiment Station.

A. E. Ferber Woodland conservationist, Soil Conservation Service, Denver, Colo.

Milton Fireman Agricultural Extension Service, University of California, Riverside.

Walter E. Fleming Entomologist, Fruit Insects Section, Entomology Research Branch, Agricultural Research Service.

C. J. Francis Director, Engineering Division, Soil Conservation Service, Washington.

Bernard Frank, Assistant chief, Division of Watershed Management Research, Forest Service, Washington, D. C. Formerly assistant chief forester, Tennessee Valley Authority.

Maurice Fried Soil scientist, Soil and Water Conservation Research Branch, Agricultural Research Service, Beltsville, Md.

Ernest J. George Silviculturist, Horticultural Crops Research Branch, Agricultural Research Service, Northern Great Plains Field Station, Mandan, N. Dak.

Joel E. Giddens Associate professor of agronomy, College Experiment Station, University of Georgia, Athens.

Perrin H. Grissom Agronomist in charge of soil fertility and irrigation research, Delta Branch, Mississippi Agricultural Experiment Station, Stoneville.

H. J. Haas Soil scientist, Soil and Water Conservation Research Branch, Department of Agriculture, Northern Great Plains Field Station, Mandan, N. Dak.

Howard R. Haise Technical staff specialist of research activities in irrigation requirements and practices, Western Soil and Water Management Section, Soil and Water Conservation Research Branch, Agricultural Research Service, Beltsville, Md.

William J. Hanna Associate professor of soils, Rutgers University, New Brunswick, N. J.

John J. Hanway Associate professor of agronomy in charge of the Soil Testing Laboratory, Iowa State College, Ames.

Lowell S. Hardin Head, Department of Agricultural Economics, Purdue University, Lafayette, Ind.

V. L. Harper, Assistant chief, in charge of research, Forest Service, Washington, D. C. Formerly director, Northeastern Forest Experiment Station, Forest Service, Upper Darby, Pa.

Earl O. Heady Professor of agricultural economics, Iowa State College, Ames.

A. M. Hedge In charge of farm and ranch planning activities, Soil Conservation Service, Washington, D. C.

747

Trimble R. Hedges Professor, agricultural economics, and agricultural economist, Experiment Station and on the Giannini Foundation, University of California, Davis.

J. R. Henderson Extension agronomist, University of Florida, Gainesville.

Sterling B. Hendricks Chemist, Agricultural Research Service, Washington, D. C.

W. L. Hill Chemist, Fertilizer and Agricultural Lime Section, Soil and Water Conservation Research Branch, Agricultural Research Service, Beltsville, Md.

J. A. Hobbs Associate agronomist, Kansas Agricultural Experiment Station, Manhattan.

E. A. Hollowell Principal agronomist, Crops Research Division, Agricultural Research Service, Beltsville, Md.

R. S. Holmes Chemist, Soil and Water Conservation Research Branch, Agricultural Research Service, Beltsville, Md.

G. M. Horner Project leader of investigations of soil management, Soil and Water Conservation Research Branch, Pullman, Wash.

Walter C. Hulburt Agricultural engineer, leader of Fertilizer Distributing Machinery Project, Agricultural Research Center.

D. B. Ibach Production Economics Research Branch, Agricultural Research Service, Washington, D. C.

K. D. Jacob Head, Fertilizer and Agricultural Lime Section, Soil and Water Conservation Research Branch, Agricultural Research Service, Beltsville, Md.

C. M. Johnson Associate chemist, Department of Soils and Plant Nutrition, University of California, Berkeley. Formerly with the Western Regional Research Laboratory of the Department of Agriculture.

E. W. Johnson Horticulturist, Horticultural Crops Research Branch, Agricultural Research Service, Southern Great Plains Field Station, Woodward, Okla.

J. R. Johnston Area supervisor, Texas-Oklahoma-New Mexico Area, Western Section, Soil and Water Conservation Research Branch, Agricultural Research Service, Department of Agriculture, Amarillo, Tex.

Howard V. Jordan Project leader, Southern Regional Sulfur Project, Mississippi Agricultural Experiment Station, State College.

J. J. Jurinak Junior soil chemist, University of California, Davis.

Charles E. Kellogg Assistant administrator for Soil Survey, Soil Conservation Service, Washington 25, D. C. Formerly on the staffs of Michigan State University, University of Wisconsin, and North Dakota State College. Author, *The Soils That Support Us;* The *Soil Survey Manual; Our Garden Soils; Food, Soil, and People.*

A. A. Klingebiel Director of Soils Survey Interpretation, Soil Conservation Service, Washington, D. C.

H. C. Knoblauch Director, State Experiment Stations Division, Agricultural Research Service, Washington, D. C.

B. A. Krantz Supervisory soil scientist, Soil and Water Conservation Research Branch, Department of Agriculture, Billings, Mont.

L. T. Kurtz Professor of soil fertility, University of Illinois, Urbana.

E. L. Langsford Head, Southern Field Research Section, Production Economics Research Branch, Agricultural Research Service, Washington, D. C.

K. Lawton Professor of soil science, Michigan State University, East Lansing.

Paul E. Lemmon. Soil scientist (forestry), Soil Conservation Service, Portland, Oreg.

Edgar R. Lemon Soil scientist, Soil and Water Conservation Research Branch, Agricultural Research Service, Ithaca, N. Y. Formerly agent (soil scientist), College Station, Tex.

W. E. McQuilkin Research specialist, Northeastern Forest Experiment Station, Forest Service, Upper Darby, Pa.

John R. Magness Head, Fruit and Nut Crops Section, Agricultural Research Service, Beltsville, Md.

John H. Martin Agricultural Research Service, Beltsville, Md. Research agronomist, Office of International Relations; author (with W. H. Leonard), *Principles of Field Crop Production.*

Curtis May Principal pathologist, Horticultural Crops Research Branch, Agricultural Research Service, Beltsville, Md.

A. Mehlich Research associate professor of soils, North Carolina State College, Raleigh.

R. J. Miears On the staff, Rice Experiment Station, Louisiana State University, Crowley.

R. J. Muckenhirn Professor of soils and assistant director, Wisconsin Agricultural Experiment Station, University of Wisconsin, Madison.

R. B. Musgrave Professor of field crops, Cornell University, Ithaca, N. Y.

L. B. Nelson Soil and Water Conservation Research Branch, Agricultural Research Service, Beltsville, Md.

E. L. Newman Chemical engineer, Division of Chemical Development, Tennessee Valley Authority, Wilson Dam, Ala.

E. B. Norum Professor of soils, North Dakota Agricultural College, Fargo.

S. S. Obenshain Agronomist, Virginia Agricultural Experiment Station; professor of agronomy, Virginia Polytechnic Institute, Blacksburg.

Sterling R. Olsen Soil scientist, Soil and Water Conservation Research Branch, Agricultural Research Service, Colorado State University, Fort Collins.

Carl E. Ostrom Chief, Division of Forest Management Research, Southeastern Forest Experiment Station, United States Forest Service, Asheville.

J. K. Patterson Assistant professor of agronomy, State College of Washington, Pullman.

R. W. Pearson Soil fertility work project leader, Eastern Soil and Water Management Section, Soil and Water Conservation Research, Agricultural Research Service, Auburn, Ala.

H. B. Peterson Head, Department of Agronomy, Utah State University, Logan.

W. H. Pierre Professor of soils and head, Department of Agronomy, Iowa State College, Ames.

John T. Presley Field Crops Research Branch, Agricultural Research Service, Beltsville, Md.

T. H. Quackenbush Irrigation engineer, Engineering Division, Soil Conservation Service, Washington, D. C.

W. A. Raney Soil physics work project leader, Eastern Section, Soil and Water Conservation Research Branch, Agricultural Research Service, Beltsville, Md. Formerly soil physicist, Mississippi Agricultural Experiment Station.

Ralph A. Read Research forester, Rocky Mountain Forest and Range Experiment Station, United States Forest Service, University of Nebraska, Lincoln.

Ronald C. Reeve Irrigation and drainage engineer, United States Salinity Laboratory, Riverside, Calif., and technical staff specialist on salinity and drainage, Western Soil and Water Management Section, Soil and Water Conservation Research Branch.

H. M. Reisenauer Associate professor of soils, State College of Washington, Pullman. Head, State soil testing laboratory.

R. F. Reitemeier Soil scientist and project leader, Soil and Water Conservation Research Branch, Agricultural Research Service, Beltsville, Md.

H. W. Reuszer Associate microbiologist, Department of Agronomy, Purdue University Agricultural Experiment Station. Formerly staff member, New Jersey and Colorado Agricultural Experiment Stations and Soil Conservation Service and Alabama Agricultural Experiment Station.

Walter Reuther Chairman, Department of Horticulture, University of California Citrus Experiment Station, Riverside. Formerly principal horticulturist, U. S. Horticultural Station, Orlando, Fla.

L. A. Richards Physicist, United States Salinity Laboratory, Agricultural Research Service, Riverside, Calif.

S. J. Richards Associate irrigation engineer and vice chairman, Department of Irrigation and Soils, Citrus Experiment Station, University of California, Riverside.

F. F. Riecken Professor of soils, Iowa State College, Ames.

R. R. Robinson Eastern Soil and Water Management Section, Soil and Water Conservation Research Branch, Agricultural Research Service, Beltsville, Md.

T. Hayden Rogers Head, Department of Agronomy, University of Georgia, Athens. Formerly professor, Alabama Polytechnic Institute.

Darrell A. Russel Assistant soil chemist in charge of soil testing research, North Louisiana Hill Farm Experiment Station, Homer. Formerly director, Eastern Branch Soil Testing Laboratory, Iowa Agricultural Extension Service; author, *A Laboratory Manual for Soil Fertility Students*.

M. B. Russell Head, Department of Agronomy, University of Illinois, Urbana. Past president, Soil Science Society of America, and Commission I, Soil Physics of the International Society of Soil Science.

749

Orlin J. Scoville Head, Farming Efficiency Section, Production Economics Research Branch, Agricultural Research Service, Washington, D. C.

Lloyd F. Seatz Professor of agronomy and agronomist in charge of research into trace elements, University of Tennessee, Knoxville.

G. Donald Sherman Chairman, Department of Soils and Agricultural Chemistry; senior chemist and professor of agriculture, University of Hawaii, Honolulu.

Roy W. Simonson Director of Soil Classification and Correlation, Soil Conservation Service, Washington, D. C.

F. B. Smith Microbiologist and head, Department of Soils, University of Florida, Gainesville. Formerly secretary-treasurer, American Society of Agronomy, and secretary, Soil Science Society of America.

Guy D. Smith Director, soil survey investigations, Soil Conservation Service.

W. A. Starr Professor of soils, State College of Washington, Pullman.

J. G. Steele Chief, Soil Survey Reports, Soil Conservation Service, Beltsville, Md.

A. D. Stoesz Head plant materials technician, Division of Plant Technology, Soil Conservation Service, Washington, D. C. Formerly chief, Regional Nursery Division, Soil Conservation Service, Lincoln, Nebr.

Earl L. Stone, Jr., Charles Lathrop Pack Associate Professor of Forest Soils, Department of Agronomy, Cornell University.

P. R. Stout Director, Kearney Foundation of Soil Science; professor of soil science, Department of Soils and Plant Nutrition, University of California, Berkeley. Formerly chairman, Division of Plant Nutrition.

R. A. Struchtemeyer Professor and head, Department of Agronomy, University of Maine, Orono.

N. W. Stuart Principal physiologist, Horticultural Crops Research Branch, Agricultural Research Service, Beltsville, Md.

M. B. Sturgis Professor of agronomy and head, Department of Agronomy, Louisiana State University, Baton Rouge.

Sterling A. Taylor Professor, soil physics, Agronomy Department, Utah State University, Logan.

M. D. Thorne Head, Department of Agronomy, Oklahoma Agricultural and Mechanical College, Stillwater. Formerly irrigation work project leader, Eastern Soil and Water Management Section, Soil and Water Conservation Research Branch, Agricultural Research Service.

Wynne Thorne Director, Utah Agricultural Experiment Station, Logan.

M. L. Upchurch Head, Western Field Research Section, Production Economics Research Branch, Agricultural Research Service, Washington, D. C.

Frank G. Viets, Jr. Supervisory soil scientist, Soil and Water Conservation Research Branch, Department of Agriculture, Fort Collins, Colo.

C. H. Wadleigh Chief, Soil and Water Conservation Research Branch, Beltsville, Md. Formerly head, Soil and Plant Relationships Section, Soil and Water Conservation Research Branch. Past president, American Society of Plant Physiologists.

R. E. Wagner Head, Department of Agronomy, University of Maryland, College Park. Formerly project leader, Western Pasture and Range Project, Field Crops Research Branch, Agricultural Research Service.

R. K. Walker Superintendent, Louisiana State University Rice Experiment Station, Crowley. Consulting director, International Basic Economy Corporation Rice Research Program, Venezuela.

C. H. Wasser Professor, Range management and dean, College of Forestry and Range Management, Colorado State University, Fort Collins.

Eric Winters Associate director, Tennessee Agricultural Experiment Station, University of Tennessee, Knoxville.

Frank W. Woods Research forester, Southern Forest Experiment Station, United States Forest Service, Marianna, Fla.

William J. Zaumeyer Horticultural Crops Research Branch, Agricultural Research Service, Beltsville, Md.

A. W. Zingg Technical staff specialist, Western Section, Soil and Water Conservation Research Branch, Agricultural Research Service, Fort Collins, Colo.

Glossary

another phase. Nutrients in solution (ions) carrying a positive charge become attached to (adsorbed by) negatively charged soil particles.

AERATION, SOIL The exchange of air in soil with air from the atmosphere. The composition of the air in a well-aerated soil is similar to that in the atmosphere; in a poorly aerated soil, the air in the soil is considerably higher in carbon dioxide and lower in oxygen than the atmosphere above the soil.

AEROBIC (1) Conditions with oxygen gas as a part of the environment. (2) Living or acting only in the presence of air or free oxygen. (3) Pertaining to the activity of organisms that grow under aerobic conditions, such as aerobic decomposition.

A HORIZON The surface horizon of a mineral soil having maximum biological activity, or eluviation (removal of materials dissolved or suspended in water), or both.

ABC SOIL A soil with a complete profile, including an A, a B, and a C horizon.

ABSORBING COMPLEX The materials in the soil that hold water and chemical compounds, mainly on their surfaces. They are chiefly the fine mineral matter and organic matter.

AC SOIL A soil with an incomplete profile, including an A and a C horizon, but no B horizon. Commonly such soils are young, like those developing from alluvium or on steep, rocky slopes.

ACID SOIL Generally, a soil that is acid throughout most or all of the parts of it that plant roots occupy. Commonly applied to only the surface-plowed layer or to some other specific layer or horizon of a soil. Practically, this means a soil more acid than pH 6.6; precisely, a soil with a pH value less than 7.0. A soil having a preponderance of hydrogen over hydroxyl ions in the soil solution.

ACTINOMYCETES A group of soil microorganisms which produce an extensive threadlike network. They resemble the soil molds in some respects but are more like the bacteria in size.

ADDITIVE A material added to fertilizer to improve its chemical or physical condition. An additive to liquid fertilizer might prevent crystals from forming in the liquid at temperatures where crystallization would normally take place.

ADSORB Removal of a substance in solution to a solid surface or a separate phase; to accumulate on a surface.

ADSORPTION The attachment of compounds or ionic parts of salts to a surface or

AGGREGATE (OF SOIL) Many fine soil particles held in a single mass or cluster, such as a clod, crumb, block, or prism. Many properties of the aggregate differ from those of an equal mass of unaggregated soil.

ALKALI SOIL Generally, a highly alkaline soil. Specifically, an alkali soil has so high a degree of alkalinity—pH 8.5 or higher—or so high a percentage of exchangeable sodium— 15 percent or higher—or both, that the growth of most crop plants is reduced. (In former years this term was also applied loosely to both alkali and saline soils. The term is also applied by some to those uncommon soils that contain highly alkaline salts, such as sodium carbonate.)

ALKALINE SOIL Generally, a soil that is alkaline throughout most or all of the parts of it occupied by plant roots; although the term is commonly applied to only a specific layer or horizon of a soil. Precisely, any soil horizon having a pH value greater than 7.0; practically, a soil having a pH above 7.3.

ALLUVIAL SOILS Soils developing from transported and relatively recently deposited material (alluvium) with little or no modification of the original materials by soil-forming processes. (Soils with well-developed profiles that have formed from alluvium are grouped with other soils having the same kinds of profiles, not with the alluvial soils.)

ALLUVIUM Sand, mud, and other sediments deposited on land by streams.

ALUMINO-SILICATES Compounds containing aluminum, silicon, and oxygen atoms as main constituents.

AMENDMENT Any material, such as lime, gypsum, sawdust, or synthetic conditioners, that is worked into the soil to make it more productive. Strictly, a fertilizer is also an amendment, but the term "amendment" is used most commonly for added materials other than fertilizer.

AMINO ACIDS Amino acids are nitrogen-containing organic compounds, large numbers of which link together in the formation of a protein molecule. Each amino acid molecule contains one or more amino ($-NH_2$) groups and at least one carboxyl ($-COOH$) group. In addition, some amino acids (cystine and methionine) contain sulfur.

AMMONIA A colorless gas composed of one atom of nitrogen and three atoms of hydrogen. Ammonia liquefied under pressure is used as a fertilizer.

AMMONIFICATION The formation by organisms of ammonium compounds from nitrogen-containing organic materials.

AMMONIUM ION The positively charged NH_4^+ ion. The form in which nitrogen occurs in many commercial fertilizers.

ANAEROBIC Living or functioning in the absence of air or free oxygen.

ANHYDROUS Dry, or without water. Anhydrous ammonia is water free; in contrast to the water solution of ammonia commonly known as household ammonia.

ANION An ion carrying a negative charge of electricity.

ANTHROPIC SOIL A soil produced from a natural soil or other earthy deposit by the work of man that has new characteristics that make it different from the natural soil. Examples include deep, black surface soils resulting from centuries of manuring, and naturally acid soils that have lost their distinguishing features because of many centuries of liming and use for grass.

ANTIBIOSIS Opposed to living. Antibiotics suppress some micro-organisms.

APATITE A native phosphate of lime. The name is given to the chief mineral of phosphate rock and the inorganic compound of bone.

AQUA AMMONIA A water solution of ammonia.

AQUIFER A water-bearing formation through which water moves more readily than in adjacent formations of lower permeability.

ARID CLIMATE A very dry climate like that of desert or semidesert regions where there is only enough water for widely spaced desert plants. The limits of precipitation vary widely according to temperature, with an upper limit for cool regions of less than 10 inches and for tropical regions of as much as 20 inches. (The precipitation-effectiveness index ranges from 0 to about 16.)

ARID REGION Areas where the potential water losses by evaporation and transpiration are greater than the amount of water supplied by precipitation. In the United States this area is broadly considered to be the dry parts of the 17 Western States.

ASH The nonvolatile residue resulting from the complete burning of organic matter. It is commonly composed of oxides of such elements as silicon, aluminum, iron, calcium, magnesium, and potassium.

ASSIMILATION Conversion of substances taken in from the outside into living tissue of plants or animals.

AUTOTROPHIC Capable of using (oxidizing) simple chemical elements or compounds, such as iron, sulfur, or nitrates, to obtain energy for growth.

AUXINS Organic substances which cause lengthening of the stem when applied in low concentrations to shoots of growing plants.

AVAILABLE NUTRIENT IN SOILS The part of the supply of a plant nutrient in the soil that can be taken up by plants at rates and in amounts significant to plant growth.

AVAILABLE WATER IN SOILS The part of the water in the soil that can be taken up by plants at rates significant to their growth; usable; obtainable.

AZONAL SOILS A general group of soils having little or no soil profile development. Most of them are young. In the United States, Alluvial soils, Lithosols, and Regosols are included in the azonal group.

B HORIZON A soil horizon, usually beneath an A horizon, or surface soil, in which (1) clay, iron, or aluminum, with accessory organic matter, have accumulated by receiving suspended material from the A horizon above it or by clay development in place; (2) the soil has a blocky or prismatic structure; or (3) the soil has some combination of these features. In soils with distinct profiles, the B horizon is roughly equivalent to the general term "subsoil."

BANDING (OF FERTILIZERS) The placement of fertilizers in the soil in continuous narrow ribbons, usually at specific distances from the seeds or plants. The fertilizer bands are covered by the soil but are not mixed with it.

BASE SATURATION The relative degree to which soils have metallic cations absorbed. The proportion of the cation-exchange capacity that is saturated with metallic cations.

BASIN IRRIGATION (OR LEVEL BORDERS) The application of irrigation water to level areas that are surrounded by border ridges or levees. Usually irrigation water is applied at rates greater than the water intake rate of the soil. The water may stand on uncropped soils for several days until the soil is well soaked; then any excess may be used on other fields. The water may stand a few hours on fields having a growing crop.

BASIN LISTING A method of tillage that creates small basins by damming lister furrows at regular intervals of about 4 to 20 feet. This method is a modification of ordinary listing and is carried out approximately on the contour on nearly level or gently sloping soils as a means of encouraging water to enter the soil rather than to run off the surface.

BC SOIL A soil with a B and a C horizon but with little or no A horizon. Most BC soils have lost their A horizons by erosion.

BEDDING SOIL Arranging the surface of fields by plowing and grading into a series of elevated beds separated by shallow ditches for drainage.

BEDROCK The solid rock underlying soils and other earthy surface formations.

BENCH TERRACES An embankment constructed across sloping soils with a steep drop on the downslope side.

BLOWOUT An area from which soil material has been removed by wind. Such an area appears as a nearly barren, shallow depression with a flat or irregular floor consisting of a resistant layer, an accumulation of pebbles, or wet soil lying just above a water table.

BOG SOIL An intrazonal group of soils with mucky or peaty surface soils underlain by peat. Bog soils usually have swamp or marsh vegetation and are commonest in humid regions.

BONDS Chemical forces holding atoms together to form molecules.

BORDER IRRIGATION Irrigation in which the water flows over narrow strips that are nearly level and are separated by parallel, low-bordering banks or ridges.

BROAD-BASE TERRACE A low embankment, with such gentle slopes that it can be farmed, constructed across sloping soils approximately on the contour. Broad-base terraces are used on pervious soils to reduce runoff and soil erosion.

BROWN FOREST SOILS An intrazonal group of soils that have dark-brown surface horizons, relatively rich in humus, grading through lighter colored soil into the parent material. They are characterized by a slightly acid or neutral reaction and a moderately high amount of exchangeable calcium. They are commonly developed under deciduous forests from parent materials relatively rich in bases, especially calcium.

BROWN PODZOLIC SOILS A zonal group of soils with thin mats of partly decayed leaves over thin, grayish-brown mixed humus and mineral soil. They lie over yellow or yellowish-brown, acid B horizons, slightly richer in clay than the surface soils. These soils develop under deciduous or mixed deciduous and coniferous forests in cool-temperate humid regions, such as parts of New England, New York, and western Washington.

BROWN SOILS A zonal group of soils having a brown surface horizon that grades below into lighter colored soil. These soils have an accumulation of calcium carbonate at 1 to 3 feet. They develop under short grasses, bunchgrasses, and shrubs in a temperate to cool semiarid climate.

BUFFER, BUFFERING Substances in the soil that act chemically to resist changes in reaction or pH. The buffering action is due mainly to clay and very fine organic matter. Highly weathered tropical clays are less active buffers than most less weathered silicate clays. Thus with the same degree of acidity, or pH, more lime is required to neutralize (1) a clayey soil than a sandy soil, (2) a soil rich in organic matter than one low in organic matter, or (3) a sandy loam in Michigan, say, than a sandy loam in central Alabama.

BUFFER STRIPS Established strips of perennial grass or other erosion-resisting vegetation, usually on the contour in cultivated fields, to reduce runoff and erosion.

BULK DENSITY The mass or weight of oven-dry soil per unit bulk volume, including air space. This mass in relation to the weight of a unit volume of water, was formerly called "apparent density" or "volume weight."

C HORIZON The unconsolidated rock material in the lower part of the soil profile like that from which the upper horizons (or at least a part of the B horizon) have developed.

CALCAREOUS SOIL A soil containing calcium carbonate, or a soil alkaline in reaction because of the presence of calcium carbonate. A soil containing enough calcium carbonate to effervesce (fizz) when treated with dilute hydrochloric acid.

CALICHE A broad term for the more or less cemented deposits of calcium carbonate in many soils of warm-temperate areas, as in the Southwestern States. When it is very near the surface or exposed by erosion, the material hardens. (Caliche is also used for deposits of sodium nitrate in Chile and Peru.)

CAPILLARY POROSITY The volume of small pores within the soil that hold water against the force of gravity.

CAPILLARY WATER The water retained in the fine pores in soil by surface tension that moves as a result of capillary forces.

CARBOHYDRATES Compounds containing carbon, hydrogen, and oxygen. Usually the hydrogen and oxygen occur in the proportion of 2 to 1, such as in glucose ($C_6H_{12}O_6$).

CARBON One of the commonest chemical elements, occurring in lampblack, coal, and coke in varying degrees of purity. Compounds of carbon are the chief constituents of living tissue.

CARBON DIOXIDE A colorless gas (CO_2) composed of carbon and oxygen and normally found in small amounts in the air. It is one of the end products of the burning (oxidation) of organic matter, or carbon-containing compounds.

CARBON-NITROGEN RATIO The ratio of the weight of organic carbon to the weight of total nitrogen in a soil or in an organic material.

CATALASE An enzyme capable of decomposing hydrogen peroxide into water and oxygen: $2H_2O_2 \rightarrow 2H_2O + O_2$.

CATALYST A material that increases the rate of a chemical reaction.

CATENA A group of soils, within a specific soil zone, formed from similar parent materials but with unlike soil characteristics because of differences in relief or drainage.

CATION An ion carrying a positive charge of electricity. The common soil cations are calcium, magnesium, sodium, potassium, and hydrogen.

CATION EXCHANGE The exchange of cations held by the soil-adsorbing complex with other cations. Thus if a soil-absorbing complex is rich in sodium, treatment with calcium sulfate (gypsum) causes some calcium cations to exchange with some sodium cations.

CATION-EXCHANGE CAPACITY A measure of the total amount of exchangeable cations that can be held by the soil. It is expressed in terms of milliequivalents per 100 grams of soil at neutrality (pH 7) or at some other stated pH value. (Formerly called base-exchange capacity.)

CELLULOSE The principal constituent of the cell walls of higher plants. It is made up of glucose molecules arranged in long chains and has the chemical formula $(C_6H_{10}O_5)_x$. The long molecules give it a fibrous nature. Cotton fibers are almost pure cellulose. Paper is mainly cellulose separated by chemical processes from wood or other plant remains.

CHELATES A type of chemical compound in which a metallic atom is firmly combined with a molecule by means of multiple chemical bonds. The term refers to the claw of a crab illustrative of the way in which the atom is held.

CHERNOZEM SOILS A zonal group of soils having deep, dark to nearly black surface horizons and rich in organic matter, which grades into lighter colored soil below. At 1.5 to 4 feet, these soils have layers of accumulated calcium carbonate. They develop under tall and mixed grasses in a temperate to cool subhumid climate.

CHERT A structureless form of silica, closely related to flint, which breaks into angular fragments. Soils developed from impure limestones containing fragments of chert and having abundant quantities of these fragments in the soil mass are called cherty soils.

CHESTNUT SOILS A zonal group of soils with dark-brown surface horizons, which grade into lighter colored horizons beneath. They have layers of accumulated calcium carbonate at 1 to 4 feet. They are developed under mixed tall and short grasses in a temperate to cool and subhumid to semiarid climate. Chestnut soils occur in regions a little more moist than those having Brown soils and a little drier than those having Chernozem soils.

CHISEL A tillage machine with one or more soil-penetrating points that can be drawn through the soil to loosen the subsoil, usually to a depth of 12 to 18 inches.

CHITIN A nitrogen containing polysaccharide found in the outer part of insects.

CHLOROPHYLL The constituent responsible for the green color of plants. Chlorophyll is important in photosynthesis in plants, the process by which sugar is manufactured.

CHLOROPLASTS Small bodies in cells of plants in which the green pigment chlorophyll is concentrated.

CHLOROSIS A condition in plants resulting from the failure of chlorophyll (the green coloring matter) to develop, usually because of deficiency of an essential nutrient. Leaves of chlorotic plants range from light green through yellow to almost white.

CLAY As a soil separate, the mineral soil particles less than 0.002 mm. in diameter. As a soil textural class, soil material that contains 40 percent or more of clay, less than 45 percent of sand, and less than 40 percent of silt.

CLAY LOAM Soil material that contains 27 to 40 percent of clay and 20 to 45 percent of sand.

CLAY MINERAL Naturally occurring inorganic crystalline material in soils or other earthy deposits of clay size—particles less than 0.002 mm. in diameter.

CLAYPAN A compact, slowly permeable soil horizon rich in clay and separated more or less abruptly from the overlying soil. Claypans are commonly hard when dry and plastic or stiff when wet.

CLOD A mass of soil produced by plowing or digging, which usually slakes easily with repeated wetting and drying, in contrast to a *ped*, which is a natural soil aggregate.

COLLOID, SOIL Colloid refers to organic or inorganic matter having very small particle size and a correspondingly large surface area per unit of mass. Most colloidal particles are too small to be seen with the ordinary compound microscope. Soil colloids do not go into true solution as sugar or salt do, but they may be dispersed into a relatively stable suspension and thus be carried in moving water. By treatment with salts and other chemicals, colloids may be flocculated, or aggregated, into small crumbs or granules that settle out of water. (Such small crumbs of aggregated colloids can be moved by rapidly moving water or air just as other particles can be.) Many mineral soil colloids are really tiny crystals and the minerals can be identified with X-rays and in other ways.

COLLUVIUM Mixed deposits of soil material and rock fragments near the base of rather steep slopes. The deposits have accumulated through soil creep, slides, and local wash.

COMPANION CROP A crop grown with another crop, usually a small grain with which alfalfa, clover, or other forage crops are sown. (Formerly such small grain crops were known as nurse crops, but because the small grain does not "nurse" the other crop this older term is being abandoned.)

COMPLEX, SOIL An intimate mixture of tiny areas of different kinds of soil that are too small to be shown separately on a publishable soil map. The whole group of soils must be shown together as a mapping unit and described as a pattern of soils.

COMPOST A mass of rotted organic matter made from waste plant residues. Inorganic fertilizers, especially nitrogen, and a little soil usually are added to it. The organic residues usually are piled in layers, to which the fertilizers are added. The layers are separated by thin layers of soil. The whole pile is kept moist and allowed to decompose. The pile is usually turned once or twice. The principal purpose in making compost is to permit the organic materials to become crumbly and to reduce the carbon-nitrogen ratio of the material. Compost is sometimes called artificial or synthetic manure.

CONCRETIONS Hard grains, pellets, or nodules from concentrations of compounds in the soil that cement the soil grains together. The composition of some concretions is unlike that of the surrounding soil. Concretions can be of various sizes, shapes, and colors.

CONDITIONER (OF FERTILIZER) A material added to a fertilizer to prevent caking and to keep it free flowing.

CONDUCTANCE Conducting power, the reciprocal of resistance.

CONDUCTIVITY, ELECTRICAL A physical quantity that measures the readiness with which a medium transmits electricity. Commonly used for expressing the salinity of irrigation waters and soil extracts because it can be directly related to salt concentration. It is expressed in mhos per centimeter (or millimhos per centimeter or micromhos per centimeter at 25° C.).

CONSISTENCE The combination of properties of soil material that determine its resistance to crushing and its ability to be molded or changed in shape. Consistence depends mainly on the forces of attraction between soil particles. Consistence is described by such words as loose, friable, firm, soft, plastic, and sticky.

CONSOLIDATE (SOIL) To place into a compact mass and thus increase density and reduce pore space.

CONSUMPTIVE USE The water used by plants in transpiration and growth, plus water vapor loss from adjacent soil or snow, or from intercepted precipitation in any specified time. Usually expressed as equivalent depth of free water per unit of time.

CONTINENTAL CLIMATE A general term for the climate typical of great land masses where wide ranges in temperature and other weather conditions occur because the area is not greatly influenced by nearness to the sea. Much of the United States has a continental climate.

CONTOUR An imaginary line connecting points of equal elevation on the surface of the soil. A contour terrace is laid out on a sloping soil at right angles to the direction of the slope and level throughout its course. In contour plowing, the plowman keeps to a level line at right angles to the direction of the slope, which usually results in a curving furrow.

CONTOUR BASINS Basins made by levees or borders built on contours with occasional cross levees.

CONVEYANCE LOSS Loss of water from a conduit due to leakage, seepage, and evaporation.

CREEP, SOIL The downward mass movement of sloping soil. The movement is usually slow and irregular and occurs most commonly when the lower soil is nearly saturated with water.

CRUMB STRUCTURE Very porous granular structure in soils.

CRUST A thin, brittle layer of hard soil that forms on the surface of many soils when they are dry. An exposed hard layer of materials cemented by calcium carbonate, gypsum, or other binding agents. Most desert crusts are formed by the exposure of such layers through removal of the upper soil by wind or running water and their subsequent hardening.

CYTOCHROME An iron-containing pigment that plays a major role in respiration.

CYTOPLASM The portion of the protoplasm of a cell outside the nucleus.

D LAYER Any stratum underlying the soil profile that is unlike the material from which the soil has been formed.

DAMPING-OFF Sudden wilting and death of seedling plants resulting from attack by micro-organisms.

DEALKALIZATION Removal of exchangeable sodium (or alkali) from the soil, usually by chemical treatment and leaching.

DEEP PERCOLATION A general term for the downward movement of water beyond the reach of plant roots.

DEEP SOIL Generally, a soil deeper than 40 inches to rock or other strongly contrasting material. Also, a soil with a deep black surface layer; a soil deeper than about 40 inches to the parent material or to other unconsolidated rock material not modified by soil-forming processes; or a soil in which the total depth of unconsolidated material, whether true soil or not, is 40 inches or more.

DEFLOCCULATE To separate or to break up soil aggregates into the individual particles; to disperse the particles of a granulated clay to form a clay that runs together or puddles.

DEGRADATION (OF SOILS) The change of one kind of soil to a more highly leached kind, such as the change of a Chernozem to a Podzol.

DEHYDRATION Removal or loss of water.

DENITRIFICATION The process by which nitrates or nitrites in the soil or organic deposits are reduced to ammonia or free nitrogen by bacterial action. The process results in the escape of nitrogen into the air and is therefore wasteful.

DESALINIZATION Removal of salts from saline soil, usually by leaching.

DESERT SOIL A zonal group of soils that have light-colored surface soils and usually are underlain by calcareous material and frequently by hard layers. They are developed under extremely scanty scrub vegetation in warm to cool, arid climates.

DESILTING AREA An area used for removing the sediment from flowing water, especially by vegetation.

DESORPTION The removal of sorbed materials from surfaces.

DETAILED SOIL MAP A soil map showing the kinds of soil. The soil boundaries have been plotted on a base map or aerial photograph from observations made throughout their course and the kinds of soil are classified and the boundaries shown in all the detail significant to soil use and management. Most of the soils shown on such maps are phases of soil types.

DIFFUSION The transport of matter as a consequence of the movement of the constituent particles. The intermingling of two gases or liquids in contact with each other takes place by diffusion.

DIPOLAR Having two poles as a result of separation of electric charge. A dipolar molecule orients in an electric field.

DISPERSION OF SOIL Deflocculation of the soil and its suspension in water.

DIVALENT MANGANOUS ION The chemical element manganese (Mn^{+2}) in its lowest valence state.

DRAINAGE (A PRACTICE) The removal of excess surface water or excess water from within the soil by means of surface or subsurface drains.

DRAINAGE, SOIL (1) The rapidity and extent of the removal of water from the soil by runoff and flow through the soil to underground spaces. (2) As a condition of the soil, soil drainage refers to the frequency and duration of periods when the soil is free of saturation. For example, in well-drained soils, the water is removed readily, but not rapidly; in poorly drained soils, the root zone is waterlogged for long periods and the roots of ordinary crop plants cannot get enough oxygen; and in excessively drained soils, the water is removed so completely that most crop plants suffer from lack of water.

DRIFT Material of any sort deposited by geological processes in one place after having been removed from another. Glacial drift includes the materials deposited by glaciers and by the streams and lakes associated with them.

DROP-INLET DAM A dam through which overflow water is carried through a shallow, sloping pipe in order to drop water from one level to another for gradient control and for stabilization of a waterway.

DROUGHT A period of dryness, especially a long one. Usually considered to be any period of soil moisture deficiency within the plant root zone. A period of dryness of sufficient length to deplete soil moisture to the extent that plant growth is seriously retarded.

DRY FARMING Generally, producing crops that require some tillage in subhumid or semiarid regions without irrigation. The system usually involves periods of fallow between crops during which water from precipitation is absorbed and retained.

DRY SANDS Sandy deposits, with low water-holding capacity, in which there has been no clear development of soil characteristics since deposition.

DRY WEIGHT PERCENTAGE (OF WATER IN SOIL) The weight of water expressed as a percentage of the ovendry weight of soil.

DUFF The matted, partly decomposed organic surface layer of forested soils.

DUNE A mount or ridge of loose sand piled up by the wind. Occasionally during periods of extreme drought, granulated soil material of fine texture may be piled into low dunes, sometimes called clay dunes.

DUST MULCH A loose, dry surface layer of a cultivated soil, formerly thought to be effective in reducing the loss of moisture from the underlying soil.

ECOLOGY The branch of biology that deals with the mutual relations among organisms and between organisms and their environment.

EFFLUENT The outflowing of water from a subterranean storage space. (Also used generally for gases and other liquids.)

ELECTROLYTE Any conductor of electric current in which chemical change accompanies the passage of the current and the amount of the change is proportional to the amount of current passed. Usually electrolytes are solutions of substances in a liquid, such as salt in water. A substance that forms a conductor of electricity when added to a solvent. Thus, common table salt becomes an electrolyte when added to water.

ELUVIATION The movement of material from one place to another within the soil in either true solution or colloidal suspension. Soil horizons that have lost material through eluviation are said to be eluvial; those that have received material are illuvial. With an excess of rainfall over evaporation, eluviation may take place either downward or laterally according to the direction of water movement. The term refers especially to the movement of soil colloids in suspension; leaching refers to the removal of soluble materials such as salt in true solution.

ENVIRONMENT All external conditions that may act upon an organism or soil to influence its development, including sunlight, temperature, moisture, and other organisms.

ENZYMES Substances produced by living cells which can bring about or speed up chemical reaction. They are organic catalysts.

EQUILIBRIUM A state of balance between opposing soil forces or actions.

ERODIBLE (SOIL) Soil susceptible to erosion.

EROSION The wearing away of the land surface by detachment and transport of soil and rock materials through the action of moving water, wind, or other geological agents.

EROSIVE (WIND OR WATER) Used in reference to wind or water having sufficient velocity to cause erosion. Not to be confused with erodible as a quality of soil.

EVAPOTRANSPIRATION The loss of water from a soil by evaporation and plant transpiration.

EXCHANGE CAPACITY (See cation-exchange capacity.)

EXCHANGEABLE This word describes the ions in the absorbing complex of the soil that can be exchanged with other ions. For example, when acid soils are limed, calcium ions exchange for hydrogen ions in the complex; when alkali soils are treated with gypsum, calcium ions exchange for sodium ions that can be leached away.

EXCHANGEABLE SODIUM Sodium that is attached to the surface of soil particles which can be exchanged with other positively charged ions in the soil solution, such as calcium and magnesium.

FALLOW Cropland left idle in order to restore productivity, mainly through accumulation of water, nutrients, or both. Summer fallow is a common stage before cereal grain in regions of limited rainfall. The soil is tilled for at least one growing season to control weeds, to aid decomposition of plant residues, and to encourage the storage of moisture for the succeeding grain crop. Bush or forest fallow is a rest period under woody vegetation between crops.

FELDSPARS Primary alumino-silicate minerals having a three-dimensional framework structure.

FERRIC IRON   An oxidized or high-valence form of iron (Fe^{+3}) responsible for red, yellow, and brown colors in soils. Fe^{+++}.

FERROUS IRON   A reduced or low-valence form of iron (Fe^{+2}), imparting a blue-gray appearance to some wet subsoils on long standing.

FERTILITY, SOIL   The quality of a soil that enables it to provide compounds, in adequate amounts and in proper balance, for the growth of specified plants, when other growth factors such as light, moisture, temperature, and the physical condition of the soil are favorable.

FERTILIZER   Any natural or manufactured material added to the soil in order to supply one or more plant nutrients. The term is generally applied to largely inorganic materials other than lime or gypsum (mineral fertilizers) sold in the trade.

FERTILIZER GRADE   An expression that indicates the percentage of plant nutrients in a fertilizer. Thus a 10–20–10 grade contains 10 percent nitrogen (N), 20 percent phosphoric oxide (P$_2$O$_5$), and 10 percent potash (K$_2$O). This convention is in common use even though the nitrogen, phosphorus, and potassium are present in other forms.

FIELD CAPACITY   The amount of moisture remaining in a soil after the free water has been allowed to drain away into drier soil material beneath; usually expressed as a percentage of the ovendry weight of soil or other convenient unit. It is the highest amount of moisture that the soil will hold under conditions of free drainage after excess water has drained away following a rain or irrigation that has wet the whole soil. For permeable soils of medium texture, this is about 2 or 3 days after a rain or thorough irrigation. Although generally similar for one kind of soil, values vary with previous treatments of the soil.

FIELD MOISTURE   The water that soil contains under field conditions.

FILM WATER   The water held on the surfaces of soil particles that does not drain away, although it moves rapidly under suction gradients. Most of it is available to plant roots.

FINE-TEXTURED SOIL   Roughly, clayey soil containing 35 percent or more of clay.

FIRST BOTTOM   The normal flood plain of a stream, subject to frequent or occasional flooding.

FIXATION (IN SOIL)   The conversion of a soluble material, such as a plant nutrient like phosphorus, from a soluble or exchangeable form to a relatively insoluble form.

FLOCCULATE   To aggregate or clump together individual tiny soil particles, especially fine clay, into small groups or granules. The opposite of deflocculate, or disperse.

FLOOD IRRIGATION   Irrigation by running water over nearly level soil in a shallow flood.

FLOOD PLAIN   The nearly flat lands along streams that overflow during floods.

FLUORAPATITE   A member of the apatite group of minerals, rich in fluorine. Most common mineral in raw rock phosphate.

FOLIAR DIAGNOSIS   Estimation of the plant-nutrient status of plant or the plant-nutrient requirements of a soil for producing a crop through chemical analyses or color manifestations of plant leaves or by both methods together.

FOLIAR FERTILIZATION   Fertilization of plants by applying chemical fertilizers to their foliage.

FOOD, PLANT   The organic compounds elaborated by a plant within its cells. (Sometimes used loosely for plant nutrients.)

FORAGE   Unharvested plant material which can be used as feed by domestic animals. Forage may be grazed or cut for hay.

FOREST LAND   Land bearing a stand of trees at any age or stature, including seedlings, and of species attaining a minimum of 6 feet average height at maturity; or land from which such a stand has been removed but on which no other use has been substituted. The term is commonly limited to land not in farms; forests on farms are commonly called woodland or farm forests.

FRAGIPANS   Dense and brittle pans or layers in soils that owe their hardness mainly to extreme density or compactness rather than to high clay content or cementation. Removed fragments are friable, but the material in place is so dense that roots cannot penetrate and water moves through it very slowly because of small pore size.

FREE   Often said of silica, ferric oxide, or calcium carbonate. The condition of the substance within a mixture when it is not chemically combined with the other components of the mixture. For example, iron oxide in soils may be by itself as free iron oxide, or it may be combined with other elements in a mineral.

FUNGI   Forms of plantlife, lacking chlorophyll and unable to make their own food.

GENESIS, SOIL   The mode of origin of the soil, with special reference to the processes responsible for the development of the solum, or true soil, from the unconsolidated parent material.

GLEY SOIL A soil horizon in which water-logging and lack of oxygen have caused the material to be a neutral gray in color. The term "gleyed" is applied, as in "moderately gleyed soil," to soil horizons with yellow and gray mottling caused by intermittent water-logging.

GRANULAR, FERTILIZER A fertilizer composed of particles of roughly the same composition, about one-tenth inch in diameter. This kind of fertilizer contrasts with the normally fine or powdery fertilizer.

GRANULAR STRUCTURE Soil structure in which the individual grains are grouped into spherical aggregates with indistinct sides. Highly porous granules are commonly called crumbs. A well-granulated soil has the best structure for most ordinary crop plants.

GRAVITATIONAL WATER IN SOILS The water in the large pores of the soil that drains away under the force of gravity with free under-drainage. Well-drained soils have such water only during and immediately after rains or applications of irrigation water. In poorly drained soils, this water accumulates in the pores at the expense of air. Under such conditions, the soil lacks oxygen for the roots of most crop plants and is said to be water-logged.

GRAY-BROWN PODZOLIC SOILS A zonal group of soils having thin organic coverings and thin organic-mineral layers over grayish-brown leached layers that rest upon brown B horizons richer in clay than the soil horizon above. These soils have formed under deciduous forests in a moist temperate climate.

GREAT SOIL GROUP Any one of several broad groups of soil with fundamental characteristics in common. Examples are Chernozem, Gray-Brown Podzolic, and Podzol.

GROUND WATER Water that fills all the unblocked pores of underlying material below the water table, which is the upper limit of saturation.

GROUND-WATER PODZOL An intrazonal group of soils, developed from imperfectly drained sandy deposits in humid regions, with thin organic and organic-mineral layers over light-gray or white leached layers that rest on dark-brown B horizons irregularly cemented with iron, organic matter, or both.

HARDPAN A hardened or cemented soil horizon or layer. The soil material may be sandy or clayey and may be cemented by iron oxide, silica, calcium carbonate, or other substances.

HEAD Difference in elevation of water-producing discharge. (Sometimes used incorrectly for the size of irrigation streams.)

HEAVY SOIL An old term formerly used for clayey or fine-textured soils. (The term originated from the heavy draught on the horses when plowing.)

HORIZON SOIL A layer of soil, approximately parallel to the soil surface, with distinct characteristics produced by soil-forming processes.

HUMIC ACIDS Alkali soluble end products of the decomposition of organic matter in soil and in composts. The term sometimes is used interchangeably for humus.

HUMID CLIMATE A climate with enough precipitation to support a forest vegetation, although there are exceptions where the plant cover includes no trees, as in the Arctic or high mountains. The lower limit of precipitation may be as little as 15 inches in cool regions and as much as 60 inches in hot regions. The precipitation-effectiveness index ranges between 64 and 128. A climate having a high average relative humidity.

HUMIFICATION A process or condition of decay in which plant or animal remains are so thoroughly decomposed that their initial structures or shapes can no longer be recognized.

HUMUS The well-decomposed, more or less stable part of the organic matter in mineral soils.

HYDRAULIC EQUILIBRIUM (OF WATER IN SOIL) The condition for zero flow rate of liquid or film water in soil. This condition is satisfied when the pressure gradient force is just equal and opposite to the gravity force.

HYDRONIUM IONS The predominant form of occurrence of hydrogen ions in solution, each hydrogen ion being associated with a single water molecule; H_3O^+.

HYDROUS Containing water.

HYDROXYAPATITE A member of the apatite group of minerals rich in hydroxyl groups. A nearly insoluble calcium phosphate.

HYGROSCOPIC Capable of taking up moisture from the air.

HYGROSCOPIC COEFFICIENT The amount of moisture in a dry soil when it is in equilibrium with some standard relative humidity near a saturated atmosphere (about 98 percent), expressed in terms of percentage on the basis of ovendry soil.

IGNEOUS ROCK Rock produced through the cooling of melted mineral matter. When the cooling process is slow, the rock contains fair-sized crystals of the individual minerals, as in granite.

759

ILLITE A series of micalike, nonexpandable, or slightly expandable alumino-silicate clay minerals in which two silica layers alternate with one alumina layer; also called hydrous micas.

ILLUVIATION An accumulation of material in a soil horizon through the deposition of suspended mineral and organic matter originating from horizons above. Since at least part of the fine clay in the B horizons (or subsoils) of many soils has moved into them from the A horizons above, these are called illuvial horizons.

IMMATURE SOIL A soil lacking clear individual horizons because of the relatively short time for soil-building forces to act upon the parent material since its deposition or exposure.

IMMOBILIZATION (OF PLANT NUTRIENTS) The conversion of an available plant nutrient in the soil from an inorganic to an organic form in living tissue. Thus the addition of fresh straw or sawdust to the soil may greatly increase the number of bacteria. These remove available nitrogen and phosphorus from the soil and immobilize them within their cells.

IMPERVIOUS SOIL A soil through which water, air, or roots penetrate slowly or not at all. No soil is absolutely impervious to water and air all the time.

INHERITED SOIL CHARACTERISTICS Any characteristic of a soil that is due directly to the nature of the material from which it formed, as contrasted to the characteristics that are wholly or partly the result of soil-forming processes acting on parent material. For example, some soils are red because the parent material was red; although the color of most red soils is due to soil-forming processes.

INORGANIC Refers to substances occurring as minerals in nature or obtainable from them by chemical means. Refers to all matter except the compounds of carbon, but includes carbonates.

INORGANIC NITROGEN Nitrogen in combination with mineral elements, not in animal or vegetable form. Ammonium sulfate and sodium nitrate are examples of inorganic nitrogen combinations, while proteins contain nitrogen in organic combination.

IN PLACE (*in situ*) (1) Formed or accumulated on the spot. A rock may decay and break down into small particles where it is first exposed in the land surface. It is then said to have weathered in place or in situ. (2) As a mass appears in the soil before any disturbance. For example, the deeper part of a profile may be massive and show no signs of structure in place but break down into lumps of regular size and shape when removed.

INTAKE RATE The rate, usually expressed in inches per hour, at which rain or irrigation water enters the soil. This rate is controlled partly by surface conditions (infiltration rate) and partly by subsurface conditions (permeability). It also varies with the method of applying water. The same kind of soil has different intake rates under sprinkler irrigation, border irrigation, and furrow irrigation.

INTERTILLED CROP A crop having or requiring cultivation during growth.

INTRAZONAL SOIL Any one of the great groups of soils having more or less well-developed soil characteristics that reflect a dominating influence of some local factor of relief or of parent material over the normal influences of the climate and the vegetation on the soil-forming processes. Such groups of soils may be geographically associated with two or more of the zonal groups of soils having characteristics dominated by the influence of climate and vegetation.

ION An electrically charged particle. As used in soils, an ion refers to an electrically charged element or combination of elements resulting from the breaking up of an electrolyte in solution. Since most soil solutions are highly dilute, many of the salts exist as ions. For example, all or part of the potassium chloride (muriate of potash) in most soils exists as potassium ions and chloride ions. The positively charged potassium ion is called a cation and the negatively charged chloride ion is called an anion.

ISOTOPE One of two or more forms of a chemical element having the same atomic number and position in the periodic table of elements, but distinguishable by differences of weight.

KAOLIN MINERALS A group of nonswelling clay minerals in which one layer or sheet of silicon and oxygen alternates with a sheet made up of aluminum, oxygen, and hydrogen.

LACUSTRINE DEPOSITS Materials deposited from lake water. Many nearly level soils have developed from such deposits from old lakes that have long since disappeared.

LAND The total natural and cultural environment within which production takes place. Land is a broader term than soil. In addition to soil, its attributes include other physical conditions such as mineral deposits and water supply; location in relation to centers of commerce, populations, and other land; the size of the individual tracts or holdings; and existing plant cover, works of improvement, and the like. Some use the term loosely in other senses: As defined above, but without the economic or cultural criteria, especially in the expression "natural land"; as a synonym for "soil"; for the solid surface of the earth; and also for earthy surface formations, especially in the geomorphological expression "land form."

LAND-CAPABILITY CLASSIFICATION A grouping of kinds of soil into special units, subclasses, and classes according to their capability for intensive use and the treatments required for sustained use.

LANDSCAPE The sum total of the characteristics that distinguish a certain kind of area on the earth's surface and give it a distinguishing pattern in contrast to other kinds of areas. Any one kind of soil is said to have a characteristic natural landscape, and under different uses it has one or more characteristic cultural landscapes.

LAND-USE PLANNING The development of plans for the uses of land that, over long periods, will best serve the general welfare, together with the formulation of ways and means for achieving such uses.

LATTICE The structural framework of a clay mineral which is made up by the orderly arrangement of the various ionic components of the mineral. The mineral is held together by the chemical bonds exerted toward each other by the various ions in the mineral. The structural pattern repeats itself indefinitely and regularly; the atoms are linked according to definite angles and distances. For example, micas and alumino-silicate clay minerals have layer lattices consisting of alternate silica and alumina layers.

LEACHING The removal of materials in solution by the passage of water through soil.

LEVEL TERRACE A broad surface channel or embankment constructed across sloping soil on the contour, as contrasted to a graded terrace, which is built at a slight angle to the contour. A level terrace can be used only on soils that are permeable enough for all of the storm water to soak into the soil so that none breaks over the terrace to cause gullies.

LEVELING (OF LAND) The reshaping or modification of the land surface to a planned grade to provide a more suitable surface for the efficient application of irrigation water and to provide good surface drainage.

LEY A term used in English writing for pastures or meadows. A short ley is roughly equivalent to our "rotation" pasture or meadow, and a long ley to our "longtime" pastures and meadows, often incorrectly called permanent.

LIGHT SOIL An old term formerly used for sandy or coarse-textured soils.

LIGNIN An organic substance that incrusts the cellulose framework of plant cell walls. It is made up of modified phenyl propane units. It is dissolved only with difficulty and is more inert chemically and biologically than other plant constituents. Lignin increases with age in plants.

LIME Generally the term lime, or agricultural lime, is applied to ground limestone (calcium carbonate), hydrated lime (calcium hydroxide), or burned lime (calcium oxide), with or without mixtures of magnesium carbonate, magnesium hydroxide, or magnesium oxide, and materials such as basic slag, used as amendments to reduce the acidity of acid soils. In strict chemical terminology, lime refers to calcium oxide (CaO), but by an extension of meaning it is now used for all limestone-derived materials applied to neutralize acid soils.

LIME REQUIREMENT The amount of standard ground limestone required to bring a 6.6-inch layer of an acre (about 2 million pounds in mineral soils) of acid soil to some specific lesser degree of acidity, usually to slightly or very slightly acid. In common practice, lime requirements are given in tons per acre of nearly pure limestone, ground finely enough so that all of it passes a 10-mesh screen and at least half of it passes a 100-mesh screen.

LITHOSOL A soil having little or no evidence of soil development and consisting mainly of a partly weathered mass of rock fragments or of nearly barren rock.

LOAM The textural class name for soil having a moderate amount of sand, silt, and clay. Loam soils contain 7 to 27 percent of clay, 28 to 50 percent of silt, and less than 52 percent of sand. (In the old literature, especially English literature, the term "loam" applied to mellow soils rich in organic matter, regardless of the texture. As used in the United States, the term refers only to the relative amounts of sand, silt, and clay; loam soils may or may not be mellow.)

LOAMY SOIL A general expression for soils of intermediate texture between the coarse-textured or sandy soils, on the one hand, and the fine-textured or clayey soils on the other. Sandy loams, loams, silt loams, and clay loams are regarded as loamy soils.

LOESS Geological deposit of relatively uniform, fine material, mostly silt, presumably transported by wind. Many unlike kinds of soil in the United States have developed from loess blown out of alluvial valleys and from other deposits during periods of aridity.

LUXURY CONSUMPTION The intake by a plant of an essential nutrient in amounts exceeding what it needs. Thus if potassium is abundant in the soil, alfalfa may take in more than is required.

MACROPORE Large or noncapillary pores. The pores, or voids, in a soil from which water usually drains by gravity. Is differentiated from micropore, or capillary pore, space, which consists of voids small enough that water is held against gravity by capillarity. Sandy soils have a large macropore, or noncapillary, pore space and a small micropore, or capillary, pore space. Nongranular clayey soils are just the reverse.

MANURE Generally, the refuse from stables and barnyards, including both animal excreta and straw or other litter. In some other countries the term "manure" is used more broadly and includes both farmyard or animal manure and "chemical manures," for which the term "fertilizer" is nearly always used in the United States.

MARL An earthy deposit, consisting mainly of calcium carbonate commonly mixed with clay or other impurities. It is formed chiefly at the margins of fresh-water lakes. It is commonly used for liming acid soils.

MATURE SOIL Any soil with well-developed soil horizons having characteristics produced by the natural processes of soil formation and in near equilibrium with its present environment.

MECHANICAL ANALYSIS The physical analysis of soil materials to determine the amounts of the various soil separates, or grain-size fractions.

MECHANICAL STABILITY Resistance of soil to breakdown by mechanical forces such as tillage or abrasion from windborne soil particles; strength of coherence; mechanical strength.

MEDITERRANEAN CLIMATE A general term for warm-temperature climates that are dry in the warm season and moist in the cool season.

MELLOW SOIL A porous, softly granular soil easily worked without becoming compacted.

METABOLISM Life functions that are a result of building up foods within the living body and using the foods for energy sources for various life processes. The synthesis of foods and their use as sources of energy.

METAMORPHIC ROCK A rock that has been greatly altered from its previous condition through the combined action of heat and pressure. For example, marble is a metamorphic rock produced from limestone, gneiss is one produced from granite, and slate is produced from shale.

METHOXYL A chemical grouping composed of a carbon atom linked to an oxygen atom and 3 hydrogen atoms. The conventional symbol is $-OCH_3$.

MICAS Primary alumino-silicate minerals in which two silica layers alternate with one alumina layer. They separate readily into thin sheets or flakes.

MICRO- A prefix meaning very small, as in micro-organism; one-millionth of something; that which makes use of a microscope, as in microbiology. Macro- implies large.

MICROCLIMATE The local climatic condition near the ground resulting from the modification of the general climatic condition by local differences in relief, exposure, and cover.

MICRONUTRIENTS Nutrients that plants need in only small, trace, or minute amounts.

MICRO-ORGANISMS Forms of life too small to be seen with the unaided eye, or barely discernible.

MICRORELIEF Small-scaled differences in relief, such as small mounts, swales, or pits that are a few feet across and have differences in elevation of a few inches to around 3 feet that are significant to soil-forming processes, to growth of plants, or to preparing the soil for cultivation.

MILLIMHOS Units of conductance.

MINERAL SOIL A general term for a soil composed chiefly of mineral matter, in contrast to an organic soil, which is composed chiefly of organic matter.

MINERALIZATION The release of mineral matter from organic matter, especially through microbial decomposition.

MOISTURE STRESS The tension at which water is held by the soil.

MOISTURE TENSION The force at which water is held by soil; usually expressed as the equivalent of a unit column of water in centimeters; 1,000 cm. equal 1 atmosphere equivalent tension. Moisture tension increases with dryness and indicates the degree of work required to remove soil moisture for use by plants.

MOLECULE A group of atoms bonded together in a characteristic pattern.

MONOVALENT CATIONS Ions having a single positive charge; having a deficiency of one electron from the neutral state.

MONTMORILLONITE A finely platy, alumino-silicate clay mineral that expands and contracts with the absorption and loss of water. It has a high cation-exchange capacity and is plastic and sticky when moist.

MOR Raw humus; a type of forest humus layer of unincorporated organic material,

762

usually matted or compacted or both; distinct from the mineral soil, unless the latter has been blackened by washing in organic matter.

MORPHOLOGY, SOIL The constitution of the soil including the texture, structure, consistence, color, and other physical, chemical, and biological properties of the various soil horizons that make up the soil profile.

MOTTLED Soil horizons irregularly marked with spots of color. A common cause of mottling is imperfect or impeded drainage although there are other causes, such as soil development from an unevenly weathered rock. Different kinds of minerals may cause mottling.

MUCK Highly decomposed organic soil material developed from peat. Generally, muck has a higher mineral or ash content than peat and is decomposed to the point that the original plant parts cannot be identified.

MULCH A natural or artificially applied layer of plant residues or other materials on the surface of the soil. Mulches are generally used to help conserve moisture, control temperature, prevent surface compaction or crusting, reduce runoff and erosion, improve soil structure, or control weeds. Common mulching materials include compost, sawdust, wood chips, and straw. Sometimes paper, fine brush, or small stones are used.

MULCH TILLAGE Tillage of the soil and treatment of crop residues in ways to leave plant materials within or on the soil surface to form a mulch.

MULL A humus-rich layer of forested soils consisting of mixed organic and mineral matter. A mull blends into the upper mineral-layers without an abrupt change in soil characteristics.

MYCELIA The threadlike bodies of simple organisms, such as the common bread mold.

MYCORHIZA (MYCORRHIZA) The morphological association, usually symbiotic, of fungi and roots of seed plants. The feeding roots are enshrouded and partially penetrated by fine filaments of fungi; such roots commonly are more branched and lose their root hairs.

NECROSIS Death associated with discoloration and dehydration of all or parts of plant organs, such as leaves.

NEMATOCIDE Any substance that can be used to kill nematodes.

NEMATODES Very small worms abundant in many soils and important because many of them attack and destroy plant roots.

NEUTRAL SOIL A soil that is neither significantly acid nor alkaline. Strictly, a neutral soil has pH of 7.0; in practice, a neutral soil has a pH between 6.6 and 7.3.

NITRIFICATION The formation of nitrates and nitrites from ammonia (or ammonium compounds), as in soils by micro-organisms.

NITROGEN FIXATION Generally, the conversion of free nitrogen to nitrogen combined with other elements. Specifically in soils, the assimilation of free nitrogen from the soil air by soil organisms and the formation of nitrogen compounds that eventually become available to plants. The nitrogen-fixing organisms associated with legumes are called symbiotic; those not definitely associated with the higher plants are nonsymbiotic.

NORMAL SOIL A soil having a profile in near equilibrium with its environment; developed under good but not excessive drainage from parent material of mixed mineral, physical, and chemical composition. In its characteristics it expresses the full effects of the forces of climate and living matter.

NUCLEIC ACIDS Complex compounds found in the nuclei of plant and animal cells and usually combined with proteins as nucleoproteins.

NUTRIENT, PLANT Any element taken in by a plant, essential to its growth, and used by it in elaboration of its food and tissue.

ORDER The highest category in soil classification. The three orders are zonal soils, intrazonal soils, and azonal soils.

ORGANIC SOIL A general term applied to a soil or to a soil horizon that consists primarily of organic matter, such as peat soils, muck soils, and peaty soil layers. Organic in chemistry refers to the compounds of carbon.

OSMOTIC A type of pressure exerted in living bodies as a result of unequal concentration of salts on both sides of a cell wall or membrane. Water will move from the area having the least salt concentration through the membrane into the area having the highest salt concentration and, therefore, exerts additional pressure on this side of the membrane.

OXIDATION A chemical change of an element or compound involving the addition of oxygen or its chemical equivalent. A chemical change that involves an increase of positive valence or a decrease of negative valence. For example, if iron is changed from the ferrous state (in which it has 2 positive valences) to the ferric state (in which it has 3 positive valences), the iron is said to be oxidized. The reverse process is reduction. During the burning of fuel, oxygen is added to carbon to form carbon dioxide; in the rusting of iron, the addition of oxygen forms a red iron oxide.

OXIDE A compound of any element with oxygen alone.

PAN A layer or soil horizon within a soil that is firmly compacted or is very rich in clay. Examples include hardpans, fragipans, claypans, and traffic pans.

PARENT MATERIAL The unconsolidated mass of rock material (or peat) from which the soil profile develops.

PARTS PER MILLION (p.p.m.) A notation for indicating small amounts of materials. The expression gives the number of units by weight of the substance per million weight units of ovendry soil. The term may be used to express the number of weight units of a substance per million weight units of solution.

PEAT Unconsolidated soil material consisting largely of undecomposed or only slightly decomposed organic matter accumulated under conditions of excessive moisture.

PED An individual natural soil aggregate such as a crumb, prism, or block, in contrast to a clod, which is a mass of soil brought about by digging or other disturbance.

PEDOLOGY The science that treats of soil.

PERCOLATION The downward movement of water through soil.

PERMANENT PASTURE Pasture that occupies the soil for a long time in contrast to rotation pasture, which occupies the soil for only a year or two in a rotation cycle with other crops. As used in the humid parts of the United States, the term "permanent pasture" is equivalent to the European "long ley."

PERMEABILITY, SOIL The quality of a soil horizon that enables water or air to move through it. It can be measured quantitatively in terms of rate of flow of water through a unit cross section in unit time under specified temperature and hydraulic conditions. Values for saturated soils usually are called hydraulic conductivity. The permeability of a soil may be limited by the presence of one nearly impermeable horizon even though the others are permeable.

pH A numerical designation of relatively weak acidity and alkalinity as in soils and other biological systems. Technically, pH is the common logarithm of the reciprocal of the hydrogen-ion concentration of a solution. A pH of 7.0 indicates precise neutrality, higher values indicate increasing alkalinity, and lower values indicate increasing acidity.

PHASE, SOIL The subdivision of a soil type or other classificational soil unit having variations in characteristics not significant to the classification of the soil in its natural landscape but significant to the use and management of the soil. Examples of the variations

recognized by phases of soil types include differences in slope, stoniness, and thickness because of accelerated erosion.

PHOTOSYNTHESIS The process of conversion by plants of water and carbon dioxide into carbohydrates under the action of light. Chlorophyll is required for the conversion of the light energy into chemical forms.

PITTING The making of shallow pits in the soil to retain rainwater of snowmelt. In short-grass rangelands pitting is done mainly with an offset disk or pitting machine.

PLANOSOL An intrazonal group of soils with eluviated surface horizons underlain by claypans or fragipans, developed on nearly flat or gently sloping uplands in humid or sub-humid climates.

PLATY SOIL STRUCTURE Soil aggregates with thin vertical axes and long horizontal axes. Flat, tabular; a three-dimensional object that has one dimension much smaller than the other two.

PLOW LAYER Equals surface soil.

PODZOL A zonal group of soils having surface organic mats and thin, organic-mineral horizons above gray leached horizons that rest upon illuvial dark-brown horizons developed under coniferous or mixed forests or under heath vegetation in a cool-temperate, moist climate.

PODZOLIC SOIL Soils that have part or all of the characteristics of the Podzol soils, especially leached surface soils that are poorer in clay than the B horizons beneath.

PODZOLIZATION The process by which soils are depleted of bases, become more acid, and have developed leached surface layers from which clay has been removed.

POLYNUTRIENT FERTILIZER A fertilizer containing more than one major plant nutrient.

POLYSACCHARIDES Compounds formed by chemical union of two or more simple sugars.

PORE SPACE The fraction of the bulk volume or total space within soils that is not occupied by solid particles.

POROSITY, SOIL The degree to which the soil mass is permeated with pores or cavities. Porosity can be generally expressed as a percentage of the whole volume of a soil horizon that is unoccupied by solid particles. In addition, the number, sizes, shapes, and distribution of the voids is important. Generally, the pore space of surface soil is less than one-half of the soil mass by volume, but in some soils it is more than half. The part of the pore space that consists of small pores that hold water by capillary is called capillary porosity.

The part that consists of larger pores that do not hold water by capillary and free drainage is called noncapillary porosity.

PRAIRIE SOILS A zonal group of soils having dark-colored surface horizons grading through brown soil material to lighter colored parent material at 2 to 5 feet, formed under tall grasses in a temperate, humid climate. The term has a restricted meaning in soil science and does not apply to all soils developed in treeless landscapes.

PRECIPITATION-EFFECTIVENESS (P–E) INDEX The sum of the 12 monthly quotients of precipitation divided by evaporation.

PRIMARY MINERAL A mineral which occurs, or originally occurred, in igneous rocks; examples are micas and feldspars.

PRISMATIC SOIL STRUCTURE Prismlike structural aggregates with the vertical axes of the aggregates longer than the horizontal axes.

PRODUCTIVITY (OF SOIL) The present capability of a kind of soil for producing a specified plant or sequence of plants under a defined set of management practices. It is measured in terms of the outputs or harvests in relation to the inputs of production factors for a specific kind of soil under a physically defined system of management.

PROFILE (SOIL) A vertical section of the soil through all its horizons and extending into the parent material.

PROTEIN Any of a group of nitrogen-containing compounds that yield amino acids on hydrolysis and have high molecular weights. They are essential parts of living matter and are one of the essential food substances of animals.

PROTOPLASM The basic, jellylike substance in plant and animal cells; it carries out all their life processes.

PUDDLED SOIL Dense, massive soil artificially compacted when wet and having no regular structure. The condition commonly results from the tillage of a clayey soil when it is wet.

PULVERANT A term applied to ungranulated fertilizers, those which are largely powdered. Pulverant fertilizers are dusty and blow readily.

PURINES A group of closely related compounds containing carbon, hydrogen, and nitrogen. Uric acid, an example, is formed from proteins as an end product of animal metabolism. Uric acid is the chief nitrogenous compound in the excrement of birds.

QUICK TESTS Simple and rapid chemical tests of soils designed to give an approximation of the nutrients available to plants.

Interpretations of results depend upon previous standardization with field trials of fertilizers and vary among different kinds of soil.

RADIATION The propagation of energy in the form of waves.

RANGE (or rangeland) Land that produces primarily native forage plants suitable for grazing by livestock, including land that has some forest trees.

REACTION, SOIL The degree of acidity or alkalinity of a soil mass, expressed in either pH value or in words, as follows:

	pH
Extremely acid	Below 4.5.
Very strongly acid	4.5–5.0.
Strongly acid	5.1–5.5.
Medium acid	5.6–6.0.
Slightly acid	6.1–6.5.
Neutral	6.6–7.3.
Mildly alkaline	7.4–7.8.
Moderately alkaline	7.9–8.4.
Strongly alkaline	8.5–9.0.
Very strongly alkaline	9.1 and higher.

RED PODZOLIC SOILS Formerly used for a zonal group of soils having thin organic and organic-mineral horizons over a yellowish-brown leached horizon that rests upon an illuvial red horizon developed under deciduous or mixed deciduous and coniferous forests in a warm to warm-temperate humid climate. These are now placed in the Red-Yellow Podzolic group.

REDUCTION Any chemical change involving the removal of oxygen or its chemical equivalent. A chemical change involving a decrease of positive valence or an increase of negative valence. The reverse of oxidation.

REGOLITH The unconsolidated mantle of weathered rock and soil material on the earth's surface; the loose earth materials above solid rock. Only the upper part of this, modified by organisms and other soil-building forces, is regarded by soil scientists as soil. In soil mechanics, however, most American engineers speak of the whole regolith, even to great depths, as "soil."

REGOSOL An azonal group of soils that includes those without definite genetic horizons developing from deep unconsolidated or soft rocky deposits.

RELIEF Elevations or inequalities of the land surface, considered collectively.

RENDZINA An intrazonal group of soils, usually with brown or black friable surface horizons, underlain by light-gray or pale-yellow soft calcareous material, developed under grass vegetation or mixed grass and forest vegetation, in humid and semiarid regions.

RESIDUAL FERTILIZER The amount of fertilizer that remains in the soil after one or more cropping seasons.

RESIDUAL MATERIAL Unconsolidated and partly weathered parent material for soils presumed to have developed from the same kind of rock as that on which it lies. The term "residual" is sometimes incorrectly applied to soils, but it can be applied correctly only to the material from which soils are formed.

RHIZOBIA The bacteria that can live in symbiotic relations with leguminous plants within nodules on their roots. The normal result of the association is the fixation of nitrogen from the air into forms that can be used by living plants.

RHIZOSPHERE The bounding surface of plant roots. The soil space in the immediate vicinity of the plant roots in which the abundance and composition of the microbial population are influenced by the presence of roots.

ROOT ZONE The part of the soil that is invaded by plant roots.

RUNOFF The surface flow of water from an area; or the total volume of surface flow during a specified time.

SALINE SOIL A soil containing enough soluble salts to impair its productivity for plants but not containing an excess of exchangeable sodium.

SALINE-ALKALI SOIL A soil having a combination of a harmful quantity of salts and either a high degree of alkalinity or a high amount of exchangeable sodium, or both, so distributed in the soil profile that the growth of most crop plants is less than normal.

SALTATION The movement of soil and mineral particles by intermittent leaps from the ground when the particles are being moved by wind or water.

SALTS The products, other than water, of the reaction of an acid with a base. Salts commonly found in soils break up into cations (sodium, calcium, etc.) and anions (chloride, sulfate, etc.) when dissolved in water.

SAND Individual rock or mineral fragments in soils having diameters ranging from 0.5 mm to 2.0 mm. Usually sand grains consist chiefly of quartz, but they may be of any mineral composition. The textural class name of any soil that contains 85 percent or more of sand and not more than 10 percent of clay.

SANDY CLAY Soil of this textural class contains 35 percent or more of clay and 45 percent or more of sand.

SANDY CLAY LOAM Generally, soil of this textural class contains 20 to 35 percent clay, less than 28 percent silt, and 45 percent or more of sand.

SANDY LOAM Generally, soil of the sandy loam class of texture has 50 percent sand and less than 20 percent clay.

SANDY SOILS A broad term for soils of the sand and loamy sand classes; soil material with more than 70 percent sand and less than 15 percent clay.

SEDIMENTARY ROCK A rock composed of particles deposited from suspension in water. Chief groups of sedimentary rocks are conglomerates, from gravels; sandstones, from sand; shales, from clay; and limestones, from soft masses of calcium carbonate. There are many intermediate types. Some wind-deposited sands have been consolidated into sandstones.

SEEPAGE The escape of water through the soil, or water emerging from an area of soil along an extensive line of surface, in contrast to springs where the water emerges from a local spot.

SEMIARID CLIMATE A climate characteristic of the regions intermediate between the true deserts and subhumid areas. In the semiarid climate the precipitation-effectiveness (P–E) index ranges between 16 and 32. The upper limit of the average annual precipitation in cool semiarid regions is as low as 15 inches and in warm regions as much as 45 inches. The vegetation is close-growing or scattered short grass, bunchgrass, or shrubs. Soils in such regions that can take in nearly all of the rain that falls and that can hold it for crop plants can be used for crops under dry-farming methods but irrigation is common where water is available.

SEPARATE, SOIL One of the individual-size groups of mineral soil particles—sand, silt, or clay.

SERIES, SOIL A group of soils that have soil horizons similar in their differentiating characteristics and arrangement in the soil profile, except for the texture of the surface soil, and are formed from a particular type of parent material. Soil series is an important category in detailed soil classification. Individual series are given proper names from place names near the first recorded occurrence. Thus names like Houston, Cecil, Barnes, and Miami are names of soil series that appear on soil maps and each connotes a unique combination of many soil characteristics.

SERPENTINE ROCKS Rocks consisting of acid magnesium silicate.

SESQUIOXIDES Oxides of trivalent cations, such as iron and aluminum.

SIEROZEM SOILS A zonal group of soils having brownish-gray surface horizons that grade through lighter colored material into accumulated calcium carbonate, developed under mixed shrub vegetation in a temperate to cool-arid climate.

SILICA An important soil constituent composed of silicon and oxygen. The essential material of the mineral quartz.

SILICA-SESQUIOXIDE RATIO The ratio of the number of molecules of silica to the number of molecules of alumina plus iron oxide in a soil or in the clay fraction of a soil. The more highly weathered materials of warm-temperate humid regions and especially of the Tropics generally have low ratios. The clay in soils with low ratios usually are less active, physically and chemically, than those with high ratios.

SILT (1) Individual mineral particles of soil that range in diameter between the upper size of clay, 0.002 mm., and the lower size of very fine sand, 0.05 mm. (2) Soil of the textural class silt contains 80 percent or more of silt and less than 12 percent of clay. (3) Sediments deposited from water in which the individual grains are approximately of the size of silt, although the term is sometimes applied loosely to sediments containing considerable sand and clay.

SILT LOAM Soil material having (1) 50 percent or more of silt and 12 to 27 percent of clay or (2) 50 to 80 percent of silt and less than 12 percent of clay.

SILTY CLAY Soil of this textural class has 40 percent or more of clay and 40 percent or more of silt.

SILTY CLAY LOAM Soil of this textural class has 27 to 40 percent of clay and less than 20 percent of sand.

SINGLE GRAIN SOIL A structureless soil in which each particle exists separately, as in dune sand.

SLICK SPOT A small area of "alkali" or Solonetz soil.

SLIP The downslope movement of a mass of soil under wet or saturated conditions; a microlandslide that produces microrelief in soils.

SLOPE The incline of the surface of a soil. It is usually expressed in percentage of slope, which equals the number of feet of fall per 100 feet of horizontal distance.

SOIL (1) The natural medium for the growth of land plants. (2) A dynamic natural body on the surface of the earth in which plants grow, composed of mineral and organic materials and living forms. (3) The collection of natural bodies occupying parts of the earth's surface that support plants and that have properties due to the integrated effect of climate and living matter acting upon parent material, as conditioned by relief, over periods of time.

A soil is an individual three-dimensional body on the surface of the earth unlike the adjoining bodies. (The area of individual soils ranges from less than one-half acre to more than 300 acres.)

A kind of soil is the collection of soils that are alike in specified combinations of characteristics. Kinds of soil are given names in the system of soil classification. The terms "the soil" and "soil" are collective terms used for all soils, equivalent to the word "vegetation" for all plants.

SOIL ASSOCIATION A group of defined and named kinds of soil associated together in a characteristic geographic pattern. Except on detailed soil maps, it is not possible to delineate the various kinds of soil so that on all small-scale soil maps the areas shown consist of soil associations or two or more kinds of soil that are geographically associated.

SOIL CHARACTERISTIC A feature of a soil that can be seen and/or measured in the field or in the laboratory on soil samples. Examples include soil slope and stoniness as well as the texture, structure, color, and chemical composition of soil horizons.

SOIL CLIMATE The moisture and temperature conditions existing within the soil.

SOIL CONSERVATION The efficient use and stability of each area of soil that is needed for use at its optimum level of developed productivity according to the specific patterns of soil and water resources of individual farms, ranches, forests, and other land-management units. The term includes the positive concept of improvement of soils for use as well as their protection and preservation.

SOIL MANAGEMENT The preparation, manipulation, and treatment of soils for the production of plants, including crops, grasses, and trees.

SOIL POPULATION The group of organisms that normally live in the soil.

SOIL QUALITY An attribute of a soil that cannot be seen or measured directly from the soil alone but which is inferred from soil characteristics and soil behavior under defined conditions. Fertility, productivity, and erodibility are examples of soil qualities (in contrast to soil characteristics).

SOIL SURVEY A general term for the systematic examination of soils in the field and in the laboratories, their description and classification, the mapping of kinds of soil, and the interpretation of soils according to their adaptability for various crops, grasses, and trees, their behavior under use or treatment for plant production or for other purposes, and their productivity under different management systems.

SOLONCHAK SOILS An intrazonal group of soils with high concentrations of soluble salts in relation to those in other soils, usually light colored, without characteristic structural form, developed under salt-loving plants, and occurring mostly in a subhumid or semiarid climate. In soil classification, the term applies to a broad group of soils and is only approximately equivalent to the common term "saline soil."

SOLONETZ SOILS An intrazonal group of soils having surface horizons of varying degrees of friability underlain by dark-colored hard soil, ordinarily with columnar structure (prismatic structure with rounded tops). This hard layer is usually highly alkaline. Such soils are developed under grass or shrub vegetation, mostly in subhumid or semiarid climates. This term is used for a broad group of soils that include many so-called alkali soils in the western part of the United States. (Where the hard, clayey layer is overlain with a light-colored leached layer, the soils are called solodized Solonetz.)

SOLUM The upper part of a soil profile, above the parent material, in which the processes of soil formation are active. The solum in mature soils includes the A and B horizons. Usually the characteristics of the material in these horizons are quite unlike those of the underlying parent material. The living roots and other plant and animal life characteristic of the soil are largely confined to the solum.

SPECIFIC HEAT The amount of heat required to change the temperature of unit mass 1 degree.

SPECIFICITY Limited to a particular organism, compound, or set of conditions.

SPHAGNUM A group of mosses which grow in moist places. By annual increments of growth, deep layers of fibrous and highly absorbent peat may be built up. Sphagnum grows best in cool, humid regions.

STORAGE CAPACITY The amount of water that can be stored in the soil for future use by plants and evaporation.

STRATIFIED Composed of, or arranged in, strata, or layers, such as stratified alluvium. The term is confined to geological materials. Layers in soils that result from the processes of soil formation are called horizons; those inherited from the parent material are called strata.

STRESS (SOIL MOISTURE) A term used for the total energy with which water is held in the soil, including tension of soil moisture and additional effects of salts in the soil water. It can be expressed in any convenient pressure unit.

STRIPCROPPING The practice of growing crops in a systematic arrangement of strips, or bands. Commonly cultivated crops and sod crops are alternated in strips to protect the soil and vegetation against running water or wind. The alternate strips are laid out approximately on the contour on erosive soils or at approximate right angles to the prevailing direction of the wind where soil blowing is a hazard.

STRUCTURE, SOIL The arrangement of primary soil particles into compound particles or clusters that are separated from adjoining aggregates and have properties unlike those of an equal mass of unaggregated primary soil particles. The principal forms of soil structure are platy, prismatic, columnar (prisms with rounded tops), blocky (angular or subangular), and granular. Structureless soils are (1) single grain—each grain by itself, as in dune sand, or (2) massive—the particles adhering together without any regular cleavage as in many claypans and hardpans. ("Good" or "bad" tilth are terms for the general structural condition of cultivated soils according to particular plants or sequences of plants.)

STUBBLE MULCH A mulch consisting of the stubble and other crop residues left in and on the surface of the soil as a protective cover during the preparation of a seedbed and during at least part of the growing of the succeeding crop.

SUBHUMID CLIMATE A climate intermediate between semiarid and humid with sufficient precipitation to support a moderate to heavy growth of short and tall grasses, or shrubs, or of these and widely spaced trees or clumps of trees. The precipitation-effectiveness (P–E) index ranges from about 32 to 64. The upper limit of rainfall in subhumid climates may be as low as 20 inches in cold regions and as high as 60 inches in hot regions.

SUBIRRIGATION Irrigation through controlling the water table in order to raise it into the root zone. Water is applied in open ditches or through tile until the water table is raised enough to wet the soil. Some soils along streams are said to be naturally "subirrigated."

SUBSOIL The B horizons of soils with distinct profiles. In soils with weak profile development, the subsoil can be defined as the soil below the plowed soil (or its equivalent of surface soil), in which roots normally grow. Although a common term, it cannot be defined accurately. It has been carried over from early days when "soil" was conceived only as the plowed soil and that under it as the "subsoil."

SUBSOILING The tillage of the soil below the normal plow depth, usually to shatter a hardpan or claypan.

768

SUBSTRATUM Any layer lying beneath the solum or true soil. It is applied to both parent materials and to other layers unlike the parent material, below the B horizon or the subsoil.

SUBSURFACE TILLAGE Tillage with a sweep-like plow or blade that does not turn over the surface cover or incorporate it into the lower part of the surface soil.

SUCTION (OF SOIL WATER) The equivalent negative pressure in soil water. It is the pressure reduction required to extract water from soil. Suction, measured in pressure units, indicates the tenacity with which water is held by surface force action in soil. Experimentally, the suction of water in soil is the pressure difference required across a permeable membrane to produce hydraulic equilibrium between water in soil that is subject to surface force action and free water in bulk on the other side of the membrane. Also, soil suction; soil moisture suction.

SUPPLEMENTAL IRRIGATION A general term sometimes used for irrigation during dry periods in regions where normal precipitation supplies most of the moisture for crops.

SURFACE SOIL The soil ordinarily moved in tillage, or its equivalent in uncultivated soil, about 5 to 8 inches in thickness.

SYMBIOSIS The living together of two different organisms with a resulting mutual benefit. A common example includes the association of rhizobia with legumes; the resulting nitrogen fixation is sometimes called symbiotic nitrogen fixation. Adjective: Symbiotic.

SYNTHESIS Combination of simple molecules to form another substance—for example, the union of carbon dioxide and water under the action of light in photosynthesis.

TENSIOMETER A device for measuring the tension with which water is held in the soil. It is a combination of a porous cup and a vacuum gage.

TENSION, SOIL-MOISTURE The equivalent negative pressure of suction of water in soil.

TERRACE An embankment or ridge constructed across sloping soils on the contour or at a slight angle to the contour. The terrace intercepts surplus runoff in order to retard it for infiltration into the soil and so that any excess may flow slowly to a prepared outlet without harm.

TERRACE (GEOLOGICAL) A nearly flat or undulating plain, commonly rather narrow and usually with a steep front, bordering a river, a lake, or the sea. Although many old terraces have become more or less hilly through dissection by streams, they are still regarded as terraces.

TEXTURAL CLASS Kinds of soil material according to the proportions of sand, silt, and clay. The principal textural classes in soil, in increasing order of the amount of silt and clay, are as follows: Sand, loamy sand, sandy loam, loam, silt loam, silt, sandy clay loam, clay loam, silty clay loam, sandy clay, silty clay, and clay. These class names are modified to indicate the size of the sand fraction or the presence of gravel, cobbles, and stones. For example, terms such as loamy fine sand, very fine sandy loam, gravelly loam, stony clay, and cobbly loam, are used on detailed soil maps. These terms apply only to individual soil horizons or to the surface layer of a soil type, as in the name "Miami silt loam." Commonly the various horizons of any one kind of soil belong in different soil textural classes.

TEXTURE, SOIL The relative proportions of the various size groups of individual soil grains in a mass of soil. Specifically, it refers to the proportions of sand, silt, and clay.

TILLAGE The operation of implements through the soil to prepare seedbeds and rootbeds.

TILTH, SOIL The physical condition of a soil in respect to its fitness for the growth of a specified plant or sequence of plants. Ideal soil tilth is not the same for each kind of crop nor is it uniform for the same kind of crop growing on contrasting kinds of soil.

TOPOGRAPHY The shape of the ground surface, such as hills, mountains, or plains. Steep topography indicates steep slopes or hilly land; flat topography indicates flat land with minor undulations and gentle slopes.

TOPSOIL A general term used in at least four different senses: (1) A presumed fertile soil or soil material, usually rich in organic matter, used to topdress roadbanks, lawns, and gardens; (2) the surface plow layer of a soil and thus a synonym for surface soil; (3) the original or present dark-colored upper soil, which ranges from a mere fraction of an inch to 2 or 3 feet on different kinds of soil; and (4) the original or present A horizon, varying widely among different kinds of soil. Applied to soils in the field, the term has no precise meaning unless defined as to depth or productivity in relation to a specific kind of soil.

TRACE ELEMENTS An old term used for the elements found in plants in only small amounts, including several that are essential to plant growth, others that are essential to animals even though not to plants, and others having no known biological functions. (See micronutrients.)

TRACER TECHNIQUES The use of small amounts of radioactive isotopes to follow normal elements. The tracer is readily detected and measured by its radioactivity.

TRAFFIC PANS Subsurface layers in soil that have been so compacted by the application of weight (e. g., by machines, tractors, etc.) that the penetration of water and roots is interfered with. Because the traffic of machines is not the only cause of these pans, some persons call them pressure pans.

TRANSPIRATION Loss of water vapor from the leaves and stems of living plants to the atmosphere.

TYPE, SOIL A subgroup or category under the soil series based on the texture of the surface soil. A soil type is a group of soils having horizons similar in differentiating characteristics and arrangement in the soil profile and developed from a particular type of parent material. The name of a soil type consists of the name of the soil series plus the textural class name of the upper part of the soil equivalent to the surface soil. Thus Miami silt loam is the name of a soil type within the Miami series.

UNHUMIFIED Organic matter prior to its decomposition into humus.

UPLAND SOILS High ground; ground elevated above the lowlands along rivers or between hills.

VALENCE The combining capacity of atoms or groups of atoms. Sodium (Na^+) and potassium (K^+) are monovalent, while calcium (Ca^{++}) is divalent.

VIRGIN SOIL A soil that has not been significantly disturbed from its natural environment.

VISCOSITY, OF FLUID Property of stickiness of liquid or gas due to its cohesive and adhesive characteristics.

VOLATILIZATION The evaporation or changing of a substance from liquid to vapor.

WATER RATIO (IN SOIL) The fraction of the total bulk volume of soil that is filled with water.

WATER REQUIREMENT (OF PLANTS) Generally, the amount of water required by plants for satisfactory growth during the season. More strictly, the number of units of water required by a plant during the growing season in relation to the number of units of dry matter produced. The water requirement varies with climatic conditions, soil moisture, and soil characteristics. Factors unfavorable to plant growth, such as low fertility, disease, and drought, increase the water requirement.

WATER RETENTION The physical property of soil that is based on surface force action and that makes it necessary to do work in order to remove water from soil pores and from soil surface.

WATER TABLE The upper limit of the part of the soil or underlying rock material that is wholly saturated with water. In some places an upper, or perched, water table may be separated from a lower one by a dry zone.

WATER-HOLDING CAPACITY The capacity (or ability) of soil to hold water; field capacity is the amount held against gravity or 1 atmosphere tension or pF 2.7. The moisture-holding capacity of sandy soils is usually considered to be low while that of clayey soils is high. Often expressed in inches of water per foot depth of soil.

WATERLOGGED A condition of soil in which both large and small pore spaces are filled with water. (The soil may be intermittently waterlogged because of a fluctuating water table or waterlogged for short periods after rain.)

WATERSHED In the United States, the term refers to the total area above a given point on a stream that contributes water to the flow at that point. Synonyms are "drainage basin" or "catchment basin." In some other countries, the term is used for the topographic boundary separating one drainage basin from another.

WEATHERING The physical and chemical disintegration and decomposition of rocks and minerals.

WILTING POINT (OR PERMANENT WILTING POINT) The moisture content of soil, on an ovendry basis, at which plants (specifically sunflower plants) wilt and fail to recover their turgidity when placed in a dark humid atmosphere. The percentage of water at the wilting point approximates the minimum moisture content in soils under plants in the field at depths below the effects of surface evaporation.

YELLOW PODZOLIC SOILS Formerly used for a zonal group of soils having thin organic and organic-mineral layers over grayish-yellow leached horizons that rest on yellow B horizons, developed under coniferous or mixed coniferous and deciduous forests in a warm-temperate to warm, moist climate. These soils are now combined into the Red-Yellow Podzolic group.

Index

774

SCIENTIFIC NAMES

LIBRARY
JUNIOR COLLEGE DISTRICT
ST. LOUIS

INVENTORY '81

INVENTORY 1983

FALL 77

Surface
Soil

Sub-
soil

Soil Material
(NONSOIL)

THE IDEAL ARABLE SOIL

THE farmer makes his arable soil from a natural soil or old arable soil. He develops and maintains a deep rooting zone, easily penetrated by air, water, and roots. It holds water between rains, but allows the excess to pass through it. It has a balanced supply of nutrients. It neither washes away during rains nor blows away with high winds. THE combination of practices to use depends